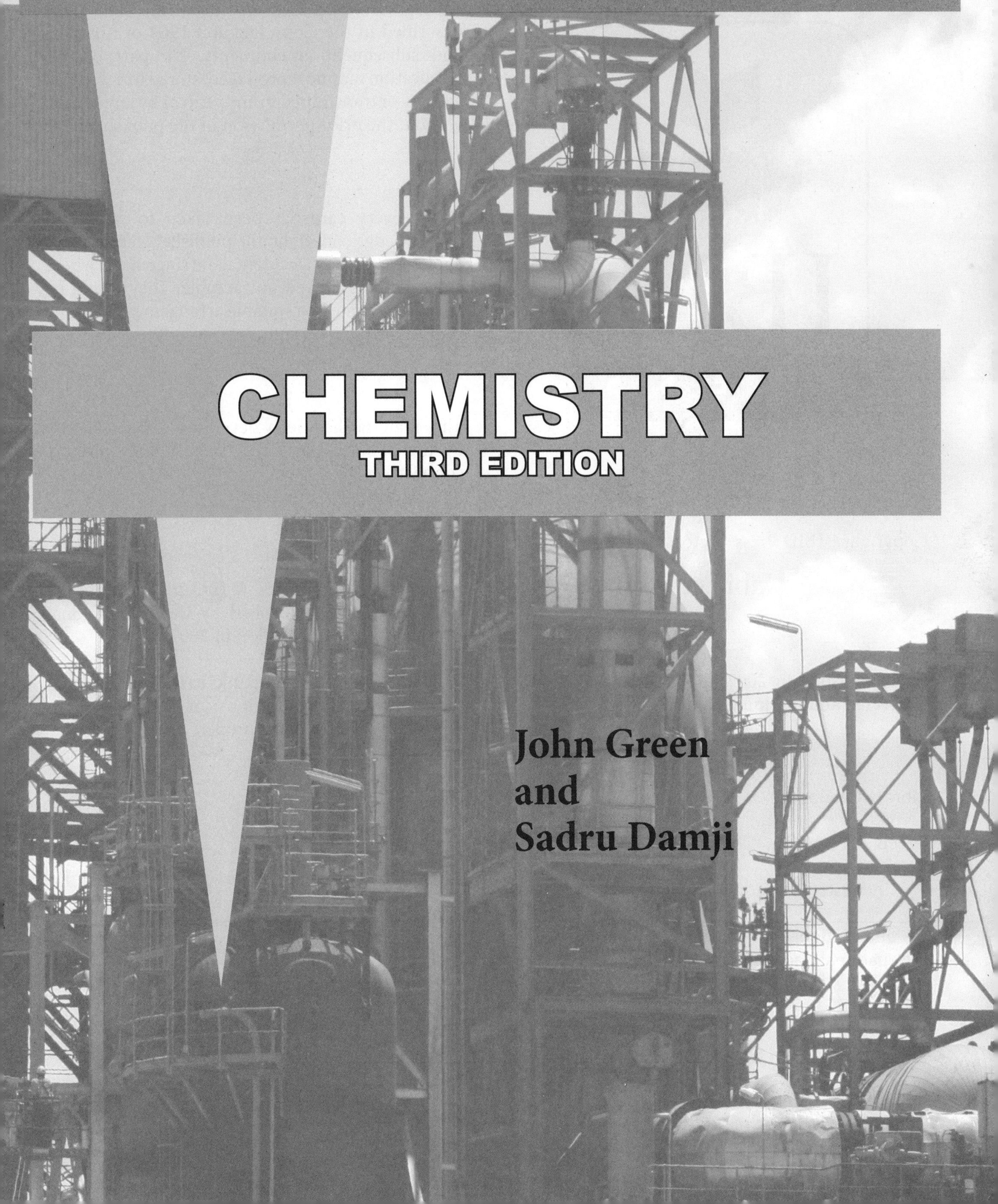

INTERNATIONAL BACCALAUREATE

CHEMISTRY

THIRD EDITION

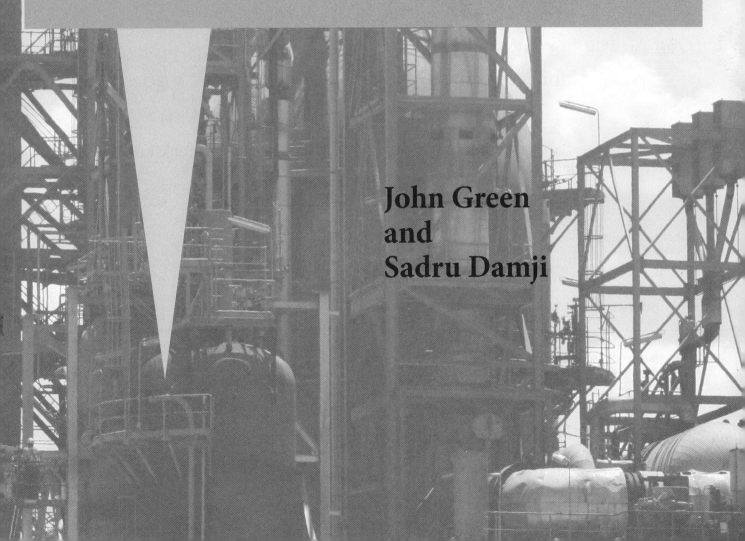

John Green
and
Sadru Damji

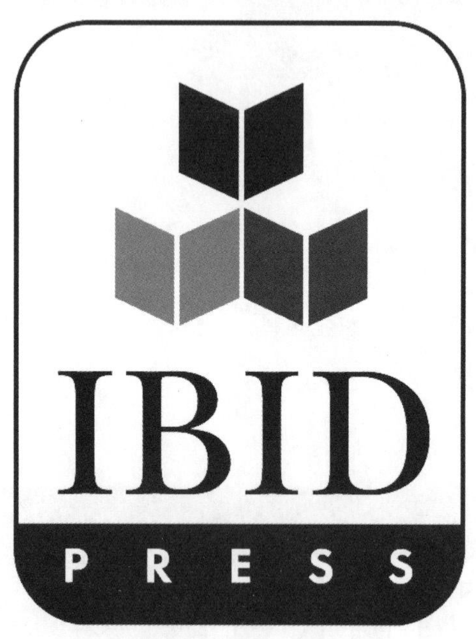

www.ibid.com.au

First published in 2007 by IBID Press, Victoria. Corrected and reprinted January 2008.

Library Catalogue:

Green, J & Damji S.

1. Chemistry, 3rd. edition.

2. International Baccalaureate. Series Title: International Baccalaureate in Detail

ISBN: 978-1-876659-08-0

IBID Press express their thanks to the International Baccalaureate Organization for permission to reproduce its intellectual property.

Cover design by Adcore.

Published by IBID Press, 36 Quail Crescent, Melton, 3337, Australia.

Printed in China through Trojan Press Book Printers

PREFACE TO THE THIRD EDITION

This textbook and CD have been produced independently of IBO as a resource to support the teaching of the Chemistry course of the International Baccalaureate. The examples and questions do not necessarily reflect the views of the official senior examining team appointed by the International Baccalaureate Organisation. The statements from the IB syllabus are reproduced with the permission of the IBO.

In writing this book the authors hope to share material that they have found useful over the years with other Chemistry teachers in the context of the revised International Baccalaureate Chemistry syllabus. Those familiar with this course will find a close correlation between the order in which the book deals with topics and the order in which they appear in the syllabus. The text is accompanied by a series of exercises, most of which have accompanying answers on the CD, making this a useful resource for self-study to reinforce normal classroom teaching.

The arrangement of material according to the IBO syllabus guide is clearly indicated in the Table of Contents, the topic lists on the chapter title pages and also with side tabs for Core, AHL, Options and Extended. HL material for Topics 12-20 has been included in Chapters 2-10 respectively. The category to which the contents of a particular page belongs can be ascertained by looking at the side tabs in the outer margin of the book and/or the syllabus statement (in the coloured boxes) which have been copied directly from the guide for Chemistry (©IBO 2007) and are used with permission.

Coming from different continents the authors have tried to bring some uniformity to the writing style and nomenclature - for example the name of the element 'sulphur' should now appear as 'sulfur'. Nevertheless there will almost certainly be some inconsistencies and we hope that these will be taken as a positive reflection of the international nature of publication.

We hope that you, the reader, will find some of the same satisfaction in using this book that we have experienced in its production.

The authors

Editor's note

This project has involved teachers, authors, proof readers, artists and many other people on several continents. It has been done within an extremely tight timeframe and involved thousands of emails across the world and many different software applications. We are pleased, and trust that you will also be pleased with the final product which went to Press with no known errors. However we know from experience that some typographic and other errors have escaped our proofing process and will emerge as students and teachers start using the books and CDs. We are very keen to identify and correct these errors.

If you wish, you can help us and yourself in the following ways

- Send us an email at rory@ibid.com.au with details of any errors that you notice
- Please visit www.ibid.com.au for errata sheets which will be produced promptly and be freely available as necessary
- Check our website and other publicity regarding our 'Student Guides to Internal Assessment' and 'Volumes of Investigations' for the Core, HL and Options in Biology, Chemistry and Physics. These materials are currently in preparation and are due for publication later this year.

THE AUTHORS

Sadru Damji
Dr Sadru Damji has been IB Deputy Chief Examiner, Principal Moderator for Internal Assessment in Chemistry, Science Curriculum Development Committee, and Chemistry Subject Committee member responsible for writing the earlier IB Subject Guide. Sadru has been a Team Leader for setting, marking and moderating IB examinations for many years and continues to enjoy the opportunity to do so. He was part of the team that produced Phase 1 and Phase 2 of the Teacher Support Material on the Online Curriculum Centre (OCC) as well as being the OCC subject faculty member for several years advising and guiding teachers. As an experienced, dedicated and passionate teacher for both the SL and HL programs, Sadru has presented workshops and trained IB teachers around the world for over 25 years, has learnt a great deal from colleagues, and brings a wealth of experience from these interactions in writing this book.

John Green
Dr John Green has been involved with the IB since joining Kristin School, New Zealand, in 1987, after extensive teaching experience in the UK at Repton and Manchester Grammar School. There, as IB coordinator, he was responsible for the introduction of the IB into the school, the first in New Zealand to offer the programme. John is involved in IB Chemistry as an assistant examiner at HL and previously at SL, as a setter of examination questions and, under the previous programme, he was overall moderator for the SL practical programme. In this role he was involved in a small way with the major syllabus revision in the mid 1990s. At various times John has been present at both Chemistry and Final Grade Award meetings and has run many IB Chemistry workshops in the Asia-Pacific region. John also teaches Theory of Knowledge and has been an assessor for the course. In 1996 John moved to Hong Kong where he is currently Director of Studies at the Li Po Chun United World College.

Acknowledgements

The Publisher wishes to gratefully acknowledge the advice and assistance of the following people in the development and production of these materials to support the teaching of IB Chemistry.

Authors
Sadru Damji and John Green

Proof readers
Chris Talbot and Neville Lawrence

Artwork and graphics
IBID Press and authors

Layout
Chris Houlahan and Colin Flashman

Project management and editing
Science Teaching And Resources (S.T.A.R.)

In particular the authors would like to express their deep gratitude to Chris Talbot, currently teaching IB Chemistry at the Anglo-Chinese School in Singapore for all of his assistance with the publication of this and previous editions of this book. He has worked tirelessly to suggest ways in which the material produced by the authors could be improved and extended and, without his 'eagle eye' many more inconsistencies and typographical errors would have slipped through. Chris has also kindly contributed some exercises, answers and glossary terms.

This book is dedicated to the many supportive family members and colleagues of those people involved in its production during the last 12 months or so.

CONTENTS

Chapter 1 QUANTITATIVE CHEMISTRY

1.1 The mole concept and Avogadro's constant 4
1.2 Formulas 6
1.3 Chemical equations 14
1.4 Mass and gaseous volume relationships in chemical reactions 18
1.5 Solutions 26
Appendix 34

Chapter 2 ATOMIC STRUCTURE

2.1 The atom 47
2.2 The mass spectrometer 52
2.3 Electron arrangement 54
12.1 Electron configuration 61

Chapter 3 PERIODICITY

3.1 The periodic table 70
3.2 Physical properties 72
3.3 Chemical Properties 76
13.1 Trends across period 3 (AHL) 82
13.2 First row D-block elements (AHL) 84

Chapter 4 CHEMICAL BONDING

4.1 Ionic bonding 97
4.2 Covalent bonding 101
14.1 Shapes of molecules and ions (AHL) 110
14.2 Hybridization (AHL) 114
14.3 Delocalization of electrons (AHL) 118
4.3 Intermolecular forces 122
4.4 Metallic bonding 126
4.5 Physical properties 127
4.2 Covalent bonding (cont) 130

Chapter 5 ENERGETICS

5.1 Exothermic & endothermic reactions 135
5.2 Calculation of enthalpy changes 138
5.3 Hess's law 141
5.4 Bond enthalpies 144
15.1 Standard enthalpy changes of reaction (AHL) 147
15.2 Born-Haber cycle (AHL) 151
15.3 Entropy (AHL) 155
15.4 Spontaneity (AHL) 157

Chapter 6 KINETICS

6.1 Rates of reaction 161
6.2 Collision theory 167
16.1 Rate Expression (AHL) 170
16.2 Reaction mechanism (AHL) 175
16.3 Activation energy (AHL) 179

Chapter 7 EQUILIBRIUM

7.1 Dynamic equilibrium 181
7.2 The position of equilibrium 184
17.1 Liquid-vapour equilibrium (AHL) 192
17.2 The equilibrium law (AHL) 194
Extension Material 197

Chapter 8 ACIDS AND BASES

8.1 Theories of acids and bases 207
8.2 Properties of acids and bases 212
8.3 Strong and weak acids & bases 213
8.4 The pH scale 215
18.1 Calculations involving acids & bases (AHL) 217
18.2 Buffer solutions (AHL) 221
18.3 Salt Hydrolysis (AHL) 224
18.4 Acid–base titrations (AHL) 225
18.5 Indicators (AHL) 228

Chapter 9 OXIDATION & REDUCTION

9.1 Introduction to Oxidation & reduction 232
9.2 Redox equations 236
Extension Material 239
9.3 Reactivity 241
9.4 Voltaic cells 243
19.1 Standard electrode potentials (AHL) 245
9.5 Electrolytic cells 250
19.2 Electrolysis (AHL) 251

Chapter 10 ORGANIC CHEMISTRY

10.1 Introduction 255
20.1 Introduction (AHL) 261
10.2 Alkanes 265
10.3 Alkenes 267
10.4 Alcohols 271
10.5 Halogenoalkanes 273
10.6 Reaction pathways 275
20.5 Reaction pathways (AHL) 276
20.2 Nucleophilic substitution reactions (AHL) 277
20.3 Elimination reactions (AHL) 280
20.4 Condensation reactions (AHL) 281
20.6 Stereoisomerism (AHL) 283

Chapter 11 MEASUREMENT AND DATA PROCESSING

11.1 Uncertainty and error in measurement 289
11.2 Uncertainties in calculated results 292
11.3 Graphical techniques 295

Chapter 12 Option A: MODERN ANALYTICAL CHEMISTRY

A1 Analytical techniques 299
A2 Principles of spectroscopy 299
A3 Infrared spectroscopy 302
A4 Mass spectrometry 304
A5 Nuclear magnetic resonance (NMR) spectroscopy 307
A9 Nuclear magnetic resonance (NMR) spectroscopy (HL) 308
A6 Atomic absorption (AA) spectroscopy 310
A7 Chromatography 312
A10 Chromatography (HL) 314
A8 Visible and ultraviolet (UV-Vis) spectroscopy (HL) 318

Chapter 13 Option B: HUMAN BIOCHEMISTRY

B1 Energy 323
B2 Proteins 324
B3 Carbohydrates 331
B4 Lipids 334
B5 Micronutrients and macronutrients 341
B6 Hormones 343
B7 Enzymes (HL) 346
B8 Nucleic acids 351
B9 Respiration (HL) 356

Chapter 14 Option C: CHEMISTRY IN INDUSTRY AND TECHNOLOGY

C1 Iron, steel and aluminium 364
C2 The oil industry 370
C3 Addition polymers 372
C4 Catalysts 374
C5 Fuel cells and rechargeable batteries 379
C6 Liquid crystals 382
C7 Nanotechnology 385
C8 Condensation polymers (HL) 389
C9 Mechanisms in the organic chemicals industry (HL) 392
C10 Silicon and photovoltaic cells (HL) 393
C11 Liquid crystals (HL) 395
C12 The chlor–alkali industry (HL) 397

Chapter 15 Option D: MEDICINES AND DRUGS

D1 Pharmaceutical products 405
D2 Antacids 410
D3 Analgesics 412
D4 Depressants 415
D5 Stimulants 419
D6 Antibacterials 422
D7 Antivirals 424
D8 Drug action (HL) 425
D9 Drug design (HL) 427
D10 Mind altering drugs (HL) 431

Chapter 16 Option E: ENVIRONMENTAL CHEMISTRY

E1 Air pollution 437
E2 Acid deposition 444
E3 Greenhouse effect 447
E4 Ozone depletion 449
E5 Dissolved oxygen in water 451
E6 Water treatment 452
E7 Soil 455
E8 Waste 459
E9 Ozone depletion (HL) 461
E10 Smog (HL) 463
E11 Acid deposition (HL) 465
E12 Water and Soil (HL) 466

Chapter 17 Option F: FOOD CHEMISTRY

F1 Food groups 475
F2 Fats and oils 476
F3 Shelf life 477
F4 Colour 481
F5 Genetically modified foods 486
F6 Texture 487
F9 Stereo-chemistry in food (HL) 488
(HL material from F7, F8 and F10 has been integrated)

Chapter 18 Option G: FURTHER ORGANIC CHEMISTRY

G1 Electrophilic addition reactions 495
G2 Nucleophilic addition reactions 497
G4 Addition–elimination reactions 498
G3 Elimination reactions 499
G5 Arenes 500
G6 Organometallic chemistry 502
G7, G11 Reaction pathways (SL and HL) 503
G8 Acid–base reactions 504
G9 Addition–elimination reactions 506
G10 Electrophilic substitution reactions 507

Glossary 513

Index 553

QUANTITATIVE CHEMISTRY

1

1.1 The mole concept and Avogadro's constant

1.2 Formulas

1.3 Chemical equations

1.4 Mass and gaseous volume relationships in chemical reactions

1.5 Solutions

SOME FUNDAMENTAL CONCEPTS

Chemistry is a science that deals with the composition, structure and reactions of matter. It is involved with looking at the properties of materials and interpreting these in terms of models on a sub-microscopic scale. Investigations form an important part of any study of chemistry. This involves making observations, and using these in the solution of problems. A typical investigation requires choosing a problem, working out a way of attempting to solve it, and then describing both the method, the results and the manner in which these are interpreted. Namely, "a scientist chooses, imagines, does and describes". Along with many other syllabuses, practical investigations are a requirement of IB Chemistry.

Matter occupies space and has mass. It can be subdivided into **mixtures** and **pure substances**. Mixtures consist of a number of different substances, not chemically combined together. Thus the ratio of these components is not constant from one sample of mixture to another. The different components of a mixture often have different **physical properties** (such as melting point and density) and **chemical properties** (such as flammability and acidity). The properties of the mixture are similar to those of the components (e.g. a match burns in both air and pure oxygen), though they will vary with its exact composition. The fact that the different components of the mixture have different physical properties means that the mixture can be separated by physical means, for example by dissolving one component whilst the other remains as a solid. A pure substance cannot be separated in this way because its physical properties are constant throughout all samples of that substance. Similarly all samples of a pure substance have identical chemical properties, for example pure water from any source freezes at 0 °C.

Pure substances may be further subdivided into **elements** and **compounds**. The difference between these is that an element cannot be split up into simpler substances by chemical means, whilst a compound can be changed into these more basic components.

The interpretation on a sub-microscopic scale is that all substances are made up of very tiny particles called **atoms**. Atoms are the smallest particles present in an element which can take part in a chemical change and they cannot be split by ordinary chemical means.

An **element** is a substance that only contains one type of atom, so it cannot be converted into anything simpler by chemical means. (note; 'type' does not imply that all atoms of an element are identical. Some elements are composed of a mixture of closely related atoms called **isotopes** (refer to Section 2.1). All elements have distinct names and symbols. Atoms can join together by **chemical bonds** to form compounds. Compounds are therefore made up of particles (of the same type), but these particles are made up of different types of atoms chemically bonded together. This means that in a **compound**, the constituent elements will be present in fixed proportions such as H_2O (water), H_2SO_4 (sulfuric acid), CO_2 (carbon dioxide) and NH_3 (ammonia). The only way to separate a compound into its component elements is by a chemical change that breaks some bonds and forms new ones, resulting in new substances. The physical and chemical properties of a compound are usually totally unrelated to those of its component elements. For example a match will not burn in water even though it is a compound of oxygen.

If a substance contains different types of particles, then it is a mixture. These concepts in terms of particles are illustrated in Figure 101. Copper, water and air provide good examples of an element, a compound and a mixture respectively.

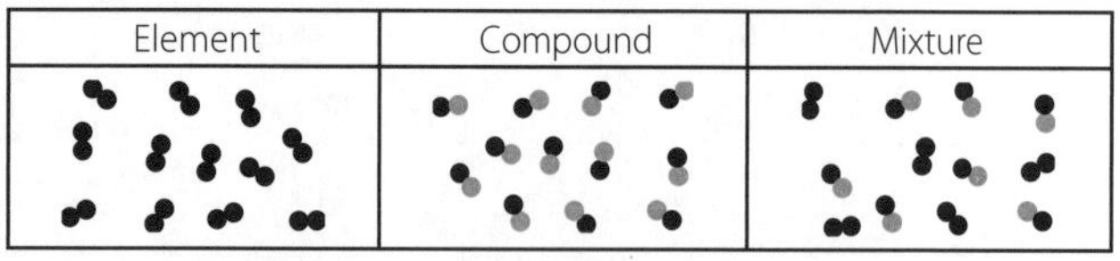

Element	Compound	Mixture

Figure 101 The particles in an element, a compound and a mixture

The term **molecule** refers to a small group of atoms joined together by covalent bonds (refer to Section 4.2). If the atoms are of the same kind, then it is a molecule of an element, if different it is a molecule of a compound. Most elements that are gases are **diatomic** (composed of molecules containing two atoms). Examples are hydrogen gas (H_2), nitrogen gas (N_2) and oxygen gas (O_2). The halogens (F_2, Cl_2, Br_2 and I_2) are also diatomic in all physical states. The noble gases (He, Ne, Ar, Kr, Xe and Rn) however are **monatomic** (i.e. exist as single atoms).

The properties of a typical element, compound and mixture are shown in Figure 102.

THE TYPES OF ATOMS

There are 92 kinds of atoms, and hence 92 chemical elements, that occur naturally and about another seventeen that have been produced artificially. Only about thirty of these elements are usually encountered in school chemistry and most of this would deal with about half of these, shown in bold type in Figure 103. Each element is given a **symbol** that is used to write the formulas of the compounds that it forms. The significance of the **atomic number** and **relative atomic mass** of the elements will be explained in Sections 2.1 and 1.3).

Figure 103 shows the common elements and some of their characteristics.

- Parts of the names where there are common spelling difficulties have been underlined.
- You should know the symbols for the elements, especially those in **bold** type. Most of them are closely related to the name of the element (e.g. chlorine is Cl). Elements that were known in early times have symbols that relate to their Latin names (e.g. Ag, silver, comes from *Argentium*).
- Note that the first letter is always an upper case letter and the second one a lower case, so that, for example Co (cobalt) and CO (carbon monoxide) refer to very different substances.

Substance	Proportions	Properties	Separation
Element Copper - a pure element	Contains only one type of atom.	These will depend on the forces between the atoms of the element.	Cannot be converted to a simpler substance by chemical means.
Compound Water - a compound of oxygen and hydrogen	Always contains two hydrogen atoms for every oxygen atom.	Totally different from its elements, e.g. water is a liquid, but hydrogen and oxygen are gases.	Requires a chemical change, e.g. reacting with sodium will produce hydrogen gas.
Mixture Air - a mixture of nitrogen, oxygen, argon, carbon dioxide etc.	The proportions of the gases in air, especially carbon dioxide and water vapour, can vary.	Similar to its constituents, e.g. supports combustion like oxygen.	Can be carried out by physical means, e.g. by the fractional distillation of liquid air.

Figure 102 The properties of a typical element, compound and mixture

Element	Symbol	Atomic Number	Relative Atomic Mass
Hydrogen	**H**	**1**	**1.01**
Helium	He	2	4.00
Lithium	Li	3	6.94
Beryllium	Be	4	9.01
Boron	B	5	10.81
Carbon	**C**	**6**	**12.01**
Nitrogen	**N**	**7**	**14.01**
Oxygen	**O**	**8**	**16.00**
Fluorine	F	9	19.00
Neon	Ne	10	20.18
Sodium	**Na**	**11**	**22.99**
Magnesium	**Mg**	**12**	**24.31**
Aluminium	**Al**	**13**	**26.98**
Silicon	Si	14	28.09
Phosphorus	**P**	**15**	**30.97**
Sulfur	**S**	**16**	**32.06**
Chlorine	**Cl**	**17**	**35.45**
Argon	Ar	18	39.95
Potassium	**K**	**19**	**39.10**
Calcium	**Ca**	**20**	**40.08**
Chromium	Cr	24	52.00
Manganese	Mn	25	54.94
Iron	**Fe**	**26**	**55.85**
Cobalt	Co	27	58.93
Nickel	Ni	28	58.71
Copper	**Cu**	**29**	**63.55**
Zinc	**Zn**	**30**	**65.37**
Bromine	Br	35	79.90
Silver	Ag	47	107.87
Iodine	I	53	126.90
Barium	Ba	56	137.34
Lead	**Pb**	**82**	**207.19**

Figure 103 The common elements

TOK Numbers in Chemistry

Try to imagine what it must have been like to have been an alchemist about 500 years ago. Apart from trying experiments out for yourself, you might be able to read in some books (if you had enough money to buy them - they were very expensive in those days) experiments other people had done, but there was probably little order to it. There was no theoretical paradigm underpinning observations, no framework within which to relate substances other than superficial groupings such as substances that change colour when heated, substances that burn, substances that dissolve.

This all changed with John Dalton's atomic theory, propounded in the early 19th century, which is the basis of modern chemistry:

- Elements are made of tiny particles called atoms
- All atoms of a given element are identical.
- The atoms of a given element are different from those of any other element .
- Atoms of one element can combine with atoms of other elements to form compounds. A given compound always has the same relative numbers of the different types of atoms.
- Atoms cannot be created, divided into smaller particles, nor destroyed in the chemical process. A chemical reaction simply changes the way atoms are grouped together.

The second point might need slight amendment to take account of isotopes, but apart from that this is more or less what we take for granted nowadays. Even though we now take it for granted, it was not universally accepted until late in the 19th century - a common feature of any paradigm change.

So where did atomic theory come from? Did Dalton just dream up these rules? Far from it, his atomic theory was the crowning achievement of quantitative chemistry, pioneered notably by Antoine Lavoisier, during the preceding half century. These scientists for the first time started to systematically record the masses of the reactants and products during their reactions. Having numbers allowed people to use mathematics in their application of deductive logic to discover patterns in their results. The patterns discovered led scientists to postulate about the existence of atoms (an idea that goes back to the ancient Greeks) and to propose that these had

Exercise

1. A grey solid when heated vapourised to form pure white crystals on the cooler parts of the test tube leaving a black solid as the residue. It is likely that the original solid was

   A an element.
   B a metal.
   C a pure compound.
   D a mixture.

2. Which one of the following is a chemical property rather than a physical property?

   A Boiling point
   B Density
   C Flammability
   D Hardness

3. Which one of the following is a physical change rather than a chemical change?

   A Combustion
   B Distillation
   C Decomposition
   D Neutralisation

4. State whether the sketches below represent elements, compounds or mixtures.

   A B C D E

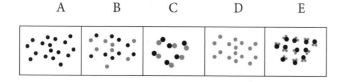

5. State whether the following refer to an element, a compound or a mixture:

   (a) Easily separated into two substances by distillation.
   (b) Its components are always present in the same proportions.
   (c) Its properties are similar to those of its components.
   (d) Cannot be broken down by chemical means.
   (e) Very different properties to its components.

1.1 THE MOLE CONCEPT AND AVOGADRO'S CONSTANT

1.1.1 Apply the mole concept to substances.

1.1.2 Determine the number of particles and the amount of substance (in moles).

Atoms and **molecules** are inconceivably minute, with equally small masses. The masses of all atoms are not however the same and it is often convenient to be able to weigh out amounts of substances that contain the same number of atoms or molecules. The same amount of any substance will therefore contain the same number of particles and we measure the **amount of substance** in **moles**. It is for this reason that the **mole concept** is important.

Amount of substance, *n* (the number of moles), is a quantity that is proportional to the number of particles in a sample of substance: its units are moles (mol). A mole of a substance contains 6.02×10^{23} particles of the substance (this very large number is expressed in scientific notation; for further explanation of scientific notation refer to Appendix 1A). This is the same number of particles as there are atoms in exactly 12 g of the C-12 ($^{12}_{6}C$) isotope.

Since a mole of carbon atoms weighs 12 g, an atom of carbon (C) weighs only: 1.995×10^{-23} g atom^{-1}.

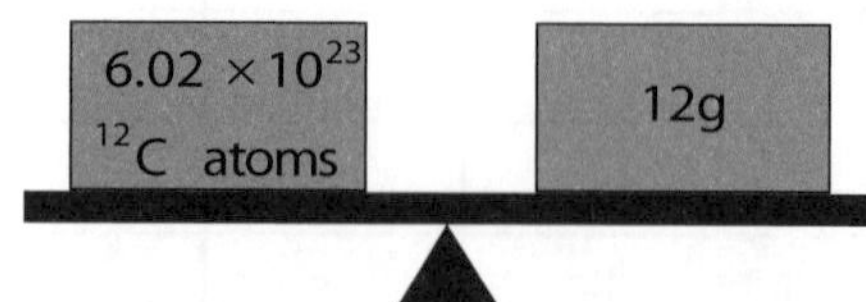

Figure 105 Avogadro's number

The value 6.02×10^{23} mol^{-1} is called the Avogadro's Constant (L or N_A). The particles may be atoms, molecules, ions, formula units, etc., but should be specified. For example, 1 mol of carbon contains 6.02×10^{23} carbon (C) atoms (and weighs 12 g), where as 1 mol of water, H_2O, contains 6.02×10^{23} H_2O molecules or $3 \times 6.02 \times 10^{23}$ atoms since each water molecule contains a total of 3 atoms.

$$\text{Number of moles} = \frac{\text{Number of particles}}{6.02 \times 10^{23}}$$

This can be written as $n = \frac{N}{6.02 \times 10^{23}}$ or $N = n \times 6.02 \times 10^{23}$.

A sample of water that contains 3.01×10^{25} water molecules therefore contains $\frac{3.01 \times 10^{25}}{6.02 \times 10^{23}} = 50$ moles of water molecules.

This is very similar to saying that 36 oranges is equivalent to 3 dozen oranges ($\frac{36}{12} = 3$).

The formula may be rearranged to calculate the number of particles. For example 0.020 moles of carbon dioxide will contain $0.020 \times 6.02 \times 10^{23} = 1.2 \times 10^{22}$ molecules of CO_2.

This number of molecules of carbon dioxide will contain 1.2×10^{22} atoms of carbon but 2.4×10^{22} (i.e. $2 \times 1.2 \times 10^{22}$) atoms of oxygen, because each molecule contains one atom of carbon, but two atoms of oxygen and the total number of atoms is 3.6×10^{22} (i.e. $3 \times 1.2 \times 10^{22}$). Note, therefore, how important it is to state what particles are being referred to.

TOK The scale of chemistry

'Chemistry deals with enormous differences in scale. The magnitude of Avogadro's constant is beyond the scale of our everyday experience'.

© IBO 2007

Dealing with very large and very small scales is almost impossible for the human brain - maybe it would disconcert our egos to be continually aware that we are infinitesimal dots living on an infinitesimal dot! So how can we try to come to terms with the enormous and minute numbers we meet in science? One approach is to try to apply the scale to things we are familiar with. For example if sand were made up of cubic grains $1/10^{th}$ mm on each side, then what length of a beach 60 m deep and 1 km wide would 1 mole (i.e. 6×10^{23}) of these form? The answer is about 10,000 km of it!!! Coming from the other end, suppose the population of the whole world (let's say 4000 million people) were turned into atoms of gold (quite big, heavy atoms) our combined mass would be about one-millionth of a microgram, too small for any balance to detect (our grains of sand above would weigh about 2 μg) and we would form a cube with a side of about $^1/_{50}$ μm, a factor of ten below the theoretical range of the best optical microscope. Hence we would not be able to detect ourselves! Fortunately we have mathematics to rely on, so we do not have to depend on being able to imagine these scales!

Exercise 1.1

(Take the value of Avogadro's constant as 6.02×10^{23} mol^{-1}.)

1. Calculate how many atoms are there in 5 moles of sulfur atoms.

   A 1.20×10^{23}
   B 6.02×10^{23}
   C 6.02×10^{115}
   D 3.01×10^{24}

2. Which one of the following is not the same number as the rest?

   A The number of molecules in 4 moles of CO_2.
   B The number of hydrogen atoms in 2 moles of H_2O.
   C The number of chloride ions in 4 moles of $CaCl_2$.
   D The number of hydrogen atoms in 1 mole of C_3H_8.

3. The number of atoms present in 0.10 mol of ethene (C_2H_4) is:

   A 3.61×10^{22}
   B 6.02×10^{22}
   C 3.61×10^{23}
   D 6.02×10^{23}

4. One mole of water contains

   A 6.02×10^{23} atoms of hydrogen.
   B 2.01×10^{23} atoms of oxygen.
   C 6.02×10^{23} atoms in total.
   D 6.02×10^{23} molecules of water.

5. The number of atoms present in 36 molecules of glucose ($C_6H_{12}O_6$) is

   A 24
   B 36
   C 24×36
   D $24 \times 36 \times 6.02 \times 10^{23}$

6. The mass of one atom of carbon -12 is:

   A 1 g.
   B 12 g.
   C $12 \times 6.02 \times 10^{23}$ g.
   D $12 / 6.02 \times 10^{23}$ g.

CORE

7. A sample of phosphoric(V) acid H_3PO_4 contains 1.2×10^{23} molecules.

   (a) Calculate how many moles of phosphoric(V) acid is this.
   (b) Calculate how many atoms of phosphorus will there be.
   (c) Calculate how many atoms of hydrogen will it contain.

8. (a) Calculate how many molecules are there in 6 moles of hydrogen sulfide (H_2S).

   (b) The formula of gold(III) chloride is $AuCl_3$. Calculate how many chloride ions are there in 0.30 moles of gold(III) chloride.

1.2 FORMULAS

1.2.1 Define the terms relative atomic mass (A_r) and relative molecular mass (M_r).

1.2.2 Calculate the mass of one mole of a species from its formula.

© IBO 2007

The atomic mass, A, of an element indicates how heavy an atom of that element is compared to an atom of another element where a standard, the carbon-12 isotope ($^{12}_{6}C$), is assigned a value of exactly 12 g mol^{-1}. Atomic mass therefore has units of g mol^{-1}, hence A(C) = 12.01 g mol^{-1} and A(Cl) = 35.45 g mol^{-1}. **Formula mass** is the sum of the atomic masses of the atoms in the compound formula (so it also has units of g mol^{-1}), and usually refers to ionic compounds. Similarly **molecular mass** is the sum of the atomic masses of all the atoms in one molecule (again expressed in units of g mol^{-1}).

The relative atomic mass, A_r, is the ratio of the average mass per atom of an element to $^1/_{12}$ of the mass of an atom of the C-12 isotope. A_r therefore has no units. Thus, A_r(C) = 12.01 and A_r(Cl) = 35.45. This scale is approximately equal to a scale on which a hydrogen atom has a relative atomic mass of 1. Relative atomic masses are shown on the **periodic table** and those of the common elements are given in Figure 103. Most are approximately whole numbers, but some are not because these elements exist as mixtures of **isotopes** (refer to Section 2.1). With **elements**, especially the common gaseous elements, it is very important to differentiate between the relative atomic mass and the **relative molecular mass**. Thus nitrogen, for example, has a relative atomic mass of 14.01, but a relative molecular mass of 28.02 because it exists as diatomic molecules (N_2). The relative molecular mass, M_r, similarly indicates how heavy a molecule is compared to the C-12 isotope and, like the concept of relative atomic mass, is defined as the ratio of the average mass of a molecule of the substance to $^1/_{12}$ of the mass of an atom of the C-12 ($^{12}_{6}C$) isotope, so M_r also has no units.

Molar mass, M, is the mass of one mole of any substance such as atoms, molecules, ions, etc., where the carbon-12 ($^{12}_{6}C$) isotope is assigned a value of exactly 12 g mol^{-1} and is a particularly useful term as it applies to any entity. The molar mass should be accompanied by the formula of the particles. Consider chlorine, where ambiguity is possible because the molar mass of chlorine atoms (Cl) is 35.45 g mol^{-1}, but the molar mass of chlorine molecules (Cl_2) is 70.90 g mol^{-1}. The molar mass, *M*, of a compound is determined by adding the atomic masses of all the elements in the compound.

Thus $M(CO_2)$ = 12.01 + (2 × 16.00) = 44.01 g mol^{-1} of CO_2 and the molar mass of sulfuric acid (H_2SO_4) is: (2 × 1.01) + 32.06 + (4 × 16.00) = 98.08 g mol^{-1} of H_2SO_4.

If a substance contains water of crystallisation, then this must be included in the molar mass, for example the molar mass of sodium sulfate heptahydrate crystals ($Na_2SO_4.7H_2O$) is: (2 × 22.99) + 32.06 + (4 × 16.00) + (7 × 18.02) = 268.18 g mol^{-1} of $Na_2SO_4.7H_2O$.

If the mass of a substance and its formula are given, the amount of substance,

$$n = \frac{\text{Mass (g)}}{\text{Molar Mass (g mol}^{-1})} \qquad n = \frac{m}{M}$$

You can calculate any one quantity given the other two. Thus the mass, m = n (mol) × M (g mol^{-1}) (m=n . M), and M (g mol^{-1}) = m (g) / n (mol) $(M = \frac{m}{n})$

Exercise 1.2

1. The molar mass of iron(III) sulfate $Fe_2(SO_4)_3$ will be

   A 191.76 g mol^{-1}
   B 207.76 g mol^{-1}
   C 344.03 g mol^{-1}
   D 399.88 g mol^{-1}

2. A certain substance has a molar mass (to 2 significant figures) of 28 g mol^{-1}. Which of the following is not a possible formula?

   A CH_2O
   B Si
   C C_2H_4
   D CO

3. Calculate the molar mass of the following substances (correct to 1 decimal place).

   (a) HI
   (b) $NaClO_3$
   (c) $(NH_4)_2HPO_4$
   (d) $(CO_2H)_2.2H_2O$
   (e) Chromium(III) oxide
   (f) Iodine trichloride

Moles and Mass

1.2.3 Solve problems involving the relationship between the amount of substance in moles, mass and molar mass.

© IBO 2007

It follows from the above that the mass of one mole of any substance will be equal to its molar mass in grams. If one mole of fluorine atoms has a mass of 19 g, then 76 g of fluorine atoms will contain four moles of fluorine atoms, hence the amount of substance may be calculated from its molar mass using the formula

Amount of substance,

$$n = \frac{\text{Mass (g)}}{\text{Molar Mass (g mol}^{-1})} \qquad n = \frac{m}{M}$$

4.904 g of sulfuric acid will therefore contain:

$$\frac{m}{M} = \frac{4.904 \text{ g}}{98.08 \text{ g mol}^{-1}}$$

$$= 0.05000 \text{ moles of sulfuric acid}$$

[**Note** - It is important to pay attention to significant figures in calculations. A short description of the scientific notation and significant figures is given later in the chapter.]

The equation may be rearranged to calculate the molar mass from the mass and the amount of substance, or to find the mass from the amount and the molar mass. For example the mass of 3.00 moles of carbon dioxide is

$$n \times M = 3.00 \text{ mol} \times 44.01 \text{ g mol}^{-1}$$
$$= 132 \text{ g of carbon dioxide}$$

Similarly if 0.200 moles of a substance has a mass of 27.8 g, then its molar mass (M) will be

$$M = \frac{m}{n} = \frac{27.8 \text{ g}}{0.200 \text{ mol}} = 139 \text{ g mol}^{-1}$$

Knowing the mass of a given number of atoms or molecules means that the mass of one atom or molecule can be calculated. For example as the molar mass of the hydrogen atom is 1.01 g mol^{-1}, 6.02×10^{23} atoms of hydrogen have a mass of 1.01 g, hence the mass of a single atom is:

$$\frac{1.01 \text{ g mol}^{-1}}{6.02 \times 10^{23} \text{ atoms mol}^{-1}}$$

$$= 1.68 \times 10^{-24} \text{ g atom}^{-1}$$

Similarly the mass of one molecule of glucose ($C_6H_{12}O_6$, $M = 180.18$ g mol^{-1}) is:

$$\frac{180.18 \text{ g mol}^{-1}}{6.02 \times 10^{23} \text{ molecules mol}^{-1}}$$

$$= 2.99 \times 10^{-22} \text{ g molecule}^{-1}$$

Exercise 1.2.3

1. Determine the mass of 0.700 moles of Li_2SO_4 taking its molar mass as exactly 110 g mol^{-1}.

   A 15.4 g
   B 77 g
   C 110 g
   D 157 g

2. 0.200 moles of a substance has a mass of 27.0 g. Determine the molar mass of the substance.

   A 13.5 g mol^{-1}
   B 27 g mol^{-1}
   C 54 g mol^{-1}
   D 135 g mol^{-1}

3. One drop of water weighs 0.040 g. Calculate how many molecules are there in one drop, taking the molar mass of water as exactly 18 g þmol^{-1}.

   A 1.3×10^{21}
   B 2.4×10^{22}
   C 3.3×10^{22}
   D 3.9×10^{22}

4. Determine the mass (in g) of one molecule of sulfuric acid (H_2SO_4).

   A 98.08
   B $98.08 \div (6.02 \times 10^{23})$
   C $98.08 \div 7$
   D $98.08 \div (7 \times 6.02 \times 10^{23})$

5. A polymer molecule has a mass of 2.5×10^{-20} g. Determine the molar mass of the polymer.

   A 1.4×10^{4} g mol^{-1}
   B 2.4×10^{43} g mol^{-1}
   C 6.7×10^{-5} g mol^{-1}
   D 4.2×10^{-44} g mol^{-1}

6. Calculate (correct to 3 significant figures) the mass of

   (a) 3.00 moles of ammonia.
   (b) ¼ mole of Li_2O.
   (c) 0.0500 moles of aluminium nitrate.
   (d) 3.01×10^{23} molecules of PCl_3.
   (e) 2.60×10^{22} molecules of dinitrogen monoxide.

7. Calculate how many moles are there in

   (a) 28.1 g of silicon.
   (b) 303 g of KNO_3.
   (c) 4000 g of nickel sulfate.
   (d) 87.3 g of methane.

8. a) 0.30 moles of a substance has a mass of 45 g. Determine its molar mass.

   b) 3.01×10^{25} molecules of a gas has a mass of 6.40 kg. Determine its molar mass.

9. Some types of freon are used as the propellant in spray cans of paint, hair spray, and other consumer products. However, the use of freons is being curtailed, because there is some suspicion that they may cause environmental damage. If there are 25.00 g of the freon CCl_2F_2 in a spray can, calculate how many molecules are you releasing to the air when you empty the can.

10. Vitamin C, ascorbic acid, has the formula $C_6H_8O_6$.

   a) The recommended daily dose of vitamin C is 60.0 milligrams. Calculate how many moles are you consuming if you ingest 60 milligrams of the vitamin.
   b) A typical tablet contains 1.00 g of vitamin C. Calculate how many moles of vitamin C does this represents.
   c) When you consume 1.00 g of vitamin C, calculate how many oxygen atoms are you eating.

1.2.4 Distinguish between the terms empirical formula and molecular formula.

1.2.5 Determine the empirical formula from the percentage composition or from other experimental data.

1.2.6 Determine the molecular formula when given the empirical formula and experimental data.

Percentage Composition and Empirical Formula

Knowing the formula of a substance and the molar masses of the elements, then the percentage composition may be found by calculating the proportion by mass of each element and converting it to a percentage. For example the molar mass of carbon dioxide is

$$12.01 + (2 \times 16.00) = 44.01 \text{ g mol}^{-1}$$

Oxygen constitutes 32.00 g mol^{-1} of this (2×16.00), so that the percentage of oxygen by mass in carbon dioxide is:

$$\frac{32.00}{44.01} \times 100 = 72.71\% \text{ oxygen by mass.}$$

The empirical formula, sometimes called the simplest formula, of a compound indicates:

- the elements present in the compound
- the simplest whole number ratio of these elements

It may be found by dividing the coefficients in the molecular formula by their highest common factor, for example the molecular formula of glucose is $C_6H_{12}O_6$, so its empirical formula is CH_2O.

If the mass of the elements in a compound is found by experiment (empirical means "by experiment"), then the amount of each element may be found using its molar mass and the formula:

$$n = \frac{m}{M}$$

Example 1

2.476 g of an oxide of copper is found to contain 2.199 g of copper. Determine its empirical formula.

Solution

The oxide therefore contains 0.277 g (2.476g – 2.199g) of oxygen. The amount of each element can therefore be calculated using the molar masses (O = 16.00 g mol^{-1}; Cu = 63.55 g mol^{-1}).

$$\text{Amount of oxygen} = \frac{0.277\text{ g}}{16.00\text{ g mol}^{-1}} = 0.01731\text{ mol}$$

$$\text{Amount of copper} = \frac{2.199\text{ g}}{63.55\text{ g mol}^{-1}} = 0.03460\text{ mol}$$

The whole number ratio of oxygen to copper may be found by dividing through by the smaller number

Ratio of O : Cu = 0.01731: 0.3460 = 1: 1.999 (dividing by 0.01731)

The simplest whole number ratio of oxygen to copper is therefore 1: 2, so that the empirical formula is Cu_2O.

In some cases this does not give whole numbers and then multiplying by a small integer will be necessary. For example a ratio of Fe:O of 1:1⅓ gives a whole number ratio of 3:4 when multiplied by 3. Percentage composition data can be used in a similar way.

Example 2

Determine the empirical formula of a compound of phosphorus and oxygen that contains 43.64% phosphorus by mass.

Solution

In 100 g, there are 43.64 g of phosphorus and 56.36 g (i.e. 100 – 43.64 g) of oxygen.

$$\text{Amount of phosphorus} = \frac{43.64\text{ g}}{30.97\text{ g mol}^{-1}} = 1.409\text{ mol}$$

$$\text{Amount of oxygen} = \frac{56.36\text{ g}}{16.00\text{ g mol}^{-1}} = 3.523\text{ mol}$$

The whole number ratio of phosphorus to oxygen may be found by dividing through by the smaller number:

Ratio of P : O = 1.409 : 3.523
= 1 : 2.5 (dividing by 1.409)
= 2 : 5 (multiplying by 2)

In this case it is necessary to multiply by a small integer, in this case 2, in order to produce a whole number ratio. The empirical formula is, therefore, P_2O_5.

Similar techniques may also be applied to calculate the amount of water of crystallisation in hydrated salts, by calculating the ratio of the amount of water to the amount of anhydrous salt.

In summary:

- Calculate the amount (in moles) of each element (or component).
- Find the simplest whole number ratio between these amounts.

EXPERIMENTAL METHODS

Empirical formulas can often be found by direct determination, for example converting a weighed sample of one element to the compound and then weighing the compound to find the mass of the second element that combined with the first (see exercise 1.5, Q 13). Another method is to decompose a weighed sample of a compound containing only two elements, so that only one element remains and then finding the mass of that element. This second method is similar to the one that is usually used to determine the formula of a hydrated salt (see exercise 1.5, Q 14). There are also many other methods for determining percentage composition data, too numerous to mention.

The percentage composition of organic compounds is usually found by burning a known mass of the compound in excess oxygen, then finding the masses of both carbon dioxide (all the carbon is converted to carbon dioxide) and water (all the hydrogen is converted to water) formed. The mass of oxygen can be found by subtracting the mass of these two elements from the initial mass, assuming that this is the only other element present.

Example 1

2.80 g of an organic compound, containing only carbon and hydrogen forms 8.80 g of carbon dioxide and 3.60 g of water when it undergoes complete combustion. Determine its empirical formula.

Solution

Amount of CO_2 = amount of C

$$\text{Amount of C} = \frac{m}{M} = \frac{8.80 \text{ g}}{44.0 \text{ g mol}^{-1}} = 0.200 \text{ mol}$$

Amount of H_2O = ½ amount of H

$$\text{Amount of } H_2O = \frac{m}{M} = \frac{3.60 \text{ g}}{18.0 \text{ g mol}^{-1}} = 0.200 \text{ mol}$$

Therefore amount of H = 2 × 0.200
= 0.400 mol

Ratio C : H = 0.200 : 0.400 = 1 : 2;
Therefore the empirical formula is CH_2.

Example 2

Consider vitamin C, a compound that contains carbon, hydrogen and oxygen only. On combustion of 1.00 g vitamin C, 1.50 g CO_2 and 0.408 g H_2O are produced. Determine the empirical formula of vitamin C.

Solution

All the carbon in the CO_2 came from the vitamin C. The mass of carbon in 1.50 g CO_2 can be easily calculated.

$$\text{Amount of } CO_2 = \frac{m}{M} = \frac{1.50 \text{ g}}{44.0 \text{ g mol}^{-1}} = 0.03408 \text{ mol}$$

Since each CO_2 contains 1 C

$$m_C = n_C \times A(C) = 0.0340(8) \text{ mol} \times 12.01 \text{ g mol}^{-1} = 0.409 \text{ g C}$$

1.50 g CO_2 contains 0.409 g of C
all of which came from vitamin C.

Similarly, all the H in the H_2O is from the vitamin C:

18.02 g H_2O contains 2.02 g H

$$\therefore 0.408 \text{ g } H_2O \text{ contains } 0.408 \text{ g} \times \frac{2.02}{18.02} = 0.0457 \text{ g of hydrogen}$$

The rest must therefore be oxygen:

∴ Mass of oxygen = (1.00 – 0.409 – 0.0457) g
= 0.54(5) g

Once the proportion by mass of the elements is known, the mole ratios can be calculated:

	C	H	O
m (g):	0.409	0.0457	0.54(5)
A_r:	12.01	1.01	16.00
n (mol):	0.0341	0.0452	0.0341
divide by smallest number:			
	1.00	1.33	1.00
	1 :	1⅓ :	1
	3 :	4 :	3

Therefore the empirical formula of vitamin C is $C_3H_4O_3$

MOLECULAR FORMULA

The molecular formula of a compound indicates:

- the elements present in the compound
- the actual number of atoms of these elements in one molecule

Hence the molar mass can be calculated from the molecular formula, as can the percentage composition by mass and the empirical formula. Note that the molecular formula of a compound is a multiple of its empirical formula, e.g., for butane, its molecular formula is C_4H_{10} and its empirical formula is C_2H_5. Other examples are shown in Figure 106. It therefore follows the relative molecular divided by the relative empirical mass is a whole number.

n.b.The relative empirical mass is the sum of the relative atomic masses of the atoms in the empirical (simplest) formula.

The relative molecular mass, M_r, for a compound can be determined experimentally using mass spectrometry (refer to Section 2.2), or from physical properties such as the density of the substance in the gas phase (refer to Section 1.4) making it possible to determine the molecular formula of the compound provided the empirical formula is known.

It can be seen from Figure 106 that ethyne and benzene both have the same empirical formula (CH), but the relative molar mass of ethyne is ≈ 26, whereas that of benzene is ≈ 78, so the molecular formula of ethyne must be C_2H_2 (2 × CH) whereas that of benzene is C_6H_6 .

In the case of the compound with the empirical formula P_2O_5, the molecular formula could actually be P_2O_5 or it could be P_4O_{10}, P_6O_{15}, P_8O_{20} etc. The relative empirical mass of P_2O_5 is 141.94 .

In order to know which molecular formula is correct, it is necessary to have information about the approximate molar mass of the substance. The molar mass of this oxide of phosphorus is found to be ≈ 280 g mol^{-1}. It must therefore contain two P_2O_5 units, hence the molecular formula is P_4O_{10}.

Compound	Percentage composition	Empirical Formula	M_r	Molecular Formula
Ethane	$\%H = 6 \times {}^{1.01}/_{30.08} = 20.1\%$; $\%C = 2 \times {}^{12.01}/_{30.08} = 79.9\%$	CH_3	30.08	C_2H_6
Hexene	$\%H = 12 \times {}^{1.01}/_{84.18} = 14.4\%$; $\%C = 6 \times {}^{12.01}/_{84.18} = 85.6\%$	CH_2	84.18	C_6H_{12}
Benzene	$\%H = 6 \times {}^{1.01}/_{78.12} = 7.8\%$; $\%C = 6 \times {}^{12.01}/_{78.12} = 92.2\%$	CH	78.12	C_6H_6
Ethyne	$\%H = 2 \times {}^{1.01}/_{26.04} = 7.8\%$; $\%C = 2 \times {}^{12.01}/_{26.04} = 92.2\%$	CH	26.04	C_2H_2

Figure 106 The percentage composition and empirical formulas of some hydrocarbons

Example 1

A hydrocarbon contains 92.24% by mass of carbon and its M_r = 78.1. Determine its molecular formula.

Solution

	C	H
m (g):	92.24	(100-92.24) = 7.76
M_r:	12.01	1.01
n (mol):	1 :	1

Simplest formula is CH, and its relative empirical mass = 12.01 + 1.01 = 13.02

Since M_r = 78.1; molecular formula is C_6H_6.

CORE

Example 2

The percentage of carbon, hydrogen and nitrogen in an unknown compound is found to be 23.30%, 4.85% and 40.78% respectively. Calculate the empirical formula of the compound.

Solution

Since % ≠ 100, the rest must be oxygen. ∴ % oxygen = (100 – 23.30 – 4.85 – 40.78) = 31.07% O

Assume 100 g sample, then percentages become masses in grams:

	C	H	N	O
m (g):	23.30	4.85	40.78	31.07
A_r:	12.01	1.01	14.00	16.00
$n = m/A_r$ (mol):				
	1.940	4.80	2.913	1.942
divide by smallest n				
	1	2.5	1.5	1
	2	5	3	2

∴ The empirical formula is $C_2H_5N_3O_2$

Exercise 1.2.4

1. Determine the percentage by mass of silver in silver sulfide (Ag_2S).

   A 33.3%
   B 66.7%
   C 77.1%
   D 87.1%

2. Of the following, the only empirical formula is

   A N_2F_2
   B N_2F_4
   C HNF_2
   D H_2N_2

3. A compound of nitrogen and fluorine contains 42% by mass of nitrogen. If the molar mass of the compound is about 66 g mol^{-1}, determine its molecular formula.

   A NF
   B N_2F_2
   C NF_2
   D N_2F

4. An organic compound which has the empirical formula CHO has a relative molecular mass of 232. Its molecular formula is:

   A CHO
   B $C_2H_2O_2$
   C $C_4H_4O_4$
   D $C_8H_8O_8$

5. 3.40 g of anhydrous calcium sulfate (M = 136 g mol^{-1}) is formed when 4.30 g of hydrated calcium sulfate is heated to constant mass. Calculate how many moles of water of crystallisation are combined with each mole of calcium sulfate.

   A 1
   B 2
   C 3
   D 4

6. 2.40 g of element Z combines exactly with 1.60 g of oxygen to form a compound with the formula ZO_2. Determine the relative atomic mass of Z.

   A 24.0
   B 32.0
   C 48.0
   D 64.0

7. Of the following, the only empirical formula is

   A $C_{12}H_{22}O_{11}$
   B $C_6H_{12}O_6$
   C C_6H_6
   D C_2H_4

8. A certain compound has a molar mass of about 56 g mol^{-1}. All the following are possible empirical formulas for this compound except

   A CH_2
   B CH_2O
   C C_3H_4O
   D CH_2N

9. The empirical formula of a compound with the molecular formula $C_6H_{12}O_3$ is

   A $C_6H_{12}O_3$
   B $C_3H_6O_2$
   C C_2H_3O
   D C_2H_4O

10. What percentage of 'chrome alum' [$KCr(SO_4)_2.12H_2O$; M = 499.4 g mol^{-1}] is water.

   A $\frac{18.01}{499.4} \times 100$

   B $\frac{12 \times 18.01}{499.4} \times 100$

   C $\frac{18.01}{499.4 - 18.01} \times 100$

   D $\frac{12 \times 18.01}{499.4 - (12 \times 18.01)} \times 100$

11. What percentage by mass of sodium thiosulfate pentahydrate ($Na_2S_2O_3.5H_2O$) is water.

12. a) 2.0 g of an oxide of iron contains approximately 0.60 g oxygen and 1.4 g iron. Determine the empirical formula of the oxide.

    b) A compound of silicon and fluorine contains about 73% fluorine by mass. Determine its empirical formula.

    c) A compound of carbon, hydrogen and oxygen only, with a molar mass of ≈90 g mol^{-1} contains 26.6% carbon and 2.2% hydrogen by mass. Determine its molecular formula.

13. 1.000 g of tin metal burns in air to give 1.270 g of tin oxide. Determine the empirical formula of the oxide.

14. A 1.39 g sample of hydrated copper(II) sulfate ($CuSO_4.xH_2O$) is heated until all the water of hydration is driven off. The anhydrous salt has a mass of 0.89 g. Determine the formula of the hydrate.

15. The red colour of blood is due to haemoglobin. It contains 0.335% by mass of iron. Four atoms of iron are present in each molecule of haemoglobin. If the molar mass of iron is 55.84 g mol^{-1}, estimate the molar mass of haemoglobin.

16. A 200.0 mg sample of a compound containing potassium, chromium, and oxygen was analyzed and found to contain 70.8 mg chromium and 53.2 mg potassium. Calculate the empirical formula of the sample.

17. The molecular formula of the insecticide DDT is $C_{14}H_9Cl_5$. Calculate the molar mass of the compound and the percent by mass of each element.

18. The percentages of carbon, hydrogen, and oxygen in vitamin C are determined by burning a sample of vitamin C weighing 1.000 g. The masses of CO_2 and H_2O formed are 1.500 g and 0.408 g, respectively.

    a) Calculate the masses and amounts of carbon and hydrogen in the sample.
    b) Determine the amount of oxygen in the sample.
    c) From the above data, determine the empirical formula of vitamin C.

19. The percentages by mass of carbon, hydrogen and nitrogen in an unknown compound are found to be 23.30%, 4.85%, and 40.78%, respectively. (Why do. these not add up to 100%?). Determine the empirical formula of the compound. If the molar mass of the compound is 206 g mol^{-1}, determine its molecular formula.

20. Efflorescence is the process by which some hydrated salts lose water of crystallisation when exposed to the air. 'Washing soda' ($Na_2CO_3.10H_2O$) is converted to the monohydrate ($Na_2CO_3.H_2O$) when exposed to the air. Determine the percentage loss in mass of the crystals.

1.3 CHEMICAL EQUATIONS

CORE

1.3.1 Deduce chemical equations when all reactants and products are given.

1.3.2 Identify the mole ratio of any two species in a chemical equation.

1.3.3 Apply the state symbols (s), (l), (g) and (aq).

CHEMICAL FORMULAS

Chemical formulas are a shorthand notation for elements, ions and compounds. They show the ratio of the number of atoms of each element present and, in the case of molecules or ions held together by covalent bonds, it gives the actual number of atoms of each element present in the molecule or ion. For example, the formula for magnesium chloride, which is ionically bonded, is $MgCl_2$. This tells us that in magnesium chloride there are twice as many chloride ions as there are magnesium ions. The formulas of ionic compounds can be deduced from the electrical charges of the ions involved (refer to Section 4.1).The formula for glucose, which is a molecular covalent compound, is $C_6H_{12}O_6$. This tells us that a molecule of glucose contains six carbon atoms, twelve hydrogen atoms and six oxygen atoms. The formulas of covalent compounds have to be memorised or deduced from their names.

The carbonate ion, which is a covalently bonded ion, has the formula CO_3^{2-}. This tells us that the carbonate ion consists of a carbon atom bonded to three oxygen atoms, that has also gained two electrons (hence the charge). Brackets are used to show that the subscript affects a group of atoms, for example the formula of magnesium nitrate is $Mg(NO_3)_2$, showing that there are two nitrate ions (NO_3^-) for every magnesium ion (Mg^{2+}). Sometimes brackets are also used to indicate the structure of the compound, for example urea is usually written as $(NH_2)_2CO$ rather than CN_2H_4O, to show that it consists of a carbon joined to two $-NH_2$ groups and an oxygen. The ending of the names of ions often indicate their composition. For example the ending *-ide* usually indicates just the element with an appropriate negative charge (e.g. sulfide is S^{2-}). The ending *-ate* usually indicates the the ion contains the element and oxygen atoms (e.g. sulfate is SO_4^{2-}). The ending *-ite*, also indicates an ion containing oxygen, but less oxygen than the *-ate* (e.g. sulfite is SO_3^{2-}).

Sometimes compounds are hydrated, that is they contain water molecules chemically bonded into the structure of the crystals. This is known as water of crystallisation or hydration and it is indicated by the formula for water following the formula of the substance and separated from it by a dot. For example in hydrated sodium sulfate crystals seven molecules of water of crystallisation are present for every sulfate ion and every two sodium ions, so its formula is written as $Na_2SO_4 \cdot 7H_2O$. When the crystals are heated this water is frequently given off to leave the anhydrous salt (Na_2SO_4). Similarly blue hydrated copper(II) sulfate crystals ($CuSO_4{\cdot}5H_2O$) forms white anhydrous copper(II) sulfate ($CuSO_4$) when strongly heated.

Exercise 1.3

1. The formula of the cadmium ion is Cd^{2+} and that of the benzoate ion is $C_6H_5COO^-$. Determine the formula of cadmium benzoate.

   A $Cd(C_6H_5COO)_2$
   B CdC_6H_5COO
   C $Cd_2(C_6H_5COO)_2$
   D $Cd_2C_6H_5COO$

2. An ore contains calcium hydroxide, $Ca(OH)_2$ in association with calcium phosphate, $Ca_3(PO_4)_2$. Analysis shows that calcium and phosphorus are present in a mole ratio of 5:3. Which of the following best represents the composition of the ore?

   A $Ca(OH_2) \cdot Ca_3(PO_4)_2$
   B $Ca(OH)_2 \cdot 2\,Ca_3(PO_4)_2$
   C $Ca(OH)_2 \cdot 3\,Ca_3(PO_4)_2$
   D $Ca(OH)_2 \cdot 4\,Ca_3(PO_4)_2$

3. If the formula of praseodymium oxide is PrO_2, Determine the formula of praseodymium sulfate.

   A Pr_2SO_4
   B $PrSO_4$
   C $Pr_2(SO_4)_3$
   D $Pr(SO_4)_2$

4. Write the formulas of the following common compounds:

   a) Sulfuric acid
   b) Sodium hydroxide
   c) Nitric acid
   d) Ammonia
   e) Hydrochloric acid
   f) Ethanoic acid
   g) Copper (II) sulfate
   h) Carbon monoxide
   i) Sulfur dioxide
   j) Sodium hydrogencarbonate

5. Write the formulas of the following substances:

   a) Sodium chloride
   b) Copper (II) sulfide
   c) Zinc sulfate
   d) Aluminium oxide
   e) Magnesium nitrate
   f) Calcium phosphate
   g) Hydroiodic acid
   h) Ammonium carbonate
   i) Methane
   j) Phosphorus pentachloride

CORE

CHEMICAL EQUATIONS

A **chemical equation** is a record of what happens in a chemical reaction.

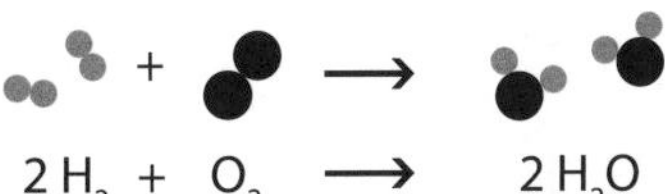

$$2\,H_2 + O_2 \longrightarrow 2\,H_2O$$

It shows the formulas (molecular formulas or formula units) of all the reactants (on the left hand side) and all the products (on the right hand side). It also gives the number of each species that are required for complete reaction. The example shows the reaction of hydrogen and oxygen to produce water.

Note that all of the elements that are gases and take part in chemical reactions (i.e. not the noble gases) are diatomic. Hence hydrogen gas is H_2 not H and chlorine gas is Cl_2 not Cl. The two non-gaseous halogens are also diatomic and so bromine is alwayswritten as Br_2 and iodine as I_2.

The first stage in producing an equation is to write a word equation for the reaction. The reaction of calcium carbonate with hydrochloric acid, for example, which

TOK When are symbols necessary in aiding understanding and when are they redundant?

How often when reading a news article do we say to ourselves "Why is that relevant?"; for example why do we need to know that the woman who appeared in court for shop-theft was age 37, or even that it was a woman come to that? (Though the English language, having "he" and "she", but no gender neutral equivalent would make this difficult - what about other languages?) If pressed a journalist would probably talk about "human interest". The same thing however arises in science - how much information does the person reading or work require; what is relevant and what irrelevant. In the case of state symbols then certainly it is relevant if the focus is thermochemistry because changes of state (like ice melting) involve heat changes. They are also probably useful when considering equilibrium (which side of the equation has most moles of gas?) or kinetics (water in the gas phase is much more "dilute" than as a liquid) and in electrolysis (molten and aqueous sodium chloride give different products). If the focus is purely stoichiometric however then the information may be redundant, for example

$$C_6H_6 + 3\,H_2 \longrightarrow C_6H_{12}$$

one mole of benzene, whether it is in the liquid or gas phase, will still react with three moles of hydrogen (pretty safe to assume this is a gas!). Probably the best policy is to consider that you really do not know what use an equation may be put to, and so include state symbols just to be on the safe side (as we have in this book), but whether it adds human interest to these equations is another matter!

produces calcium chloride, carbon dioxide and water can be represented as

$$\text{Calcium carbonate + Hydrochloric acid} \longrightarrow \text{Calcium chloride + Carbon dioxide + Water}$$

The next stage is to replace the names of the compounds with their formulas, so that this equation becomes:

$$CaCO_3 + HCl \longrightarrow CaCl_2 + CO_2 + H_2O$$

Finally, because matter cannot be created or destroyed (at least in chemical reactions) and the charge of the products must be equal to that of the reactants, the equation must be balanced with respect to both number of atoms of each element and the charge by placing coefficients, also called stoichiometric coefficients, in front of some of the formulas. These multiply the number of atoms of the elements in the formula by that factor and represent the number of moles of the species required. In the example above, there are two chlorines on the right hand side, but only one on the left hand side. Similarly the hydrogen atoms do not balance. This can be corrected by putting a '2' in front of the hydrochloric acid, so the final balanced equation is

$$CaCO_3 + 2\ HCl \longrightarrow CaCl_2 + CO_2 + H_2O$$

This means that one formula unit of calcium carbonate will just react completely with two formula units of hydrochloric acid to produce one formula unit of calcium chloride, one molecule of carbon dioxide and one molecule of water. Scaling this up means that one mole of calcium carbonate reacts with two moles of hydrochloric acid to produce one mole of calcium chloride, one mole of carbon dioxide and one mole of water. The amounts of substances in a balanced equation are known as the stoichiometry of the reaction, hence these equations are sometimes referred to as stoichiometric equations. One corollary of balancing chemical equations is that as a result mass is conserved.

Note that the formulas of compounds can never be changed, so balancing the equation by altering the subscripts, for example changing calcium chloride to $CaCl_3$ or water to H_3O, is incorrect.

It is sometimes helpful to show the physical state of the substances involved and this can be done by a suffix, known as a state symbol placed after the formula. The state symbols used are; (s) - solid, (l) - liquid, (g) - gas and (aq) - aqueous solution. State symbols should be used as a matter of course as it gives more information about a reaction and in some cases, such as when studying thermochemistry, their use is vital. Adding these, the equation for the reaction between calcium carbonate and hydrochloric acid becomes

$$CaCO_3\,(s) + 2\ HCl\,(aq) \longrightarrow CaCl_2\,(aq) + CO_2\,(g) + H_2O\,(l)$$

It is often better to write the equation for a reaction occurring in aqueous solution as an **ionic equation**. This is particularly true for precipitation reactions, acid-base reactions and redox reactions. An example would be the reaction between aqueous lead nitrate and aqueous sodium chloride to precipitate lead chloride and leave a solution of sodium nitrate.

$$Pb(NO_3)_2\,(aq) + 2\ NaCl(aq) \longrightarrow PbCl_2\,(s) + 2\ NaNO_3\,(aq)$$

When soluble ionic compounds, as well as strong acids and bases, dissolve in water they totally dissociate into their component ions and so the equation above would be more correctly written as:

$$Pb^{2+}\,(aq) + 2\ NO_3^-\,(aq) + 2\ Na^+\,(aq) + 2\ Cl^-\,(aq) \longrightarrow PbCl_2\,(s) + 2\ Na^+\,(aq) + 2\ NO_3^-\,(aq)$$

This shows that the reaction actually involves just the lead ions and chloride ions. The hydrated nitrate ions and sodium ions are present in both the reactants and products and so do not take part in the reaction. They are known as **spectator ions**. The spectator ions can therefore be cancelled from both sides so that the net ionic equation becomes:

$$Pb^{2+}(aq) + 2\ Cl^-(aq) \longrightarrow PbCl_2\,(s)$$

Ionic equations are far more general than normal equations. This ionic equation, for example, states that any soluble lead compound will react with any soluble chloride to form a precipitate of lead chloride. For example the reaction

$$Pb(CH_3COO)_2\,(aq) + MgCl_2\,(aq) \longrightarrow PbCl_2\,(s) + Mg(CH_3COO)_2\,(aq)$$

would have exactly the same ionic equation:

$$Pb^{2+}\,(aq) + 2\ Cl^-\,(aq) \longrightarrow PbCl_2\,(s)$$

In order to know which salts are soluble there are certain simple rules that it is useful to remember:

Always soluble – salts of Na^+, K^+, NH_4^+ and NO_3^-

Usually soluble - salts of Cl^- and SO_4^{2-}, but AgCl, $PbCl_2$, $PbSO_4$ and $BaSO_4$ are insoluble

Usually insoluble - salts of OH^-, O^{2-}, CO_3^{2-} and PO_4^{3-}, but Na^+, K^+, NH_4^+ salts soluble

Common slightly soluble substances – $Ca(OH)_2$ and Ca SO_4

Exercise 1.3.1

1. Which one of the following equations best represents the reaction between iron and hydrochloric acid?

   A $Fe + HCl \longrightarrow FeCl + H$
   B $Fe + HCl \longrightarrow FeCl + H_2$
   C $Fe + 2\ HCl \longrightarrow FeCl_2 + H_2$
   D $Fe + 2\ HCl \longrightarrow FeCl_2 + 2\ H$

2. What numerical value of Q is required to balance the equation below?

   $$2\ H_2S + Q\ O_2 \longrightarrow 2\ SO_2 + 2\ H_2O$$

   A 2
   B 3
   C 4
   D 6

3. The equation for the reaction of sodium sulfate with barium nitrate to form a precipitate of barium sulfate is

   $$Ba(NO_3)_2 + Na_2SO_4 \longrightarrow BaSO_4 + 2\ NaNO_3$$

   Which one of the following is the correct ionic equation for this reaction?

   A $Ba^{2+} + SO_4^{2-} \longrightarrow BaSO_4$
   B $Na^+ + NO_3^- \longrightarrow NaNO_3$
   C $Ba^{2+} + Na_2SO_4 \longrightarrow BaSO_4 + 2\ Na^+$
   D $Ba(NO_3)_2 + SO_4^{2-} \longrightarrow BaSO_4 + 2\ NO_3^-$

4. Insert coefficients, to balance the following equations.

   (a) $CaO + HNO_3 \longrightarrow Ca(NO_3)_2 + H_2O$
   (b) $NH_3 + H_2SO_4 \longrightarrow (NH_4)_2SO_4$
   (c) $HCl + ZnCO_3 \longrightarrow ZnCl_2 + H_2O + CO_2$
   (d) $SO_2 + Mg \longrightarrow S + MgO$
   (e) $Fe_3O_4 + H_2 \longrightarrow Fe + H_2O$
   (f) $K + C_2H_5OH \longrightarrow KC_2H_5O + H_2$
   (g) $Fe(OH)_3 \longrightarrow Fe_2O_3 + H_2O$
   (h) $CH_3CO_2H + O_2 \longrightarrow CO_2 + H_2O$
   (i) $Pb(NO_3)_2 \longrightarrow PbO + NO_2 + O_2$
   (j) $NaMnO_4 + HCl \longrightarrow NaCl + MnCl_2 + Cl_2 + H_2O$

5. Write balanced equations for the following reactions.

   (a) Copper(II) carbonate forming copper (II) oxide and carbon dioxide.
   (b) Nickel oxide reacting with sulfuric acid to form nickel sulfate and water.
   (c) Iron and bromine reacting to give iron(III) bromide.
   (d) Lead(IV) oxide and carbon monoxide forming lead metal and carbon dioxide.
   (e) Iron(II) chloride reacting with chlorine to form iron(III) chloride.
   (f) Ethanol burning in air to form carbon dioxide and water.
   (g) Silver reacting with nitric acid to form silver nitrate, nitrogen dioxide and water.
   (h) Manganese(IV) oxide reacting with hydrochloric acid to form manganese(II) chloride, chlorine and water.
   (i) Sulfur dioxide reacting with hydrogen sulfide to form sulfur and water.
   (j) Ammonia reacting with oxygen to form nitrogen monoxide and water.

CORE

1.4 MASS AND GASEOUS VOLUME RELATIONSHIPS IN CHEMICAL REACTIONS

1.4.1 Calculate theoretical yields from chemical equations.

1.4.2 Determine the limiting reactant and the reactant in excess when quantities of reacting substances are given.

1.4.3 Solve problems involving theoretical, experimental and percentage yield.

Reacting masses

Stoichiometry is the study of quantitative (i.e., numerical) aspects of chemical equations. A balanced equation gives the amount in moles of each substance in the reaction, making it possible to calculate the masses of reactants or products in the reaction. In chemical reactions matter cannot be created or destroyed, so that the total mass of the products is equal to the total mass of the reactants. If a gas is given off or absorbed, then the mass of the solids and liquids will appear to change, but if the gas is taken into account, mass is conserved.

Chemical equations give the amounts of substances related by a chemical reaction. Consider the reaction of methane with oxygen:

$$CH_{4\,(g)} + 2\,O_{2\,(g)} \longrightarrow CO_{2\,(g)} + 2\,H_2O_{(l)}$$

One mole of methane (i.e. 16 g) will react with two moles of oxygen molecules (i.e. 64 g) to form one mole of carbon dioxide (i.e. 44 g) and two moles of water (i.e. 36 g). The total mass is 80 g on both sides of the equation, in accordance with the principle of conservation of mass, but the equation allows us to predict that burning 16 g of methane will consume 64 g (= 2 × 32) of oxygen. What if only 4 g of methane is burnt? This is $^4/_{16} = ^1/_4$ of the amount of methane, so it will consume ¼ of the amount of oxygen, i.e. 16 g.

If the molar masses are known, the masses of substances related in a chemical equation may be calculated by applying the formula $n = \frac{m}{M}$

These calculations are best thought of as being carried out in three stages as illustrated in the examples below:

Example 1

Consider that you had 10.00 g of sodium hydroxide. What mass of hydrated sodium sulfate crystals ($Na_2SO_4{\bullet}7H_2O$) could be produced by reaction with excess sulfuric acid?

Solution

Stage One - Calculate the amount of the substance whose mass is given.

$$\text{Amount of NaOH} = \frac{m}{M} = \frac{10.00\text{ g}}{40.00\text{ g mol}^{-1}}$$

$$= 0.2500\text{ mol}$$

Stage Two - Use the balanced equation to calculate the amount of the required substance.

$$2\,NaOH + H_2SO_4 \longrightarrow Na_2SO_4 + H_2O$$

2 mol　　　　　　1 mol

$\therefore$ mol Na_2SO_4 = ½ mol NaOH

0.2500 mol NaOH

$\therefore$ ½ × 0.2500 mol Na_2SO_4

= 0.1250 mol

Stage Three - Calculate the mass of the required substance from the amount of it.

Mass of hydrated sodium sulfate

$= n \times M$

$= 0.1250\text{ mol} \times 268.18\text{ g mol}^{-1}$

$= 33.52\text{ g}$

(N.B. the molar mass of the hydrated salt must be used)

The procedure is exactly the same irrespective of whether the calculation starts with the mass of reactant and calculates the mass of product, or calculates the mass of reactant required to give a certain mass of product, as illustrated by a second example.

Example 2

What mass of sodium hydrogencarbonate must be heated to give 8.80 g of carbon dioxide?

Solution

Stage One

$$\text{Amount of } CO_2 = \frac{8.80 \text{ g}}{44.01 \text{ g mol}^{-1}} = 0.200 \text{ mol}$$

Stage Two

$$2\,NaHCO_3 \longrightarrow Na_2CO_3 + CO_2 + H_2O$$

2 mol 1 mol

$2 \times 0.200 = 0.400$ mol 0.200 mol

Stage Three

Mass of $NaHCO_3$ $= 0.400 \text{ mol} \times 84.01 \text{ g mol}^{-1}$
$= 33.6$ g

Example 3

Calculate the mass of O_2 required for the combustion of 0.250 mol propane gas, $C_3H_{8\,(g)}$.

Solution

Stage One

Aleady completed;
we are given the moles of propane (0.250)

Stage Two

$$C_3H_8\,(g) + 5\,O_2\,(g) \longrightarrow 3\,CO_2\,(g) + 4\,H_2O\,(l)$$

1 mol C_3H_8 5 mol O_2

0.250 mol C_3H_8 $0.25 \times 5 = 1.25$ mol O_2

Stage Three

Mass of O_2 required $= 1.25 \text{ mol} \times 32.0 \text{ g mol}^{-1}$
$= 40.0$ g

In summary

- Calculate the amount of the substance whose mass is given.
- Use the balanced equation to calculate the amount of the required substance.
- Calculate the mass of the required substance from the amount of it.

Exercise 1.4

1. When butane is burnt in excess air, the following reaction takes place

$$2\,C_4H_{10\,(g)} + 13\,O_{2\,(g)} \longrightarrow 8\,CO_{2\,(g)} + 10\,H_2O_{(l)}$$

Calculate how many moles of oxygen are required to react with five moles of butane.

A 6.5
B 13
C 32.5
D 65

2. When magnesium is added to aqueous silver nitrate, the following reaction takes place

$$Mg_{(s)} + 2\,AgNO_{3\,(aq)} \longrightarrow 2\,Ag_{(s)} + Mg(NO_3)_{2\,(aq)}$$

What mass of silver is formed when 2.43 g of magnesium is added to an excess of aqueous silver nitrate.

A 107.9 g
B 21.6 g
C 10.8 g
D 5.4 g

3. When heated potassium chlorate(V) decomposes to form potassium chloride and oxygen. The unbalanced equation is:

$$KClO_{3\,(s)} \longrightarrow KCl_{(s)} + O_{2\,(g)}$$

(a) Balance the equation.
(b) Calculate how many moles of $KClO_3$ are needed to produce 0.60 moles of oxygen.
(c) What mass of $KClO_3$ is needed to produce 0.0200 moles of KCl?

4. What mass of copper(II) sulfate pentahydrate ($CuSO_4 \cdot 5H_2O$) can be produced by reacting 12.00 g of copper(II) oxide with an excess of sulfuric acid?

5. Pure compound A contains 63.3% manganese and 36.7% oxygen by mass. Upon heating compound A, oxygen is evolved and pure compound B is formed which contains 72.0% manganese and 28.0% oxygen by mass.

   (a) Determine the empirical formula for compounds A and B.
   (b) Write a balanced equation which represents the reaction that took place.
   (c) Calculate how many grams of oxygen would be evolved when 2.876 g of A is heated to form pure B.

Limiting reagents

The quantities of reactants related in the section above are the precise amounts, or stoichiometric amounts, required to just react with each other. More commonly there will be an excess of all of the reagents except one, so that all of this last reagent will be consumed. This reagent is known as the **limiting reagent** because it is the amount of this that limits the quantity of product formed. It may be identified by calculating the amount of each reagent present and then dividing by the relevant coefficient from the equation. The reagent corresponding to the smallest number is the limiting reagent.

Example

Consider the reaction:

$$H_2O_{2\,(aq)} + 2KI_{(aq)} + H_2SO_{4\,(aq)} \longrightarrow I_{2\,(s)} + K_2SO_{4\,(aq)} + 2H_2O_{(l)}$$

What mass of iodine is produced when 100.00 g of KI is added to a solution containing 12.00 g of H_2O_2 and 50.00 g H_2SO_4?

Solution

The mole ratio from the equation is

H_2O_2	:	KI	:	H_2SO_4
1	:	2	:	1

The actual mole ratio of reagents present is

$$\frac{12.00}{34.02} \qquad \frac{100.00}{166.00} \qquad \frac{50.00}{98.08}$$

$$= 0.3527 : 0.6024 : 0.5098$$
$$= 1 : 1.708 : 1.445$$

Ratio divided by coefficient

$$= 1 : 0.854 : 1.445$$

It can be seen that even though there is the greatest mass of potassium iodide, it is still the limiting reagent, owing to its large molar mass and the 2:1 mole ratio. The maximum yield of iodine will therefore be ½ × 0.6024 = 0.3012 moles. This is the theoretical yield, which can, if required, be converted into a mass:

$$\text{Theoretical yield} = n \times M$$
$$= 0.3012\ \text{mol} \times 253.8\ \text{g mol}^{-1}$$
$$= 76.44\ \text{g}$$

There is an excess of both hydrogen peroxide and sulfuric acid. The amounts in excess can be calculated:

0.6024 moles of potassium iodide will react with:

½ × 0.6024 = 0.3012 moles of both H_2O_2 and H_2SO_4 (both a 2:1 mole ratio).

Mass of H_2O_2 reacting = 0.3012 mol × 34.02 g mol^{-1} = 10.24 g,

Mass of H_2SO_4 reacting = 0.3012 × 98.08 = 29.54 g,

therefore mass in excess = 50.00 – 29.54
= 20.46 g

In practice the theoretical yield based on the balanced chemical equation is never achieved owing to impurities in reagents, side reactions and other sources of experimental error. Supposing 62.37 g of iodine was eventually produced, the **percentage yield** can be calculated as follows:

$$\text{Percentage yield} = \frac{62.37}{76.44} \times 100 = 81.59\%.$$

Exercise 1.4.1

1. Consider the reaction:

$$2\,Al\,(s) + 3\,I_2\,(s) \longrightarrow 2\,AlI_3\,(s)$$

Determine the limiting reagent and the theoretical yield of the product from:

(a) 1.20 mol aluminium and 2.40 mol iodine.
(b) 1.20 g aluminium and 2.40 g iodine.
(c) Calculate how many grams of aluminium are left over in part b.

2. Freon-12 (used as coolant in refrigerators), is formed as follows:

$$3\,CCl_4\,(l) + 2\,SbF_3\,(s) \longrightarrow 3\,CCl_2F_2\,(g) + 2\,SbCl_3\,(s)$$

150 g tetrachloromethane is combined with 100 g antimony(III) fluoride to give Freon-12 (CCl_2F_2).

(a) Identify the limiting and excess reagents.
(b) Calculate how many grams of Freon-12 can be formed.
(c) How much of the excess reagent is left over?

3. Aspirin is made by adding acetic anhydride to an aqueous solution of salicylic acid. The equation for the reaction is:

$$2\,C_7H_6O_3\,(aq) + C_4H_6O_3\,(l) \longrightarrow 2C_9H_8O_4\,(aq) + H_2O\,(l)$$

salicylic acid, acetic anhydride ⟶ aspirin, water

If 1.00 kg of salicylic acid is used with 2.00 kg of acetic anhydride, determine:

(a) the limiting reagent.
(b) the theoretical yield.
(c) If 1.12 kg aspirin is produced experimentally, determine the percentage yield.

AVOGADRO'S HYPOTHESIS AND THE MOLE CONCEPT APPLIED TO GASES

1.4.4 Apply Avogadro's law to calculate reacting volumes of gases.

1.4.5 Apply the concept of molar volume at standard temperature and pressure in calculations.

1.4.6 Solve problems involving the relationship between temperature, pressure and volume for a fixed mass of an ideal gas.

1.4.7 Solve problems relating to the ideal gas equation, PV=nRT.

1.4.8 Analyse graphs relating to the ideal gas equation.

At constant temperature and pressure it is found that a given volume of any gas always contains the same number of particles (i.e. molecules except in the case of the noble gases) at the same temperature and pressure. In other words, equal amounts of gases at the same temperature and pressure occupy the same volume! This is known as **Avogadro's hypothesis.** It means that in reactions involving gases the volumes of reactants and products, when measured at the same temperature and pressure, are in the same ratio as their coefficients in a balanced equation. For example when carbon monoxide reacts with oxygen to form carbon dioxide, the volume of oxygen required is only half the volume of carbon monoxide consumed and carbon dioxide formed:

$$2\,CO_{(g)} + O_{2\,(g)} \longrightarrow 2\,CO_{2\,(g)}$$

2 vol 1 vol 2 vol

This may be used to carry out calculations about the volume of gaseous product and the volume of any excess reagent:

CORE

CORE

Example 1

10 cm^3 of ethyne is reacted with 50 cm^3 of hydrogen to produce ethane according to the equation:

$$C_2H_{2\,(g)} + 2\,H_{2\,(g)} \longrightarrow C_2H_{6\,(g)}$$

Calculate the total volume and composition of the remaining gas mixture, assuming that temperature and pressure remain constant.

Solution

Ratio of volume of reactants to products is in the ratio of the coefficients:

$$C_2H_{2\,(g)} + 2\,H_{2\,(g)} \longrightarrow C_2H_{6\,(g)}$$

1 vol	2 vol	1 vol
10 cm^3	20 cm^3	10 cm^3

Hence it can be seen that the hydrogen is in excess:

Volume of remaining hydrogen = 50 cm^3 - 20 cm^3 = 30 cm^3

The total volume of the gas mixture that remains is 40 cm^3, comprising of 10 cm^3 ethane and 30 cm^3 hydrogen.

If the temperature and pressure are specified, then the volume of any gas that contains one mole may be calculated. This is known as the **molar volume**. At standard temperature and pressure (abbreviated to stp; i.e. 1 atm = 101.3 kPa and 0 °C = 273 K) this volume is 22.4 dm^3. [Note: 1 dm^3 = 1 dm × 1 dm × 1 dm = 10 cm × 10 cm × 10 cm = 1000 cm^3 = 1 litre (L)] This is called the molar gas volume, V_m, and contains 6.02×10^{23} molecules for a molecular gas (or 6.02×10^{23} atoms for noble gases). V_m is the same for all gases (under ideal conditions; see Ideal Gas Equation).

The concept of molar volume allows one to solve a variety of problems in which gases are involved in terms of the mole concept. For example the amount of gas can be calculated from the volume of the gas under these conditions using the formula:

$$\text{Amount of gas} = \frac{\text{Volume of gas}}{\text{Molar volume}}$$

This may be abbreviated to:

$$n = \frac{V_{stp}}{22.4}$$

where V_{stp} is the volume of gas in dm^3 at 273 K and 101.3 kPa.

Example 2

Calculate how many moles of oxygen molecules are there in 5.00 dm^3 of oxygen at s.t.p..

Solution

$$n = \frac{V_{stp}}{22.4} = \frac{5.00}{22.4} = 0.223 \text{ mol}$$

This equation may also be rearranged to calculate the volume of gas under these conditions, knowing the amount of gas. The relationship between the amount of gas and its volume can then be used in calculations in the same way as the relationship between mass and molar mass.

Example 3

What mass of sodium hydrogencarbonate must be heated to generate 10.0 dm^3 of carbon dioxide, measured at standard temperature and pressure?

Solution

***Stage One** - Calculate the amount of the substance for which data is given.*

$$n = \frac{V_{stp}}{22.4} = \frac{10.00 \text{ dm}^3}{22.4 \text{ mol dm}^{-3}} = 0.446 \text{ mol}$$

***Stage Two** - Use the balanced equation to calculate the amount of the required substance.*

$$2\,NaHCO_3 \longrightarrow Na_2CO_3 + H_2O + CO_2$$

2 moles 1 mole

$2 \times 0.446 = 0.892$ moles 0.446 moles

***Stage Three** - Calculate the result for the required substance from the number of moles.*

Mass of sodium hydrogencarbonate

$= n \times M$

$= 0.892 \text{ mol} \times 84.0 \text{ g mol}^{-1}$

$= 74.9$ g.

Example 4

What volume of air (assumed to contain 20% oxygen by volume), measured at s.t.p., is required for the complete combustion of 1.000 kg of gasoline, assuming that this is totally composed of octane (C_8H_{18})?

Solution

***Stage One** - Calculate the amount of the substance for which data is given.*

$$n = \frac{m}{M_r} = \frac{1000}{114.2} = 8.76 \text{ mol}$$

***Stage Two** - Use the balanced equation to calculate the amount of the required substance.*

$$2\,C_8H_{18} \;+\; 25\,O_2 \longrightarrow 16\,CO_2 \;+\; 18\,H_2O$$

2 moles 25 mole

8.76 $\frac{1}{2} \times 25 \times 8.76$

$= 109.5$ moles

***Stage Three** - Calculate the result for the required substance from the number of moles.*

Volume of oxygen $= n \times 22.4$

$= 109.5 \times 22.4$

$= 2543 \text{ dm}^3$

Volume of air $= 2543 \times {}^{100}/_{20}$

$= 12260 \text{ dm}^3$

Exercise 1.4.2

1. According to the equation below, what volume of nitrogen dioxide would you expect to be formed from 20 cm^3 of nitrogen monoxide, assuming that the volumes are measured at the same temperature and pressure?

$$2\,NO\,(g) + O_2\,(g) \longrightarrow 2\,NO_2\,(g)$$

   A 10 cm^3
   B 15 cm^3
   C 20 cm^3
   D 30 cm^3

2. Four identical flasks are filled with hydrogen, oxygen, carbon dioxide and chlorine at the same temperature and pressure. The flask with the greatest mass will be the one containing

   A hydrogen.
   B oxygen.
   C carbon dioxide.
   D chlorine.

3. Calculate how many moles of hydrogen molecules are there in 560 cm^3 of hydrogen gas measured at s.t.p:.

   A 0.0250
   B 0.050
   C 25.0
   D 50.0

4. What volume would 3.20 g of sulfur dioxide ocupy at s.t.p.?

   A 0.56 dm^3
   B 1.12 dm^3
   C 2.24 dm^3
   D 4.48 dm^3

5. Potassium nitrate ($M = 101 \text{ g mol}^{-1}$) decomposes on heating as shown by the equation below. What mass of the solid must be heated to produce 10.0 dm^3 of oxygen gas, measured at s.t.p.?

$$2\,KNO_3\,(s) \longrightarrow 2\,KNO_2\,(s) + O_2\,(g)$$

   A $101 \times \frac{22.4}{10.0}$ g
   B $101 \times \frac{10.0}{22.4}$ g
   C $\frac{1}{2} \times 101 \times \frac{10.0}{22.4}$ g
   D $2 \times 101 \times \frac{10.0}{22.4}$ g

CORE

6. A mixture of 20 cm^3 hydrogen and 40 cm^3 oxygen is exploded in a strong container. After cooling to the original temperature and pressure (at which water is a liquid) what gas, if any, will remain in the container?

7. To three significant figures, calculate how many methane molecules are there in 4.48 dm^3 of the gas at standard temperature and pressure?

8. If 3.00 dm^3 of an unknown gas at standard temperature and pressure has a mass of 6.27 g, Determine the molar mass of the gas.

9. Determine the density of ammonia, in g dm^{-3}, at s.t.p..

10. Sulfur dioxide, present in flue gases from the combustion of coal, is often absorbed by injecting powdered limestone into the flame, when the following reactions occur:

$$CaCO_3\,(s) \longrightarrow CaO\,(s) + CO_2\,(g)$$

$$CaO\,(s) + SO_2\,(g) \longrightarrow CaSO_3\,(s)$$

What volume of sulfur dioxide, measured at s.t.p., can be absorbed by using 1 tonne (1.00×10^6 g) of limestone in this way?

THE IDEAL GAS EQUATION

An '**ideal gas**' is one in which the particles have negligible volume, there are no attractive forces between the particles and the kinetic energy of the particles is directly proportional to the absolute temperature. For many real gases this approximation holds good at low pressures and high temperatures, but it tends to break down at low temperatures and high pressures (when the separation of molecules is reduced), especially for molecules with strong intermolecular forces, such as hydrogen bonding (e.g. ammonia). In an ideal gas the pressure and volume of the gas are related to the amount and temperature of the gas by the Ideal Gas Equation:

$$P.V = n.R.T$$

R is known as the Ideal Gas Constant and its numerical value will depend on the units used to measure pressure, P, and volume, V and n (n.b. Temperature, T must be expressed in Kelvin -not degrees Celsius). If P is in kPa, n is in moles, and V is in dm^3, then R has a value of 8.314 J K^{-1} mol^{-1}.

The ideal gas equation may be used to find any one of the terms, provided that the others are known or remain constant. For example we can calculate the volume occupied by 1 mole of a gas (so n=1) at 20.0° C (so T = 293.0 K, note that this conversion to Kelvin is vital!) and normal atmospheric pressure (101.3 kPa):

Hence the volume of a gas under known conditions may be used to calculate the amount of a gas. Similarly if the volume of a known mass of gas (or the density of the gas) is measured at a particular temperature and pressure, then the ideal gas equation may be used, along with the formula $n = \frac{m}{M}$, to calculate the molar mass of the gas.

Example

3.376 g of a gas occupies 2.368 dm^3 at 17.6° C and a pressure of 96.73 kPa, determine its molar mass.

Solution

(note: temperature is in K)

$$n = \frac{PV}{RT} = \frac{96.73 \times 2.368}{8.314 \times 290.6} = 0.09481$$

$$M = \frac{m}{n}$$

$$= \frac{3.376}{0.09481}$$

$$= 35.61 \text{ g mol}^{-1}$$

This technique may also be used to determine the molar mass of a volatile liquid by making the measurements at a temperature above the boiling point of the liquid.

THE EFFECT OF CONDITIONS ON THE VOLUME OF A FIXED MASS OF IDEAL GAS

In order to convert the volume, pressure and temperature of a given amount of ideal gas (so n and R are both constant) from one set of conditions (1) to another set of conditions (2), when the third variable remains constant, the ideal gas equation simplifies to:

Boyle-Mariotte Law $P_1V_1 = P_2V_2$

(at constant n and T)

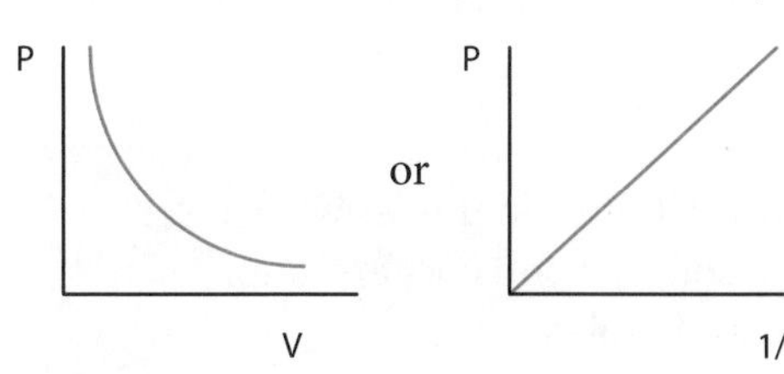

Charles' Law $\frac{V_1}{T_1} = \frac{V_2}{T_2}$

(at constant n and P)

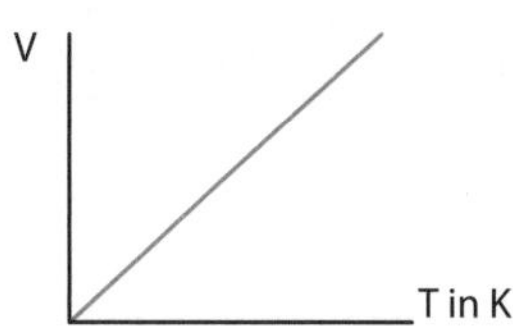

Pressure (Gay Lussac's) Law $\frac{P_1}{T_1} = \frac{P_2}{T_2}$ (at constant n and V)

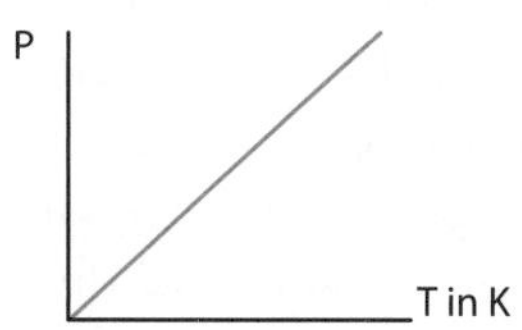

These may be combined into the expression:

$$\frac{P_1V_1}{T_1} = \frac{P_2V_2}{T_2}$$

In this and the preceding equations, T must be expressed in Kelvin, but P and V may be expressed in any units provided the same units are used consistently throughout the calculation.

Example

A syringe contains 50 cm^3 of gas at 1.0 atm pressure and 20 °C. What would the volume be if the gas were heated to 100 °C, whilst at the same time compressing

Solution

it to 5 atm?

$$\frac{P_1V_1}{T_1} = \frac{P_2V_2}{T_2}$$

$$\therefore \frac{1.0 \times 50}{293} = \frac{5.0 \times V_2}{373}$$

$$V_2 = 50 \times \frac{1.0}{5.0} \times \frac{373}{292} = 13 \text{ cm}^3$$

Exercise 1.4.3

1) A sealed flask contains 250 cm^3 of gas at 35°C and atmospheric pressure. The flask is then heated to 350°C. The pressure of the gas will increase by a factor of about

A 2
B 10
C 250
D 585

2) The pressure on 600 cm^3 of gas is increased from 100 kPa to 300 kPa at constant temperature. What will the new volume of gas be?

A 200 cm^3
B 300 cm^3
C 1200 cm^3
D 1800 cm^3

3) 1 dm^3 of gas in a container at -73°C is allowed to expand to 1.5 dm^3, what must the temperature be increased to so that the pressure remains constant?

A –36°C
B 0°C
C 27°C
D 73°C

4) 4.00 dm^3 of air at 0°C and a pressure of 2.00 atmospheres, is heated to 273°C and the pressure increased to 8 atmospheres. What will the new volume of the gas be?

A 1.00 dm^3
B 2.00 dm^3
C 8.00 dm^3
D 32.00 dm^3

5) A 2.00 dm^3 of a gas at a pressure of 1000 kPa is allowed to expand at constant temperature until the pressure decreases to 300 kPa. What will the new volume of the gas be?

A 3.00 dm^3
B 3.33 dm^3
C 6.00 dm^3
D 6.66 dm^3

CORE

6) What volume is occupied by 0.0200 g of oxygen gas at 27 °C and a pressure of 107 kPa?

A 0.466 dm^3
B 0.029 dm^3
C 0.015 dm^3
D 0.002 dm^3

7) In a particular experiment aluminium was reacted with dilute hydrochloric acid according to the equation:

$$2\ Al\ (s) + 6\ HCl\ (aq) \longrightarrow 2\ AlCl_3\ (aq) + 3\ H_2\ (g)$$

355 cm^3 of hydrogen was collected at 25.0 °C a pressure of 100.0 kPa.

a) Calculate how many moles of hydrogen were collected.
b) If 0.300 g of aluminium was used with excess acid, determine the percentage yield of hydrogen.

8) A steel cylinder contains 32 dm^3 of hydrogen at 4×10^5 Pa and 39 °C. Calculate

a) The volume that the hydrogen would occupy at s.t.p. (0 °C and 101.3 kPa)
b) The mass of hydrogen in the cylinder.

9) The following readings were taken during the determination of the molar mass of a gas by direct weighing. If the experiment was carried out at 23 °C and 97.7 kPa, calculate the molar mass of the gas.

Mass of evacuated flask 183.257 g
Mass of flask and gas 187.942 g
Mass of flask filled with water 987.560 g

10) Two 5 dm^3 flasks are connected by by a narrow tube of negligible volume. Initially the two flasks are both at 27 °C and contain a total of 2 moles of an ideal gas. One flask is heated to a uniform temperature of 127 °C while the other is kept at 27 °C. Assuming their volume does not alter, calculate the number of moles of gas in each flask of the gas and the final pressure.

1.5 SOLUTIONS

1.5.1 Distinguish between the terms solute, solvent, solution and concentration (g dm^{-3} and mol dm^{-3}).

1.5.2 Solve problems involving concentration, amount of solute and volume of solution.

Sometimes when a substance is mixed with a liquid, it disperses into sub-microscopic particles (i.e. atoms, molecules or ions) to produce a homogenous mixture of two or more substances - this is known as a **solution**. The liquid, present in excess, in which the dispersion occurs is known as the **solvent** and the substance dissolved in it, which can be a solid, a liquid or a gas, is known as the **solute**. A **solution** is different from a **suspension** (fine particles of solid in a liquid) because it is transparent, does not settle out and cannot be separated by filtration.

The **solubility** of a substance is the quantity of that substance that will dissolve to form a certain volume of solution in that solvent (water is assumed unless another solvent is stated). The units vary from source to source (the quantity may be in moles or grams, and this may be in 100 cm^3 or in 1 dm^3), so this is always worth checking. It is important to also note that solubility varies with temperature. With solids it usually (though not always) increases with temperature, for gases it decreases with temperature. If a certain volume of solution contains a small amount of dissolved solid it is said to be dilute and if it contains a large amount of solute it is said to be concentrated. Care must be taken not to replace these with the terms weak and strong, as these have a very different meaning in chemistry (refer to Section 8.3). A **saturated solution** is one in which no more solute will dissolve at that temperature, and excess solute is present. Sometimes, temporarily, the concentration of a solute (or its component ions) can exceed its solubility and in this case the solution is referred to as a **supersaturated solution**. This can occur if the temperature of a solution is changed, or more commonly, if the substance is produced in a chemical reaction. In this case the excess solid will eventually separate from the solution as a **precipitate**.

CONCENTRATION

The **concentration** (c) is the amount of substance (n) contained within a given volume (V) of solution. In chemistry this is given as the number of moles of the substance in one cubic decimetre (dm^3; note that this volume is equivalent to 1 litre). Concentration can therefore be calculated using the formula:

$$\text{Concentration (of solution)} = \frac{\text{Amount of solute}}{\text{Solution volume in dm}^3}$$

This can be written as: $c = \frac{n}{V}$

Example 1

Calculate the concentration of the solution formed when 4.00 moles of glucose are dissolved in 5.00 dm^3 of water.

Solution

$$c = \frac{n}{V}$$

$$c = \frac{4.00 \text{ mol}}{5.00 \text{ dm}^3}$$

$$= 0.800 \text{ mol dm}^{-3}$$

Although the preferred unit for concentration is mol dm^{-3}, because 1 dm^3 is equal to 1 litre (L), concentration may also be quoted as mol/L, mol/dm^3, mol L^{-1}, or even just 'M'. 2 M sulfuric acid is therefore sulfuric acid with a concentration of 2 moles per litre. International convention however recommends that this use of 'M', and the use of the term 'molarity' instead of concentration, be discontinued as M is the notation commonly used for molar mass.

Because we frequently refer to the concentrations of species in chemistry, the convention has arisen that square brackets around a symbol means 'the concentration of', so that [NaCl] = 0.5 mol dm^{-3} means the concentration of sodium chloride is 0.5 mol dm^{-3}.

The concentration of the solution formed by dissolving a given mass of a substance may be found by substituting in the concentration formula above, having first calculated the amount of the substance using the formula $n = \frac{m}{M}$.

Example 2

If 2.00 g of sodium hydroxide is dissolved in 200 cm^3 of water, determine the concentration of the resulting solution.

Solution

$$\text{Amount of NaOH} = \frac{2.00 \text{ g}}{40.0 \text{ g mol}^{-1}}$$

$$= 0.0500 \text{ mol}$$

$$[\text{NaOH}] = \frac{0.0500 \text{ mol}}{0.200 \text{ dm}^3}$$

$$= 0.250 \text{ mol dm}^{-3}$$

Note that the 200 cm^3 of water has to be converted to 0.200 dm^3 before it can be substituted in the equation. Similarly this process can be modified to calculate the amount (and hence the mass) of solute present, or the volume of the solution required.

Example 3

What mass of hydrated copper (II) sulfate crystals ($CuSO_4{\cdot}5H_2O$) is present in 17.3 cm^3 of a 0.279 mol dm^{-3} solution of copper (II) sulfate?

Solution

$$\text{Amount of CuSO}_4 \text{ (n)} = c \times V$$

$$= 0.279 \text{ mol dm}^{-3} \times 0.0173 \text{ dm}^3$$

$$= 0.00483 \text{ mol}$$

$$\text{Mass of CuSO}_4{\cdot}5\text{H}_2\text{O} = n \times M$$

$$= 0.00483 \text{ mol} \times 249.7 \text{ g mol}^{-1}$$

$$= 1.21 \text{ g}$$

Soluble ionic compounds split up into their component ions when dissolved in water. The concentrations of the individual ions will depend on how many of these ions are produced when the substance dissolves. In a 2 mol dm^{-3} solution of aluminium sulfate, for example, the concentration of the aluminium ions is 4 mol dm^{-3} and that of the sulfate ions is 6 mol dm^{-3}, as illustrated by the equation below

$$Al_2(SO_4)_3 \text{ (aq)} \longrightarrow 2\,Al^{3+} \text{ (aq)} + 3\,SO_4^{\;2-} \text{ (aq)}$$

$Al_2(SO_4)_3$	Al^{3+}	SO_4^{2-}
1 mole	2 moles	3 moles
2 mol dm^{-3}	4 mol dm^{-3}	6 mol dm^{-3}

CORE

CORE

A concentrated solution may have solvent added to produce a more dilute one; since the amount of solute remains the same on dilution, then increasing the volume decreases its concentration. Because the amount of solute before and after dilution is constant: ($n_b = n_a$) and $n = cV$, the concentrations and volumes before and after dilution are related by the expression:

$$n = c_1 \times V_1 = c_2 \times V_2$$

where c_1 and V_1 are the initial concentration and volume and c_2 and V_2 the final concentration and volume. Note that c and V can be in any units provided that the same units are used on both sides of the equation.

Example 4

Calculate the volume to which 20.0 cm^3 of 7.63 mol dm^{-3} hydrochloric acid must be diluted to produce a solution with a concentration of exactly 5.00 mol dm^{-3}.

$$c_1 \times V_1 = c_2 \times V_2$$

Solution

Substituting:

$$7.63 \times 20.0 = 5.00 \times V_2$$

Hence:

$$V_2 = 20.0 \times \frac{7.63}{5.00}$$

$$= 30.5 \text{ cm}^3$$

Therefore the 20.0 cm^3 of the original acid must be diluted to 30.5 cm^3. Assuming that there is no volume change on dilution 30.5 cm^3 - 20.0 cm^3 = 10.5 cm^3 of water must be added.

Exercise 1.5

1. Calculate how many moles of hydrochloric acid are present in 0.80 dm^3 of a solution with a concentration of 0.40 mol dm^{-3}.

   A 0.32
   B 0.5
   C 0.8
   D 2

2. Sodium phosphate has the formula Na_3PO_4. Determine the concentration of sodium ions in a 0.6 mol dm^{-3} solution of sodium phosphate?

   A 0.2 mol dm^{-3}
   B 0.3 mol dm^{-3}
   C 0.6 mol dm^{-3}
   D 1.8 mol dm^{-3}

3. What volume of a 0.5 mol dm^{-3} solution of sodium hydroxide can be prepared from 2 g of the solid?

   A 0.05 litres
   B 0.1 litres
   C 0.4 litres
   D 0.5 litres

4. What are the concentrations of the solutions produced by dissolving

   a) 3.0 moles of nitric acid in 4.0 dm^3 of solution?
   b) 2.81 g of KOH in 2.00 dm^3 of solution?
   c) 5.00 g of magnesium sulfate heptahydrate in 250 cm^3 of solution?

5. Calculate how many moles are there in the following:

   a) 7.0 dm^3 of sulfuric acid of concentration 0.30 mol dm^{-3}.
   b) 50 cm^3 of a 0.040 mol dm^{-3} solution of lithium chloride.
   c) 15.0 cm^3 of a solution made by dissolving 5.80 g of zinc chloride in 2.50 dm^3 of solution.

6. What volume of solution could you produce in the following cases?

   a) 1 mol dm^{-3} copper(II) chloride from 0.4 moles of the solid.

b) 0.0200 mol dm^{-3} $NaNO_3$ starting from 5.00 g of the solid.
c) 0.50 mol dm^{-3} sulfuric acid starting with 20 cm^3 of a concentrated 18 mol dm^{-3} solution.

7. How would you prepare 500 cm^3 of a 0.100 mol dm^{-3} NaCl solution?

8. How would you prepare 1.2 dm^3 of a 0.40 mol dm^{-3} solution of hydrochloric acid starting from a 2.0 mol dm^{-3} solution?

9. 500 cm^3 of 0.500 mol dm^{-3} NaCl is added to 500 cm^3 of 1.00 mol dm^{-3} Na_2CO_3 solution. Calculate the final concentration of Na^+ ions in solution.

10. When hydrochloric acid is added to aqueous lead (II) nitrate, solid lead (II) chloride is precipitated. If 10 cm^3 of 2 mol dm^{-3} hydrochloric acid is added to 40 cm^3 of 0.5 mol dm^{-3} aqueous lead nitrate, determine the concentration in the final solution of

    a) nitrate ions
    b) chloride ions
    c) hydrogen ions
    d) lead (II) ions.

TITRATION CALCULATIONS

CORE

Titration is a technique which involves measuring the volume of one solution which just reacts completely with another solution.

Usually one of the solutions will have an accurately known concentration and this will be used to find the concentration of the other solution. The solution of accurately known concentration is called a **standard solution**. Its concentration can be checked by titrating it against a solution of a **primary standard**, which is prepared by dissolving a precisely known mass of pure solute to make an accurately known volume of solution, using a **volumetric flask**.

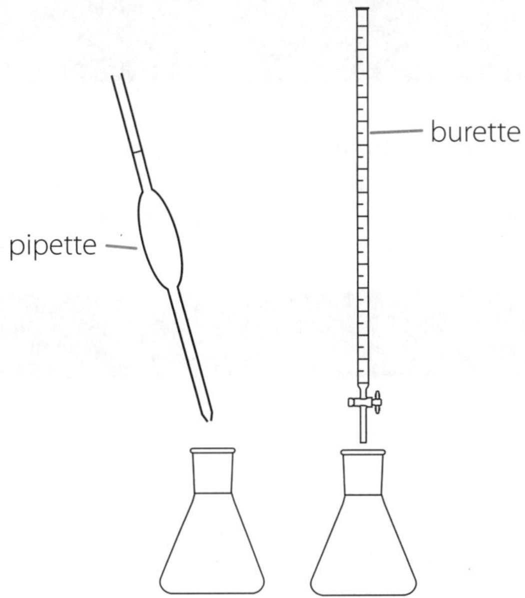

Figure 107 Pipette and burette

A primary standard must:

- be available in very pure form
- have a relatively high molar mass
- be stable as both the solid and in solution
- be readily soluble in water
- react completely in a known manner

Sodium carbonate and potassium hydrogenphthalate are commonly used as primary standards for acid-base titrations. Although acid-base titrations are the most common, the technique is not restricted to these. Redox, precipitation and compleximetric titrations are also frequently encountered.

An accurately known volume of one of the solutions will be measured out into a conical flask with a **pipette (pipet)**, which is designed to deliver exactly the same volume each time it is used. An **indicator** will usually be added and the second solution run in from a **burette** (**buret**), until the indicator just changes colour. The burette is fitted with a tap and is calibrated so as to accurately measure a variable volume of solution. The volume of the second solution required, called the **titre**, can be found by subtracting the initial burette reading from the final one.

The amount of solute can be calculated from the volume of the solution of known concentration. The amount of the unknown may then be found using the balanced equation. Finally the concentration of the unknown may be calculated from this and the volume of the second solution used. The three stages involved are closely analogous to those used in reacting mass calculations.

Example 1

It is found that 10.00 cm^3 of 0.2000 mol dm^{-3} aqueous sodium carbonate requires 25.00 cm^3 of hydrochloric acid to just neutralise it. Determine the concentration of the hydrochloric acid.

Solution

Stage One *- Calculate the amount in the solution of known concentration*

Amount of sodium carbonate = $c \times V$
= 0.200 mol dm^{-3} × 0.0100 dm^{-3}
= 0.00200 mol

Stage Two *- Use a balanced equation to calculate the amount of the unknown*

$$Na_2CO_3 + 2\,HCl \longrightarrow 2\,NaCl + CO_2 + H_2O$$

Na_2CO_3	2 HCl
1 mol	2 mol
0.00200 mol	2 × 0.00200
	= 0.00400 mol

Stage Three *- Calculate the concentration of the unknown solution*

$$[HCl] = \frac{n}{V} = \frac{0.00400\ mol}{0.02500\ dm^3} = 0.160\ mol\ dm^{-3}$$

Example 2

If the volume of NaOH solution required to neutralize 1.325 g hydrated ethanedioic acid ($H_2C_2O_4{\cdot}2H_2O$) is 27.52 cm^3, calculate the concentration of the sodium hydroxide solution.

Solution

Stage One

M_r = (2.02+24.02+64.00+4.04+32.00)
= 126.08

Amount of ethanedioic acid $= \frac{1.325}{126.08}$

= 0.010509 mol

Stage Two

Since ethanedioic acid is diprotic, the balanced chemical equation for the neutralization reaction is:

$$H_2C_2O_4 + 2\,NaOH \longrightarrow Na_2C_2O_4 + 2\,H_2O$$

$H_2C_2O_4$	2 NaOH
1	2
0.010509 mol	2 × 0.010509 mol
	= 0.021018 mol

Stage Three

27.52 cm^3 = 0.02752 dm^3,

Hence [NaOH] $= \frac{0.021018}{0.02750}$

= 0.07638 mol dm^{-3}

Note the conversion of volume to dm^3 and correct rounding to 4 significant figures at the end of the calculation.

Example 3

A titration technique can also be used to investigate the stoichiometry of an equation by finding out the amounts of the various reagents that react together.

It is found that 10.0 cm^3 of iodine solution of concentration 0.131 mol dm^{-3}, just reacts completely with 20.4 cm^3 of aqueous sodium thiosulfate of concentration 0.128 mol dm^{-3}. Calculate the stoichiometry of the reaction between iodine and the thiosulfate ion.

Calculate the amounts of each of the reagents involved

Solution

Amount of iodine = c × V
= 0.131 mol dm^{-3}× 0.01 dm^3
= 1.31 × 10^{-3} mol

(n.b. 10 cm^3= 0.01 dm^3)

Amount of thiosulfate = c × V
= 0.128 mol dm^{-3} × 0.0204 dm^3
= 2.61 × 10^{-3} mol

Then calculate the ratio of these:

Ratio of moles I_2 : moles $S_2O_3^{2-}$ = 1.31 × 10^{-3} : 2.61 × 10^{-3}
= 1 : 2

Exercise 1.5.1

1. Sulfuric acid from an automobile battery reacts with sodium hydroxide according to the equation.

$$2\,NaOH\,(aq) + H_2SO_4\,(aq) \longrightarrow Na_2SO_4\,(aq) + 2\,H_2O\,(l)$$

It is found that 10 cm^3 of the acid is just neutralised by 32 cm^3 of 2.0 mol dm^{-3} aqueous sodium hydroxide. Determine the concentration of the battery acid.

A 0.63 mol dm^{-3}
B 1.6 mol dm^{-3}
C 3.2 mol dm^{-3}
D 6.4 mol dm^{-3}

2. The amount of copper(II) ions present in a solution may be estimated by adding excess iodide ions and then titrating the iodine formed with aqueous thiosulfate ions. The equations involved are:

$$2\,Cu^{2+}(aq) + 4\,I^-\,(aq) \longrightarrow 2\,CuI\,(s) + I_2\,(aq)$$

$$2\,S_2O_3^{2-}\,(aq) + I_2\,(aq) \longrightarrow S_4O_6^{2-}\,(aq) + 2\,I^-\,(aq)$$

Calculate how many moles of thiosulfate will be required for each mole of copper (II) ions.

A 1
B 2
C 4
D 8

3. Which one of the following is not an important property for a primary standard?

A Purity
B Stability as a solid
C Stability in solution
D Bright colour

4. 20 cm^3 of hydrochloric acid was just neutralised by 25.0 cm^3 of a solution of potassium hydroxide of concentration 0.500 mol dm^{-3}.

(a) Calculate how many moles of potassium hydroxide were used in the reaction.
(b) Calculate how many moles of hydrochloric acid this reacted with.
(c) What was the concentration of the hydrochloric acid?

5. 25.0 cm^3 of saturated calcium hydroxide solution (limewater) required 7.50 cm^3 of 0.0500 mol dm^{-3} nitric acid to just neutralise it.

(a) Calculate how many moles of nitric acid were used.
(b) Calculate how many moles of calcium hydroxide did this react with.
(c) Determine the concentration of the calcium hydroxide in grams per litre.

6. A 0.245 g sample of a mixture of calcium chloride and sodium nitrate is dissolved in water to give 50.0 cm^3 of solution. This solution is titrated with 0.106 mol dm^{-3} aqueous silver nitrate which reacts with the chloride ions present to form insoluble silver chloride. The end point is reached after 37.7 cm^3 of the silver nitrate solution has been added.

(a) Write a balanced chemical equation for the reaction, including state symbols.
(b) Calculate the amount of silver nitrate used in the titration.
(c) Calculate the amount of calcium chloride present in the solution.
(d) Calculate the percentage by mass of calcium chloride in the original mixture.

CORE

7. The number of moles of water of crystallisation (x) present in hydrated ammonium iron(II) sulfate, $Fe(NH_4)_2(SO_4)_2{\cdot}xH_2O$, can be determined by oxidising the iron(II) ions with aqueous potassium permanganate in acidified solution. The ionic equation for the reaction is

$$MnO_4^- (aq) + 5\ Fe^{2+} (aq) + 8\ H^+ (aq) \longrightarrow Mn^{2+} (aq) + 5\ Fe^{3+} (aq) + 4\ H_2O\ (l)$$

It is found that when 0.980 g of the compound is dissolved in 25.0 cm^3 of water and titrated with 0.0300 mol dm^{-3} aqueous permanganate, 16.7 cm^3 are required for complete reaction.

(a) Calculate the amount of potassium permanganate used in the titration.

(b) Calculate the amount of iron(II) ions present in the solution.

(c) Given that the molar mass of $Fe(NH_4)_2(SO_4)_2$ is 284 g mol^{-1}, calculate the mass of anhydrous solid that must have been present.

(d) Calculate the mass of water present in the crystals and hence the value of *x*.

8. Concentrated hydrochloric acid has a density of 1.15 g cm^{-3} and contains 30.0% by mass hydrogen chloride.

(a) Determine the concentration of the hydrochloric acid.

(b) What volume of this must be diluted to 5.00 dm^3 to give a solution of concentration 0.200 mol dm^{-3}.

9. 0.130 g of a sample of impure iron was dissolved in excess dilute sulfuric acid to form iron(II) sulfate. This was then titrated with a 0.0137 mol dm^{-3} solution of dichromate ions ($Cr_2O_7^{2-}$) and was found to be just sufficient to reduce 27.3 cm^3 of the solution to chromium(III) ions (Cr^{3+}).

(a) Write a balanced ionic equation for the titration reaction.

(b) Calculate the amount of dichromate ion used in the reaction.

(c) Calculate the amount of iron(II) ions present in the solution.

(d) Calculate the percentage purity (by mass) of the iron.

10. 1.552 g of a pure carboxylic acid (Y—COOH) is titrated against 0.4822 mol dm^{-3} aqueous sodium hydroxide and 26.35 cm^3 are found to be required for complete neutralisation. Calculate the molar mass of the acid and hence deduce its probable formula.

BACK TITRATION

Sometimes reactions occur too slowly for a titration to be employed. This, for example, is usually the case when insoluble solid reagents are used. Back titration is usually employed for quantitative work with substances of this kind. In this technique the sample (say an insoluble base) is reacted with a known excess of one reagent (in this case a known volume of a standard solution of acid). When the reaction with the sample is complete a titration is then carried out (in the example with an alkali of known concentration), to determine how much of the reagent in excess remains unreacted. By knowing the initial amount of the reagent and the amount remaining as excess, then the amount that has reacted with the sample can be calculated. This is clarified by Figure 108.

Amount of standard acid - known from volume and concentration	
Amount of acid reacting with the sample - unknown	Amount of acid reacting with the standard alkali used in the titration - known from volume and concentration

Figure 108 Illustration of the principle of back titration

The total (known) amount of acid must be the sum of the amount that reacted with the alkali (known) and the amount that reacted with the sample (unknown) so the latter can be calculated.

Back titration can be used to determine the percentage by mass of one substance in an impure mixture. For example a sample of calcium hydroxide, a base, containing non-basic impurities can be reacted with excess hydrochloric acid. The excess amount of hydrochloric acid can then be determined by titrating with aqueous sodium hydroxide of known concentration. If the total amount of acid is known and the excess determined, the difference gives the amount that reacted with calcium hydroxide. Thus the mass of calcium hydroxide and its percentage in the mixture can be calculated by 'back titration'. This is illustrated in the example below.

Example

0.5214 g of impure calcium hydroxide was dissolved in 50.00 cm^3 of 0.2500 mol dm^{-3} hydrochloric acid. When the reaction was complete, 33.64 cm^3 of 0.1108 mol dm^{-3} aqueous sodium hydroxide was required to just neutralise the excess acid. Assuming that the impurities do not react, what percentage of the sample was calcium hydroxide?

Solution

Amount of alkali in titration

$= c \times V$

$= 0.1108\ mol\ dm^{-3} \times 0.03364\ dm^3$

$= 0.003727\ mol$

$$HCl\ (aq) + NaOH\ (aq) \longrightarrow NaCl\ (aq) + H_2O\ (l)$$

1: 1 reaction therefore 0.003727 moles of HCl react with the NaOH added.

Amount of acid used initially

$= c \times V$

$= 0.2500\ mol\ dm^{-3} \times 0.05000\ dm^3$

$= 0.01250\ mol$

Amount of acid reacting with calcium hydroxide

$= 0.01250\ mol - 0.003727\ mol$

$= 0.008773\ mol$

$$Ca(OH)_2\ (s) + 2HCl\ (aq) \longrightarrow CaCl_2\ (aq) + 2\ H_2O\ (l)$$

2:1 ratio therefore 0.004386 $\left(= \frac{1}{2} \times 0.008773 \right)$ moles of calcium hydroxide react with the hydrochloric acid.

Mass of $Ca(OH)_2 = n \times M$

$= 0.004386\ mol \times 74.10\ g\ mol^{-1}$

$= 0.3250\ g$

$$\text{Percent by mass of } Ca(OH)_2 = 100 \times \frac{0.3250}{0.5214}$$

$$= 62.34\%$$

The same technique can be used to determine the percentage of calcium carbonate (a base) in egg shell or a sample of impure limestone.

Exercise 1.5.2

1. Aspirin is a sparingly soluble monobasic acid. 1.0 g of impure aspirin ($C_9H_8O_4$) was added to 10 cm^3 of 1.0 mol dm^{-3} aqueous sodium hydroxide. The excess base was then titrated with 0.20 mol dm^{-3} hydrochloric acid and 25 cm^3 were needed to neutralise the excess alkali.

   a) Calculate how many moles of hydrochloric acid were used.
   b) Calculate how many moles of sodium hydroxide were taken initially.
   c) Calculate how many moles of aspirin were present in the tablet.
   d) What mass of aspirin does this correspond to?
   e) What was the percentage purity of the aspirin?

2. A 20.0 g block of impure marble was dissolved in 250 cm^3 of 2.00 mol dm^{-3} nitric acid. When the block completely dissolved, 25.0 cm^3 of the solution was titrated with 1.00 mol dm^{-3} aqueous sodium hydroxide and 17.0 cm^3 were required for neutralisation. What percent by mass of the marble was calcium carbonate. What assumptions did you make in calculating this?

3. 0.600g of a metal M was dissolved in 200 cm^3 of 0.500 mol dm^{-3} hydrochloric acid. 25.0 cm^3 of 2.00 mol dm^{-3} aqueous sodium hydroxide were required to neutralise the excess acid. Calculate the molar mass of the metal assuming that the formula of its chloride is:

   a) MCl
   b) MCl_2
   c) MCl_3

   Which do you consider to be the more likely value? Why?

CORE

CORE

APPENDIX

1A SCIENTIFIC NOTATION

Scientific notation is a method of expressing large or small numbers as factors of the powers of 10. One can use exponents of 10 to make the expression of scientific measurements more compact, easier to understand, and simpler to manipulate (0.0000000013 m compared with 1.3×10^{-9} m and 7500000 g compared to 7.5×10^{6} g — note: these may also be found as $1.3 \bullet 10^{-9}$ m and $7.5 \bullet 10^{6}$ g where the point represents multiplication).

To express numbers in scientific notation, one should use the form: $a \times 10^{b}$ where a is a real number between 1 and 10 (but not equal to 10), and b is a positive or negative integer.

This form works for 7500000, a large number as follows:

1. Set a equal to 7.5, which is a real number between 1 and 10.

2. To find b, count the places to the right of the decimal point in a to the original decimal point. There are 6 places to the right (+6) from the decimal point in a to the original decimal point, so $b = 6$. The number is expressed as 7.5×10^{6}.

For a large number, the exponent of 10 (b) will be a POSITIVE integer equal to the number of decimal places to the RIGHT from the decimal point in a to the original decimal point.

For 0.0000000013, a small number:

1. *Set a* = 1.3, which is a real number between 1 and 10.

2. To find b, count the places to the left of the decimal point in a, finishing up at the original decimal point. There are 9 places from the left (–9) of the decimal point, so b = –9. This is expressed as 1.3×10^{-9}.

For a small number, the exponent of 10 will be a NEGATIVE integer equal to the number of decimal places to the LEFT from the decimal point in a to the original decimal point.

Manipulating numbers in this form is also easier, especially multiplying and dividing. In multiplying the first part of the numbers (the 'a' s) are multiplied, the exponents are added and then the decimal place adjusted.

Example 1

Calculate the number of oxygen molecules in 5.00×10^{-8} moles of oxygen.

Solution

$$\begin{aligned} N &= n \times 6.02 \times 10^{23} \\ &= 5 \times 10^{-8} \times 6.02 \times 10^{23} \\ &= (5 \times 6.02) \times 10^{(-8+23)} \\ &= 30.1 \times 10^{15} \\ &= 3.01 \times 10^{16} \end{aligned}$$

Similarly, in dividing numbers, the first part of the numbers (the 'a' s) are divided, the exponents subtracted and then the decimal place adjusted.

Example 2

Calculate the mass of a protein molecule that has a molar mass of 1.76×10^{4} g mol^{-1}.

Solution

$$\begin{aligned} m &= \frac{M}{6.02 \times 10^{23}} \\ &= \frac{1.76 \times 10^{4}}{6.02 \times 10^{23}} \\ &= \left(\frac{1.76}{6.02}\right) \times 10^{(4-23)} \\ &= 0.292 \times 10^{-19} \\ &= 2.92 \times 10^{-20} \text{g} \end{aligned}$$

Exercise 1.5.2

1. Which one of the following numbers is in correct scientific notation?

   A 862×10^5
   B 0.26×10^5
   C 4.73×10^5
   D $2.93 \times 10^{5.2}$

2. The number 57230.357 is best shown in scientific notation as

   A 5.7230357×10^{-4}
   B 57230357×10^{-3}
   C 5.7230357×10^4
   D 5.7230357×10^8

3. 2.872×10^{-4} is best written as a normal number in the form

   A 0.0002872
   B 28720
   C −42.872
   D −28720

4. Write the following in scientific notation:

   a) 437600
   b) 0.00000023
   c) 415000000
   d) 0.0372
   e) 476.8
   f) 3.26

5. Write the following as normal numbers:

   a) 8.2×10^5
   b) 6.29×10^{-3}
   c) 2.7138×10^{11}
   d) 2×10^{-7}
   e) 4.2×10^1
   f) 5.89×10^{-1}

1B SIGNIFICANT FIGURES

The accuracy of a measurement depends on the quality of the instrument one uses for measuring and on the carefulness of the measurement. When a measurement is reported, the number of significant figures, can be used to represent one's own precision and that of the instrument. So significant figures should show the limits of accuracy and where the uncertainty begins. Section 11.1 discusses this subject in much more detail.

Measuring with an ordinary meter stick, you might report the length of an object as 1.4 m, which means you measured it as being longer than 1.35 m, but shorter than 1.45 m. The measurement 1.4 has *two* significant figures. If you had a better ruler, or were more careful, you might have reported the length as 1.42 m, which means that you measured the object as being longer than 1.415 m, but shorter than 1.425 m. The measurement 1.42 has *three* significant figures.

The last digit in a significant figure is uncertain because it reflects the limit of accuracy.

Significant zeros

You may have to decide whether zeros are significant in three different situations.

1. *If the zeros precede the first non-zero digit, they are not significant*. Such zeros merely locate the decimal point; i.e., they define the magnitude of the measurement. For example, 0.00014 m has two significant figures, and 0.01 has one significant figure.

2. *If the zeros are between non-zero digits, they are significant*. For example, 103307 kg has six significant figures while 0.04403 has four significant figures.

3. *If the zeros follow non-zero digits, there is ambiguity if no decimal point is given*. If a volume is given as 300 cm^3, you have no way of telling if the final two zeros are significant. But if the volume is given as 300. cm^3, you know that it has three significant figures; and if it is given as 300.0 cm^3, it has four significant figures.

Note: You can avoid ambiguity by expressing your measurements in scientific notation. Then if you record your final zeros in *a*, they are significant. So, if you report '300 cm^3' as 3×10^2 cm^3, it has only one significant figure; 3.0×10^2 cm^3 has two significant figures; and 3.00×10^2 has three significant figures. A number such as 20700 in which the last two zeros are not significant is probably better written as 2.07×10^4, to avoid ambiguity.

CORE

CORE

Using significant figures in calculations

For multiplication and division, a result can only be as accurate as the factor with the least number of significant figures that goes into its calculation.

Note: Integers or whole numbers and constants do not alter your calculation of significant figures. For example, the volume of a sphere is $v = {}^4/_3\pi r^3$. The 4 and 3 are exact whole numbers, while the constant pi can be reported to any desired degree of accuracy (3.14159...). The result for the volume will depend only on the accuracy of the measurement for the radius r.

Rounding off

The rounding off rules are simple: If the digit following the last reportable digit is:

- 4 or less, you drop it
- 5 or more, you increase the last reportable digit by one

For addition and subtraction, the answer should contain no more digits to the right of the decimal point than any individual quantity i.e. use the least number of decimal places.

For multiplication and division, use the least number of significant figures.

Note: You may wonder just when to round off. The answer is, round off when it's most convenient. With calculators and computers, it's as easy to carry six or seven digits as it is to carry three or four. So, for economy and accuracy, do your rounding off at the last step of a calculation.

Exercise 1.16

1. The number of significant figures in 0.0003701 is

   A 3
   B 4
   C 7
   D 8

2. A calculator display shows the result of a calculation to be 57230.357. If it is to be reported to 4 significant figures, it would be best recorded as

   A 5723
   B 57230
   C 5.723×10^{-4}
   D 5.723×10^{4}

3. If a sample of a metal has a mass of 26.385 g and a volume of 5.82 cm^3, its density is best recorded as

   A 4.5 g cm^{-3}
   B 4.53 g cm^{-3}
   C 4.534 g cm^{-3}
   D 4.5335 g cm^{-3}

4. A bottle of mass 58.32 g contains 0.373 kg of water and a crystal of mass 3000.6 mg. To how many significant figures should the total mass be recorded?

   A 2
   B 3
   C 4
   D 5

5. Give the results of the following calculations to the appropriate degree of accuracy.

   (a) 0.037×0.763

   (b) $200.1257 \div 7.2$

   (c) $3.76 \times 10^5 - 276$

   (d) $0.00137 + 3.762 \times 10^{-4}$

   (e) $3 \times 10^8 \times 7.268$

FURTHER WORKED EXAMPLES

There are only four formulas used in these worked examples, though these formulas may be rearranged or combined together depending on what is required and the data available. These four formulas are:

$$\text{Number of moles} = \frac{\text{Number of particles}}{6.02 \times 10^{23}}$$

$$n = \frac{N}{6.02 \times 10^{23}}$$

$$\text{Number of moles} = \frac{\text{Mass of substance}}{\text{Molar mass of substance}}$$

$$n = \frac{m}{M}$$

$$\text{Number of moles of gas} = \frac{\text{Volume of gas}}{\text{Molar volume at same T \& P}}$$

$$n = \frac{V}{V_m}$$

Pressure × Volume = R × Moles of gas × Absolute temperature

$$P.v = n.R.T$$

$$\text{Concentration of solution} = \frac{\text{Moles of solute}}{\text{Volume in dm}^3}$$

$$n = \frac{n}{V}$$

1. Finding the amount of substance from the number of particles.

Determine the amount of substance in 2.408×10^{21} molecules of ammonia.

SOLUTION

Required - n Known - N (2.408×10^{21} particles)

Therefore use:

$$n = \frac{N}{6.02 \times 10^{23}}$$

Substituting:

$$n = \frac{N}{6.02 \times 10^{23}}$$

$$= \frac{2.408 \times 10^{21}}{6.02 \times 10^{23}}$$

= 0.004 moles of ammonia.

2. Finding number of particles from the amount of substance.

Calculate how many molecules are there in 15.0 moles of water.

SOLUTION

Required - N Known - n (15.0 moles)

Therefore use:

$$n = \frac{N}{6.02 \times 10^{23}}$$

Substituting:

$$15.0 = \frac{N}{6.02 \times 10^{23}}$$

Rearranging:

$$N = 15.0 \times 6.02 \times 10^{23}$$

$= 9.03 \times 10^{24}$ molecules of water.

3. Finding the amount of substance from the mass and the molar mass

Determine the amount of substance in 12.00 g of barium sulfate.

(Ba = 137.34 g mol^{-1}, S = 32.06 g mol^{-1}, O = 16.00 g mol^{-1})

SOLUTION

Required - n Known - m (12 g) & M (from formula).

Therefore use:

$$n = \frac{m}{M}$$

Molar mass of $BaSO_4$ = 137.34 + 32.06 + (4 × 16.00)
= 233.40 g mol^{-1}

Substituting:

$$n = \frac{m}{M}$$

$$= \frac{12.00}{233.40}$$

= 0.0514 moles of barium sulfate.

CORE

4. Finding mass from the amount of substance and molar mass.

Determine the mass of 0.500 moles of borax crystals, $Na_2B_4O_7{\cdot}10H_2O$

($Na = 22.99\ g\ mol^{-1}$, $O = 16.00\ g\ mol^{-1}$, $B = 10.81\ g\ mol^{-1}$, $H = 1.01\ g\ mol^{-1}$)

SOLUTION

Required - m Known - n (0.500 mole) & M (from formula)

Therefore use: $n = \frac{m}{M}$

Molar mass of $Na_2B_4O_7{\cdot}10H_2O$

$= (2 \times 22.99) + (4 \times 10.81) + (7 \times 16.00) + (10 \times 18.02)$

$= 381.42\ g\ mol^{-1}$

Substituting:

$$n = \frac{m}{M}$$

$$0.500 = \frac{m}{381.42}$$

Rearranging

$$m = 0.500\ mol \times 381.42\ g\ mol^{-1}$$

$= 191$ g of borax crystals.

5. Finding the molar mass from the mass and amount of substance

5.42 g of a substance is found to contain 0.0416 moles. Determine its molar mass.

SOLUTION

Required - M Known - n (0.0416 mol) & m (5.42 g)

Therefore use: $n = \frac{m}{M}$

Substituting:

$$n = \frac{m}{M}$$

$$0.416\ mol = \frac{5.42\ g}{M}$$

Rearranging:

$$M = \frac{5.42\ g}{0.0416\ mol}$$

$$= 130\ g\ mol^{-1}.$$

6. Finding the percentage composition

Gypsum is a naturally occuring form of calcium sulfate ($CaSO_4{\cdot}2H_2O$). What percentage by mass of gypsum is water?

($Ca = 40.08\ g\ mol^{-1}$; $S = 32.06\ g\ mol^{-1}$; $O = 16.00\ g\ mol^{-1}$; $H = 1.01\ g\ mol^{-1}$)

SOLUTION

Required - % H_2O

Known - molar masses of gypsum and water.

Molar mass of gypsum

$= 40.08 + 32.06 + (4 \times 16.00) + (2 \times 18.02)$

$= 172.18\ g\ mol^{-1}$

Mass of water in this $= 2 \times 18.02$

$= 36.04$

$$\text{Percentage of water} = \frac{36.04}{172.16} \times 100$$

$= 20.93$ %

7. Finding the empirical formula from mass data

5.694 g of an oxide of cobalt yielded 4.046 g of the metal on reduction. What was the empirical formula of the oxide?

($Co = 58.93\ g\ mol^{-1}$; $O = 16.00\ g\ mol^{-1}$)

SOLUTION

Required - molar ratio of Co to O.

Known - the masses and molar masses of Co and O.

$$\text{Amount of cobalt in the oxide} = \frac{m}{M}$$

$$= \frac{4.046\ g}{58.93\ g\ mol^{-1}}$$

$= 0.06866$ moles.

$$\text{Amount of oxygen in the oxide} = \frac{m}{M}$$

$$= \frac{5.694\ g - 4.046\ g}{16.00\ g\ mol^{-1}}$$

$= 0.1030$ moles

Ratio of cobalt to oxygen $= 0.06866 : 0.1030$

$$= 1 : \frac{0.1030}{0.06866}$$

$= 1 : 1.500$

$= 2 : 3$

Therefore the empirical formula of the oxide is Co_2O_3.

8. Finding the empirical formula from percentage composition data

Treatment of metallic copper with excess of chlorine results in a yellow solid compound which contains 47.2% copper, and 52.8% chlorine. Determine the simplest formula of the compound.

($Cu = 63.55\ g\ mol^{-1}$; $Cl = 35.45\ g\ mol^{-1}$)

SOLUTION

Required - molar ratio of Cu to Cl.
Known - the percentages by mass and molar masses of Cu and Cl.

In 100.0 g of compound there are 47.2 g of copper and 52.8 g of chlorine.

$$\text{Amount of Cu} = \frac{m}{M} = \frac{47.2\ g}{63.55\ g\ mol^{-1}} = 0.7427\ mol$$

$$\text{Amount of Cl} = \frac{m}{M} = \frac{52.8\ g}{35.45\ g\ mol^{-1}} = 1.489\ mol$$

Ratio of amounts of Cu : Cl = 0.7427 : 1.489
= 1 : 2.005 = 1 : 2

The empirical formula is therefore $CuCl_2$.

9. Finding the empirical formula of a hydrate from percentage composition data.

When hydrated strontium hydroxide crystals are strongly heated, they decrease in mass by 54.2% to leave the anhydrous solid. Determine the formula of the hydrate.

($Sr = 87.62\ g\ mol^{-1}$; $O = 16.00\ g\ mol^{-1}$; $H = 1.01\ g\ mol^{-1}$)

SOLUTION

Knowing that the strontium ion is Sr^{2+} (in Group 2 of the Periodic Table) and that the hydroxide ion is OH^-, the formula of strontium hydroxide can be calculated as $Sr(OH)_2$. (N.B. positive and negative charges must cancel.)

Required - molar ratio of to $H_2O : Sr(OH)_2$
Known - the molar masses and masses of these in 100 g of the hydrate.

$$\text{Amount of } H_2O = \frac{m}{M} = \frac{54.2\ g}{18.02\ g mol^{-1}} = 3.008\ mol$$

$$\text{Amount of } Sr(OH)_2 = \frac{100\ g - 54.2\ g}{121.64\ g\ mol^{-1}} = 0.3765\ mol$$

Ratio of amounts of $H_2O : Sr(OH)_2$ = 3.008 : 0.3765
= 7.989 : 1

The formula of the hydrate must be $Sr(OH)_2 \cdot 8H_2O$.

10. The molecular formula from molar mass and combustion data.

Vitamin C, a compound of carbon hydrogen and oxygen only, is found in many fruits and vegetables. The percentages, by mass, of carbon, hydrogen, and oxygen in vitamin C are determined by burning a sample of vitamin C weighing 2.00 mg. The masses of carbon dioxide and water formed are 3.00 mg and 0.816 mg, respectively. By titration its molar mass is found to be about 180 g mol^{-1}. From these data, determine the molecular formula of vitamin C.

($O = 16.00\ g\ mol^{-1}$; $C = 12.01\ g\ mol^{-1}$; $H = 1.01\ g\ mol^{-1}$).

SOLUTION

Required - molar ratio of C, H and O.
Known - the molar masses and masses of CO_2 and H_2O formed by the combustion of 2.00 mg of the compound and the approximate molar mass.

Firstly calculate that amounts of CO_2 and H_2O:

$$\text{Amount of } CO_2 = \frac{3.00 \times 10^{-3}\ g}{44.01\ g\ mol^{-1}} = 6.816 \times 10^{-5} \text{ moles.}$$

$$\text{Amount of } H_2O = \frac{m}{M} = \frac{8.16 \times 10^{-4}\ g}{18.02\ g\ mol^{-1}} = 4.528 \times 10^{-5} \text{ moles.}$$

CORE

The amounts of C and H in the 2.00 mg of vitamin C must have been 6.816×10^{-5} and 9.056×10^{-5} (as it is H_2O) respectively.

Calculate the mass of oxygen in the sample by subtraction and hence the amount:

Mass of oxygen
$= 0.002 - (12.01 \times 6.816 \times 10^{-5}) - (1.01 \times 9.056 \times 10^{-5})$
$= 1.090 \times 10^{-3}$ g.

Amount of oxygen $= \frac{m}{M}$

$= \frac{1.090 \times 10^{-3}}{16.00}$

$= 6.812 \times 10^{-5}$ moles.

Ratio of amounts of C : H : O
= 6.816 : 9.056 : 6.812
= 1 : 1.33 : 1
= 3 : 4 : 3

The empirical formula of vitamin C must be $C_3H_4O_3$,

The molar mass of this would be approximately
$(3 \times 12) + (4 \times 1) + (3 \times 16) = 88$

The observed molar mass is ≈ 180,
so it is composed of $\frac{188}{88} \approx 2$ of these units.

The molecular formula of vitamin C is therefore
$2 \times (C_3H_4O_3) = C_6H_8O_6$.

11. Reacting mass calculations

When aqueous silver nitrate is added to an aqueous solution containing chromate ions, a brick-red precipitate of silver chromate (Ag_2CrO_4) forms. What mass of silver chromate could be obtained from a solution containing 5.00 g of silver nitrate?

(Ag = 107.87 g mol^{-1}; Cr = 52.00 g mol^{-1};
O = 16.00 g mol^{-1}; N = 14.01 g mol^{-1})

SOLUTION

Required: mass of silver chromate
Known: mass and molar mass of, hence the amount of $AgNO_3$.
equation, hence the amount of Ag_2CrO_4.
molar mass of Ag_2CrO_4, hence calculate the mass from the amount.

Amount of $AgNO_3 = \frac{m}{M}$

$= \frac{5.00}{169.88}$

$= 0.02943$ moles.

Equation:
$$Na_2CrO_4 + 2\ AgNO_3 \longrightarrow Ag_2CrO_4 + 2\ NaNO_3$$

2 moles 1 mole
0.02943 moles 0.01472 moles

Mass of $Ag_2CrO_4 = n \times M$
$= 0.01472 \times 331.74$
$= 4.89$ g.

12. The amount of reactant required.

When potassium nitrate is heated, it decomposes to potassium nitrite and oxygen. What mass of potassium nitrate must be heated to produce 10 g of oxygen?

(Potassium nitrite is KNO_2; K = 39.10 g mol^{-1};
O = 16.00 g mol^{-1}; N = 14.01 g mol^{-1})

SOLUTION

Required: mass of potassium nitrate.
Known: mass and molar mass of O_2, hence the amount of O_2.
equation, hence the amount of KNO_3.
molar mass of KNO_3, hence calculate the mass from the amount.

Amount of $O_2 = \frac{m}{M}$

$= \frac{10}{32.00}$

$= 0.3215$ moles.

Equation:
$$2\ KNO_3 \longrightarrow 2\ KNO_2 + O_2$$

2 moles 1 mole
0.3125×2 moles 0.3125 moles

Mass of $KNO_3 = n \times M$
$= 0.625 \times 101.11$
$= 63.19$ g.

13. Finding the molar mass of a gas from the mass of a sample under standard conditions.

10.4 g of a gas occupies a volume of 3.72 dm^3 at standard temperature and pressure. Determine the molar mass of the gas.

SOLUTION

Required: M
Known: m (10.4 g) and V (3.72 dm^3)

Therefore use $n = \frac{V}{V_m}$ to find n

and then use $n = \frac{m}{M}$ to find M.

$$\text{Moles of gas} = \frac{V}{22.4} = \frac{3.72}{22.4} = 0.166 \text{ moles}$$

$$\text{Molar mass} = \frac{m}{n} = \frac{10.4}{0.166} = 62.7 \text{ g mol}^{-1}.$$

14. Finding the volume of gas produced in a reaction.

When hydrogen peroxide is added to a manganese(IV) oxide catalyst it undergoes catalytic decomposition to water and oxygen. What volume of oxygen, measured at standard temperature and pressure, can be produced from a solution containing 17 g of hydrogen peroxide?

SOLUTION

Required - V
Known - m (17 g) and M (34 g mol^{-1})

Therefore use $n = \frac{m}{M}$ to find $n(H_2O_2)$,

use balanced equation to find $n(O_2)$,

and then use $n = \frac{V}{V_m}$ to find V.

$$\text{Moles of } H_2O_2 = \frac{m}{M} = \frac{17}{34} = 0.5 \text{ moles.}$$

Balanced equation:

$$2\,H_2O_2 \longrightarrow 2\,H_2O + O_2$$

2 moles 1 mole
0.5 moles 0.25 moles

$$\text{Volume of oxygen} = n \times 22.4 = 0.25 \times 22.4 = 5.6 \text{ dm}^3.$$

15. Volume of .a known amount of gas under given conditions.

A lighter contains 0.217 mol of butane. What volume would this occupy if it were released on top of a mountain where the temperature was 5°C and the pressure was 92.0 kPa?

SOLUTION

Required: V
Known: n (0.217 mol),
T (5 °C = 278K) and
P (92.0 kPa)

$$V = \frac{n.R.T}{P}$$

$$V = \frac{0.217 \times 8.314 \times 278}{92.0} = 5.45 \text{ dm}^3$$

16. Calculating the pressure of a known gas under given conditions.

A test tube of volume 25 cm^3 sealed with a bung contains 0.1 cm^3 of water. It is heated to a temperature of 200°C, what pressure, in atmospheres, will the vapourised water create inside the test tube?

(O = 16.00 g mol^{-1}; H = 1.01 g mol^{-1}).

SOLUTION

Required: P
Known: V (25 cm^3 = 0.025 dm^3),
m (0.1 cm^3 will have a mass of 0.1 g) and
T (200 °C = 473K)

therefore use

$$n = \frac{m}{M} \text{ followed by } P = \frac{n.R.T}{V}$$

$$\text{amount of water} = \frac{0.1}{(2 \times 1.01) + 16.00} = 0.005549 \text{ mol}$$

$$P = \frac{0.005549 \times 8.314 \times 473}{0.025} = 873 \text{ kPa}$$

$$= {}^{873}/_{101.3} = 8.62 \text{ atm}$$

17. Finding the number of molecules in a given volume of gas under specified conditions.

Calculate the number of molecules in a classroom that measures 5.00 m × 6.00 m with a height of 2.50 m on a day when the temperature in the room is 27.0 °C and the pressure is 100.0 kPa.

SOLUTION

Required: N

Known: V (5 × 6 × 2.5 m^3),
T (27 °C = 300 K),
P (100.0 kPa)

Therefore use $n = \frac{P.V}{R.T}$

followed by $N = n \times 6.02 \times 10^{23}$

$$n = \frac{100 \times [(6 \times 5 \times 2.5) \times 10^3]}{8.314 \times 300}$$

= 3007 mol

N = 3007 × 6.02 × 10^{23}

= 1.81 × 10^{27} molecules

18. Finding the mass of a given volume of gas at specified conditions and how the conditions mutually affect each other.

A gas cylinder containing 50.0 dm^3 of hydrogen has a pressure of 70.0 atm at 20 °C.

a) What mass of hydrogen does it contain?

b) What volume of hydrogen would this produce at atmospheric pressure?

c) If the bursting pressure of the cylinder were 100 atm to what temperature would the cylinder have to be heated for it to explode?

SOLUTION

a) Required: m

Known: V (50.0 dm^3),
T (20 °C = 293 K),
P (70.0 atm = 7091 kPa)

Therefore use $n = \frac{P.V}{R.T}$

followed by m = n × M

$$n = \frac{7091 \times 50}{8.314 \times 293} = 146 \text{ mol}$$

m = 146 × 2
= 291 g of hydrogen

b) Required: V at 1.00 atm

Known: V (50.0 dm^3) at 70.0 atm

Therefore use $P_1 \times V_1 = P_2 \times V_2$

Substituting:

$$70 \times 50 = 1 \times V_2$$

Rearanging: V_2 = 3500 dm^3

c) Required: T at which P = 100 atm

Known: P at (20 °C = 293 K)

Therefore use $\frac{P_1}{T_1} = \frac{P_2}{T_2}$

$\frac{100}{T_1} = \frac{70}{293}$ therefore $T_1 = 293 \times \frac{100}{70}$

= 419 K or 146 °C

19. Finding the concentration from the amount of substance and the volume.

Determine the concentration of the solution produced when 0.02 moles of magnesium sulfate is dissolved to give 40 cm^3 of solution.

SOLUTION

Required: c

Known: n (0.02 mole) and
V (0.04 dm^3).

Therefore use: $c = \frac{n}{V}$

Substituting $c = \frac{0.02}{0.040}$

= 0.5 mol dm^{-3}.

20. Volume from concentration and amount of substance

What volume of 0.200 mol dm^{-3} nitric acid contains 5.00 × 10^{-2} moles of the acid?

SOLUTION

Required: V

Known: n (5 × 10^{-2} moles) and
c (0.2 mol dm^{-3}).

Therefore use: $V = \frac{n}{c}$

Substituting $V = \frac{n}{c}$

$= \frac{5.00 \times 10^{-2}}{0.200}$ dm^3

= 250 cm^3

$m = n \times M$
= 0.80 mol × 342.34 g mol^{-1}
= 270 g.

21. Concentration from mass and volume

What concentration is the solution formed when 2.00 g of solid potassium chloride is dissolved in 250 cm^3 of solution?

(K = 39.10 g mol^{-1}, Cl = 35.45 g mol^{-1}).

SOLUTION

Required: c
Known: m (2.00 g),
M (39.1 + 35.45g mol^{-1}) and
V (0.250 dm^3).

Therefore: first use $n = \frac{m}{M}$ to find n and then $c = \frac{n}{V}$.

Substituting: $n = \frac{m}{M}$

$= \frac{2.00}{74.55}$

= 0.02683 moles.

$c = \frac{n}{V}$

$= \frac{0.02683}{0.250}$

= 0.107 mol dm^{-3}.

22. Mass from concentration and volume.

What mass of solid will remain when 2.0 dm^3 of a 0.40 mol dm^{-3} solution of sucrose ($C_{12}H_{22}O_{11}$) is evaporated to dryness?

(O = 16.00 g mol^{-1}; C = 12.01 g mol^{-1};
H = 1.01 g mol^{-1}).

SOLUTION

Required: m
Known: c (0.40 mol dm^3),
M (342.34 g mol^{-1}) and
V (2 dm^3).

Therefore: first use $n = c \times V$ to find n
and then $m = n \times M$

Substituting: $n = c \times V$
=0.40 mol dm^{-3} × 2.0 dm^3
= 0.80 moles.

23. Calculating concentration from titration results.

It is found that 33.7 cm^3 of hydrochloric acid just neutralises 20 cm^3 of aqueous sodium carbonate with a concentration of 1.37 mol dm^{-3}. Determine the concentration of the acid.

SOLUTION

Required: c
Known: c_{alkali} (1.37 mol dm^{-3}),
V_{alkali} (0.02 dm^3),
V_{acid} (0.0337 dm^3)

Therefore:
first use $n = c_{alkali} \times V_{alkali}$ to find the amount of alkali used;
then use the balanced equation to calculate the amount of acid required.
finally use $c = \frac{n}{V_{acid}}$ to calculate the concentration of the acid.

Substituting: $n = c_{alkali} \times V_{alkali}$

= 1.37 mol dm^{-3} × 0.02 dm^3
= 0.0274 moles

Balanced equation:

$2\,HCl + Na_2CO_3 \longrightarrow 2\,NaCl + H_2O + CO_2$

2 HCl	Na$_2$CO$_3$
2 moles	1 mole
0.0548	0.0274

Substituting: $c = \frac{n}{V_{acid}}$

$= \frac{0.0548}{0.0337}$

= 1.63 mol dm^{-3}.

24. A complex titration calculation to find the concentration of a reactant.

10.0 cm^3 of household bleach (active ingredient ClO^-) is diluted to a total volume of 250 cm^3. 20.0 cm^3 is then added to 1 g of potassium iodide (an excess) and the iodine produced is titrated with 0.0206 sodium thiosulfate. Using starch solution as an indicator the end point is found after 17.3 cm^3 has been added. The equations for the reactions taking place are:

CORE

$$2\,ClO^-\,(aq) + 2\,I^-\,(aq) + 2\,H^+\,(aq) \longrightarrow 2\,Cl^-\,(aq) + I_2\,(aq) + H_2O\,(l)$$

$$2\,S_2O_3^{\;2-}\,(aq) + I_2\,(aq) \longrightarrow S_4O_6^{\;2-}\,(aq) + 2\,I^-\,(aq)$$

Calculate the concentration of the active ingredient in the bleach as the percentage of sodium chlorate(I) (i.e. mass of NaClO in 100 cm^3).

(Cl = 35.45 g mol^{-1}, Na = 22.99 g mol^{-1}, O = 16.00 g mol^{-1})

SOLUTION

Required: *First of all, initial c_{NaClO}, then convert to mass of NaClO*

Known: $c_{S_2O_3}$ (0.0206 mol dm^{-3}),
$V_{S_2O_3}$ (17.3 cm^3) and
V_{NaClO} (20.0 × $^{10}/_{250}$ cm^3)

Therefore: use $n = c \times V$ successsively followed by $m = n \times M$

Moles ClO^- = $c_{NaClO} \times V_{NaClO}$

= 2 × moles I_2

= moles $S_2O_3^{\;2-}$

= $c_{S_2O_3} \times V_{S_2O_3}$

$c_{NaClO} \times 0.020 \times {}^{10}/_{250}$

= 0.0206 × 0.0173

$$c_{NaClO} = \frac{0.0206 \times 0.0173 \times 250}{0.020 \times 10}$$

= 0.445 mol dm^{-3}

Mass of NaClO in 100 cm^3 = $c_{NaClO} \times {}^{100}/_{1000} \times M_{NaClO}$

Mass of NaClO in 100 cm^3
= 0.445 × 0.1 × (22.99 + 35.45 + 16.00)
= 3.32 g

Therefore the percent of active ingredient in the bleach is 3.32%.

25. Diluting an acid.

250 cm^3 of hydrochloric acid with a concentration of exactly 0.1 mol dm^{-3} is to be prepared using hydrochloric acid with a concentration of 1.63 mol dm^{-3}. What volume of this must be diluted?

SOLUTION

Required: $V_{starting}$

Known: $c_{starting}$ (1.63 mol dm^{-3}),
c_{final} (0.1 mol dm^{-3}) and
V_{final} (0.25 dm^3)

Therefore: first use $n = c_{final} \times V_{final}$ to find the amount required

then $V_{starting} = \dfrac{n}{c_{starting}}$

to calculate the volume of the acid required.

Substituting: $n = c_{final} \times V_{final}$
= 0.1 mol dm^{-3} × 0.25 dm^3 = 0.025 moles.

$$V_{starting} = \frac{n}{c_{starting}} = \frac{0.025}{1.63}$$

= 0.0154 dm^3
= 15.4 cm^3.

26. Finding the percentage of a component in a mixture by titration.

'Iron tablets', to prevent anaemia, often contain hydrated iron(II) sulfate ($FeSO_4{\bullet}7H_2O$). One such tablet weighing 1.863 g was crushed, dissolved in water and the solution made up to a total volume of 250 cm^3. When 10 cm^3 of this solution when added to 20 cm^3 of dilute sulfuric acid and titrated with aqueous 0.002 mol dm^{-3} potassium pemanganate, was found on average to require 24.5 cm^3 to produce a permanent pink colouration. Given that the equation for the reaction between iron(II) ions and permanganate ions is

$$MnO_4^- + 5\,Fe^{2+} + 8\,H^+ \longrightarrow Mn^{2+} + 5\,Fe^{3+} + 4\,H_2O$$

calculate the percentage of the tablet that was iron(II) sulfate.

(Fe = 55.85 g mol^{-1}; S = 32.06 g mol^{-1}; O = 16.00 g mol^{-1})

SOLUTION

Required: the mass of iron(II) sulfate in the tablet, hence the percentage by mass.

Known: the volume of permanganate solution reacting with a fraction of the tablet.

Therefore: Find the amount of permanganate used.
Hence find the amount of iron reacting.
Hence find the amount of iron in total tablet.
Hence find the mass of the iron(II) sulfate and the percentage.

Amount of permanganate $= c \times V$
$= 0.002 \times 0.0245$
$= 4.90 \times 10^{-5}$ moles.

$MnO_4^- + 5\,Fe^{2+} + 8\,H^+ \longrightarrow Mn^{2+} + 5\,Fe^{3+} + 4\,H_2O$

MnO_4^-	Fe^{2+}
1 mole	5 moles
4.90×10^{-5}	$(5 \times 4.90 \times 10^{-5})$ $= 2.45 \times 10^{-4}$

There are 2.45×10^{-4} moles of iron(II) in 10 cm^3 of solution, so in 250 cm^3 there are

$$2.45 \times 10^{-4} \times \frac{250}{10} = 6.125 \times 10^{-3} \text{ moles.}$$

Mass of iron(II) sulfate $= n \times M$
$= 6.125 \times 10^{-3} \times 278.05$
$= 1.703$ g.

Percentage by mass of iron(II) sulfate $= \frac{1.703}{1.863} \times 100$

$= 91.4\%$

27. Finding the concentration of the solution produced by a reaction.

1.86 g of lead carbonate is added to 50.0 cm^3 (an excess) of nitric acid. Determine the concentration of lead nitrate in the resulting solution.

(Pb = 207.19 g mol^{-1}; O = 16.00 g mol^{-1}; C = 12.01 g mol^{-1})

SOLUTION

Required: c
Known: m (1.86 g), M (283.2); V (0.050 dm^3)

Therefore: first use $n = \frac{m}{M}$ to find the amount of lead carbonate,then use the balanced equation to find the amount of lead nitrate, and finally use $c = \frac{n}{V}$ to find the concentration.

Substituting: $n = \frac{m}{M}$

$= \frac{1.86}{267.2}$

$= 0.006961$ moles.

$PbCO_3 + 2\,HNO_3 \longrightarrow Pb(NO_3)_2 + H_2O + CO_2$

$PbCO_3$	$Pb(NO_3)_2$
1 mole	1 mole
0.006961	0.006961

$c = \frac{n}{V}$

$= \frac{0.006961}{0.050}$

$= 0.139$ mol dm^{-3}.

28. Calculating the limiting reagent.

1.34 g of magnesium are added to 120 cm^3 of a 0.200 mol dm^{-3} solution of silver nitrate. What mass of silver will be formed?

(Ag = 107.87 g mol^{-1}, Mg = 24.31 g mol^{-1})

SOLUTION

Required: m_{Ag}
Known: c_{Ag} (0.20 mol dm^{-3});
V_{Ag} (0.12 dm^3);
m_{Mg} (1.34 g)

Therefore: use $n = \frac{m}{M}$ to find the amount of Mg, then use $n = c \times V$ to find the amount of Ag^+, use a balanced equation to find the limiting reagent and the amount of Ag, and finally calculate the mass using $m = n \times M$.

$n = \frac{m}{M}$

$= \frac{1.34}{24.31}$

$= 0.05512$ moles of magnesium.

$n = c \times V$
$= 0.200 \times 0.120$
$= 0.024$ moles of silver nitrate.

$Mg + 2\,Ag^+ \longrightarrow 2\,Ag + Mg^{2+}$

	Mg	Ag^+
In theory -	1	2
Actually -	0.05512	0.024

Magnesium is in excess as only 0.012 moles are required. The silver is the limiting reagent and therefore it controls the yield of the metal:

$$Mg + 2\,Ag^{+} \longrightarrow 2\,Ag + Mg^{2+}$$

2	2
0.024	0.024

$m = n \times M$
$= 0.024 \times 107.87$
$= 2.59$ g.

29. Calculating the number of molecules from the concentration

The concentration of gold in seawater is approximately 10^{-10} mol dm^{-3}. Calculate how many gold atoms will there be in the average drop (0.04 cm^3) of seawater.

SOLUTION

Required: N
Known - c (10^{-10} mol dm^{-3}) and V (4×10^{-5} dm^3)

Therefore: use $n = c \times V$ to find the amount of gold, then use $N = n \times 6.02 \times 10^{23}$ to find the number of gold atoms.

Substituting: $n = c \times V$
$= 10^{-10} \times 4 \times 10^{-5}$
$= 4 \times 10^{-15}$

$N = n \times 6.02 \times 10^{23}$
$= 4 \times 10^{-15} \times 6.02 \times 10^{23}$
$= 2.41 \times 10^{9}$

i.e. each drop has over 2 billion gold atoms in it!

30. Calculating molar mass by back titration.

2.04 g of an insoluble, dibasic organic acid were dissolved in 20.0 cm^3 of 2.00 mol dm^{-3} aqueous sodium hydroxide. The excess alkali required 17.6 cm^3 of 0.50 mol dm^{-3} hydrochloric acid to neutralise it. Determine the molar mass of the acid.

SOLUTION

Required: moles of acid in known mass and hence molar mass

Known: volumes and concentrations of excess alkali and neutralising acid

Therefore: find amount of excess alkali and neutralising acid,
use these to calculate the amount of the organic acid,

find the molar mass of the organic acid from the mass and amount

Amount of excess alkali $= c \times V$
$= 2.00 \times 0.020$
$= 0.040$ moles.

Amount of neutralising acid $= c \times V$
$= 0.50 \times 0.0176$
$= 0.0088$ moles.

Amount of alkali reacting with organic acid
$= 0.040 - 0.0088$
$= 0.0312$ moles

$$H_2A + 2\,NaOH \longrightarrow Na_2A + 2\,H_2O$$

1 moles	2 mole
0.0156	0.0312

Hence 0.0156 moles of the organic acid has a mass of 2.04 g

Molar mass of the organic acid $= \dfrac{m}{n}$

$= \dfrac{2.04}{0.0156}$

$= 131$

ATOMIC STRUCTURE

2.1 The atom

2.2 The mass spectrometer

2.3 Electron arrangement

12.1 Electron configuration (AHL)

CORE

2.1 THE ATOM

2.1.1 State the position of protons, neutrons and electrons in the atom.

2.1.2 State the relative mass and relative charge of protons, electrons and neutrons.

2.1.3 Define the terms mass number (A), atomic number (Z) and isotopes of an element.

2.1.4 Deduce the symbol for an isotope given its mass number and atomic number.

2.1.5 Calculate the number of protons, neutrons and electrons in atoms and ions from the mass number, atomic number and charge.

2.1.6 Compare the properties of the isotopes of an element.

2.1.7 Discuss the use of radioisotopes

In 1807 *John Dalton* proposed his **atomic theory** - that all matter was made up of a small number of different kinds of atoms, that were indivisible and indestructible, but which could combine in small whole numbers to form compounds.

From the point of view of chemical change this theory remains largely true, i.e. atoms, or most of the atom, remains intact throughout chemical reactions. We now know, however, that atoms are not indivisible and are in fact composed of many smaller subatomic particles. Even though much of the atom does not change in chemical reactions, the outermost part of the atom (known as the valence electron shell) is crucial to chemical interactions, so knowing about the atomic structure of atoms allows us to understand how atoms join together to form compounds and why different atoms react in different ways.

ATOMIC STRUCTURE

Three important types of **subatomic particles** are the proton, the neutron and the electron. The proton and neutron have a much greater mass than the electron and are very tightly bound together to form the nucleus of the atom. Hence the nucleus contains all the positive charge and nearly all the mass (>99.9%) of the atom. It is very much smaller than the atom - if the nucleus were 1 metre across, then the electrons would be about 10 kilometres away, so most of the atom is empty space. The electrons occupy shells around the nucleus. The proton and electron carry a single positive and a single negative charge respectively, whilst the neutron is electrically neutral. The

Particle	Proton	Neutron	Electron
Relative mass	1	1	$\frac{1}{1840} \approx 5\text{x}10^{-4}$
Relative electrical charge	+1	0	1
Where found	In the nucleus	In the nucleus	Shells around the nucleus

Figure 201 The subatomic particles

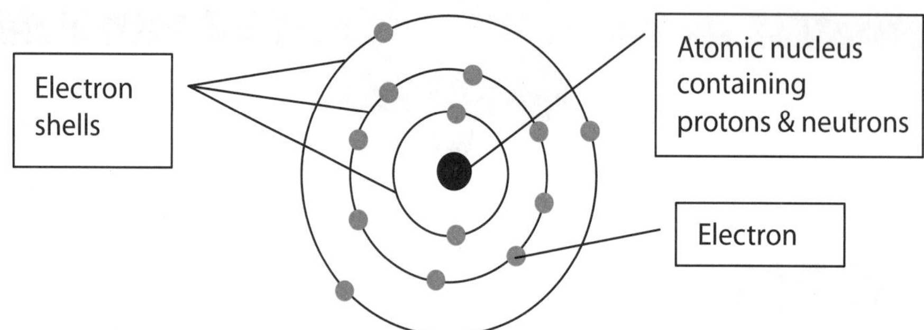

Figure 202 A diagrammatic representation of the atom

characteristics of these subatomic particles are given in Figure 201 and a diagrammatic representation of the atom is given in Figure 202.

The fundamental difference between atoms of different elements lies in the number of protons in the nucleus. An element consists of atoms which have the same number of protons in their nuclei. This is known as the **atomic number** (Z) of the element. Each element has one more proton than the preceding element in the periodic table. The sum of the protons and neutrons in the nucleus is known as the **mass number** (A). The atomic number and mass number of an element may be indicated by a subscript and a superscript respectively, placed before the symbol for the element ($^{A}_{Z}X$), e.g. for aluminium:

$$\text{Mass number} \longrightarrow {}^{27}_{13}\text{Al} \longleftarrow \text{Atomic number}$$

Mass number ⟶ 27
Atomic number ⟶ 13
Al

This is sometimes written Al-27. The number of neutrons can be found by subtracting the atomic number from the mass number, e.g. in the case of aluminium there are 27–13 = 14 neutrons in the nucleus. For lighter elements, the numbers of protons and neutrons are approximately equal, but elements with many protons require a higher proportion of neutrons because of the greater repulsion between the larger number of protons. Lead, for example, has 82 protons and (207–82) 125 neutrons (i.e. the p:n ratio is approximately 2:3).

In order to preserve electrical neutrality, the number of electrons in an atom is equal to the number of protons, so that aluminium has 13 electrons, which exist outside of the nucleus in shells of differing energies, as is discussed in greater detail later in Sections 2.3 and 2.4.

Atoms can gain or lose electrons to form ions, which have a net electrical charge because the numbers of protons and electrons are no longer equal. If an atom gains electrons, as non-metals tend to, then it will form a negatively charged ion (or anion), because there are now more electrons than protons. The ion will have one negative charge for each electron gained. For example an oxygen atom tends to gain two electrons to form the O^{2-} ion. An atom, especially of a metal, may also lose electrons to form a positive ion (or cation), because there are now more protons than electrons. The ion will have one positive charge for each electron lost. For example aluminium tends to lose three electrons to form the Al3+ ion. In chemical reactions, atoms **never** gain or lose protons. It is the interactions of the electrons that determine the chemical properties.

Knowing the atomic number (or name of the element), mass number and charge on a particle it is possible to calculate the numbers of protons, neutrons and electrons present.

TOK What use are scientific models?

What is the significance of the model of the atom in the different areas of knowledge? Are the models and theories that scientists create accurate descriptions of the natural world, or are they primarily useful interpretations for prediciton, explanation and control of the natural world? What is the purpose of a model? In what way, for example, would our perception of a new building change if we saw a model of it rather than just reading about its dimensions, or even looking at plans of it? Probably in some way it helps to make it more "real". We can better grasp what it is like and relate it to things we are more familiar with. Do theoretical models, like the chemical "model" of the atom, do the same thing as physical models? The answer is probably a qualified "yes". Models certainly help us to explain and have a better understanding of rather abstract concepts (actually, it is interesting to try to pin down just exactly what we mean by these words "explanation" and "understanding"!).

By a qualified yes I mean it is important not to stretch analogies too far. If we want to think of electrons as being rather like planets going around the sun, then probably, like planets, they have angular momentum, but we would probably not spend too much time looking for smaller particles going around the electrons just because many of the planets have moons! A model, or map (they have many similarities) is often only useful for its intended purpose. It would be difficult to use a street map of London to work out the best route between Holborn and Paddington on the train, just as the underground map would not be very helpful when working out how to walk from Piccadilly to Westminster Bridge. The particle model of light is really useful trying to explain the photo-electric effect, but not very helpful when it comes to interference patterns. Asking which light is really like is probably a bit like asking which of the two maps, London is really like!

For example in the ion $^{58}Ni^{2+}$ there will be 28 protons (because the atomic number of nickel must be 28), 30 neutrons (58 – 28) and 26 electrons (28 in a nickel atom minus 2 to give the +2 charge). Similarly in the ion $^{31}P^{3-}$ there will be 15 protons, 16 neutrons and 18 electrons.

Many elements are composed of slightly differing types of atoms known as **isotopes**. These atoms all have the same number of protons (which makes them still the same element), but differ in the number of neutrons in the nucleus. Isotopes therefore have the same atomic number, but different mass numbers. Chlorine for example occurs naturally as a mixture of two isotopes. Both contain 17 protons, but one contains 18 neutrons and the other contains 20 neutrons, so the symbols for the two isotopes respectively are:

$$^{35}_{17}Cl \text{ and } ^{37}_{17}Cl$$

Both isotopes of chlorine have the same number of electrons and, as it is the number of electrons that determines the chemical properties of a substance, both isotopes have identical chemical properties. Physical properties often also depend on the mass of the particles and so different isotopes will often have slightly different physical properties such as density, rate of diffusion etc.

Natural chlorine contains approximately 75% ^{35}Cl and 25% ^{37}Cl. These percentages, known as the natural abundances of the isotopes, give the proportions of the different isotopes of chlorine, in the element and in all compounds of chlorine are often found by mass spectrometry (see Section 2.2). The existence of isotopes must therefore be taken into account in calculating the relative atomic mass of the element, which is the weighted mean. In chlorine, for example, out of 100 chlorine atoms, on average, 75 will have a mass of 35 and 25 will have a mass of 37, so the relative atomic mass of chlorine is:

$$\frac{(75 \times 35) + (25 \times 37)}{100} = 35.5$$

Similarly, if an element is only composed of two major isotopes and the molar mass is known, the natural abundances of the two isotopes can be calculated. For example iridium is composed almost entirely of 191Ir and ^{193}Ir. Knowing that its molar mass is 192.2 g mol^{-1}, the naturally occuring percentages of the two isotopes may be calculated:

Let the % of $^{191}Ir = x$, then the % of $^{193}Ir = (100\text{-}x)$

$$191 \, x/100 + 193 \, (100\text{-}x)/100 = 192.2$$

$$191\,x + 19300 - 193\,x = 192.2 \times 100$$

$$2\,x = 19300 - 19220$$

$$= 80$$

$$\text{therefore} \quad x = 40$$

Iridium is therefore 40% ^{191}Ir and 60% ^{193}Ir

Usually if an element has an atomic mass that is greater than 0.1 from being an integer, it is a sign that it is composed of a mixture of isotopes, though some elements that are composed of isotopes have atomic masses that are almost integers. For example bromine consists of approximately equal amounts of ^{79}Br and ^{81}Br to give an atomic mass of almost exactly 80. Many elements have naturally occurring isotopes, but often these are only present in low percentages. This is the case in the isotopes of hydrogen ($^{2}_{1}H$ - deuterium and $^{3}_{1}H$ - tritium) and carbon ($^{13}_{12}C$ and $^{14}_{12}C$).

Radioactive isotopes of all elements can be produced by exposing the natural element to a flux of slow moving neutrons in a nuclear reactor. This results in the nucleus of the atom capturing an additional neutron. These "radioisotopes" have many uses. Sometimes, as is the case with carbon-14, the rate of radioactive decay can be used to date objects. Naturally occurring carbon in living organisms contains a fixed proportion of carbon-14 owing to exchange with carbon in the atmosphere. On death this interchange stops and the proportion of carbon-14 starts to decrease. After about 5,700 years the proportion of carbon-14 will have fallen to about half its initial value.

Another use of radioisotopes is as "tracers". This relies on the fact that the radioactive isotopes behave chemically, and thus biologically, in an identical manner to the stable isotopes. For example the activity of the thyroid gland, which preferentially absorbs iodine, can be measured by monitoring the increase in radioactivity of the gland after taking a drink containing traces of iodine radioisotopes (typically ^{125}I and ^{131}I).

Some radiosotopes produce gamma rays and hence can be a source of quite intense radioactivity. Cobalt-60 is an example of this and radiation from cobalt-60 sources is used in radiation treatment for cancer and industrially in devices such as those monitoring the thickness of steel plate from a rolling mill.

Exercise 2.1

1. Which of the following are usually found in the nucleus of an atom?

   A Electrons and neutrons only.
   B Neutrons only.
   C Protons neutrons and electrons.
   D Protons and neutrons only.

2. The number of neutrons in an atom of $^{138}_{56}Ba$ is

   A 56
   B 82
   C 138
   D 194

3. How many electrons would have about the same mass as a proton or a neutron?

   A 200
   B 500
   C 2000
   D 5000

4. Which one of the following is not a common use of radioactive isotopes?

   A As a fuel in fuel cells
   B Irradiating tumours in patients with cancer.
   C Measuring the rate of uptake of a drug that has been swallowed.
   D Finding the age of rocks.

5. Radioisotopes of normally stable elements are

   A chemically extracted from the natural element
   B mined from scarce underground deposits.
   C formed from the stable element in nuclear reactors.
   D produced through chemical reactions of the stable element

6 Identify the following subatomic particles:

   a) The particle that has a much lower mass than the others.
   b) The particle that has no electrical charge.
   c) The particle that is not found in the nucleus.
   d) The number of these in the nucleus is equal to the atomic number.
   e) The particle that is gained or lost when ions are formed

7. Calculate the numbers of protons, neutrons and electrons in the following:

Element	Mass No.	Protons	Neutrons	Electrons
Helium	4			
Nitrogen	14			
Aluminium	27			
Manganese	55			
Iodine	127			

8. Boron has atomic number 5. It comprises two isotopes, one with five neutrons, the other with six.

   a) Define the term "isotope".
   b) Calculate the mass numbers of the two isotopes and represent them in the form ${}^{x}_{y}B$.
   c) In naturally occurring boron, 20% of the atoms contain five neutrons and 80% six neutrons. Calculate the relative atomic mass of boron.

9. Describe how you might use a sample of calcium phosphate, containing traces of a radioisotope of phosphorus, to measure the rate of uptake of phosphorus by the root systems of various plants.

10. Naturally occurring copper is a mixture of two isotopes. One of these has 29 protons and 34 neutrons, the other one two more neutrons. Complete the following table for both isotopes:

	No. Protons	No. Neutrons	No. Electrons	Atomic No.	Mass No.
Isotope 1	29	34			
Isotope 2					

If the relative atomic mass of copper is 63.55, calculate the natural abundances of the two isotopes.

11. Give the numbers of protons, neutrons and electrons in the following isotopes:

Isotope	Number of		
	protons	neutrons	electrons
${}^{3}_{1}H$			
${}^{15}_{7}N$			
${}^{57}_{26}Fe$			
${}^{90}_{38}Sr$			
${}^{235}_{92}U$			

12. Complete the following table:

Species	Number of		
	protons	neutrons	electrons
$^{3}H^{-}$			
$^{24}Mg^{2+}$			
	13	14	10
	16	18	18
$^{4+}$	22	26	

AHL

2.2 THE MASS SPECTROMETER

2.2.1 Describe and explain the operation of a mass spectrometer.

2.2.2 Describe how the mass spectrometer may be used to determine relative, atomic masses using the ^{12}C scale.

2.2.3 Calculate non-integer relative atomic masses and abundance of isotopes from given data

A **mass spectrometer** is an instrument which separates particles according to their masses and records the relative proportions of these. In a mass spectrometer the substance is firstly converted to atoms or molecules in the vapour phase (A). These are then turned into positive ions (B) and accelerated (C). The fast moving ions are deflected (D) - the lighter the particle the greater the deflection. Finally particles of a particular mass, which can be adjusted, will be detected (E). The body of the instrument must be maintained at a high vacuum by a pump (F).

Region A contains the vapourised substance. If it is already a gas, then it will contain the gas at low pressure, if the sample is a solid or liquid, it must be heated to produce the vapour. This is connected to the rest of the mass spectrometer by a fine tube, or capillary, so that the transfer of material into the body of the instrument occurs very slowly. This is vital as the body of the mass spectrometer must be kept at a high vacuum for its correct operation, which depends on particles being able to pass through it without colliding with any other particles.

In region B, the particles are converted from neutral atoms or molecules into positive ions. This is usually done by bombarding them with fast moving electrons that are accelerated between the two plates shown. These electrons collide with electrons in the particle knocking them out and leaving a positive ion.

$$X(g) + e^{-} \longrightarrow X^{+}(g) + 2e^{-}$$

In region C, these positive ions are accelerated by the high electrical potential difference between the two parallel

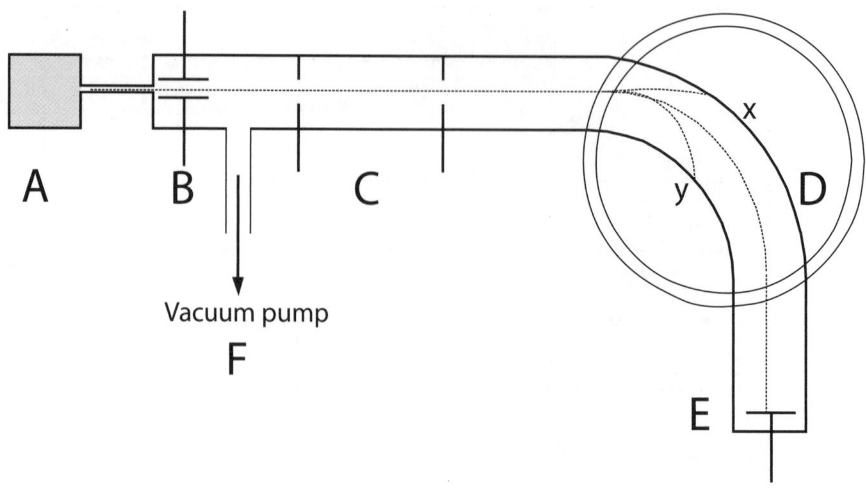

Figure 207 A diagram of a simple mass spectrometer

TOK Reality or imagination?

None of these particles can be (or will be) directly observed. Which ways of knowing do we use to interpret indirect evidence, gained through the use of technology? Do we believe or know of their existence. Do we know electrons exist or do we believe electrons exist? Are they more like this book, for which most of us agree we have concrete evidence, or are they more like God, where (if we believe in Him, or Her, - English strikes again!) the evidence is more circumstantial? Let's go back to the discovery of the electron, late in the 19th Century; what was the necessity to come up with this hypothesis? Under certain circumstances rays could be observed, as a glow on a fluorescent screen, and these were easily deflected by electric or magnetic fields in a way that led to it being postulated they were caused by particles (under some circumstances you can observe single flashes of light) having a negative charge. Their production also seemed to leave much more massive particles with a positive charge. This was interpreted as evidence that atoms (already constraining ourselves within Dalton's paradigm) might be comprised of particles with unequal masses and opposite charges. Onward to the photo-electric effect, an electric current and the hydrogen atom spectrum; things we can observe directly for which we invoke the electron as an explanation.

Postulating the existence of the electron certainly allows us to relate many apparently unrelated phenomena, but is that existence? I guess it depends what you mean by exist? Postulating there is a publisher out there explains why I get e-mails enquiring why this chapter is late, why I sometime get large piles of proofs to read through and why, just occasionally, my bank account seems to have increased slightly. But is that the same sort of existence as meeting him in Melbourne (or at least me imagining that there is this person there at the same time as I am imagining that a place called Melbourne really exists and I am in it, at the same time as I have this wonderful sensation that seems to go with imagining I am enjoying a meal with him)?

Back to solipsism - why am I even bothering to imagine I am writing all of this when I have no evidence at all (not even in my own brain!) that you the reader are out there reading it!

electrodes with holes in their centres. In region D these fast moving ions enter a magnetic field produced by an electromagnet. The poles, shown as circles, are above and below the plane of the diagram. This causes the fast moving ions to deflect, as shown. Particles of a certain mass (dependent on the field strength) will continue round the tube and strike the detector plate. Those with a greater mass will not be deflected as much and those with a smaller mass will be deflected more (deflection depends on the charge to mass ratio $^{m}/_{z}$). These will strike the wall of the instrument at (x) and (y) respectively. This means that only ions of a certain mass are detected at E, usually by means of the current flow required to neutralise the positive charge that they carry - the greater the number of particles of a given mass that are present, the greater the current.

By varying the strength of the magnetic field, ions of different masses can be brought to focus on the detector. In this way the relative abundances of ions of different masses produced from the sample can be determined. This is known as a mass spectrum. Usually the electron bombardment is adjusted to produce ions with only a single charge. Any doubly charged ions will be deflected more than the singly charged ions and will in fact behave in the same way as a singly charged ion of half the mass. That is why the x-axis is labelled $^{m}/_{z}$, where m is the relative mass of the species and z its relative charge. For example $^{32}S^{2+}$ will be observed at $^{m}/_{z}$ = 16.

To summarise, the main operations are:

A	vapourised sample introduced
B	ionisation by electron bombardment
C	positive ions accelerated by electrical field
D	ions deflected by a magnetic field
E	detector records ions of a particular mass
F	vacuum prevents molecules colliding

The mass spectrometer has many applications, but one of the simplest is to determine the natural abundances of the isotopes of a particular element and hence allow

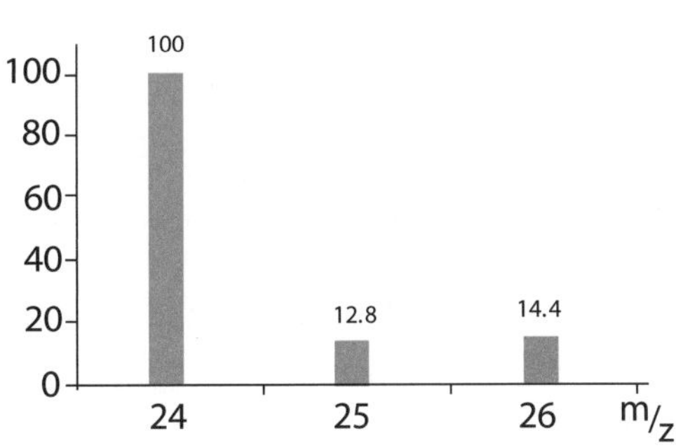

Figure 208 The mass spectrum of magnesium

AHL

calculation of its atomic mass. If for example a sample of magnesium was vapourised in the mass spectrometer, the resulting mass spectrum would be similar to that shown below.

The relative abundance is recorded so that either the most abundant isotope is given a value of 100 and the others recorded as a proportion of this, or the abundances are given as percentages of the whole.

The natural abundances of the three isotopes of magnesium and hence its relative atomic mass can be calculated from these data:

$$^{24}Mg = 100 \times \frac{100}{127.2} = 78.6\%$$

$$^{25}Mg = 100 \times \frac{12.8}{127.2} = 10.0\%$$

$$^{26}Mg = 100 \times \frac{14.4}{127.2} = 11.3\%$$

Relative atomic mass of magnesium =
$(24 \times 0.786) + (25 \times 0.100) + (26 \times 0.113) = 24.3$

With molecules, the relative molecular mass of the molecule can be found. The ionisation process often causes the molecule to break into fragments and the resulting 'fragmentation pattern' acts like a fingerprint to identify the compound.

Exercise 2.2

1. Describe briefly how in the mass spectrometer

   a) the atoms are converted into ions.
   b) the ions of different mass are separated.
   c) the ions are detected.

2. Germanium (atomic number 32) contains 20% germanium-70, 27% germanium-71, 8% germanium-72, 37% germanium-73 and 8% germanium-74. Draw a graph of the mass spectrum that you would expect germanium to produce. If an atom of germanium-70 lost two electrons to become a doubly charged ion, at what $^{m}/_{z}$ would it appear?

3. The graph shows the mass spectrum of the element which contains 76 protons in its nucleus.

   a) Write down, in the form $^{A}_{Z}X$, the isotopes that it is composed of with their natural abundances (as a %).
   b) Calculate the relative atomic mass of the element.

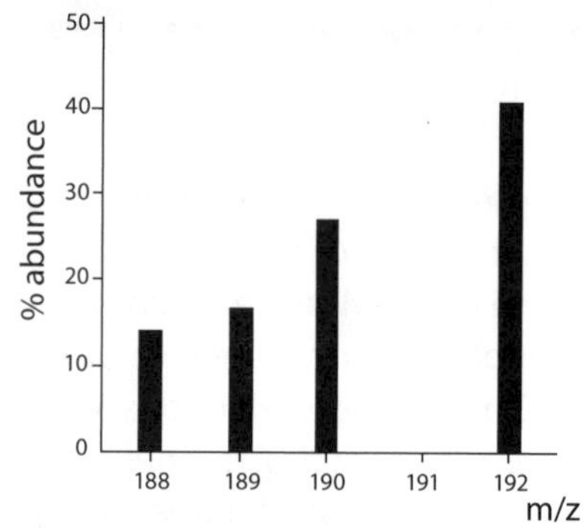

4 Lead has a molar mass of 207.2 g mol^{-1}. Assuming that it is composed entirely of ^{206}Pb, ^{207}Pb and ^{208}Pb, and that the percentages of the two lightest isotopes are equal, calculate the relative percentages of these isotopes in the natural element.

2.3 ELECTRON ARRANGEMENT

2.3.1 Describe the electromagnetic spectrum.

2.3.2 Distinguish between a continuous spectrum and a line spectrum.

ATOMIC EMISSION SPECTRA

The study of the emission of light by atoms and ions is the most effective technique for deducing the electronic structure of atoms. Here the term "light" is being used rather loosely to indicate electromagnetic radiation. This covers radiation from gamma rays through to radio waves, as illustrated in Figure 210 below, that has many properties in common. Familiar visible light is just the very small region of this spectrum that our eyes happen to be sensitive to.

The best evidence for the fact that electrons in an atom surround the nucleus in certain allowed energy levels, or orbitals comes from a study of the emission spectra of elements. When an element is excited it will often emit light of a characteristic colour (e.g. the red of neon signs). In the case of gases this can be achieved by passing an electrical discharge through the gas at low pressure. For many metals the same effect can be observed when their compounds are heated directly in a Bunsen flame. This is the basis of the 'flame tests' for metals. For example, the alkali metals all impart a characteristic colour to the flame:

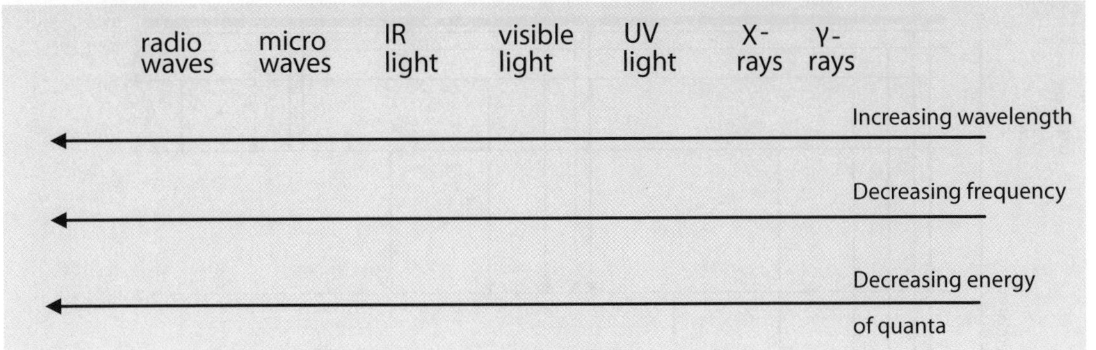

Figure 210 The electromagnetic spectrum

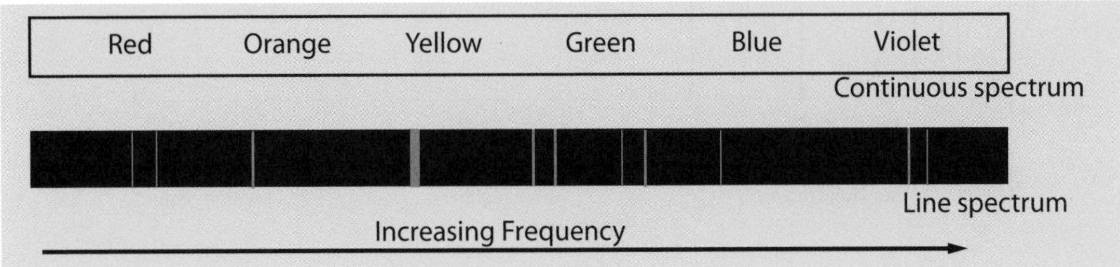

Figure 211 Continuous and line spectra

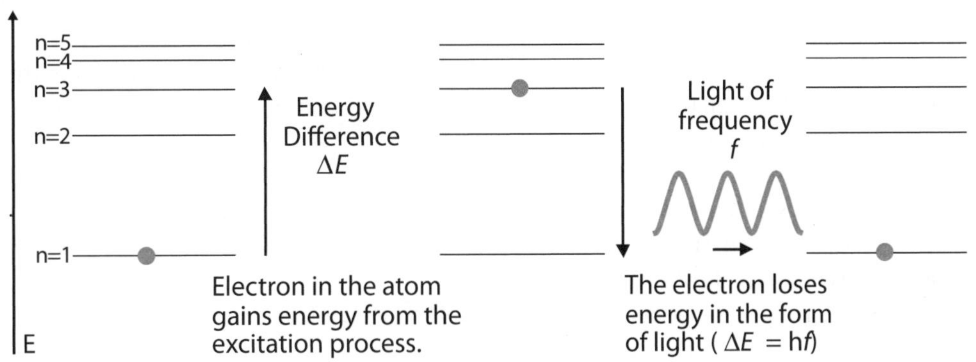

Figure 212 The origin of line spectra

lithium - red, sodium - yellow, potassium – lilac, this is the basis of atomic absorption spectroscopy If the light is passed through a spectroscope, containing a prism or diffraction grating, to separate out the different colours, then what is observed is not a continuous spectrum (like a rainbow) as is observed with normal 'white' light, which contains all frequencies. Instead, it comprises very bright lines of specific colours with black space in between. This is known as a line spectrum and is illustrated in Figure 211. Each element has its own characteristic line spectrum that can be used to identify it.

When an atom is excited its electrons gain energy and move to a higher energy level. In order to return to lower energy levels, the electron must lose energy. It does this by giving out light. This is illustrated in Figure 212.

The frequency (f), and hence colour, of the light depends on the amount of energy lost by the electron (ΔE), according to the equation:

$$\Delta E = h\,f \qquad (h \text{ is Planck's constant})$$

The colour of light is sometimes defined by its wavelength (λ) rather than its frequency (f). The two are related by the equation $c = f.\lambda$ ($c = 3 \times 10^{-8}$ m s^{-1}, the velocity of light) i.e. the greater the frequency, the shorter the wavelength.

Because there are only certain allowed energy levels within the atom, there are a limited number of amounts of energy (ΔE) that the electron can lose. This means that only certain frequencies of light can be emitted, hence the line spectrum. A continuous spectrum would imply that an electron in an atom could have any energy.

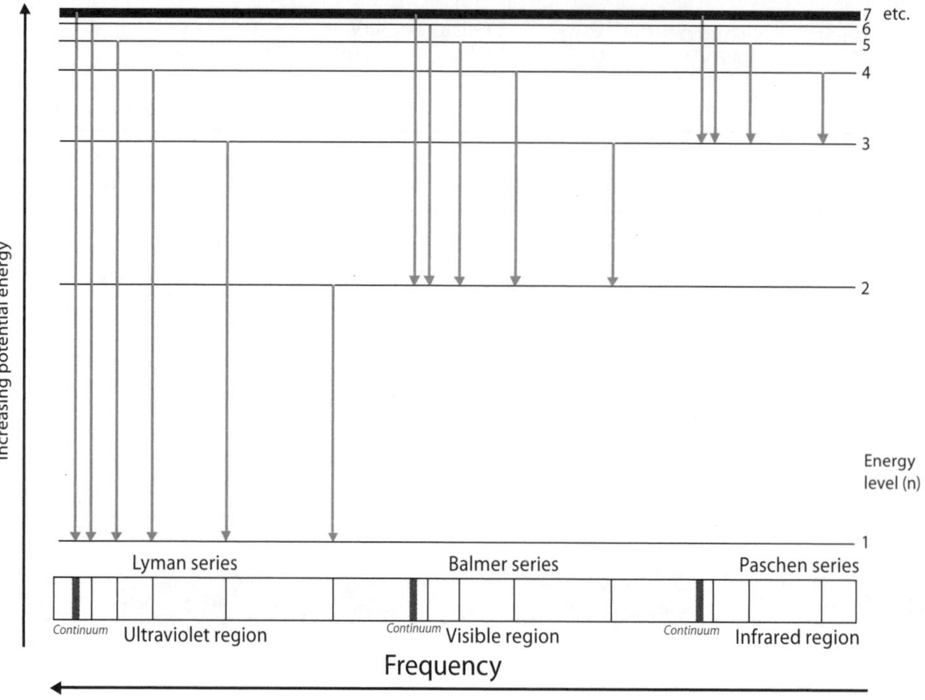

Figure 213 Explanation of the atomic emission spectrum of hydrogen

By studying the frequencies of the lines in the emission spectrum of an element, the energies of the various energy levels in its atoms may be found. The situation is not quite as simple as has been portrayed because there are sub-levels within the main allowed levels and this makes the spectra significantly more complex, nevertheless they may still be used to determine the allowed energy levels for electrons within an atom. It is found that the energy levels are not evenly spaced, like the rungs of a ladder, but that the higher the energy, the smaller the difference in energy between successive energy levels becomes (See Figure 212). This means that the lines in a spectrum will converge (i.e. get closer together) with increasing frequency. The limit of this convergence indicates the energy required to completely remove the electron from the atom (i.e. to ionise it) and so it may be used to determine the ionisation energy.

2.3.3 Explain how the lines in the emission spectrum of hydrogen are related to the energy levels of electrons.

THE ATOMIC EMISSION SPECTRUM OF HYDROGEN

The **emission spectrum** of the hydrogen atom is the simplest emission spectrum, because having only one electron, there is none of the electron-electron repulsion which causes the principal energy levels to split into different sub-levels. When a potential difference is applied across hydrogen gas at low pressure, electromagnetic radiation is emitted. As explained above, this is not uniform but concentrated into bright lines, indicating the existence of only certain allowed electron energy levels within the atom. It was by a study of these lines that the electronic structure of the hydrogen was deduced, though it is simpler to start, as below, with the accepted electronic structure and show how this results in the observed spectrum.

The spectrum is divided into a number of distinct series, named after the people who discovered them, which occur in different spectral regions as shown (there are also further series at longer wavelengths which are not shown). Each series corresponds to transitions in which the electron falls to a particular energy level. The reason

TOK The role and implications of technology

I'm so old I even remember back to when we thought that being able to reproduce music via a groove on a piece of vinyl that rotated at $33^1/_3$ rpm was a pretty neat idea! It prompts me to go even further back in time and muse upon what it is that we really mean by "technology". Is using a stick to dig up roots applying technology? What is the cut-off point? Dictionary definitions seem to hinge around applying scientific discoveries to manufacturing, so maybe "using technology to further science"? (but since it comes out of science anyway, it sounds a bit circular!) Can we consider knowledge as being "manufactured", as opposed to being "discovered"? Now there's a fundamental difference that it's probably worth devoting some thought to!

If we have two solutions of potassium manganate(VII) (permanganate – it forms purple solutions) we can tell at a glance which is the more concentrated (making a couple of assumptions on the way?). Is this knowledge essentially different to that we would obtain from putting them in a spectrophotometer and reading that at 525 nm (in the green region – why here when the solution is purple?) one had an absorbance of 1.374 and the other an absorbance of 0.867? (Maybe there would be a couple more assumptions to add!) How do the knowledge implications change again if we shift the wavelength to 280 nm (in the ultraviolet region) and take two apparently colourless solutions of benzoic acid and find one has an absorbance greater than the other? Both look the same so are we sure there's a difference? (Yet more assumptions – how many do we need to make us start to feel uneasy?)

There's a saying that "seeing is believing" (or did they mean "knowing"?), but from TOK classes on perception we probably now know the pitfalls that lie there. Wassabe and Guacamole are a very similar shade of green, and remembering a recent horrendous mistake in which millions of taste buds died, maybe we shouldn't put too much faith in any one sense?

why they occur in different spectral regions is that as the energy levels increase, they converge (i.e. get closer together in energy). This means that all transitions to the n=1 level include the large n=1 to n=2 energy difference and so they are all high energy transitions found in the ultraviolet region. For similar reasons all transitions to the n=2 level are in the visible region etc.

Each series has a very similar structure of lines that become closer together going towards higher frequencies. This is another result of the convergence of energy levels. Each series ends in a brief continuum at the high frequency end where the lines become too close together to be separated. The cut off of this is the energy emitted when an electron completely outside the atom ($n=\infty$) falls to the particular level involved. In the case of the Lyman series, this corresponds to the ionisation energy of the hydrogen atom, which can be found from the high frequency cut off of the continuum.

The reverse can happen, that is a hydrogen atom can absorb light of a particular frequency and this will excite an electron from a lower energy level to a higher one. This is known as an absorption spectrum. It appears as black lines (caused because a particular frequency is absorbed) in a continuous spectrum. Only the Lyman series (in the ultraviolet region) is observed in the absorption spectrum because in hydrogen atoms the electrons are normally in the lowest energy level (n=1) and so can only move to higher energy levels from that energy level.

2.3.4 Deduce the electron arrangement for atoms and ions up to Z = 20.

Electronic Structure and the Periodic Table

The most stable energy levels, or shells, are those closest to the nucleus and these are filled before electrons start to fill the higher levels. There is a maximum number of electrons that each energy level can hold. The first can hold up to two electrons, the second up to eight electrons. Beyond this the situation becomes more complex. The number of electrons in each orbital is known as the electronic structure of the atom. For example aluminium has 13 electrons so its electronic structure is 2.8.3. i.e. it has 2 electrons in the first level, 8 in the second (so both of these are filled) and the remaining 3 in the third. Different isotopes of an element have the same number of electrons

CORE

H 1							He 2
Li 2,1	Be 2,2	B 2,3	C 2,4	N 2,5	O 2,6	F 2,7	Ne 2,8
Na 2,8,1	Mg 2,8,2	Al 2,8,3	Si 2,8,4	P 2,8,5	S 2,8,6	Cl 2,8,7	Ar 2,8,8
K 2,8,8,1	Ca 2,8,8,2						

Figure 214 Electronic structure in relation to the periodic table

TOK Which ways of knowing allow us access to the microscopic world?"

I was intrigued reading this one – what is the implication of the phrase "image of an invisible world"? Does it imply that we believe this image we have is in some way real? Probably that depends a lot on what we mean by real and whether we think that reality is "out there" or "in here" (i.e. in our minds)? Making a sharp turn to avoid a return to solipsism, even if we accept there is a physical world out there, is the world you perceive the same as the world I perceive? If I say "Eiffel Tower", is what pops up as my mental image the same as what pops up as your mental image and can we claim either of them corresponds to reality? In that case if I say "electrons in "sodium" probably the image we see in our brain does not correspond to reality either, just to a model we find useful?

What about our ways of knowing about this world? If "us" means you or me (unless you're a Nobel Laureate) the answer is probably maily through our eyes (reading books like this one as well as looking at things you access on your computer) and ears (listening to what your teacher tells you in class, or what you hear on television). These are ways we have of finding out what other people think, or have thought – in other words we get second hand knowledge on Authority. We then process that in our brains, hopefully applying logic and critical thinking skills and maybe a little creativity, to construct our world referred to in the previous paragraph. Sometimes we will note inconsistencies and enquire further to resolve these – we "stand on the shoulders of giants" as Newton would have it. That might enable us (especially if we are called Newton or Einstein) to have an effect on the way the other "us" (i.e. the human race) knows about the invisible world, by doing science experiments, prompted by our rational thoughts, that change the accepted knowledge that everybody else learns.

Once again in cutting edge science the primary path of perception is vision – we read meters, note numbers on digital displays, look at the chemicals in test tubes. It's very rarely that we engage any of our other senses. But that is obtaining data, which is a long way from obtaining knowledge (think how they are related, and what about 'information'?). Again knowing is probably what happens to all of these things we see when they whizz round in our brain and interact, perhaps allowing us to suggest new and better models for what seems to be out there. Just be careful that your world view is not too different from that of everybody else. It could make for a very uncomfortable life - they have special places where they put people like that!

and the same electronic structure, hence they exhibit identical chemical properties.

It is the electrons, especially those in the outermost shell, or valence shell, that determine the physical and chemical properties of the element. For example elements with three or less electrons in the valence level, with the exception of boron, are metals, the others non-metals. It is therefore not surprising that the **electronic structure** of an element is closely related to its position in the periodic table, which can therefore act as a memory aid for electronic structure. The period (horizontal row) gives the number of energy levels that contain electrons and the group (number of vertical columns from the left) gives the number of electrons in the valence level. This is shown in Figure 214.

Phosphorus, for example is in the third period, so it has electrons in the first three energy levels, and in the fifth group, so it has five electrons in the valence level. Its electronic structure is therefore 2,8,5.

Example

List the electron arrangement of chlorine and identify the element with n = 2 that has the same number of valence (outer shell) electrons.

Solution

The electron arrangement of chlorine is 2.8.7. Fluorine is the element with n = 2 that also has 7 valence electrons since both chlorine and fluorine are in group 7/17.

Exercise 2.3

1. An atom has an atomic number of 13 and a mass number of 27. How many electrons will it have in its valence level?

   A 1
   B 2
   C 3
   D 5

2. Which of the following would produce a line spectrum rather than a continuous spectrum?

   A A yellow (sodium) street light.
   B A normal filament light bulb.
   C Sunlight.
   D A white hot piece of steel.

3. Which of the following colours corresponds to light of the highest energy

   A Yellow
   B Red
   C Green
   D Blue

4. Which one of the following is not a valid electronic structure?

   A 2,8,4
   B 2,6
   C 2,9,1
   D 2,8,8,2

5. Which one of the following electron transitions in a hydrogen atom would produce light in the visible region of the spectrum?

   A n=2 to n=1
   B n=5 to n=4
   C n=6 to n=2
   D n=4 to n=1

6. Which one of the following is not true for both absorption and an emission spectra?

   A They are the result of the movement of electrons between energy levels.
   B The electrons can move between any two energy levels.
   C The frequency of the light is related to the difference in the energy levels.
   D There is a convergence towards the high frequency end.

7. Which of the following transitions in the hydrogen atom would produce light of the shortest wavelength?

   A n=2 to n=1
   B n=5 to n=4
   C n=6 to n=2
   D n=4 to n=1

8. Given the atomic numbers of the following elements, write their simple electronic structures:

   a) Beryllium (At. No. = 4)
   b) Aluminium (At. No. = 13)
   c) Fluorine (At. No. = 9)
   d) Argon (At. No. = 18)
   e) Sulfur (At. No. = 16)

9. Two particles have the following composition:

   A: 37 protons; 38 neutrons, 37 electrons
   B: 37 protons; 40 neutrons, 37 electrons

   a) What is the relationship between these particles?
   b) These two particles have very similar chemical properties. Explain why.

10. Explain why, in the hydrogen atom spectrum:

   a) only light of certain frequencies is observed.
   b) different series are observed in different spectral regions.
   c) these series all converge at the high frequency end.

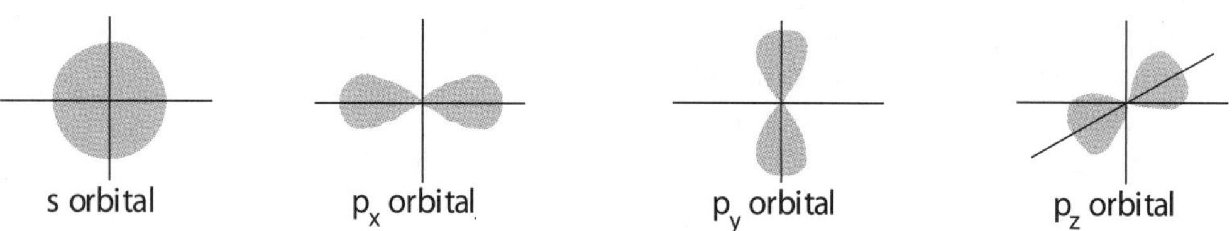

Figure 215 An illustration of the electron distribution in s- and p-orbitals

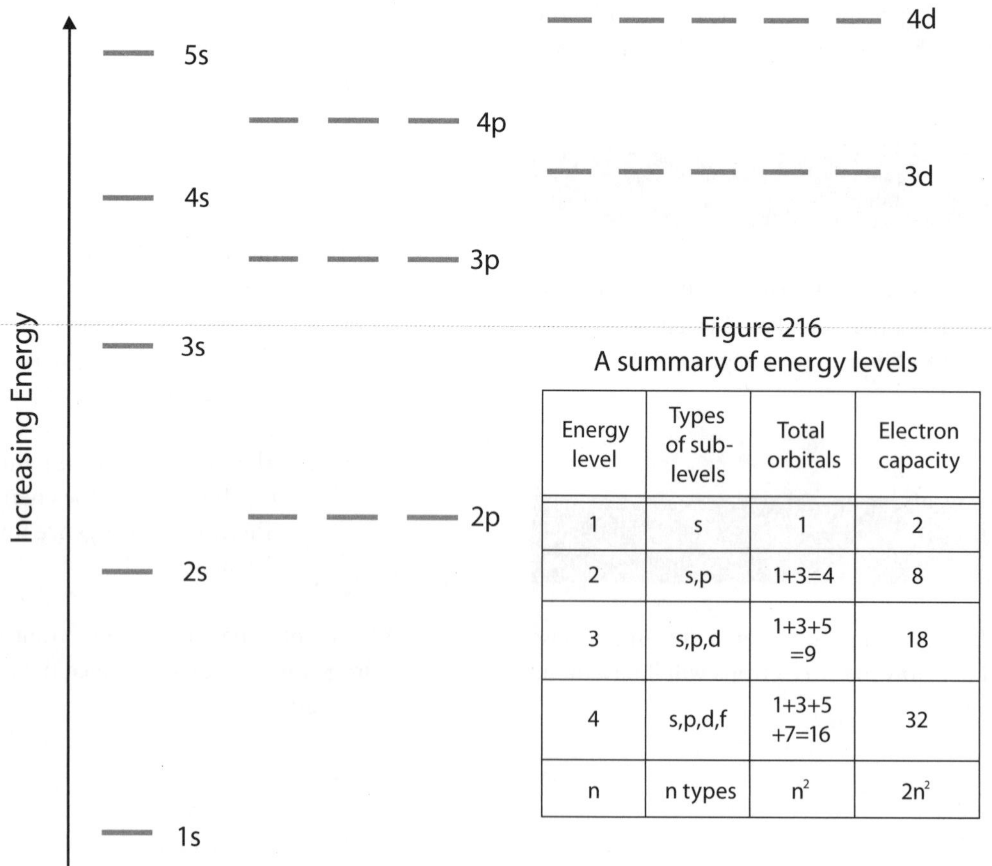

Figure 216
A summary of energy levels

Energy level	Types of sub-levels	Total orbitals	Electron capacity
1	s	1	2
2	s,p	1+3=4	8
3	s,p,d	1+3+5 =9	18
4	s,p,d,f	1+3+5 +7=16	32
n	n types	n^2	$2n^2$

Figure 216 The electron energy levels in a typical atom

HIGHER LEVEL

12.1 ELECTRON CONFIGURATION (AHL)

12.1.3 State the relative energies of s, p, d and f orbitals in a single energy level.

12.1.4 State the maximum number of orbitals in a given energy level.

12.1.5 Draw the shape of an s orbital and the shapes of the p_x, p_y and p_z orbitals.

The nucleus of the atom is surrounded by electrons arranged in specific energy levels and sub-levels. The different sub-levels differ in the shape of the electron distribution. Each energy sub-level is divided into orbitals each of which can contain up to two electrons, which must have opposite spins, as a consequence of the Pauli exclusion principle, which says that no two electrons in an atom can be in exactly the same state (that is, they cannot be in the same place at the same time). The evidence to support this model of electronic structure, illustrated in Figure 2.16, comes mainly from the study of atomic spectra, as described above.

The energy level closest to the nucleus only contains one sub-level and one orbital. This orbital has spherical symmetry and as orbitals of this shape are known as 's' orbitals, it is referred to as the 1s orbital. It can hold two electrons of opposite spins which are conventionally illustrated as upward and downward pointing arrows..

The second energy level has two sub-levels. The 's' sub-level has one 's' orbital, with spherical symmetry, and the 'p' sub-level has three 'p' orbitals, which have a "figure of eight" electron distribution. These all have the same energy under normal conditions and differ in that one is oriented along the x-axis, a second along the y-axis and the third along the z-axis (see Figure 210). Each orbital can again hold two electrons making six p-electrons and a total of eight in the second level. Owing to increased electron-electron repulsion, the p-orbitals are at a slightly higher energy than the s- orbitals in all atoms except hydrogen.

The third energy level has three sub-levels. The 's' and 'p' sub-levels contain two s-electrons and six p-electrons respectively. It also has five 'd' orbitals, all of the same energy (unless in the presence of ligands), but with even more complex shapes. The d-orbitals can therefore hold ten electrons, giving a total of eighteen for the third level. There is however a complication in that the 3d-orbitals are at a higher energy than the 3p-orbitals and they occur, in most atoms, at a slightly higher energy than the 4s-orbital. In the fourth energy level, as well as the s-orbital, the three p-orbitals and the five d-orbitals, there are also seven 'f'-orbitals. These orbitals (up to and including the 4d) and their relative energies for a typical atom are shown in Figure 211.

12.1.6 Apply the Aufbau principle to electron configurations, Hund's rule and the Pauli exclusion principle to write the electron configurations for atoms up to Z = 54.

Filling electron energy levels

The electrons in atoms always adopt the lowest energy configuration possible by filling one sub-level completely before starting to fill the sub-level of next highest energy. This is known as the ***'Aufbau'*** (building up) principle. In hydrogen therefore, the electron occupies the 1s orbital and in helium this is doubly filled; the two electrons are paired, and drawn as ↑↓ (showing opposite spins). nl^x notation is used to describe the electron configuration of an atom where n is the main energy level, l the sub-level, and x is the number of electrons in the sub-level, hence the electronic structures of these atoms can be written as $1s^1$ and $1s^2$ respectively. The first energy level is now full, so in lithium, the third electron must occupy the s-orbital of the second level, and with beryllium this is doubly filled (paired electrons) so that their respective electronic structures are $1s^2\ 2s^1$ and $1s^2\ 2s^2$. The fifth electron in boron now occupies one of the 2p orbitals, giving an electronic structure of $1s^2\ 2s^2\ 2p^1$. Carbon has six electrons so there is the possibility of these electrons occupying separate p-orbitals, with similar spins (217 a), separate p-orbitals with opposite spins (217 b) or the same p-orbital with opposite spins (217 c):

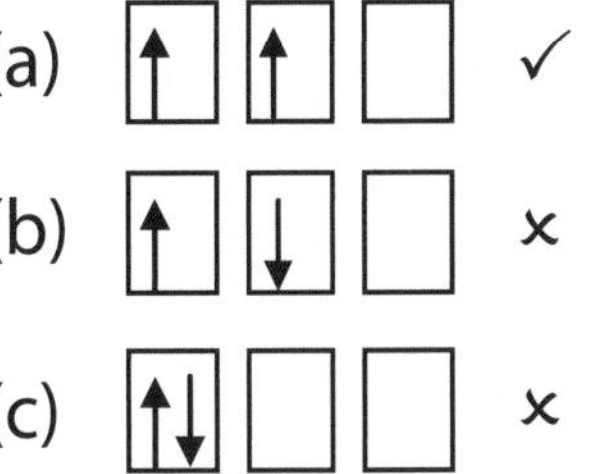

Figure 217 Possible ways for two electrons to occupy orbitals of the same energy

It turns out that (217 a) is the most stable configuration (this is known as **Hund's rule**, or the principle of 'maximum multiplicity'; sub-level orbitals are singly occupied as far as possible by electrons with the same spin) and so in carbon the two outer electrons singly occupy two of the p-orbitals and in nitrogen all three p-orbitals are singly occupied, the electronic structures being $1s^2\ 2s^2\ 2p^2$ and $1s^2\ 2s^2\ 2p^3$ respectively. Going from oxygen, through fluorine to neon, these orbitals are each doubly filled, the electronic structures in this order being $1s^2\ 2s^2\ 2p^4$, $1s^2\ 2s^2\ 2p^5$ and $1s^2\ 2s^2\ 2p^6$. The arrangement of electrons in the p-orbital of some of these atoms is illustrated in Figure 218.

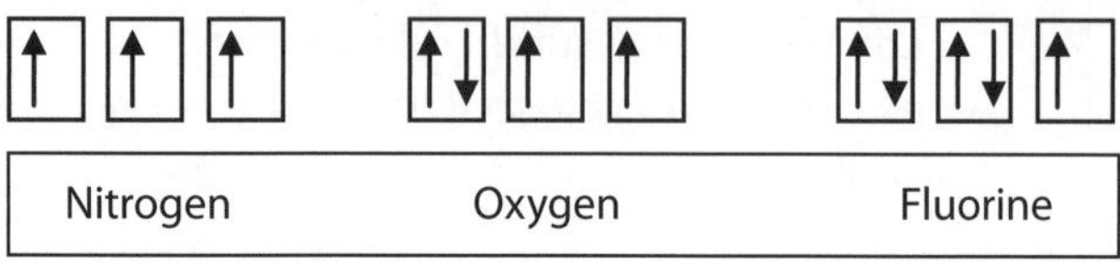

Figure 218 Occupancy of the 2p orbitals in some atoms

At sodium the outer electrons start to occupy the third energy level in a manner totally analogous to the filling of the second energy level until argon ($1s^2\ 2s^2\ 2p^6\ 3s^2\ 3p^6$) is reached. At this point, the 4s level is at a lower energy than the 3d level and so this is the next to be filled in potassium and calcium. With longer electronic structures, an abbreviated form may be written in which the symbol for a noble gas in square brackets indicates filled inner shells as for that gas, so the abbreviated electronic structure of potassium can be written as [Ar] $4s^1$ and the full electronic structure as $1s^2\ 2s^2\ 2p^6\ 3s^2\ 3p^6\ 4s^1$. The electronic structure for calcium can be similarly written as [Ar] $4s^2$ or $1s^2\ 2s^2\ 2p^6\ 3s^2\ 3p^6\ 4s^2$.

Starting at scandium the 3d orbitals are gradually filled, each orbital being first singly occupied (Hund's rule), as far as manganese ([Ar] $3d^5\ 4s^2$) and then doubly filled (thought chromium and copper are exceptions to this, see below), until at zinc ([Ar] $3d^{10}\ 4s^2$) the 3d and 4s sub-levels are both fully filled. From gallium to krypton the 4p orbital is filled in the usual manner. The order in which the orbitals of an atom are filled according to the Aufbau principle is also illustrated in Figure 219.

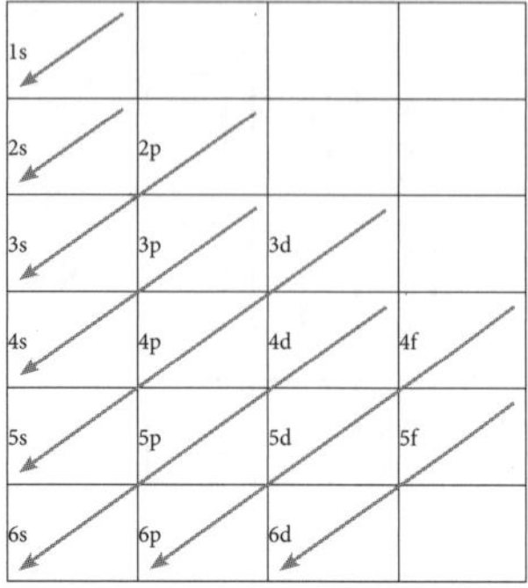

Figure 219 The order of electrons filling sub-levels

There are two exceptions to the filling of the 3d orbital, both associated with a 4s-electron being used to generate the additional stability associated with a half-filled and fully filled 3d orbital. Chromium is [Ar] $3d^5\ 4s^1$ rather than [Ar] $3d^4\ 4s^2$ and copper [Ar] $3d^{10}\ 4s^1$ rather than [Ar] $3d^9\ 4s^2$. A peculiarity of these (first row d-block) elements, with both d and s electrons in the valence shell, is that when the elements between scandium and zinc form cations, the first electrons that they lose are the 4s electrons, even though this orbital was filled before the 3d orbitals. This is a consequence of a change in the relative stabilities of the 3d and 4s orbitals, which occurs as the 3d orbital starts to fill, that means that the ion with the most d-electrons is the more stable. Therefore, for example, the electronic structure of the iron(II) ion, formed by the loss of two electrons from an iron atom ([Ar] $3d^6\ 4s^2$) is [Ar] $3d^6$ not [Ar] $3d^4\ 4s^2$. The 3d and 4s sublevels are close in energy, so that once the $4s^2$ electrons are lost, the 3d electrons also behave as valence electrons, for example, Fe^{3+} is [Ar] $3d^5$. This accounts for many of the unique properties of these elements.

The electronic structures of the elements are related to the position of the element in the periodic table. In the elements on the far left of the periodic table, the s-orbitals are being filled up, so this is known as the s-block. Similarly in the middle d-block of the periodic table the d-orbitals are being filled and in the right hand p-block, the p-orbitals are being filled. The f-block is traditionally separated from the main table, though it should be placed between the s-block and the d-block, as is found in the "long form" of the table, as shown diagrammatically in Figure 220.

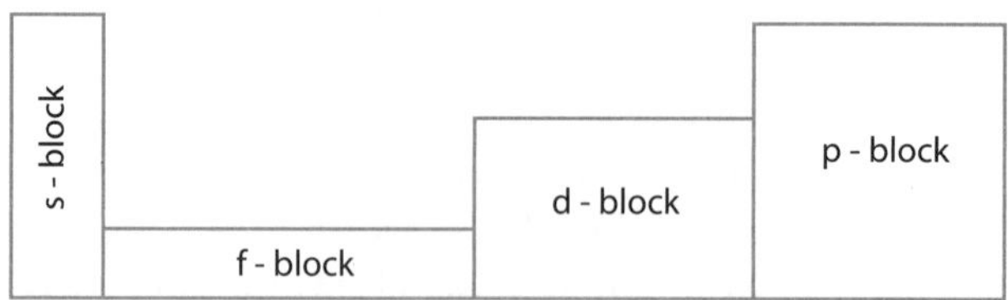

Figure 220 The 'long form' of the periodic table

Value of l	0	1	2	3
Value of m	0	−1 0 +1	−1 −1 0 +1 +2	−3 to +3
Value of n 1	1s ↑↓			
2	2s ↑↓	2p ↑↓ ↑↓ ↑↓		
3	3s ↑↓	3p ↑↓ ↑↓ ↑↓	3d ↑↓ ↑↓ ↑↓ ↑↓ ↑↓	
4	4s	4p ↑↓ ↑↓ ↑↓	4d ↑↓ ↑↓ ↑↓ ↑↓ ↑↓	4f 7 × ↑↓

Figure 221 Interpretation of orbitals in terms of quantum numbers table

EXTENSION

Quantum Numbers

Electrons have a wave as well as a particle nature. Their wave-like nature in atoms can be described by the **Schrödinger wave equation**. This involves four constants, called quantum numbers, and a solution for the equation is only possible if the values of these quantum numbers lie within certain limits. The principal quantum number (n) must be a positive integer. The azimuthal (or subsidiary) quantum number (l) can have integer values from zero to (n – 1). The magnetic quantum number (m) can have integer values from –l to +l (including zero), whilst the spin quantum number (s) can be ±½. This interpretation corresponds exactly with the electron orbital concept outlined above. The principal quantum number dictates the main or principal energy level, the azimuthal quantum number the sub-level (l=0 is an s-sublevel; l=1 is a p-sublevel; l=2 is a d-sublevel; l=3 is an f-sublevel etc.), the magnetic quantum number the particular orbital within the sub-level (i.e. p_x, p_y and p_z) with the spin quantum number differentiating between the two electrons in that orbital. This correspondence is shown in Figure 221 in which ↑ represents s=+½ and ↓ represents s=−½:

A more precise statement of the **Pauli exclusion principle** is that no two electrons in a given atom can have the same four quantum numbers.

Ionisation Energies

12.1.1 Explain how evidence from first ionization energies across periods accounts for the existence of the main energy levels and sub-levels in an atom.

12.1.2 Explain how successive ionisation energy data is related to the electron configuration of an atom.

The **ionisation energy** of an atom is the minimum amount of energy required to remove a mole of electrons from a mole of gaseous atoms to form a mole of gaseous ions, that is, using Q as the symbol for the element, it is the energy required for the change:

$$Q(g) \longrightarrow Q^{+}(g) + e^{-}$$

The second ionisation energy is similarly the energy required to remove a second mole of electrons from the ion produced by the loss of one electron, that is the energy required for the change:

$$Q^{+}(g) \longrightarrow Q^{2+}(g) + e^{-}$$

Note that these are both endothermic changes, because work has to be done to remove a negatively charged electron from the attraction of a positively charged nucleus. The magnitude of the ionisation energy will depend on the charge on the nucleus. This will be counteracted by the repulsion, or "shielding" of electrons in filled inner orbitals. To a first approximation, each electron in a filled inner shell will cancel one unit of nuclear charge and after these have been subtracted, the remaining nuclear charge is referred to as the effective nuclear charge (ENC see Figure 222). The third factor that affects the ionisation energy is the repulsion that the electron experiences from other electrons within the same shell.

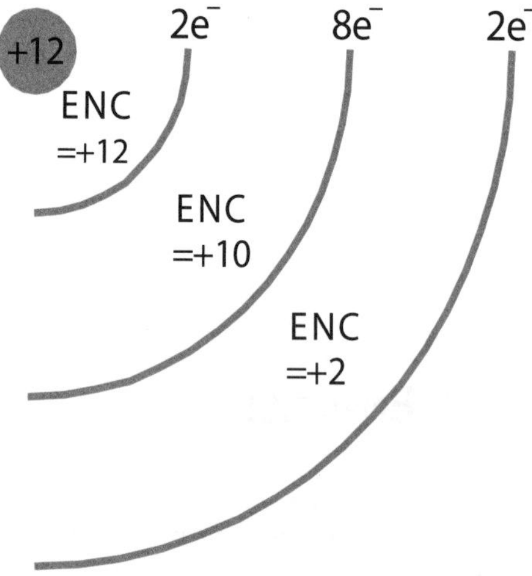

Figure 222 The effective nuclear charge (ENC) for the electrons in magnesium

Successive Ionisation Energies

The more electrons that have been removed from an atom, the greater the energy required to remove the next electron. When the successive electrons are all in the same energy level this is because of a reduction in the amount of electron-electron repulsion and hence the greater nuclear-electron attraction that results causes the remaining electrons to move closer to the nucleus. Consider for example the successive ionisation energies for the magnesium atom, shown in Figure 223 below. The two outer electrons experience the same effective nuclear charge. The first one to be removed is also repelled by the other valence electron, but this force is absent when the second electron is removed. After the first electron is lost, the second outer electron is attracted closer to the nucleus, hence the higher ionisation energy.

Similarly, from the third to the tenth ionisation energy the electrons are being removed from the second energy level, where again the electrons all experience the same effective nuclear charge (+10). In the case of the third ionisation energy this nuclear attraction is counteracted by the repulsion of seven other electrons in the same valence shell, but in the case of the fourth ionisation energy there are only six other electrons repelling the electron being lost, so the remaining valence electrons are now attracted closer to the nucleus and the ionisation energy increases. This trend continues as the remaining second shell electrons are removed. The last two electrons in the second shell have slightly higher ionisation energies than would be anticipated from this trend because they are being removed from the s sub-shell which is slightly more stable than the p sub-shell.

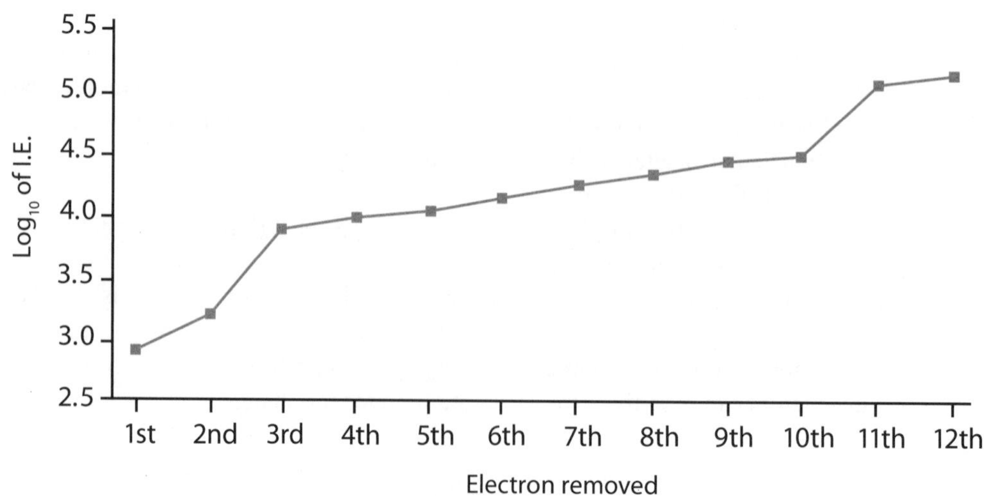

Figure 223 The energy required for the removal of successive electrons from a magnesium atom.

Element	Na	Mg	Al	Si	P	S	Cl	Ar
Group	1	2	13	14	15	16	17	0
Electronic structure	2.8.1	2.8.2	2.8.3	2.8.4	2.8.5	2.8.6	2.8.7	2.8.8
1st IE	496	738	578	789	1,010	1,000	1,251	1,520
2nd IE	4,560	1,450	1,820	1,580	1,900	2,250	2,300	2,670
3rd IE	6,910	7,730	2,750	3,230	2,910	3,360	3,820	3,930
4th IE	9,540	10,500	11,600	4,360	4,960	4,560	5,160	5,770
5th IE	13,400	13,600	14,800	16,100	6,270	7,010	6,540	7,240
6th IE	16,600	18,000	18,400	19,800	21,269	8,500	9,360	8,780
7th IE	20,100	21,700	23,300	23,800	25,400	27,100	11,000	12,000
8th IE	25,500	25,700	27,500	29,300	29,900	31,700	33,600	13,800
9th IE	28,900	31,600	31,900	33,900	35,900	36,600	38,600	40,800
10th IE	141,000	35,400	38,500	38,700	41,000	43,100	44,000	46,200

(Note all values are kJ mol^{-1} correct to 3 sig fig.)

Figure 224 Ionisation data for thel elements from sodium (Na) to argon (Ar)

Sometimes with successive ionisation energies the next electron must be removed from a filled inner energy level, so that this electron will experience a much higher effective nuclear charge (see Fig. 222) and there is a sudden large rise in ionisation energy. This is the case for the third and the eleventh electrons to be removed from magnesium. Note the use of the logarithmic scale in Figure 223. This makes the shell structure more obvious because, if a linear scale were used, all of the first ten ionisation energies would lie very close to the x-axis.

Consider the detailed ionisation energy data for the period sodium to argon shown below in Figure 224. Looking at these data it can be seen that the sudden increase in ionization energy (see shaded cells), corresponding to starting to remove electrons from the 2p sub-shell, occurs after the removal of one more electron going across the period. Similarly the very high 10th ionization of sodium corresponds to removing an electron from the 1s orbital. Apart from these, the data shows that there is a steady increase in successive ionization energies for every element (decrease in e^{-}-e^{-} repulsion) and a steady increase going across the period (increase in nuclear charge).

VARIATION OF IONISATION ENERGY

WITHIN THE GROUP

Going down a group of the periodic table, the ionisation energy of the elements decreases. This is because whilst the effective nuclear charge remains approximately constant (the extra nuclear charge being approximately cancelled out by an extra filled electron shell), the electrons that are being lost are in successively higher energy levels and hence further from the nucleus.

An example would be the first ionisation energy of the elements of Group 1, the alkali metals, given in Figure 225). In lithium, for example, the electron is lost from the 2s sub-shell at a distance of 152 pm from the nucleus. In sodium it is lost from the 3s sub-shell which is 186 pm from the nucleus, hence the lower ionisation energy (see Figure 226).

This trend can be seen for these elements and perhaps even more clearly for the noble gases, the peak ionisation energies, in Figure 227.

AHL

Element	Li	Na	K	Rb	Cs
I.E. (kJ mol^{-1})	526	502	425	409	382

Figure 225 First ionisation energies for the alkali metals

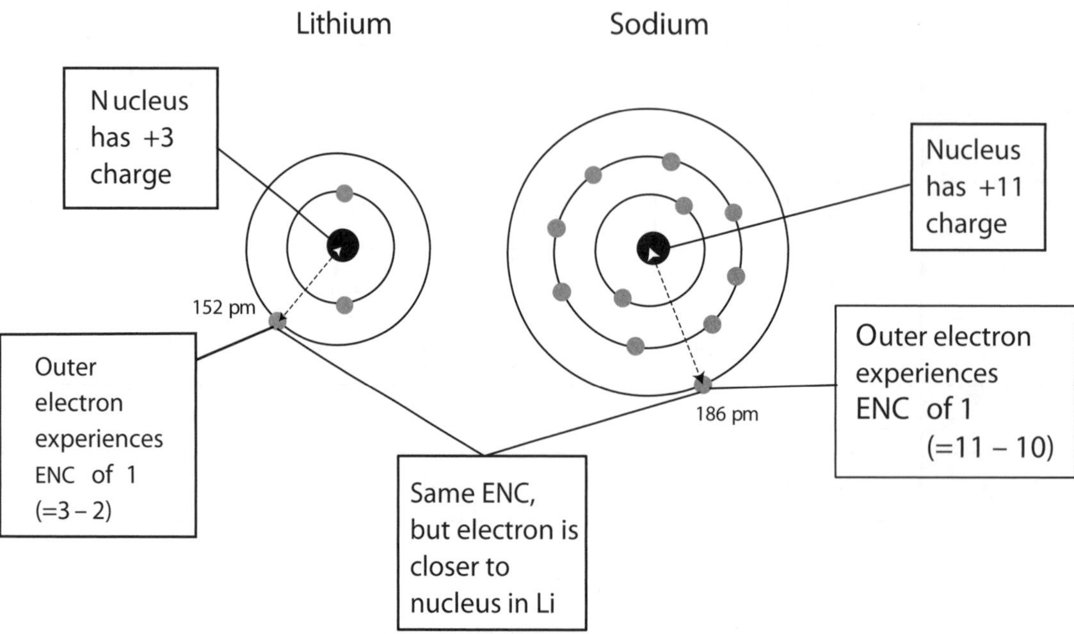

Figure 226 A simplified electronic structure of lithium and sodium illustrating effective nuclear charges

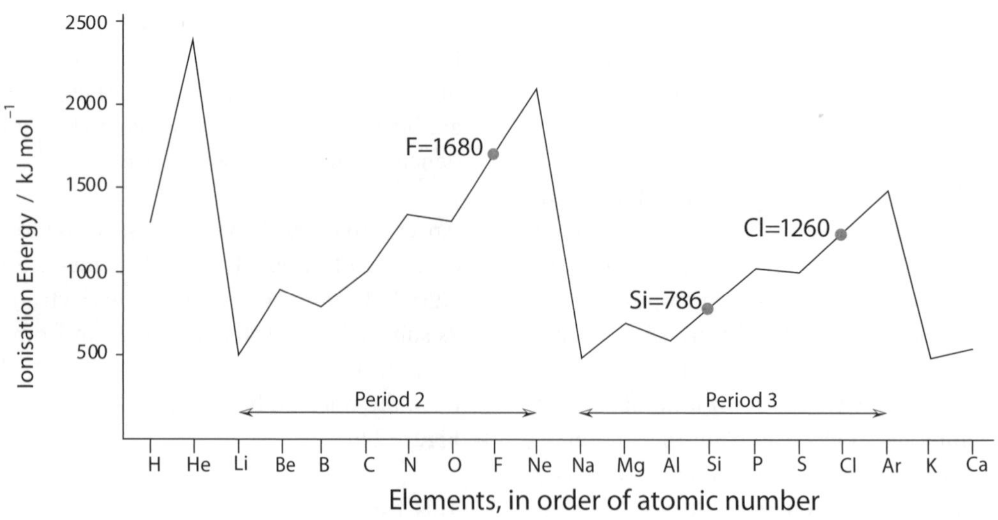

Figure 227 The variation of first ionisation energy with atomic number

THE VARIATION OF IONISATION ENERGY ACROSS A PERIOD

The ionisation energies of successive elements (in kJ mol^{-1}) is shown in Figure 224.

Overall, going across a period (for example period 2 from Li to Ne, or period 3 from Na to Ar), it can be seen that the ionisation energy increases. This is because of the increase in the charge on the nucleus which, as the electrons being removed are all in the same energy level, increases the effective nuclear charge, and hence the ionisation energy.

The increase is not however a smooth one. Going from the second to the third element in each period (Be to B and Mg to Al) there is a decrease. This is because the electron removed from the third element is in a p-subshell (e.g. B is $1s^2\ 2s^2\ 2p^1$) whereas that being lost from the second element is from an s-subshell (e.g. Be is $1s^2\ 2s^2$). The p-subshell is at a slightly higher energy than the s-subshell and this more than counteracts the effect of the increase in nuclear charge, so the result is a decrease in ionisation energy.

There is also a slight decrease going from the fifth to the sixth element in each period (N to O and P to S). This is because in the fifth element each of the p-orbitals is singly filled, whereas with the sixth element one of these must be doubly filled as shown in Figure 228.

Nitrogen

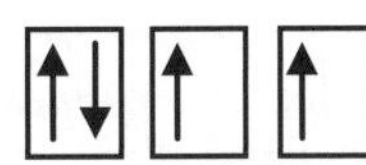

Oxygen

Figure 228 The 2p electron structure in nitrogen and oxygen

There is greater electron-electron repulsion between the two electrons that share the same orbital, which more than counteracts the effect of the increase in nuclear charge, hence oxygen has a lower ionisation energy than nitrogen.

Isoelectronic species are those which have the same electronic structure. For example S^{2-},Cl^-, Ar, K^+, and Ca^{2+} all have an electronic stucture $1s^2\ 2s^2\ 2p^6\ 3s^2\ 3p^6$. In the order shown the charge on the nucleus gradually increases (from +16 for S to +20 for Ca), so that the attraction for the electrons becomes greater and the ionisation energies gradually increase.

Exercise 12.1

1. The electronic structure $1s^2\ 2s^2\ 2p^6\ 3s^2\ 3p^6$ would be found in

   A neon atoms
   B sodium ions
   C sulfide ions
   D chlorine atoms

2. Which one of the following elements has the lowest first ionisation energy?

   A Argon
   B Magnesium
   C Sodium
   D Lithium

3. How many 3d electrons are present in the ground state of a cobalt atom?

   A 6
   B 7
   C 8
   D 9

4. The first three ionisation energies of aluminium (in kJ mol^{-1}) are 584, 1823 & 2751. The fourth ionisation energy (in kJ mol^{-1}) is most likely to be about:

   A 3000
   B 5000
   C 10 000
   D 100 000

5. The first ionisation energy of aluminium is slightly lower than that of magnesium because

   A magnesium has a higher nuclear charge.
   B the outer electron in aluminium is in a p-orbital not an s-orbital.
   C in aluminium the electron is being lost from a doubly filled orbital.
   D the radius of the aluminium atom is greater than the magnesium atom.

6. Which one of the following atoms would have the highest fourth ionisation energy?

   A C
   B N
   C Si
   D P

AHL

7. How many unpaired electrons are there in the Cr^{3+} ion?

A 0
B 1
C 3
D 6

8. Which one of the following would require the most energy for the removal of one more electron?

A F^-
B Ne
C Na^+
D Mg^{2+}

9. Write the complete electron configurations of:

a) Mn
b) S
c) Mg^{2+}
d) Fe^{3+}
e) Cu

AHL

10. Arrange the following in order of increasing ionisation energy

Li Na Ne N O

11. a) Sketch a graph to show how you would expect the successive ionisation energies of silicon to vary with the number of electrons removed.
b) Explain how this provides evidence that the electrons in atoms are arranged in distinct energy levels.
c) Explain why, within one of these levels, the amount of energy required to remove an electron varies with the number of electrons removed.

12. Explain why

a) the first ionisation energy of lithium is greater than that of sodium.
b) the first ionisation energy of oxygen is less than that of nitrogen.
c) the first ionisation energy of beryllium is greater than that of boron.

13. A particular metal cation M^{3+} has the electronic structure [Ar] $3d^2$.

a) Identify the metal concerned.
b) Write the electronic structure of the metal atom.
c) Explain why the electronic structure of the ion could not be the electronic structure of a neutral atom.

14. The graph below shows the logarithm of the successive ionisation energies of a particular element with atomic number less than or equal to 20.

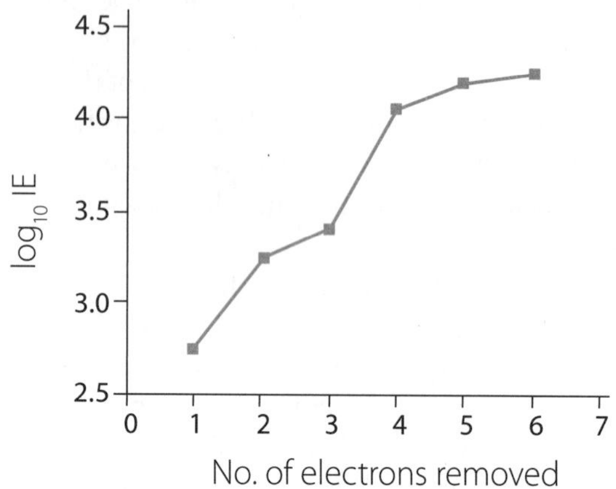

a) Identify the element.
b) Predict the approximate value of the logarithm of the seventh ionisation energy.
c) How would you expect the equivalent successive ionisation energies of the element immediately above it in the periodic table to compare in magnitude?

15. The table below gives successive ionisation data for a number of elements in $kJmol^{-1}$.

Element	First IE	Second IE	Third IE	Fourth IE
A	580	1800	2700	11600
B	900	1800	14800	21000
C	2080	4000	6100	9400
D	590	1100	4900	6500
E	420	3600	4400	5900

a) Which two elements are probably in the same group of the periodic table?
b) Which element is probably in group 3 of the periodic table? How can you tell?
c) Which two elements probably have consecutive atomic numbers?
d) Which element is most probably a noble gas? Give two pieces of evidence for this.

PERIODICITY

3.1 The periodic table

3.2 Physical properties

3.3 Chemical Properties

13.1 Trends across Period 3 (AHL)

13.2 First-row d-block elements (AHL)

TOK Phlogiston and a paradigm shift?

'The early discoverers of the elements allowed chemistry to make great steps with limited apparatus, often derived from the pseudoscience of alchemy. Lavoisier's discovery of oxygen, which overturned the phlogiston theory of heat, could be discussed as an example of a paradigm shift.'

Fire, and out ability to control it, is one of the major things that has helped us advance beyond other animals. Looking at flames two things are obvious – there is something coming out of the thing that's burning and the process gives out heat and light. Heat seemed part of many natural processes (sunlight and hot-springs), but what could be causing the flame. This is where phlogiston (from the Greek phlogistos, meaning burnt up or flammable) came in – it was the material released when things burnt. There seemed to be less of things after they burnt (compare the ashes that remain to the piece of wood they came from) so it all made sense. The theory is attributed to Johann Becher, a German physician and alchemist, who lived in the middle of the 17th century. It was the accepted theory of combustion for at least a century and so was probably the explanation for combustion in the first edition of Encyclopaedia Britannica in 1768? It is a bit disturbing to reflect on what in the current edition will be considered nonsense a couple of centuries from now! About a century later however scientists were starting to make more accurate quantitative observations and they noted that some substances (magnesium would be a good example) gained mass when they burnt. It is perhaps interesting to reflect whether previous results to the contrary (i.e. that metals lost weight when they burnt), by such eminent people as Robert Boyle, were a result of poor technique or through wanting the results to fit in with the theory! (Of course you would never "edit" the results of your chemistry experiments to "improve them?) As so often when a paradigm seems to be refuted, some people tried to keep the phlogiston theory alive, even if it meant postulating that it had a negative mass! The real death blow for phlogiston came with the work of Lavoisier in the late 18th century, who produced oxygen and showed that it was necessary for combustion. The discovery of oxygen is variously attributed to Scheele (a German), Priestley (an Englishman) and Lavoisier (a Frenchman) – which you support probably depends on what you feel the word "discover" implies and maybe on where you come from!

3.1 THE PERIODIC TABLE

3.1.1 Describe the arrangement of elements in the periodic table in order of increasing atomic number.

3.1.2 Distinguish between the terms group and period.

3.1.3 Apply the relationship between the electron configuration of elements and their position in the periodic table up to Z = 20.

3.1.4 Apply the relationship between the number of electrons in the highest occupied energy level for an element and its position in the periodic table.

The relationship between electronic structure and chemical properties of the elements is one of the key concepts in chemistry. This lies at the heart of the **periodic table** which is a most valuable arrangement of the elements to which chemical properties can be related. The usual form of the periodic table is that shown diagrammatically in Figure 301, but in many places in this chapter (e.g. Figure 302) the "short form" of the periodic table, in which the transition metals are omitted (also shown in Figure 301), is used for clarity.

In the periodic table, the elements are arranged in order of increasing atomic number, reading from left to right, top to bottom (as in reading English). This means that knowing the atomic number, the position of an element can be found by counting down the squares in this way. Try it, using the periodic table in Figure 302, for phosphorus (Z=15).

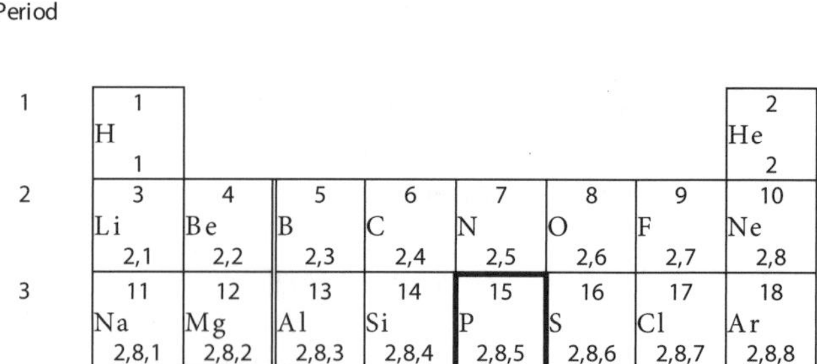

Period \ Group →	1	2	3/13	4/14	5/15	6/16	7/17	0
1	1 H 1							2 He 2
2	3 Li 2,1	4 Be 2,2	5 B 2,3	6 C 2,4	7 N 2,5	8 O 2,6	9 F 2,7	10 Ne 2,8
3	11 Na 2,8,1	12 Mg 2,8,2	13 Al 2,8,3	14 Si 2,8,4	15 P 2,8,5	16 S 2,8,6	17 Cl 2,8,7	18 Ar 2,8,8
4	19 K 2,8,8,1	20 Ca 2,8,8,2						

Figure 302 The first twenty elements in the periodic table and their electronic structures

A group is a vertical column consisting of elements with the same number of electrons in the outer energy level, which gives these elements similar chemical properties. These are numbered above the column and originally they were numbered from 0 to 7, but recently the system has been changed to 0 to 17 to include the d–block elements. This is less ambiguous, though both are shown. It is then found that going across a horizontal row (known as a period) the chemical properties gradually change from those of reactive metals to those of reactive non–metals, with the noble gases in the final group at the far right. Consider this for the first twenty elements shown in Figure 302.

Valence electrons are electrons in the outermost energy level (the highest energy level) of an atom. These are usually the electrons that take part in a chemical reaction and determine the physical and chemical properties of the element. It is therefore not surprising that the position of an element in the periodic table is closely related to its electronic structure, so this can be used as a memory aid. A period is a series of elements arranged according to increasing atomic number, which begins with the first element having one electron in a new main energy level, in which the same electron energy level (or shell) is being filled. Period 1 fills the n = 1 level, period 2 the n = 2 level etc. Hence the period an element is in gives the number

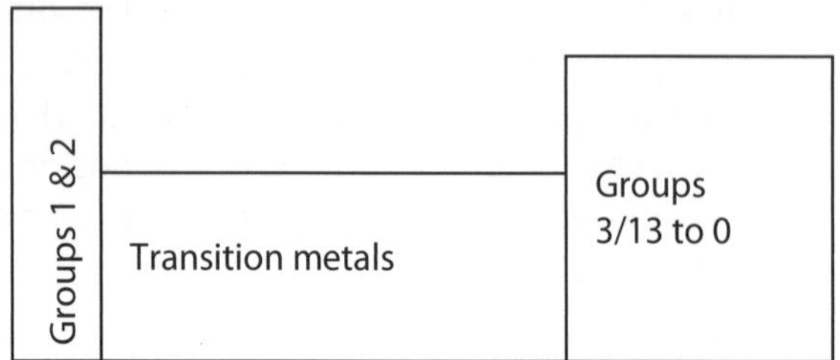

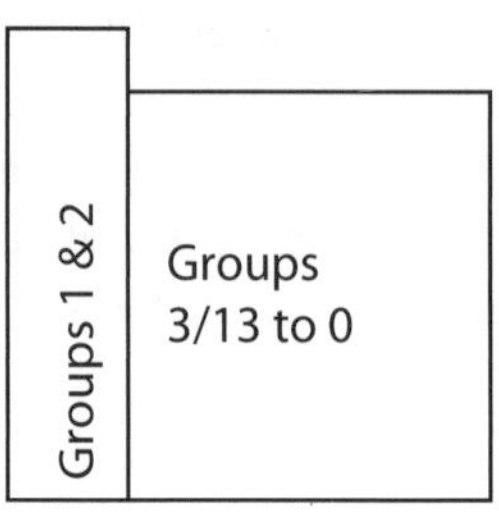

Figure 301 Forms of the periodic table

of energy levels that contain electrons. On the other hand, the group number (or the group number minus 10 in the modern numbering of groups 13 to 17) gives the number of electrons in the valence shell. This is also shown in Figure 302. Phosphorus, for example is in the third period, so it has electrons in the first three energy levels, and in the fifth group, so it has five electrons (or 5-10) in the valence level. Its electronic structure is therefore 2,8,5.

The first element in each period (such as sodium, Na) therefore has only one electron in its outer shell. The elements in this first group are known as the alkali metals. The last but one element in each period (such as chlorine, Cl) requires one more electron to complete its outer shell. The elements in this last but one group are known as the halogens. The final element in each period (such as argon, Ar) has all its electron shells filled. These elements have little chemical reactivity and are known as the noble gases. Periodicity is the regular repeating of properties according to the arrangement of elements in the periodic table (they occur at regular intervals). It is found that chemical and physical properties of elements show periodicity if the elements are arranged in order of increasing atomic numbers and these are discussed in sections 3.2 and 3.3 respectively.

TOK Risk-taking and science

The predictive power of Mendeleev's periodic table can be seen as an example of a "scientist" as a "risk taker". © IBO 2007

There is no doubt at all that when he proposed his periodic table Mendeleev put his neck on the line. Not only did he predict that there were some elements still to be found, he also made many detailed predictions about their properties, for example his predictions with regard to Germanium (which Mendeleev referred to as eka-silicon) are given below, along with the properties it was found to have after its discovery in 1886, about 15 years after it had been predicted by Mendeleev.

Property	Mendeleev's prediction	Actual property
Relative atomic mass	72.0	72.6
Density	5.5 g cm^{-3}	5.35 g cm^{-3}
Appearance	Light grey solid	Dark grey solid
Reaction with air	Will react to form a dioxide	Reacts to form GeO_2
Reaction with water	Reacts only with difficulty	Reacts only if red hot
Reaction with acids	Slight reaction	Does not react with common acids
Reaction with alkalis	No reaction	Does not react with common alkalis
Properties of its oxide	High melting point; density 4.7 g cm^{-3}; few acid base reactions	Melts at 1115 °C; density 4.23 g cm^{-3}; very weak base
Properties of its chloride	Will form a liquid tetrachloride which boils at under 100 °C	$GeCl_4$ is a liquid at room temperature and boils at 84 °C

Whether being a risk-taker is a good thing or not is also worth some thought, and probably evolution, through survival of the fittest, is the final arbiter. Having a long tail is obviously a risk for a male peacock when trying to escape from a fox, so do the extra peahens he attracts compensate for this risk? Will he survive long enough to mate with them? In scientific terms it could be argued there is now less risk attached to proposing a new theory than there once was as a result of Karl Popper, a 20th Century Austrian philosopher. Popper said "Our belief in any particular natural law cannot have a safer basis than our unsuccessful critical attempts to refute it.", in other words science progresses by people trying to disprove existing theories. About a century ago it would have been a major disgrace in the scientific world to have had a theory disproved, but now it would be seen as valuable because it stimulated the work that eventually disproved the theory which led (hopefully) to the proposal of a better theory. Now a real risk-taker would set out to disprove the theory of gravity by bungee jumping without the cord!

Exercise 3.1

1. In the periodic table, reading from left to right and top to bottom, the elements are arranged in order of

   A the number of protons in their nucleus.
   B the number of neutrons in their nucleus.
   C increasing relative atomic mass.
   D increasing mass number.

2. An element has 13 electrons orbiting the nucleus. In which group of the periodic table will it be found?

   A Group 1
   B Group 2
   C Group 3
   D Group 4

3. Find the element chlorine in the periodic table.

   a) How many electrons will it have in its outer shell?
   b) How many fully filled electron shells does it have?
   c) Give the symbol of another element in the same period as chlorine.
   d) Give the symbol of another element in the same group as chlorine.
   e) What name is given to the elements in this group?

3.2 PHYSICAL PROPERTIES

3.2.1 Define the terms first ionization energy and electronegativity.

3.2.2 Describe and explain the trends in atomic radii, ionic radii, first ionization energies, electronegativities and melting points for the alkali metals (Li $\rightarrow$ Cs) and the halogens (F $\rightarrow$ I).

3.2.3 Describe and explain the trends in atomic radii, ionic radii, first ionization energies and electronegativities for elements across period 3.

3.2.4 Compare the relative electronegativity values of two or more elements based on their positions in the periodic table.

Going down a group of the periodic table, for successive elements there are more energy levels filled with electrons, so the outer electrons are in higher energy levels and farther from the nucleus. The extra charge on the nucleus is approximately cancelled out by additional filled shells of electrons, so the charge acting on the valence electrons (the **Effective Nuclear Charge**) is approximately the same for each element. As a result the valence electrons are further from the nucleus and the radius of the atoms and the ions formed from these atoms, both increase. The electrons are also less strongly attacted by the nucleus so that the **ionisation energy** (the minimum amount of energy required to remove an electron from one mole of gaseous atoms,) and the **electronegativity** (a measure of how strongly the atom attracts the electrons in a covalent bond) both decrease going down the group. These trends are illustrated in Figure 303 using as examples, for atomic and ionic radius, the alkali metals (Group 1), for ionisation energy the noble gases (Group 0) and the halogens (Group 7/17) for electronegativity.

Going across a period of the periodic table, the number of protons in the nucleus and hence the charge on the nucleus increases. This means that going across the period the electrons, which are all in the same energy level, are more strongly attracted and hence move closer to the nucleus causing the atomic and ionic radii (for isoelectronic ions, i.e. those with the same electronic structure) to both decrease. The ionization energy and the

(a) The trend in atomic radius going down Group 1

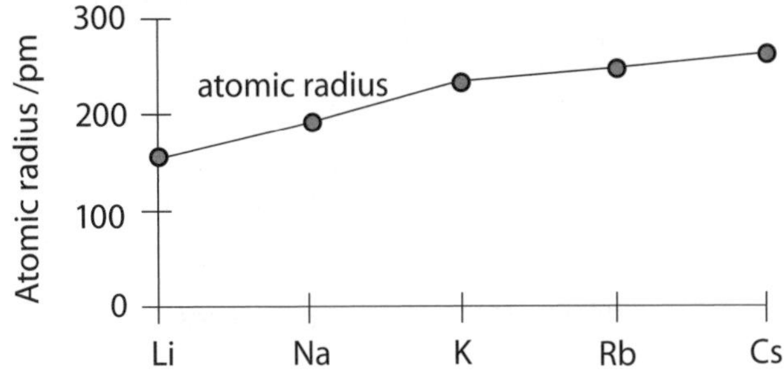

(b) The trend in ionization energy going down Group 0

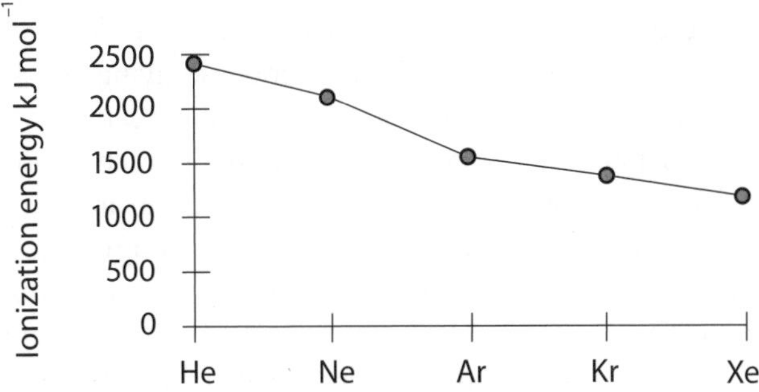

(c) The trend in electronegativity going down Group 17

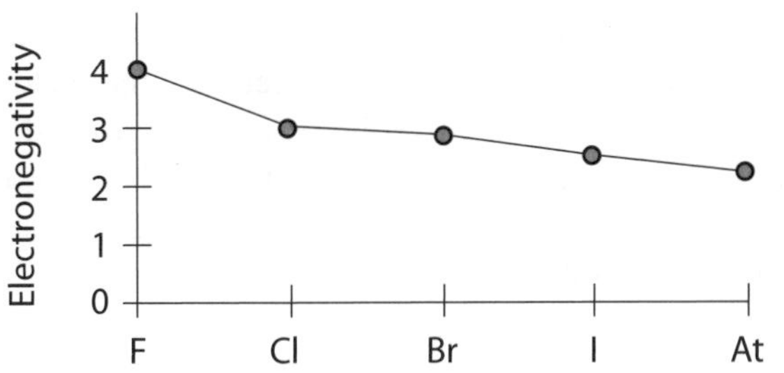

Figure 303 a, b, c Some trends in various atomic properties on going down different groups of the periodic table

(a) Variation in atomic radius across the third period

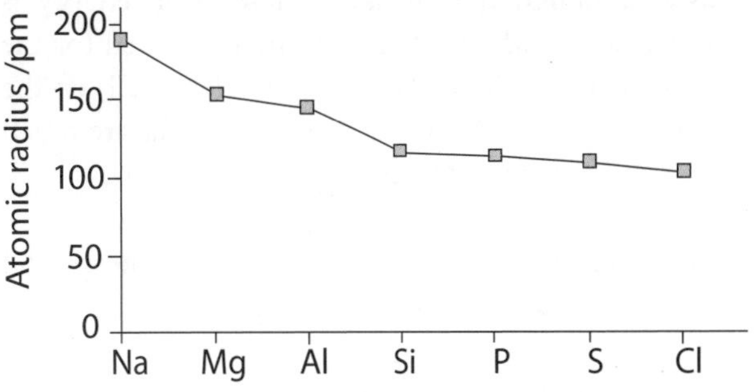

(b) Variation in ionization energy across the third period

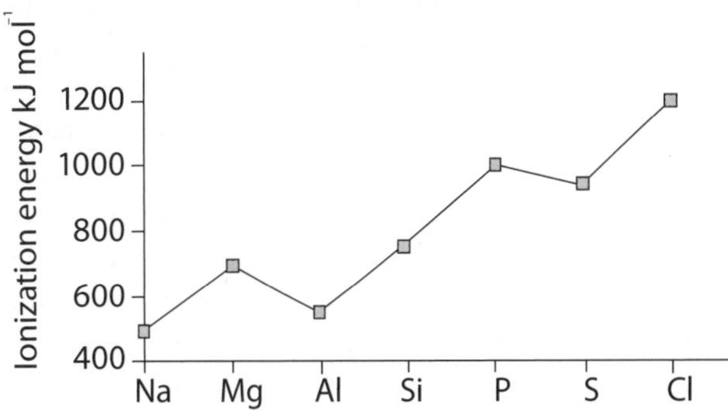

(c) Variation in electronegativity across the third period

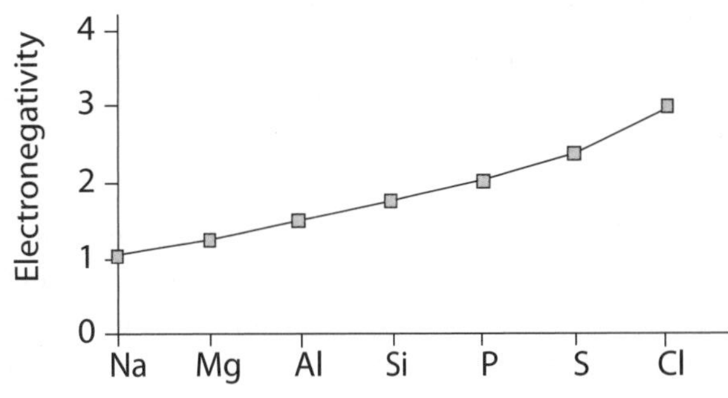

Figure 304 a,b,c Variations in some atomic properties on going across the third period of the periodic table

Li ⟶ **F**

Decreasing atomic & ionic radius
Increasing electronegativity
and ionization energy

I ⟶ **F**

Decreasing atomic & ionic radius
Increasing electronegativity and
ionization energy

Figure 305 Periodic trends in some atomic properties

electronegativity both increase overall going across the period as the attraction of the nucleus for the electrons increases, although the change in ionization energy is by no means smooth. These trends are illustrated for the chemically reactive elements of period 3 (Na → Cl) on the graphs in Figure 304. Note that these variations are much greater than those found within a group.

The overall trends in atomic radius, ionization energy and electronegativity are summarised in Figure 305.

The size of an atom always decreases when it is converted into a positive ion (cation). This may be because the whole of an outer shell of electrons has been lost (e.g. when Cs turns into Cs^+, see to Figure 306) or because the loss of the electron results in less electron–electron repulsion between the valence electrons (e.g. when Mg turns into Mg^+, in which 12 protons are now pulling on only 11 electrons).

Conversely the size of an atom always increases when it is converted into a negative ion (anion), because the additional electron results in an increase in repulsion between the valence electrons (e.g. when F turns into F^-, in which 10 electrons repel each other more than the 9 electrons in the F atom, see Figure 306).

Almost every common cation (i.e. positive ion) is smaller than any anion (i.e. negative ion), the converse only being true for the extremities such as Cs^+ and F^-, illustrated in the scale drawings shown in Figure 306. H^- is also quite small.

Physical properties, such as melting point, boiling point and density also depend on the nature of the bonding between the particles of the element. This is dealt with in much greater detail in Chapter 4, which should be read in conjunction with this section. Clear periodicity patterns are visible in a graph of the melting points of the elements against atomic number, shown in Figure 307.

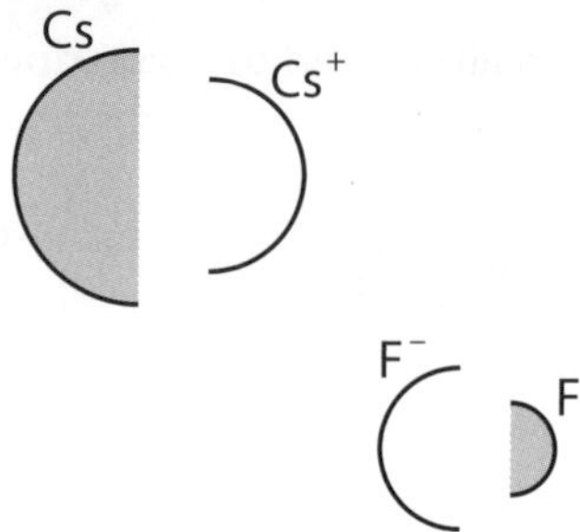

Figure 306 Atom and ion sizes

At the left of the period the elements (Li, Na, K) are metallic and going across the period the strength of the metallic bonding increases as there is an increase in nuclear charge. As a result both the number of mobile valence electrons increases and the atomic radius decreases, giving rise to an increase in the melting points (as the metal cations are held closer and more tightly). At the centre of each period (C, Si) giant covalently bonded structures occur in which every atom is joined to all the others by very strong covalent bonds, hence have very high melting points. Following this the melting points suddenly drop (N, P) as the elements here have non-polar, simple molecular structures and only weak **van der Waals' forces** exist between the molecules. Melting points are low, and depend on mass and size of the molecules P_4, S_8, and Cl_2. This is further emphasised with the noble gases (He, Ne, Ar), which exist as single atoms with very weak van der Waals' forces and hence very low melting points. It must be remembered that the melting point is only a measure of the difference in the strength of the forces between particles between the solid and liquid state, rather than a measure of the absolute magnitude of such forces, as boiling point represents.

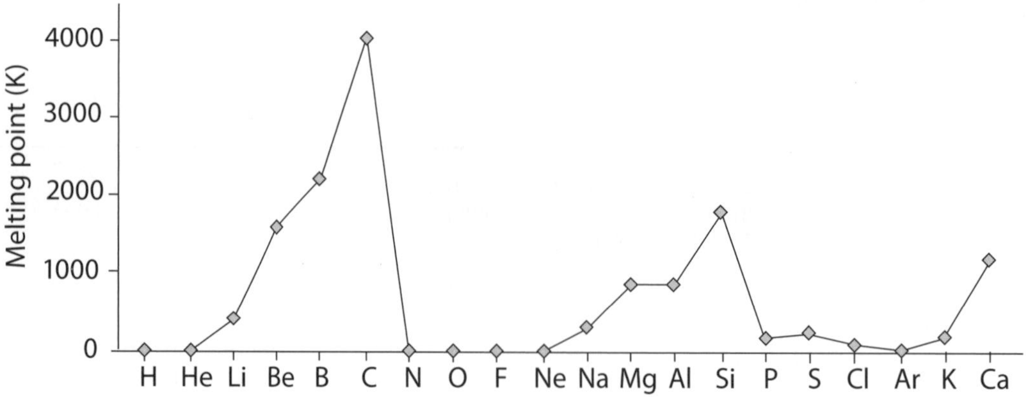

Figure 307 The melting points of the first twenty elements

Element	Na	Mg	Al	Si
Group	1	2	13	14
e^- arrangement	$1s^2\,2s^2\,2p^6\,3s^1$ 2.8.1	$1s^2\,2s^2\,2p^6\,3s^2$ 2.8.2	$1s^2\,2s^2\,2p^6\,3s^2\,3p^1$ 2.8.3	$1s^2\,2s^2\,2p^6\,3s^2\,3p^2$ 2.8.4
# Valence e^-	1	2	3	4
1st I.E. (in eV)	5.1	7.6	6.0	8.1
2nd IE	47.3	15.0	18.8	16.3
3rd IE	71.7	80.1	28.4	33.5
4th IE	98.9	109.3	120.0	45.1
5th IE	139	141	154	167

Figure 308 IE data for some elements

Exercise 3.2

1. Which one of the following has the lowest electronegativity?

   A Boron
   B Beryllium
   C Magnesium
   D Carbon

2. Which one of the following has the smallest radius?

   A K
   B K^+
   C Ca
   D Ca^{2+}

3. The circles below represent the relative sizes of the F^-, Na^+, Mg^{2+}, K^+ and ions, but not necessarily in that order. Which one of the following would give them in this order?

   A II, I, III, IV
   B III, I, II, IV
   C I, II, III, IV
   D III, II, I, IV

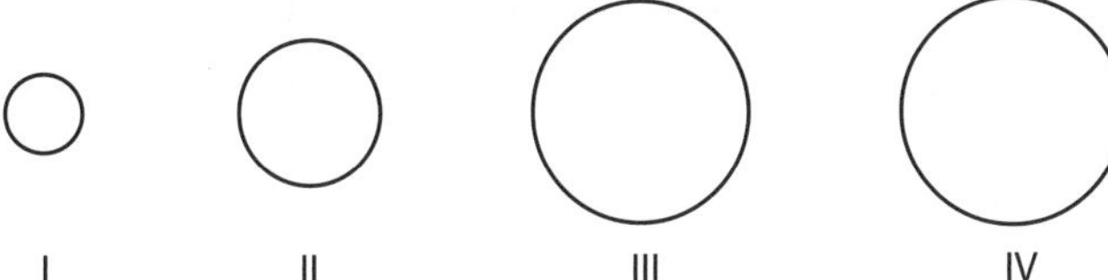

4. Going across a given short period, in which group are you most likely to find the element with the highest melting point?

   A Group 0
   B Group 2
   C Group 4
   D Group 6

5. Arrange the following in order of increasing atomic radius

   Mg Cs Ca Al Ba

6. For each of the following properties, state how you would expect it to change in the direction indicated and give reasons for the change based on concepts such as nuclear charge, shielding, electron–electron repulsion and atomic/ionic radius.

   a) The electronegativity going down a group.
   b) The atomic radius going across a period.
   c) The radius of an anion compared to its parent atom.
   d) The first ionization energy going down a group.
   e) The radius of a series of isoelectronic species (i.e. species having the same electronic structure, such as Cl^-, Ar, Na^+) with increasing atomic number.

CORE

3.3 CHEMICAL PROPERTIES

3.3.1 Discuss the similarities and differences in the chemical properties of elements in the same group.

THE ALKALI METALS

The **alkali metals** Li, Na, K, Rb and Cs (Fr has not been included because of its scarcity and nuclear instability) are soft malleable metals with low melting points and low densities. The low density is a result of the atoms of the alkali metals being the largest atoms in their period of the periodic table, and the softness and low melting points result from the fact that each atom can only contribute one electron to the metallic bonding, so this is less strong than for many other metals. The metals become softer and the melting point decreases (refer to Figure 310) going down the group as the attraction between the nucleus and the outer electrons becomes less, as a result of the increase in the size of the atoms.

Alkali metals are chemically very reactive and tarnish rapidly on exposure to air. The metals all have just one electron in their valence electron shell. This electron is very easily lost and this is the major reason why they are very reactive metals. They always form ions with a single positive charge in their compounds. They combine directly with reactive non-metals such as oxygen, chlorine, bromine and iodine to form ionically bonded compounds:

$$4Li\ (s) + O_2\ (g) \longrightarrow 2Li_2O\ (s) \quad (2 \times Li^+ \text{ and } O^{2-})$$

(Na and K form more complex oxides)

$$2Na\ (s) + Cl_2\ (g) \longrightarrow 2NaCl\ (s)\ (Na^+ \text{ and } Cl^-)$$

$$2K\ (s) + Br_2\ (l) \longrightarrow 2KBr\ (s) \quad (K^+ \text{ and } Br^-)$$

$$2Cs\ (s) + I_2\ (s) \longrightarrow 2CsI\ (s) \quad (Cs^+ \text{ and } I^-)$$

Going down the group, as the atomic radius increases, the ionization energy of the elements decreases, the reactivity of the elements increases. This is best illustrated by the reaction of the elements with water. All of the metals react with water to form a solution of the metal hydroxide and hydrogen gas, according to the equation below (M represents the alkali metal):

$$2M\ (s) + 2H_2O\ (l) \longrightarrow 2M^+\ (aq) + 2OH^-\ (aq) + H_2\ (g)$$

for example in the case of sodium:

$$2Na\ (s) + 2H_2O\ (l) \longrightarrow 2Na^+\ (aq) + 2OH^-\ (aq) + H_2\ (g)$$

With lithium, the reaction occurs slowly and steadily. In the case of sodium the reaction is vigorous, producing enough heat to melt the sodium which fizzes around on the surface quite vigorously. With potassium the reaction is violent and the heat produced is enough to ignite the hydrogen evolved, which burns with a purple flame. In all cases the solution becomes strongly alkaline owing to the formation of hydroxide ions.

Alkali Metals	$_3Li$	$_{11}Na$	$_{19}K$	$_{37}Rb$	$_{55}Cs$
Electronic Structure	2,1	2,8,1	2,8,8,1	2,8,8,18,1	2,8,8,18,18,1
Melting Point – K	454	371	336	312	302
Increasing atomic and ionic radius →					
Decreasing ionization energy →					
Decreasing electronegativity →					

Figure 310 Properties of the alkali metals

THE HALOGENS

The **halogens** F, Cl, Br and I (At has not been included because of its scarcity and nuclear instability) are very reactive non–metals that occur in the penultimate group of the periodic table, hence they all require just one electron to complete their valence shell.

All of the elements exist as diatomic molecules (F_2, Cl_2, Br_2, I_2) in which the atoms are joined by single covalent bonds. Going down the group their state, at room temperature and pressure, changes as the strength of the van der Waals' forces between the molecules increases with molar mass. Fluorine and chlorine are gases, bromine a liquid and iodine a solid that forms a purple vapour on heating. The halogens are are all quite electronegative elements. They require just one electron to complete their valence shell, hence they readily gain electrons to form the singly charged halide ions (F^-, Cl^-, Br^-, I^-). The ease with which they gain electrons decreases going down the group, as the electrons gained are further from the nucleus and hence less strongly attracted. This means that, in contrast to the alkali metals, the reactivity of the halogens decreases going down the group.

The halogens are only slightly soluble in water as they are non–polar and hence can only bond by weak van der Waals' forces to the polar water molecules. Concentrated solutions of chlorine have a green tinge and those of bromine darken from yellow through orange to brown as the concentration increases. In non–polar solvents, such as hexane, iodine forms the violet solution that would be expected, but in polar solvents, such as water and ethanol, the solution is a brown colour. In aqueous solution the halogens dissociate slightly to form an acidic solution:

$$X_2\,(aq) + H_2O\,(l) \longrightarrow H^+\,(aq) + X^-\,(aq) + HOX\,(aq)$$

(where X is the halogen and HOX is a weak acid)

For example with chlorine:

$$Cl_2\,(aq) + H_2O\,(l) \longrightarrow H^+\,(aq) + Cl^-\,(aq) + HOCl\,(aq)$$

The compound HOX can readily donate its oxygen to other substances, so it acts as an oxidant. Chloric(I) acid (HOCl) will, for example, oxidise coloured dyes to colourless products. The second stage of the test for chlorine, in which it turns moist blue litmus paper from blue to red (the acidic solution) and then bleaches it to colourless, depends on this reaction. As a result chloric(I)acid, and its conjugate base the chlorate(I) ion (OCl^-) are used as bleaches (e.g. for paper). They are also toxic to microbes, hence they are used as disinfectants and chlorine is used in water treatment.

The halogens combine with metals to give ionically bonded salts containing the halide ion. These salts are usually white and soluble in water giving colourless solutions. The common insoluble halides are those of lead and silver (though the lead(II) salts are moderately soluble in boiling water). These insoluble salts can be precipitated by adding solutions containing the halide ion to a soluble salt containing the metal ion. Lead(II) iodide (PbI_2) is easily recognised because of its bright yellow colour and this is a convenient test for the iodide ion. The usual test for halide ions is however to add dilute nitric acid (to prevent carbonates etc. giving a precipitate) followed by aqueous silver nitrate to a solution of the unknown substance. The

Halogens	${}_{9}F$	${}_{17}Cl$	${}_{35}Br$	${}_{53}I$
Electronic Structure	2,7	2,8,7	2,8,8,7	2,8,8,18,7
Colour	Pale yellow	Yellow green	Red brown	Black/dark purple
State at room T & P	Gas	Gas	Liquid	Solid
Increasing atomic and ionic radius →				
Decreasing ionization energy →				
Decreasing electronegativity →				

Figure 311 Properties of the halogens

formation of a precipitate (see equation below) indicates that a chloride, bromide or iodide ion is present (note that because AgF is soluble, the fluoride does not give a precipitate). Silver chloride (AgCl) is white, but rapidly darkens through purple to black in sunlight through photodissociation to silver and chlorine. Silver bromide (AgBr) is an off–white (or cream) colour and silver iodide (AgI) a pale yellow.

$$Ag^+(aq) + Cl^-(aq) \longrightarrow AgCl(s);$$
white precipitate, that darkens in light

$$Ag^+(aq) + Br^-(aq) \longrightarrow AgBr(s);$$
cream precipitate

$$Ag^+(aq) + I^-(aq) \longrightarrow AgI(s);$$
pale yellow precipitate

Both the electronegativity and oxidising power of the halogens decrease going down the group as the size of the atoms increases and the attraction between the nucleus and the electrons becomes less. As a result, going down the group, the elements become less powerful oxidising agents. This means that a higher halogen will displace a lower halogen from its salts, for example, chlorine will oxidise iodide ions to iodine and this may be detected by the solution changing colour from colourless to brown. A lower halogen cannot however displace a higher halogen from its salts, e.g. iodine will not oxidise chloride ions to chlorine:

$$Cl_2(aq) + 2\,I^-(aq) \longrightarrow I_2(aq) + 2\,Cl^-(aq) \quad ✓$$

$$I_2(aq) + 2\,Cl^-(aq) \longrightarrow Cl_2(aq) + 2\,I^-(aq) \quad ✗$$

The results of displacement reactions of this type, and precipitation reactions with aqueous silver ions, are summarised in Figure 313.

Halide ion / Reagent	F^-	Cl^-	Br^-	I^-
Aqueous Ag^+	No reaction	White precipitate (turns black in sunlight) $Ag^++Cl^- \longrightarrow AgCl$	Cream precipitate $Ag^++Br^- \longrightarrow AgBr$	Pale yellow precipitate $Ag^++I^- \longrightarrow AgI$
Chlorine	No reaction	No reaction	Solution turns yellow then brown $Cl_2+2Br^- \longrightarrow Br_2+2Cl^-$	Solution goes yellow then black precipitate $Cl_2+2I^- \longrightarrow I_2+2Cl^-$
Bromine	No reaction	No reaction	No reaction	Solution goes yellow then black precipitate $Br_2+2I^- \longrightarrow I_2+2Br^-$
Iodine	No reaction	No reaction	No reaction	No reaction

Figure 313 Summary of some reactions of the halide ions

Period 3 elements	Na	Mg	Al	Si	P	S	Cl	Ar
Electronic structure	2,8,1	2,8,2	2,8,3	2,8,4	2,8,5	2,8,6	2,8,7	2,8,8
Boiling point / K	1156	1380	2740	2528	553	718	238	87
Metallic / non-metallic	Metallic			Metalloid		Non-metallic		Inert gas
Decreasing atomic radius →								
Increasing ionisation energy →								
Increasing electronegativity →								
Decreasing metallic character →								
Increasing hydrolysis of chlorides →								
Increasing acidic oxides →								

Figure 314 Trends across period 3

3.3.2 Discuss the changes in nature, from ionic to covalent and from basic to acidic, of the oxides across period 3.

TRENDS IN THE OXIDES OF THE PERIOD 3 ELEMENTS

Going across a period of the periodic table, the nature of the elements changes, as shown in Figure 315. At the left hand side the elements (e.g. Na & Mg) have relatively low ionization energies and so they bond to other elements to form ionic compounds in which they have lost their valence electrons and exist as cations. This is typical metallic behaviour. The oxides of these elements are therefore ionic and contain the oxide ion. The oxide ion can form a bond to hydrogen ions and as a result these ionic oxides act as bases dissolving in water to give alkaline solutions and neutralising acids to produce a salt and water:

$$O^{2-}\text{ (s)} + H_2O\text{ (l)} \longrightarrow 2OH^-\text{(aq)}$$

$$O^{2-}\text{ (s)} + 2H^+\text{ (aq)} \longrightarrow H_2O\text{ (l)}$$

With sodium oxide:

$$Na_2O\text{ (s)} + H_2O\text{ (l)} \longrightarrow 2Na^+\text{ (aq)} + 2OH^-\text{ (aq)}$$

With magnesium oxide:and hydrochloric acid

$$MgO\text{ (s)} + 2HCl\text{ (aq)} \longrightarrow Mg^{2+}\text{ (aq)} + 2Cl^-\text{ (aq)}$$

Aluminium oxide is amphoteric (that is, it will react with and hence dissolve in, both acids and alkalis):

$$Al_2O_3\text{ (s)} + 6H^+\text{ (aq)} \longrightarrow 2Al^{3+}\text{ (aq)} + 3H_2O\text{ (l)}$$

$$Al_2O_3\text{ (s)} + 2OH^-\text{ (aq)} + 3H_2O\text{ (l)} \longrightarrow 2Al(OH)^{4-}\text{ (aq)}$$

CORE

Formula	Na_2O	MgO	Al_2O_3	SiO_2	P_2O_5	SO_3	Cl_2O_7
Ratio of Atoms	2 : 1	2 : 2	2 : 3	2 : 4	2 : 5	2 : 6	2 : 7
Bonding	Ionic	Ionic	Highly polar covalent	Polar covalent	Polar covalent	Polar covalent	Polar covalent
Acid-base Character	Basic	Basic	Amphoteric	Weakly acidic	Acidic	Acidic	Acidic
Other Oxides	Na_2O_2				P_2O_3	SO_2	ClO_2 & Cl_2O

Figure 315 Some properties of the period 3 oxides

It therefore displays the properties of both metallic and non–metallic oxides. Refer to Figure 315.

Moving towards the middle of the periodic table the ionization energy becomes too great for cation formation and the elements tend towards non–metallic behaviour. In this region the elements (e.g. C and Si) bond by means of covalent bonds. Carbon dioxide reacts reversibly with water to form a weakly acidic solution

$$CO_2\,(g) + H_2O\,(l) \rightleftharpoons H^+\,(aq) + HCO_3^-\,(aq)$$

Silicon dioxide has little acid–base activity, but it does show weakly acidic properties by slowly dissolving in hot concentrated alkalis to form silicates.

$$SiO_2\,(s) + 2OH^-\,(aq) \longrightarrow SiO_3^{2-}\,(aq) + H_2O\,(l)$$

At the far right of the period the elements (except for the noble gases) continue to be able to form covalent bonds by sharing electrons with other non-metals, but gaining an additional electron also becomes energetically feasible. This means that these elements (e.g. S and Cl) also have the option of combining with metals to form ionic compounds in which they exist as anions (e.g. S^{2-} and Cl^-).

The oxides of these elements react completely when dissolved in water to form acidic solutions. For example phosphorus(V) oxide reacts to form a solution of phosphoric(V) acid a weak acid and sulfur trioxide reacts to form a solution of sulfuric acid, a strong acid:

$$P_4O_{10}\,(s) + 6H_2O\,(l) \longrightarrow 4H^+\,(aq) + 4H_2PO_4^-\,(aq)$$

$$SO_3\,(s) + H_2O\,(l) \longrightarrow H^+\,(aq) + HSO_4^-\,(aq)$$

These trends in the properties of the compounds of the elements on going across the third period are discussed in considerably more detail in the next section.

Exercise 3.3

1. The reactivity of the alkali metals increases in the order

   A Na, K, Li
   B K, Na, Li
   C Li, Na, K
   D Li, K, Na

2. An aqueous solution of chlorine acts as a bleach. This is because the solution

   A acts as an oxidant and converts the coloured dye to a colourless product.
   B acts as a base and converts the coloured dye to a colourless product.
   C acts as a reductant and converts the coloured dye to a colourless product.
   D acts as an acid and converts the coloured dye to a colourless product.

3. Going down the halogen group the state of the elements, at room temperature and pressure, changes from gas to liquid to solid. The reason for this is that

   A the strength of the bonds between the atoms increases.
   B the strength of the forces between the molecules increases.
   C the polarity of the molecules increases.
   D the electronegativity of the atoms decreases.

4. On going across a period of the periodic table, the elements tend to become less metallic in character. Which one of the following is not an indication of this trend?

   A There is an overall increase in molar mass.
   B There is an increase in electronegativity.
   C There is an overall increase in ionization energy.
   D There is a change in bond type from ionic to covalent.

5. Which one of the following is not true of the alkali metals?

   A They have a high density.
   B They form ionic compounds.
   C Their chlorides dissolve in water to form neutral solutions.
   D Their oxides dissolve in water to form alkaline solutions.

6. a) Write a balanced equation for the reaction of sodium with water.
   b) What would be seen as this reaction occurred?
   c) To what class of chemical reactions does this belong?
   d) Describe how the change in the character of this reaction can be used to compare the reactivity of sodium with those of lithium and potassium.

7. Give the colours of the following:

   a) Iodine vapour.
   b) The precipitate initially formed when aqueous barium chloride reacts with aqueous silver nitrate.
   c) The colour this changes to when exposed to sunlight for a long time.
   d) The colour of the solution when chlorine is bubbled through aqueous sodium bromide.
   e) The precipitate formed by the reaction of aqueous solutions of lead(II) nitrate and potassium iodide.

8. When aqueous silver nitrate is added to a colourless aqueous bromide solution, in the presence of excess nitric acid, an off–white precipitate forms. The experimenter assumes that this shows the presence of bromide ions in the solution.

   a) If this is the case, write a balanced ionic equation for the formation of the precipitate.

   A colleague suggests that this would also be the expected result if the solution had contained a mixture of chloride and iodide ions.

   b) How could the experimenter test his colleague's hypothesis? Describe what s/he should do, and give the results you would expect for both the bromide ion and the mixture of chloride and iodide ions. Write balanced equations for any reactions that you describe.

CORE

9. For each of the following pairs, state whether a reaction would or would not occur on mixing, explaining your reasoning. In cases where a reaction does occur, write an ionic equation for the reaction and state any colour change you would expect to see.

   a) chlorine and aqueous sodium bromide.
   b) bromine and aqueous potassium fluoride.
   c) bromine and aqueous calcium iodide.
   d) iodine and aqueous magnesium bromide.

10. Properties of the elements and their compounds often show regular variations with respect to their position in the periodic table.

   a) Describe the general trend in acid–base character of the oxides of the elements in the third period (Na to Ar). Give one example each of an acidic oxide and a basic oxide and show with equations how these oxides react with water.
   b) How does the oxidising strength of the halogens vary down the group? Account for this trend.
   c) How does the reducing strength (i.e. the ability to donate electrons) of the alkali metals vary down the group? Account for this trend.

HIGHER LEVEL

13.1 TRENDS ACROSS PERIOD 3 (AHL)

13.1.1 Explain the physical states (under standard conditions) and the electrical conductivity (in the molten state) of the chlorides and oxides of the elements in period 3 in terms of their bonding and structure.

13.1 .2 Describe the reactions of chlorine and the chlorides referred to in 13.1.1 with water.

AHL

The position of the elements in the periodic table is related to the type of chemical bonding that occurs in their compounds, which in turn has an effect on the formulas and properties of the compounds. The physical properties that result from different types of chemical bonding are more fully discussed in chapter 4 and this should be referred to when reading this section.

OXIDES OF PERIOD 3

As the number of valence electrons increases, going across the period there is a steady increase in the number of electrons available for bond formation and hence in the number of oxygen atoms that each element bonds to. The formulas of the highest oxides of the period 3 elements display distinct periodicity, with each successive element bonding to an extra half oxygen – Na_2O, MgO, Al_2O_3, SiO_2, P_4O_{10} (equivalent to P_2O_5), SO_3, Cl_2O_7 .(see Figure 315 & 316) Often at the right of the periodic table more than one oxide exists and these contain the element in different oxidation states. For example phosphorus can form phosphorus(III) oxide (P_4O_6; P in a +3 oxidation state) as well as phosphorus(V) oxide (P_4O_{10}; P in a +5 oxidation state). Similarly sulfur forms sulfur dioxide (SO_2; +4 state) as well as sulfur trioxide (SO_3; +6 state),whereas chlorine forms dichlorine monoxide(Cl_2O; +1 state) and the explosive chlorine dioxide (ClO_2 +4 state), as well as dichlorine heptoxide (Cl_2O_7; +7 state).

The oxides of the elements on the left of the periodic table (Na and Mg) are ionically bonded and hence are solids with high melting and boiling points. In the centre of the periodic table silicon dioxide exists as a giant covalent lattice in which each atom is joined to all the others by strong covalent bonds. As a result it is a solid with very high melting and boiling points. To the right of the period, molecular covalent bonding occurs, so that the compounds are gases, liquids or low melting point solids as a result of the relatively weak forces that exist between the molecules. The molten oxides of the first two elements (sodium and magnesium) can conduct owing to the presence of mobile ions in the liquid, but the oxides of the non-metals do not conduct in the liquid state. Aluminium oxide shows characteristics of both ionic and covalent bonding. It has an exceptionally high melting point and is a poor conductor of electricity in the liquid phase.

The acid-base properties of the oxides of period 3 were described in the previous section.

CHLORIDES OF PERIOD 3

The formulas of the highest chlorides of the period 3 elements also display a marked periodicity, though this is not as complete as that displayed by the oxides (see Figure 316). Going across the period each element bonds to one more chlorine – NaCl, $MgCl_2$, $AlCl_3$ (more correctly written as Al_2Cl_6 in its gaseous state), $SiCl_4$ and PCl_5. Once again at the right hand side other chlorides exist in which the element has a different oxidation state, for example PCl_3 (P in a +3 state) exists as well as PCl_5 (P in a +5 state).

The chlorides of metals, such as sodium chloride and magnesium chloride, are ionically bonded, crystalline solids with high melting points. When added to water these chlorides dissolve without chemical reaction, to give solutions in which the component ions can behave independently.

$$NaCl\,(s) \xrightarrow[\text{water}]{} Na^+\,(aq) + Cl^-\,(aq)$$

Even though aluminium is a metal the behaviour of many of its compounds, especially when anhydrous, is more typical of non–metals. This is a result of the small size and high charge of the ion that aluminium forms. Aluminium chloride for example, although a solid, sublimes at the surprisingly low temperature of 178 °C to give a vapour consisting mainly of Al_2Cl_6 molecules. When added to water, anhydrous aluminium chloride undergoes vigorous hydrolysis (that is splitting by the action of water) in which the bonds between aluminium and chlorine are broken and a stongly acidic solution is formed.

$$AlCl_3\,(s) + 3H_2O\,(l) \longrightarrow Al(OH)_3\,(s) + 3H^+\,(aq) + 3Cl^-\,(aq)$$

Even hydrated aluminium chloride produces quite acidic solutions owing to the dissociation of the water molecules associated with the small, highly charged, Al^{3+} ion.

The giant convalent structure, found for the oxides of the elements in the middle of the period, is not generally found for the chlorides because chlorine usually forms only one bond, making an extended lattice impossible. The chlorides of non–metals, such as silicon tetrachloride and the chlorides of phosphorus, all have molecular covalent structures. As a result of the weak forces between their molecules these compounds have low melting and boiling points. When added to water a hydrolysis reaction occurs, in which the bonds between the element and chlorine are replaced by bonds between the element and oxygen. The result is an acidic solution containing hydrogen ions, chloride ions and the oxide, or an oxyacid of the element. For example with silicon tetrachloride:

$$SiCl_4\,(l) + 2\,H_2O(l) \longrightarrow SiO_2\,(s) + 4\,H^+(aq) + 4\,Cl^-(aq)$$

In the case of the chlorides of phosphorus, such as phosphorus trichloride (or phosphorus(III) chloride), the oxyacid formed also dissociates:

$$PCl_3\,(l) + 3\,H_2O(l) \longrightarrow P(OH)_3\,(aq) + 3\,H^+(aq) + 3\,Cl^-(aq)$$

$P(OH)_3$ or H_3PO_3 is phosphoric(III) acid; a weak acid that partially dissociates as shown:

$$H_3PO_3\,(aq) \rightleftharpoons H^+\,(aq) + H_2PO_3^-\,(aq)$$

Similarly with phosphorus pentachloride (or phosphorus(V) chloride),

$$PCl_5\,(s) + 4H_2O\,(l) \longrightarrow H_3PO_4\,(aq) + 5H^+\,(aq) + 5Cl^-\,(aq)$$

H_3PO_4 is phosphoric(V) acid; a strong acid that fully dissociates as shown below.

$$H_3PO_4\,(aq) \longrightarrow H^+\,(aq) + H_2PO_4^-\,(aq)$$

Chlorine itself (Cl_2), which may be regarded as "chlorine chloride", fits in with this pattern of behaviour, being a molecular covalent substance that reacts with water in an analogous hydrolysis reaction.

Because of the presence of mobile ions, sodium and magnesium chlorides conduct electricity when molten or in aqueous solution. The chlorides of the remaining elements of period 3 do not conduct electricity in the molten state, as would be expected for molecular covalent compounds. In aqueous solution however they do conduct electricity because of the ions formed in the chemical reactions above.

The trends in the properties of the elements, chlorides and oxides of the elements from sodium to chlorine are summarised in Figure 316.

AHL

Element	Na	Mg	Al	Si	P	S	Cl
Bonding	Metallic			Giant covalent	Molecular covalent		
Chloride							
Formula	NaCl	$MgCl_2$	$AlCl_3$	$SiCl_4$	PCl_5 PCl_3	Complex	Cl_2
Bonding	Ionic		Intermediate	Molecular covalent			
Oxide							
Formula	Na_2O	MgO	Al_2O_3	SiO_2	P_4O_{10} P_4O_6	SO_3 SO_2	Cl_2O_7 Cl_2O
Bonding	Ionic		Intermediate	Giant covalent	Molecular covalent		
Acid/base properties	Sol. basic	Insol. basic	Amphoteric	Insol. acidic	Soluble acidic		

Figure 316 The period 3 elements, their chlorides and their oxides

Exercise 13.1

1. Going across the third period of the periodic table, there is a steady change in the formulae of the oxides formed. Which one of the following oxides is not an example of this trend?

   A Al_2O_3
   B Na_2O
   C SO_2
   D P_4O_{10}

2. Hydrolysis is a reaction in which

   A water adds on to a molecule.
   B water splits up a molecule.
   C water is a product.
   D water acts as a catalyst.

3. a) When sodium chloride is added to water the resulting solution is a good electrical conductor. The same is true of the solution formed when phosphorus trichloride is added to water, but for slightly different reasons. Explain this behaviour, writing equations for any reactions involved.

   b) Given a sample of the two solutions produced by adding these two chlorides to water describe, giving the results that would be observed,

      i a test to show that both contained the chloride ion.
      ii a test that would tell which solution was formed from which chloride.

4. The oxides of the elements in the third period show a trend in acid-base properties going across the period. Choose specific examples of three oxides, one basic, one amphoteric and one acidic, then use these examples to illustrate this trend, writing balanced equations for any chemical reactions involved.

5. There is a trend in the chemical character of the elements in the third period (Na to Ar). Describe this briefly with respect to the bonding present in the element and its chloride. Explain these in terms of trends that occur in atomic properties such as nuclear charge, ionization energy and electronegativity.

AHL

13.2 FIRST ROW D-BLOCK ELEMENTS (AHL)

13.2.1 List the characteristic properties of transition elements.

13.2.2 Explain why Sc and Zn are not considered to be transition elements.

The **d-block elements** are those that occur in the central block of the periodic table, i.e the groups headed by the elements scandium to zinc, in which the d-subshell of an atom is being filled with electrons. A subset of these elements, known as the **transition elements**, are those in which the element has a partially filled d-sublevel in one of its common oxidation states.

The elements of the d-block are all dense, hard metallic elements. The electronic structures differ by the addition of one more d-electrons for each successive element, but note the two exceptional electronic structures of chromium and copper. In these elements there is only one electron present in the 4s sublevel, with the 'missing' electron being present in the 3d sublevel so as to gain the additional stability associated with a half filled and fully filled d-sublevel respectively. This again shows how similar in energy the 3d and 4s sublevels are.

Since the 3d electrons quite effectively shield the outer 4s electrons, the first ionization energy remains relatively constant. As a result the d-block elements have many similar chemical and physical characteristics. The ease with which the 3d electrons are lost decreases as the nuclear charge increases, resulting in a trend from the maximum oxidation state being the most stable at the start of the series to the +2 oxidation state being the most stable at the end. As a result of their partially filled d-sublevel, the transition metals have certain properties in common, which are not generally shared by other metals (including Sc and Zn), some of these are:

- a variety of stable oxidation states
- the ability to form complex ions
- the formation of coloured ions
- catalytic activity

Element	Sc	Ti	V	Cr	Mn	Fe	Co	Ni	Cu	Zn
Electronic structure	[Ar] $3d^1 4s^2$	[Ar] $3d^2 4s^2$	[Ar] $3d^3 4s^2$	[Ar] $3d^5 4s^1$	[Ar] $3d^5 4s^2$	[Ar] $3d^6 4s^2$	[Ar] $3d^7 4s^2$	[Ar] $3d^8 4s^2$	[Ar] $3d^{10} 4s^1$	[Ar] $3d^{10} 4s^2$

Decreasing stability of maximum oxidation state →

Increasing stability of +2 oxidation state →

Figure 318 Electronic structure and oxidation state stability of the d-block elements (first row)

13.2.3 Explain the existence of variable oxidation number in ions of transition elements.

VARIABLE OXIDATION STATES

The **s-block metals**, such as sodium and calcium, have s–electrons that are easily lost, but the ionization energies for the inner electrons are so high that these are never lost in chemical reactions, as shown in Figure 319 for calcium. For this reason they always have the same oxidation states in their compounds +1 for group 1 and +2 for group 2. Transition metals have slightly higher effective nuclear charges and so their first ionization energies are a little higher, but there is no sudden increase in successive ionization energies in the same way as there is with the s–block elements (until all the 3d and 4s electrons have been lost), as can be seen for chromium in Figure 319. This is because the 3d and 4s electrons have similar energies. The oxidation state of transition metals therefore depends on how strongly oxidising the environment is, which depends on the presence of species that readily gain electrons.

It can be seen by referring to Table 320, that one of the most commonly found oxidation states of transition metals is the +2 state which corresponds to the loss of the two 4s electrons. This is a very stable state on the right of the d–block where the high nuclear charge increases the difference in energy between the 3d and 4s electrons, but becomes an increasingly powerful reductant going to the left. Ti^{2+}, for example, does not exist in aqueous solution because it reduces water to hydrogen. The second commonly found oxidation state, going as far as manganese, is that which corresponds to the loss of all the 3d and 4s valence electrons (+3 for Sc; +4 for Ti etc.). These are stable on the left of the d–block, but become increasingly powerful oxidants going across the period as the energy required to produce these states becomes quite high (see Fig. 319). The highest oxidation states usually occur as oxyanions, such as dichromate(VI) ($Cr_2O_7^{2-}$) and permanganate (also referred to as manganate(VII); (MnO_4^-). There are also a few other commonly encountered states, such as Cr^{3+} and Fe^{3+}, which do not fit into this pattern. These common oxidation states are summarised in Table 320.

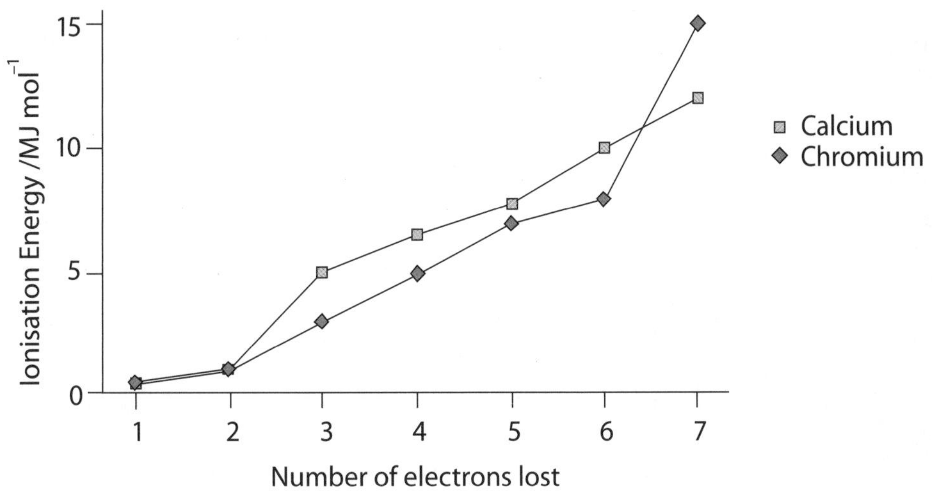

Figure 319 The successive ionisation energies of calcium and chromium

AHL

TOK The historical development of the Periodic Table

Although the periodic table, in its modern form, is organised in terms of atomic numbers and electronic structure, it originated from a study of the periodicity of chemical properties. No sooner had theoretical chemistry been put on a sound footing in the early 18th century by the recognition of the elements as fundamental building blocks, through the work of Boyle, Lavoisier and Dalton, and the determination of the relative atomic masses of these, especially by Berzelius and Cannizzaro, than chemists started to notice that certain elements had very similar chemical properties. Döbereiner noticed that if three elements had similar chemical properties then one element often had a relative atomic mass approximately mid–way between the other two. Examples of this are Li (7), Na (23), K (39) and Cl (35), Br (80), I (127). Döbereiner named these groups 'triads'. Newlands then noticed that every eighth element, when placed in order of increasing relative atomic mass, showed similar chemical properties and referred to these as 'octaves'. The examples given above fit in with this as do many others (note the noble gases had not been discovered at this date). There were however still many anomalies, for example copper was in the same group as sodium and potassium!

The name most closely associated with the periodic table is undoubtedly that of Mendeléev. He extended and rearranged Newland's table, separating groups into two subgroups that gave better correspondence with chemical properties. Another innovation was that he left gaps in the table to improve the fit, and predicted that elements would be discovered to fit these gaps. The early ones correspond to the elements we now know as scandium, gallium and germanium. Mendeléev gave detailed predictions of the physical and chemical properties that he expected these undiscovered elements to have and his predictions proved to be remarkably accurate – a classic example of scientific methodology in action. Mendeléev's periodic table is shown in Table 17 below with his gaps marked by stars (*):

The modern periodic table is similar to that of Mendeléev, except that the elements have been re–ordered according to atomic number (otherwise argon would be classified as an alkali metal!), the noble gases have been added and the d– and f–block metals have been collected together as separate groups in the centre of the table.

Series	Group 1	Group 2	Group 3	Group 4	Group 5	Group 6	Group 7	Group 8
1	H							
2	Li	Be	B	C	N	O	F	
3	Na	Mg	Al	Si	P	S	Cl	
4	K	Ca	*	Ti	V	Cr	Mn	Fe,Co,Ni
5	Cu	Zn	*	*	As	Se	Br	
6	Rb	Sr	Y	Zr	Nb	Mo	*	Ru,Rh,Pd
7	Ag	Cd	In	Sn	Sb	Te	I	
8	Cs	Ba	Dy	Ce	*	*	*	
9	*	*	*	*	*	*	*	
10	*	*	Er	La	Ta	W	*	Os,Ir,Pt
11	Au	Hg	Tl	Pb	Bi	*	*	
12	*	*	*	Th	*	U		

Figure 317 Mendeléev's Periodic Table

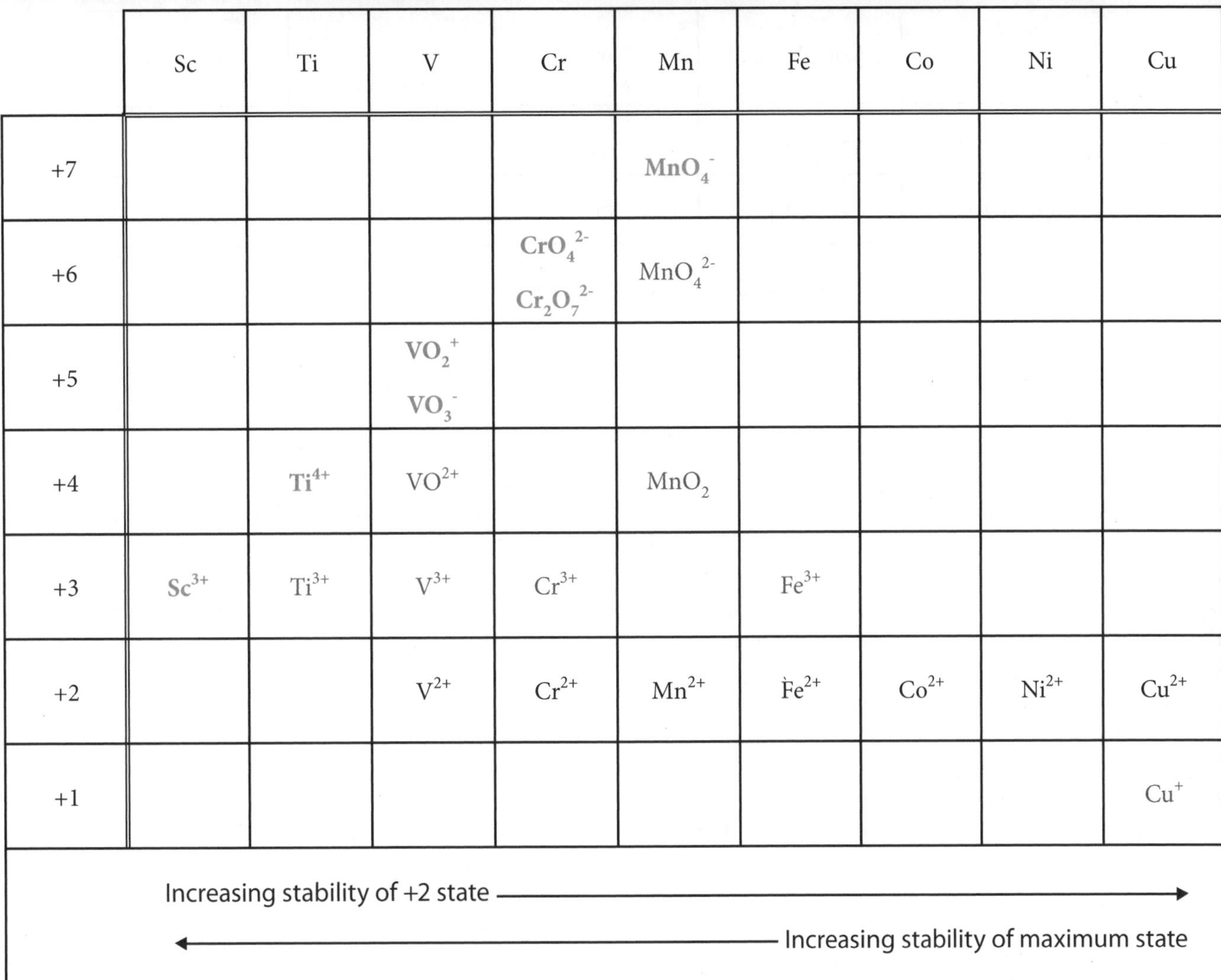

	Sc	Ti	V	Cr	Mn	Fe	Co	Ni	Cu
+7					MnO_4^-				
+6				CrO_4^{2-} $Cr_2O_7^{2-}$	MnO_4^{2-}				
+5			VO_2^+ VO_3^-						
+4		Ti^{4+}	VO^{2+}		MnO_2				
+3	Sc^{3+}	Ti^{3+}	V^{3+}	Cr^{3+}		Fe^{3+}			
+2			V^{2+}	Cr^{2+}	Mn^{2+}	Fe^{2+}	Co^{2+}	Ni^{2+}	Cu^{2+}
+1									Cu^+

Increasing stability of +2 state →

← Increasing stability of maximum state

Figure 320 Common oxidation states of the d–block elements

Note that the variety of oxidation states increases to a maximum at manganese and in the second half of the d–block far fewer oxidation states are found because the greater nuclear charge causes an increase in the ionization energies of the 3d electrons. The stability of the half– filled and fully filled 3d level (encountered before in the unusual electronic structures of Cr and Cu) also affects the stability of oxidation states. In manganese the +2 state, which has a half filled shell ([Ar]$3d^5$), is much more stable than the +3 ([Ar]$3d^4$) state and the +4 ([Ar]$3d^3$) state (usually only encountered as manganese(IV) oxide, MnO^2), which are therefore quite strong oxidants. With iron however the reverse is true because it is the +3 state that has the half filled shell ([Ar]$3d^5$) and the +2 state ([Ar]$3d^6$) is quite strongly reducing. In copper, the existence of the +1 state is due to the stability of the filled shell ([Ar]$3d^{10}$). Note that because the Cu^+ ion has a full 3d sub–shell, like Zn^{2+}, its compounds are not coloured.

13.2.4 Define the term 'ligand'.

13.2.5 Describe and explain the formation of complexes of d–block elements.

THE FORMATION OF COMPLEX IONS

The ions of d–block metals and those in the lower section of the p–block (such as lead) have low energy unfilled d– and p–orbitals. These orbitals can accept a lone pair of electrons from species, known as ligands, to form a dative bond between the ligand and the metal ion. For example an ammonia molecule can donate its non-bonding electron pair to a copper(II) ion.

	Complex Ion	Charge on Complex Ion	Oxidation State of Metal Ion	Similar to
$[Cu(NH_3)_4]Cl_2$	$[Cu(NH_3)_4]^{2+}$	2+	+2	$CaCl_2$
$[K_2(CuCl_4)]$	$(CuCl_4)^{2-}$	2-	+2	K_2SO_4

Figure 322 Two compounds of complex ions

This behaviour, in which one species donates an electron pair whilst another accepts it, is **Lewis acid–base** behaviour. Species which contain ligands bonded to a central metal ion are known as complex ions, a common example being the deep blue complex ion $[Cu(NH_3)_4]^{2+}$ formed when excess aqueous ammonia is added to a solution of a copper(II) salt. Note that the complex ion is written in square brackets. The charge is the sum of the charge on the central metal ion and the charges on the ligands. For example the charge on the $[CoCl_4]^{2-}$ ion is the sum of the +2 charge on the cobalt and the four –1 charges on the chloride ions (+2 – 4 = –2).

Ligands are species that can donate a pair of non-bonding electrons to the central metal ion in the complex; the most common examples are water, ammonia, chloride ion and cyanide ion. Most complex ions have either six ligands arranged octahedrally around the central atom (usually found with water and ammonia ligands), or four ligands arranged tetrahedrally (usually found with chloride ion ligands), though some examples of linear complex ions with a two ligands are found. These are illustrated in Figure 321.

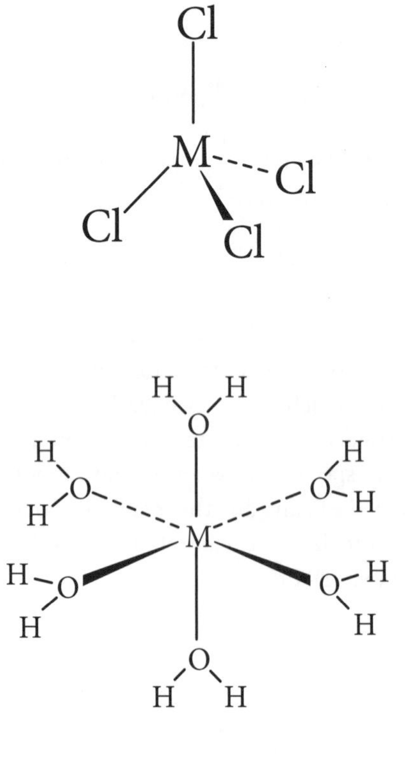

Cl
M
Cl Cl Cl

H H O H O H H O H M H O H O H H O H H

Figure 321 Tetrahedral and octahedral complex ions

The number of ligands around the central ion is known as the coordination number of the complex ion, hence the coordination number of the metal ion in the ammine is 2, in the chloroanion is 4 and in the aqua ion is 6. The term "coordination number" also has a similar use in describing crystal structures.

Complex ions can have either a positive charge (∴ cations) or a negative charge (∴anions) and hence form salts with ions of the opposite charge as illustrated in Figure 322 above. Both complexes are water soluble and conduct electricity in aqueous solution. Some complex ions are however neutral because the charge on the metal ion and the ligands cancel. An example would be $[Pt(NH_3)_2Cl_2]$. Being uncharged this is almost insoluble and behaves as a molecular species. With aqueous silver nitrate it does not form a precipitate showing that in the complex ion the chloride ions are strongly bonded to the central metal ion and are not free to react with the silver ions (see also the chromium(III) species in Figure 324).

The formation of complex ions stabilises certain oxidation states and hence affects the $E^{\ominus}$ value of the related redox system. For example the value for the $[Fe(H_2O)_6]^{+}$/ $[Fe(H_2O)_6]^{2+}$ couple is +0.77 V, whereas that for the $Fe(CN)_6^{3-}$/ $Fe(CN)_6^{4-}$ couple is +0.36V, in other words the presence of the cyanide ligand stabilises the iron(III) state. The formation of a complex ion can also have a major effect on the colour of a metal ion in solution. Aqueous cobalt(II) salts, for example contain the hexaaquacobalt(II) ion, which is a pink colour. If concentrated hydrochloric acid is added to this, the solution turns blue owing to the formation of the tetrachlorocobalt(II) ion:

$$[Co(H_2O)_6]^{2+}(aq) + 4Cl^-(aq) \rightleftharpoons [CoCl_4]^{2-}(aq) + 6H_2O\,(l)$$

Pink Blue

This is an example of a ligand exchange reaction. For most transition metal ions, such as cobalt(II) and copper(II)

Metal ion	Water Octahedral	Ammonia Octahedral/Sq. planar	Chloride ion Tetrahedral
Cobalt(II)	Pink $[Co(H_2O)_6]^{2+}$	Straw $[Co(NH_3)_6]^{2+}$	Blue $[CoCl_4]^{2-}$
Nickel(II)	Green $[Ni(H_2O)_6]^{2+}$	Blue $[Ni(NH_3)_6]^{2+}$	Yellow-green $[NiCl_4]^{2-}$
Copper(II)	Blue $[Cu(H_2O)_6]^{2+}$	Deep blue $[Cu(NH_3)_4]^{2+}$	Yellow $[CuCl_4]^{2-}$

Figure 323 Some common complex ions and their colours

ligand replacement takes place freely in aqueous solution, but for others, such as chromium(III) and cobalt(III) there is a significant activation energy barrier to this, hence the complex ion is unusually stable, as for example the chromium(III) complex ions given in Figure 324.

Some examples of common complex ions and their colours are given Figure 323.

ISOMERISM IN COMPLEX IONS

Complex ions exhibit many types of **isomerism** analogous to those found with organic compounds. Firstly there is formula isomerism (analogous to structural isomerism) associated with which species are acting as ligands and hence directly bonded to the metal ion. There are for example three forms of chromium(III) chloride hexahydrate that vary in the way the chloride ions are bonded. Because the bonding of the ligand to the metal ion is very stable in this case, the number of chloride ions present as free chloride ions can be found by titration with aqueous silver nitrate. These isomers are summerised in Figure 324 below:

Stereoisomerism also occurs in complex ions. The simplest examples of geometric isomerism occurs in square planar transition metal complexes such as $Pt(NH_3)_2Cl_2$ (note that as it contains Pt^{2+}, this is an electrically neutral complex), which exists in both *cis*– and *trans*– forms:

Geometric isomerism can also occur in six coordinate octahedral complexes such as $[Co(NH_3)_4Cl_2]^+$ depending

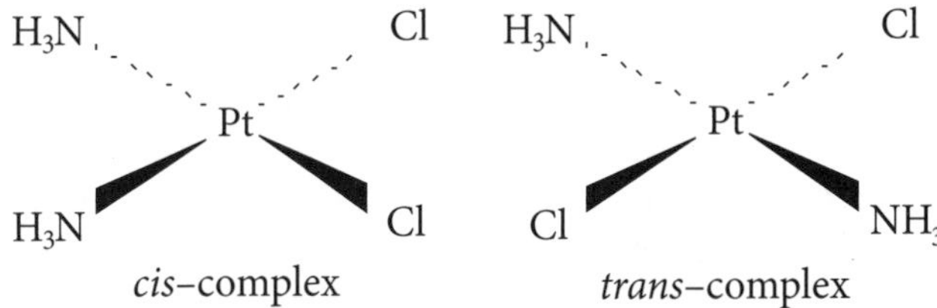

Figure 325 cis- and trans- forms

on whether the two chloride ligands occupy adjacent (*cis*) or opposite (*trans*) sites.

The ligands considered up to now can only form one bond to the metal ion, they are monodentate ligands. With bidentate ligands (i.e. those that can form two rather than one bond to a metal ion) such as diaminoethane

Formula	Colour	Amount of chloride precipitated by $Ag^+(aq)$
$[Cr(H_2O)_4Cl_2]^+Cl^-.2H_2O$	Dark green	1 mol
$[Cr(H_2O)_5Cl]^{2+}(Cl^-)_2.H_2O$	Light green	2 mol
$[Cr(H_2O)_6]^{3+}(Cl^-)_3$	Grey-blue	3 mol

Figure 324 Isomers of hydrated chromium(III) chloride hexahydrate

($H_2N-CH_2-CH_2-NH_2$ shown as N⌒N below) non-superimposable mirror image forms can occur, giving rise to enantiomerism. An example is the complex ion $[Co(H_2N-CH_2-CH_2-NH_2)_3]^{3+}$, shown below:

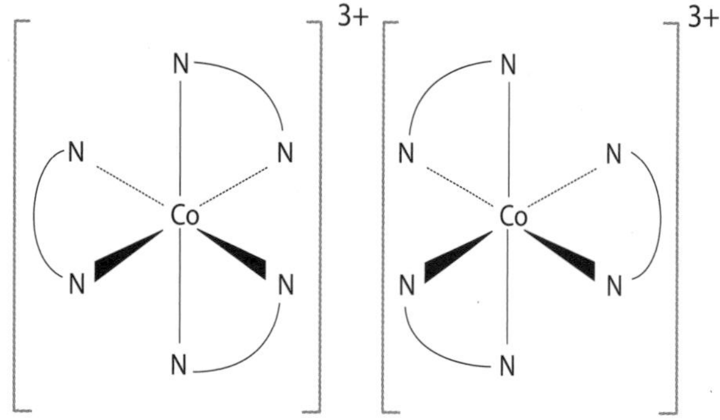

Figure 326 The two enantiomers of the complex ion $[Co(H_2N-CH_2-CH_2-NH_2)_3]^{3+}$

AHL

13.2.6 Explain why some complexes of d-block elements are coloured.

Coloured ions

In an isolated atom all of the d-orbitals have exactly the same energy, but if an atom or ion is surrounded by charged ions or polar molecules, the effect of the electric field from these has a different effect on the various d-orbitals. Because of their symmetry the orbitals are often split up into two different groups. For octahedral complex ions three orbitals are at low energy and two orbitals at higher energy. The difference in energy between these two groups of orbitals varies slightly with the nature of the species surrounding the metal ion, but the frequency of the light corresponding to this (linked by the formula $\Delta E = h.f$) occurs in the visible region. This means that when white light passes through a compound of a transition metal, light of a particular frequency is absorbed and an electron is promoted from a lower energy orbital to a higher energy orbital, as shown in the Figure 327 below.

The light that passes through therefore appears coloured because some of the frequencies have been absorbed. In the case of most copper(II) compounds, red and yellow light are absorbed so that they look a blue-green colour, that is. we see the transmitted light which is the complementary colour of the absorbed light. The exact shade depends slightly on the species surrounding the copper, so that the hexaaquacopper(II) ion is light blue but the tetraamminecopper(II) ion is dark blue.

If there are no electrons in the d-orbitals, as is the case for Sc^{3+} and Ti^{4+}, then there are no d-electrons to move and the compounds are colourless. If the d-orbitals are all completely filled, as is the case with Zn^{2+}, then there are no vacant orbitals for the electrons to move into and again the compounds are colourless.

13.2.7 State examples of the catalytic action of transition elements and their compounds.

13.2.8 Outline the economic significance of catalysts in the Contact and Haber processes.

Catalytic activity

The catalytic behaviours of **transition metals** and their ions are mainly caused by a combination of two properties already mentioned. Firstly they form complex ions with species that can donate lone pairs of electrons. This results in close contact between the different ligands, as well as between the metal and the ligand. Secondly transition metal ions have a wide variety of relatively stable oxidation states, so they can readily gain and lose electrons in redox reactions.

d-block element catalysts can either be heterogeneous or homogeneous, though the former are more common. Many enzymes involved in catalysing redox reactions also contain transition metal ions near the active site (refer to Chapter 13). In a heterogeneous catalyst the surface of the metal or compound provides an active surface on which the reaction can occur with a reduced activation energy. A common example of heterogeneous catalysis is

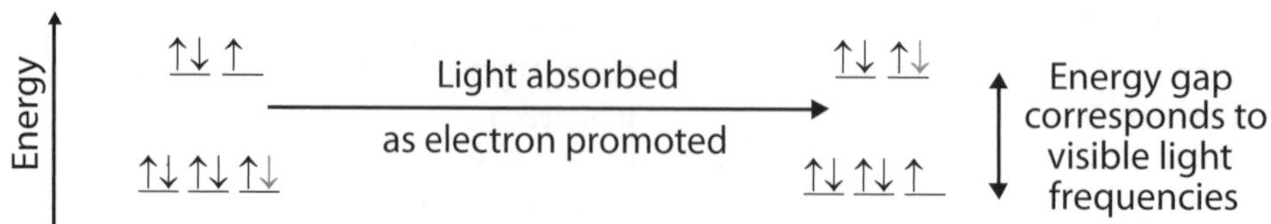

Figure 327 The interaction between transition metal ions and light

manganese(IV) oxide which catalyses the decomposition of hydrogen peroxide to water and oxygen.

$$2H_2O_2(aq) \xrightarrow{MnO_2} 2H_2O(l) + O_2(g)$$

Another example is nickel catalysing the reaction between hydrogen and an alkene to produce an alkane.

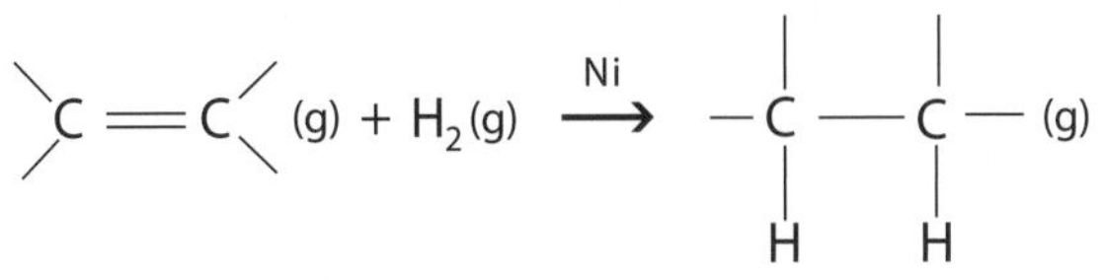

$$>C{=}C< (g) + H_2(g) \xrightarrow{Ni} -\overset{|}{\underset{H}{C}}-\overset{|}{\underset{H}{C}}- (g)$$

Figure 328 Production of an alkane

Here bonding to the metal surface not only brings the molecules into close contact, but also electrons from the bonds are used to bond to the metal atoms. This weakens the bonds in the molecules and lowers the activation energy.

Platinum and palladium are found in the catalytic converters fitted to the exhaust systems of cars to reduce the emission of pollutants such as carbon monoxide and oxides of nitrogen, e.g.

$$2\,CO + 2\,NO \xrightarrow{Pd/Pt} 2\,CO_2 + N_2$$

Many other important industrial catalysts involve transition metals, such as iron in the **Haber process** and vanadium(V) oxide in the **Contact process**.

$$\text{Haber process: } N_2(g) + 3H_2(g) \overset{Fe}{\rightleftharpoons} 2NH_3(g)$$

$$\text{Contact process: } 2SO_2(g) + O_2(g) \overset{V_2O_5}{\rightleftharpoons} 2SO_3(g)$$

The economic importance of the chemical industry rests on the food, clothes, medicines and the great variety of consumer articles that it produces. One of the signs of the economic development of a country is the state of its chemical industry because the chemical industry can take essentially simple and often cheap raw materials and turn them into much more valuable products. For example, the Haber process which exploits the 'free' supply of nitrogen (it still costs money to extract the nitrogen) from the atmosphere and converts it into ammonia and then into explosives upon which wars and conflicts have become dependent (the commercialization of this process likely prolonged World War I by at least one year). It is also vital in the production of fertilizers that are now vital for our supply of food. Nitrogen is an element vital for plant growth, so the major use of ammonia is in the manufacture of fertilizers such as ammonium salts and urea. It is also used in the manufacture of nitrogen containing polymers such as nylon.

Sulfuric acid is considered the "king of chemicals" and is relatively easy to produce. Sulfuric acid has numerous uses in the chemical industry – indeed the tonnage of it used annually gives a good indication of the extent of a country's chemical industry. These uses include manufacture of fertilizers (especially converting insoluble phosphate rock to soluble 'superphosphate'), polymers, detergents, paints and pigments. It is also widely used in the petrochemicals industry and in the industrial processing of metals. One of its minor, though possibly most familiar uses, is as the electrolyte in automobile batteries.

In homogeneous catalysis, the catalyst is in the same phase as the reactants. In these reactions a particular metal ion is oxidised in one stage and then reformed by being reduced in a second stage. A good example is the role of iron(II)/(III) in catalysing the slow reaction between acidified hydrogen peroxide and iodide ions. The iron(II) is oxidised by the peroxide to iron(III).

$$H_2O_2(aq) + 2H^+(aq) + 2Fe^{2+}(aq) \longrightarrow 2H_2O(l) + 2Fe^{3+}(aq)$$

This is then reduced by the iodide ions to reform iron(II).

$$2I^-(aq) + 2Fe^{3+}(aq) \longrightarrow I_2(s) + 2Fe^{2+}(aq)$$

These reactions occur more rapidly than the direct reaction because they both have lower activation energies than the direct reaction.

Examples of enzymes containing transition metals include the presence of iron in heme, the active part of haemoglobin responsible for carrying oxygen in the blood, and of cobalt in vitamin B12 which is vital factor in the production of red blood cells as well as having other functions. The structures of these two enzymes are given in Figures 329 and 330.

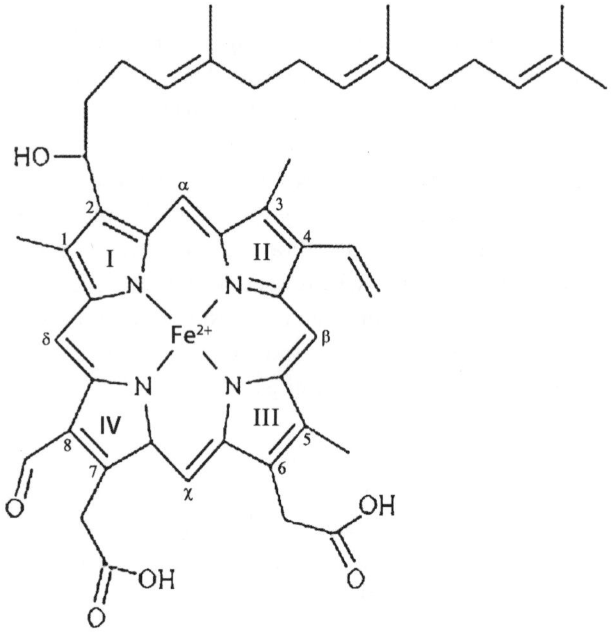

Figure 329 The structure of a heme group from cytochrome oxidase

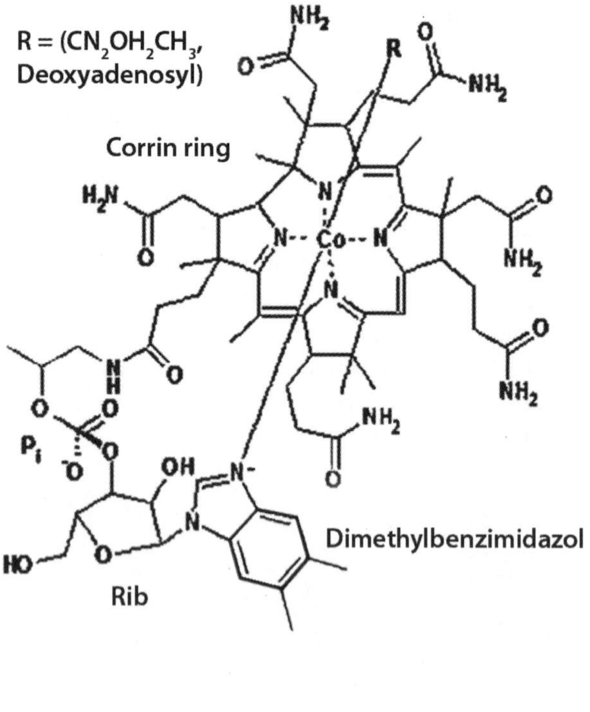

Figure 330 The structure of Vitamin B12

EXTENSION

The chemistry of individual

TRANSITION METAL ELEMENTS

Titanium has an electronic structure [Ar] $3d^2\ 4s^2$. Titanium is actually a component of a number of quite common minerals. It is however relatively difficult to extract from these, hence the high price of the metal. Nevertheless because of its low density, high strength and corrosion resistance it finds widespread use in the aerospace industry. Its most common oxidation state in compounds is the +4 state and, as titanium dioxide (found naturally as rutile), it finds widespread use as a white pigment in paint and cosmetic products. The easily hydrolysed tetrachloride is employed as a catalyst in the Ziegler-Natta polymerisation of alkenes. Titanium(III) ions, produced by reducing titanium(IV) compounds with zinc, are powerful reductants in aqueous solution and titanium(II) is so powerfully reducing it will reduce water to hydrogen.

Vanadium has an electronic structure [Ar] $3d^3\ 4s^2$ and can exist in a variety of oxidation states from +2 to +5, the higher ones existing as various oxy-ions. For example vanadium(V) can exist as VO_2^+ and VO_3^-, as well as the more familiar vanadium(V) oxide (V_2O_5, used as a catalyst in the Contact process). If zinc is added to an acidic solution of the yellow vanadate(V) ion (VO_3^-) a notable series of colour changes take place as it is reduced firstly to blue vanadium(IV), then to green vanadium(III) and finally to the lavender coloured vanadium(II). These lower oxidation states are gradually more powerful reductants.

Chromium has an electronic structure [Ar] $3d^5\ 4s^1$ (n.b. like copper an exception in only having one 4s electron). Its common oxidation states are +3 and +6. Compounds of chromium(III), such as chromium(III) oxide, Cr_2O_3, and the hexaaquachromium(III) ion, $[Cr(H_2O)_6]^{3+}$, are usually a dark green colour. Dark green chromium(III) hydroxide is precipitated when aqueous alkali is added to solutions of chromium(III) salts. Like aluminium hydroxide, it is amphoteric and redissolves in high concentrations of hydroxide ions to give a dark green solution containing the chromate(III) ion (also called chromite):

$$Cr^{3+}\,(aq) + 3OH^-\,(aq) \longrightarrow Cr(OH)_3\,(s)$$

$$Cr(OH)_3\,(s) + OH^-\,(aq) \longrightarrow Cr(OH)_4^-\,(aq)$$

The common compounds of chromium(VI) are the dark red–brown oxide, CrO_3^- which in many ways resembles SO_3, as well as the yellow chromate(VI), CrO_4^{2-}, and orange dichromate(VI), $Cr_2O_7^{2-}$, ions derived from it.

$$2CrO_3(s) + H_2O(l) \longrightarrow 2H^+(aq) + Cr_2O_7^{2-}(aq)$$

The chromate(VI) and dichromate(VI) ions are in an acid–base equilibrium. If acid is added to the yellow chromate, then the equilibrium shifts to the right to give the orange dichromate. This change can be reversed by adding an alkali:

$$\underset{\text{Yellow}}{2\,H^+(aq) + 2\,CrO_4^{2-}(aq)} \rightleftharpoons \underset{\text{Orange}}{Cr_2O_7^{2-}(aq)} + H_2O(l)$$

The dichromate(VI) ion is a strong oxidant in acidic solution, being reduced to the green chromium(III) ion:

$$\underset{\text{Orange}}{Cr_2O_7^{2-}(aq)} + 14\,H^+(aq) + 6\,e^- \longrightarrow \underset{\text{Green}}{2Cr^{3+}(aq)} + 7\,H_2O(l)$$

Manganese has an electronic structure [Ar] $3d^5\ 4s^2$. Its common oxidation states are +2, +4, +6 and +7. The most common manganese(VII) compound is the permanganate ion (or manganate(VII) ion), MnO_4^-, which has a very intense purple colour. It is a very powerful oxidant and the other common oxidation states can be formed by its reduction under various conditions, depending on the pH at which the reaction occurs. In very strongly alkaline conditions, the dark green manganate(VI) ion is the product:

$$MnO_4^-(aq) + e^- \longrightarrow MnO_4^{2-}(aq)$$

In approximately neutral solution, a brown precipitate of manganese(IV) oxide forms:

$$MnO_4^-(aq) + 4H^+(aq) + 3e^- \longrightarrow MnO_2(s) + 2H_2O(l)$$

In acidic solution the almost colourless (in concentrated solution, very pale pink) manganese(II) ion is the product. This reaction is frequently used in titrations to determine the concentrations of easily oxidised species, such as SO_3^{2-} and Fe^{2+}.

$$MnO_4^-(aq) + 8H^+(aq) + 5e^- \longrightarrow Mn^{2+}(aq) + 4H_2O(l)$$

Manganese(IV) oxide is itself a powerful oxidant, for example oxidising concentrated hydrochloric acid to chlorine:

$$MnO_2(s) + 4\,HCl(aq) \longrightarrow MnCl_2(aq) + 2\,H_2O(l) + Cl_2(g)$$

It is most commonly encountered because of its ability to catalyse the decomposition of hydrogen peroxide.

When aqueous alkali is added to solutions of manganese(II) salts a flesh coloured precipitate of manganese(II) hydroxide is formed. This rapidly darkens in the presence of air as manganese(II) hydroxide is oxidised to manganese(III) hydroxide by oxygen in aqueous solution:

$$Mn^{2+}(aq) + 2OH^-(aq) \longrightarrow Mn(OH)_2(s)$$

$$4Mn(OH)_2(s) + 2H_2O(l) + O_2(g) \longrightarrow 4Mn(OH)_3(s)$$

Iron has an electronic structure [Ar] $3d^6\ 4s^2$. Its two common oxidation states are +2 and +3. Iron(II) compounds are usually pale green in colour. Iron(III) compounds usually vary from yellow to brown in colour. The two oxidation states are readily interconverted ($E^\theta = 0.77$ V) so that iron(II) acts as a mild reductant and iron(III) as a mild oxidant:

$$Fe^{3+}(aq) + e^- \rightleftharpoons Fe^{2+}(aq)$$

Oxygen in the air will oxidise iron(II) to iron(III), the higher the pH the faster the reaction. As a result iron(II) compounds are often contaminated with traces of iron(III).

The oxidation state of iron in aqueous solution can be readily detected by adding aqueous alkali until a precipitate of the hydroxide forms. Iron(II) hydroxide is green, though it turns brown on standing as a result of aerial oxidation (similar to that of manganese(II) hydroxide above though the reaction is rather slower), and iron(III) hydroxide is red–brown:

$$Fe^{2+}(aq) + 2OH^-(aq) \longrightarrow \underset{\text{Green precipitate}}{Fe(OH)_2(s)}$$

$$Fe^{3+}(aq) + 3OH^-(aq) \longrightarrow \underset{\text{Red–brown precipitate}}{Fe(OH)_3(s)}$$

When thiocyanate (SCN^-) ions are added to a solution of an iron(III) compound an intense blood–red coloured complex ion is formed. Iron(II) salts, if pure, give no reaction. The major reaction is that shown below, though further ligand exchange is possible and the precise product will depend ion the concentration of thiocyanate ions.

$$[Fe(H_2O)_6]^{3+} + SCN^- \longrightarrow [FeSCN(H_2O)_6]^{2+} + H_2O$$

Cobalt has an electronic structure [Ar] $3d^7\ 4s^2$ and is used in a variety of steels. Its most stable oxidation state is the +2 state, which in dilute aqueous solution exists as the pink $[Co(H_2O)_6]^{2+}$ ion. Adding aqueous alkali to its solutions precipitates out the hydroxide, which though initially blue, slowly changes to a pink colour:

$$Co^{2+}(aq) + 2OH^-(aq) \longrightarrow \underset{\text{Blue, then pink precipitate}}{Co(OH)_2(s)}$$

EXTENSION

When concentrated hydrochloric acid is added to solutions containing the hexaaqua cobalt(II) ion the colour gradually changes from pink through shades of purple, eventually yielding the deep blue tetrachloro ion:

$$\underset{\text{Pink}}{[Co(H_2O)_6]^{2+}(aq)} + 4\,Cl^-(aq) \longrightarrow \underset{\text{Blue}}{[CoCl_4]^{2-}(aq)} + 6\,H_2O(l)$$

The cobalt(III) state also exists but it is generally a powerful oxidant, oxidising water to oxygen in aqueous solution. Ammonia ligands however stabilise the cobalt(III) state so that when aqueous ammonia is added to cobalt(II) compounds the straw coloured solution, formed when the initial green precipitate redissolves, gradually darkens as dissolved oxygen oxidises the cobalt(II) hexammine complex to the cobalt(III) hexammine complex.

$$4\,[Co(NH_3)_6)]^{2+} + O_2 + 2\,H_2O \longrightarrow 4\,[Co(NH_3)_6)]^{3+} + 4\,OH^-$$

In the presence of chloride ions it is also possible to produce an interesting variety of isomers, similar to those given in Figure 324 for complex ions containing chromium(III) with chloride and water ligands, that are kinetically stable to ligand exchange reactions.

Nickel has an electronic structure [Ar] $3d^8\,4s^2$ and its only significant oxidation state is the +2 state formed by the loss of the two 4s electrons. The metal is widely used in a variety of steels and in alloys used to make coins. Nickel(II) compounds are generally pale green and in aqueous solution exist as the green hexaaqua ion, $[Ni(H_2O)_6]^{2+}$. This precipitates out the pale green nickel(II) hydroxide when aqueous alkali is added:

$$Ni^{2+}(aq) + 2\,OH^-(aq) \longrightarrow \underset{\text{Pale green}}{Ni(OH)_2(s)}$$

If ammonia is added the initial precipitate readily redissolves to form a a pale blue solution containing the hexaammine complex:

$$\underset{\text{Green}}{[Ni(H_2O)_6]^{2+}(aq)} + 6\,NH_3(aq) \longrightarrow \underset{\text{Pale blue}}{[Ni(NH_3)_6]^{2+}(aq)} + 6\,H_2O(l)$$

Copper has an electronic structure [Ar] $3d^{10}\,4s^1$ (again note that this is an exception, having only one 4s–electron). The most common oxidation state of copper is the copper(II) state. Copper(II) compounds are usually blue coloured though some, such as the carbonate, are green and both copper(II) oxide and copper(II) sulfide are black. Most copper(II) compounds are water soluble forming the pale blue hexaaquacopper(II) ion, but this is readily converted into other complex ions. Adding concentrated hydrochloric acid produces the yellow tetrachlorocopper(II) anion. Adding aqueous ammonia, initially produces a pale blue precipitate of copper(II) hydroxide, but this readily redissolves in excess of the reagent to give a dark blue solution containing the tetraamminecopper(II) cation:

$$\underset{\text{Pale blue}}{[Cu(H_2O)_6]^{2+}(aq)} + 4\,Cl^-(aq) \rightleftharpoons \underset{\text{Yellow}}{[CuCl_4]^{2-}(aq)} + 6\,H_2O(l)$$

$$\underset{\text{Pale blue}}{[Cu(H_2O)_6]^{2+}(aq)} + 4\,NH_3(aq) \rightleftharpoons \underset{\text{Dark blue}}{[Cu(NH_3)_4(H_2O)_2]^{2+}(aq)} + 4\,H_2O(l)$$

The reaction to precipitate blue copper(II) hydroxide also occurs when other aqueous alkalis are added to solutions of copper(II) salts:

$$Cu^{2+}(aq) + 2OH^-(aq) \longrightarrow Cu(OH)_2(s)$$

Copper can also exist in a +1 oxidation state. This state has a completely filled d– subshell (like Ag^+ and Zn^{2+}), so that most of its compounds are colourless. The ion is unstable in aqueous solution forming copper metal and copper(II) ions:

$$2\,Cu^+(aq) \longrightarrow Cu(s) + Cu^{2+}(aq)$$

Note that in this reaction the copper(I) is simultaneously oxidised and reduced. Reactions of this type are known as disproportionation reactions.

Insoluble copper(I) salts are stable however, the most common being copper(I) iodide, which is a white solid formed by the reduction of copper(II) compounds with iodide ions. The iodine, formed at the same time, can be removed by adding excess aqueous thiosulfate.

$$2\,Cu^{2+}(aq) + 4\,I^-(aq) \longrightarrow 2\,CuI(s) + I^2\,(aq)$$

Copper(I) oxide is a red–brown solid that is formed when copper(II) compounds are reduced under alkaline conditions, for example in Fehling's solution where tartrate ions complex the copper(II) ions to prevent copper(II) hydroxide precipitating:

$$2Cu^{2+}(aq) + 2OH^-(aq) + 2e^- \longrightarrow Cu_2O\,(s) + H_2O\,(l)$$

Transition metals form a number of relatively small highly charged ions, such as Cr^{3+} and Fe^{3+}. In aqueous solution the water ligands of these hydrated ions dissociate to make the solution acidic, in a similar way to Al^{3+}.

$$[M(H_2O)_6]^{3+}(aq) \rightleftharpoons [M(H_2O)_5OH]^{2+}(aq) + H^+(aq)$$

EXTENSION

Exercise

1. The oxidation state that occurs for the greatest number of first row transition metals is

   A +1
   B +2
   C +3
   D +4

2. The high oxidation states of transition metals are

   A usually found to the right hand side of the transition series.
   B usually found to involve simple ions.
   C usually powerful oxidants.
   D usually colourless.

3. Transition metal ions are frequently coloured because

   A they absorb infrared radiation and re–emit it as visible light.
   B of the vibrations of the ligands surrounding them.
   C of the movement of electrons between d–orbitals.
   D light causes them to spontaneously change their oxidation state.

4. The colour of the complex ion formed between cobalt(II) ions and excess chloride ions is

   A green.
   B yellow.
   C pink.
   D blue.

5. Which one of the following elements is not classified as a transition metal?

   A Cu
   B Zn
   C Mn
   D Ti

6. Explain briefly why

   a) Potassium always occurs as a +1 ion in its compounds and calcium as a + 2 ion, but compounds of manganese are known in which the oxidation state of the manganese varies from +2 to +7.
   b) There is a slight change in the shade of green of an aqueous solution of nickel(II) sulfate, when concentrated hydrochloric acid is added.
   c) Ammonia forms complex ions with cobalt(II) ions, but methane does not.

7. Describe what would be seen during the following:

   a) A few drops of aqueous ammonia are added to aqueous copper(II) sulfate and then a large excess is added.
   b) Sulfur dioxide gas (a strong reducing agent) is bubbled through acidified potassium dichromate(VI).
   c) Aqueous iron(II) sulfate is warmed with excess aqueous hydrogen peroxide and then aqueous sodium hydroxide is added to the product.
   d) Solid manganese(IV) oxide is added to aqueous hydrogen peroxide.

8. Catalysts containing transition metals or their compounds, are important in many industrial processes. Choose **two** examples of this and in each case:

   a) Name the catalyst.
   b) Write a balanced equation for the reaction that it catalyses.

   Explain the difference between homogeneous and heterogeneous catalysis and state which category your chosen examples belong to.

9. Give the formulaes of the complex ion(s) or oxyanion(s) of the first row of d–block elements (Sc to Zn) corresponding to each of the following:

   a) A blue solution that turns green then yellow when concentrated hydrochloric acid is added.
   b) The ion formed when excess aqueous ammonia is added to aqueous copper(II) sulfate.
   c) A blue solution that turns pink when water is added to it.
   d) An orange solution that turns yellow when alkali is added to it.
   e) A purple solution that goes dark green when concentrated alkali and a reductant are added.

10. The cyanide ion (CN^-) can form two complex ions with iron ions. The formulae of these are $Fe(CN)_6^{4-}$ and $Fe(CN)_6^{3-}$.

   a) What shape would you expect these to have?
   b) What is the oxidation state of the iron in the two complex ions?
   c) What feature of CN^- allows it to form complex ions with transition metals?

11. Account for the following observations:

   a) Ti^{2+} will reduce water to hydrogen, but Ca^{2+} will not.
   b) V^{3+} compounds are coloured but Sc^{3+} compounds are not.
   c) V^{3+} can act as both an oxidising agent and a reducing agent, whilst Sc^{3+} is neither.
   d) Cu^+ has colourless compounds but Cu^{2+} compounds are coloured.
   e) $Co(NH_3)_3Cl_3$ exists in a number of isomeric forms.

12. The complex ion $[Co(H_2NCH_2CH_2NH_2)_2Cl_2]^+$ is octahedral and exists as two different geometric isomers.

   a) Draw these isomers so as to illustrate how the geometric isomerism arises.

   One of these two isomers can also exist in two enantiomeric forms.

   b) Draw these isomers so as to illustrate how the enantiomerism arises and explain why. enantiomers of the other geometric isomer do not occur.
   c) Name a vitamin that contains cobalt and state a metabolic function of this vitamin.

CHEMICAL BONDING

4

4.1 Ionic bonding

4.2 Covalent bonding

14.1 Shapes of molecules and ions (AHL)

14.2 Hybridization (AHL)

14.3 Delocalization of electrons (AHL)

4.3 Intermolecular forces

4.4 Metallic bonding

4.5 Physical properties

4.2 Covalent bonding (cont)

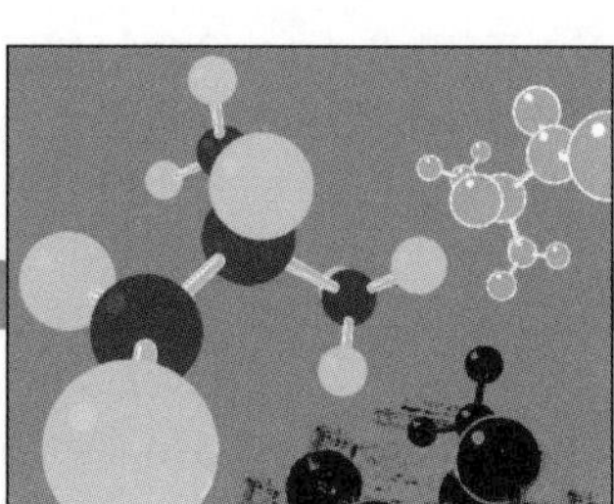

A **chemical bond** is an interaction between atoms or ions that results in a reduction in the potential energy of the system which hence becomes more stable. The formation of a chemical bond between atoms involves the interaction of the electrons in the valence shells of the atoms. There are three idealised types of chemical bond, namely ionic, covalent and metallic, though there are examples of bonds intermediate between these. The bond type depends on the extent to which the atoms involved attract the bonding electrons, that is, on their **electronegativities**. If the elements have very different electronegativities then ionic bonding results. If they both have quite high electronegativities then the bonding will be covalent, whereas if they both have low electronegativities they form a metallic bond. Each type of bonding gives rise to distinctive physical properties of the substance formed.

4.1 IONIC BONDING

4.1.1 Describe the ionic bond as the electrostatic attraction between oppositely charged ions.

4.1.2 Describe how ions can be formed as a result of electron transfer.

4.1.3 Deduce which ions will be formed when elements in groups 1, 2 and 3 lose electrons.

4.1.4 Deduce which ions will be formed when elements in groups 5, 6 and 7 gain electrons.

4.1.5 State that transition elements can form more than one ion.

4.1.6 Predict whether a compound of two elements would be ionic from the position of the elements in the periodic table or from their electronegativity values.

4.1.7 State the formula of common polyatomic ions formed by non-metals in periods 2 and 3.

4.1.8 Describe the lattice structure of ionic compounds.

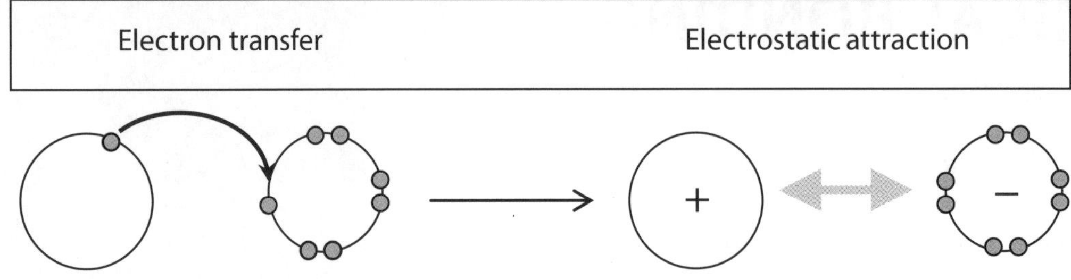

Figure 401 Ionic bonding

Ionic bonding occurs between elements that have a large difference in electronegativity. In ionic bonding a metal atom with a low electronegativity loses electrons to form a positively charged ion, or **cation** and a non-metal atom with a high electronegativity gains electrons to form a negatively charged ion, or **anion**. As a result there is an electrostatic attraction between these ions which results in ionic bonding as illustrated in Figure 401.

This means that we can predict that the bonding in barium selenide is ionic because barium (Ba) is a metal (in Group 2) and selenium (Se) is a non-metal (in Group 6). Almost all metal compounds are ionic. They are made up of a regular array of positively and negatively charged particles, called ions, held together by electrostatic attraction. In simple cases these ions are isoelectronic with (that is they have the same electronic structure as) the noble gases. The three dimensional arrangement between cations and anions of opposite charges in ionic crystals accounts, resulting in very strong electrostatic attractions, for the high melting points and stability of ionic solids.

In ionic bonding the number of electrons lost varies from metal to metal, but the elements in the s-block of the periodic table lose all of the electrons in their **valence level**. Sodium, which has an electronic structure 2,8,1, therefore loses just its one outer electron to give a sodium ion, with an electronic structure 2,8 (isoelectronic with Ne). This carries a single positive charge because it has one more proton than electron (11 p^+ compared to 10 e^-).

$$Na \longrightarrow Na^+ + e^-$$

(2,8,1) (2,8)

Similarly calcium has two valence electrons (2,8,8,2) and so it forms an ion with an electronic structure 2,8,8 (isoelectronic with Ar) that has two positive charges.

The number of electrons lost by metals outside of the s-block is less easy to predict, especially in the case of the transition metals, and a particular metal can form stable ions with different charges, for example iron can form both Fe^{2+} (the iron(II) ion) and Fe^{3+} (the iron(III) ion). This means that the charges on the ions must be learnt and those most commonly met are given in Figure 404, from which it can be seen that a 2+ charge is by far the most common.

Non-metals usually gain electrons to fill the valence level of the atom. Chlorine therefore, with an electronic structure 2,8,7, requires one electron to fill its valence level, so it forms an ion with an electronic structure 2,8,8 (isoelectronic with Ar), which carries a single negative charge because it has one more electron than proton (18 e^- compared to 17 p^+).

$$Cl + e^- \longrightarrow Cl^-$$

(2,8,7) (2,8,8)

Similarly oxygen (2,6) requires two electrons to fill its valence level and so it forms an ion with an electronic structure 2,8 (isoelectronic with Ne) that has two negative charges.

Hence in forming sodium chloride the sodium atom can be considered to have transferred an electron to the chlorine atom. Similarly in forming calcium oxide the calcium atom transfers two electrons to the oxygen atom. No electron sharing occurs between the ions in ionic bonding.

The anions and cations have opposite electrical charges and are attracted together into a **crystal lattice** in which each anion is surrounded by cations and *vice versa*. A single layer of such a lattice, formed by ions of equal charge, is shown in Figure 402.

The lattice naturally extends in three dimensions, so that there would be an anion above and below each cation and *vice versa* as illustrated in Figure 403.

An ionic substance is therefore held together by strong electrostatic attractions in all three dimensions. This means that there are no molecules present in ionic

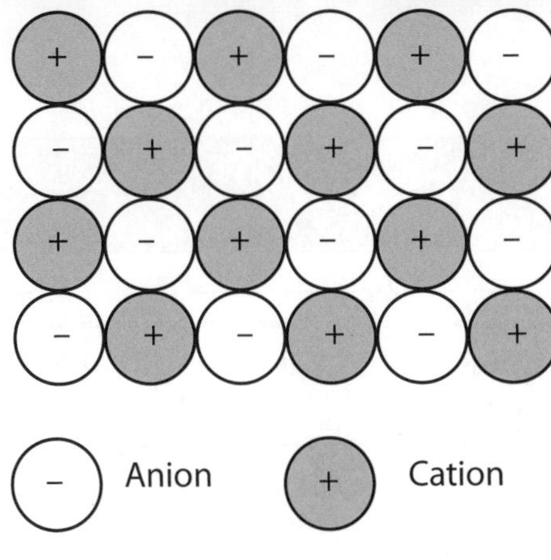

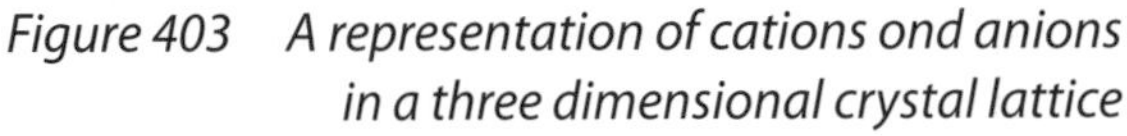

Figure 402 A layer of an ionic lattice

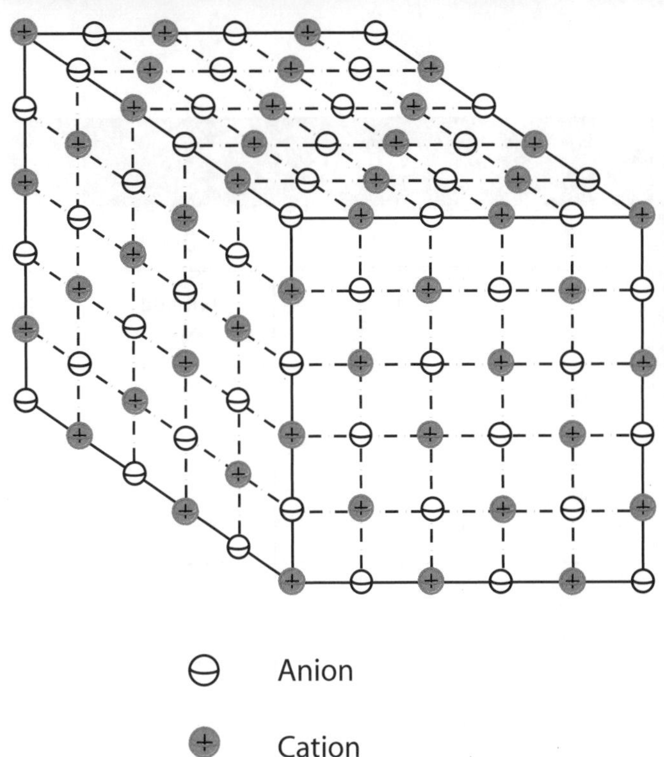

Figure 403 A representation of cations ond anions in a three dimensional crystal lattice

substances. Because of the way in which bonding occurs, ionic compounds have distinctive physical properties:

- Hard, brittle crystalline solids.
- Relatively high melting and boiling points.
- Do not conduct electricity when solid, but do when molten or in aqueous solution.
- Are more soluble in water than other solvents.

Groups of atoms, joined together by covalent bonds can also have an electrical charge and so form compounds with ions of the opposite charge by ionic bonding. The sulfate ion (SO_4^{2-}), for example, consists of a sulfur atom and four oxygen atoms, joined by covalent bonds, which has gained two extra electrons to give a charge of 2–. Table 404 gives the electrical charges carried by common anions and cations. Note:

- Simple anions change the ending of the names of the atoms to -ide, e.g. chlorine gives the chloride ion.
- Anions that end in -ate contain oxygen e.g. sulfate.

Ionically bonded compounds are simply named according to the names of the two ions involved, the cation being given first, so that Al_2O_3 is aluminum oxide and $Cr(OH)_3$ is chromium(III) hydroxide. Note that the bracketed Roman numerals are used for transition metals, which have multiple oxidation states, to give the oxidation number of the metal in the compound, which is usually equal to the charge on the cation.

Converting from the name to the formula requires a knowledge of the ratio that the ions combine in. Ionic compounds must contain cations and the anions in such a ratio that their charges cancel each other to give an electrically neutral compound. If they have equal, but opposite charges, as for example with zinc and sulfide ions, then this requires just an equal number of each, so the formula of zinc sulfide is simply ZnS. In other cases the formula must give the ratio of the different ions, so that copper(II) fluoride is CuF_2, because for each doubly charged copper(II) ion there must be two singly charged fluoride ions. When multiplying groups of atoms, they must be enclosed in brackets, so that ammonium sulfate has the formula $(NH_4)_2SO_4$.

A simple way of predicting the formula of an ionic compound is to 'swap' the numbers of the charges on the ions involved. For example, the formula of calcium phosphate can be predicted as $Ca_{\mathbf{3}}(PO_4)_{\mathbf{2}}$, by 'swapping' the bold numbers of the charges on the ions - $Ca^{\mathbf{2}+}$ and $PO_4^{\mathbf{3}-}$, that is, the '**2**' charge for the calcium becomes the phosphate subscript and *vice versa*. The formulas of acids can be predicted by combining the hydrogen ion (H^+) with the appropriate anion, hence nitric acid (H^+ and NO_3^-) has the formula HNO_3. However, it must be remembered that the pure acids contain covalently bonded molecules.

Anions			Cations			
1–	2–	3–	1+	← 2+	→	3+
Fluoride F^-	Oxide O^{2-}	Nitride N^{3-}	Hydrogen H^+	Magnesium Mg^{2+}	Calcium Ca^{2+}	Aluminium Al^{3+}
Chloride Cl^-	Sulfide S^{2-}		Sodium Na^+	Manganese Mn^{2+}	Iron(II) Fe^{2+}	Chromium(III) Cr^{3+}
Bromide Br^-			Potassium K^+	Cobalt Co^{2+}	Nickel Ni^{2+}	Iron(III) Fe^{3+}
Iodide I^-			Copper(I) Cu^+	Copper(II) Cu^{2+}	Zinc Zn^{2+}	
			Silver Ag^+	Lead Pb^{2+}	Tin Sn^{2+}	
Hydroxide OH^-	Carbonate CO_3^{2-}	Phosphate PO_4^{3-}	Ammonium NH_4^+			
Nitrate NO_3^-	Sulfate SO_4^{2-}					

Figure 404 The charges on common anions and cations

Using Lewis structures, a pair of electrons can be represented by dots, crosses, a combination of dots and crosses or by a line. For example, a chlorine molecule can be shown as:

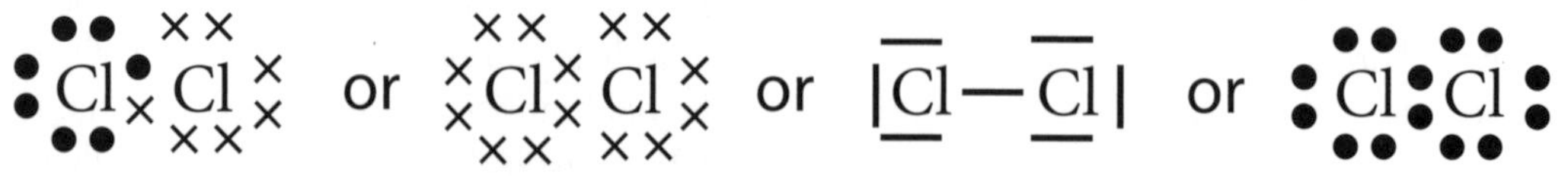

Cl Cl or Cl Cl or |Cl—Cl| or Cl Cl

Note: Cl — Cl is not a Lewis structure

Figure 405 Lewis structure for Cl_2

Exercise 4.1

1. An element has an atomic number of 16. What will be the charge on the ions that it forms?

   A +2
   B +1
   C −1
   D −2

2. The electronic structures of five elements are given below. Which one of these will be most likely to form an ion with a charge of 2+?

   A 2,1
   B 2,4
   C 2,6
   D 2,8,2

3. Which one of the following elements is most likely to be capable of forming cations with different charges?

   A Be
   B V
   C Sr
   D Cs

4. Name the following compounds:

   a) KBr b) Li_3N c) BaS
   d) AlI_3 e) BeO

5. The table below gives the electronic structures of pairs of elements, A and B. On the basis of these electronic structures, predict the ions that these elements would form and hence the formula of the compound that would result.

	Element A	Element B
a)	2,1	2,8,7
b)	2,6	2,8,8,2
c)	2,8,1	2,8,6
d)	2,8,3	2,7
e)	2,5	2,8,2

4.2 COVALENT BONDING

4.2.1 Describe the covalent bond as the electrostatic attraction between a pair of electrons and positively charged nuclei.

4.2.2 Describe how the covalent bond is formed as a result of electron sharing.

4.2.3 Deduce the Lewis (electron dot) structures of molecules and ions for up to four electron pairs on each atom.

4.2.4 State and explain the relationship between the number of bonds, bond length and bond strength.

4.2.5 Predict whether a compound of two elements would be covalent from the position of the elements in the periodic table, or from their electronegativity values.

Covalent bonding occurs between atoms that have quite high electronegativities, that is usually between non-metals (under some circumstances metals in high oxidation states can also form covalent bonds). In covalent bonding the two atoms involved share some of their valence electrons since neither element loses electrons easily. The attraction of the two positively charged nuclei for these shared pairs of electrons results in the two atoms being bonded together as illustrated in Figure 406.

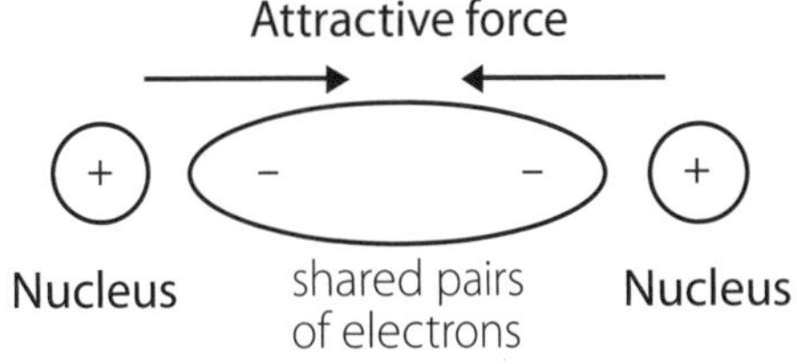

Figure 406 Covalent bonding as a result of electron pair sharing

In contrast to ionic bonding and metallic bonding, the interaction involves two specific atoms. A single covalent bond consists of a shared pair of electrons, a double bond two shared pairs and a triple bond three. Usually each atom involved contributes one electron, but in some circumstances one atom can donate both electrons. In this case the bond is known as a **dative covalent bond** (refer to the end of this page). When forming covalent bonds, the atoms involved usually fill their valence level, so that the number of bonds formed is equal to the number of electrons needed for this. As a result the noble gases, which have filled valence shells, rarely form compounds. It also means that atoms in compounds (except for hydrogen) usually have eight electrons in their valence shell. This is often known as the **octet rule**. Carbon has an electronic structure of 2,4 and so requires four more electrons to fill its valence level. It therefore forms four bonds, as shown in Figure 406.

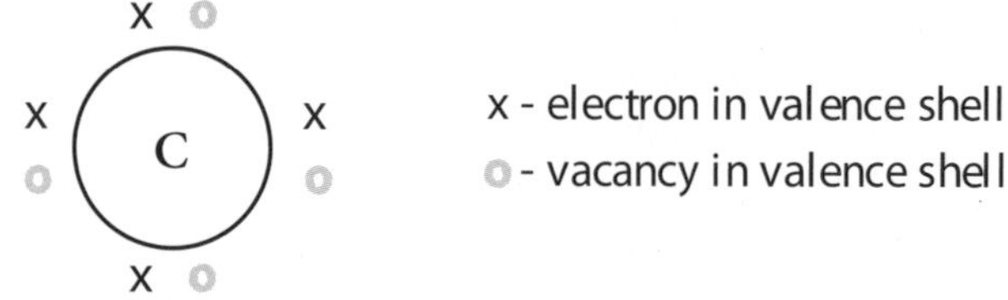

Figure 406 The valence level in carbon, showing vacancies

Similarly fluorine, (which has an electronic structure 2,7) and hydrogen (1) both require just one electron to fill their valence levels and so form just one bond. Oxygen (2,6) requires two electrons and normally forms 2 bonds, whilst nitrogen (2,5) forms 3 bonds.

If carbon and fluorine form a compound, because carbon forms four bonds and fluorine only forms one, four fluorines are required for each carbon and so the formula is CF_4. This can be represented as a **structural formula,** in which each covalent bond is shown as a line joining the atoms involved, or as a **Lewis structure** (electron dot diagram), which shows all the valence electrons of the atoms involved, or as a combination of these in which each electron pair is represented by a line (or a pair of crosses or a combination of a pair of dots, crosses and lines). These representations of CF_4 are given in Figure 407, with two styles of Lewis electron structure on the lower line. The Lewis structure shows that the atoms involved all have filled valence shells in the molecule.

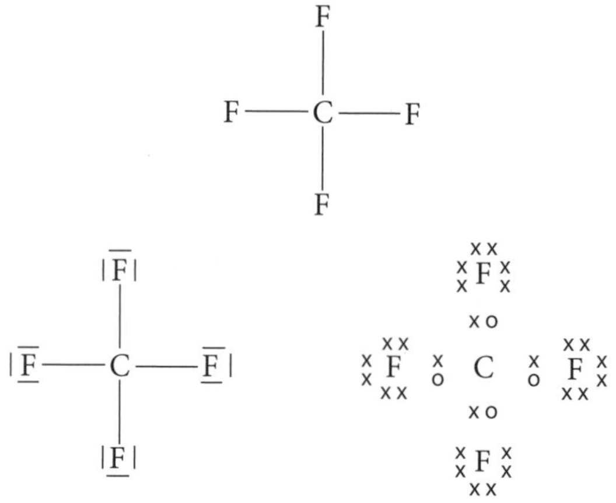

Figure 407 Bonding in carbon tetrafluoride

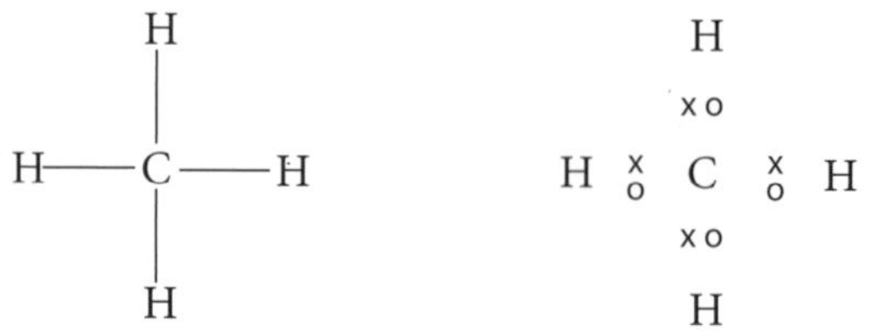

Figure 408 Bonding in methane

Figure 408 shows the bonding in CH_4 illustrated as both a structural formula (left), which in this case is the same as the simple Lewis structure, and the "dot & cross" Lewis structure.

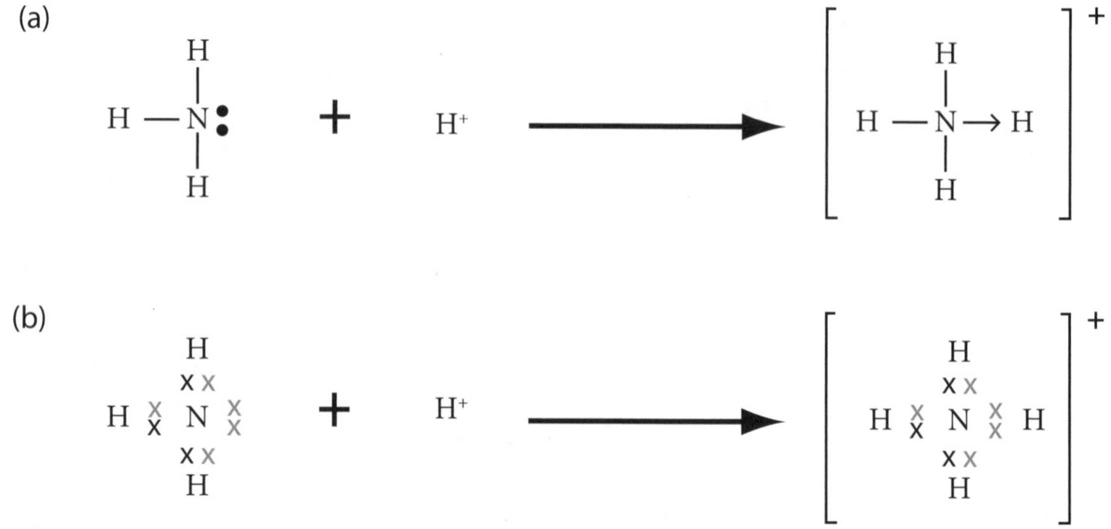

(a)

(b)

Figure 409 Bonding in the Ammonium ion

Sometimes in a covalent bond both of the electrons that form the bond originate from the same atom. A bond of this type is known as **dative bond**, though it is also sometimes referred to as a **coordinate bond**, or as a donor-acceptor bond. It is however equivalent to a normal covalent bond in every way apart from the origin of the electrons. The simplest example of a bond of this type is the bond formed between an ammonia molecule (NH_3) and a hydrogen ion to form the ammonium ion (NH_4^+), illustrated in Figure 409. In structural formulas a dative bond is often indicated by an arrow pointing in the direction the electron pair is donated and this is illustrated in Figure 409(a) whilst 409(b) shows it as a Lewis diagram. Dative bonds also occur in the triple bond formed in carbon monoxide, in all acid base interactions and in all ligand metal ion interactions

If two pairs of electrons are shared a double bond is formed, which joins the atoms more tightly and closer together than a single bond (as there are now two electron pairs pulling the two nuclei closer together). Carbon forms four bonds and oxygen forms two bonds, so that two oxygens are needed for each carbon, giving carbon dioxide. The oxygen and carbon atoms are joined by double bonds, which are represented as double lines in the structural formula. The diagrams for these are given in Figure 410.

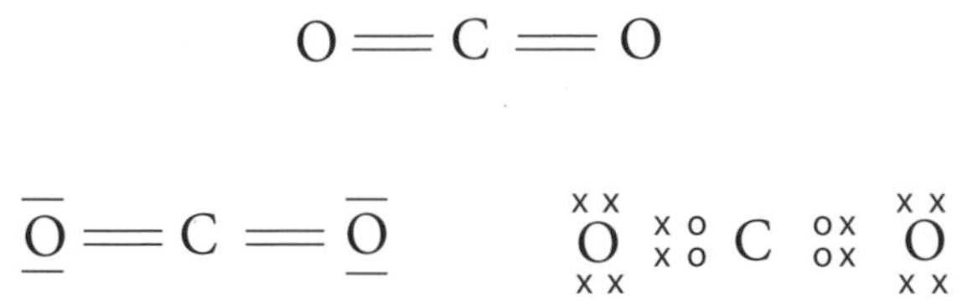

O ═ C ═ O

$\overline{\underline{O}}$ ═ C ═ $\overline{\underline{O}}$ $\qquad$ xx O xx $\begin{smallmatrix}x o\\x o\end{smallmatrix}$ C $\begin{smallmatrix}o x\\o x\end{smallmatrix}$ xx O xx

Figure 410 The bonding In CO_2

Figure 410 shows the bonding in CO_2 illustrated as both a structural formula (top) and two styles of Lewis diagram (lower line)

Again notice that the valence shells of both the carbon and oxygen are filled. Ethene is an example of an organic molecule that contains a double bond, and is an example of an unsaturated molecule. Its structural formula is given in Figure 414.

Two atoms can also share three pairs of electrons giving an even stronger triple bond. A nitrogen atom has five electrons in its valence level (electronic structure 2,5) and so requires three more electrons to fill it. In a nitrogen molecule therefore, the two nitrogen atoms are held together by a triple bond to form a nitrogen molecule, as shown in Figure 411.

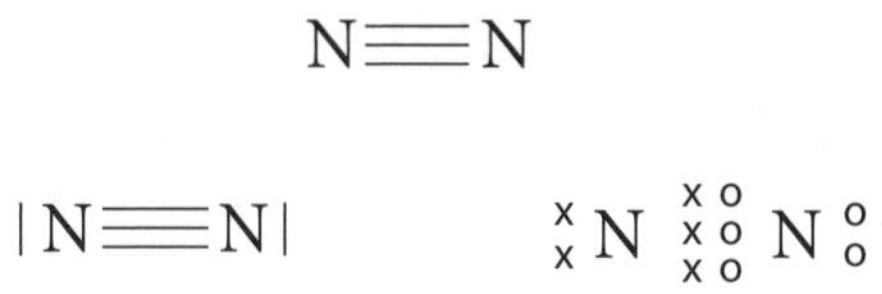

N≡N

|N≡N| $\qquad$ $\begin{smallmatrix}x\\x\end{smallmatrix}$ N $\begin{smallmatrix}x o\\x o\\x o\end{smallmatrix}$ N $\begin{smallmatrix}o\\o\end{smallmatrix}$

Figure 411 The bonding in N_2

Figure 411 shows the bonding in N_2 illustrated as both a structural formula (top) and two styles of Lewis diagram(lower line).

Again note that the valence shells of both nitrogen atoms are filled. Ethyne is an example of an unsaturated organic molecule containing a triple bond (See Figure 414).

The types of diagrams above represent three of the stages involved in drawing a "dot & cross" Lewis diagram:

1 Decide how many bonds each atom involved forms. For many simple molecules this equals the number of electrons required to fill the outer electron shell, for more complicated cases see "Molecules with more or less than four electron pairs" under Section 14.1).

2 Decide on which is/are the central atom(s) (i.e. the one that has most bonds) and join the atoms together with bonds, so that all the atoms have the required number of bonds - this gives the structural formula. (n.b. if more than one structural formula is possible then the species most likely displays delocalised bonding, refer to Section 4.7).

3 Each bond will involve one electron from each of the atoms it joins (unless it is a dative bond). Subtract these from the total number of electrons in the valence shell of each atom to calculate the number of electrons present as non-bonding electrons. Draw a line to represent each of these pairs - this gives a simple Lewis diagram. If the species is an ion, then show the charge on the atoms with unpaired electrons.

4 To produce a "dot and cross" (sometimes referred to as an "electron dot") Lewis structure, replace each bond and each line by an electron pair. The electrons may be all represented by 'x's, or preferably a mixture of 'x's and 'o's can be used to indicate which atom the electron originally came from.

5 If the species is an ion rather than a molecule then one electron needs to be added for each negative charge and one removed for each positive charge. The

Hydrogen cyanide	Methanoate ion
Carbon (2,4) forms four bonds, nitrogen (2,5) three and hydrogen (1) one in order to complete their valence shells.	Carbon (2,4) forms four bonds, oxygen (2,6) two and hydrogen (1) one in order to complete their valence shells.
The structural formula accounts for all of the carbon and hydrogen valence electrons, as the carbon has eight in its valence shell and the hydrogen one. The structural formula however only accounts for three of nitrogen's five valence electrons, so it must have a non- bonding pair. The simple Lewis diagram is therefore: H−C≡N|	The structural formula accounts for two electrons around the hydrogen and eight electrons around the carbon. The double bonded to the oxygen only accounts for two of its six electrons so there must also be two non-bonding pairs. The single bond to the other oxygen only accounts for one of its electrons so there are five more valence electrons to account for, two pairs and an unpaired electron*. 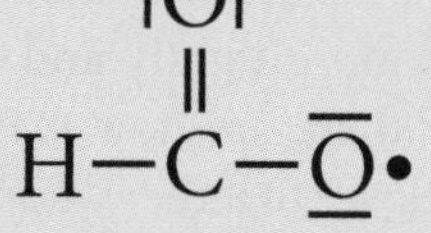 |O| ‖ H−C−O̅•
There is one pair of electrons in the C−H bond and three pairs of electrons in the triple C≡N bond, so the "dot & cross" Lewis structure is:  H ˣₒ C ˣₒˣₒˣₒ N ₒₒ	Replacing each bond by a pair of electrons, replacing the lines by non-bonding pairs and taking into account the unpaired electron on the oxygen, is the first stage in producing the "electron dot" Lewis structure.
Hydrogen cyanide is a neutral molecule so there is no need to add or remove electrons.	Finally the electron that causes the negative charge needs to be shown in the Lewis structure and the overall charge shown outside the square brackets: 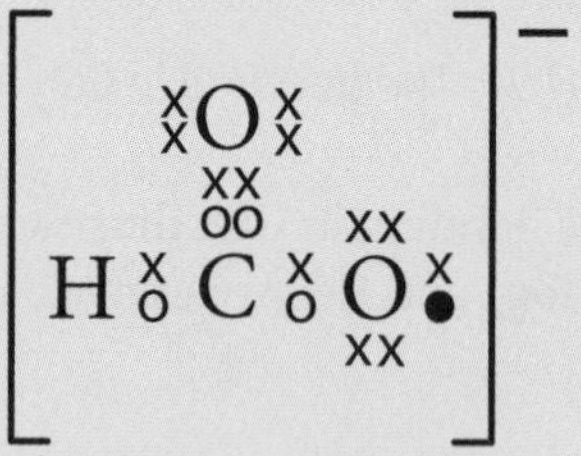 [ˣₓOˣₓ / ˣˣ ₒₒ / H ˣₒ C ˣₒ ˣˣOˣ• ˣˣ]⁻

* Note for the methanoate ion that a second structure could be drawn in whih the bonding to the oxygens is interchanged. This indicates that delocalised bounding probably occurs see Section 4.7

Figure 412 Constructing Lewis diagrams for hydrogen cyanide molecule and methanoate ion

electrons should be added/removed so as to give full valence shells of paired electrons. It may be useful to indicate such electrons by a '□' or '•'

This process is illustrated for the hydrogen cyanide molecule (HCN) and the methanoate ion (HCO_2^-) in Figure 412:

An alternative way to determine the Lewis structure, if each atom has an octet of electrons surrounding it (as is the case with C, N and O), is to follow the following procedure:

1. Count the total number of valence electrons from the group the atoms are in, accounting for any charge(s) present (add one for each "–" and subtract one for each "+").
2. Count the number of atoms requiring octets and hence calculate the resulting number of electrons needed (ignore hydrogens as their electrons all comprise part of other octets).
3. Take the difference between these two figures and add the number of electrons involved in bonds (as they are counted in two octets) to give the number of electrons in lone pairs (x). Hence there are $\frac{x}{2}$ lone pairs.

Using, the carbonate ion, CO_3^{2-} as an example:

1. Number of valence e^- = 4 + (3 × 6) +2 (added for 2– charge) = $24e^-$
2. Number of octets required = 4; ∴ number of electrons needed = 4 × 8 = $32e^-$

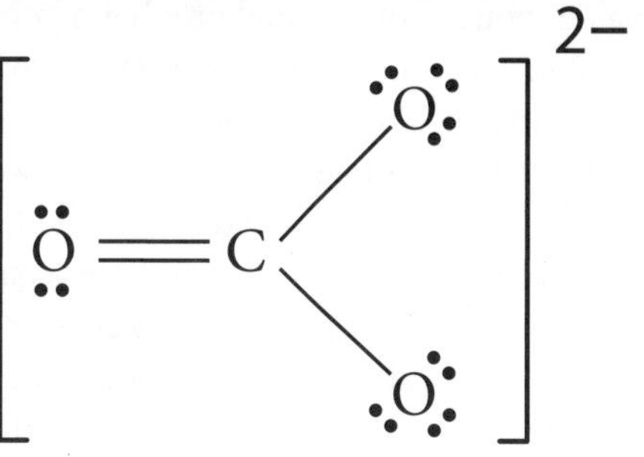

Figure 413 The Lewis structure for CO_3^{2-}

3. Number of e^- short = (32 – 24) = $8e^-$; plus $8e^-$ in bonds to give a total of $16e^-$; thus 8lone pairs required.

Now to produce the Lewis diagram, draw a double bond between C and (any) O, and single bond between C and the other two oxygens.

Carbon with 4 bonds now has its octet complete

Draw lone e^- pairs around the other oxygen atoms to complete their octet.

Show the 2^- charge on the ion [in square brackets] as in Figure 413.

Organic molecules, such as ethane, ethene and ethyne show the effect of single, double and triple bonding on the length and strength of the carbon-carbon bond as shown in Figure 414:

Covalent bonding can lead to two very different types of structures. Usually, as in all the examples so far considered,

	Ethane (single C–C bond)	Ethene (double C–C bond)	Ethyne (triple C–C bond)
Structural formula	$H_3C–CH_3$ (H–C–C–H, each C with two further H)	$H_2C=CH_2$	H–C≡C–H
Lewis diagram	H ˣₒ C ˣₒ C ˣₒ H, each C with H above and below (xo pairs)	C ˣₒˣₒ C, each C with H above and below (xo pairs)	H ˣₒ C ˣₒˣₒˣₒ C ˣₒ H
C–C bond length (pm)	154	134	121
C–C bond energy (kJ mol^{-1})	346	598	837

Figure 414 The structure of some simple hydrocarbons

the covalent bonds hold a small number of atoms together to form discrete units called **molecules**. Although the covalent bonds holding the molecule together are strong, the forces between molecules are much weaker (refer to Section 4.8), so that individual molecules are easily separated from each other. As a result molecular covalent solids have characteristic physical properties, such as being quite soft in the solid state, not conducting electricity, being more soluble in non-polar solvents than in water and having low melting and boiling points (often existing as liquids or gases at room temperature and pressure). This too is discussed in more detail in Section 4.8.

Sometimes, the whole lattice of a solid can be held together by strong covalent bonds. These 'covalent network', or 'giant covalent' structures are very different, being very hard and having very high melting and boiling points (again refer to Section 4.8) .

Exercise 4.2

1. An element forms a covalently bonded compound with hydrogen, that has the formula XH_3, where X is the element. In which group of the periodic table would you expect to find X?

   A Group 1
   B Group 14
   C Group 15
   D Group 17

2. "Two atoms each provide two electrons that are shared by the two atoms". This is a description of a

   A single covalent bond.
   B double covalent bond.
   C triple covalent bond
   D quadruple covalent bond.

3. A non-metal usually forms two covalent bonds in its compounds. How many electrons will it have in its valence level?

   A 2
   B 4
   C 6
   D 8

4. The noble gases do not usually form chemical compounds because

   A they have very stable nuclei.
   B the bonds between their atoms are very strong.
   C they already have complete valence electron levels.
   D they are not polar.

5. Which one of the following compounds contains both ionic and covalent bonds?

   A SiO_2
   B BaF_2
   C Na_2CO_3
   D Cl_2O

6. From the electronic structures of the following pairs elements deduce the numbers of covalent bonds, if any, that each would normally form, and hence predict the formulaes of the compound you would expect to result.

   a) helium and sulfur
   b) chlorine and hydrogen
   c) nitrogen and chlorine
   d) silicon and fluorine
   e) phosphorus and oxygen

7. From the electronic structures of the pairs of elements given, predict the type of bonding that you would expect in the compound they form.

   a) 2,4 and 1
   b) 2,8,5 and 2,8,7
   c) 2,1 and 2,8,6
   d) 2,6 and 2,7
   e) 2,8 and 3,2,6

8. Draw Lewis diagrams of the following molecules:

   a) HCl b) O_2 c) PH_3

   d) F_2O e) H_2CO

4.2.7 Predict the shape and bond angles for species with four, three and two negative charge centres on the central atom using the valence shell electron pair repulsion theory (VSEPR).

4.2.8 Predict whether or not a molecule is polar from its molecular shape and bond polarities.

SHAPES OF MOLECULES AND IONS

Molecules with 4 electron pairs

Covalent molecules all have distinct shapes. The shape of a molecule is determined by repulsion between the electron pairs in the valence shell. This is known as Valence Shell Electron Pair Repulsion **(VSEPR) theory**. Most common molecules have filled valence levels that contain four pairs of electrons. In order to be as widely separated as possible and hence minimise their potential energy, these electron pairs distribute themselves so that they are pointing towards the corners of a tetrahedron (a regular triangular based pyramid) with angles of 109.5°. If all of the electron pairs are bonding pairs, as for example in methane, CH_4, then this is also the shape of the molecule (See Figure 415).

Some molecules also contain non-bonding, or 'lone' pairs of electrons and these affect the shape of the molecule. In order to determine this it is vital to draw a correct Lewis structure for the species before any attempt is made to predict its shape. In ammonia, NH_3, if there were only the three pairs of bonding electrons, then these would point to the corners of an equilateral triangle with the nitrogen atom at its centre and angles would be 120°. The pair of electrons on the nitrogen that is not involved in the bonding (the lone pair or non-bonding pair), repels the bonding electrons so the molecule has the shape of a triangular pyramid. Similarly, if it were not for its two pairs of non-bonding electrons, the water molecule would be linear and not bent. The basic shapes of these common molecules is summarised in Figure 415.

CORE

Number of non-bonding electron pairs	Example	Lewis diagram	Shape and bond angle
None	Methane	H xx C xx H, with H above and below (four shared pairs)	Tetrahedral 109.5°
One	Ammonia	H xx N xx H, with H above; lone pair xx below	Trigonal pyramidal 107°
Two	Water	xx O xx H, with H below; two lone pairs xx	Non-linear ('bent') 'angular' or 'V-shaped'. 104°

Figure 415 The shapes of common molecules

In all of these structures, the angles between all of the bonds might be expected to be the tetrahedral angle of 109.5° and this is the angle that is found in methane and other molecules that contain just four bonding pairs. The repulsion between a lone pair and a bonding pair is however greater than that between two bonding pairs. As a result the presence of a lone pair distorts the geometry, causing a slight reduction in the bond angle. If there is just one lone pair, as in ammonia, the bond angle is about 107°, whilst the presence of two lone pairs, as in water, reduces the bond angle to about 104°.

Note that in describing the shape of the molecule only the atoms and not the lone pairs are considered so that even though water has four regions of high electron density that have approximate tetrahedral orientation, its shape is described as non-linear (bent, angular or V-shaped) because that is the orientation of the atoms. It is important to indicate the angle as other non-linear molecules (such as ozone, O_3) can have angles of about 120°.

Molecules with less than four electron pairs

As discussed above, the shape of a molecule is determined by repulsion between the regions of high electron density in the valence level, that is, covalent bonds and non-bonding (or 'lone') electron pairs. The former arises when elements in groups 2 and 3/13 form covalent bonds, or when elements in the later groups form multiple bonds (which with regard to the shape of the molecule are the same as single ones) and hence have a reduced number of electron dense regions close to the nucleus. Ethene and ethyne (see Figure 4.15) are good examples of this.

If there are two regions of high electron density, then the result will be a linear molecule with 180° bond angle, as is found in gaseous beryllium chloride ($BeCl_2$) and in carbon dioxide. If there are three regions of high electron density then these will point towards the corners of an equilateral triangle with angles of 120°. If they are all bonding pairs then a trigonal planar molecule results, such as boron trifluoride. If one is a non-bonding pair, as in sulfur dioxide or ozone, then a bent (V-shaped; angular) molecule results. As would be expected from their effect in ammonia and water, the presence of the lone pair in sulfur dioxide reduces the bond angles to ~117° (less than 120°). These structures are given in Figure 416.

Nunber of regions of high electron density	Number of non-bonding electron pairs	Example	Shape and bond angle
Two	None	Carbon dioxide	Linear 180° O=C=O
Three	None	Boron trifluoride	Trigonal planar 120° F—B(F)F
Three	One	Sulfur dioxide	Non-linear (V-shaped) 117° O=S=O (with lone pair)

Figure 416 The shapes of common molecules with less than four regions of high electron density

Number of regions of high electron density	Number. of non-bonding electron pairs	Example	Shape and bond angle(s)
Five	None	Phosphorus pentafluoride	Trigonal bipyramidal 90° & 120° 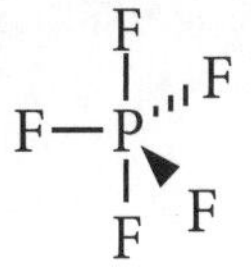
Five	One	Sulfur tetrafluoride	'Saw horse' 90° & ≈ 117° 
Five	Two	Iodine trichloride	T-shaped 90° 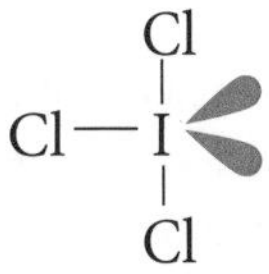
Five	Three	Xenon difluoride	Linear 180° 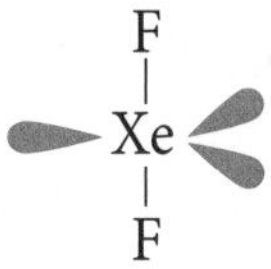
Six	None	Sulfur hexafluoride	Octahedral 90° 
Six	One	Bromine pentafluoride	Square pyramid ≈ 88° 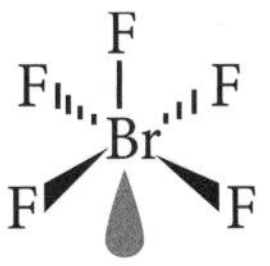
Six	Two	Xenon tetrafluoride	Square planar 90° 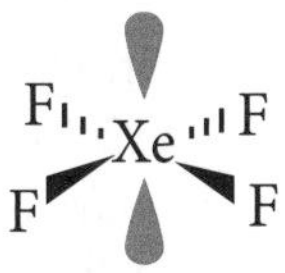

Figure 418 The shapes of common molecules with more than four regions of high electron density

AHL

HIGHER LEVEL

14.1 SHAPES OF MOLECULES AND IONS (AHL)

14.1.1 Predict the shape and bond angles for species with five and six negative charge centres using the VSEPR theory.

MOLECULES WITH MORE THAN FOUR ELECTRON PAIRS

Molecules with more than four negative charge centres arise because elements in the third (Al to Ar) and lower periods of the p-block can 'promote' one or more electron from a doubly filled s- or p-orbital into an unfilled low energy d-orbital. This increases the number of unpaired electrons available, and hence the number of bonds that can be formed by two for each electron promoted. Phosphorus ([Ne] $3s^2 3p^3$) for example usually has three unpaired electrons and forms the chloride PCl_3. By promoting one of its s-electrons it can take on the electron configuration ([Ne] $3s^1 3p^3 3d^1$) which has five unpaired electrons and so can form the chloride PCl_5. Molecules of this kind have more than eight outer electrons and so are said to have an **expanded valence shell**. This usually occurs only when the element forms strong polar covalent bonds (which in practice means to very electronegative elements) to small atoms (so that they can fit around the central atom without severe repulsion). As a result in many molecules with expanded valence shells the central atom is bonded to fluorine, oxygen or chlorine, especially fluorine. For example sulfur forms SF_6 and iodine IF_7.

In some molecules with expanded valence shells, there may be five or six regions of high electron density. Application of VSEPR theory shows that these will give molecular shapes based on the trigonal bipyramid (5 negative regions) and the octahedron or square bipyramid (6 negative regions). The trigonal bipyramid has two types of electron rich regions, two axial ones (each at 90° to three other pairs and at 180° to the fourth) and three equatorial ones (each at 90° to two other pairs and at 120° to the remaining two). Non-bonding electron pairs always occupy the equatorial positions, presumably because this minimises electron-electron repulsion. In the octahedral or square bipyramid arrangement, all of the positions are equal, but if there are two non-bonding pairs in an octahedral arrangement then these take positions opposite to each other to give a square planar shape (for example in XeF_4) so that they are separated as far as possible. It is of course vital to draw correct Lewis structures to determine the geometry of a molecule or ion, so as to find the number of lone pairs. As with tetrahedral based shapes, the presence of a lone pair causes slight distortion of the bond angles. Note that in all these cases, the central atom has more than an octet of electrons. These basic shapes and some common examples are summarised in Figure 418.

SHAPES OF MOLECULES WITH MULTIPLE AND DELOCALISED BONDS

As will be seen later, quite a number of molecules and ions involve π-bonds (refer to Section 4.6) and delocalised bonds (refer to Section 4.7). When predicting the shape of these, exactly the same theory applies. The shape is dictated by the σ-bonds and the non-bonding electron pairs. π-bonds do not affect the shape of the molecule and hence it does not matter whether the delocalised structure or one of the resonance structures derived from a Lewis diagram is considered, as both give identical answers. This is illustrated below for the nitrate ion, which has three regions of high electron density (charge centres, or centres of negative charge) around the nitrogen and hence is trigonal planar and has bond angles of 120°.

Resonance structure

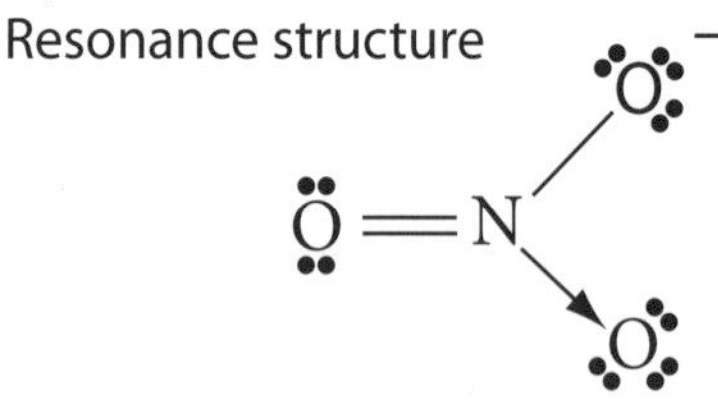

Delocalised

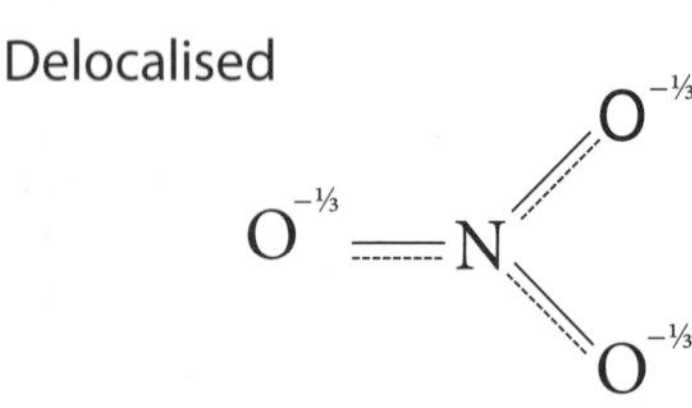

Figure 417 Nitrate structures

Consider for example the shapes of the three species NO_2^+, NO_2 and NO_2^-. Oxygen will normally form two bonds and nitrogen three, so the requirements of simple bonding theory cannot be satisfied in NO_2 which has an odd number of electrons (each oxygen has 6 valence electrons and nitrogen has 5). Oxygen can however also accept an electron pair to form a dative bond and this does meet the bonding requirements, except that it will be noted that there is a single unpaired electron on the nitrogen atom. (Species with unpaired valence electrons are called free radicals and are usually very reactive. NO_2 by being relatively stable is a notable exception. Further details of free radicals are given later). In NO_2^+ this unpaired electron is lost and in NO_2^- an additional electron has been gained to give a non-bonding electron pair on the nitrogen. The Lewis structures are therefore:

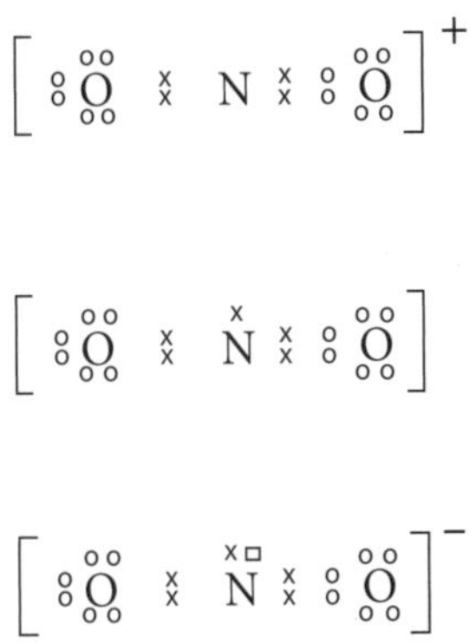

[O N O]$^+$

[O N O]

[O N O]$^-$

Figure 419 Lewis Structures of NO_2 species

It can therefore be seen that, because it has only two regions of negative charge around the nucleus, NO_2^+ will be linear with a bond angle of 180° and that NO_2^- with three centers of electron charge (one of which is a lone electron pair) will be trigonal planar with a bond angle of just less than 120°, probably about 117°. In the case of NO_2, because there is only a single lone electron rather than a lone pair, it is likely that it will be non-linear, but because the repulsion caused by a single electron will be less than that from a pair of electrons, the bond angle will be between 120° and 180° (it is in fact 134°). It is an arbitrary decision in all of these structures which of the oxygen atoms to join with a single bond and which with a double. This gives a clear indication that they are resonance structures, so that the actual species will involve delocalised π-bonds and be a resonance hybrid of the possible resonance structures (refer to Section 4.7). Similar considerations show that the carbonate ion (CO_3^{2-}) is trigonal planar.

Exercise 14.1

1. (AHL) Which one of the following molecules would you not expect to be planar?

   A SCl_4
   B C_2H_4
   C BCl_3
   D XeF_4

2. If a molecule has a trigonal pyramid shape, how many non-bonding pairs of electrons are there in the valence level of the central atom?

   A 1
   B 2
   C 3
   D 4

3. What shapes would you predict for the following molecules?

   a) SiF_4
   b) PCl_3
   c) H_2S
   d) NF_3
   e) CCl_4

4. Draw Lewis diagrams for and hence predict the shape, giving approximate bond angles, for $^+CH_3$, $^-CH_3$ and $\bullet CH_3$ (i.e. a methyl radical).

5. Sketch the shapes and predict the bond angles in each of the following species:

   a) H—CO—OH
   b) CH_3—NH_2
   c) H—CN
   d) ICl_2^- (AHL)

AHL

4.2.6 Predict the relative polarity of bonds from electronegativity values.

4.2.8 Predict whether or not a molecule is polar from its molecular shape and bond polarities.

CORE

Polarity

Polarity in covalent bonding and molecules

In covalent bonding, the bonds consist of electrons shared between the atoms. This sharing is not equal, unless the two atoms involved are identical (such as the two chlorine atoms in a Cl_2 molecule), because different atoms have different **electronegativities**, that is, have different attraction for electrons in a covalent bond (the most commonly met electronegativity scale is the Pauling electronegativity, used here, which assigns a value between 0 and 4 to indicate how strongly an atom will attract electron pairs in a covalent bond – the larger the number the greater the attracting power). The more electronegative atom will attract the electrons more strongly than the less electronegative one and that will result in it having a slight negative charge. The less electronegative atom will therefore be slightly deficient in electrons and so will have a slight positive charge. A covalent bond in which the atoms have fractional electrical charges (referred to as delta plus and delta minus and shown as δ+ and δ-) is known as a **polar bond**. In hydrogen chloride, for example, the chlorine atom is more electronegative than the hydrogen, which has the lowest electronegativity of all the common non-metals, and so the chlorine attracts the shared electrons more strongly. The hydrogen therefore has a slight positive charge and the chlorine a slight negative charge, as illustrated in Figure 420.

$H^{\delta+}$  $Cl^{\delta-}$

Figure 420 Illustrating a polar bond in hydrogen chloride

The **electronegativity** of an element can be judged from its position in the periodic table. All of the elements that form covalent bonds have quite high electronegativities, otherwise they would bond in a different way. The electronegativity of atoms increases across a period of the periodic table and also increases going up a group, so that the electronegativities fall into a series:

B & Si < P & H < C & S & I < Br < Cl & N < O < F

High Very high Extremely high

The greater the difference in electronegativity of the atoms involved, the greater the polarity of the bond and hence the electrical charges on the atoms involved. For example compared to the H–Cl the bond, the H–F bond is more polar and the H–I bond less polar. In the extreme case of very large electronegativity differences (e.g. sodium and chlorine) the electron can be considered to have been transferred, resulting in ionic bonding.

In some cases, such as hydrogen chloride, the polar bonds result in the molecule having a resultant dipole, that is, there is a positive and a negative end to the molecule. In carbon dioxide, even though the carbon-oxygen bonds are polar, their effects cancel out because of the symmetry of the molecule. The centres of positive and negative charge are in the same place, so that there is no overall **dipole**. In other molecules, such as water, because the shape is not so symmetrical, the effects of the polar bonds do not cancel, so that the molecule does have an overall dipole. Carbon dioxide and water molecules are compared in Figure 421.

$O^{\delta-} = C^{\delta+} = O^{\delta-}$

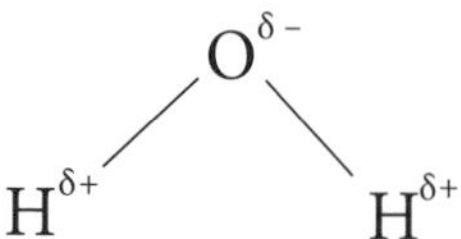

Figure 421 Comparing a non-polar molecule (Carbon Dioxide) with a polar molecule (Water)

In summary, for a molecule to be polar:

- it must contain polar bonds, and
- its shape must be such that the centres of positive and negative charges are not in the same place.

The **dipole moment** is a measure of the polarity of a molecule. Non-polar molecules have a zero dipole moment. For other molecules the more polar the molecule, the greater the dipole moment. Methane for example has a dipole moment of zero, hydrogen iodide has a value of 0.42 Debye, hydrogen chloride 1.05 Debye and hydrogen fluoride a value of 1.91 Debye.

Another way to represent the polarity of a bond is by means of arrows drawn next to the bond (with the head pointing to the more electronegative element). If because of symmetry the arrows on the various bonds in a molecule cancel each other out (that is, their vector sum is zero, so that when when placed head-to tail, these arrows return to the same point) then the molecule will be non-polar (for example, CO_2). If they do not then the molecule will be polar and the vector sum of the polar bonds will give the molecular dipole (for example in H_2O). Molecular polarity can be indicated by an arrow drawn next to the molecule. By convention the head of the arrow points in the direction of the partial negative charge. This is illustrated below for polar trichloromethane ($CHCl_3$) and non-polar tetrachloromethane (CCl_4), both of which are tetrahedral:

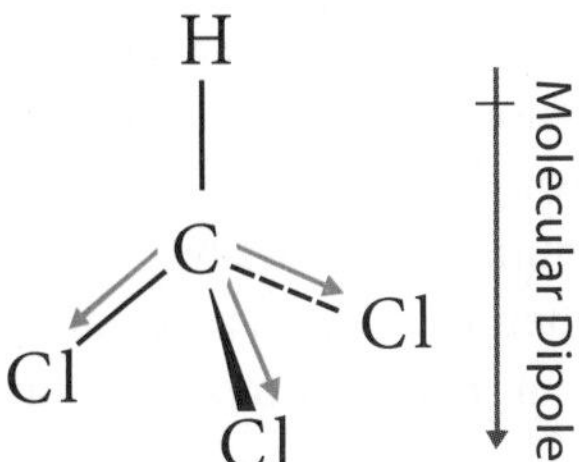

Trichloromethane, polar bonds do not cancel, so it is a polar molecule. (Note: the C—H bond has a low polarity and is generally ignored.)

Tetrachloromethane, polar bonds cancel (equal and symmetrical) so it is a non-polar molecule.

Figure 422 Using bond polarity vectors to predict molecular polarity

Similar consideration of the polar bonds in symmetrical molecules such as methane (CH_4) and ethene (C_2H_4) will indicate that these are non-polar, whereas less symmetrical molecules such as ammonia (NH_3), chloromethane (CH_3Cl) and dichloromethane (CH_2Cl_2) are polar.

Experimentally, it is easy to tell if a liquid is polar or not by bringing an electrostatically charged rod close to a jet of liquid running out of a burette. If it is polar (such as $CHCl_3$, C_2H_5OH or $(CH_3)_2CO$) the stream of liquid will be attracted to the rod, if non-polar (such as CCl_4 or hexane, C_6H_{14}) it will be unaffected. This occurs because, in the electrical field produced by the rod, the molecules orientate themselves so that the end closest to the rod has the opposite charge to the rod, meaning that the electrostatic force of attraction is greater than the force of repulsion.

Exercise 14.1

1. Which one of the following bonds would be the most polar?

   A C—N
   B S—O
   C Si—F
   D P—Cl

2. Carbon and chlorine form a series of compounds: CH_4; CH_3Cl; CH_2Cl_2; $CHCl_3$; CCl_4. Which of these will be polar molecules?

   A CCl_4 only
   B CH_3Cl and $CHCl_3$ only
   C CH_3Cl, CH_2Cl_2 and $CHCl_3$ only
   D CH_3Cl, CH_2Cl_2, $CHCl_3$ and CCl_4 only

3. State whether you would expect the molecules below to be polar or non-polar.

   a) SiF_4 b) PCl_3 c) H_2S
   d) NF_3 e) CCl_4

4. Which atom in the following bonds would you expect to carry a partial negative charge?

   a) H—N b) O—P c) C—F
   d) S—S e) B—O

5. Two molecules are shown below

   A)

   B)

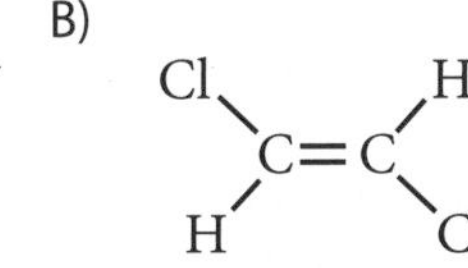

   a) In the molecules there are three kinds of bonds (C=C, C—Cl and C—H). Which would you expect to be the most polar and which the least?
   b) Which one of these molecules would you expect to be polar and which non- polar? Explain why.
   c) Given unlabelled samples of the two liquids, how could you use this property to identify them. Say exactly what you would do and what result you would expect in each case.

6. For each of the following species :

   i) draw the Lewis structure, including all non-bonding electrons.

CORE

ii) give a sketch of the shape (including bond angles) of the molecule.
iii) state whether it would be polar or non-polar.

a) $BeCl_2$ (g)
b) H_2CO
c) N_2F_2 (2 isomeric forms exist)
d) ICl_4^- (AHL)
e) PF_4^- (AHL)

HIGHER LEVEL

14.2 HYBRIDIZATION (AHL)

AHL

14.2.2 Explain hybridization in terms of the mixing of atomic orbitals to form new orbitals for bonding.

14.2.3 Identify and explain the relationships between Lewis structures, molecular shapes and types of hybridization (sp, sp^2 and sp^3).

When carbon and hydrogen form methane (CH_4), a perfectly tetrahedal molecule in which carbon bonds to four hydrogens results. How can this be explained when carbon has only two unpaired electrons with which to form bonds in its ground state? Firstly one of the pair of electrons in the s-orbital is 'promoted' to the vacant p-orbital to produce a carbon atom in an excited state which has four unpaired electrons (see below, this is similar to the electron promotion in valence shell expansion). One of these is however an s-electron and the others are p-electrons, and it seems most unlikely that these would produce four entirely equivalent bonds with hydrogen atoms. Similarly, consider the oxygen atom ($1s^22s^22p^4$). Since electrons go singly into p orbitals before pairing begins, the oxygen atom has one paired and two unpaired electrons ($2p_x^2$, $2p_y^1$, $2p_z^1$). If only the p_y and p_z orbitals are involved in the bonding then the bond angle in H_2O should be 90° (since the p_y orbital is at 90° to the p_z orbital). This is not the case in water and again some explanation is required.

The theory used to explain these is **hybridization** which states that when an atom bonds the atomic orbitals involved in forming the σ-bonds, or accommodating the lone pairs of electrons, interact with each other to form an equal number of highly directional **hybrid orbitals** of equal energy. In the cases above this results in four equivalent sp^3 hybrid orbitals, as illustrated for carbon in figure 424:

Note that the total energy has not changed, it has just been redistributed equally amongst the four new hybrid orbitals. Because of electron-electron repulsion these hybrid orbitals are directed towards the corners of a regular tetrahedron.

In other words, when atoms join together to form molecules (except in the case of hydrogen), their outer atomic orbitals interact with each other to produce hybrid orbitals. This process of hybridization gives the same number of hybrid orbitals as the atomic orbitals involved, but these orbitals are all of the same energy, are symmetrically arranged around the atom and are more directional so as to produce greater interaction with the orbitals of the other atoms. The precise type of hybridization that occurs depends on the number of σ-bonds and non-bonding electron pairs that have to be accommodated about the atom. If there are two of these, then the hybridization will involve one s-orbital and one p-orbital and so is known as sp hybridization. This produces two hybrid orbitals at 180° to each other (as for example in CO_2 and C_2H_2). If three electron pairs are to be accommodated, then it involves one s-orbital and two p-orbitals to give sp^2 hybridization, with a trigonal planar symmetry (as for example in BF_3 and $H_2C{=}O$), and if four

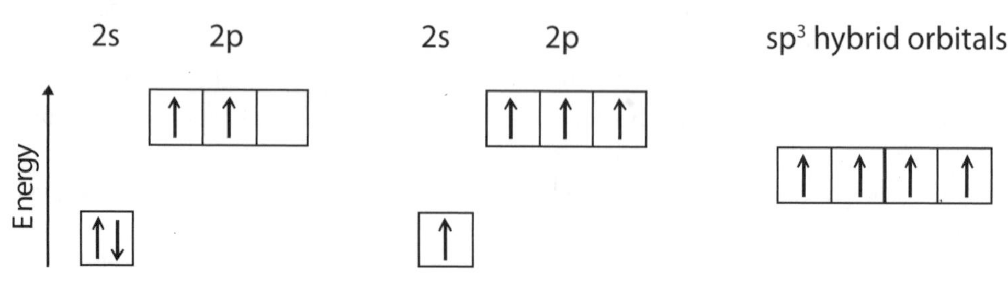

Figure 424 sp^3 hybrid orbitals

TOK Is hybridization a real process or a mathematical device?

Now the person who wrote this sounds just like my friends who, when I tell them of my plans for the future, say to me "Get real!" I suppose that "really" gets to the heart of things. What is reality? I suppose first of all you have to agree there is a reality – an external universe outside of my head (no, not your head, my head because you only exist in there). Once that is over, the question must then what attributes would something have to have for me to be sure that it was part of this physical world – we mulled over this a bit with regard to atoms and sub-atomic particles, but perhaps hybridisation is a little bit different – it's not supposed to be an object, but a process and what do we mean by a process being real.

Do we actually need it? What does it help us to explain? It is useful and are there simpler alternatives? I suppose that what it helps to explain is how all of these different shaped atomic orbitals (and again it's interesting to reflect on the evidence for these) can give rise to equal bonds in molecules like methane. So hybridisation is a bit like saying you take a large, green wine bottle, along with 3 small, colourless beer bottles, melt them and use the glass to make four identical pale green bottles for fizzy water. Isn't it enough to say in the atom there were atomic orbitals and in the molecule there are molecular orbitals and we don't really need to know a lot about how one became the other? This is the basis of the "molecular orbital" approach which youhave started to meet through σ-bonds and π-bonds.Hybridization seems to work mathematically, meaning that if you put in the atomic wave functions and carry out some fancy mathematical transformations, lo and behold out come things with a similar symmetry to common molecular shapes. Perhaps it's a bit like saying that long division is real (whatever that might mean) because if I have148 pieces of candy to share out amongst the 13 students in my class I can calculate I'll have to eat five myself (or maybe 18?). Again I'm just not sure that it helps my understanding of anything.

The contrast between mathematical devices and reality in the statement is an interesting one, Just like the first part of Bertrand Russell's famous quotation about"Mathematics is a subject in which people never know what they are talking about and never know whether it is true." Is what they are talking about the real world? Is mathematics discovered, in which case it is part of the real world (Didn't somebody once say that God was the great geometer, so maybe we are all part of a mathematical device?), or invented, in which case it is a product of human imagination and no more real than that may be. Anyway the statement seems to have prejudged the issue. Can't something be both? The Laws of Physics seem to be very well expressed in mathematical terms, so maybe all of mathematics is real? If so can both Euclidean and non-Euclidean geometry be real at the same time? I think I'll go off to find out more about imaginary numbers, and don't dare tell me that they're real!

such regions then an s-orbital and three p-orbitals interact to give four tetrahedrally orientated sp^3 hybrid orbitals (as for example in CCl_4 and C_2H_6). These hybrid orbitals are shown in Figure 425:

It can be seen that the shapes of these hybrid orbitals correspond to the shapes found for molecules according to electron repulsion theory (refder to the VSEPR theory in section 4.3) and the best way to determine the hybridization around an atom is by considering the shape of the molecule.

In ethyne (C_2H_2) for example, we can conclude that the carbon atoms are sp hybridized because of the linear shape of the molecule.

H—C≡C—H Linear

Note that hybrid orbitals can just form σ-bonds; π-bonds are only produced by the sideways interaction of unhybridized p-orbitals. (For an explanation of σ- and π-bonds refer to Section 4.6) The hybridization process of the carbons in this case are represented in Figure 426.

No. of orbitals	Hybridization	Shape
2	sp	Linear
3	sp^2	Trigonal planar
4	sp^3	Tetrahedral

Figure 425 The shapes of hybrid orbitals

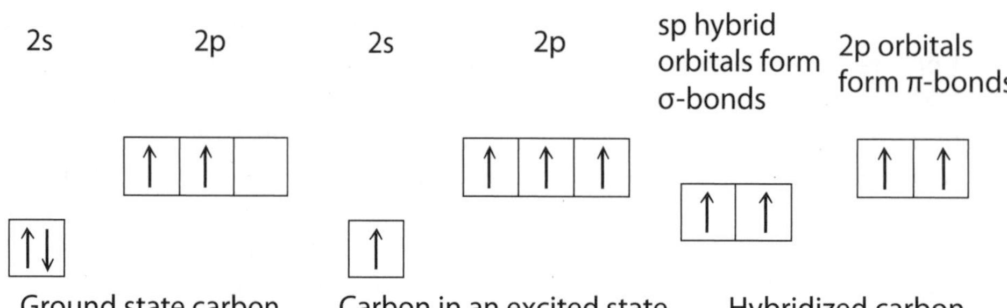

Figure 426 Hybridization of carbon in ethyne

Another example is ammonia, which has sp^3 hybridization because its trigonal pyramid shape can only result from a tetrahedral geometry. In this case however the sp^3 hybrid orbitals are not all used for bonding as one accommodates a lone pair of electrons. The hybridization can be represented as:

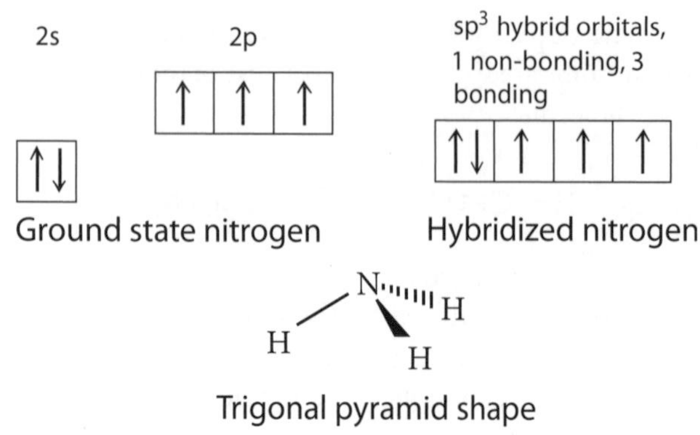

Figure 427 Hybridisation in ammonia

Another way to predict the hybridization present is from the Lewis structure. In this case the number of orbitals required around the central atom will be equal to the sum of the number of bonds (single, double or triple all count as one as each only involves one σ-bond) and the number of lone pairs. In water for example, there are two bonds and two lone pairs so that four orbitals are required, hence the hybridization will be sp^3. A second example would be the carbon atom in ethene which must be sp^2 hybridized in order to form bonds to three other atoms with no lone pairs. The relevant Lewis structures are gien in figure 428

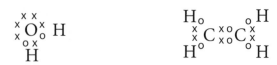

Figure 428 The Lewis structures of the molecules whose hybridization is discussed above

14.2.1 Describe σ and π bonds.

Exercise 14.2

1. The carbon atoms in ethane (C_2H_6), ethene (C_2H_4) and ethyne (C_2H_2) provide examples of the three common types of hybridization. In the order given above the type of hybridization corresponds to

   A sp, sp^2, sp^3
   B sp, sp^3, sp^2
   C sp^3, sp^2, sp
   D sp^3, sp, sp^2

2. The hybridization of the boron atom in boron trifluoride is described as sp^2.

   a) Use this example to explain what is meant by the term 'hybridization'.
   b) Why may we conclude that this kind of hybridization occurs in boron trifluoride?
   c) Boron trifluoride can react with a fluoride ion to give the tetrahedral BF_4^- ion. What type of hybridization would you expect the boron in this to have?

MULTIPLE BONDS

When a double bond forms between two atoms, the two bonds are not identical. The first bond is formed by the "end on" interaction of electrons in a s-orbital, or more commonly a hybrid orbital (see Section 4.5). When they interact they produce a bond in which the electron density is at its greatest on the inter-nuclear axis (an imaginary line joining the two nuclei) and is symmetrical about it. Bonds of this type are called σ (pronounced sigma) bonds.

The second bond in a double bond is formed by the "side on" interaction of electrons in p-orbitals at right-angles to the inter-nuclear axis. This bond has a low electron density on the inter-nuclear axis, but regions of high electron density on opposite sides of it. Bonds of this type are called π (pronounced pi) bonds. The formation of sigma and pi bonds is shown in Figure 429.

Single bonds are always σ-bonds, double bonds are always made up of one σ-bond plus one π-bond, whereas triple bonds are one σ-bond plus two π-bonds, with the π- bonds being at 90° to each other (that is, one with high electron density above and below the inter-nuclear axis, the other with high electron density in front of and behind it as you view the page). This is illustrated in Figure 430.

AHL

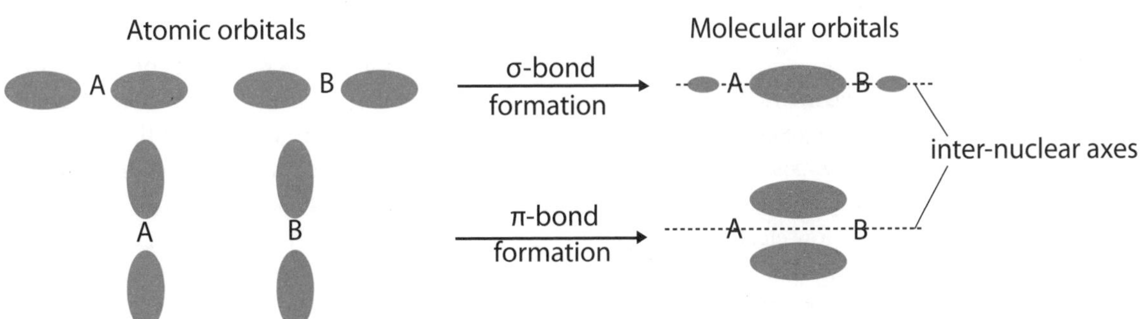

Figure 429 The formation of σ-bonds and π-bonds from the interaction of atomic orbitals

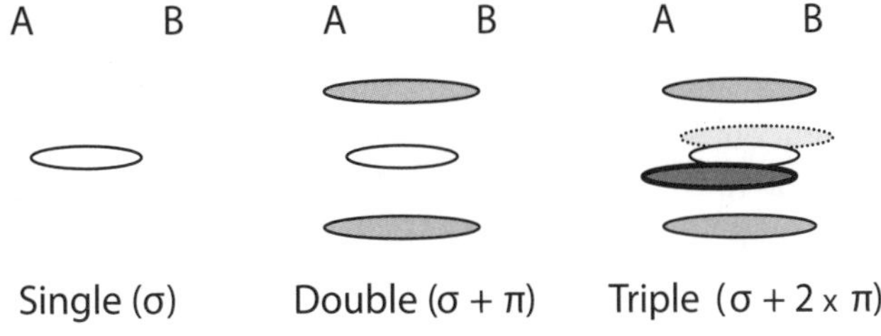

Figure 430 The molecular orbitals comprising single, double and triple bonds

Because there are more electrons between the two nuclei, double and triple bonds result in them being more strongly bonded than single bonds, so pulling the atoms closer together. This means that going from single to double to triple bonds the bond energies increase and the bond lengths decrease, as shown in Figure 431 using carbon-carbon bonds as examples.

Bond type	Bond energy - kJ mol^{-1}	Bond length pm
Single (C—C)	348	154
Double (C=C)	612	134
Triple (C≡C)	837	120

Figure 431 The bond energies and bond lengths of carbon-carbon bonds

This is also true for other types of bonds. For example ethanoic acid contains two carbon-oxygen bonds, one single and one double, and it is found that the double bond is significantly shorter and stronger than the single. Similarly in the second period of the periodic table, the bond energy decreases going from nitrogen (N≡N, 944 kJ mol^{-1}, one of the strongest covalent bonds), through oxygen (O=O, 496 kJ mol^{-1}) to fluorine (F—F, 158 kJ mol^{-1}, one of the weakest covalent bonds).

Exercise 14.2

1. Which one of the following correctly describes a π-bond?

   A It is formed by the interaction of s-orbitals and has a high electron density on the internuclear axis.
   B It is formed by the interaction of s-orbitals and has a low electron density on the internuclear axis.
   C It is formed by the interaction of p-orbitals and has a high electron density on the internuclear axis.
   D It is formed by the interaction of p-orbitals and has a low electron density on the internuclear axis.

2. Carbon and oxygen can bond either by a single bond (as in CH_3—OH), a double bond (as in O=C=O), or a triple bond (as in C≡O).

   a) Describe these three types of bonds in terms of σ-bonds and π-bonds.
   b) How would you expect the length of the carbon-oxygen bond to vary in the three examples given?

14.3.1 Describe the delocalization of π electrons and explain how this can account for the structures of some species.

14.3 DELOCALIZATION OF ELECTRONS (AHL)

A π-bond results from the "sideways" interaction of p-orbitals on two atoms, each containing one electron. On some occasions this interaction can involve more that two atoms and the p-orbitals on these atoms may contain differing numbers of electrons. This results in what is known as a **delocalized π-bond**. Delocalization in poly-atomic species allows the π electrons to spread over more than two nuclei (i.e. the π valence electrons provided by an individual atoms are not held around that atom but are mobile and shared by a number of atoms). This spreading out of the electrons that gives the species a lower potential energy (making it more stable) than it would have if it were composed of simple double and single bonds. Delocalization can hence be used to explain observations that are not readily accounted for in other ways.

The best known occurrence of delocalization is in benzene, C_6H_6, which is a planar, regular hexagonal shaped molecule, in which all of the carbon-carbon bond lengths and angles are equal. Simple bonding theory would predict that the carbon-carbon bonds in the ring would be alternately double and single (see Figure 432 a). This however would not lead to a regular hexagonal shape, as double bonds are shorter than single ones. The description involving delocalization is that each carbon atom in benzene is sp^2 hybridized. One of these orbitals forms a σ-bond to the hydrogen atom it is attached to, the other two form σ-bonds to the carbons on either side. The remaining electron (carbon has four valence electrons, three of which have been used to form the three σ-bonds) is in a p-orbital perpendicular to the plane of the σ-bonds. These p-orbitals on each carbon atom interact to produce a delocalized π-bond, which gives rings of high electron density above and below the ring of carbon atoms (see Figure 432 b).

(a) Possible "resonance" structures in terms of localized single and double bonds

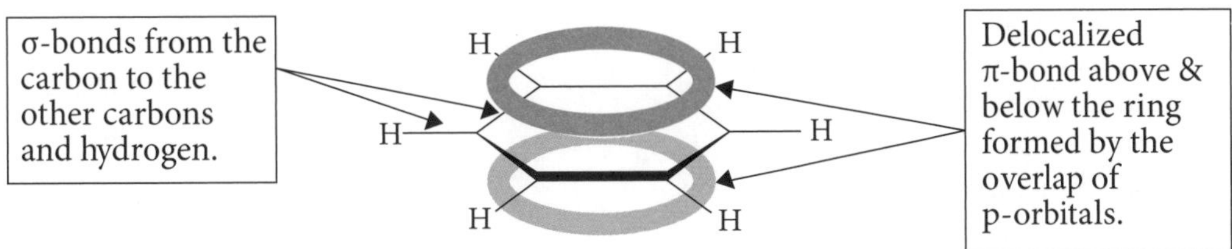

(b) Delocalized description

Figure 432 Some descriptions of the bonding in benzene

An alternative approach (the "valence bond" model as opposed to the "molecular orbital" model above) is to consider the bonding in relation to the possible Lewis structures. If there are two or more equivalent structures that can be drawn for a molecule, as shown for benzene in Figure 432 (a), then what actually occurs will be mid-way between these various possibilities. The equivalent simple structures are called "resonance structures" and the actual species that exists is referred to as a "resonance hybrid" of these structures, because the species cannot be described adequately by a single structure involving just single and double bonds. Resonance structures have the same sigma bonds but differ in the arrangement of the pi bonds.

The "bond order" is the average of the number of bonds of the different resonance structures. In the case of benzene each bond is single in one resonance structure and double in the other, so the bond order is 1½. The resonance hybrid is always more stable than any of the resonance structures, the difference in stability being known as the resonance energy (the terms delocalisation energy and stabilisation energy are also sometimes used). This means that, for example, thermochemical calculations based on resonance structures give incorrect results.

Cyclohexene reacts with hydrogen to form cyclohexane and this reaction releases 119 kJ mol^{-1} of heat energy. If benzene contained three double bonds (i.e. it was 1,3,5-cyclohexatriene) then it would be reasonable to expect it to release three times this amount of energy (i.e. 357 kJ mol^{-1}).

In fact only 207 kJ mol^{-1} of heat energy is released when benzene is fully hydrogenated so that the delocalization of the π-bonds results in benzene being more stable by about 150 kJ mol^{-1}. This is illustrated in Figure 433.

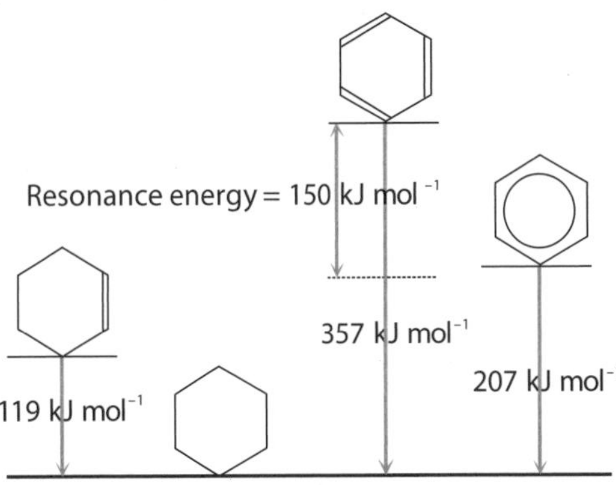

Figure 433 The hydrogenation of benzene

Graphite, an allotrope of carbon, has bonding that is very similar to that in benzene. The hydrogens on benzene are replaced by other carbons, so that each carbon is bonded to three other carbons by σ-bonds, formed by sp^2 hybrid orbitals, and the p-orbitals on the carbon atoms interact to form a delocalized π-bond that extends in two dimensions throughout the layer of the graphite crystal. This gives a carbon-carbon bond order (the average of the bonds between the atoms) of 1⅓. The structure of graphite is shown in Figure 454.

Another example of delocalized bonding is the carbonate ion shown in Figure 434. There are three equivalent resonance structures that can be drawn for this. Note the use of the double headed arrow ($\longleftrightarrow$) used to join resonance structures. This should never be confused with, or substituted for, the equilibrium arrow ($\rightleftharpoons$). The resonance hybrid has all the carbon–oxygen bonds part way between single and double bonds (specifically, the bond order is 1⅓ as each is a double bond in one of the three resonance structures), with the negative charge equally distributed over all of the oxygens (to be more precise each oxygen has a ⅔– charge as it carries a negative charge in two of the three resonance structures). The description of the carbonate ion in terms of delocalized bonding would be that the central carbon is sp^2 hybridized and that it forms σ-bonds to the three oxygens. There is then a delocalized π-bond formed by the four p-orbitals on the carbon and the three oxygens that also accommodates the extra electrons which give the ion its negative charge.

It is sometimes difficult deciding exactly when delocalization is likely to occur. Ethanoic acid and its anion, the ethanoate ion, are very similar however delocalization occurs in the anion, but not in the acid. The way that this may be predicted is from the fact that only one valid Lewis structure can be drawn for the acid, but there are two valid equivalent Lewis structures for the anion (see Figure 435). The evidence that this interpretation is correct is that in the acid the two carbon–oxygen bond lengths are different, but in the anion the two bonds are equal and their length is between the lengths of the bonds in the acid.

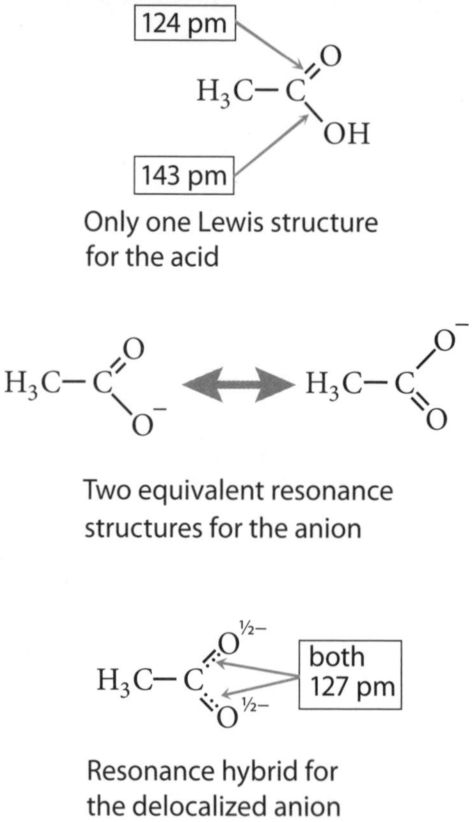

124 pm

$H_3C-C(=O)OH$

143 pm

Only one Lewis structure for the acid

$H_3C-C(=O)O^- \longleftrightarrow H_3C-C(O^-)=O$

Two equivalent resonance structures for the anion

H_3C-C ($O^{½-}$, $O^{½-}$)

both 127 pm

Resonance hybrid for the delocalized anion

Figure 435 Bonding in ethanoic acid and the ethanoate ion

Two other examples of common species in which delocalization occurs are ozone (O_3) and the nitrite ion (NO_2^-, also known as the nitrate(III) ion). In ozone the contributing resonance structures each have the central atom forming a dative single bond to one oxygen and a double bond to the other. A delocalized π-bond description would be that the oxygens all have sp^2 hybridization and the p-orbitals perpendicular to this interact to form a delocalized π -bond above and below the plane of the oxygen atoms, giving a bond order of 1½ in ozone.

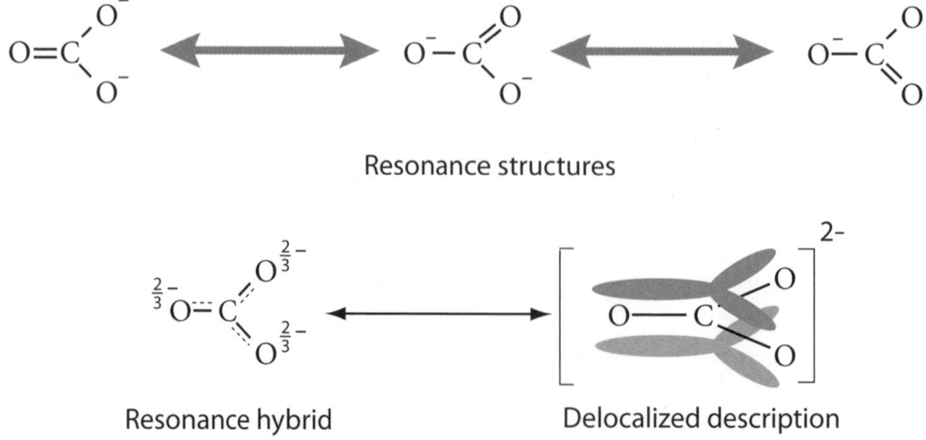

$O=C(O^-)O^- \longleftrightarrow O^--C(=O)O^- \longleftrightarrow O^--C(O^-)=O$

Resonance structures

$^{\frac{2}{3}-}O\text{---}C(O^{\frac{2}{3}-})(O^{\frac{2}{3}-})$ ⟷ $[O—C(O)(O)]^{2-}$

Resonance hybrid

Delocalized description

Figure 434 Delocalization in the carbonate ion

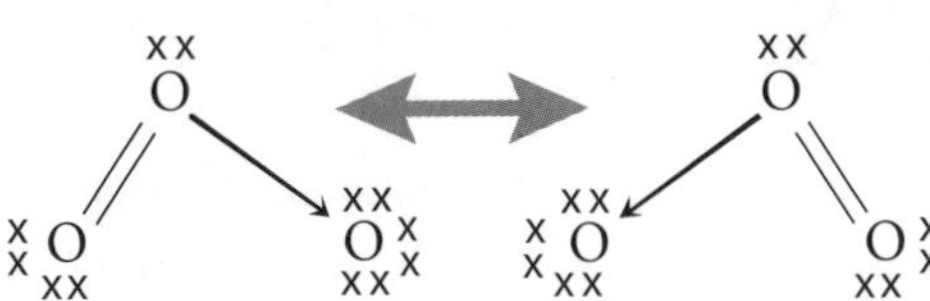

Resonance structures

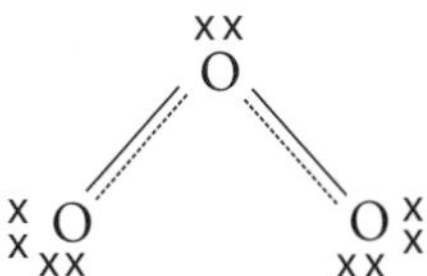

Resonance hybrid

Figure 436 Resonance structures

This predicts that the oxygen-oxygen bond length will be part way between the single bond found in hydrogen peroxide (HO—OH, 146 pm) and the double bond in the oxygen molecule (O=O, 121 pm). The **empirically** determined value of 128 pm fits with this prediction. Lewis diagrams for the possible resonance structures for the nitrite ion, which is isoelectronic with ozone, are shown below along with the resonance hybrid:

Resonance structures

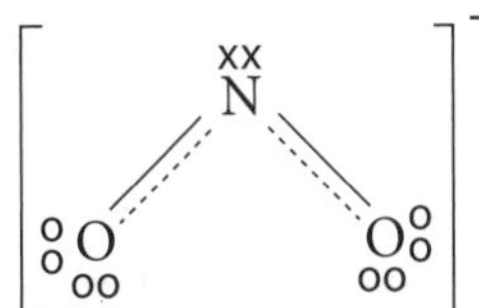

Resonance hybrid

Figure 437 Resonance Lewis structures

Note that the predicted nitrogen-oxygen bond order is 1½ and that the charge is shared equally over the two oxygen atoms. A similar approach can be used to predict the bonding in the nitrate(V) ion (see question 2 in Exercise 4.7).

Exercise 14.3

1. Which one of the following species cannot be adequately described by a single Lewis diagram?

   A NH_4^+
   B HCO_3^-
   C C_2H_2
   D OH^-

2. a) Draw a Lewis diagram for the nitrate(V) ion.

   b) Explain how this fails to adequately describe the shape of the nitrate(V) ion.

   c) How is the bonding better described using the concept of delocalization?

   d) Describe how the atomic orbitals interact to produce a delocalized bond.

   e) What bond order would you expect for the N—O bond in the nitrate(V) ion and what charge would you expect each oxygen atom to carry?

   f) How would you expect the lengths of the N—O bonds in nitric(V) acid (HNO_3)to compare with those in the nitrate(V) ion?

4.3 INTERMOLECULAR FORCES

CORE

4.3.1 Describe the types of intermolecular forces (attractions between molecules that have temporary dipoles, permanent dipoles or hydrogen bonding) and explain how they arise from the structural features of molecules.

4.3.2 Describe and explain how intermolecular forces affect the boiling points of substances.

Covalent bonding between atoms can result in either a giant structure such as diamond, or in a simple molecular structure such as methane. In the latter weak forces exist between the molecules. If it were not for these then molecular covalent compounds would never condense to liquids and solids when cooled. There are three types of these intermolecular forces that will be dealt with in order of increasing strength.

VAN DER WAALS' FORCES

These forces are also sometimes referred to as **London forces** (after the Polish physicist *Fritz London*), or dispersion forces. They exist between all species as a result of the fact that a temporary dipole on one molecule resulting from the random movements of the electrons, especially in the valence shell, has an inductive effect on the neighbouring molecules. Thus, if one end of a molecule has an instantaneous negative charge then the electrons in a neighbouring molecule will be repelled from that end of the molecule resulting in an instantaneous positive charge. The net result is that the attractive forces between molecules are on average stronger than the repulsive forces, as illustrated in Figure 438.

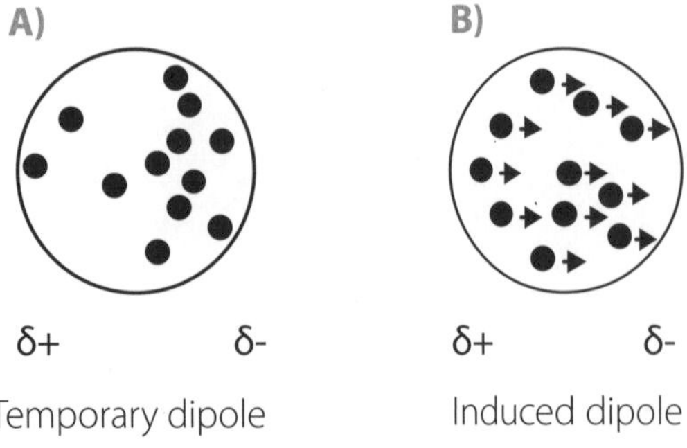

Figure 438 Illustrating van der Waals' forces

At this moment in time in "A" there are, by chance, more electrons on the right hand side than on the left hand side, which results in the right hand side of "A" having a temporary partial negative charge. This repels the electrons in "B", as shown, inducing the left hand side of B to acquire a positive charge, resulting in an attractive force. This however does not last owing to the random, independent movement of electrons.

The strength of this force increases with the molar mass of the molecule, owing to an increase in the number of electrons and hence the size of the instantaneous dipoles. This effect can be seen, for example in the noble gases (helium boils at 4 K, xenon at 165 K) and the alkanes (methane boils at 111 K, hexane at 341 K). Another example of this trend is the halogens which all exist as non-polar diatomic molecules. As the molar mass of the molecules increases, so does the boiling point as shown in Figure 439:

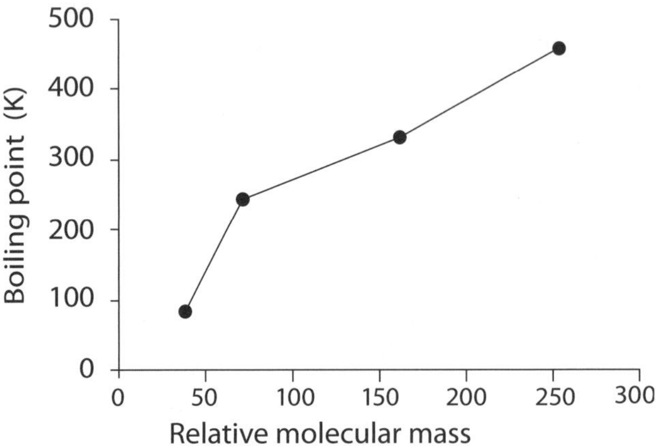

Figure 439 The variation of boiling point of the halogens with molar mass

These forces are only effective over a short range and so they are very dependent on the surface area of the molecules that come into close contact with each other. The more elongated the molecule, the stronger the van der Waals' forces and the higher the boiling point. Pentane, CH_3–CH_2–CH_2–CH_2–CH_3 boils at 309 K, whereas its almost spherical isomer, dimethylpropane, $(CH_3)_4C$ boils at 283 K. Under certain circumstances **van der Waals' forces** can become quite strong, such as those between polymer chains in some common plastics, such as polythene. These long thin molecules have both a high molar mass and a very large surface area.

DIPOLE-DIPOLE FORCES

These occur because of the electrostatic attraction between molecules with permanent dipoles.

Electrostatic attraction

$H^{\delta+}—Cl^{\delta-}$ ||||||||||||||||||||| $H^{\delta+}—Cl^{\delta-}$

These are significantly stronger than van der Waals' forces in molecules of a similar size, so that, even though both have similar molar masses, the boiling point of polar hydrogen chloride (188 K) is significantly higher than that of non-polar fluorine (85 K). Similarly, as shown in Figure 440, the boiling points of the non-polar noble gases (Ar, Kr and Xe) are considerably lower than the polar hydrogen halides of a similar molar mass (HCl, HBr and HI), because both will have van der Waals' forces between their particles, but in addition to these the hydrogen halides will have **dipole-dipole forces**:

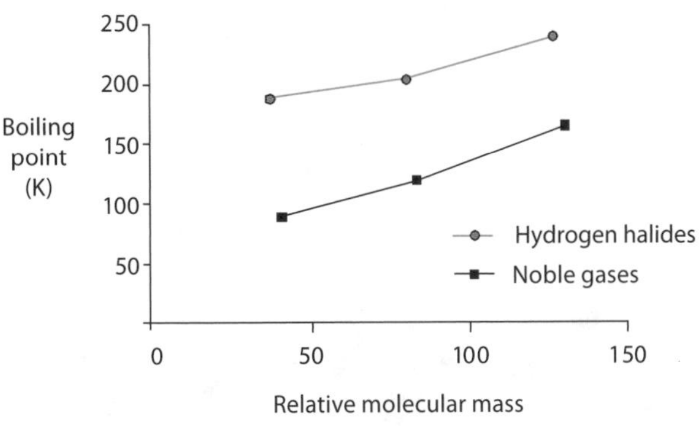

Figure 440 A comparison of the boiling points of polar and non-polar substances

HYDROGEN BONDING

This occurs most markedly in molecules that contain hydrogen bonded to highly electronegative and small nitrogen, oxygen or fluorine atoms. It occurs as a result of the interaction of a non-bonding electron pair on one of these atoms with a hydrogen atom that is carrying a relatively high partial positive charge, as a result of being bonded to another of these small, very electronegative atoms. As such it may be thought of as being part way between a dipole-dipole bond and a dative covalent bond. In the hydrogen bond, for maximum strength, the two atoms and the hydrogen should all be in a straight line. The **hydrogen bonding** interaction is illustrated in Figure 441 (in which X and Y are N, O or F).

$X^{\delta-}$: Hydrogen bond $H^{\delta+}—Y^{\delta-}$

Figure 441 An illustration of hydrogen bonding

Hydrogen bonding is usually considerably stronger than other intermolecular forces and has a large effect on the physical properties of the substances in which it occurs (refer to Section 4.10). Hydrogen peroxide (H_2O_2), of a similar molar mass to fluorine and hydrogen chloride mentioned above, has a boiling point of 431 K (158 °C) - an increase of > 250 °C over hydrogen chloride. Another set of examples is that propane C_3H_8 ($M_r = 44$), which has only van der Waals' forces, boils at 231 K, ethanal CH_3–CO–H ($M_r = 44$) which is polar but cannot hydrogen bond, boils at 294 K, whereas ethanol CH_3CH_2OH ($M_r = 46$), which has intermolecular hydrogen bonds, boils at 352 K.

Hydrogen bonding has a profound effect on the boiling points of the hydrides of nitrogen (NH_3), oxygen (H_2O) and fluorine (HF) when compared to those of other

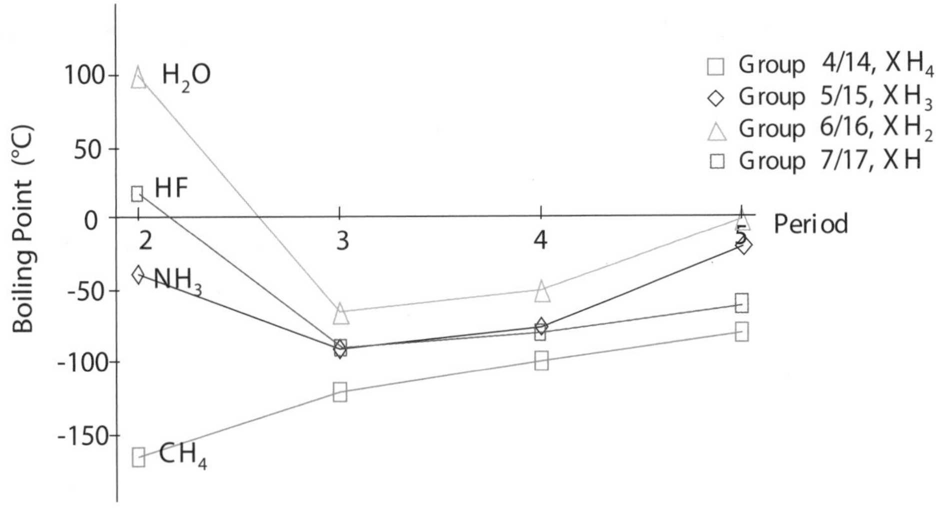

Figure 442 The effect of hydrogen bonding on the boiling points of some hydrides

elements in the same group of the periodic table. This is shown in Figure 442.

In the case of the group 4/14 compounds, the hydrides are tetrahedral and hence non-polar, so that the only forces between them are van der Waals' forces. As a result they are always the compounds with the lowest boiling points. All of the other hydrides are less symmetrical and so will have some resultant dipole and hence a degree of dipole-dipole interaction as well as the van der Waals' forces. It can be seen that going from period 5 to period 4 to period 3 the boiling points decrease in all of the groups, because of the reduction in the strength of the van der Waals' forces with decreasing molar mass. In group 4/14 this trend continues into period 2, with methane (CH_4) but in the other groups there is a sharp increase in boiling point on going from period 3 to period 2. This is explained by the existence of hydrogen bonding between molecules of ammonia (NH_3), water (H_2O) and hydrogen fluoride (HF), as well as van der Waals' forces. The deviation is most marked for water because each water molecule has two hydrogen atoms and two non-bonding electron pairs,which allows it to form two hydrogen bonds per molecule. Ammonia has only one non-bonding electron pair and hydrogen fluoride has only one hydrogen atom, so in both cases they can form only one hydrogen bond per molecule, as illustrated in Figure 443.

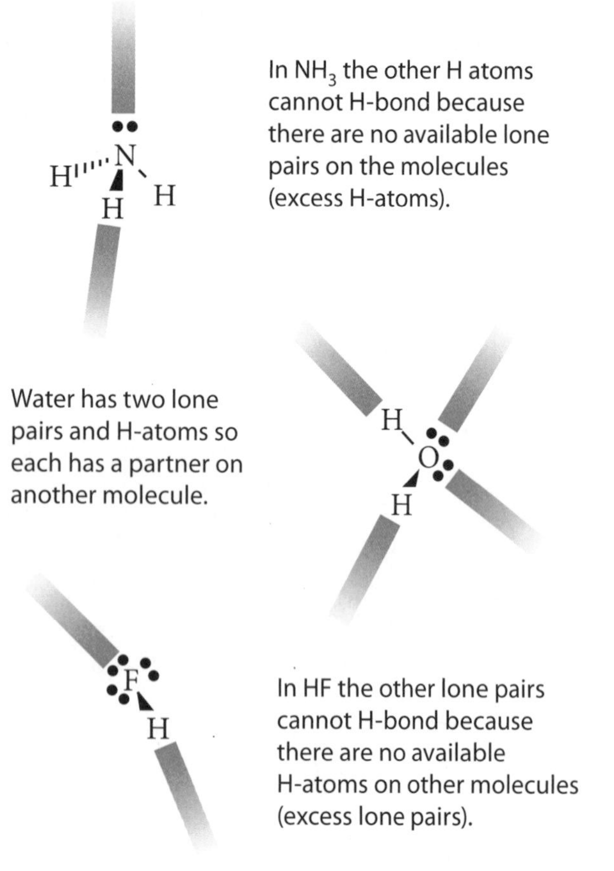

In NH_3 the other H atoms cannot H-bond because there are no available lone pairs on the molecules (excess H-atoms).

Water has two lone pairs and H-atoms so each has a partner on another molecule.

In HF the other lone pairs cannot H-bond because there are no available H-atoms on other molecules (excess lone pairs).

Figure 443 The number of hydrogen bonds formed by some common hydrides

Water is one of the most strongly hydrogen bonded substances and this affects many other physical properties, such as the molar enthalpy of fusion (6.0 kJ mol^{-1} for H_2O and only 2.4 kJ mol^{-1} for H_2S) and molar enthalpy of vaporization (41 kJ mol^{-1} for H_2O and only 19 kJ mol^{-1} for H_2S). It also accounts for many of its anomalous physical properties, such as ice having a density less than that of water. Because each water molecule can form four hydrogen bonds, ice has a structure in which each water molecule is hydrogen bonded to four others with tetrahedral symmetry.

This produces a structure very similar to the diamond structure, but with hydrogen bonds instead of covalent bonds, compare that of ice in Figure 444 below with that of diamond in Figure 452. This is a very open structure with large empty spaces enclosed in it, hence the low density. Thus ponds and lakes freeze from the surface downwards. As the water cools at the surface, it becomes less dense and stays on top until it freezes. The layer of ice on the surface helps to insulate the water underneath from further heat loss and fish and plants survive under the ice. Even when ice melts, this structure persists to some extent, which is why the density of liquid water increases when heated from 0 °C to 4 °C, the exact opposite of the effect of temperature on density in almost all other liquids.

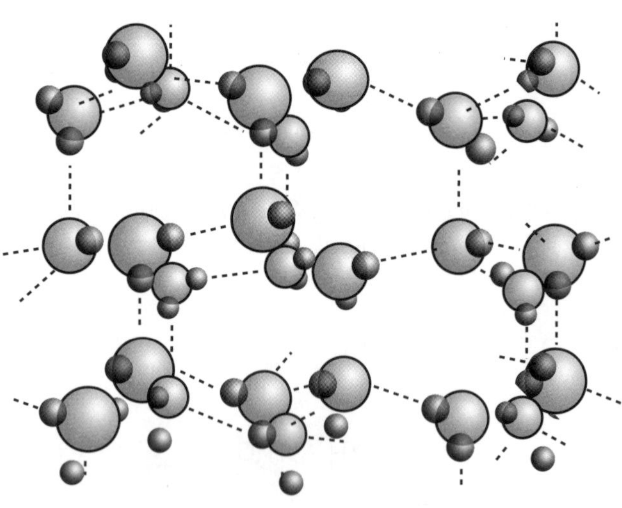

Figure 444 The structure of ice

The properties of many organic compounds are affected by the fact that hydrogen bonding can occur between their molecules, for example ethanoic acid (CH_3–CO–OH, M_r = 60, b.p. 391 K) is a liquid at room temperature and pressure, whereas butane (CH_3–CH_2–CH_2–CH_3, M_r = 58, b.p. 273 K) is a gas. Even in the gaseous state or in non-aqueous solution, the hydrogen bonding between pairs of ethanoic acid molecules persists, as shown below, so that its relative molecular mass appears to be $\approx$ 120.

Figure 445 Hydrogen bonding in **dimers** of ethanoic acid

Butane and other substances that cannot hydrogen bond are insoluble in water, because their presence would disrupt the hydrogen bonding between water molecules, whereas ethanoic acid can form its own hydrogen bonds to water and hence is fully miscible. Indeed ethanoic acid is even more strongly hydrogen bonded in aqueous solution than compounds such as ethanol because it has two oxygen atoms (>C=O and —O—H) that can form hydrogen bonds to water molecules. Water solubility even extends to compounds such as propanone (CH_3—CO—CH_3), which cannot form hydrogen bonds to other propanone molecules (it has no suitable hydrogen atom), but which can hydrogen bond to water molecules (the >C=O oxygen bonds to the hydrogen atom of a water).

Hydrogen bonding is also of great biological importance. It provides the basis for the pairing of bases in DNA and the α-helix and β-sheet secondary structures of protein molecules. The α-helix is in fact an example of intra-molecular hydrogen bonding, i.e. hydrogen bonding within a molecule. This type of bonding can also occur in much simpler molecules and explains why the boiling point of 2-nitrophenol (216 °C), which mainly bonds intra-molecularly and hence has weaker intermolecular forces, is significantly lower than that of 4-nitrophenol (279 °C), which mainly bonds inter-molecularly, as shown in Figure 446.

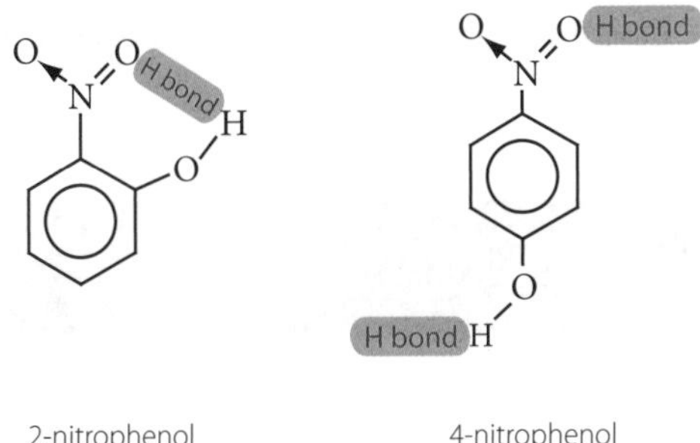

Figure 446 Hydrogen bonding in nitrophenols

In brief the consequences of hydrogen bonding for a substance are:

- Higher boiling point and lower volatility,
- Greater solubility in water,
- Higher viscosity.

Exercise 4.3

1. In which one of the following compounds would hydrogen bonding occur?

   A $COCl_2$
   B PH_3
   C H_2CO
   D CH_3OH

2. Which one of the following molecules would you expect to have the highest boiling point?

   A CH_3-CH_2-CH_2-CH_2-CH_2-CH_3
   B CH_3-CH(CH_3)-CH_2-CH_2-CH_3
   C CH_3-CH_2-CH(CH_3)-CH_2-CH_3
   D CH_3-C(CH_3)$_2$-CH_2-CH_3

3. In which of the following substances would there be the strongest forces between the molecules?

   A SiH_4
   B $H_2C=O$
   C CH_3-CH_3
   D O_2

4. Which one of the following usually produces the weakest interaction between particles of similar molar mass?

   A Hydrogen bonding
   B Covalent bonds
   C Dipole-dipole forces
   D Van der Waals' forces

5. In which one of the following substances is hydrogen bonding **not** significant?

   A Ice
   B Polythene (polyethene)
   C DNA
   D Protein

6. Explain the following observations in terms of the intermolecular forces that exist.

   a) At room temperature and pressure chlorine is a gas, bromine a liquid and iodine a solid.
   b) Water is a liquid at room temperature and pressure, but hydrogen sulfide is a gas.
   c) Ethanol (CH_3CH_2OH) has a much higher boiling point than its isomer methoxymethane (CH_3OCH_3).

CORE

d) Pentan-1-ol boils at 137 °C, whereas pentan-3-ol boils at 116 °C.

e) The boiling point of sulfur dioxide is 24 °C higher than that of chlorine.

7. Explain why the boiling points of hydrogen fluoride, water and ammonia are significantly higher than those of the analogous compounds in the next period. What other effects on physical properties occur as a consequence of the bonding you describe? Give specific examples.

4.4 METALLIC BONDING

4.4.1 Describe the metallic bond as the electrostatic attraction between a lattice of positive ions and delocalized electrons.

4.4.2 Explain the electrical conductivity and malleability of metals.

Metallic bonding occurs between atoms which all have low electronegativities. In a metal the atoms are all packed together as closely as possible in three dimensions - like oranges packed into a box. A regular arrangement of this type is known as a **close-packed lattice**. Because the metal atoms have low ionization energies and many low energy unfilled orbitals, the valence electrons are delocalized amongst (that is, shared by) all the atoms, so that no valence electron belongs to any particular atom, and they are free to move throughout the metal. The atoms, having lost their valence electrons, are positively charged and are therefore better described as being cations. The attraction of these positive ions for the mobile electrons provides the force which holds the structure together. Thus a metallic structure is often described as consisting of a lattice of positive ions filled by a mobile 'sea' of valence electrons, as illustrated in Figure 447.

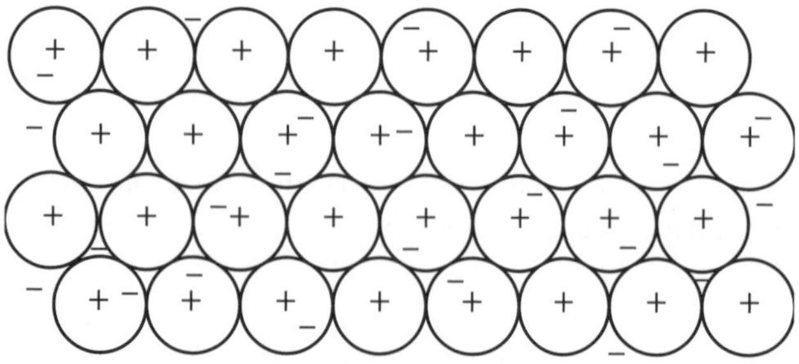

+ positive ion
– electron

Figure 447 Bonding in metals

The attraction is between the ions and the mobile electrons and not between the ions themselves, so that the layers of ions can slide past each other without the need to break the bonds in the metal. This means that metals are **malleable** and **ductile**. If an atom of a different size is introduced (for example, carbon in steel) then it is less easy for the planes to slide, hence alloys (metals containing more than one type of atom) are usually harder than pure metals.

The delocalized electrons are free to move from one side of the lattice to the other when a potential difference is applied, so that they can carry an electric current. Metals are therefore good conductors of electricity. These mobile electrons also make them good conductors of heat and their interaction with light produces the lustre characteristic of metals, at least when freshly cut.

The strength of the bond between the metal atoms depends on how many electrons each atom shares with the others. For example, the melting point of potassium (one valence electron per atom) is 337 K, calcium (two valence electrons per atom) is 1123 K and scandium (three valence electrons per atom) is 1703 K. It also depends on how far from the positive nucleus the electrons in the 'sea' are (i.e. depends on the ionic radius). For example, going down group 1 the melting point decreases from lithium (454 K), through sodium (371 K) to potassium (337 K). In some cases, such as sodium, the metallic bonding is quite weak, so that the substance is soft and has low melting and boiling points. In most cases however metallic bonding is strong, so that the solid is quite hard, though still malleable, and has high melting and boiling points. Mercury, a metal that is one of two elements that is a liquid at room temperature and pressure (bromine is the other), is an obvious exception.

Exercise 4.4

1. Use the commonly accepted model of metallic bonding to explain why:

   a) the boiling points of the metals in the third period increase from sodium to magnesium to aluminium.

   b) most metals are malleable.

   c) all metals conduct electricity in the solid state.

4.5 PHYSICAL PROPERTIES

4.5.1 Compare and explain the properties of substances resulting from different types of bonding.

The physical properties of a substance depend on the forces between the particles of the chemical species that it is composed of. The stronger the bonding between these particles, the harder the substance and the higher the melting and boiling points, though the melting point is also very dependent on the extent to which the bonding depends on the existence of a regular lattice structure. The presence of impurities in a substance disrupts the regular lattice that its particles adopt in the solid state, weakening the bonding. Hence the presence of impurities always lowers (and broadens) the melting point of a substance. For this reason, melting point determination is often used to check the purity of molecular covalent compounds. Similarly, alloys have lower melting points than the weighted mean of their component metals. The volatility, that is, how easily the substance is converted to a gas, also depends on the strength of forces between particles. Electrical conductivity depends on whether the substance contains electrically charged particles that are free to move through it when a potential difference is applied. Dissolving involves the intimate mixing of the particles of two substances (the **solute** and **solvent**). In order for one substance to dissolve in another the forces between the two types of particles in the mixture must be as strong, or stronger, than that between the particles in the two pure substances, though entropy changes also play an important role in determining solubility.

In metals the hardness, **volatility**, melting point and boiling point all depend upon the number of valence electrons that the individual metal atom contributes to the delocalized electrons. It is the mobility of these delocalized electrons that allows metals to conduct electricity in all physical states.

The malleability and ductility of metals results from the fact that the bonding is between the metal ions and these electrons, and not between the ions themselves. This allows one layer of the lattice to slide over another without the need to break the bonding.

The forces between metal atoms are often quite strong and metal atoms cannot form bonds of comparable strength to substances that are held together by bonding of a different type (that is, ionic or covalent). As a result metals do not dissolve in other substances unless they react with them chemically (for example, sodium in water). Metals can however dissolve in other metals to form mixtures of variable composition called alloys, for example brass is an alloy of copper and zinc. Mercury, as a liquid metal, forms a wide range of alloys, known as amalgams. To a limited extent non-metals can also be dissolved into metals to form alloys, the most common example being steel, which is iron with a small percentage of dissolved carbon. Alloys usually retain metallic properties, though an alloy is generally less malleable and ductile than the pure metal because the varying size of atoms in the lattice means that it is less easy for the layers to slide over each other as shown in Figure 448.

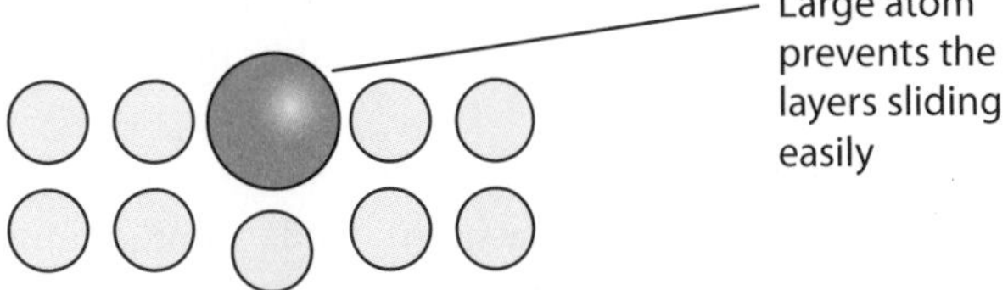
Large atom prevents the layers sliding easily

Figure 448 The lattice structure of an alloy

The ions in an ionic compound are held together by strong electrostatic forces operating in all three dimensions (see Figure 402 & 403), so that they are non-volatile, with high melting points and high boiling points. Hence they are all solids at room temperature and pressure. If one layer moves a fraction then ions of the same charge will come next to each other and so repulsion rather than attraction will result. This causes the substance to break, hence ionic solids as well as being hard, are also brittle.

The particles that make up an ionic solid are electrically charged ions. In the solid however, these are firmly held in place and cannot move to carry an electric current. However when the substance is molten, or in solution, the ions can move freely and carry an electric current. Ionic compounds therefore conduct when molten and in solution, but not in the solid state.

The strong forces between the ions mean that ionic substances are insoluble in most solvents. Water however is a highly polar molecule; hence water molecules can bond to both anions and cations because of the attraction between the partial charge on the atoms of the water molecule and the charge on the ion. The interaction between ions and the polar water molecules, known as ion-dipole interactions, is illustrated in Figure 449.

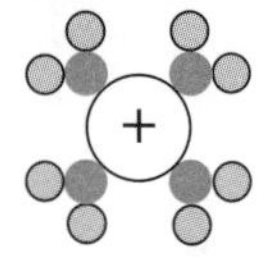

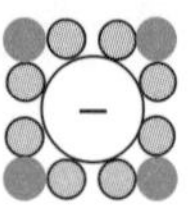

● The oxygen atoms carry a slight negative charge

○ The hydrogen atoms carry a slight positive charge

Figure 449 The hydration of anions and cations by polar water molecules

As a result of this hydration of the ions, ionic substances are more soluble in water than in non-polar solvents. If however the forces between the ions are very strong, then the ionic substance will not even dissolve in water. There are definite patterns to the solubility of ionic compounds and the **solubility** of most ionic substances can be correctly predicted using a few simple solubility rules:

- All nitrates are soluble.
- All sodium, potassium and ammonium compounds are soluble.
- All sulphates are soluble, except $BaSO_4$ and $PbSO_4$; $CaSO_4$ is only sparingly soluble.
- All chlorides, bromides and iodides are soluble, except those of silver. Lead halides are sparingly soluble in cold water, but quite soluble in boiling water.
- All other compounds are insoluble, though some, such as $Ba(OH)_2$ and $Ca(OH)_2$ are sparingly soluble.

The hydration enthalpy (that is, the enthalpy change when one mole of gaseous ions is converted to one mole of hydrated ions) is a measure of the strength of the interaction of the water molecule with the ion. It depends on the charge to size ratio (its charge density): this increases with the charge on the ion and decreases with the size of the ion. It is also greater for cations than for anions as a result of their smaller size and the angular shape of the water molecule giving better packing. As a result the hydration energy is greatest for small, highly charged cations such as the aluminium ion Al^{3+}.

In the substances of the two kinds described above the bonding is uniform throughout the substance and this kind of structure is described as a 'giant' structure. Covalent bonding can lead to two very different structures. The first of these is a giant covalent structure (also known as network covalent or macromolecular structure) such as in diamond and silica, SiO_2. In these, all of the atoms in the lattice are joined to each other by strong covalent bonds, so that giant covalent substances are very hard and have very high melting and boiling points. The strong forces holding the substance together also means that giant covalent substances are solids at room temperature and pressure, and insoluble in all solvents. All of the electrons are usually firmly held in the covalent bonds so the substance does not conduct electricity (with the exception of graphite, see Figure 455).

By contrast, in the second type of covalent structure, known as a molecular covalent structure, there are strong covalent bonds (intramolecular forces) between the atoms making up the molecule, but only weak intermolecular forces between these molecules (refer to Section 4.9). Because the bonds between one molecule and another are so weak, molecular covalent substances are often liquids or gases at room temperature and pressure, whereas the other structure types almost always give rise to solids.

The physical state depends on the strength of the intermolecular forces. In the case of the halogens, as the molar mass and hence the strength of the van der Waals' forces increases (refer to Section 4.9) the state of the element (at room temperature and pressure) changes from gas (F_2 and Cl_2) to liquid (Br_2) to solid (I_2).

Molecular covalent substances are usually quite soft as a result of the weak forces between the molecules of the solid. They will often dissolve in non- polar solvents, such as hexane, which also have weak van der Waals' forces between the molecules, but are insoluble in very polar solvents like water. This is because water is very strongly hydrogen bonded, so that inclusion of a non-polar molecule into its structure would require the breaking of these bonds. Substances that dissociate to form ions in water, such as hydrogen chloride are an exception to this, as are substances which can form hydrogen bonds to water. As with giant covalent substances, the electrons in molecular covalent substances are firmly held in the covalent bonds and so they do not conduct electricity. The bonding in a molecular covalent substance is illustrated in Figure 450.

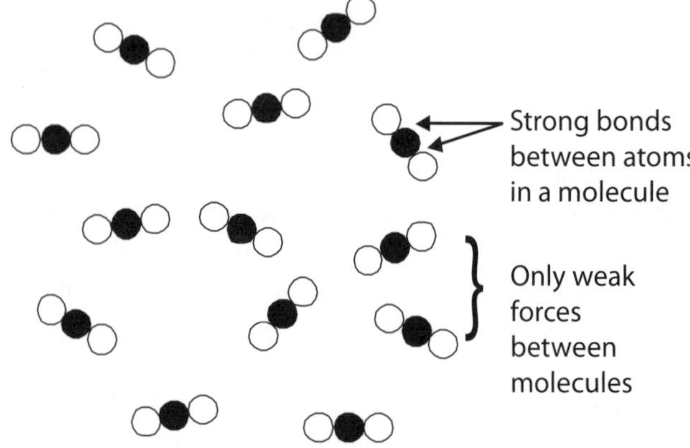

Figure 450 An illustration of molecular covalent bonding

Hydrogen bonding can however have a large effect on the properties of molecular covalent substances. These forces are much stronger than other intermolecular forces so that hydrogen bonded substances have much higher melting and boiling points than molecules of a similar molar mass that cannot hydrogen bond. For example, at room temperature and pressure ethanol (CH_3–CH_2–OH) is a liquid (b.p. = 351 K), whereas its isomer methoxymethane (CH_3–O–CH_3), which is unable to form hydrogen bonds, is a gas (b.p. = 248 K). In solids, hydrogen bonding can often result in the crystals being harder, and more brittle, than those solids with other types of intermolecular forces. Sucrose (sugar) would be a good example of such a substance. Molecules that can hydrogen bond, such as ethanol and sucrose, are usually quite soluble in water. This is because the molecule can form hydrogen bonds to the water molecules to compensate for the water-water hydrogen bonds that are broken. In alcohols the hydroxyl (—OH) group forms hydrogen bonds, but the hydrocarbon chain disrupts the hydrogen bonding in the water. This means that as the length of the hydrocarbon chain increases, the solubility of the alcohol in water decreases. This also explains why ethanoic acid (CH_3–CO–OH) is fully miscible with water, but hexanoic acid (C_5H_{11}–CO–OH) and benzoic acid (C_6H_5–CO–OH) are only sparingly soluble.

The physical properties associated with different types of structure are summarised in Figure 451, along with some typical examples.

	Giant Metallic	**Giant Ionic**	**Giant Covalent**	**Molecular Covalent**
Hardness and malleability	Variable hardness, malleable rather than brittle	Hard, but brittle	Very hard, but brittle	Usually soft and malleable unless hydrogen bonded
Melting and boiling points	Very variable, dependent on number of valence electrons, but generally high	High: melting point usually over 500 °C	Very high melting point, usually over 1000 °C	Low melting point, usually under 200 °C. Liquids and gases are molecular covalent
Electrical and thermal conductivity	Good as solids and liquids	Do not conduct as solids, but do conduct when molten or in solution	Do not conduct in any state (graphite is an exception)	Do not conduct in any state
Solubility	Insoluble, except in other metals to form alloys	More soluble in water than other solvents	Insoluble in all solvents	More soluble in non-aqueous solvents, unless they can hydrogen bond to water or react with it
Examples	Iron, copper, lead, mercury, brass	Sodium chloride, calcium oxide	Carbon (diamond) silicon dioxide (quartz, sand)	Carbon dioxide, ethanol, iodine

Figure 451 Structural types and physical properties - a summary

4.2 COVALENT BONDING (CONT)

4.2.9 Describe and compare the structure and bonding in the three allotropes of carbon (diamond, graphite and C_{60} fullerene).

4.2.10 Describe the structure of and bonding in silicon and silicon dioxide.

CARBON AND SILICON

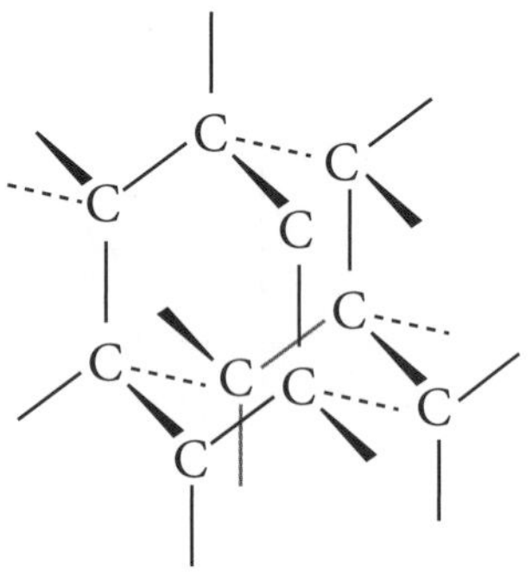

Figure 452 The covalent structure of diamond

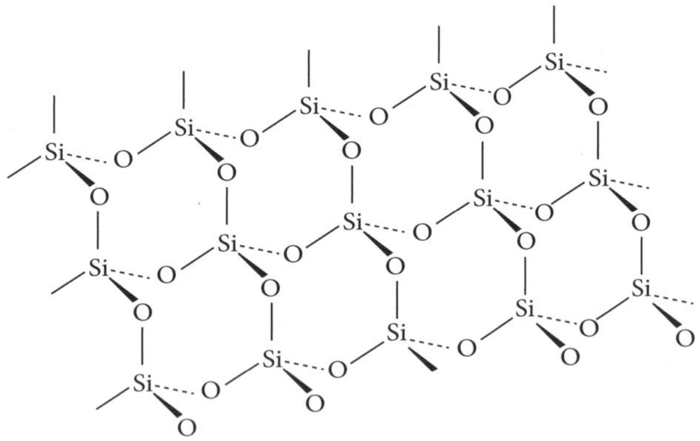

Figure 453 The bonding in silicon dioxide

Diamond is the most common example of a substance that has a giant three dimensional covalent structure. Each carbon atom in diamond is sp^3 hybridised and is joined to four others arranged tetrahedrally, so that there is strong bonding in all three dimensions. The arrangement of carbon atoms in diamond is illustrated in Figure 452. This explains why crystals of diamond are exceptionally hard and why it has very high melting and boiling points. Diamond is probably the best example of a **giant covalent structure**.

Silicon, also forming four covalent bonds, has an almost identical crystal structure to diamond. The sideways overlap between the p-orbitals of the larger atoms is less so other allotropes that involve π-bonding do not occur. Silicon dioxide (SiO_2, sometimes called silica), which occurs commonly as quartz and (in a less pure form) sand, has a very similar structure to silicon and diamond, except that each carbon is replaced by a silicon and the C-C bonds are replaced by an oxygen 'bridging' between the silicon atoms. A two dimensional diagram of the bonding is shown in Figure 453 below."

Graphite is another **allotrope** of carbon. Allotropes are different forms of an element that exist in the same physical state (ozone and diatomic oxygen molecules are another example of allotropes). It is unusual in that it comprises a giant covalent network in two dimensions, but has only weak van der Waals' forces between these sheets of carbon atoms, see Figure 454. There is a delocalized π-bond between all of the sp^2 hybridized carbon atoms in a given sheet, so that the bond order of the carbon-carbon bonds is 1⅓, hence the carbon–carbon bond length is slightly less than that found in diamond. The distance between the sheets is quite large and the forces between them quite small, hence they can easily slide over each other. This results in graphite having a lower density than diamond, being a soft solid used as a lubricant and, as layers of carbon are easily rubbed off on to paper, it is used in 'lead' pencils. The delocalized electrons between the layers are free to move so that graphite can conduct electricity in two dimensions.

The **fullerenes** are a recently discovered allotrope of pure carbon. They contain approximately spherical molecules made up of five- and six- membered carbon rings. The fullerene that has been most completely investigated is C_{60} (whose shape resembles a soccer ball), illustrated in Figure 455. In fullerenes each sp^2 hybridised carbon is bonded by sigma bonds to three other carbons, but because the surface of the sphere is not planar, there is only a little delocalization of the unpaired bonding electrons (contrast to graphite) and electrons cannot flow easily from one C_{60} molecule to the next. Hence the electrical conductivity,

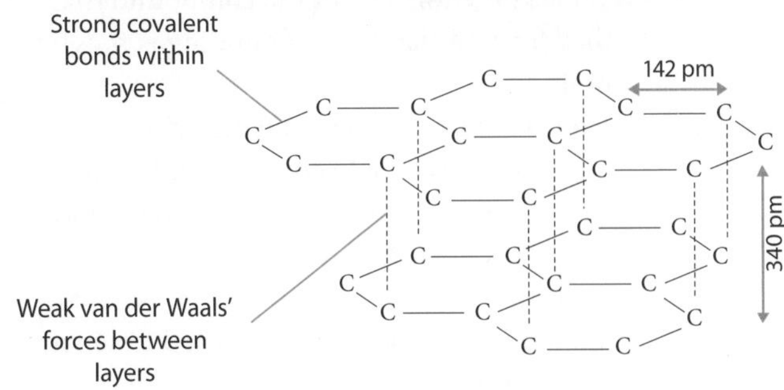

Figure 454 The structure of graphite

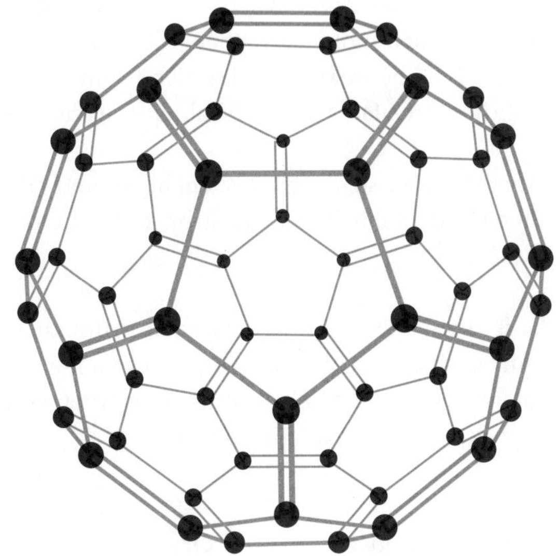

Figure 455 The structure of fullerene-60 (C_{60})

whilst greater than that of diamond, is much less than that of graphite and some fullerene derivatives, for example $C_{60}K_3$, have unusual electrical properties. Chemically C_{60} behaves as an electron deficient molecule readily accepting electrons from reducing agents to form anions with a variety of charges. Addition reactions, similar to those found in alkenes, can also occur. Unlike diamond and graphite, fullerenes are molecular, hence they will dissolve in non-polar solvents and have comparitively low melting points. For example C_{60} is moderately soluble in non-polar solvents, such as methylbenzene, and sublimes at about 800 K. With such open, spherical molecules, fullerenes have interesting compressibility properties. Closely related to the fullerenes are the nanotubes, which comprise capped cylinders of carbon atoms bonded in a very similar manner to the fullerenes.

Exercise 4.2

1. A substance that is a gas at standard temperature and pressure is likely to

   A have a molecular covalent structure.
   B be a compound of a metal.
   C have a giant covalent structure.
   D have its atoms held together by metallic bonds.

2. If an element in group 2 of the periodic table formed a compound with an element in group 7/17 of the periodic table, the compound formed is likely to

   A conduct electricity in the solid state.
   B have a low boiling point.
   C dissolve in non-polar solvents.
   D be a crystalline solid.

3. Ethanol (C_2H_5OH) is a molecular covalent compound. When pure ethanol boils the gas consists of

   A a mixture of carbon dioxide and water.
   B carbon, hydrogen and oxygen.
   C water and ethanol.
   D ethanol only.

4. Which one of the following substances would you expect to have the lowest boiling point?

   A $CsCl$
   B $SrSO_4$
   C Sc_2O_3
   D $AsCl_3$

5. Which one of the following would not conduct an electric current?

   A Solid sodium chloride
   B Liquid sodium chloride
   C Aqueous sodium chloride
   D Solid mercury

6. Which one of the following substances would you expect to be most soluble in water?

   A $CH_3-CH_2-CH_2-CH_2-CH_2-CH_3$
   B $H_2N-CH_2-CH_2-CH_2-CH_2-NH_2$
   C $Cl-CH_2-CH_2-CH_2-CH_2-Cl$
   D $CH_3-CH_2-CH_2-O-CH_2-CH_2-CH_3$

AHL

7. Molten lead and molten lead(II) bromide both conduct electricity. Which one of the following statements relating to this is true?

   A Both undergo a chemical change when they conduct.
   B Both conduct by the movement of charged particles.
   C Both will also conduct in the solid state.
   D Both contain mobile electrons.

8. Rubidium chloride (RbCl) is an ionic compound, naphthalene (C_6H_8) is a molecular covalent solid, scandium (Sc) is a metal and silicon carbide (SiC)by has a giant covalent structure.

   a) Which of these substances would you expect to have the highest melting point?
   b) Which of these substances would you expect to have the lowest melting point?
   c) Which of these substances would you expect to be soluble in water?
   d) Which of these substances would you expect to conduct electricity as a solid?
   e) Which of these substances would you expect to be soluble in a non-polar solvent, such as hexane?
   f) Which of these substances would you expect to conduct electricity only when molten, or in solution?
   g) Which of these substances would you expect to be malleable?
   h) Which of these substances is an element rather than a compound?
   i) Which of these substances would you expect to be the hardest solid?
   j) Which of these substances contains charged particles?

9. Magnesium is a silver-grey metal, iodine a black crystalline non-metal. Under suitable conditions, they will react together to form a white compound, magnesium iodide.

   a) Give two physical properties that you would expect to be different for magnesium and iodine.
   b) How would the appearance of a mixture of magnesium and iodine compare with that of their compound?
   c) What is the formula of the compound that they form? What kind of bonding is present in it?
   d) How would you expect the behaviour of magnesium iodide to compare with that of a mixture of magnesium and iodine if both were shaken with water?
   e) Describe how a non-polar solvent, such as tetrachloromethane could be used to separate the mixture of magnesium and iodine into its components.

10. In cookery class Anita expresses surprise that sugar melts so much more easily than salt, when in many other ways they are similar. Her friend Jenny, wanting to show off the fact that she is taking science, says

    "That's because sugar has covalent bonds and salt has ionic bonds. Ionic bonds are stronger than covalent ones"

    As is often the case, there is some truth in what Jenny says. Using suitable examples, explain why this statement as it stands is not accurate and then express more accurately what Jenny meant.

11. Ethanoic acid (CH_3-CO-OH) reacts with sodium hydroxide to form sodium ethanoate (CH_3–CO–O^- Na^+) and with ethanol to form ethyl ethanoate (CH_3–CO–O–CH_2–CH_3). Explain why ethanoic acid and sodium ethanoate both dissolve in water, but ethyl ethanoate does not.

12. The graph below shows the melting points of representative oxides of the elements in the third period of the periodic table. Explain how the type of bonding present in these compounds varies across the period and how this is reflected in the graph.

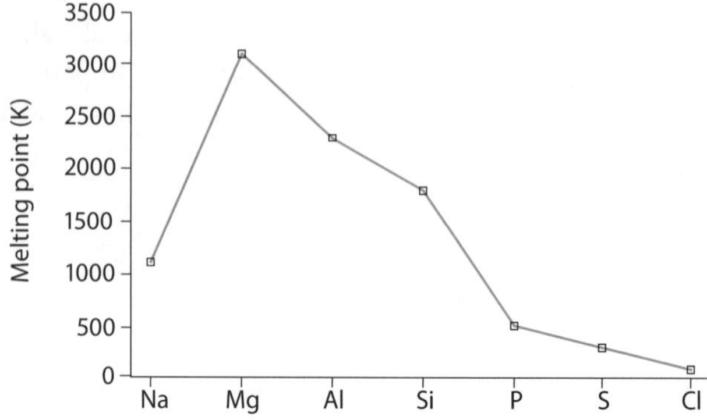

CRYSTAL TYPE	PARTICLES IN CRYSTAL	PRINCIPAL ATTRACTIVE FORCES BETWEEN PARTICLES	MELTING POINTS and BOILING POINTS	ELECTRICAL CONDUCTIVITY OF LIQUID (IN MOLTEN STATE)	CHARACTERISTICS OF THE CRYSTALS	CONDITIONS FOR FORMATION	EXAMPLES
IONIC NETWORK CRYSTALS	Positive and negative ions due to electron transfer from active metal to active non-metal, e.g., $Na^+ \ldots Cl^-$, NaCl $Ca^{2+} \ldots O^{2-}$, CaO $2K^+ \ldots SO_4^{2-}$, K_2SO_4	Attractions between oppositely charged ions. Strong ionic bonding.	High. Non-volatile due to three dimensional arrangement of anions and cations.	High. Electrolyte in molten form or in aqueous solution. Non- electrolytes as solids.	Solid. Hard, brittle. Most dissolve in polar solvents e.g. H_2O.	Metal - non-metal combination. Formed between atoms of greatly differing electronegativity (between elements of Groups 1, 2 and 3 and 6 and 7).	NaCl, CaO, K_2SO_4, KCl, CaF_2, Cs_2S, MgO
COVALENT NETWORK CRYSTALS / NETWORK SOLIDS / GIANT STRUCTURES, OR MACRO-MOLECULAR	Non-metal atoms	Covalent bonds (i.e., electron sharing) throughout the whole crystal. Very strong.	Very high. Non-volatile due to 3D network arrangement.	Diamond: nil Graphite solid: moderate conductor; Fullerene: poor conductor.	Solids. Very hard. Insoluble in most ordinary liquids.	Most are formed by two elements of Group 4, e.g. C, Si	Diamond, Si, SiO_2, graphite. Fullerene-60
METAL NETWORK CRYSTALS	Lattice of positive ions surrounded by delocalized / mobile valence electrons.	Metallic bonding. Attraction of mobile valence electrons by positive nuclei. Strong.	Most are medium to high. Non-volatile.	Very high due to presence of mobile valence electrons.	Usually solids. Most are hard yet malleable, ductile. High thermal conductivity. Insoluble in liquids. Usually soluble in molten metals.	Formed by electropositive metallic elements with low electronegativity.	Na, Cu, Ca (¾ of the periodic table elements are metals)

Figure 463 Characteristics of Crystalline Solids - A Summary

CRYSTAL TYPE	PARTICLES IN CRYSTAL	PRINCIPAL ATTRACTIVE FORCES BETWEEN PARTICLES	MELTING POINTS and BOILING POINTS	ELECTRICAL CONDUCTIVITY OF LIQUID (IN MOLTEN STATE)	CHARACTERISTICS OF THE CRYSTALS	CONDITIONS FOR FORMATION	EXAMPLES
(SIMPLE) MOLECULAR CRYSTALS (a) POLAR	Polar molecules containing elements of high electronegativity (i.e. non-metals).	Electrostatic attraction between dipoles. Intermediate strength.	Intermediate-low molar mass compounds tend to be volatile.	Very low or non-conductors when solids, liquids and in aqueous solution. A few (e.g. HCl) react with H_2O to form electrolyte.	Many polar substances are soluble in polar solvents.	Formed from asymmetrical distribution of electron cloud containing polar covalent bonds. Such bonds are formed between atoms having a moderate difference in electronegativity.	ICl, SO_2, HCl
(b) H-BONDING	H bonded to N, O, or F	Strengthened by hydrogen bonding if H is bonded to O, F or N.	Hydrogen-bonding increases boiling and melting points.		Most small hydrogen bonded substances are soluble in polar solvents.	Hydrogen-bonding if H is bonded to F, N, O.	Hydrogen bonding in: H_2O, H_2O_2, HF, NH_3 alcohols, amines, organic acids.
(c) NON-POLAR	Non-polar molecules or atoms (in the case of noble gases).	Strong covalent bonds between atoms. van der Waals' forces (weak, temporary, instantaneous dipoles) between molecules.	Low; Volatile	Non-conductors when solid and as liquid.	Soft. Usually gases or volatile liquids. Most are soluble in non-polar or slightly polar solvents. Insoluble in polar water.	Formed between atoms or from symmetrical molecules containing covalent bonds between like atoms or atoms having a small difference in electronegativity.	H_2, Cl_2, S_8, C_6H_6, CH_4, N_2, CO_2, CCl_4, I_2. Noble gases: simple atomic substances.

ENERGETICS

5.1 Exothermic and endothermic reactions

5.2 Calculation of enthalpy changes

5.3 Hess's law

5.4 Bond enthalpies

15.1 Standard enthalpy changes of reaction (AHL)

15.2 Born-Haber cycle (AHL)

15.3 Entropy (AHL)

15.4 Spontaneity (AHL)

5

CORE

5.1 EXOTHERMIC & ENDOTHERMIC REACTIONS

5.1.1 Define the terms exothermic reaction, endothermic reaction and standard enthalpy change of reaction ($\Delta H^{\ominus}$).

5.1.2 State that combustion and neutralization are exothermic processes.

5.1.3 Apply the relationship between temperature change, enthalpy change and the classification of a reaction as endothermic or exothermic.

5.1.4 Deduce, from an enthalpy level diagram, the relative stabilities of reactants and products and the sign of the enthalpy change for the reaction.

Thermochemistry is the study of energy changes associated with chemical reactions. Most chemical reactions absorb or evolve energy, usually in the form of heat, though chemical reactions can also produce light and mechanical energy. Thermochemistry studies the amounts of energy (measured in joules, J) associated with these changes. It is important to note that the energy evolved or absorbed in a reaction is unrelated to the rate of the reaction, which refers to how fast a reaction takes place.

Enthalpy (H, also known as heat content) is the total energy of a system, some of which is stored as chemical potential energy in the chemical bonds. In chemical reactions, bonds are broken and made, but the energy absorbed in breaking bonds is almost never exactly equal to that released in making new bonds. As a result, all reactions are accompanied by a change in the potential energy of the bonds and hence an **enthalpy change**. There is no 'absolute zero' for enthalpy, so absolute enthalpies for particular states cannot be measured, but the change in enthalpy that occurs during a reaction can be measured. This enthalpy change of reaction can be measured and is given the symbol ΔH. It is equal to the difference in enthalpy between the reactants and the products (see

Figure 502) assuming that the reaction occurs with no change in temperature or pressure, or that these conditions are restored to their initial values. If this is the case and any other factors affecting a system's enthalpy do not change, then ΔH is equal to the change in the potential energy of the chemical bonds. Strictly speaking the term enthalpy change only applies to reactions that occur at **constant pressure**, but in the laboratory using open beakers and test tubes, this is most often the case.

A useful comparison may be made with gravitational potential energy. If an object gains gravitational potential energy, then it must absorb energy from its surroundings (for example, from the muscles of the person lifting it) and if this is in the form of heat energy, heat is lost from the surroundings and they cool down. Similarly if a chemical reaction leads to an increase in enthalpy (i.e. the total enthalpy of the products is greater than the total enthalpy of the reactants, so the enthalpy change, ΔH, is positive), then heat energy is absorbed from the surroundings and either they get cooler or heat from an external source must be provided. This is described as an **endothermic reaction.** If the chemicals lose enthalpy (i.e. the enthalpy change, ΔH, is negative), then the heat energy lost by the chemicals is gained by the surroundings and they get hotter. This is described as an **exothermic reaction**. A comparison would be that a falling object loses gravitational potential energy and this is converted into sound (and a little heat) when it hits the floor. Most **spontaneous reactions** (that is, ones that occur, without heating, on mixing the reagents and hence are capable of doing useful work) are exothermic, but spontaneous endothermic reactions do occur (for example, dissolving ammonium chloride in water). This is summarised in Figure 501:

Enthalpy changes during the course of a reaction may also be represented by **energy level diagrams**. In an exothermic reaction the products are more stable than the reactants (bonds made are stronger than bonds broken), so that ΔH is negative. In an endothermic reaction the opposite is true. This is shown in Figure 502 below for both an exothermic and an endothermic reaction. In these energy level diagrams, the horizontal axis (x–axis) signifies the transition from reactants to products and hence is sometimes referred to as the reaction coordinate.

The numerical value of an enthalpy change for a reaction is best shown by writing the balanced chemical equation for the reaction, with the enthalpy change written alongside it. It is vital to include state symbols in all thermochemical equations because changes of state have their own enthalpy changes associated with them. The enthalpy change will of course vary with the amount of the limiting reagent, so by convention it is given for molar amounts in the equation as it is written. The units may therefore be given as kilojoules per mole, kJ mol^{-1} (to indicate that it refers to molar quantities) or simply as kilojoules, kJ (because it may not be for one mole of all the species involved). The former convention is used throughout this book. Using the thermal decomposition of sodium hydrogencarbonate as an example, a thermochemical equation would be:

Type of reaction	Heat energy change	Temperature change	Relative enthalpies	Sign of ΔH
Exothermic	Heat energy evolved	Becomes hotter	$H_p < H_r$	Negative (–)
Endothermic	Heat energy absorbed	Becomes colder	$H_p > H_r$	Positive (+)

Figure 501 Summary of exothermic and endothermic changes

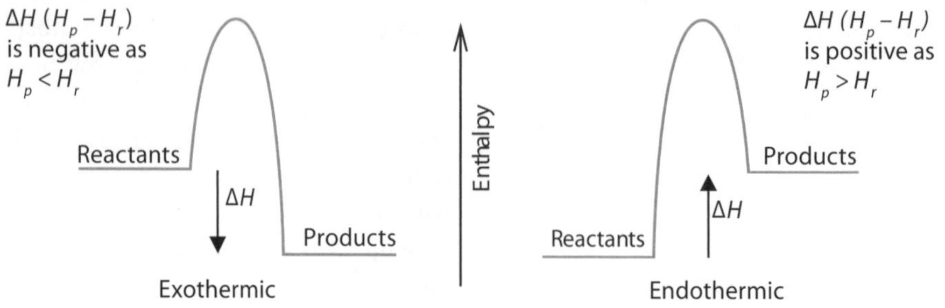

Figure 502 Energy level diagrams of reactions

$$2\,NaHCO_3\,(s) \longrightarrow Na_2CO_3\,(s) + H_2O\,(l) + CO_2\,(g)$$
$$\Delta H = +91.6\ kJ\ mol^{-1}$$

Note that ΔH is positive, indicating the reaction is endothermic. It is advisable to actually put in the '+' sign rather than just assuming that its absence indicates a positive quantity, as this concentrates the mind on whether the sign should be positive or negative. It is however also correct, though perhaps less common to write:

$$NaHCO_3\,(s) \longrightarrow \tfrac{1}{2}Na_2CO_3\,(s) + \tfrac{1}{2}H_2O\,(l) + \tfrac{1}{2}CO_2\,(g)$$
$$\Delta H = +45.8\ kJ\ mol^{-1}$$

so as to focus on the amount of sodium hydrogencarbonate. Hence the need to always quote an equation (with state symbols). Note that the basic unit of enthalpy is the Joule (J), but the quantities involved in chemical enthalpy changes are quite large, so that it is more convenient to use kilojoules (kJ, 1 kJ = 10^3 J).

By definition an enthalpy change must occur at constant pressure, but the exact numerical value will depend slightly on the exact conditions, such as the pressure and the temperature at which the reaction is carried out. For convenience **thermochemical standard conditions** have been defined as a temperature of 25 °C (298 K), a pressure of 101.3 kPa (1 atm) with all solutions having a concentration of 1 mol dm^{-3}. Note that the temperature is different from standard temperature and pressure (s.t.p.) for gases, which is 0 °C (273 K); the pressure is however the same. Thermochemical quantities that relate to standard conditions are often indicated by a 'standard' sign (⊖) as a superscript after the quantity (e.g. $\Delta H^{\ominus}$), or even more correctly by also including the absolute temperature as a subscript (e.g. $\Delta H^{\ominus}_{298}$). Frequently however, as in this text, the temperature is omitted.

Exercise 5.1

1. If a reaction is endothermic

   A ΔH is negative and heat is absorbed.
   B ΔH is positive and heat is absorbed.
   C ΔH is positive and heat is evolved.
   D ΔH is negative and heat is evolved.

2. A reaction gives out heat. This means that

   A the reaction only involves making new bonds.
   B the reaction only involves breaking existing bonds.
   C the bonds made are stronger than the bonds broken.
   D the bonds broken were stronger than the bonds made.

3. In the enthalpy level diagram shown

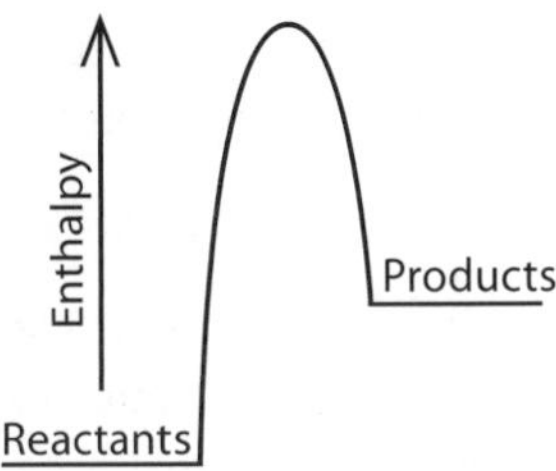

   A the reactants are more stable than the products and the reaction is endothermic.
   B the products are more stable than the reactants and the reaction is endothermic.
   C the reactants are more stable than the products and the reaction is exothermic.
   D the products are more stable than the reactants and the reaction is exothermic.

4. When magnesium is added to dilute sulfuric acid, the temperature of the acid rises.

   a) Write a balanced equation for the reaction of magnesium with sulfuric acid.
   b) Is the reaction exothermic or endothermic?
   c) Explain what this implies in terms of the chemical potential energy contained in the reactants and the products.
   d) Draw an energy level diagram for this reaction, clearly label on this the enthalpy of reaction.

CORE

5. Consider the formation of chlorine monoxide (Cl_2O) from its elements.

   a) What bonds must be broken? Does this process absorb or release energy?
   b) What bonds are made? Does this process absorb or release energy?
   c) Explain what is meant by the term "enthalpy change".
   d) In this case the bonds made are less strong than those broken, will the enthalpy change be positive or negative ?
   e) Will the formation of (Cl_2O) from its elements be an endothermic or exothermic change?

5.2 CALCULATION OF ENTHALPY CHANGES

5.2.1 Calculate the heat energy change when the temperature of a pure substance is changed.

5.2.2 Design suitable experimental procedures for measuring the heat energy changes of reactions.

5.2.3 Calculate the enthalpy change for a reaction using experimental data on temperature changes, quantities of reactants and mass of water.

5.2.4 Evaluate the results of experiments to determine enthalpy changes.

The **temperature** of a system is a measure of the average kinetic energy of the particles present. More specifically the absolute temperature (in Kelvin, K) is proportional to the mean kinetic energy and is independent of the amount of substance present. Heat, on the other hand, is a measure of the total energy in a substance and does depend on the amount of substance present. Thus, to raise the temperature of 100 g water by 1 °C requires five times the heat neeed to raise the temperature of 20 g water by 1 °C.

When the temperature of a substance increases, **heat energy** must be absorbed from the surroundings. The amount of heat required will depend on how much of the substance there is to heat (its mass, m), what the substance is made of (its **specific heat capacity**, c) and the amount by which its temperature is being increased (ΔT). The amount of heat energy released when a substance cools can be calculated in the same way:

$$\text{Heat energy} = m.c.\Delta T$$

For example the energy required to heat 50.0 g of water (specific heat capacity = 4.18 J g^{-1} K^{-1}) from 20.0 °C to 60.0°C (ΔT = 40.0 °C) is:

$$\begin{aligned}\text{Heat energy} &= m.c.\Delta T \\ &= 50.0\text{ g} \times 4.18\text{ J g}^{-1}\text{ K}^{-1} \times 40.0\text{ °C} \\ &= 8360\text{ J} \quad\text{or}\quad 8.36\text{ kJ}\end{aligned}$$

The specific heat capacity depends on the substance whose temperature is being changed, because some materials require more heat energy to bring about a change in temperature. For example from the specific heats of aluminium and gold (Al: 0.90 J g^{-1} °C^{-1}; Au: 0.13 J g^{-1} °C^{-1}) it can be seen that gold requires about 7 times less energy to raise its temperature than aluminum does. Sometimes the heat capacity of an object is referred to. This is the amount of energy required to increase its temperature by 1 °C (i.e. m.c). Thus heating a calorimeter with a heat capacity of 50 J K^{-1} by 12 °C will require 50 × 12 = 600 J of energy.

Calorimetry is a technique used to measure the enthalpy associated with a particular change. In this the temperature change of a liquid inside a well insulated container, known as a calorimeter, is measured before and after the change. For many chemical reactions a styrofoam (i.e. expanded polystyrene) cup is a convenient calorimeter because it has a very low (that is, for most purposes, negligible) heat capacity and it is a good insulator. If calorimeters made of other materials are used, for example a copper calorimeter in a combustion experiment, then the heat absorbed by the calorimeter must be added to that absorbed by the liquid:

$$\text{Heat absorbed} = (m.c.\Delta T)_{\text{liquid}} + (m.c.\Delta T)_{\text{calorimeter}}$$

Calorimetry depends on the assumption that all the heat absorbed or evolved changes the temperature of the calorimeter and its contents, that is, that no heat is gained from/lost to the surroundings. That is why it is important that calorimeters are well insulated. Nevertheless heat exchange with the surroundings is the major source of error in all thermochemistry experiments in school laboratories. It may be minimised by increasing the insulation, especially by fitting an insulated lid, but significant errors are inevitable, especially in reactions where a gas is evolved. Errors in combustion experiments, where a hot gas is being used to heat liquid in a calorimeter, are even greater. This source of error always leads to temperature rises that are less than would be expected and hence to ΔH values that are numerically less than literature values. The thermometer used often has a precision uncertainty of ±0.1°C or greater, so that uncertainty in the value of the temperature change is often the major source of imprecision.

The enthalpy change that occurs in a reaction is quoted for molar amounts in the chemical equation as it is usually written, so for example the equation

$$2\ Mg(s) + O_2\ (g) \longrightarrow 2\ MgO(s) \qquad \Delta H = -1200\ \text{kJ mol}^{-1}$$

means that 1200 kJ of heat are evolved (as ΔH is negative) when 2 moles of magnesium react completely with 1 mole of oxygen molecules. Thus if 0.600 g of magnesium (= $^{0.600}/_{24.3}$ moles) is burnt, then the amount of heat produced is:

$$\tfrac{1}{2} \times {}^{0.600}/_{24.3} \times 1200 = 14.8\ \text{kJ}$$

Often chemical reactions occur in aqueous solution and the energy evolved or absorbed alters the temperature of the water the reactants are dissolved in. Water is usually in excess and has a very high specific heat capacity, so that to a first approximation, the heat energy required to change the temperature of the other substances present may be ignored, in comparison to that needed to heat the water.

If for example 20.0 cm^3 of exactly 2 mol dm^{-3} aqueous sodium hydroxide is added to 30.0 cm^3 of hydrochloric acid of the same concentration, the temperature increases by 12.0 °C. The total volume of aqueous solution is 50.0 cm^3 (20.0 + 30.0) and the density of water (also assumed for dilute aqueous solutions) is 1.00 g cm^{-3}, hence the mass of the aqueous solution is 50.0 g. The amount of heat required to heat the water can be calculated:

$$\text{Heat energy} = m.c.\Delta T$$

$$= 50.0\ \text{g} \times 4.18\ \text{J g}^{-1}\ {}^\circ\text{C}^{-1} \times 12.0\ {}^\circ\text{C}$$

$$= 2508\ \text{J or } 2.51\ \text{kJ}$$

This heat is equal to the heat energy evolved, for the quantities specified. by the reaction:

$$H^+\ (aq) + OH^-\ (aq) \longrightarrow H_2O\ (l)$$

The hydroxide ion is the limiting reagent (amount of NaOH = $c.V$ = 2 × 0.0200 = 0.0400 moles, amount of HCl = 2 × 0.0300 = 0.0600 moles), so the reaction of 0.0400 moles evolved this amount of heat energy. The enthalpy of reaction per mole can therefore be calculated as:

$$2.508 \times {}^{1}/_{0.0400} = 62.7\ \text{kJ mol}^{-1}$$

But as the reaction is exothermic the sign of ΔH must be negative, therefore

$$\Delta H = -62.7\ \text{kJ mol}^{-1}.$$

TOK Experimental and theoretical values

What criteria do we use in judging whether discrepancies between experimental and theoretical values are due to experimental limitations or theoretical assumptions?

I'm much better at chemistry than Charlie. I spend more time reading through my notes, I never miss a chemistry class, I hand in all my assignments on time and I get A-grades for them, whereas Charlie's book is in mint condition, his seat in class is as often empty as it is occupied and as for assignments ... ... Just one nagging problem; he always gets a higher mark than me in tests. Our dumb teacher always manages to set questions he knows the answer to, and when it comes to multiple choice he is so lucky with his guesses.

Science is sometimes like that, what should be true sometimes doesn't quite correspond to reality and we have to ask whether the problem lies with "what should be true" (i.e. the theory) how we measure reality (i.e. the experiment) or perhaps both. Probably working out where the problem lies involves looking at both very carefully. With regard to the experimental results we need to consider the precision uncertainty of our measurements and how reproducible they are. If after a number of repetitions the values seem to differ consistently in the same direction to theory we then probably need to carefully examine the method for systematic errors – are we always making the same mistake without realising it. In thermo-chemical determinations of enthalpy changes of reaction explaining a smaller numerical value, through a smaller than expected temperature change owing to heat exchange with the environment, or not taking into account the specific heat capacity of the container, is easy. Variations in the opposite direction require more imagination. With the theory, what assumptions are we making? Have we evidence regarding their validity? Are there factors we haven't considered, like overlooking state changes if using bond enthalpies?

CORE

Exercise 5.2

In this section, assume the specific heat capacity of water and all dilute aqueous solutions to be 4.18 kJ dm^{-3} K^{-1} (equivalent to 4.18 J g^{-1} K^{-1}).

1. How much heat energy is required to increase the temperature of 10 g of nickel (specific heat capacity 440 J kg^{-1} K^{-1}) from 50 °C to 70 °C?

   A 4.4 J
   B 88 J
   C 4400 J
   D 88000 J

2. Copper has a specific heat capacity of 400 J kg^{-1} K^{-1}. If a 50 g cylinder of copper absorbs 800 J of energy, by how much will its temperature rise?

   A 5 °C
   B 20 °C
   C 40 °C
   D 320 °C

3. The enthalpy of combustion of ethanol (C_2H_5OH) is 1370 kJ mol^{-1}. How much heat is released when 0.200 moles of ethanol undergo complete combustion?

   A 30 kJ
   B 274 kJ
   C 1370 kJ
   D 6850 kJ

4. $H_2 (g) + ½ O_2 (g) \longrightarrow H_2O (l)$

   ΔH for the reaction above is –286 kJ mol^{-1}. What mass of oxygen must be consumed to produce 1144 kJ of energy?

   A 4 g
   B 32 g
   C 64 g
   D 128 g

5. When 4.0 g of sulfur is burnt in excess oxygen, 40 kJ of heat is evolved. What is the enthalpy change for the combustion of sulfur?

   A 10 kJ
   B 40 kJ
   C 160 kJ
   D 320 kJ

6. In thermochemistry experiments carried out in a school laboratory the major source of error is usually

   A heat losses to the surroundings.
   B accurate measurement of the volumes of liquids.
   C innacuracies in the concentrations of the solutions.
   D impurities in the reagents.

7. When 25 cm^3 of 2 mol dm^{-3} aqueous sodium hydroxide is added to an equal volume of hydrochloric acid of the same concentration, the temperature increases by 15 °C. What is the enthalpy change for the neutralisation of sodium hydroxide by hydrochloric acid?

   A $25 \times 2 \times 15 \times 4.18$ kJ mol^{-1}
   B $50 \times 2 \times 15 \times 4.18$ kJ mol^{-1}
   C $\frac{25 \times 15 \times 4.18}{2}$ kJ mol^{-1}
   D $\frac{50 \times 15 \times 4.18}{2 \times 25}$ kJ mol^{-1}

8. When 8.00 g of ammonium nitrate completely dissolved in 100 cm^3 of water, the temperature fell from 19.0°C to 14.5°C. Calculate the enthalpy of solution of ammonium nitrate.

9. In cooking 'Crepe Suzette' a tablespoon of brandy is poured over the pancakes and then it is ignited.

   a) If the volume of brandy in a tablespoon is 10 cm^3 and the brandy is 30% ethanol by volume, what volume of ethanol is present?
   b) The density of ethanol is 0.766 g cm^{-3}. What mass of ethanol is there in the tablespoon of brandy?
   c) The molar mass of ethanol is 46 g mol^{-1}. How many moles of ethanol were there in the tablespoon?
   d) Write a balanced equation for the complete combustion of one mole of ethanol.
   e) The standard enthalpy change for this reaction is –1350 kJ mol^{-1}. How much heat is given out when the brandy on the Crepe Suzette burns?

10. A camping stove, burning butane, was used to heat 500 g of water from 20 °C until it was boiling. Heating this amount of water from 20 °C to boiling with an electrical heater requires 168 kJ of energy.

a) If the pot was made out of aluminium and it weighed 100 g, how much heat energy was required to heat the pot (the specific heat capacity of aluminium is 875 J kg^{-1} K^{-1})?

b) What is the total energy required to heat the pot and water?

c) When the water started to boil, the stove weighed 14.5 g less than it had initially. How many moles of butane (C_4H_{10}) were used to heat the pot and water?

d) Use these data to calculate the enthalpy of reaction, in kJ mol^{-1}, of butane with air?

e) The accepted value for the enthalpy of combustion of butane is 2874 kJ mol^{-1}. Explain why you think the two values are so different.

5.3 HESS'S LAW

5.3.1 Determine the enthalpy change of a reaction that is the sum of two or three reactions with known enthalpy changes.

The principle of **conservation of energy** (which Physicists call the **First Law of Thermodynamics**) states that energy cannot be created or destroyed. In chemistry terms this means that the total change in chemical potential energy (that is, enthalpy change) must be equal to the energy lost or gained by the system. It also means that the total enthalpy change on converting a given set of reactants to a particular set of products is constant, irrespective of the way in which the change is carried out. This is known as **Hess's Law**. This principle holds irrespective of whether a particular reaction could actually be carried out in practice.

For example sodium hydrogencarbonate can be directly reacted with hydrochloric acid to produce sodium chloride, carbon dioxide and water:

$$NaHCO_3(s) + HCl(aq) \longrightarrow NaCl(aq) + CO_2(g) + H_2O(l) \qquad \Delta H_1$$

The reaction, to give exactly the same products, could also be carried out by first heating the sodium hydrogencarbonate and then reacting the sodium carbonate produced with the hydrochloric acid:

$$2\ NaHCO_3(s) \longrightarrow Na_2CO_3(s) + CO_2(g) + H_2O(l) \qquad \Delta H_2$$

$$Na_2CO_3(s) + 2\ HCl(aq) \longrightarrow 2\ NaCl(aq) + CO_2(g) + H_2O(l) \qquad \Delta H_3$$

If these equations are added together, the Na_2CO_3 cancels and the result is equal to twice the overall equation given.

$$2\ NaHCO_3(s) + 2\ HCl(aq) \longrightarrow 2\ NaCl(aq) + 2\ CO_2(g) + 2\ H_2O(l)$$

Hess's Law states that the total enthalpy change for the two stage reaction must be equal to the single stage process, i.e.

$$2\ \Delta H_1 = \Delta H_2 + \Delta H_3$$

Note the factor of two occurs because the equation for the direct reaction, as usually written involves only one mole of $NaHCO_3$ being converted to one mole of NaCl, whereas the route via Na_2CO_3 would usually be written for the conversion of two moles.

This may also be shown in the form of an enthalpy cycle.

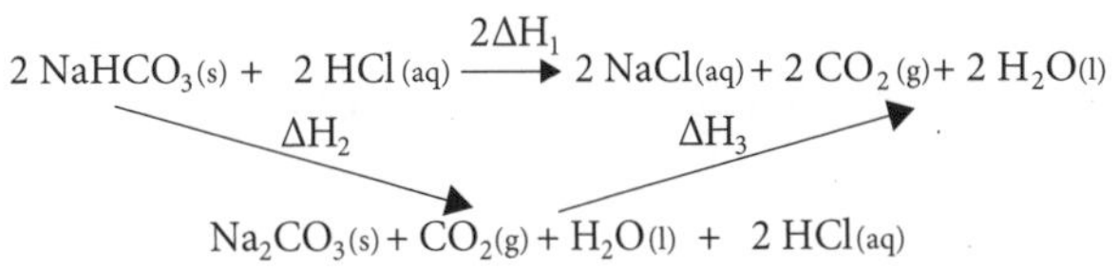

$$2\ NaHCO_3(s) + 2\ HCl(aq) \xrightarrow{2\Delta H_1} 2\ NaCl(aq) + 2\ CO_2(g) + 2\ H_2O(l)$$

ΔH_2 (to) $Na_2CO_3(s) + CO_2(g) + H_2O(l) + 2\ HCl(aq)$ ΔH_3 (to products)

Figure 504 An enthalpy cycle for the direct and indirect reaction of sodium hydrogencarbonate with dilute acid

The use of Hess's Law is particularly important in determining the enthalpy change of reactions for which direct measurement is difficult (i.e. not easy in practice) or impossible (i.e. the reaction in question does not occur). In the example considered above, ΔH_2 would be difficult to measure in practice because it involves heating the substance. Both ΔH_1 and ΔH_3 can be easily determined by standard calorimetric methods, and values of –140 kJ mol^{-1} and –370 kJ mol^{-1} can be found respectively. Hence ΔH_2 can be calculated as

$$\Delta H_2 = 2\Delta H_1 - \Delta H_3 = 2 \times (-140) - (-370) = +90 \text{ kJ mol}^{-1}$$

Another important example is the enthalpy change for the formation of compounds, such as the alkanes, which cannot be formed by the direct combination of the elements. There is an example of this below.

CORE

Example

Calculate ΔH_1 for reaction

$2\,C(s) + 2\,H_2(g) \longrightarrow C_2H_4(g)$ given:

(1) $C(s) + O_2(g) \longrightarrow CO_2(g)$; $\Delta H = -395$ kJ

(2) $H_2(g) + \frac{1}{2}\,O_2(g) \longrightarrow H_2O(l)$; $\Delta H = -287$ kJ

and (3) $C_2H_4(g) + 3\,O_2(g) \longrightarrow 2\,CO_2\,(g) + 2\,H_2O(l)$; $\Delta H = -1416$ kJ

Solution

Reverse equation (3) to get C_2H_4 in the product; this gives (–3) and change the sign of the enthalpy change:

(–3): $2\,CO_2(g) + 2\,H_2O(l) \longrightarrow C_2H_4(g) + 3\,O_2(g)$; $\Delta H = +1416$ kJ

(This has to be done since in equation (1) $C_2H_4(g)$ is on the right.)

Because this involves two moles of both water and carbon dioxide it must be added to twice equation (1) and equation (2), doubling the enthalpy change in each case, to produce the required equation:

(–3): $2\,CO_2(g) + 2\,H_2O(l) \longrightarrow C_2H_4(g) + 3\,O_2(g)$; $-\Delta H_4 = +1416$ kJ

(1): $2\,C(s) + 2\,O_2(g) \longrightarrow 2\,CO_2(g)$; $2\Delta H_2 = 2 \times (-395\text{ kJ})$

(2): $2\,H_2(g) + O_2(g) \longrightarrow 2\,H_2O(l)$; $2\Delta H_3 = 2 \times (-287\text{ kJ})$

$2\,C(s) + 2\,H_2(g) \longrightarrow C_2H_4(g)$

Therefore according to Hess's law:

$$\Delta H = 2\Delta H_1 + 2\Delta H_2 - \Delta H_3$$

$$= 2 \times (-395) + 2 \times (-287) + 1416\text{ kJ}$$

$$= +52\text{ kJ mol}^{-1}$$

As ΔH is positive this must be, an endothermic process.

The above exercise can be represented as a simple enthalpy cycle as shown in Figure 505

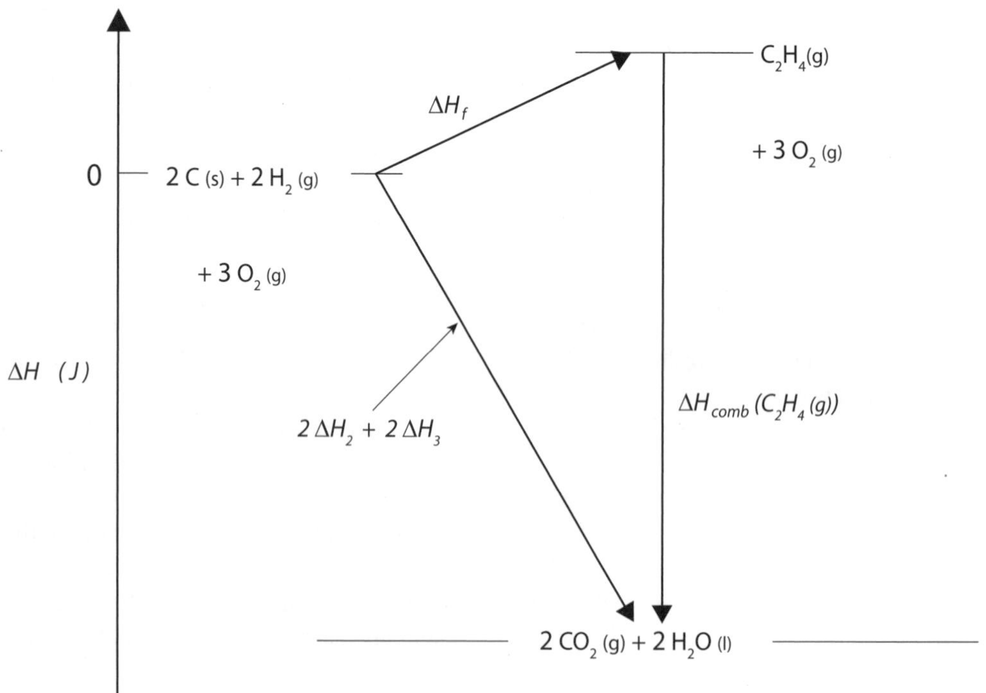

Figure 505 Illustration of the enthalpy example

Exercise 5.3

1. Below are four reactions, or series of reactions. Which of these would have an overall enthalpy change different from the others?

A $NaOH (s) + HCl (aq) \longrightarrow NaCl (aq) + H_2O (l)$

B $NaOH (s) + H_2O (l) \longrightarrow NaOH (aq)$ and $NaOH (aq) + HCl (aq) \longrightarrow NaCl (aq) + H_2O (l)$

C $NaOH (s) + CO_2 (g) \longrightarrow NaHCO_3 (s)$ and $NaHCO_3 (s) + HCl (aq) \longrightarrow NaCl (aq) + H_2O (l) + CO_2 (g)$

D $HCl (aq) + MgO (s) \longrightarrow MgCl_2 (aq) + H_2O (l)$ and $MgCl_2 (aq) + NaOH (s) \longrightarrow NaCl (aq) + Mg(OH)_2 (s)$

2. Given the enthalpy changes of the reactions below

$$2\ H_2O_2\ (aq) \longrightarrow 2\ H_2O\ (l) + O_2\ (g) \qquad \Delta H = -200\ kJ\ mol^{-1}$$

$$2\ H_2\ (g) + O_2\ (g) \longrightarrow 2H_2O\ (l) \qquad \Delta H = -600\ kJ\ mol^{-1}$$

what will be the enthalpy change for
$H_2 (g) + O_2 (g) \longrightarrow H_2O_2 (aq)$?

A -200 kJ mol^{-1}
B -400 kJ mol^{-1}
C -600 kJ mol^{-1}
D -800 kJ mol^{-1}

3. Iron and chlorine react directly to form iron(III) chloride, not iron(II) chloride, so that it is not possible to directly measure the enthalpy change for the reaction

$$Fe\ (s) + Cl_2\ (g) \longrightarrow FeCl_2\ (s)$$

The enthalpy changes for the formation of iron(III) chloride from the reaction of chlorine with iron and with iron(II) chloride are given below. Use these to calculate the enthalpy change for the reaction of iron with chlorine to form iron(II) chloride.

$$2\ Fe\ (s) + 3\ Cl_2\ (g) \longrightarrow 2\ FeCl_3\ (s) \qquad \Delta H = -800\ kJ\ mol^{-1}$$

$$2\ FeCl_2\ (s) + Cl_2\ (g) \longrightarrow 2\ FeCl_3\ (s) \qquad \Delta H = -120\ kJ\ mol^{-1}$$

4. The enthalpies of combustion of ethene, ethane and hydrogen are -1390 kJ mol^{-1}, -1550 kJ mol^{-1} and -286 kJ mol^{-1} respectively. Use these data to calculate the enthalpy of hydrogenation of ethene (i.e. the reaction of ethene with hydrogen to form ethane).

5. The decomposition of calcium carbonate to calcium oxide and carbon dioxide only takes place at very high temperatures, making the direct measurement of the enthalpy change, ΔH for this reaction difficult. Both calcium carbonate and calcium oxide react readily with dilute hydrochloric acid at room temperature.

a) Describe an experiment to find out the enthalpy change of these reactions, describing what you would do and stating what measurements you would make.
b) Which of these two experiments is likely to give the more accurate result? Explain why?
c) What further piece of data would you need so that you could use your results to find the enthalpy change for the decomposition of calcium carbonate?
d) Given this further information, describe how you would calculate the enthalpy change for this decomposition.

TOK The Unification of Ideas

As an example of the conservation of energy, this illustrates the unification of ideas from different areas of science.

When ideas from one part of science seem to explain apparently unrelated phenomena elsewhere, then you get the feeling things are really falling in place and you are on to something fairly fundamental. Newton probably experienced this when he found he could use his theory of gravity to explain the motion of the planets. Similarly Mendeleev's periodic table, originally drawn up to show regular patterns of chemical properties seems to fit in beautifully with later evidence about electron structure, which in its turn relates amazingly to quantum mechanics through the Schrödinger wave equation.

Another interesting trick is to say, suppose this wasn't true? Suppose if when I converted reactants A into products B by a different route I found that the energy change wasn't the same as for the direct conversion, what would be the consequences? It is said that Einstein started research into his theory of relativity by saying let's assume that when a light source is moving towards us and when it is moving away from us, the speed of light from the source is just the same.

5.4 BOND ENTHALPIES

5.4.1 Define the term average bond enthalpy.

5.4.2 Explain, in terms of average bond enthalpies, why some reactions are exothermic and others are endothermic.

CORE

All chemical reactions involve the making and breaking of bonds. **Bond enthalpies** are a measure of the strength of a covalent bond: the stronger the bond, the more tightly the atoms are joined together. The breaking of a chemical bond requires energy and is therefore an endothermic process. Conversely the formation of chemical bonds is an exothermic process. The amount of energy associated with the formation/breaking of a particular covalent bond is to a large extent independent of the bonding in the rest of the molecule, that is, the energy bonding a carbon atom to a hydrogen atom is about 413 kJ mol^{-1} in both methane and ethanol. This means that the average bond enthalpy may defined as the mean of the enthalpy required to break a particular covalent bond in a range of molecules. Using this concept, approximate enthalpy changes for reactions involving only covalent bonds may be calculated by considering the bonds being broken and the bonds being made in a reaction:

ΔH = the sum of the energy of bonds broken – the sum of the energy of bonds made:

$$\Delta H^\circ_{\text{reaction}} = \Sigma\, BE_{\text{bonds broken}} - \Sigma\, BE_{\text{bonds made}}$$

Note that if the bonds being broken are weaker (thus requiring less energy) than those being made (thus producing more energy), the reaction will be exothermic (ΔH is negative) and *vice versa*.

Bond enthalpies are for the conversion of a mole of gaseous molecules (not necessarily the normal state of the compound) into gaseous atoms (not the element in its standard state). The H–Cl bond energy is the enthalpy change for the reaction:

$$HCl\,(g) \longrightarrow H\,(g) + Cl\,(g) \qquad \{\text{NOT } H_2\,(g) \text{ and } Cl_2\,(g)\}$$

The fact that they refer to gases, coupled with the fact that bond enthalpy values are the average of that bond in a range of compounds and hence are only approximately constant, means that enthalpy changes calculated using bond energies are less precise than those obtained by other methods. Nevertheless, apart from a few exceptional cases such as benzene (which is resonance stabilized), the values are within about 10% of other more accurate values and hence this is a useful way of calculating approximate enthalpy changes.

Consider the formation of ammonia from nitrogen and hydrogen:

$$N_2\,(g) + 3\,H_2\,(g) \longrightarrow 2\,NH_3\,(g)$$

The enthalpies of the bonds involved are:

N≡N 945 kJ mol^{-1}; H—H 436 kJ mol^{-1}; N—H 391 kJ mol^{-1}

The bonds broken are: (N≡N) + 3 (H—H)
= 945 + (3 × 436) = 2253 kJ mol^{-1}

The bonds made are: 6 (N—H) = 6 × 391 = 2346 kJ mol^{-1}

$$\begin{aligned}\Delta H &= (\Sigma\, BE_{\text{bonds broken}} - \Sigma\, BE_{\text{bonds made}})\\ &= 2253 - 2346\\ &= -93 \text{ kJ mol}^{-1}\end{aligned}$$

The bond enthalpy concept can be used to explain various observations. For example the enthalpies of combustion of successive alkanes, which form a homologous series increase in a regular manner with the number of carbon atoms as shown in Figure 506 below.

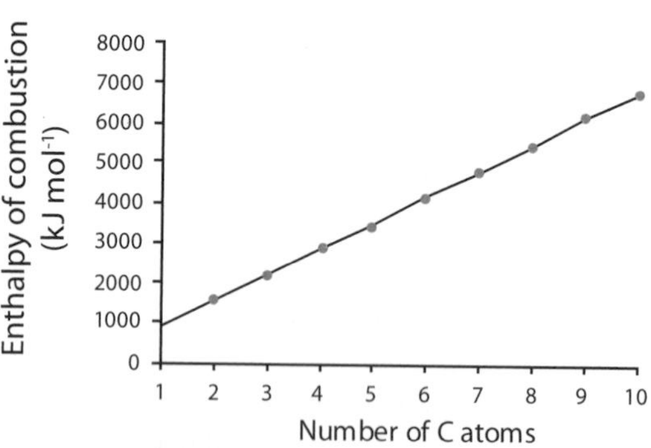

Figure 506 The enthalpies of combustion of the alkanes

This can be explained by the fact that each successive member of the series contains one more methylene group ($-CH_2-$) than the previous one. When it is burnt there will be one extra C—C bond (347 kJ mol^{-1}) and two extra C—H bonds (2 × 413 kJ mol^{-1}) and 1½ extra O=O bonds (for the extra oxygen required; 1½ × 499 kJ mol^{-1}) to break. There will however be two more C=O bonds (2 × 805 kJ mol^{-1}) and two more O—H bonds (2 × 464 kJ mol^{-1}) made from the extra carbon dioxide molecule and water molecule formed respectively. This means, taking into account that bond breaking is endothermic (positive ΔH) and bond making is exothermic (negative ΔH), that the difference in enthalpy of combustion between successive hydrocarbons will be:

$$[(347) + (2 \times 413) + (1 \times 499)] - [(2 \times 805) - (2 \times 464)]$$
$$= -616 \text{ kJ mol}^{-1}$$

approximately in keeping with the values in the graph.

Usually covalent bonds formed by smaller atoms are stronger than those of larger atoms (e.g. C—C = 348 kJ mol^{-1} and Si—Si = 226 kJ mol^{-1}). Bonds to very electronegative elements also tend to be very strong (C—C = 348 kJ mol^{-1}, C—O = 360 kJ mol^{-1} and C—F = 484 kJ mol^{-1}). Bonds between two very electronegative elements tend to be unusually weak (O—O = 146 kJ mol^{-1} and F—F = 158 kJ mol^{-1}) and the fission of bonds such as this will often be the initiation step of a chain reaction, such as the halogenation of the alkanes. Indeed if a substance has several different bonds, it is the weakest bond that is likely to break first allowing predictions to be made with regard to the reaction mechanism.

Bond strength increases from single bonds, through double bonds to triple bonds of the same element: N—N, 163 kJ mol^{-1}; N=N, 409 kJ mol^{-1} and N≡N, 944 kJ mol^{-1}. Similarly the bond enthalpy for carbon carbon bonds increases from C—C, 348 kJ mol^{-1}; C=C, 612 kJ mol^{-1} and C≡C, 837 kJ mol^{-1} and as the bonds become stronger they also become shorter. This is because the electron density in the bond increases the atraction of the nuclei for these electrons, pulling the nuclei closer together.

Various uses can therefore be made of bond enthalpy data:

- Comparing the strengths of bonds
- Understanding structure and bonding
- In calculations relating bond enthalpies to enthalpies of reaction
- Making predictions with regard to some reaction mechanisms.

Apart from a few simple molecules, such as hydrogen chloride H—Cl, it is not possible to determine bond enthalpies directly, so they must be determined indirectly. This can be done applying Hess's Law to the fundamental stages involved.

Example

Use the data provided below to obtain the value for the bond enthalpy of the C—H bond.

(1) $C\ (graphite) + 2H_2\ (g) \longrightarrow CH_4\ (g);\ \Delta H^o_1$

(2) $C\ (graphite) \longrightarrow C\ (g);\ \Delta H^o_2$

(3) $H_2\ (g) \longrightarrow 2H\ (g);\ \Delta H^o_3$

Solution

Doubling equation (3), then reversing it and equation (2) and adding equation (1) gives the equation for the formation of four C—H bonds:

$(-2 \times \Delta H_3)$: $4\,H\ (g) \longrightarrow 2\,H_2\ (g)$;
$\Delta H_{-3} = -2 \times (436)$
$= -\ 872$ kJ

(ΔH_{-2}): $C\ (g) \longrightarrow C\ (graphite);\ \Delta H_{-2} = -\ 725$ kJ

(ΔH_1): $C\ (graphite) + 2H_2\ (g) \longrightarrow CH_4\ (g);\ \Delta H_1 = -75$ kJ

Add equations (-3) + (-2) + (1) gives the equation:

(4) $C\ (g) + 4H\ (g) \longrightarrow CH_4\ (g);\ -1672$ kJ

∴ Forming each C—H bond produces $^{1672}/_4 = 418$ kJ

See Figure 507 for a graphical illustration of this method.

Note that this is an average value for the four bonds. It does not imply, and it is not true, that this is equal to the enthalpy change for the reaction:

$$CH_4\ (g) \longrightarrow CH_3\ (g) + H\ (g)$$

Note also that the standard state of carbon is defined as solid graphite, rather than the less stable allotrope diamond.

This method of determining bond enthalpies can be carried out for a variety of bonds over a large number of compounds and it is by this process that the average bond enthalpies given in data books are deduced.

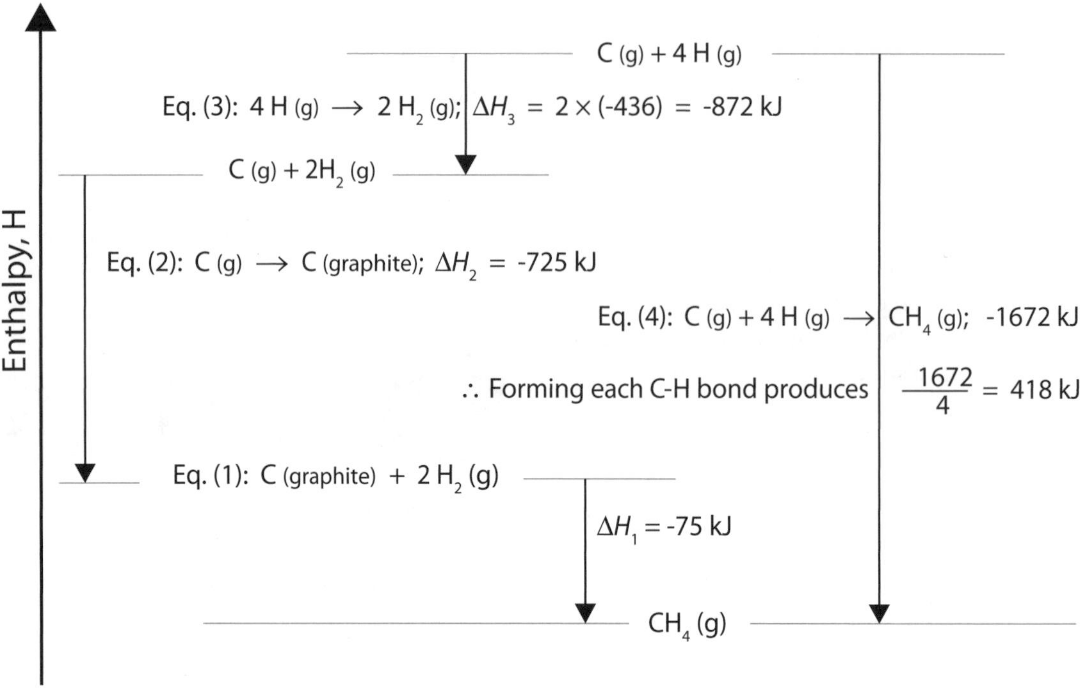

Figure 507 Solution to example illustrated as an enthalpy cycle

Exercise 5.4

1. For which of the following equations is the value of ΔH equivalent to the bond enthalpy for the carbon–oxygen bond in carbon monoxide?

   A $CO(g) \longrightarrow C(g) + O(g)$
   B $CO(g) \longrightarrow C(s) + O(g)$
   C $CO(g) \longrightarrow C(s) + O_2(g)$
   D $CO(g) \longrightarrow C(g) + O_2(g)$

2. The bond enthalpy of the bond between nitrogen and oxygen in nitrogen dioxide is 305 kJ mol^{-1}. If those of the bonds in the oxygen molecule and the nitrogen molecule are 496 kJ mol^{-1} and 944 kJ mol^{-1} respectively, what will be the enthalpy change for the reaction?

   $$N_2(g) + 2\,O_2(g) \longrightarrow 2\,NO_2(g)$$

   A +716 kJ mol^{-1}
   B +1135 kJ mol^{-1}
   C +1326 kJ mol^{-1}
   D +1631 kJ mol^{-1}

3. Given that the bond enthalpy of the carbon–oxygen bonds in carbon monoxide and carbon dioxide are 1073 kJ mol^{-1} and 743 kJ mol^{-1} respectively, and that of the bond in the oxygen molecule is 496 kJ mol^{-1}, calculate the enthalpy change for the combustion of one mole of carbon monoxide.

4. Given that the enthalpy change for the reaction

   $$N_2\,(g) + 3Cl_2\,(g) \longrightarrow 2NCl_3\,(g)$$

   is +688 kJ mol^{-1}, calculate the bond enthalpy of the N—Cl bond, given that the bond enthalpies in the nitrogen molecule and the chlorine molecule are 944 kJ mol^{-1} and 242 kJ mol^{-1} respectively.

5. Use bond enthalpy data to calculate the enthalpy change when cyclopropane reacts with hydrogen to form propane. The actual value found is –159 kJ mol^{-1}. Give reasons why you think this differs from the value you have calculated.

   [Bond enthalpies in kJ mol^{-1}: C—C 348; C—H 412; H—H 436]

6. Consider the halogens (Cl_2, Br_2, I_2) - the bond enthalpies of the halogens given in the table below. Explain the trend in these. Based on the data in the table below, predict a value for the F—F bond. Compare this to the literature value, and explain any discrepancy:

	Cl—Cl	Br—Br	I—I
B.E. / kJ mol^{-1}	243	193	151

HIGHER LEVEL

15.1 STANDARD ENTHALPY CHANGES OF REACTION (AHL)

15.1.1 Define and apply the terms standard state, standard enthalpy change of formation (ΔH_f°) and standard enthalpy change of combustion (ΔH_c°).

15.1.2 Determine the enthalpy change of a reaction using standard enthalpy changes of formation and combustion.

Just as when comparing altitudes it is useful to assign an arbitrary zero point for comparison (for example, mean sea level), so in considering enthalpies it is useful to assign an arbitrary zero. This is taken as the elements in their **standard states** under standard conditions. The enthalpy of formation of any element in its standard state is therefore zero by definition.

The **standard enthalpy change of formation** (ΔH_f°) is the amount of energy evolved or absorbed in the formation of one mole of the compound, in its standard state, from its constituent elements in their standard states. Standard state refers to the form normally found at a temperature of 25 °C (298 K) and a pressure of 101.3 kPa (1 atmosphere pressure). If allotropes exist, then one of these (usually the most stable one) is agreed on as the standard state. For example the standard state of oxygen is O_2 (g), not O_3 (g). The superscript (⊖) is sometimes placed after a quantity to indicate that its value refers to standard conditions, though this is often omitted.

Under standard conditions, sodium chloride is a solid, and the standard states of the elements, from which it is formed are solid sodium metal and gaseous chlorine molecules. The standard enthalpy of formation of sodium chloride (–411 kJ mol^{-1}) is therefore the enthalpy change for the reaction:

$$Na(s) + \frac{1}{2}Cl_2(g) \longrightarrow NaCl(s) \quad \Delta H^\circ = -411 \text{ kJ mol}^{-1}$$

The sum of the enthalpies of formation of the reactants will give the total enthalpy change to form the reactants from the component elements in their standard states. Similarly the sum of the enthalpies of formation of the products will give the total enthalpy to form the products. The enthalpy change of the reaction is therefore the difference between these, so that the enthalpy change for any reaction can be calculated using the equation:

$$\Delta H^\circ = \Sigma\Delta H^\circ_f(\text{products}) - \Sigma\Delta H^\circ_f(\text{reactants})$$

This same formula also results from a consideration of the appropriate enthalpy cycle:

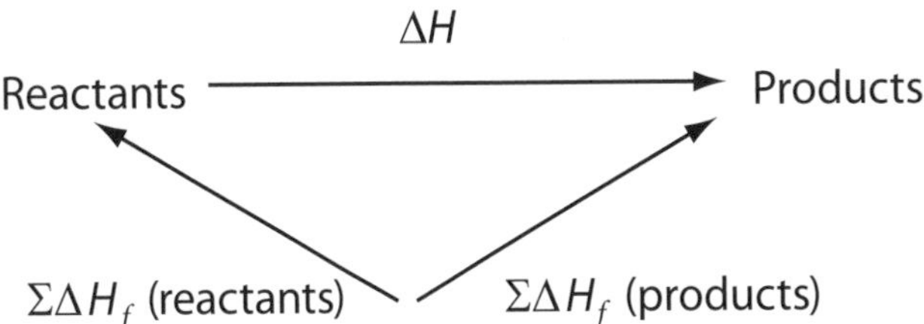

Elements in their standard states

Figure 509 Illustrating the relationship between enthalpy of reaction and standard enthalpies of formation

Consider for example the reaction of ethanol and ethanoic acid to form ethyl ethanoate and water:

$$(1) \quad C_2H_5OH\,(l) + CH_3COOH\,(l) \longrightarrow CH_3COOC_2H_5\,(l) + H_2O\,(l) \quad \Delta H^\circ_1$$

This could be thought of as the result of two hypothetical reactions, going via the elements:

$$(2) \quad C_2H_5OH\,(l) + CH_3COOH\,(l) \longrightarrow 4\,C\,(s) + 5\,H_2\,(g) + 1\tfrac{1}{2}\,O_2\,(g) \quad \Delta H^\circ_2$$

followed by

$$(3) \quad 4\,C\,(s) + 5\,H_2\,(g) + 1\tfrac{1}{2}\,O_2\,(g) \longrightarrow CH_3COOC_2H_5\,(l) + H_2O\,(l) \quad \Delta H^\circ_3$$

ΔH°_2 is $-[\Delta H_f(C_2H_5OH\,(l)) + \Delta H_f(CH_3COOH\,(l))]$ as it is the reverse of the formation of the compounds from the elements, and ΔH°_3 is even more obviously ΔH°_f ($CH_3COOC_2H_5$ (l)) + $\Delta H^\circ_f(H_2O(l))$], as it is the formation of the elements from their compounds. Applying Hess's Law:

$$\Delta H^\circ_1 = \Delta H^\circ_2 + \Delta H^\circ_3$$

$$= -[\Delta H_f(C_2H_5OH\ (l)) + \Delta H_f(CH_3COOH\ (l))] + [\Delta H_f(CH_3COOC_2H_5\ (l)) + \Delta H_f(H_2O\ (l))]$$

Substituting in appropriate values [ΔH°_f ($C_2H_5OH(l)$) = –1367 kJ mol^{-1}; ΔH°_f (CH_3COOH (l)) = –874 kJ mol^{-1}; ΔH°_f($CH_3COOC_2H_5$ (l)) = –2238 kJ mol^{-1}; ΔH°_f(H_2O (l)) = –286 kJ mol^{-1}]:

$$\Delta H^\circ_1 = -[(-1367) + (-874)] + [(-2238) + (-286)]$$
$$= 2241 - 2524$$
$$= -283 \text{ kJ mol}^{-1}$$

It is simpler however just to substitute in the equation relating ΔH° and ΔH°_f values. Consider as a second example the decomposition of ammonium nitrate:

$$NH_4NO_3(s) \longrightarrow N_2O(g) + 2\ H_2O(l)$$

The standard enthalpies of formation of the compounds involved are:

NH_4NO_3(s) –366 kJ mol^{-1}; N_2O(g) +82 kJ mol^{-1}; H_2O(l) –285 kJ mol^{-1}

Substituting in the equation:

$$\Delta H^\circ_f = \Sigma\Delta H^\circ_f(\text{products}) - \Sigma\Delta H^\circ_f(\text{reactants})$$

$$= [\Delta H^\circ_f(N_2O(g)) + 2 \times \Delta H^\circ_f(H_2O(l))] - [\Delta H^\circ_f(NH_4NO_3(s))]$$
$$= [(+82) + 2 \times (-285)] - [(-366)]$$
$$= (-488) - (-366)$$
$$= -122 \text{ kJ mol}^{-1}$$

Notice the care taken not to make mistakes with signs.

The **standard enthalpy change of combustion** (ΔH°_{comb}) is the enthalpy change when one mole of the compound undergoes complete combustion in excess oxygen under standard conditions. For example the standard enthalpy change of combustion for methane is ΔH for the reaction:

$$CH_4(g) + 2\ O_2(g) \longrightarrow CO_2(g) + 2\ H_2O(l) \qquad \Delta H^\circ_{comb} = -891 \text{ kJ mol}^{-1}$$

The standard enthalpy change of combustion is always exothermic. Note that the enthalpies of formation of many oxides (e.g. H_2O and CO_2) are equivalent to the enthalpies of combustion of the element, because both refer to the same thermochemical equation, e.g.:

$$H_2\ (g) + ½O_2\ (g) \longrightarrow H_2O\ (l)$$
both ΔH°_{comb} (H_2 (g)) and ΔH°_f(H_2O (l))

$$C\ (s) + O_2\ (g) \longrightarrow CO_2\ (g)$$
both ΔH°_{comb} (C (s)) and ΔH°_f(CO_2 (g))

Many covalent compounds will undergo combustion and hence it is often easy to determine the standard enthalpy change of combustion for molecules. An enthalpy cycle, similar to that for enthalpy of formation can be constructed using enthalpies of combustion, as shown in the example below, and this can be used to calculate a value for the enthalpy of formation:

Example

Calculate ΔH°_f(C_2H_4(g)), given: ΔH°_f(CO_2(g)) = –395 kJ mol^{-1}, ΔH°_f(H_2O (l)) = –287 kJ mol^{-1} and ΔH°_{comb} (C_2H_4 (g)) = -1416 kJ mol^{-1}.

Solution

The enthalpy diagram for this example is illustrated below

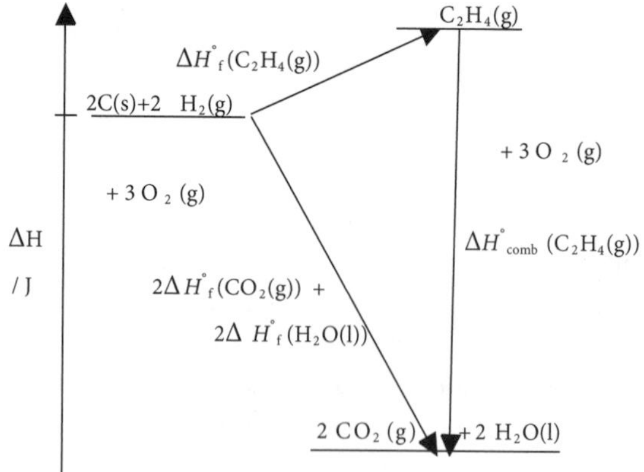

$$C_2H_4\ (g) + 3O_2\ (g) \longrightarrow 2\ CO_2\ (g) + 2H_2O\ (l) \qquad \Delta H^\circ_{comb} = -1416 \text{ kJ}$$

$$\Delta H^\circ = \Sigma\Delta H^\circ_f(\text{products}) - \Sigma\Delta H^\circ_f(\text{reactants})$$

$$\therefore \Delta H^\circ_{comb}(C_2H_4(g)) = [2\Delta H^\circ_f(CO_2(g)) + 2\Delta H^\circ_f(H_2O(l))] - [\Delta H^\circ_f(C_2H_4(g)) + 3\Delta H^\circ_f(O_2(g))]$$

AHL

Since ΔH of (O_2 (g)) = 0, this may be rearranged to give:

$$\Delta H^{\ominus}_f(C_2H_4\,(g)) = 2\,\Delta H^{\ominus}_f(CO_2\,(g)) + 2\,\Delta H^{\ominus}_f(H_2O\,(l)) - \Delta H^{\ominus}_{comb}\,(C_2H_4\,(g))$$

Substituting:

$$\Delta H^{\ominus}_f(C_2H_4\,(g)) = 2(-395) + 2(-287) - (-1416) = +\,52\text{ kJ mol}^{-1}.$$

Note that standard enthalpy of combustion data can be used to calculate values for the enthalpy of reaction directly using the enthalpy cycle below:

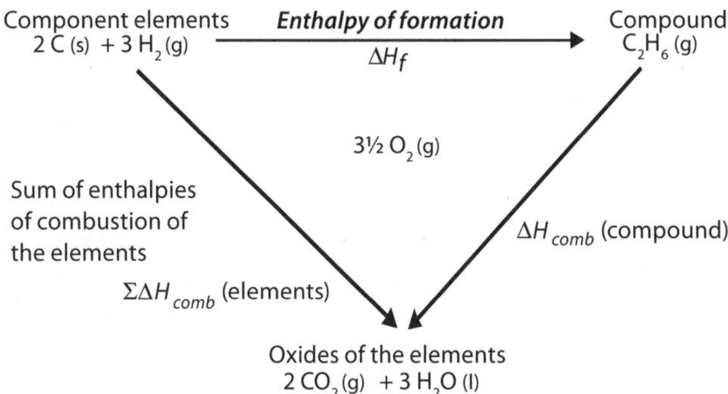

Figure 511 Finding enthalpies of reaction from enthalpies of combustion

This can be summarised by the equation:

$$\Delta H^{\ominus} = \Sigma\Delta H^{\ominus}_{comb}\,(\text{reactants}) - \Sigma\Delta H^{\ominus}_{comb}\,(\text{products})$$

Note that the position of products and reactants in this is the opposite of that for the equation using the enthalpy of formation because the enthalpy change being used is in the opposite direction (combustion is from the compound whereas formation is to the compound).

Example

Calculate the enthalpy change for the hydration of ethene, given that the enthalpy of combustion of ethene and ethanol are –1409 kJ mol^{-1} and –1371 kJ mol^{-1} respectively.

Solution

$$C_2H_4 + H_2O \longrightarrow CH_3{-}CH_2{-}OH \qquad \Delta H^{\ominus}$$

$$\Delta H^{\ominus} = \Sigma\Delta H^{\ominus}_f(\text{reactants}) - \Sigma\Delta H^{\ominus}_f(\text{products})$$

$$\Delta H^{\ominus} = -1409 - (-1371) = -38\text{ kJ mol}^{-1}$$

(n.b. ΔH_c for water is zero)

Again notice the care taken to avoid making mistakes with signs.

Similarly enthalpies of combustion can be used to find the enthalpy change of other reactions, in which the reactants and products can all be readily converted to the oxides, even if the changes cannot occur in practice.

Example

Calculate the relative stabilities of propan-1-ol and propan-2-ol from their enthalpies of combustion.

Solution

Consider the reaction:

$$CH_3{-}CH_2{-}CH_2{-}OH\,(l) \longrightarrow CH_3{-}CH(OH){-}CH_3\,(l)$$

$$\Delta H^{\ominus} = \Delta H^{\ominus}_{comb}\,(\text{propan-1-ol}) - \Delta H^{\ominus}_{comb}\,(\text{propan-2-ol})$$

$$\Delta H^{\ominus} = -2021 - (-2006) = -15\text{ kJ mol}^{-1}$$

Hence, as the conversion of propan-1-ol to propan-2-ol is exothermic, propan-2-ol is the more energetically stable of the two isomers.

One other notable enthalpy change is the standard enthalpy change of neutralisation, ΔH_{neut}, the enthalpy change when one mole of the acid (base) undergoes complete neutralisation with a strong base (acid) under standard conditions. For example the standard enthalpy change of neutralisation for ethanoic acid is $\Delta H^{\ominus}$ for the reaction:

$$CH_3COOH\,(l) + OH^-\,(aq) \longrightarrow CH_3COO^-\,(aq) + H_2O\,(l) \qquad \Delta H^{\ominus} = -56.1\text{ kJ mol}^{-1}$$

Again, this also is always exothermic. Note also that the enthalpy of neutralisation of any strong acid by any strong base is always the same because it is equal to the enthalpy change for the reaction:

$$H^+\,(aq) + OH^-\,(aq) \longrightarrow H_2O\,(l) \qquad \Delta H^{\ominus} = -57.9\text{ kJ mol}^{-1}$$

In the case of ethanoic acid the enthalpy of neutralisation is less exothermic as it is a weak acid and the dissociation of the acid is an endothermic process.

AHL

Exercise 15.1

1. Which one of the following is not a 'standard state' condition?

   A A temperature of 298 K
   B A pressure of 101.3 kPa
   C All substances in the gaseous state
   D Elements present as the standard allotrope

2. The standard enthalpy change of formation for hydrogen chloride is the enthalpy change for

   A $H_2(g) + Cl_2(g) \longrightarrow 2\,HCl(g)$
   B $\frac{1}{2}H_2(g) + \frac{1}{2}Cl_2(g) \longrightarrow HCl(g)$
   C $H(g) + Cl(g) \longrightarrow HCl(g)$
   D $H^+(g) + Cl^-(g) \longrightarrow HCl(g)$

3. Given the standard enthalpy of formation data:

   $NaHCO_3(s)$: –948; $Na_2CO_3(s)$: –1131;
   $CO_2(g)$: –395; $H_2O(l)$: –286; all in kJ mol^{-1}

   what is the enthalpy change for the reaction

   $2\,NaHCO_3(s) \longrightarrow Na_2CO_3(s) + CO_2(g) + H_2O(l)$

   A +84 kJ mol^{-1}
   B +864 kJ mol^{-1}
   C –864 kJ mol^{-1}
   D –84 kJ mol^{-1}

4. Which one of the following is the reaction for which the enthalpy change is equal to the enthalpy change of combustion for ethyne?

   A $C_2H_2(g) + 2\frac{1}{2}O_2(g) \longrightarrow 2\,CO_2(g) + H_2O(l)$
   B $C_2H_2(g) + 1\frac{1}{2}O_2(g) \longrightarrow 2\,CO(g) + H_2O(l)$
   C $2\,C_2H_2(g) + 5\,O_2(g) \longrightarrow 4\,CO_2(g) + 2\,H_2O(l)$
   D $C_2H_2(g) + 2\frac{1}{2}O_2(g) \longrightarrow 2\,CO_2(g) + H_2O(g)$

5. What value would you expect for the enthalpy change of the reaction

   $CH_3\text{—}OH(l) + CO(g) \longrightarrow CH_3\text{—}COOH(l)$

   Given that $\Delta H^{\circ}_{comb}(CH_3\text{—}OH) = -715$ kJ mol^{-1}, $\Delta H^{\circ}_{comb}(CO) = -283$ kJ mol^{-1} and $\Delta H^{\circ}_{comb}(CH_3\text{—}COOH) = -876$ kJ mol^{-1}?

   A +161 kJ mol^{-1}
   B +122 kJ mol^{-1}
   C –122 kJ mol^{-1}
   D –405 kJ mol^{-1}

6. Which one of the following enthalpy terms is not required to calculate the enthalpy of the nitrogen–fluorine bond in nitrogen trifluoride?

   A The electron affinity of fluorine.
   B The fluorine–fluorine bond enthalpy.
   C The enthalpy of atomisation of nitrogen.
   D The enthalpy of formation of nitrogen trifluoride.

7. Given the enthalpies of atomisation of phosphorus and hydrogen (+354 kJ mol^{-1} and +218 kJ mol^{-1} respectively) and the phosphorus-hydrogen bond enthalpy (321 kJ mol^{-1}), calculate the approximate enthalpy of formation of a hypothetical compound PH_5.

8. Write balanced equations for the following reactions and use standard enthalpy of formation data to calculate the standard enthalpy change associated with each:

   a) Zinc and chlorine reacting to form zinc chloride.
   b) Hydrogen sulfide and sulfur dioxide reacting to form sulfur and water.
   c) Lead(II) nitrate decomposing to lead(II) oxide, nitrogen dioxide and oxygen.

   [Standard enthalpy of formation data, in kJ mol^{-1}: $ZnCl_2(s)$ –416; $H_2S(g)$ –21; $SO_2(g)$ –297; $H_2O(l)$ –286; $Pb(NO_3)_2(s)$ –449; $PbO(s)$ –218; $NO_2(g)$ +34.]

9. Depending on whether you consider the chlorine to be converted to the element or to hydrogen chloride, it is possible to write two different equations for the combustion of dichloromethane (CH_2Cl_2). Use enthalpy of formation data to calculate the enthalpy changes of these two reactions. If the experimental value is –578 kJ mol^{-1}, what conclusions can you draw?

AHL

[Standard enthalpy of formation data, in kJ mol^{-1}:
CH_2Cl_2 (l) –121; HCl(g) –92;

CO_2 (g) –395; H_2O (l) –286]

10. In the Apollo project, the engines of the lunar module mixed methylhydrazine (CH_3—NH—NH_2) and dinitrogen tetroxide (N_2O_4), which ignite spontaneously, as fuel for the rocket.

    a) Write the most probable equation for the reaction. (It forms common simple molecules).
    b) Use enthalpy of formation data to calculate the enthalpy change for this reaction.
    c) What factors, apart from the reaction being highly exothermic, would have made this combination of fuels suitable for this application?

    [Standard enthalpy of formation data, in kJ mol^{-1}:
    CH_3NHNH_2 (l) +13.0; N_2O_4 (g) +9;
    H_2O (g) –244; CO_2 (g) –395]

11. a) How could you attempt to measure the enthalpy change for the hypothetical isomerisation of butan-1-ol (C_4H_9OH) to ethoxyethane ($C_2H_5OC_2H_5$) experimentally?

    b) Use bond energy data to calculate a value for this enthalpy change.
    c) Use enthalpy of formation data to calculate a value for this enthalpy change.
    d) Which would you expect to give the best agreement with your experimental value? Why?

    [Standard enthalpy of formation data, in kJ mol^{-1}:
    H_2O (l) –286; CO_2 (g) –395; C_4H_9OH (l) –327;
    $C_2H_5OC_2H_5$ (l) –280.

    Bond energies in kJ mol^{-1}: C—C 346; C—H 413;
    H—H 436; C—O 360; O—H 464]

12. The enthalpy of combustion data for cyclohexene, cyclohexane and benzene in the gaseous state, in kJ mol^{-1}, are –3752, –3924 and –3273.

    a) Write balanced equations for the gas phase hydrogenation of cyclohexene to cyclohexane and for benzene to cyclohexane.
    b) Use the data given, along with the enthalpy of formation of water (–286 kJ mol^{-1}) to calculate the enthalpy change for these two reactions.
    c) Explain the relationship that might have been expected between these two values.
    d) Explain why this relationship is not in fact found.

15.2 BORN-HABER CYCLE (AHL)

AHL

15.2.1 Define and apply the terms lattice enthalpy and electron affinity.

15.2.2 Explain how the relative sizes and the charges of ions affect the lattice enthalpies of different ionic compounds.

15.2.3 Construct a Born–Haber cycle for group 1 and 2 oxides and chlorides and use it to calculate an enthalpy change.

15.2.4 Discuss the difference between theoretical and experimental lattice enthalpy values of ionic compounds in terms of their covalent character.

The formation of an ionic compound can be considered as the sum of a number of individual processes converting the elements from their standard states into gaseous atoms, losing and gaining electrons to form the cations and anions respectively and finally these gaseous ions coming together to form the solid compound. The diagrammatic representation of this, shown in Figure 512, is known as the **Born–Haber cycle.**

The **standard enthalpy change of atomisation** is the enthalpy change required to produce one mole of gaseous atoms of an element from the element in the standard state. For example for sodium it is the enthalpy change for:

$$Na(s) \longrightarrow Na(g) \quad \Delta H^{\ominus}_{at} = +103 \text{ kJ mol}^{-1}$$

Note that for diatomic gaseous elements, such as chlorine, it is numerically equal to half the bond enthalpy, because breaking the bond between the atoms of one molecule produces two atoms. Considering chlorine as the example:

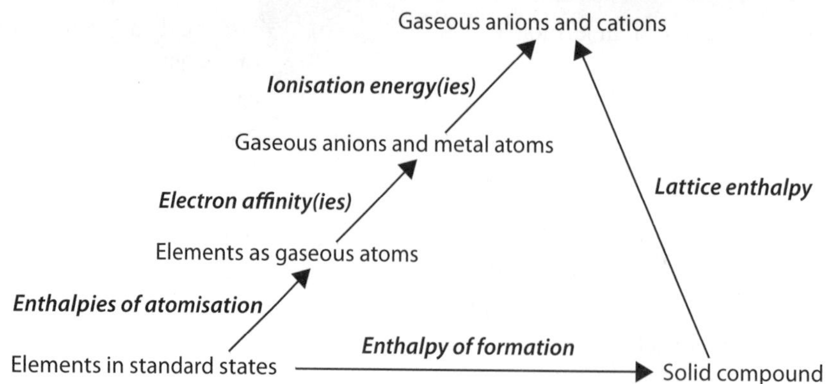

Figure 512 The Born–Haber cycle

AHL

$$Cl_2(g) \longrightarrow Cl(g) \quad \Delta H^{\ominus}_{at} = ½\ E\ (Cl—Cl) = ½\ (+242) = +121\ kJ\ mol^{-1}$$

The **electron affinity** is the enthalpy change when one mole of gaseous atoms or anions gains electrons to form a mole of negatively charged gaseous ions. For example the electron affinity of chlorine is the enthalpy change for

$$Cl(g) + e^- \longrightarrow Cl^-(g) \quad \Delta H^{\ominus} = -364\ kJ\ mol^{-1}$$

For most atoms this change is exothermic, but gaining a second electron (e.g. O^- (g) + e^- $\longrightarrow$ O^{2-} (g)) is endothermic, due to the repulsion between the electron and the negative ion.

The ionisation energy, the enthalpy change for one mole of a gaseous element or cation to lose electrons to form a mole of positively charged gaseous ions, has been met before.

Notice the **lattice enthalpy** is the energy required to convert one mole of the solid compound into gaseous ions. Using sodium chloride as the example it is the enthalpy change for:

$$NaCl(s) \longrightarrow Na^+(g) + Cl^-(g) \quad \Delta H^{\ominus} = +771\ kJ\ mol^{-1}$$

The lattice enthalpy is therefore very highly endothermic.

The direct determination of lattice enthalpies is not possible since gaseous ions are involved, but values are obtained indirectly using the Born–Haber cycle, a special case of Hess's law for the formation of ionic compounds. The Born–Haber cycle for the formation of sodium chloride is illustrated in Figure 513.

In the Born–Haber cycle, if the magnitude of every term except one is known, then the remaining value may be calculated. The lattice enthalpy of sodium chloride can therefore be calculated knowing the other terms in the cycle:

Enthalpy of formation of NaCl	$= -411\ kJ\ mol^{-1}$
Enthalpy of atomisation of Na	$= +103\ kJ\ mol^{-1}$
Enthalpy of atomisation of Cl	$= +121\ kJ\ mol^{-1}$
Electron affinity of Cl	$= -364\ kJ\ mol^{-1}$
Ionisation energy of Na	$= +500\ kJ\ mol^{-1}$

Enthalpies of atomisation + Electron affinity + Ionisation energy
= Enthalpy of formation + Lattice enthalpy

$$(+103) + (+121) + (-364) + (+500) = (-411) + \text{L.E.}$$

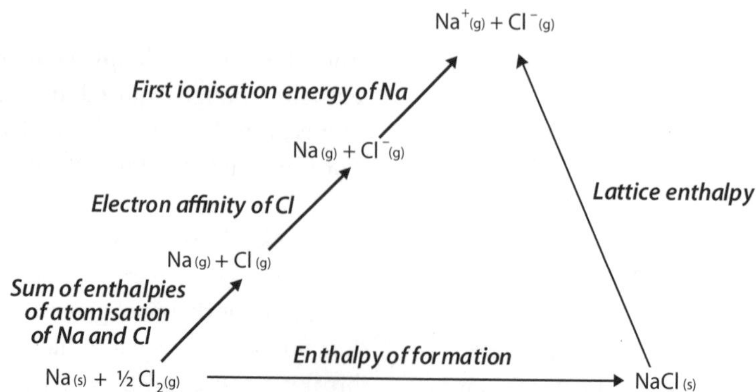

Figure 513 The theoretical steps in the formation of sodium chloride from its elements in their standard states

$\therefore$ L.E. = 411 + 103 + 121 – 364 + 500

= + 771 kJ mol^{-1}

The magnitude of the lattice enthalpy depends upon the nature of the ions involved:

- The greater the charge on the ions, the greater the electrostatic attraction and hence the greater the lattice enthalpy, and *vice versa.*
- The larger the ions, then the greater the separation of the charges and the lower the lattice enthalpy, and *vice versa.*

These trends are illustrated in Figure 514, which compares the lattice enthalpies of sodium chloride, magnesium oxide and potassium bromide, all of which crystallise with a similar lattice:

Compound	Lattice enthalpy (kJ mol^{-1})	Change from NaCl
MgO	3889	Increased ionic charge
NaCl	771	—
KBr	670	Larger ions

Figure 514 Comparison of the lattice enthalpies of some compounds

As illustrated above, the Born–Haber cycle provides a way in which lattice enthalpies can be indirectly measured through experimental techniques (an empirical value). It is also possible to calculate theoretical lattice enthalpies for ionic compounds. This is done by assuming the ionic model, then summing the electrostatic attractive and repulsive forces between the ions in the crystal lattice. As can be seen from Figure 515, this gives excellent agreement for many compounds, implying that the ionic model provides an appropriate description of the bonding in these compounds. For others however, such as the silver halides, the agreement is less good. This is interpreted as evidence for a significant degree of covalent character in the bonding of such compounds (difference in electronegativities < ~1.7). The presence of covalent character in a bond always leads to an increase in the lattice enthalpy. In the case of silver halides this increased lattice enthalpy helps to explain their insolubility and the fact that silver fluoride (the most ionic; difference in electronegativities = 2.1) is in fact soluble.

Compound	Empirical value (kJ mol^{-1}) [Born-Haber]	Theoretical value (kJ mol^{-1}) [Electrostatic summing]
Sodium chloride	766	766
Potassium bromide	672	667
Potassium iodide	632	631
Silver iodide	865	736

Figure 515 Experimental and theoretical lattice enthalpies for some compounds

Another enthalpy cycle that involves the lattice enthalpy is that for the formation of an aqueous solution from a solid ionic compound. The **enthalpy change of solution** (ΔH_{sol}; i.e. the enthalpy change when one mole of the substance is dissolved in water to form a dilute aqueous solution) is equal to the lattice enthalpy of the compound plus the sum of the hydration enthalpies of the component ions. The **enthalpy change of hydration** (ΔH_{hyd}) for an ion is the enthalpy change (always exothermic) when one mole of the gaseous ion is added to excess water to form a dilute solution - the term solvation is used in place of hydration for solvents other than water. This is illustrated below using calcium chloride as an example:

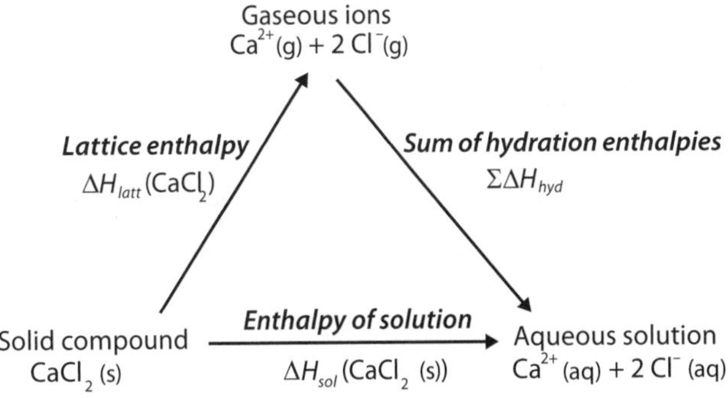

Figure 516 The enthalpy of hydration for calcium chloride

Again, if all the terms are known except one, then this one may be calculated. For example the above cycle will be used to calculate the enthalpy of solution using the lattice enthalpy for calcium chloride (+2258 kJ mol^{-1}) and the hydration enthalpies of the ions (ΔH_{hyd} (Ca^{2+}) = –1650 kJ mol^{-1} and ΔH_{hyd} (Cl^-) = –364 kJ mol^{-1}).

Enthalpy of solution = Lattice enthalpy + Sum of hydration enthalpies

$$\Delta H_{sol}(CaCl_2) = \Delta H_{lat}(CaCl_2) + \Delta H_{hyd}(Ca^{2+}) + 2\,\Delta H_{hyd}(Cl^-)$$

$$\Delta H_{sol}(CaCl_2) = +2258 + (-1650) + 2\,(-364)$$

$$= -120 \text{ kJ mol}^{-1}$$

Note that the enthalpy of solution, being the sum of two very large terms, one of which is always endothermic the other always exothermic, is usually quite small and may be either positive (endothermic) or negative (exothermic). If it is large and positive, then the compound in question will almost certainly be insoluble. Because the entropy change for the formation of a solution is always positive, this is the explanation for the lack of solubility of many inorganic compounds.

AHL

Exercise 15.2

1. The lattice enthalpy is dependent on two main factors, the size of the ions and the charge on the ions. Which combination of these would lead to the greatest lattice enthalpy?

	Size of ions	Charge on ions
A	Large	Large
B	Large	Small
C	Small	Large
D	Small	Small

2. Which one of the following quantities is not directly involved in the Born–Haber cycle?

   A Ionisation energy
   B Lattice enthalpy
   C Electronegativity
   D Enthalpy of formation

3. Which one of the following ionic solids would you expect to have the greatest lattice enthalpy?

   A RbCl
   B CaS
   C BaI_2
   D LiF

4. Calculate the lattice enthalpy of sodium chloride given the following data:

   $\Delta H_{sol}(NaCl) = -4 \text{ kJ mol}^{-1}$

   $\Delta H_{hyd}(Na^+) = -406 \text{ kJ mol}^{-1}$

   $\Delta H_{hyd}(Cl^-) = -364 \text{ kJ mol}^{-1}$

   A +774 kJ mol^{-1}
   B +766 kJ mol^{-1}
   C +46 kJ mol^{-1}
   D +38 kJ mol^{-1}

5. Which one of the following enthalpy terms will always have a different sign to the others?

   A Ionisation enthalpy
   B Enthalpy of hydration
   C Lattice enthalpy
   D Enthalpy of atomisation

6. Use the data below, relating to the formation of barium chloride, to calculate a value of the electron affinity of the chlorine atom.

   Enthalpy of atomisation of barium
   +175 kJ mol^{-1}

   Enthalpy of atomisation of chlorine
   +121 kJ mol^{-1}

   First ionisation energy of barium
   +502 kJ mol^{-1}

   Second ionisation energy of barium
   +966 kJ mol^{-1}

   Lattice enthalpy of barium chloride
   +2018 kJ mol^{-1}

   Enthalpy of formation of barium chloride
   −860 kJ mol^{-1}

7. It would be theoretically possible for calcium to form a fluoride CaF containing Ca^+ ions and the F^- ions in equal numbers. Assuming that the lattice enthalpy of the hypothetical compound is similar to that of NaF (+891 kJ mol^{-1}), use a Born– Haber cycle to calculate its enthalpy of formation using the data below.

Enthalpy of atomisation of calcium
+193 kJ mol^{-1}

F—F bond enthalpy
+158 kJ mol^{-1}

First ionisation energy of calcium
+590 kJ mol^{-1}

Electron affinity of fluorine
−348 kJ mol^{-1}

The enthalpy of formation of CaF_2 is −1214 kJ mol^{-1}. Use this to explain why it is not possible to produce CaF even if two moles of calcium are reacted with one mole of fluorine gas.

8. a) Use the data below to calculate an empirical value for the lattice enthalpy of silver bromide:

Enthalpy of atomisation of silver
+285 kJ mol^{-1}

Enthalpy of atomisation of bromine
+112 kJ mol^{-1}

First ionisation energy of silver
+732 kJ mol^{-1}

Electron affinity of bromine
−342 kJ mol^{-1}

Enthalpy of formation of silver bromide
−100 kJ mol^{-1}

b) If the electrostatic interactions in the lattice are summed to give a theoretical ionisation energy, a value of +758 kJ mol^{-1} is found for the lattice enthalpy of silver bromide. Compare this to the value obtained in the first part of the question and comment on its significance

9. The theoretical and experimentally determined lattice enthalpies for silver chloride are +833 kJ mol^{-1} and +905 kJ mol^{-1} respectively. Combine these, with the enthalpy of hydration of the component ions ($\Delta H_{hyd}(Ag^+)$ = −464 kJ mol^{-1} and $\Delta H_{hyd}(Cl^-)$ = −364 kJ mol^{-1}) to calculate two values for the enthalpy of solution of the compound. Use these to explain the fact that silver chloride is insoluble in water, yet sodium chloride is readily soluble, given that the entropy change for the formation of a solution is similar for both solid salts.

15.3 ENTROPY (AHL)

15.3.1 State and explain the factors that increase the entropy in a system.

15.3.2 Predict whether the entropy change (ΔS) for a given reaction or process is positive or negative.

15.3.3 Calculate the standard entropy change for a reaction ($\Delta S^{\ominus}$) using standard entropy values ($S^{\ominus}$).

AHL

Some states are inherently more probable than others, in the same way that the probability of rolling '7' on a pair of dice (1+6, 2+5, 3+4, 4+3, 5+2, 6+1) is much greater than that of rolling '12' (6+6 only). The probability of a state existing is known as its entropy and it is given the symbol S. In general terms the less order there is in a state, the greater the probability of the state and the greater its entropy. The **entropy** of a system is therefore a measure of the degree of disorder or randomness in a system. Thus, other factors being equal, there is an increase in entropy on changing state from solid to liquid to gas, as illustrated by the values for the states of water below:

	solid	⇒ liquid	⇒ gas
	(ice)	(water)	(steam)
Entropy	48.0	69.9	188.7 J K^{-1} mol^{-1}

Figure 518 Entropies of water

A solid, with a regular arrangement of particles, has a low entropy. When it melts, the particles can move more easily. The system has become more disordered and its entropy increases. Gas molecules move fast and independently of one another since inter-particle forces are negligible and gases have high entropy. Entropy decreases as gas pressure increases, because higher pressure reduces the volume for gas particles to move in, resulting in less disorder. When a solid or a liquid dissolves in a solvent, the entropy of the substance generally increases, however when a gas dissolves in a solvent its entropy decreases. Complex molecules, with more atoms to vibrate and move about, have higher entropies than simple ones. Hard solids with well ordered crystals, such as diamond, have lower entropy than soft, less-ordered ones such as potassium or lead.

The entropy of a perfectly ordered crystal at absolute zero is zero (that is there no randomness in the crystal or from the movement of the particles) hence, unlike enthalpy (H), absolute values of the entropy of a substance in a particular state can be measured relative to this. Real substances always have a greater randomness than this theoretical stationary perfect crystal, hence standard molar entropies of substances are always positive. The units of entropy are $J\ K^{-1}\ mol^{-1}$.

As a result, in any conversion, as well as the enthalpy change (ΔH), there is also an entropy change (ΔS). This entropy change is likely to be positive if there is a decrease in order through a decrease in the number of moles of solid, or an increase in the number of moles of gas, for example:

$$NH_4Cl\ (s) \longrightarrow NH_3\ (g) + HCl\ (g) \qquad \Delta S = +285\ J\ K^{-1}\ mol^{-1}$$

Conversely if the number of moles of gas decreases, or the number of moles of solid increases, there is an increase in order and the change in entropy is likely to be negative:

$$Pb^{2+}\ (aq) + 2\ I^-\ (aq) \longrightarrow PbI_2\ (s) \qquad \Delta S = -70\ J\ K^{-1}\ mol^{-1}$$

An increase in temperature and an increase in the number of particles (for example by a dissociation reaction), especially if some of these are of a different type, also increase entropy. The latter is, for example, the reason why, even if a reaction is slightly endothermic, a small amount of product will exist at equilibrium. This is dealt with more fully in the next section. The mixing of different types of particles (such as formation of a solution), also increases entropy, but the change in the number of particles in the gaseous state usually has a greater influence on the entropy change than any other factor.

The exact value of the entropy change can be calculated from absolute entropies using the formula:

$$\Delta S = \Sigma S\ (\text{Products}) - \Sigma S\ (\text{Reactants})$$

Consider the complete combustion of methane:

$$CH_4(g) + 2\ O_2(g) \longrightarrow CO_2(g) + 2\ H_2O(l)$$

$S(CH_4\ (g)) = 186$, $S(O_2\ (g)) = 205$,
$S(CO_2\ (g)) = 214$, $S(H_2O\ (l)) = 70$ (all in $J\ K^{-1}\ mol^{-1}$)

$$\begin{aligned}\Delta S &= [(2 \times 70) + (214)] - [(2 \times 205) + (186)] \\ &= -242\ J\ K^{-1}\ mol^{-1}\end{aligned}$$

As expected, because of the decrease in the number of moles of gas (3 to 1), there is an increase in the order of the system so the entropy change is negative. Note that, in contrast to standard enthalpies of formation, the entropy of elements, such as oxygen, is not zero.

Exercise 15.3

1. Which one of the following does not generally lead to an increase in the entropy of a system?

   A An increase in the total number of moles of particles.
   B The formation of a solution.
   C The formation of gaseous products.
   D The formation of solid products.

2. What is the entropy change associated with the Haber process?

   $$N_2(g) + 3\ H_2(g) \longrightarrow 2\ NH_3(g)$$

   [Standard entropies in $J\ K^{-1}\ mol^{-1}$: N_2 (g), 191; H_2 (g), 131; NH_3 (g), 193]

   A $-129\ J\ K^{-1}\ mol^{-1}$
   B $-198\ J\ K^{-1}\ mol^{-1}$
   C $+129\ J\ K^{-1}\ mol^{-1}$
   D $+198\ J\ K^{-1}\ mol^{-1}$

3. For each of the following state what kind of entropy change you would expect and briefly give your reasons.

   a) $Br_2\ (l) \longrightarrow Br_2\ (g)$
   b) $Ag^+\ (aq) + Cl^-\ (aq) \longrightarrow AgCl\ (s)$
   c) $2\ NO_2\ (g) \longrightarrow N_2O_4\ (g)$
   d) $2\ OH^-\ (aq) + CO_2\ (g) \longrightarrow H_2O\ (l) + CO_3^{2-}\ (aq)$
   e) $H_2\ (g) + Cl_2\ (g) \longrightarrow 2\ HCl\ (g)$

4. Calculate the enthalpy change for each of the following reactions and comment on how you could have predicted its sign without any need to perfom the calculation.

   a) $CuSO_4{\cdot}5H_2O\ (s) \longrightarrow CuSO_4\ (s) + 5\ H_2O\ (l)$
   [ΔS values, in $J\ K^{-1}\ mol^{-1}$: $CuSO_4{\cdot}5H_2O$ (s), 300; $CuSO_4$ (s), 109; H_2O (l), 70]

   b) $FeCl_2(s) + Cl_2(g) \longrightarrow FeCl_3(s)$
   [ΔS values, in $J\ K^{-1}\ mol^{-1}$: $FeCl_2$ (s), 118; $FeCl_3$ (s), 142; Cl_2 (g), 83]

   c) $Ba^{2+}\ (aq) + SO_4^{2-}\ (aq) \longrightarrow BaSO_4\ (s)$
   [ΔS values, in $J\ K^{-1}\ mol^{-1}$: Ba^{2+} (aq), 80.0; SO_4^{2-} (aq), 90.0; $BaSO_4$ (s), 132]

15.4 SPONTANEITY (AHL)

15.4.1 Predict whether a reaction or process will be spontaneous by using the sign of ΔG°.

15.4.2 Calculate ΔG° for a reaction using the equation
$\Delta G^\circ = \Delta H^\circ - T\Delta S^\circ$
and by using values of the standard free energy change of formation ΔG_f°.

15.4.3 Predict the effect of a change in temperature on the spontaneity of a reaction, using standard entropy and enthalpy changes and the equation.
$\Delta G^\circ = \Delta H^\circ - T\Delta S^\circ$

Nature tends to greater disorder, hence any change may occur spontaneously (like water flowing downhill, sodium chloride ('salt') dissolving in water or a gas expanding to fill a container) if the final state is more probable than the initial state, that is, if as a result of the change the final entropy of the universe is greater than the initial entropy of the universe (Physicists call this the Second Law of Thermodynamics). The entropy of the universe depends on both the entropy of the system and the entropy of the surroundings.

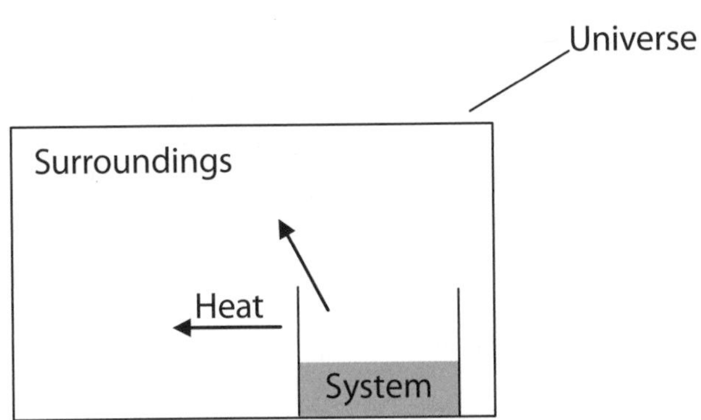

Figure 519 Illustrating the division into system and surroundings

ΔS measures the change in the entropy of the system. The major effect of chemical changes on the entropy of the surroundings results from the gain and loss of heat energy. If chemical potential energy is converted to heat energy which is then transferred to the universe (i.e. an exothermic change), then this results in an increase in the entropy of the surroundings and *vice versa* for an endothermic change. The magnitude of this entropy change is $-\Delta H^\circ/T$, where T is the absolute temperature. The condition for a spontaneous change to occur is therefore that $\Delta S_{universe}$ is positive, where $\Delta S_{universe}$ is given by:

$$\Delta S_{universe} = \Delta S_{surroundings} + \Delta S^\circ_{system} = -\Delta H^\circ/T + \Delta S^\circ_{system}$$

In other words a change will be spontaneous if:

- the final state has a lower enthalpy than the initial state (ΔH° is negative)

and

- the final state is more disordered than the initial state (ΔS° is positive).

If only one of these is the case then the outcome will depend on which factor is the dominant one at the temperature being considered.

In chemistry this condition has traditionally been considered in terms of the **Gibbs free energy change**, ΔG. The Gibbs free energy change is equal to $-T\Delta S_{universe}$. If this quantity is negative, then $\Delta S_{universe}$ must be positive, so that the process in question may occur spontaneously.

Multiplying through the equation above by $-T$ gives the expression:

$$\Delta G = \Delta H^\circ - T\Delta S^\circ$$

where ΔH° is the standard enthalpy change, ΔS° the standard entropy change of the system and T is the temperature in Kelvin. Hence for $\Delta S_{universe}$ to be positive and a change to be spontaneous, ΔG must be negative.

In other words whether a change occurs depends on two fundamental factors:

- whether it results in a product with lower enthalpy (i.e. whether ΔH° is negative)
- whether it results in a product with greater entropy (i.e. an increase in randomness so ΔS° is positive)

As a result a reaction will definitely occur if both the enthalpy change (ΔH°) is negative (i.e. it is exothermic) and the entropy change (ΔS°) is positive (i.e. it gives an increase in randomness). This does not mean that endothermic reactions (ΔH° positive) and reactions in which the randomness of the system decreases (ΔS° negative) or do not occur. Both ΔH° and ΔS° changes must be considered before deciding if a reaction will occur, that is whether it is spontaneous. The Gibbs free energy change (ΔG) ,

ΔH^{Θ}	ΔS^{Θ}	ΔG	Spontaneity
Positive, i.e. endothermic	Positive, i.e. more random products	Depends on T	Spontaneous at high temperatures, when $T\Delta S^{\Theta} > \Delta H$
Positive, i.e. endothermic	Negative, i.e. more ordered products	Always positive	Never spontaneous
Negative, i.e. exothermic	Positive, i.e. more random products	Always negative	Always spontaneous
Negative, i.e. exothermic	Negative, i.e. more ordered products	Depends on T	Spontaneous at low temperatures, when $T\Delta S^{\Theta} < \Delta H$

N.B. This assumes that the effect of temperature on the actual values of ΔH^{Θ} and ΔS^{Θ} is negligible

Figure 520 The effect of ΔH and ΔS on the spontaneity of reaction

defined in the equation above, which is a measure of the driving force of a reaction, is the criterion for predicting the spontaneity of a reaction. The way in which the sign of ΔH^{Θ} and ΔS^{Θ} affect the sign of ΔG is summarised in Figure 520:

This may be illustrated graphically as shown in Figure 521 below:

Note that ΔH does not vary much with T (so ΔH^{Θ} data can be used), but ΔG is strongly temperature dependent hence, because the entropy change (ΔS^{Θ}) is multiplied by the absolute temperature, the influence of the entropy change is always dominant at high temperature.

Figures 519 and 520 just give the conditions under which a reaction may be spontaneous, they do not actually mean that the reaction will actually take place at a measurable rate. If the reaction has a high activation energy, then the rate at which the reaction occurs may be infinitesimal, even though it is energetically feasible. For example a mixture of hydrogen and oxygen will not react at a measurable rate at room temperature and pressure, even though the reaction to form water is spontaneous, because virtually none of the molecules have sufficient kinetic energy to overcome the activation energy for the reaction.

The Gibbs free energy (ΔG) for a change is equal to the amount of energy from that system that is available to do useful work. Hence for any system in equilibrium (refer to Chapter 7) ΔG must be exactly zero, i.e. the system can do no useful work. Thus if ΔG for a reaction is zero, then when stoichiometric amounts of both reactants and products are all mixed together there will be no further change. If ΔG is slightly negative there will be a net reaction to increase the amount of products and decrease the amount of reactants.

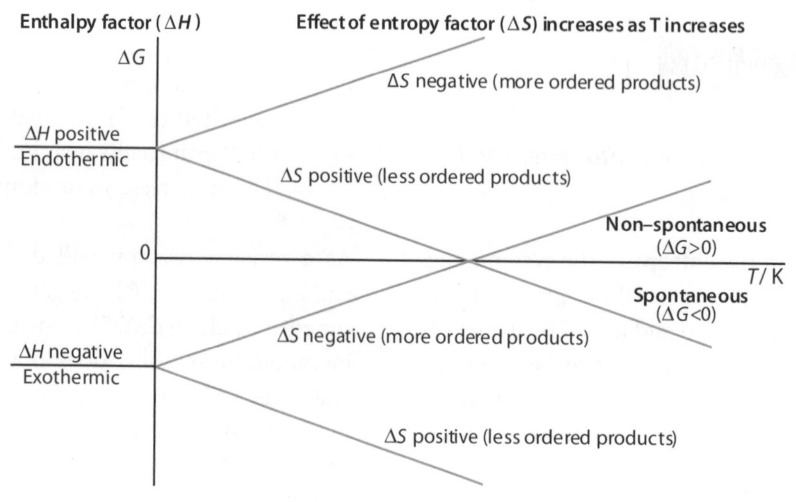

Figure 521 The conditions for spontaneity and the effect of temperature on this

This will continue until ΔG for any further change will be zero (remember standard values only apply to standard conditions, i.e. stoichiometric amounts), at which point equilibrium will be established. If ΔG is very negative then this position will be so far to the right that the reaction will effectively go to completion. Similarly if ΔG is small and positive then an equilibrium favouring the products will occur, but if ΔG is very positive the reaction will not occur.

The value of ΔG can be calculated at any given temperature from values of ΔH and ΔS for the reaction, which are in turn calculated from data about the reactants and products. Consider for example the thermal decomposition of calcium carbonate at 500 K:

$$CaCO_3\,(s) \longrightarrow CaO\,(s) + CO_2\,(g)$$

The required data are:

Substance	ΔH°_f – kJ mol^{-1}	S° – J K^{-1}mol^{-1}
$CaCO_3$(s)	–1207	93
CaO(s)	–636	40
CO_2(g)	–394	214

Figure 522 Table for the decomposition of $CaCO_3$

Using these data, values of ΔH° and ΔS° can be calculated for the reaction:

$$\Delta H = \sum H_f(\text{Products}) - \sum H_f(\text{Reactants})$$

$$= [(-636) + (-394) - [-1207]$$

$$= +177 \text{ kJ mol}^{-1} = 177\,000 \text{ J mol}^{-1}.$$

$$\Delta S = \sum \Delta S(\text{Products}) - \sum \Delta S(\text{Reactants})$$

$$= [(40) + (214)] - [93]$$

$$= +\,161 \text{ J K}^{-1} \text{ mol}^{-1}.$$

$$\Delta G = \Delta H - T\Delta S$$

$$= 177\,000 - (161 \times 500)$$

$$= 96\,500 \text{ J mol}^{-1} = 96.5 \text{ k J mol}^{-1}.$$

Note that the units for ΔG_f and ΔH°_f are usually kJ mol^{-1}. Since the units of ΔS° are J K^{-1} mol^{-1}, then units of $T\Delta S^\circ$ are J mol^{-1}. Hence it is essential to divide this by 1000 to convert it to kJ mol^{-1}. Alternatively the whole calculation can be performed in units of J mol^{-1}.

ΔG is positive, therefore at this temperature the reaction is not spontaneous and cannot occur. If the temperature is increased to 2000 K however, assuming ΔH° and ΔS° are both independent of temperature:

$$\Delta G = \Delta H - T\Delta S$$

$$= 177\,000 - (161 \times 2\,000)$$

$$= 145\,000 \text{ J mol}^{-1} = 96.5 \text{ k J mol}^{-1}.$$

The reaction is now spontaneous so that, provided there is sufficient energy to overcome the activation energy, which is the case for this reaction, the process occurs. The temperature at which the system is in perfect equilibrium (i.e. $K_c = 1$) can be calculated knowing that at equilibrium, because $\Delta G = 0$, $\Delta H^\circ = T{\cdot}\Delta S^\circ$:

$$177\,000 = T \times 161$$

$$T = \frac{177\,000}{161} = 1\,099 \text{ K}$$

ΔG° under standard conditions (298 K and 101.3 kPa) can also be calculated using the standard **Gibbs free energy of formation** (ΔG°_f) data in the same way as data on the standard enthalpy of formation (ΔH°_f) data is used to calculate standard enthalpy changes (ΔH°). The Gibbs free energy of elements in their standard state is similarly defined as zero, so that the standard Gibbs free energy change of formation is the free energy change when one mole of a compound is formed from its elements under standard conditions.

Therefore:

$$\Delta G^\circ_f = \Sigma G^\circ_f(\text{Products}) - \Sigma G^\circ_f(\text{Reactants})$$

Using this approach for the calcium carbonate example above standard free energy of formation data for the compounds in the appropriate state is:

$\Delta G^\circ_f(CaCO_3) = -1120$ kJ mol^{-1};
$\Delta G^\circ_f(CaO) = -604$ kJ mol^{-1};
$\Delta G^\circ_f(CO_2) = -395$ kJ mol^{-1}

Hence:

$$\Delta G^\circ = [(-604) + (-395)] - [-1120]$$
$$= +121 \text{ kJ mol}^{-1}$$

AHL

AHL

Exercise 15.4

1. Which of the following combinations of enthalpy change and entropy change ensures that the position of equilibrium will favour the products under all conditions?

	ΔH	ΔS
A	Positive	Positive
B	Positive	Negative
C	Negative	Positive
D	Negative	Negative

2. For the reaction of liquid phosphorus(III) chloride with chlorine gas to form solid phosphorus(V) chloride at 298 K, the entropy change is –85 J mol^{-1} K^{-1} and the enthalpy change is -124 kJ mol^{-1}. What is the approximate value of the Gibbs free energy at this temperature?

   A –200 kJ mol^{-1}
   B –100 kJ mol^{-1}
   C –40 kJ mol^{-1}
   D +40 kJ mol^{-1}

3. Under certain conditions it is possible for three moles of gaseous ethyne (C_2H_2) to polymerise to form liquid benzene (C_6H_6). Use the data provided to calculate:

   a) The entropy change of the system.
   b) The enthalpy change of the system.
   c) The entropy change of the surroundings that would result from the emission of this amount of heat energy at 25 °C.
   d) Explain how these factors combine to determine whether a spontaneous reaction is possible and predict the optimum conditions for the formation of benzene.

   Data:

	ΔH_f / kJ mol^{-1}	S / J mol^{-1} K^{-1}
Ethyne	227	201
Benzene	83	269

4. Use values of the Gibbs free energy change of formation, given below, to deduce whether the *cis–* or *trans–* isomer of but-2-ene is the more stable at 25 °C. At what temperature will the two isomers have the same stability?

   Data:

	ΔG_f kJ mol^{-1}	ΔH_f kJ mol^{-1}	S J mol^{-1} K^{-1}
***cis*–but-2-ene**	67.1	–5.7	301
***trans*–but-2-ene**	64.1	–10.1	296

5. This question refers to the graph of ΔG against temperature shown.

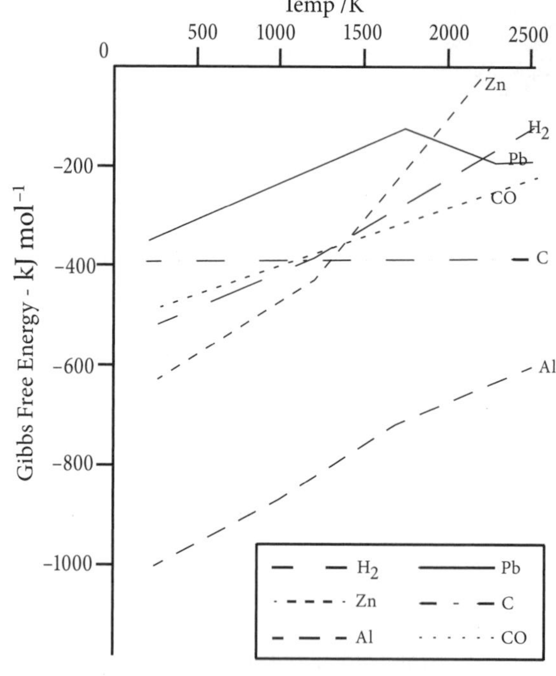

This shows the variation of ΔG for the reaction of the substance indicated with one mole of oxygen to form the most stable oxide.

   a) The line for the reaction $2Pb + O_2 \longrightarrow 2PbO$ shows two distinct changes of gradient. Explain these.
   b) Is carbon or carbon monoxide the more powerful reducing agent?
   c) Explain what it shows about the potential use of hydrogen as a reductant for:
      i Al_2O_3
      ii PbO
      iii ZnO

KINETICS

6.1 Rates of reaction

6.2 Collision theory

16.1 Rate Expression (AHL)

16.2 Reaction mechanism (AHL)

16.3 Activation energy (AHL)

6.1 RATES OF REACTION

6.1.1 Define the term rate of reaction.

6.1.2 Describe suitable experimental procedures for measuring rates of reactions.

6.1.3 Analyse data from rate experiments.

Figure 601 An explosion is a quick reaction

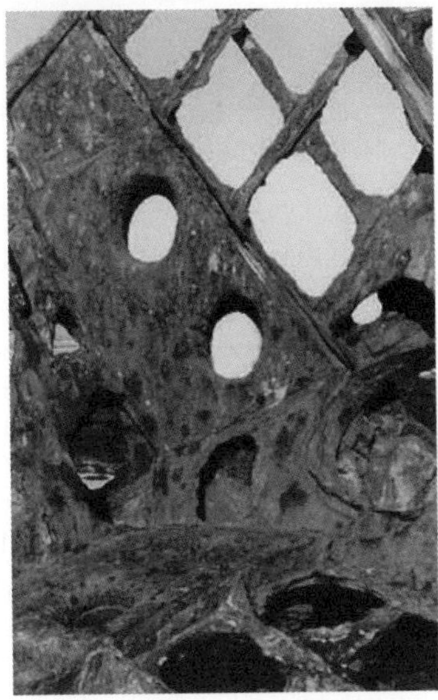

Figure 602 Corrosion is a slow reaction

Different chemical reactions occur at different rates (i.e. speeds). Some, such as the neutralisation of a strong acid by a strong base in aqueous solution, take place very rapidly whilst others, such as the rusting of iron, take place far more slowly. Rates of reactions should not be confused with how far a reaction goes - this is determined by equilibrium.

The **rate of a chemical reaction** is a measure of the speed at which products are formed, measured as the change in concentration divided by the change in time, so reaction rate has units of mol dm^{-3} s^{-1}. This is equal to the rate at which the reactants are consumed, so for a reaction:

$$R \longrightarrow P, \text{ rate} = \frac{\Delta[P]}{\Delta t} = -\frac{\Delta[R]}{\Delta t}$$

Note the minus sign for the reactants, which is necessary as the concentrations of reactants decreases with time whereas the concentrations of products increases. Rate is always positive.

The numerical value will vary according to the amount of the substance involved in the stoichiometric equation, so that in the reaction:

$$MnO_4^- (aq) + 8\,H^+ (aq) + 5\,Fe^{2+} (aq) \longrightarrow Mn^{2+} (aq) + 4\,H_2O\,(l) + 5\,Fe^{3+} (aq)$$

The rate of appearance of Fe^{3+} is five times as great as the rate at which MnO_4^- is consumed. The rate is usually considered to apply to a product that has a coefficient of one as the equation is usually written:

$$\text{Rate} = -\frac{\Delta[MnO_4^-]}{\Delta t} = \frac{1}{5}\frac{\Delta[Fe^{3+}]}{\Delta t}$$

Or more simply for a reaction: a A $\longrightarrow$ b B, then

$$\text{Rate} = \frac{1}{b}\frac{\Delta[B]}{\Delta t} = -\frac{1}{a}\frac{\Delta[A]}{\Delta t}$$

Any property that differs between the reactants and the products can be used to measure the rate of the reaction. *Refer to Section 6.2.* Whichever property is chosen, a graph is drawn of that property against time and the rate of reaction is proportional to the gradient of the curve or line ignoring the sign. Changes in the gradient of similar graphs illustrate the effect of changing conditions on the rate of reaction, without the need to convert the units to mol $dm^{-3}\,s^{-1}$.

In most cases the rate of reaction decreases with time because the concentration of the reactants decreases with time and the reaction rate usually depends on the reactant concentration. It is most common to compare initial rates, that is, the gradient of the tangent to the curve at $t = 0$. At this time the concentrations of the reagents are accurately known, as is the temperature of the system. It is also easiest to draw tangents at this time as this section of the curve is the most linear. Typical curves obtained for the consumption of a reagent and formation of a product are shown in Figure 603.

Exercise 6.1

1. The equation for a reaction is:

$$4\,NO_2\,(g) + 2\,H_2O\,(g) + O_2\,(g) \longrightarrow 4\,HNO_3\,(g)$$

Which one of the following is not numerically equal to the others?

A $-\frac{1}{2}\frac{\Delta[NO_2]}{\Delta t}$

B $-\frac{1}{2}\frac{\Delta[O_2]}{\Delta t}$

C $-\frac{\Delta[H_2O]}{\Delta t}$

D $\frac{1}{2}\frac{\Delta[HNO_3]}{\Delta t}$

2. Which of the curves on the following graph shows the greatest initial reaction rate?

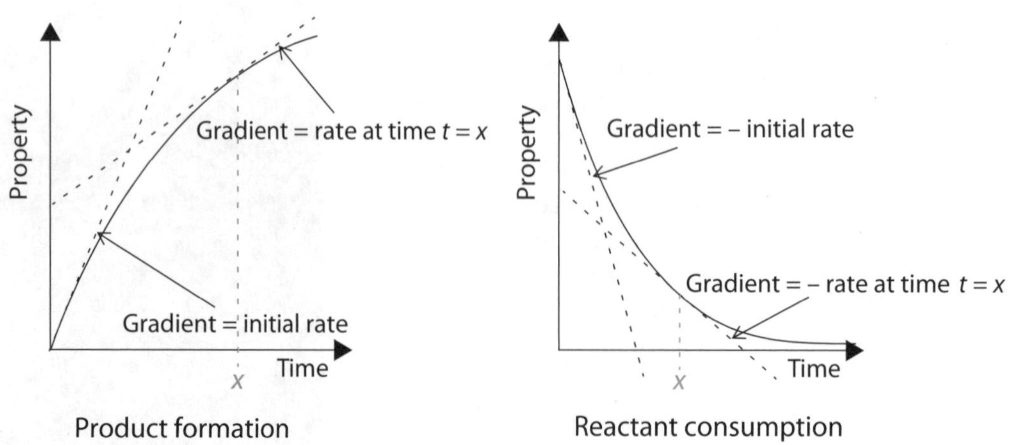

Figure 603 The variation of reaction rate with time

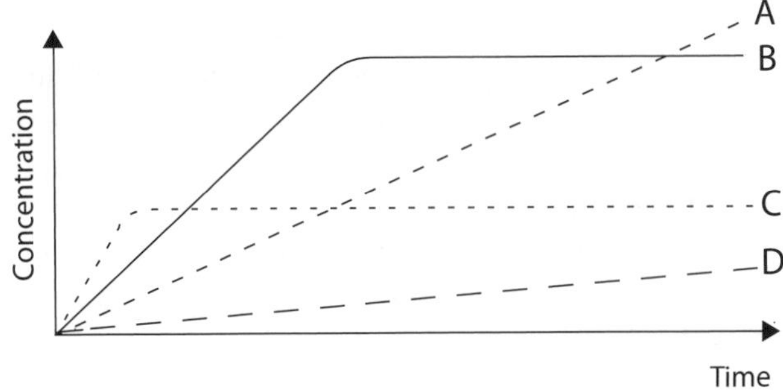

3. Iodate(V) ions oxidise iodide ions in acidic solution to form iodine and water according to the equation

$$IO_3^-\,(aq) + 5\,I^-\,(aq) + 6\,H^+(aq) \longrightarrow 3\,I_2\,(aq) + 3\,H_2O\,(l)$$

If the number of moles of each reactant consumed after one minute was measured, which would have been consumed least?

A IO_3^-
B I^-
C H^+
D They would all have been consumed to the same extent.

4. The rate of reaction between hydrogen peroxide and the iodide ions was measured by monitoring the absorption of blue light by the iodine. If the equation for the reaction is

$$H_2O_2\,(aq) + 2\,I^-(aq) + 2\,H^+(aq) \longrightarrow I_2\,(aq) + 2\,H_2O\,(l)$$

a) If 0.005 mol dm^{-3} of iodine is produced in the first 2 minutes, what is the initial reaction rate in mol dm^{-3} s^{-1}?
b) What is the rate at which
   i hydrogen peroxide is consumed?
   ii iodide ions are consumed?
   Explain why these are different.

5. The rate of reaction between zinc and sulfuric acid is measured by weighing a zinc plate, which is then placed into a beaker of the acid. Every 10 minutes it is removed, rinsed, dried and reweighed. This is continued until all of the acid is consumed.

a) Sketch the graph you would expect for the mass of the zinc plate against time in the acid.
b) At what point is the reaction rate the greatest? How can you tell?
c) Suggest another way that the rate of this reaction could have been measured.

SOME TECHNIQUES FOR MEASURING RATES

There are a variety of techniques that can be used to measure the rate of a chemical reaction and some of the more common are described below. Any property that changes between the start and end of the reaction can in principle be used. It is however best if this changes by a large amount compared to the limits of accuracy of its measurement. It is also simpler to use quantitatively if the characteristic is directly proportional to the concentration of one or more components. For these reasons monitoring the rate of reaction by observing a pH change is generally not to be recommended, because the pH, being a logarithmic scale, will only change by 0.30 for a change of $[H^+]$ by a factor of 2.

In some techniques the time taken for a particular event to occur may be used to measure the reaction rate (e.g. the time taken for a piece of magnesium ribbon to dissolve in a dilute acid). In these techniques it is important to remember that the greater the time the smaller the rate of reaction, i.e. the rate of reaction is inversely proportional to the time taken:

$$\text{Rate} \propto \frac{1}{\text{Time}}$$

If the purpose of the investigation is simply to observe the effect of some variable, such as the concentration of a particular species, on the rate of reaction, then a graph of the property proportional to concentration against time, will suffice. If however the reaction rate is required in standard units (mol dm^{-3} s^{-1}) then it will be necessary to calibrate the system so as to produce graphs of concentration against time.

Whichever technique is being used, it is important to keep the reaction mixture at a constant temperature during the reaction, because temperature has a great effect on the rate of reaction. For this reason it is usual to immerse the reaction vessel in a water bath at the required temperature. It is also preferable to immerse the reactants in the water bath, to allow them to reach the required temperature before mixing. One reason for prefering 'initial rate' data is that the effect of an endo- or exothermic reaction on the temperature of the system is minimised.

TOK The empirical nature of chemistry

I used to think all magpies were black and white. In both England and New Zealand (my two "home" countries – whatever that concept implies) the magpie (very different species in both countries – the New Zealand version is a lot heavier and doesn't have the long tail) are black and white birds. Then there's the magpie robin, a much smaller bird, and the magpie goose - both also black and white. Indeed in England Newcastle United football club are nicknamed 'the magpies' because of their black and white shirts. My simple world was turned on its head when I arrived in Hong Kong and encountered the blue magpie. Definitely a magpie shape, but with bright blue as the dominant colour (along with black and white) and a gorgeous long tail. I'm afraid I was another victim of the fundamental problem of inductive logic - you can never be sure. However, in case you're thinking you will just rely on deductive techniques, reflect for a few seconds on how you establish your premises.

All empirical science suffers in the same way - it is quite easy to prove a theory wrong, but it is never possible to prove it correct. Tomorrow somebody might come up with a piece of evidence that contradicts your theory and then it's back to the drawing boards. Falsification is so fundamental to science that the Austrian philosopher, *Karl Popper*, said that if you could not think of an experiment that would disprove your theory, then it was not a scientific theory.

In kinetics, the balanced equation tells us nothing about how changing the concentrations will affect the rate and we have to do experiments to determine the rate equation. We can then postulate mechanisms that would account for the empirical rate equation and certainly we can rule out some possible mechanisms, but even if we have a mechanism that explains the rate equation (and sometimes there can be more than one mechanism that does this, read this chapter) we can never be sure that tomorrow somebody will not come up with an alternative.

Titration

This involves removing small samples from the reaction mixture at different times and then titrating the sample to determine the concentration of either one of the reactants or one of the products at this time. The results can then be used directly to generate a graph of concentration against time. In its simplest form this is only really suitable for quite slow reactions, in which the time taken to titrate the mixture is insignificant compared to the total time taken for the reaction. One common variant that helps to overcome this difficulty is to quench the reaction before carrying out the titration. This means altering the conditions so as to virtually stop the reaction. This can be done by rapidly cooling the reaction mixture to a very low temperature or by adding an excess of a compound that rapidly reacts with one of the reactants. If for example the reaction was that of a halogenoalkane with an alkali, it could be quenched by running the reaction mixture into an excess of a strong acid. This means that the time at which the sample of the reaction mixture was quenched is much easier to determine.

Another example of a reaction that can be readily measured by this technique is the rate of reaction of hydrogen peroxide with iodide ions in acidic solution to produce iodine and water. The amount of iodine produced can be measured by titrating the mixture with aqueous sodium thiosulfate. The reaction mixture can be quenched by adding excess of an insoluble solid base, such as powdered calcium carbonate, to neutralise the acid required for reaction.

$$H_2O_2\,(aq) + 2\,H^+\,(aq) + 2\,I^-\,(aq) \longrightarrow 2\,H_2O\,(l) + I_2\,(aq)$$

Collection of an evolved gas/ increase in gas pressure

The gas produced in the reaction is collected either in a gas syringe, or in a graduated vessel over water. The volume of gas collected at different times can be recorded. This technique is obviously limited to reactions that produce a gas. In addition, if the gas is to be collected over water, this gas must not be water soluble. An alternative technique is to carry out the reaction in a vessel of fixed volume and monitor the increase in the gas pressure. These techniques would be suitable for measuring the rate of reaction between a moderately reactive metal (such as zinc) and an acid (such as hydrochloric acid), or reaction of a carbonate with acid:

$$Zn\,(s) + 2\,H^+\,(aq) \longrightarrow Zn^{2+}\,(aq) + H_2\,(g)$$

$$Na_2CO_3\,(s) + 2\,HCl\,(aq) \longrightarrow 2\,NaCl\,(aq) + CO_2\,(g) + H_2O\,(l)$$

Measurement of the mass of the reaction mixture

The total mass of the reaction mixture will only vary if a gas is evolved. To be really effective, the gas being evolved should have a high molar mass (i.e. not hydrogen), so that there is a significant change in mass, also the gas should not be significantly soluble in the solvent used. This technique would be suitable for measuring the rate of reaction between a metal carbonate (such as calcium carbonate, marble chips) and an acid (such as hydrochloric acid), by measuring the rate of mass loss resulting from the evolution of carbon dioxide.

$$CaCO_3\,(s) + 2\,H^+\,(aq) \longrightarrow Ca^{2+}\,(aq) + H_2O\,(l) + CO_2\,(g)$$

Light absorption

If a reaction produces a precipitate, then the time taken for the precipitate to obscure a mark made on a piece of paper under the reaction vessel can be used as a measure of reaction rate. For simple work comparison of the times, keeping the depth of the liquid constant will suffice; e.g. if the time taken doubles then the reaction rate is halved. A reaction that is often studied by this technique is the reaction between aqueous thiosulfate ions and a dilute acid which gives sulfur dioxide, water and a finely divided precipitate of sulfur.

$$S_2O_3^{2-}\,(aq) + 2\,H^+\,(aq) \longrightarrow H_2O\,(l) + SO_2\,(g) + S\,(s)$$

A convenient way to follow this reaction is to place a black cross/mark on a white piece of paper under the reaction mixture and to measure the time taken for the finely suspended yellow sulfur to obscure the cross.

If the reaction involves a coloured reactant or product, then the intensity of the colour can be used to monitor the concentration of that species. In its simplest form this can be done by comparing the colour by eye against a set of standard solutions of known concentration. The technique is far more precise if an instrument that measures the absorbance (which is directly proportional to concentration – refer to the Beer–Lambert law in Section A8.6, Chapter 12) such as a colorimeter or spectrophotometer is available. If a colorimeter is used then a filter of the complementary colour to that of the coloured species should be chosen – an aqueous solution of a copper(II) salt is blue because it absorbs red light, so that it is the intensity of transmitted red light not blue light that will vary with its concentration. If a spectrophotometer is used, then a wavelength near to the absorption maximum of the coloured species should be selected.

A reaction that is often studied by this technique is the reaction between propanone and iodine to form iodopropanone. The yellow-brown iodine is the only coloured species involved and so the intensity of blue light (or light of wavelength ≈450 nm if a spectrophotometer is used) passing through the solution will increase with time as the concentration of the iodine falls. Most instruments, however, give a direct reading of absorbance which has an inverse relationship to the transmitted light, so that absorbance decreases with time.

$$CH_3COCH_3\,(aq) + I_2\,(aq) \longrightarrow CH_3COCH_2I\,(aq) + H^+\,(aq) + I^-\,(aq)$$

Electrical conductivity

The presence of ions allows a solution to conduct, so if there is a significant change in the concentration of ions (especially hydrogen and hydroxide ions which have an unusually high conductivity) during the course of a reaction, then the reaction rate may be found from the change in conductivity. This is usually found by measuring the A.C. resistance between two electrodes with a fixed geometry, immersed in the solution. A reaction that is suitable for this technique would be the hydrolysis of phosphorus(III) chloride that produces dihydrogenphosphate(III) ions, hydrogen ions and chloride ions from non–ionic reactants.

$$PCl_3\,(aq) + 3\,H_2O\,(l) \longrightarrow H_2PO_3^-\,(aq) + 4\,H^+\,(aq) + 3\,Cl^-\,(aq)$$

Clock techniques

There are some reactions in which the product can be consumed by further reaction with another added substance. When all of this substance is consumed then an observable change will occur. The time taken for this corresponds to the time for a certain amount of product to have been formed and so is inversely proportional to the rate of reaction. The classic reaction studied in this way is the reaction between hydrogen peroxide and iodide ions, in the presence of acid, to form iodine and water. Thiosulfate ions are added to the system and these initially react rapidly with the iodine produced. When all of the thiosulfate has been consumed, free iodine is liberated and this colours the solution yellow, or more commonly blue–black through the addition of starch solution (which forms an intensely coloured complex with iodine) to the system.

$$H_2O_2 (l) + 2\,H^+ (aq) + 2\,I^- (aq) \longrightarrow 2\,H_2O (l) + I_2 (aq)$$

$$\downarrow$$

$$2\,S_2O_3^{2-} (aq) + I_2 (aq) \longrightarrow S_4O_6^{2-} (aq) + 2\,I^- (aq)$$

The blue colour of the iodine-starch complex suddenly appears when all of the thiosulfate has been consumed. The time taken for this to occur is inversely proportional to the rate.

Exercise 6.1

1. The rate of a chemical reaction can sometimes be determined by measuring the change in mass of the reaction flask and its contents with time. For which of the following reactions would this technique be most successful?

   A Magnesium oxide and dilute sulfuric acid.
   B Aqueous sodium chloride and aqueous silver nitrate.
   C Copper(II) carbonate and dilute hydrochloric acid.
   D Zinc and aqueous copper(II) sulfate.

2. You wish to carry out an investigation that involves the use of a conductivity meter to monitor the rate of a chemical reaction. Which of the reactions below would be the least suitable for this?

   A $H_2O_2 (aq) + 2\,H^+ (aq) + 2\,I^- (aq) \longrightarrow 2\,H_2O (l) + I_2 (aq)$

   B $Ba^{2+} (aq) + SO_4^{2-} (aq) \longrightarrow BaSO_4 (s)$

   C $POCl_3 (l) + 3\,H_2O (l) \longrightarrow 4\,H^+ (aq) + 3\,Cl^- (aq) + H_2PO_4^- (aq)$

   D $2\,H_2O_2 (aq) \longrightarrow 2\,H_2O (l) + O_2 (g)$

3. For which one of the following reactions would a colorimeter be most suitable for monitoring the reaction rate?

   A The reaction of acidified permanganate ions (manganate(VII)) ions with ethanedioic acid (oxalic acid) to form carbon dioxide, manganese(II) ions and water.
   B The reaction of magnesium carbonate with a dilute acid to form a soluble magnesium salt, carbon dioxide and water.
   C The reaction of bromobutane with aqueous sodium hydroxide to form butanol and aqueous sodium bromide.
   D The reaction of lithium with water to form aqueous lithium hydroxide and hydrogen.

4. You wish to measure the rate of reaction of acidified dichromate(VI) ions with aqueous sulfur dioxide to produce aqueous chromium(III) ions and aqueous sulfate ions at 35 °C. This reaction involves a colour change from orange to green. Discuss how you might go about doing this, the measurements you would need to take and the precautions required.

5. During your study of chemistry you will most likely have studied the way in which altering certain variables affected the rate of a chemical reaction.

   a) What reaction did you study?
   b) What technique did you use to study the rate of this reaction? Why do you think this method was appropriate?
   c) What variable did you change? How was this carried out?
   d) How could you modify the investigation to study another variable. State which variable you are now going to study and outline how you would carry this out along with any precautions you would take.

6.2 COLLISION THEORY

6.2.1 Describe the kinetic theory in terms of the movement of particles whose average energy is proportional to temperature in kelvins.

6.2.2 Define activation energy, E_a.

6.2.3 Describe the collision theory.

6.2.4 Predict and explain, using collision theory, the qualitative effects of particle size, temperature, concentration and pressure on the rate of a reaction.

6.2.5 Sketch and explain qualitatively the Maxwell–Boltzmann energy distribution curve for a fixed amount of gas at different temperatures and its consequences for changes in reaction rate.

6.2.6 Describe the effect of a catalyst on a chemical reaction.

6.2.7 Sketch and explain Maxwell–Boltzmann curves for reactions with and without catalysts.

Collisions are vital for chemical change, both to provide the energy required for a particle to change (for example, a bond to break), and to bring the reactants into contact.

As particles approach each other there is repulsion between the electron clouds of the particles. In order for reaction to occur, the collision must have sufficient **kinetic energy** to overcome this repulsion. Frequently energy is also required to break some of the bonds in the particles before a reaction can take place. Hence not all collisions lead to a reaction. This minimum amount of energy required for reaction is known as the **activation energy** (E_a) for the reaction (units of E_a: kJ mol^{-1}). This is illustrated, for an exothermic reaction, in Figure 605.

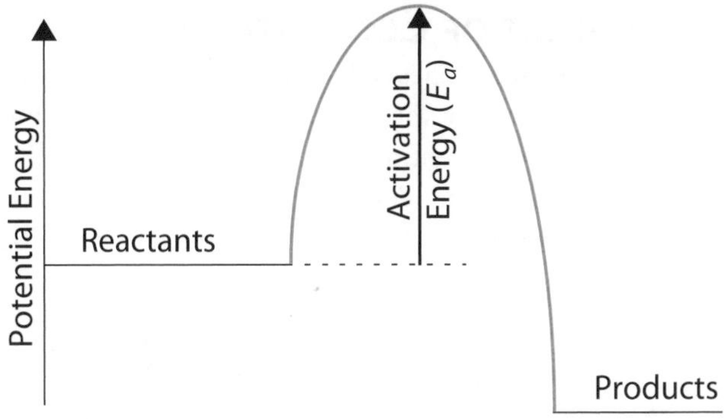

Figure 605 The principle of activation energy

The activation energy involved varies tremendously from reaction to reaction. In some cases (such as the reaction of the hydrogen ion and hydroxide ion) it is so low that reaction occurs on almost every collision even at low temperatures. In other cases (such as sugar and oxygen) it is so high that reaction at room temperature is negligible.

In order to react, the two particles involved must:

- collide with each other
- the collision must be energetic enough to overcome the activation energy of the reaction, (i.e. the collision must have $E > E_a$)
- the collision must occur with the correct geometrical alignment, that is it must bring the reactive parts of the molecule into contact in the correct way

This final factor, often called the **steric factor**, is particularly important with regard to reactions involving large organic molecules.

If anything increases the **collision rate**, then the rate of reaction increases. Similarly anything that increases the proportion of the collisions that have an energy equal to or greater than the activation energy will increase the rate of reaction. These factors are summarised in Figure 606.

Factors mainly affecting the collision rate	Factors mainly affecting the proportion with required E_a
Concentration/pressure	Temperature
Surface area	Catalyst

Figure 606 Factors affecting the rate of reaction (table)

THE EFFECT OF CONCENTRATION

The rate at which particles collide is increased by increasing the concentration of the reactants. Thus marble chips react faster with concentrated hydrochloric acid than they do with the dilute acid. For reacting gases, increasing the pressure is equivalent to increasing the concentration. The effect of concentration on rate is illustrated in Figure 607.

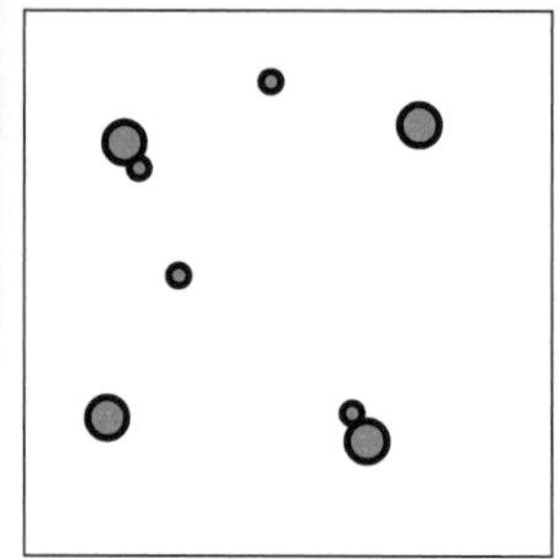

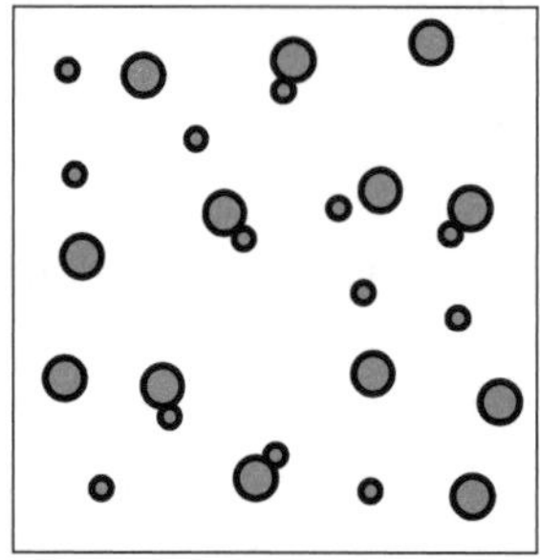

Figure 607 The effect of concentration

THE EFFECT OF SURFACE AREA

If the reaction involves substances in phases that do not mix (e.g. a solid and a liquid, or a liquid and a gas) then an increase in the surface area in contact will increase the collision rate. As a result powdered calcium carbonate reacts faster with hydrochloric acid than lumps of the solid with the same mass. This is illustrated in Figure 608.

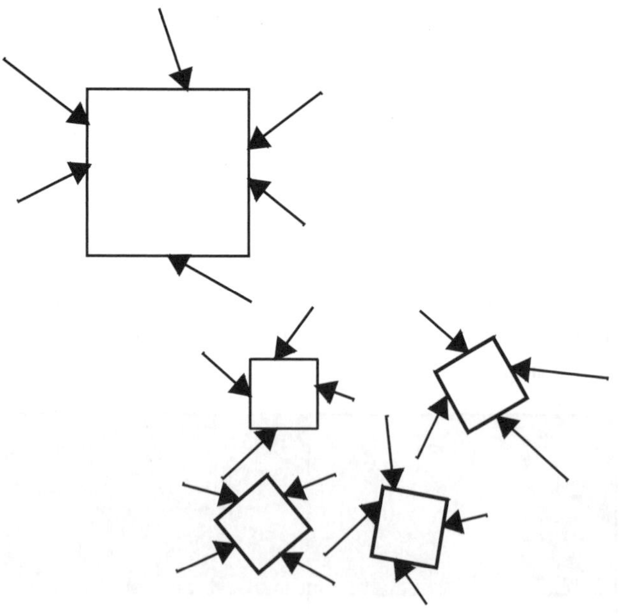

Figure 608 The effect of surface area

THE EFFECT OF TEMPERATURE

Not all particles have the same energy so there is a distribution of kinetic energy, and hence velocity, amongst the particles of the gas, known as the **Maxwell-Boltzmann distribution**, shown in Figure 609. As with cars on a freeway, some are moving more rapidly and others more slowly. The mean speed of the particles is proportional to the absolute temperature but, because the curve is asymmetric, this does not coincide with the most probable speed. The area under the curve represents the total number of particles and hence, in a closed system, this area must remain constant.

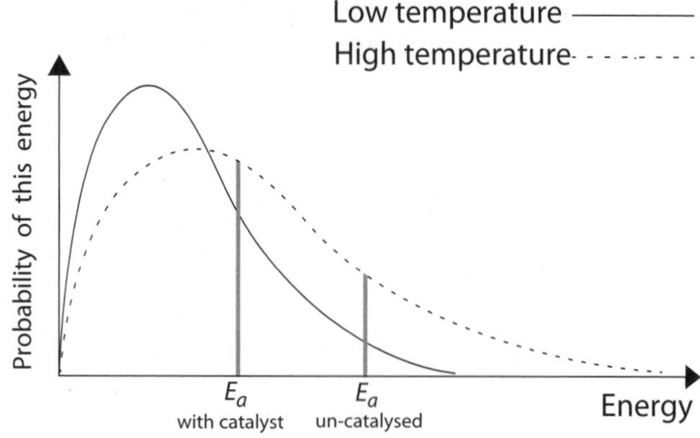

Figure 609 The effects of temperature and catalyst

As previously stated, a collision must have a certain minimum energy, the activation energy, before reaction can occur. As can be seen in Figure 609, the number of molecules with the required activation energy is much greater at a higher temperature than at a lower one. This means that marble chips react more rapidly with warm hydrochloric acid than with cold hydrochloric acid. Increasing the temperature also has a very slight effect on the collision rate, but in most cases this is insignificant compared to its effect on the proportion of collisions with the required activation energy. For many reactions an increase in temperature of 10 °C will approximately double the rate of reaction (a crude generalization), but the increase in the collision rate that this rise in temperature causes is only ≈2%. To summarise, increasing the temperature increases the frequency of collisions but, more important is the increase in the proportion of molecules with $E > E_a$. The effect of temperature on reaction rate is discussed in much more detail in Chapter 6.6.

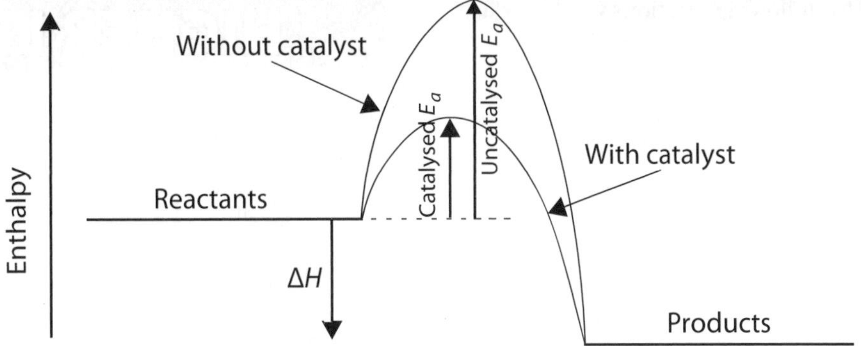

Figure 610 The effect of a catalyst

THE EFFECT OF CATALYST

A catalyst is a substance that is usually required in small amounts and can increase the rate of a chemical reaction without undergoing any overall change. Catalysts speed up a reaction by providing an alternative reaction mechanism or pathway (like a mountain pass) with a lower activation energy by which the reaction can take place. This means that a greater proportion of collisions will have the required energy to react by the new mechanism and so the reaction rate increases. Typically, the efficiency of a catalyst decreases with time as it becomes inactive due to impurities in the reaction mixture, side reactions, or if its surface becomes coated and unavailable for activity.

The way this affects the situation in terms of the Maxwell-Boltzmann distribution and the energy diagram is shown in Figures 609 & 610.

THE EFFECT OF LIGHT

Some chemical reactions are brought about by exposure to light. Examples would be the darkening of silver halides when exposed to sunlight (the basis of black and white photography) and the reaction of alkanes with chlorine or bromine (for example, the reaction of methane and chlorine). This is because reactant particles absorb light energy and this brings about either the excitation of one of the reactants (as is the case with the silver halides) or the breaking of a bond (such as the halogen—halogen bond in the halogenation of the alkanes) which initiates the reaction. It is for this reason that many chemicals are stored in brown glass containers.

Exercise 6.2

1. Which one of the following factors does not affect the rate of a chemical reaction?

   A The amounts of the reagents.
   B The concentration of the reagents.
   C The temperature of the reagents.
   D The presence of a catalyst.

2. In most chemical reactions, the rate of reaction decreases as the reaction proceeds. The usual reason for this is that

   A The energy for the reaction is running out.
   B The concentrations of the reactants are becoming lower.
   C The temperature is falling as the reaction proceeds.
   D The activation energy becomes greater.

3. In which of the following situations would you expect the rate of reaction between marble (calcium carbonate) and nitric acid to be the greatest?

   A Powdered marble and 2 mol dm^{-3} acid at 40 °C.
   B Powdered marble and 0.5 mol dm^{-3} acid at 40 °C.
   C Powdered marble and 2 mol dm^{-3} acid at 20 °C.
   B Marble chips and 0.5 mol dm^{-3} acid at 40 °C.

4. In which one of the following reactions would surface area not be a factor affecting the rate?

   A Zinc and sulfuric acid.
   B Carbon dioxide gas with limewater (aqueous calcium hydroxide).
   C Vegetable oil and aqueous sodium hydroxide.
   D Aqueous ethanedioic (oxalic) acid and aqueous potassium permanganate.

5. Which one of the following reactions must occur by more than one reaction step?

   A $H^+ (aq) + OH^- (aq) \longrightarrow H_2O (l)$

   B $2 H_2O_2 (aq) \longrightarrow 2 H_2O (l) + O_2 (g)$

   C $2 H_2 (g) + O_2 (g) \longrightarrow 2 H_2O (l)$

   D $H_2 (g) + O_3 (g) \longrightarrow H_2O (l) + O_2 (g)$

AHL

6. Explain briefly why:

   a) Increasing the concentration of the reagents usually increases the rate of a chemical reaction.
   b) A reaction does not occur every time the reacting species collide.
   c) Increasing the temperature increases the rate of reaction.

7. The rate of decomposition of an aqueous solution of hydrogen peroxide can be followed by recording the volume of gas collected over water in a measuring cylinder, against time.

   a) Sketch the graph of volume against time you would expect for the complete decomposition of a sample of hydrogen peroxide.
   b) On the same axes, use a dotted line to sketch the curve that you would expect to find if the experiment were repeated using a smaller volume of a more concentrated solution of hydrogen peroxide so that the amount of hydrogen peroxide remains constant.
   c) When lead(IV) oxide is added, the rate at which oxygen is evolved suddenly increases, even though at the end of the reaction, the lead(IV) oxide remains unchanged. Explain this.
   d) In what way, apart from altering the concentration or adding another substance, could the rate at which the hydrogen peroxide decomposes be increased?

HIGHER LEVEL

16.1 RATE EXPRESSION (AHL)

16.1.1 Distinguish between the terms rate constant, overall order of reaction and order of reaction with respect to a particular reactant.

16.1.2 Deduce the rate expression for a reaction from experimental data.

16.1.3 Solve problems involving the rate expression.

16.1.4 Sketch, identify and analyse graphical representations for zero-, first- and second-order reactions.

Altering the concentration of the reactants usually affects the rate of the reaction, but the way in which the rate is affected is not the same for all substances, nor can it be predicted from the balanced equation for the reaction. The **rate expression**, which is a mathematical function expressing the dependence of the rate on the concentrations of the reactants, must be determined experimentally. This is usually done by measuring the reaction rate whilst varying the concentration of one species but holding those of the other species constant. Consider a reaction involving reactants A, B, etc. The rate expression for this reaction takes the form:

$$\text{Rate of reaction} = -\frac{d[A]}{dt} = k[A]^m[B]^n \text{ etc}$$

The **order of reaction** is said to be 'm' in substance A, 'n' in substance B etc. The overall order of the reaction is the sum of these powers, i.e. $m + n$ etc. The constant 'k' in the rate expression is known as the rate constant.

Note that 'k' does not vary with concentration, but it varies greatly with temperature, so it is important to always state the temperature at which the rate constant was measured. Note that where a solid is involved in a reaction, 'k′ must also vary with particle size (since for example in the reaction of acid with calcium carbonate at the same concentration of acid and temperature, the rate changes as particle size changes).

Experiment	[A] mol dm^{-3}	[B] mol dm^{-3}	[C] mol dm^{-3}	Initial rate mol dm^{-3} s^{-1}
1	0.400	1.600	0.0600	4.86×10^{-3}
2	0.800	1.600	0.0600	9.72×10^{-3}
3	0.400	0.800	0.0600	4.86×10^{-3}
4	0.800	1.600	0.1800	87.5×10^{-3}

Figure 611 The effect of concentration changes on the rate of a reaction

If doubling the concentration of one species (say A), whilst the other conditions are held constant, has no effect on the initial rate of reaction, then the reaction is zero order with respect to A (as $2^0 = 1$). If doubling the concentration of A doubles the rate, then the reaction is first order with respect to A (as $2^1 = 2$). If it increases by a factor of four it is second order with respect to A (as $2^2 = 4$), by a factor of eight then third order with respect to A (as $2^3 = 8$) etc. Similar considerations apply to altering the concentrations by other factors (for example if the concentration was decreased by a factor of 3, then the rate would also decrease by a factor of 3 if the reaction was first order with respect to this reagent).

Figure 611 gives some data about the effect of varying concentrations upon the rate of a chemical reaction involving three species – A, B and C:

Comparing experiments 1 and 2, the only change is that the concentration of A has been doubled. The data in the table indicate that the rate has been doubled, so the reaction is first order with respect to A. Comparing 1 and 3, the only change is that the concentration of B has been halved, but there is no effect on the reaction rate, indicating that the reaction is zero order with respect to B (if first order it would be ½ the rate in 1, if second order, then ¼ of the rate in 1). Comparing 2 and 4 the only difference is that the concentration of C has been increased by a factor of three. The rate has increased by a factor of nine, so the reaction is second order in C (as $3^2 = 9$ – if it had been first order in C, the rate would only have increased by a factor of 3.). This means that the rate expression for this reaction is:

$$\text{Rate} = k.[A]^1[B]^0[C]^2$$

or more simply

$$\text{Rate} = k.[A][C]^2$$

Hence the reaction is third order (1 + 2) overall.

The rate constant for a reaction may be calculated provided that the rate of reaction has been measured in standard units of mol dm^{-3} s^{-1}, for known concentrations of the reagents. Consider the data in Figure 611 above. The rate constant can be calculated by substituting any set of data in the rate expression. For example using the data from experiment 1:

$$\text{Rate} = k.[A][C]^2$$

$$4.86 \times 10^{-3} = k[0.400][0.06]^2$$

$$k = \frac{4.86 \times 10^{-3}}{0.400 \times 0.06^2}$$

$$= 3.375 \text{ mol}^{-2} \text{ dm}^6 \text{ s}^{-1}$$

and using the data from experiment 2:

$$\text{Rate} = k.[A][C]^2$$

$$9.72 \times 10^{-3} = k[0.800][0.06]^2$$

$$k = \frac{9.72 \times 10^{-3}}{0.800 \times 0.06^2}$$

$$= 3.375 \text{ mol}^{-2} \text{ dm}^6 \text{ s}^{-1}$$

Note the units for the rate constant. These only hold for a reaction that is third order overall and other order reactions will have rate constants with different units.

The units can be calculated remembering that the units for rates are mol dm^{-3} s^{-1} and the units for concentrations are mol dm^{-3}. Hence the units of the rate constant are:

Zero order overall	mol dm^{-3} s^{-1}
First order overall	s^{-1}
Second order overall	mol^{-1} dm^3 s^{-1}
Third order overall	mol^{-2} dm^6 s^{-1}

In general $(\text{mol dm}^{-3})^{q-1}\,\text{s}^{-1}$ where q is the overall order

The order of reaction can also be found from a graph showing the way in which the initial rate varies with the initial concentration of the reactant, all other factors being equal. This is illustrated in Figure 612.

AHL

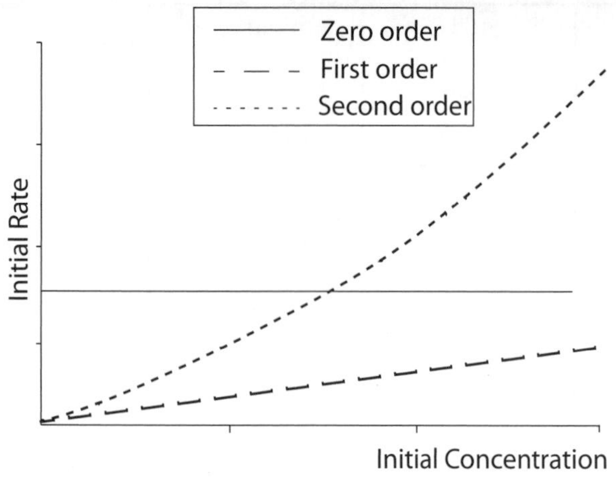

Figure 612 The effect of concentration on rate

The order of a reaction can also be found from a graph of concentration against time, which shows the effect of the reactants being used up on the rate of reaction. The gradient of the graph at any point gives the rate of reaction. If this is constant (i.e. the graph is a straight line) then the reaction must be **zero order** in the reactants whose concentrations are undergoing significant change, because the decrease in concentration is not affecting the rate of reaction (which we know from the constant gradient). If the reaction rate (the gradient of the line) is halved when the concentration is halved, then the reaction is **first order**. If halving the concentration causes the rate (gradient) to decrease by a factor of 4, the reaction is **second order** $(½)^2 = ¼$ etc. To be really useful, such experiments should have all but one reagent in large excess, so that the order in the limiting reagent is what causes the reaction rate to change.

This is in fact the basis for a very powerful technique to simplify the rate equation. Consider a reaction that is second order overall in which the initial concentration of A is 0.02 mol dm^{-3} and the initial concentration of B is 2 mol dm^{-3}. When the reaction is complete (assuming the stoichiometry is 1 mole of A reacts with 1 mole of B), the final concentration of A is zero and that of B is 1.98 mol dm^{-3}, i.e. the concentration of B remains virtually unchanged, hence:

$$\text{Rate} = k.[A].[B] \approx k'.[A] \qquad (\text{where } k' = k.[B])$$

A reaction of this type is called a "**pseudo first-order reaction**" because it obeys a first order rate law, but the observed rate constant (k′) will depend on the concentration of another species (if [B] is doubled then the reaction rate will double and the half-life will decrease to half of its initial value). The same technique (making the concentration of one reagent much less than that of the

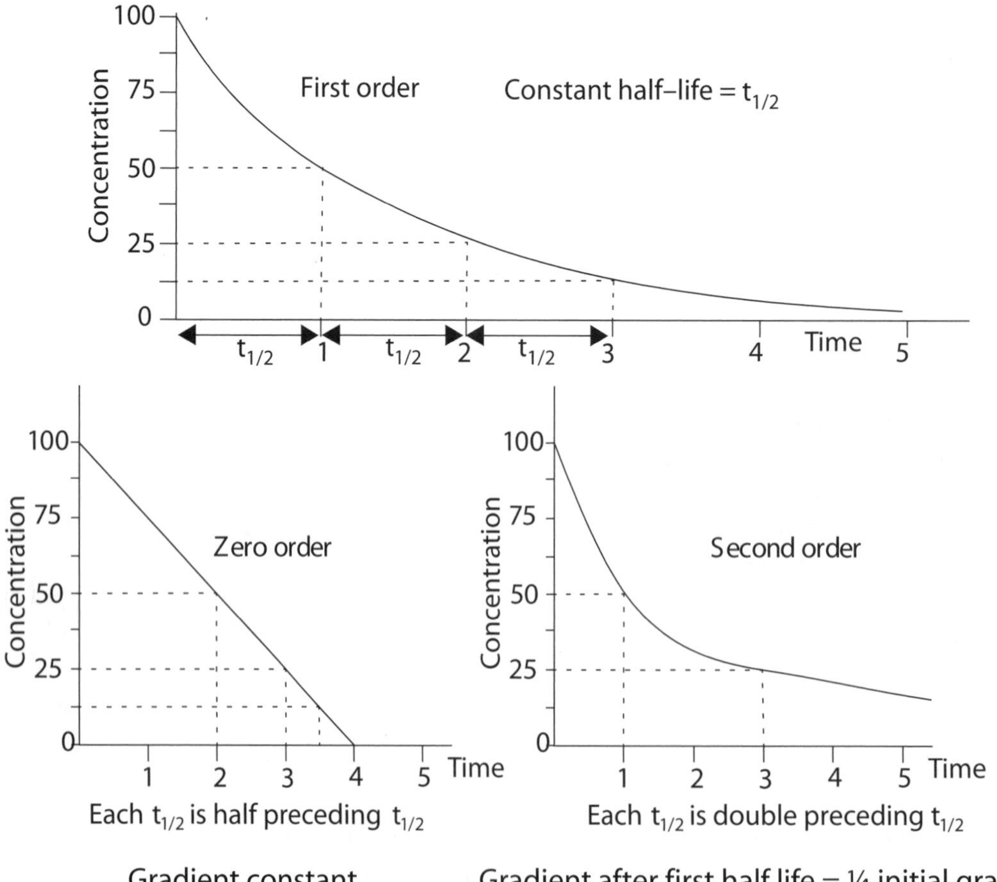

Figure 613 a, b and c. Graphs showing the variation of concentration with time for reactions of different orders

others) can be used to vary the observed order of reactions with other rate expressions.

It is easy to recognise a first order reaction from graphs of concentration (or something proportional to concentration) against time. This is because the concentration shows an exponential decrease, that is the time for the concentration to fall from its initial value to half its initial value, is equal to the time required for it to fall from half to one quarter of its initial value and from one quarter to one eighth etc. This time is known as the **half-life** $t_{½}$ of the reaction and it is illustrated in Figure 613 which shows that the successive half lives of reactions of other orders vary in characteristic ways.

The first order exponential decay is the same as that found in **radioactive decay**. Because it remains constant, the half-life is an important quantity for these systems and it can be found from an appropriate graph (such as that above) or it may be found from the rate constant (k) by substituting in the equation:

$$t_{\frac{1}{2}} = \frac{\ln 2}{k}$$

For example, if the rate constant of a first order reaction is 0.005 s^{-1}, then the half-life will be $\frac{\ln 2}{0.005}$ = 139 s.

This results from the integration of the first order rate expression. If the half-life is known, say from a concentration-time graph, then this equation may be rearranged to find the rate constant. For example if the half-life for a first order reaction is 4 minutes:

$$k = \frac{\ln 2}{(4 \times 60)} = 0.0289\ s^{-1}$$

Exercise 16.1

Questions 1 to 4 refer to the rate expression for a chemical reaction given below:

$$\text{Rate} = k[A][B]^2[H^+]$$

1. Which one of the following statements is not true about this reaction?

   A It is first order in A.
   B It is second order in B.
   C It is first order in H^+.
   D It is third order overall.

2. The units of the rate constant (k) will be:

   A mol dm^{-3} s^{-1}
   B mol s^{-1}
   C dm^3 mol^{-1} s^{-1}
   D dm^9 mol^{-3} s^{-1}

3. If the concentrations of A and B are both doubled, but the concentration of H^+ remains constant, the rate would increase by a factor of:

   A 2
   B 4
   C 8
   D 16

4. Which one of the following would lead to the greatest increase in reaction rate?

   A Doubling the concentration of A only.
   B Doubling the concentration of B only.
   C Doubling the concentration of A and H^+ only.
   D Doubling the concentration of B and H^+ only.

5. Which one of the graphs shown would indicate that a reaction was zero order in the reactant whose concentration was being varied?

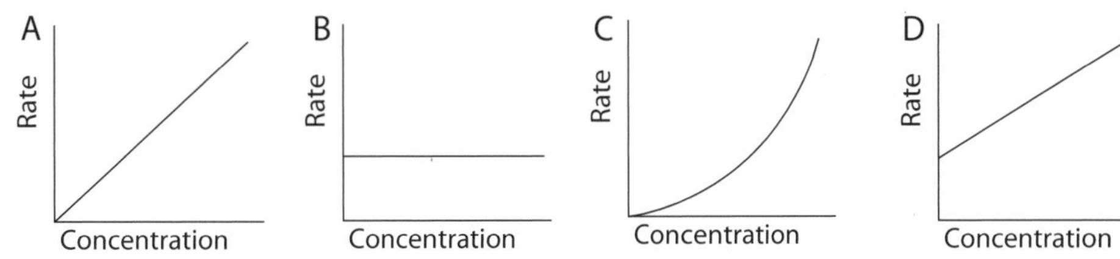

AHL

6. The following data refers to the acid catalysed iodination of propanone

$$CH_3{-}CO{-}CH_3\,(aq) + I_2\,(aq) \longrightarrow CH_3{-}CO{-}CH_2{-}I\,(aq) + H^+\,(aq) + I^-\,(aq)$$

Solution	$[CH_3{-}CO{-}CH_3]$ mol dm^{-3}	$[I_2]$ mol dm^{-3}	$[H^+]$ mol dm^{-3}	Initial Rate mol dm^{-3} s^{-1}
1	0.2	0.008	1	4×10^{-6}
2	0.4	0.008	1	8×10^{-6}
3	0.6	0.008	1	1.2×10^{-5}
4	0.4	0.004	1	8×10^{-6}
5	0.4	0.002	1	8×10^{-6}
6	0.2	0.008	2	8×10^{-6}
7	0.2	0.008	4	1.6×10^{-5}

AHL

a) From the data in the table derive the rate expression for the reaction, explaining the evidence for the dependency on each of the species.

b) Give the order with respect to $CH_3{-}CO{-}CH_3$, I_2 and H^+, and the overall order.

c) Use the data from Solution 1 to calculate the value of the rate constant.

7. The data given below refer to the hydrolysis of a 0.002 mol dm^{-3} solution of an ester by 0.2 mol dm^{-3} aqueous sodium hydroxide.

Time (s)	60	120	180	240	300	360	420	480
[ester] (mmol dm^{-3})	1.48	1.10	0.81	0.60	0.45	0.33	0.24	0.18

a) Plot a suitable graph to determine the order of the reaction with respect to the ester, explaining your method.

b) Use your graph to determine the half-life of the reaction and hence determine a value for the apparent rate constant, giving appropriate units.

c) Why does this graph give no indication of the order with respect to the hydroxide ion?

d) How would you modify the experiment to determine the dependence on hydroxide ion?

e) Assuming that it is also first order in hydroxide ion, write a new rate expression.
Use this to calculate a value for the rate constant, giving appropriate units.
Why does this differ from the value found in b) and how are the two related?

16.2 REACTION MECHANISM (AHL)

16.2.1 Explain that reactions can occur by more than one step and that the slowest step determines the rate of reaction (rate-determining step).

16.2.2 Describe the relationship between reaction mechanism, order of reaction and rate-determining step.

The chance of more than two particles colliding simultaneously with the correct geometry and minimum energy is very small. This means that if there are more than two reactants, the reaction must occur by a number of simpler reaction steps. In addition, many reactions that have apparently simple equations do not occur in this manner, but are the result of a number of steps. These steps involve species that are the product of an earlier step and are then completely consumed in a later step (so they do not appear in the stoichiometric equation). These species are known as "**intermediates**". The simple stages by which a chemical reaction occurs are known as the mechanism of the reaction. The sum of the various steps of the mechanism must equal the balanced equation for the reaction.

The various steps in the reaction mechanism will have the potential to occur at different rates. The products cannot however be formed faster than the slowest of these steps and so this is known as the rate determining step (rds). An analogy would be that if people can come off a train at the rate of 20 per second, can travel up the escalator at a rate of 10 per second, and can pass through the ticket barrier into the street at a rate of 50 per second, then they will still only reach the street at a rate of 10 people per second. Making larger doors on the train or putting in an extra ticket barrier will not make this any faster, only a change affecting the escalator, the slowest step, will increase the rate.

In summary, a mechanism is a model of how a reaction occurs. The rate of overall reaction is the rate of the slowest step. This slowest step is called the **rate determining step**. Species produced in earlier steps of the mechanism that are consumed in later steps are called intermediates. A mechanism must account for the overall stoichiometry of the reaction, the observed rate expression and any other available evidence (such as the effect of light or a catalyst).

There are only two kinds of fundamental process that can occur to bring about a chemical reaction. Firstly, a species can break up or undergo internal rearrangement to form products, which is known as a **unimolecular** process. As this only involves one species, a unimolecular step is first order in that species. Radioactive decay, for example, is unimolecular. Secondly, two species can collide and interact to form the product(s) and this is known as a **bimolecular** process. As this involves the collision of the two species then doubling the concentration of either will double the collision rate. Hence, it is first order in each and second order overall. Both unimolecular and bimolecular processes can be either reversible (lead to equilibrium) or irreversible (lead to complete reaction) depending on the relative stability of the reactants and products. Whether a particular reaction step is unimolecular or bimolecular, is known as the **molecularity** of that reaction step. In a bimolecular process, the species collide to initially give a transition state (or activated complex), which then breaks down to either form the products or reform the reactants.

A Unimolecular step	A Bimolecular step
A unimolecular step involves a single species as a reactant.	A bimolecular steps involves collision of two species (that form a transition state or an activated complex that can not be isolated).
$A \longrightarrow / \rightleftharpoons$ Products	$A + B \longrightarrow / \rightleftharpoons$ Products
Its rate law is therefore 1st order with respect that reactant.	Its rate law is 1st order with respect to each of the colliding species and is therefore 2nd order overall.
rate $\propto$ [A]	rate $\propto$ [A][B]

Figure 617 Comparing uni- and bi-molecular steps

AHL

A **transition state** is an unstable arrangement in which the bonds are in the process of being broken and formed. It therefore occurs at the maximum point on a potential energy diagram and cannot be isolated.

As outlined above, many chemical reactions occur by a series of simple steps known as the mechanism of the reaction. It is possible to write a number of mechanisms (that is a series of fundamental processes by which the reaction could occur) for any reaction and it is only possible to suggest which is the correct one by studying the kinetics of the reaction. Only species that are involved in the rate determining step, or in an equilibrium preceding it, can affect the overall rate of reaction. Hence, determining the rate expression for a reaction will help to identify the rate determining step and this will eliminate many possible mechanisms for the reaction.

Consider for example a reaction

$$2\,A + B \longrightarrow C + D$$

as an illustration of how the rate expression will depend upon the mechanism and upon which step in the mechanism is the rate determining step.

There are three particles involved in the reaction, so it is most unlikely that this occurs as a single step. Many mechanisms for the reaction could be written and these would produce a variety of rate expressions. Some examples are given in Figure 618. Note that adding together the different steps always leads to the same overall equation as shown for the first two possible mechanisms in Figure 618.

	Mechanism	Rate expression
I	$A + B \longrightarrow X + C$; Slow rds $A + X \longrightarrow D$; Fast $(A + B + A + X \longrightarrow X + C + D$ $= 2\,A + B \longrightarrow C + D$ overall)	Rate $\propto$ [A] [B]
II	$A + B \rightleftharpoons X$; Fast $A + X \longrightarrow C + D$; Slow rds $(A + B + A + X \longrightarrow X + C + D$ $= 2\,A + B \longrightarrow C + D$ overall)	Rate $\propto [A]^2$ [B]
III	$A + A \rightleftharpoons A_2$; Fast $A_2 + B \longrightarrow C + D$; Slow rds	Rate $\propto [A]^2$ [B]
IV	$A + A \rightleftharpoons A_2$; Slow rds $A_2 + B \longrightarrow C + D$; Fast	Rate $\propto [A]^2$
V	$B \longrightarrow X$; Slow rds $X + A \longrightarrow Y + C$; Fast $Y + A \longrightarrow D$; Fast	Rate $\propto$ [B]

Figure 618 Some possible mechanisms for the reaction; $2A + B \longrightarrow C + D$

Some of these mechanisms involve equilibria, a topic that is dealt with in greater detail in Chapter 7. For the present purposes it is enough to know that for the equilibrium, $A + B \rightleftharpoons X$, the [X] will depend on both the [A] and [B]. Similarly in the equilibrium, $A + A \rightleftharpoons A_2$, the $[A_2]$ will be proportional to $[A]^2$. Note also that the concentration of the intermediate (X) never appears in the rate expression.

In I, the first bimolecular step is rate determining so that the rate will depend on the rate of collisions between A and B, hence the rate will be proportional to [A].[B]. In II the second bimolecular step is rate determining so that the rate will depend on the rate of collisions between A and X, hence the rate will be proportional to [A] [X], but [X] will depend on both [A] and [B], so that taking this into account the rate depends on $[A]^2$ [B]. In V the rate depends on the unimolecular conversion of B to an intermediate X, so the rate only depends upon [B].

Note that III and IV only differ in which of the two steps is the rate determining step. This is not necessarily fixed, for example at very low [B] the second step could be the rate determining step (mechanism III), but at very high [B] the second step will become much faster so that now the first step might be rate determining (mechanism IV). Because A_2 will react with B as soon as it is formed, the first step is now no longer an equilibrium. Note also that both mechanism II and mechanism III lead to the same rate expression and so some other means (such as trying to get some information about the intermediate X) would have to be used to decide which (if either.) was operating.

Consider as another example the reaction between propanone and iodine:

$$CH_3COCH_3\,(aq) + I_2\,(aq) \longrightarrow CH_3COCH_2I\,(aq) + H^+\,(aq) + I^-\,(aq)$$

This would appear to be a simple bimolecular process, but if this were the case, then the rate of reaction would be expected to depend on the concentrations of both the

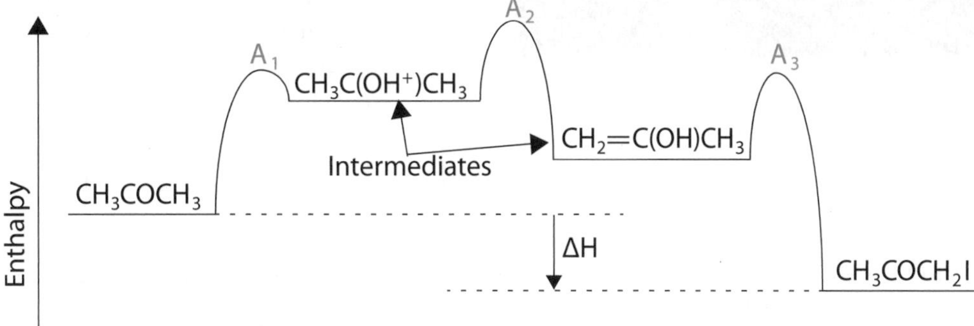

Figure 619 P.E. diagram for the iodination of propanone

propanone and the iodine hence the rate expression would be:

$$\text{Rate} = k\,[CH_3COCH_3]\,[I_2]$$

In practice it is found that the reaction is catalysed by acids and that the rate is independent of the concentration of iodine hence the reaction is first order in both propanone and hydrogen ions, but zero order in iodine. Hence the rate expression is:

$$\text{Rate} = k\,[CH_3COCH_3]\,[H^+]$$

This means that one molecule of propanone and one hydrogen ion must be involved in the rate determining step, or in equilibria occurring before this. The commonly accepted mechanism for this reaction is:

$CH_3COCH_3 + H^+ \rightleftharpoons CH_3C(OH^+)CH_3$
Fast equilibrium

$CH_3C(OH^+)CH_3 \longrightarrow CH_2{=}C(OH)CH_3 + H^+$
Slow – rate determining step

$CH_2{=}C(OH)CH_3 + I_2 \longrightarrow CH_3COCH_2I + H^+ + I^-$
Fast (does not affect rate)

This mechanism agrees with the experimentally determined rate expression. The rate expression can never prove that a particular mechanism is correct, but it can provide evidence that other possible mechanisms are wrong.

(Good TOK *point – an example of a difficulty that besets all processes of inductive logic.)*

The species $CH_3C(OH^+)CH_3$ and $CH_2{=}C(OH)CH_3$ are intermediates; they have a finite life and occur at a potential energy minimum on the reaction diagram. In this reaction mechanism there would be a number of transition states, firstly (A_1) between CH_3COCH_3 and H^+ before forming $CH_3C(OH^+)CH_3$ secondly (A_2) when $CH_3C(OH^+)CH_3$ starts to break up to form $CH_2{=}C(OH)CH_3$ and H^+ and finally (A_3) in the reaction of this with iodine. These do not have a finite life and occur at potential energy maxima on the reaction diagram. This is illustrated in Figure 619 and the differences between intermediates and transition states (activated complexes) are summarised in Figure 620.

Intermediates	Transition States
Exist for a finite time	Have only a transient existence
Occur at a P.E. minimum	Occur at a P.E. maximum
Formed in one step of a reaction and consumed in a subsequent step	Exist part way through every step of a reaction

Figure 620 Differences between intermediates and transition states

The differences between intermediates and transition states can also be illustrated by the S_N1 and S_N2 mechanisms for the nucleophilic substitution reactions of halogenoalkanes.

AHL

AHL

Exercise 16.2

1. Which one of these steps is unimolecular?

   A $NH_3 + H^+ \longrightarrow NH_4^+$
   B $H^+ + OH^- \longrightarrow H_2O$
   C $N_2O_4 \longrightarrow 2\ NO_2$
   D $H\bullet + Cl\bullet \longrightarrow HCl$

2. Which one of the following is **not** a difference between an activated complex and an intermediate?

   A An activated complex occurs at a potential energy maximum and an intermediate at a minimum.
   B An activated complex cannot take part in bimolecular reactions, but an intermediate can.
   C An activated complex does not exist for a finite time but an intermediate does.
   D An activated complex can reform the reactants, but an intermediate cannot.

3. The rate determining step of a mechanism is the one which

   A occurs most rapidly.
   B occurs most slowly.
   C gives out the most energy.
   D gives out the least energy.

4. Which one of the following mechanisms would give a first order dependence on A and zero order on B for the reaction below?

$$A + B \longrightarrow C$$

   A $A + X \longrightarrow Y$ (fast) then
   $Y + B \longrightarrow C + X$ (slow)

   B $B \longrightarrow X$ (slow) then
   $X + A \longrightarrow C$ (fast)

   C $2\ A \longrightarrow A_2$ (slow) then
   $A_2 + B \longrightarrow C$ (fast)

   D $A \longrightarrow X$ (slow) then
   $X + B \longrightarrow C$ (fast)

5. A reaction involves two reactants, A and B. The initial reaction rate was measured with different starting concentrations of A and B and the following results were obtained at 25 °C:

[A] mol dm^3	[B] mol dm^3	Initial rate mol dm^3 s^1
0.2	0.2	3.2×10^4
0.4	0.4	1.3×10^3
0.4	0.8	1.3×10^3

   a) Deduce the order of the reaction in A, in B and the overall order. Hence write a rate expression for the reaction.

   b) Calculate a value for the rate constant, giving suitable units.

   c) What initial rate would you expect if the initial concentrations of both reactants were 0.1 mol dm^{-3}?

   d) If the overall equation for the reaction is $A + B \longrightarrow C + D$, write a mechanism, indicating which step is the rate determining step, that is:
      i consistent with the rate expression found.
      ii inconsistent with the rate expression found.

16.3 ACTIVATION ENERGY (AHL)

16.3.1 Describe qualitatively the relationship between the rate constant (k) and temperature (T).

16.3.2 Determine activation energy (E_a) values from the Arrhenius equation by a graphical method.

In a fluid, there is a distribution of energy amongst the particles known as the Maxwell–Boltzmann distribution (see Section 6.3). As the temperature increases, the number of particles with a high energy increases, though there are still some particles with very little energy. The result is a flattening of the distribution curve, because the total area under it must remain constant (*refer to figure 609, reproduced again as Figure 622 for convenience*).

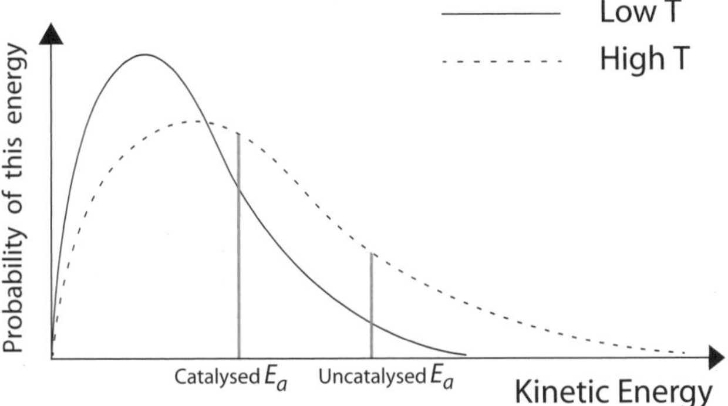

Figure 622 The distribution of kinetic energy at two different temperatures

All chemical reactions require a certain minimum energy, the activation energy (E_a), for the reaction to occur. As can be seen from Figure 622, at the higher temperature a greater proportion of the molecules have an energy greater than the activation energy, i.e. there is a greater proportion of the total area under the curve to the right of the E_a line (either the catalysed or uncatalysed) on the higher temperature curve than on the lower temperature curve. This is usually the major reason why reactions occur more rapidly at higher temperatures.

For many reactions it is found that the effect of temperature on the rate constant for a reaction (k) is given by the expression:

$$k = Ae^{\left(-\frac{E_a}{RT}\right)}$$

where E_a is the activation energy, T the absolute temperature (in Kelvin), R the gas constant (8.314 J K^{-1} mol^{-1}) and A is called the Arrhenius constant (or the pre–exponential factor). It is dependent on collision rate and steric factors, that is any requirements regarding the geometry of the colliding particles. This equation is known as the **Arrhenius equation** after the Swedish chemist, *Svante August Arrhenius*, who first proposed it.

The expression indicates that the rate constant k depends exponentially on temperature, which is why temperature has such a large effect on reaction rate. Rather satisfyingly the expression for the area under the Maxwell–Boltzmann distribution curve in excess of E_a also gives an exponential dependence if E_a>>RT. If we take logarithms to the base e (natural logarithms (ln) - a mathematical procedure you may possibly not have met) and then rearrange, the Arrhenius equation is converted to:

$$\ln k = \ln A - \left(\frac{E_a}{R}\right)\frac{1}{T}$$

This is the equation of a straight line so, as shown in Figure 623 below, a graph of ln k against $\frac{1}{T}$ will be linear with gradient $-\frac{E_a}{R}$ and an intercept on the y–axis of ln A.

The activation energy for a reaction can therefore be found by measuring the rate of reaction at different temperatures, with all the other conditions unchanged (so that rate $\propto k$), and then plotting ln(rate) against $\frac{1}{T}$ (Note again, T must be in Kelvin, not °Celsius).

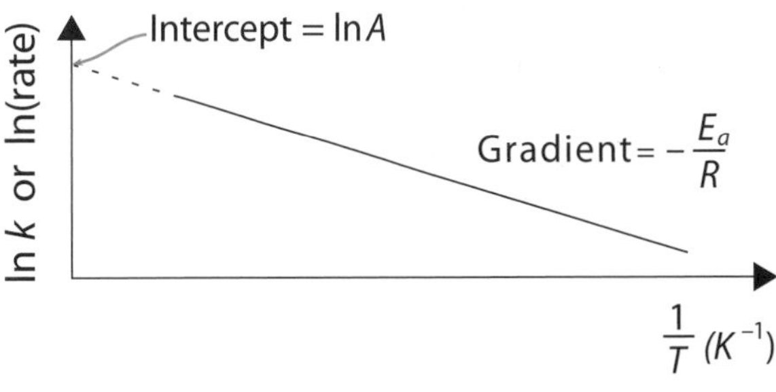

Figure 623 Determining the activation energy graphically

Exercise 16.3

1. Which one of the following is not true about the activation energy of a reaction?

   A It is related to the enthalpy change (ΔH) of the reaction.
   B It is decreased by the addition of a catalyst.
   C It is the minimum amount of energy that the reactants must have in order to form the products.
   D The greater the activation energy the lower the rate of reaction.

2. The activation energy of a chemical reaction can be determined by measuring the effect on reaction rate of varying

   A the temperature.
   B the concentration of the reagents.
   C the concentration of the catalyst.
   D the surface area in contact.

3. The temperature at which a reaction is carried out is increased from 20 °C to 40 °C. If the half-life of the reaction was initially t, the half-life at the higher temperature will be:

   A 2 t
   B ½ t
   C t^2
   D It would depend on the size of the activation energy.

4. The activation energy for the reaction below is 112 kJ mol^{-1} and ΔH is +57 kJ mol^{-1}.

$$2\,NO_2\,(g) \rightleftharpoons 2\,NO(g) + O_2\,(g)$$

   a) Draw an energy level diagram illustrating the energy changes for this reaction. Clearly mark and label the activation energy E_a and the enthalpy change (ΔH).
   b) On the same diagram, using dotted lines, show the effect of a platinum catalyst, clearly labelling the change 'With catalyst'. Would the platinum be acting as a homogeneous or heterogeneous catalyst?
   c) Is the reaction exothermic or endothermic? When it occurs will the container become hotter, or cooler?
   d) If the temperature was increased, how would this affect the rate of reaction? Explain this in terms of the collision theory of reactions (a diagram might help).
   e) What other factor (i.e. **not** temperature or catalyst) could be changed to increase the rate of reaction – be precise, remembering that these are all gases.
   f) Nitrogen dioxide is a brown gas, whereas nitrogen monoxide is colourless. Suggest how you might be able to measure the rate of reaction.

5. When aqueous solutions of benzenediazonium chloride decompose, they evolve nitrogen gas. The table below gives the volume of gas obtained at different times for such a decomposition at 70 °C.

Time min	Volume cm^3
1	5
2	9
3	13
4	17
5	21
7	28
9	33
12	40
16	48
20	54

   a) If, when decomposition was complete, the total volume of gas released was 70 cm^3, graphically determine the order of the reaction. What further data, if any, would you need to calculate a value for the rate constant?
   b) Draw the apparatus you could use to obtain such data and state what precautions you would take.
   c) If you wanted to determine the activation energy for this reaction, what further experiments would you carry out? How would you use the data from these to determine the activation energy?

AHL

EQUILIBRIUM

7

7.1 Dynamic equilibrium

7.2 The position of equilibrium

17.1 Liquid-vapour equilibrium (AHL)

17.2 The equilibrium law (AHL)

The Vapour pressure of mixtures (EXT)

Distillation and fractional distillation (EXT)

Raoult's law and deviations from ideality (EXT)

Colligative properties of solutions (EXT)

Other equilibrium constants (EXT)

7.1 DYNAMIC EQUILIBRIUM

7.1.1 Outline the characteristics of chemical and physical systems in a state of equilibrium.

Many chemical reactions go to completion because the products are much more energetically favourable than the reactants and the activation energy is low enough to allow for a rapid reaction at the ambient temperature, for example, the neutralisation of aqueous sodium hydroxide by hydrochloric acid. Other potential reactions do not occur either because, though energetically feasible, the activation energy barrier is too great for significant reaction at the ambient temperature (such as the combustion of sucrose at room temperature), or because as well as the activation energy being too high, the reactants are much more energetically stable than the products (as in the decomposition of water to hydrogen and oxygen). With some chemical systems however the energies of the reactants and products are of a similar order of magnitude so that the reaction is reversible, that is it can occur in either direction. An example is the reaction of ammonia and hydrogen chloride to form ammonium chloride. If ammonia gas and hydrogen chloride gas are mixed they react to form a white smoke of solid ammonium chloride. Conversely if ammonium chloride is heated, then some of the solid 'disappears', because it has been converted into ammonia and hydrogen chloride gas. We indicate such a **reversible reaction** by means of a double arrow as shown below:

$$NH_3\,(g) + HCl\,(g) \rightleftharpoons NH_4Cl\,(s)$$

If such a system is established in a closed vessel (so that no gases can escape) and at a constant temperature, then a **chemical equilibrium** is established.

Chemical equilibrium is the state of dynamic equilibrium that occurs in a closed system when the forward and reverse reactions of a reversible reaction occur at the same rate. If we consider mixing together two reactants A and B in the **reversible reaction**:

$$A + B \rightleftharpoons C + D$$

then initially the forward reaction occurs rapidly, but as the concentrations of the reactants fall its rate decreases. The reverse reaction initially cannot occur at all, but as soon as C and D start to form, its rate increases. Eventually the rate of the two reactions becomes equal, the concentrations reach constant values and equilibrium is established. This is shown in Figure 701.

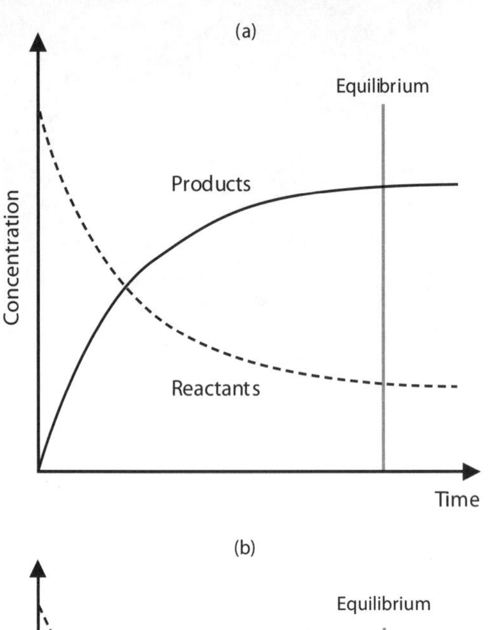

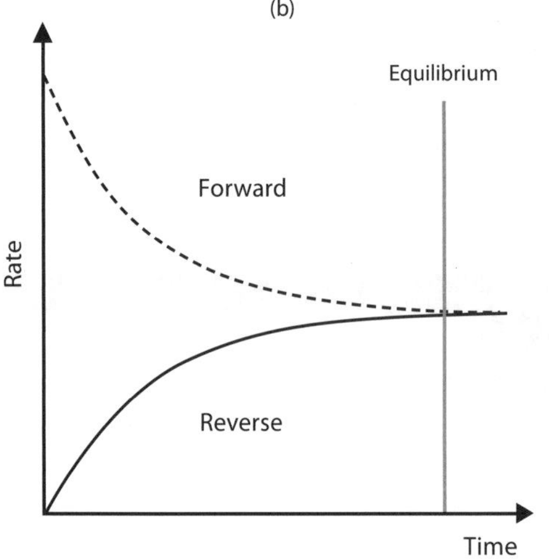

Figure 701 (a), (b) The change of concentration (a) and rate of reaction (b) with time in establishing a chemical equilibrium

In an equilibrium all of the species involved, both reactants and products, are present at a constant concentration. As a consequence, macroscopic properties of the system (that is those that can be observed or measured, such as its colour, density, pH) are constant, even though on a molecular scale there is continual interconversion of reactants and products. The concentrations of the species at equilibrium will reflect how readily they react on collision. If two species react on every collision, then the concentration required to produce a given rate of reaction will be much less than if they only have a 10% chance of reacting. In Figure 701 above, the reactants (A & B) react together far more easily than the products (C & D) because a smaller concentration is required to give the same rate of reaction. A similar equilibrium could obviously be established by mixing together C and D.

A specific example of such a system would be the introduction of one mole of liquid dinitrogen tetroxide (N_2O_4) into an evacuated, sealed one dm^3 flask at ~80 °C. The colourless dinitrogen tetroxide will initially vapourise and then start to decompose into brown nitrogen dioxide (NO_2). The rate of this decomposition will fall as the concentration of dinitrogen tetroxide decreases. Initially there is no nitrogen dioxide present to dimerise, but as more is produced the rate of the reverse reaction to form dinitrogen tetroxide will increase. Eventually the two rates will become equal and chemical equilibrium is established as indicated by the fact that the brown colour of the gas does not change any further and the pressure in the flask remains constant. Under these conditions equilibrium would occur when about 60% of the dinitrogen tetroxide has been converted to nitrogen dioxide, so that the concentration of dinitrogen tetroxide will fall to 0.4 mol dm^{-3} and the concentration of nitrogen dioxide will increase to 1.2 mol dm^{-3}, because each dinitrogen tetroxide molecule decomposes to give two nitrogen dioxide molecules. This is shown in the equation below and in Figure 702.

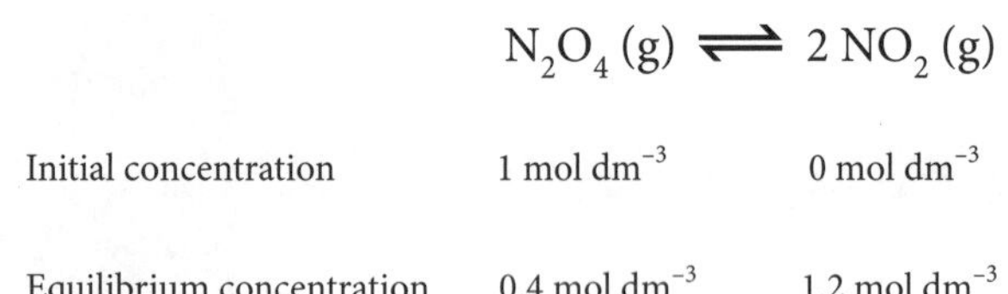

	$N_2O_4\,(g) \rightleftharpoons$	$2\,NO_2\,(g)$
Initial concentration	1 mol dm^{-3}	0 mol dm^{-3}
Equilibrium concentration	0.4 mol dm^{-3}	1.2 mol dm^{-3}

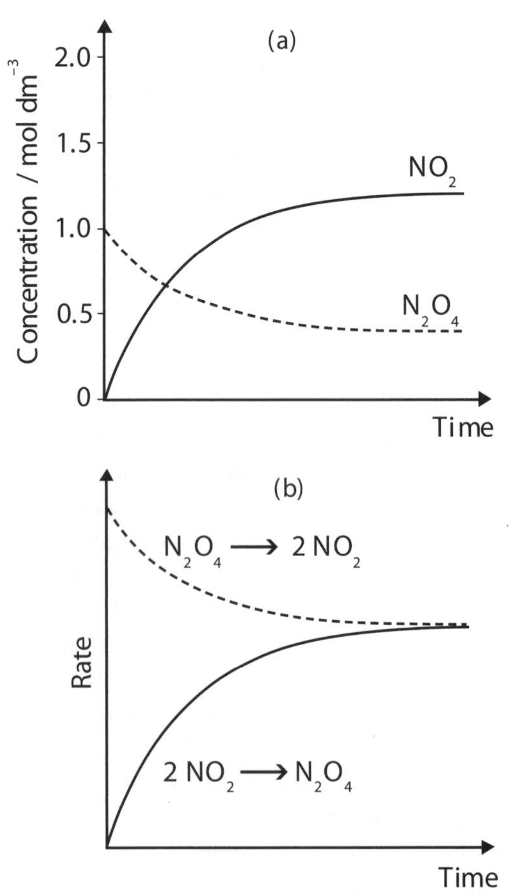

Figure 702 (a), (b) The equilibrium established by heating dinitrogen tetroxide

If 2 moles of nitrogen dioxide were cooled to 80 °C from a much higher temperature, at which there was no dintrogen tetroxide present, then the brown colour would fade to a constant value, but eventually exactly the same position of equilibrium would be reached, as shown in Figure 703.

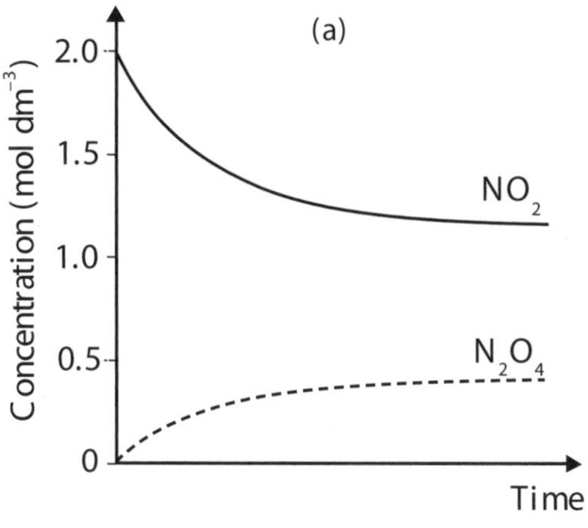

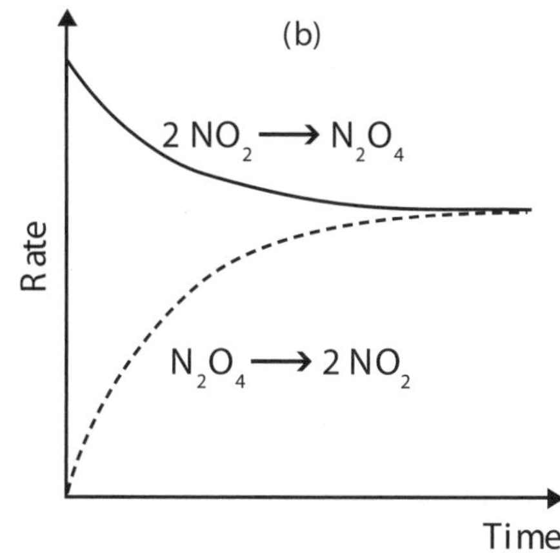

Figure 703 (a), (b) The equilibrium established by cooling nitrogen dioxide

Exercise 7.1

1. In a system at equilibrium, which of the following is not always true?

   A There are both reactants and products present.
   B The forward and reverse reactions occur at the same rate.
   C The concentrations of reactants and products are equal.
   D The concentrations of reactants and products remain constant.

2. When solid phosphorus(V) chloride is heated it decomposes to solid phosphorus(III) chloride and chlorine gas. Conversely when phosphorus(III) chloride is shaken in an atmosphere of chlorine, it forms phosphorus(V) chloride.

   a) Write a balanced equation for this reversible reaction, with phosphorus(V) chloride on the left hand side.
   b) Consider warming some phosphorus(V) chloride in an empty, sealed flask:
      i What will happen to the phosphorus(V) chloride?
      ii As time passes what will happen to the rate at which this occurs? Why?
      iii Initially, what is the rate of reaction between phosphorus (III) chloride and chlorine? Why?
      iv As time passes what will happen to the rate at which this occurs? Why?
      v Eventually what will happen to the rates of these two processes?
      vi What name is given to this state?
      vii At this point what species will be present in the flask? Will their concentrations all be equal?
   c) Would there be a difference if the phosphorus(V) chloride was heated in an open beaker? If so explain why and predict what would in fact happen.

7.2 THE POSITION OF EQUILIBRIUM

7.2.1 Deduce the equilibrium constant expression (K_c) from the equation for a homogeneous reaction.

7.2.2 Deduce the extent of a reaction from the magnitude of the equilibrium constant.

7.2.3 Apply Le Chatelier's principle to predict the qualitative effects of changes of temperature, pressure and concentration on the position of equilibrium and on the value of the equilibrium constant.

7.2.4 State and explain the effect of a catalyst on an equilibrium reaction.

7.2.5 Apply the concepts of kinetics and equilibrium to industrial processes.

The rate at which a reaction occurs depends upon the concentration of the species involved. Let us make the assumption that both the forward and reverse reaction in the equilibrium

$$A + B \rightleftharpoons C + D$$

to be first order in each species (the final result can also be proved for a more general case, but the proof is is much more complicated!) then the rate expressions for the forward and reverse reactions are:

$$\text{Forward rate} = k_f.[A][B]$$

$$\text{Reverse rate} = k_r.[C][D]$$

At equilibrium these rates are equal, so

$$k_f.[A][B] = k_r.[C][D] \text{ which rearranges to}$$

$$\frac{k_f}{k_r} = \frac{[C][D]}{[A][B]}$$

As k_f and k_r are constants, at a given temperature, their ratio must also be a constant. This is known as the equilibrium constant, K_c.

More generally, the **equilibrium constant** is given by the concentration of the products raised to the power of their stoichiometric coefficients (that is the numbers that appear before them in the balanced equation) divided by the concentrations of the reactants also raised to these powers. For a general reaction:

$$a\,A + b\,B + c\,C + ... \rightleftharpoons p\,P + q\,Q + r\,R + ...$$

The equilibrium constant is given by

$$K_c = \frac{[P]^p[Q]^q[R]^r ...}{[A]^a[B]^b[C]^c ...}$$

For example in the equilibrium between ammonia gas and oxygen gas to give nitrogen monoxide gas and water vapour:

$$4\,NH_3\,(g) + 5\,O_2\,(g) \rightleftharpoons 4\,NO\,(g) + 6\,H_2O\,(g)$$

The equilibrium constant is given by

$$K_c = \frac{[NO]^4[H_2O]^6}{[NH_3]^4[O_2]^5}\ \text{mol dm}^{-3}$$

The equilibrium constant does not have fixed units and they must be calculated in each case from the equation for K_c, using the fact that concentrations have units of mol dm^{-3}.

If the concentrations of the species involved were all 1 mol dm^{-3}, then K_c would have a value of one. If K_c is greater than one then the concentrations of products are greater than those of the reactants and the equilibrium is said to lie on the right hand side. If K_c is very large the reaction can be regarded as going to completion. If K_c is less than one the opposite is true and the equilibrium is said to lie on the left hand side. If K_c is very small, then the reaction may be considered not to occur.

The concentrations of certain substances remain constant, so these are omitted from the equilibrium constant expression. All solids have a fixed density and hence a constant concentration, so these are omitted. For example in the equilibrium:

$$NH_4Cl\,(s) \rightleftharpoons NH_3\,(g) + HCl\,(g)$$

the equilibrium constant is simply given by

$$K_c = [NH_3][HCl]\ \text{mol}^2\ \text{dm}^{-6}$$

because the constant concentration of the solid ammonium chloride is omitted. The concentration of any pure liquid is also constant as it too has a fixed density. This is particularly important for the concentration of water which is taken as constant and omitted for equilibria in dilute aqueous solutions.

The equilibrium constant for the formation of the tetrachlorocobaltate(II) ion in dilute solution is therefore written as shown below:

$$Co(H_2O)_6^{2+}\,(aq) + 4\,Cl^-\,(aq) \rightleftharpoons CoCl_4^{2-}\,(aq) + 6\,H_2O(l)$$

$$K_c = \frac{[CoCl_4^{2-}]}{[Co(H_2O)_6^{2+}][Cl^-]^4}$$

If however the concentration of water can vary because the reaction is not in aqueous solution, for example in the equilibrium below, where the pure liquids would be mixed:

$$CH_3COOH\,(l) + C_2H_5OH\,(l) \rightleftharpoons CH_3COOC_2H_5\,(l) + H_2O\,(l)$$

$$K_c = \frac{[CH_3COOC_2H_5][H_2O]}{[CH_3COOH]\,[C_2H_5OH]}$$

Water must also be included if it is in the gas phase, as for example in the reduction of carbon dioxide shown in equation (1) below, then the water must be included, for which the value for the equilibrium constant at 1000 K is given:

(1) $H_2\,(g) + CO_2\,(g) \rightleftharpoons H_2O\,(g) + CO\,(g)$

$$K_c = \frac{[CO][H_2O]}{[H_2][CO_2]}$$

$$= 0.955$$

(Note - here K_c is unitless as the units cancel)

This equilibrium could easily be written the other way round, as shown in equation (2) below, and in this case the equilibrium constant is the reciprocal of the value given above:

(2) $H_2O\,(g) + CO\,(g) \rightleftharpoons H_2\,(g) + CO_2\,(g)$

$$K_c = \frac{[H_2][CO_2]}{[CO][H_2O]}$$

$$= \frac{1}{0.955}$$

$$= 1.05 \qquad \text{(again the units cancel)}$$

Another interesting situation to consider is when the reactant in one equilibrium is the product of a previous equilibrium. For example the carbon monoxide in (2) could be the product of the reaction of carbon with steam shown in (3) below (the value of the equilibrium constant again being that at 1000 K):

(3) $H_2O\,(g) + C\,(s) \rightleftharpoons H_2\,(g) + CO\,(g)$

$$K_c = \frac{[H_2][CO]}{[H_2O]}$$

$$= 4.48 \times 10^{-4}\ mol\ dm^{-3}$$

These two equilibria can then be combined, as shown in (4) and in this case the equilibrium constant is the product of those for the two separate equilibria:

(4) $2\,H_2O\,(g) + C\,(s) \rightleftharpoons 2\,H_2\,(g) + CO_2\,(g)$

$$K_c = \frac{[H_2]^2[CO_2]}{[H_2O]^2}$$

$$= \frac{[H_2][CO_2]}{[CO][H_2O]} \times \frac{[H_2][CO]}{[H_2O]}$$

$$= 1.05 \times 4.48 \times 10^{-4}$$

$$= 4.70 \times 10^{-4}\ mol\ dm^{-3}$$

THE EFFECT OF CONDITIONS ON THE POSITION OF EQUILIBRIUM

If the conditions (such as temperature, pressure, or the concentrations of the species involved) under which the equilibrium is established are changed, then the rates of the forward and reverse reactions will no longer be equal. As a result the equilibrium is disturbed and the concentrations of the species will change until the rates once again become equal and equilibrium is once more established.

Le Chatelier's principle is a way of predicting the direction (forward or reverse) in which the position of equilibrium will change if the conditions are altered. It states

> *"If a change is made to the conditions of a chemical equilibrium, then the position of equilibrium will readjust so as to minimise the change made."*

This means that increasing a concentration of a species will result in a change that will cause that concentration to decrease again; increasing pressure will result in a change that will cause the pressure to decrease again; increasing the temperature will result in a change that will cause the temperature to decrease again. The effects of changes in the conditions of equilibrium are summarised in Figure 704.

Note that whilst changes in concentration and pressure affect the position of equilibrium and the amounts of the

CORE

Change	Effect on Equilibrium	Does K_c change?
Increase concentration	Shifts to the opposite side	No
Decrease concentration	Shifts to that side	No
Increase pressure	Shifts to side with least moles of gas	No
Decrease pressure	Shifts to side with most moles of gas	No
Increase temperature	Shifts in endothermic direction	Yes
Decrease temperature	Shifts in exothermic direction	Yes
Add catalyst	No effect	No

Figure 704 The effect of changes in conditions on the position of an equilibrium

various species present, they have no effect on the value of the equilibrium constant, K_c, because the values of the forward and reverse rate constants k_f and k_r respectively do not change. A change in temperature does however affect the rate constants, so that the value of K_c changes as well as the position of equilibrium.

If an unreactive gas is added to a fixed volume of the equilibrium, so all concentrations remain constant, then there is no effect. If however the gas is added at a constant pressure, so that the total volume has to increase, then the concentrations of all species will decrease, so the effect is similar to that of reducing the total pressure.

The presence of a catalyst reduces the activation energy of both the forward and reverse reactions by the same amount. This means that both the forward and reverse reactions are speeded up by the same factor, so even though the equilibrium is established more rapidly, neither the position of equilibrium nor the value of the equilibrium constant are affected.

Concentration

If the concentration of a species is increased, then the equilibrium moves towards the other side causing the concentration to fall to a value between the original concentration and the increased value. Conversely if the concentration of a species is reduced the equilibrium shifts towards the side of the equilibrium on which it occurs causing its concentration to increase to a value between the original concentration and the reduced value.

Consider the equilibrium:

$$\underset{\text{Yellow-Brown}}{Fe(H_2O)_6^{\ 3+}\ (aq)} + \underset{\text{Colourless}}{SCN^-\ (aq)} \rightleftharpoons \underset{\text{Blood-red}}{[Fe(H_2O)_5SCN]^{2+}\ (aq)} + H_2O\ (l)$$

If aqueous thiocyanate ions are added to an aqueous solution of an iron(III) salt, then a blood-red colouration is observed owing to the formation of the complex ion shown. If the concentration of either the thiocyanate ion or the iron(III) ion is increased, then the intensity of the colouration increases. This is in keeping with Le Chatelier's principle because the shift of the equilibrium to the right causes the concentration of the added reactant to fall again. It also shows that the reaction has not gone to completion because addition of either reactant causes an increase in the amount of product. If the concentration of iron(III) ions is decreased by adding fluoride ions (which form the very stable $FeF_6^{\ 3-}$ complex ion) then the intensity of the colouration decreases. This is in keeping with Le Chatelier's principle because the shift of the equilibrium to the left produces more aqueous iron(III) ions to counteract the reduction caused by the fluoride ions. It also shows that the reaction is reversible. Note that even though the position of equilibrium is altered, the change in concentrations is such that the value of K_c remains unchanged.

Pressure

If the total pressure of a system (P) is increased then the equilibrium shifts to the side with least moles of gas, so causing the pressure to fall to a value between the original pressure and the increased value. Conversely if the total pressure of the system is reduced the equilibrium shifts towards the side with the most moles of gas, causing the pressure to increase to a value between the original pressure and the reduced value. Consider the examples below:

$2\ SO_2\ (g) + O_2\ (g) \rightleftharpoons 2\ SO_3\ (g)$
3 moles of gas is converted to to 2 moles of gas
Increased P, equilibrium →;
Decreased P, equilibrium ←

$C\ (s) + H_2O\ (g) \rightleftharpoons CO(g) + H_2\ (g)$
1 mole of gas is converted to to 2 moles of gas
(note: carbon is a solid)
Increased P, equilibrium ←;
Decreased P, equilibrium →

$H_2\ (g) + I_2\ (g) \rightleftharpoons 2\ HI\ (g)$
2 moles of gas is converted to 2 moles of gas
Changing P has no effect

Note that even though the position of equilibrium is altered, the changes in the concentrations that result from the changes in pressure are such that the value of K_c remains unchanged.

Temperature

If the temperature of a system is increased then the equilibrium shifts in the direction of the **endothermic change**, so absorbing heat and causing the temperature to fall to a value between the original temperature and the increased value. Conversely if the temperature of the system is reduced the equilibrium shifts in the direction of the **exothermic change**, so releasing heat and causing the temperature to increase to a value between the original temperature and the reduced value. Consider the examples below:

$N_2\ (g) + O_2\ (g) \rightleftharpoons 2\ NO\ (g)$
$\Delta H = +180\ kJ\ mol^{-1}$
(i.e. forward reaction endothermic)
Increased T, K_c increases, equilibrium →;
Decreased T, K_c decreases, equilibrium ←

$2\ SO_2\ (g) + O_2\ (g) \rightleftharpoons 2\ SO_3\ (g)$
$\Delta H = -197\ kJ\ mol^{-1}$
(i.e. forward reaction exothermic)
Increased T, K_c decreases, equilibrium ←;
Decreased T, K_c increases, equilibrium →

Note that changes in temperature affect the rate constants of the forward and reverse reactions to different extents, so the actual value of K_c changes.

Explanations

Le Chatelier's principle is just a memory aid that helps us to predict the effect that a change in conditions will have on the position of an equilibrium. It is **not** an explanation of **why** these changes occur. The explanation come from a consideration of the effect of the change in conditions on the rates of the forward and reverse reactions.

Consider the effects of the changes in conditions on the equilibrium between solid phosphorus pentachloride, liquid phosphorus trichloride and gaseous chlorine:

$$PCl_5\ (s) \rightleftharpoons PCl_3\ (l) + Cl_2\ (g)\quad \Delta H = +88\ kJ\ mol^{-1}$$

If the concentration of chlorine is increased, then the rate of the reverse reaction will increase, but the forward reaction will be unaffected, so that the reaction rates are no longer equal. In order for equilibrium to be restored, the amount of the pentachloride must increase and the amount of the trichloride decrease so that the position of the equilibrium will shift to the left, hence the amount of chlorine decreases to below its new higher level, but still above the original level (see Figure 705). This is in agreement with the predictions of Le Chatelier's principle that the position of equilibrium will shift to the opposite side to the species whose concentration has been increased. Obviously a decrease in the concentration of chlorine has the opposite effect, though neither affects the value of K_c.

If the total pressure is increased then the rate of the reverse reaction will again increase, because this is the only one that involves a gas and an increase in pressure only increases the concentration of gases. The more moles of gas involved on the side of the equilibrium, the more a change in pressure will affect the rate. The result of this increase in the rate of the reverse reaction is the same as those explained above and the position of equilibrium will again shift to the left. This results in a reduction in the amount of chlorine and hence the total pressure falls below the new higher value (see Figure 706). A decrease in total pressure will have the opposite effect, but once again the value of K_c is unchanged.

If the temperature is increased, then the rates of both the forward and reverse reactions will increase, but they will not do so by the same amount. The higher the activation energy, the greater the effect of temperature on reaction rate, so that an increase in temperature will speed up the reaction in the endothermic direction (which must have the greater activation energy) more than the exothermic reaction. In this example the forward reaction is endothermic (ΔH positive), so the reverse reaction is exothermic. The effect of an increase in temperature is therefore to increase the rate constant of the forward reaction more than that of the reverse reaction. Therefore, the value of K_c increases and the reaction shifts to the right, producing more chlorine and phosphorus trichloride until the reaction rates again become equal (see Figure 707). This endothermic change absorbs heat energy and causes the temperature of the system to fall to below its new higher value. A decrease in temperature will have the opposite effect and the value of K_c will decrease.

Figures 705, 706 and 707 show the effect of changes in conditions on the equilibrium established by heating phosphorus pentachloride.

INDUSTRIAL PROCESSES

Many industrial processes involve equilibria. The aim of the process is to produce the desired product as efficiently as possible, that is rapidly, but with the minimum amount of waste and the minimum input of energy. This requires a study of both kinetics (how fast the product is made from the reactants) and equilibrium (how much of the desired product is present in the mixture produced) considerations. Two processes to which these considerations have been applied are the Haber Process, for the production of ammonia, and the Contact Process, for the production of sulfuric acid. These are considered separately in Figure 707.

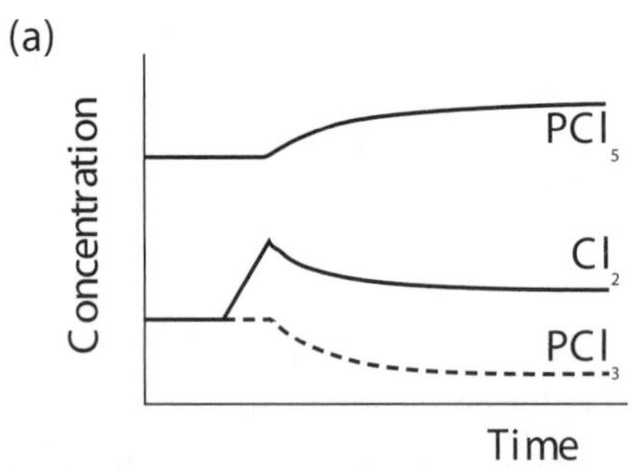

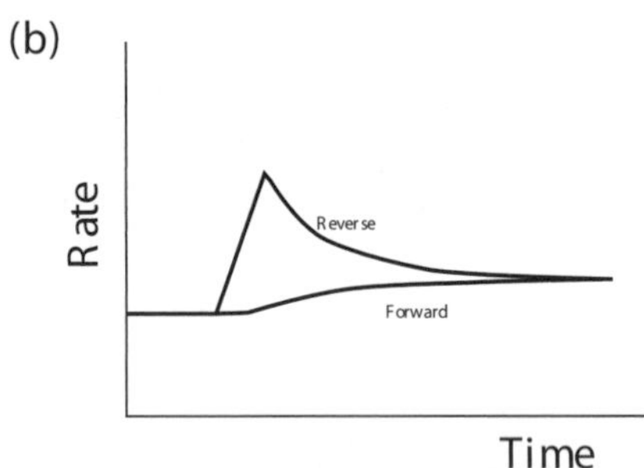

Figure 705 Increased concentration of chlorine

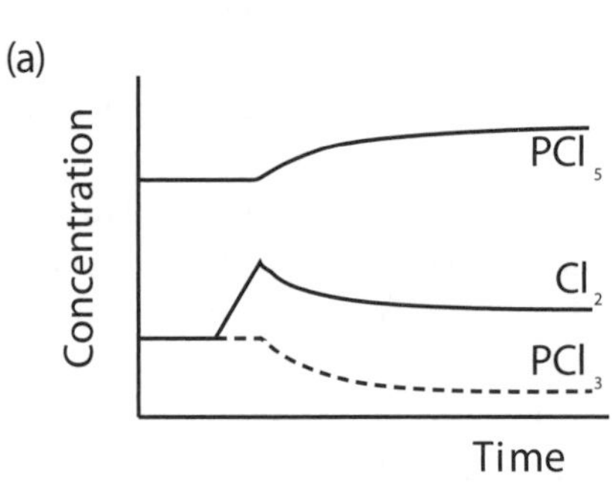

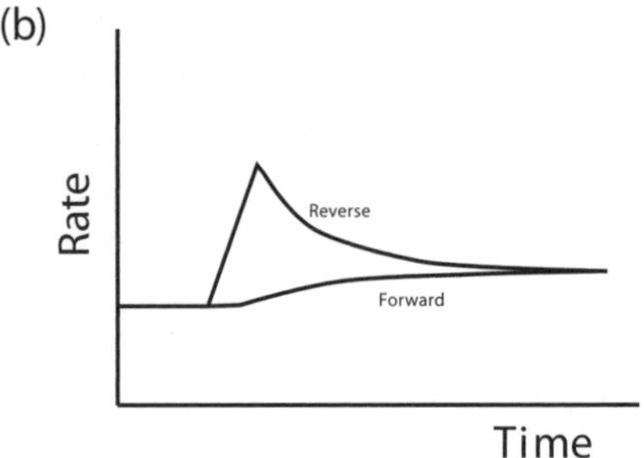

Figure 706 Increased total pressure

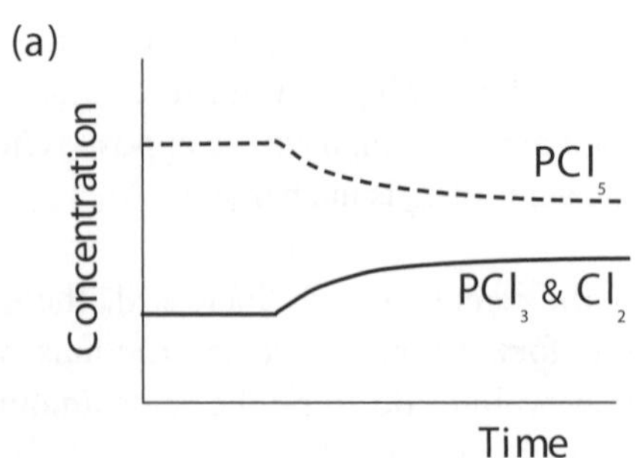

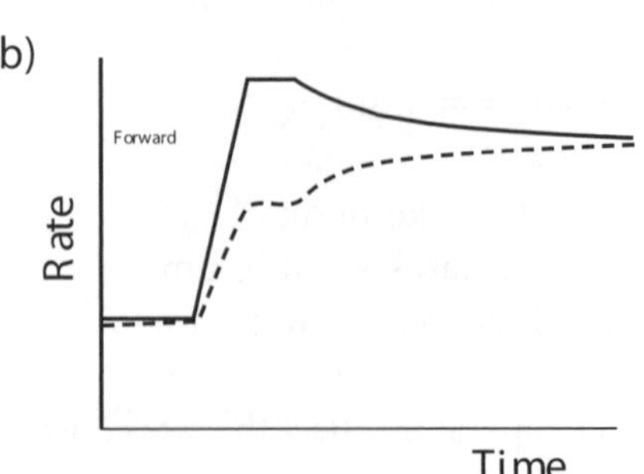

Figure 707 Increased temperature

(N.B. the 'flat' sections on the rate graph have been exaggerated to distinguish between the effects of temperatures and concentration changes)

Haber Process

The **Haber process** involves the direct combination of nitrogen and hydrogen to produce ammonia. A mixture of nitrogen and hydrogen in a 1:3 ratio by volume is compressed and passed over a heated iron catalyst where the following equilibrium is established.

$$N_2\,(g) + 3\,H_2\,(g) \rightleftharpoons 2\,NH_3\,(g)$$
$$\Delta H = -92 \text{ kJ mol}^{-1}$$

The choice of conditions for this equilibrium is critical. It can be seen that in the reaction 4 moles of gas are converted to 2 moles of gas, hence a high pressure will favour the formation of the product, as Figure 708 confirms. The provision of a high pressure is however expensive, both in terms of the capital cost of providing a plant that will resist high pressures and in terms of the operating costs of compressing gases to high pressures. The final choice will therefore be a compromise pressure that takes into account these factors.

It can be seen from the equation above that the forward reaction is exothermic (ΔH is negative), hence a low temperature would favour the products, as can be seen from Figure 708. Unfortunately low temperatures result in low rates of reaction so that even though there may be a high proportion of ammonia in the product it may take a long time for the conversion to occur. A compromise temperature is therefore chosen so as to produce the maximum mass of ammonia per hour. The use of a finely divided catalyst containing iron also increases the reaction rate.

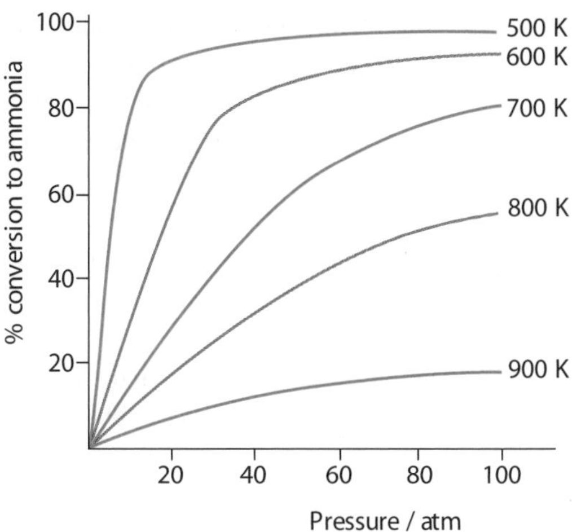

Figure 708 The effect of conditions on the proportion of ammonia at equilibrium

Typical conditions chosen for the Haber process are pressures in the range 200 – 1000 atm (20 – 100 MPa) and temperatures ≈ 700 K. The reaction is however not left for sufficient time to reach equilibrium (remember the reaction rate will decrease as equilibrium is approached – see Figure 701) and typically in the converter only about 20% of the nitrogen and hydrogen is converted to ammonia. It would be very uneconomical to waste the unchanged reactants, so the mixture of gases is cooled causing the ammonia to condense (it can hydrogen bond, unlike the reactants) so that it can be separated and the gaseous nitrogen and hydrogen recycled.

Nitrogen is an element vital for plant growth, so the major use of ammonia is the manufacture of fertilizers, such as ammonium salts and urea. It is also used in the manufacture of nitrogen containing polymers such as nylon. Ammonia can also be oxidised to produce nitric acid, involving the initial oxidation of ammonia over a platinum catalyst (see the equations below), which is used in the production of explosives such as TNT, dynamite etc. and in the dye industry.

$$4\,NH_3\,(g) + 5\,O_2\,(g) \rightleftharpoons 4\,NO\,(g) + 6\,H_2O\,(g)$$

$$2\,NO\,(g) + O_2\,(g) \rightleftharpoons 2\,NO_2\,(g)$$

$$4\,NO_2\,(g) + 2\,H_2O\,(l) + O_2\,(g) \rightleftharpoons 4\,HNO_3\,(aq)$$

Contact Process

The **Contact process** is the production of sulfuric acid by the oxidation of sulfur. Firstly pure sulfur is burnt in air to form sulfur dioxide:

$$S\,(s) + O_2\,(g) \rightleftharpoons SO_2\,(g)$$

Sulfur dioxide is mixed with air and passed over a vanadium(V) oxide catalyst to produce sulfur trioxide:

$$2\,SO_2\,(g) + O_2\,(g) \rightleftharpoons 2\,SO_3\,(g)$$
$$\Delta H = -196 \text{ kJ mol}^{-1}$$

As with the Haber Process a high pressure would favour the formation of the product (3 moles of gas going to 2), but in this case excellent conversion is achieved without the expense of a high pressure process. Hence the reactants are only compressed to the pressure needed (about 2 atm) to achieve the desired flow rate in the reactor. Similarly using pure oxygen rather than air would drive the equilibrium to the right, but again it would be an unnecessary expense. Another similarity is that the forward reaction is exothermic, so a low temperature favours the products. As with the Haber Process the temperature cannot be too low otherwise the process becomes uneconomically slow. The result is the choice of a compromise temperature (700 — 800 K) and the use of a catalyst (finely divided V_2O_5) to enhance the reaction rate. Also the oxidation to sulfur trioxide is usually done by a number of converters at

CORE

successively lower temperatures, so as to make use of high temperature to give a fast initial rate of reaction as well as a low temperature to give a high final equilibrium yield. The result is well over 90% conversion to the trioxide. After absorption of the sulfur trioxide, the gases are often passed through one more converter to ensure that the waste gases contain so little sulfur dioxide that they can be released directly into the air.

The sulfur trioxide must now be reacted with water to produce sulfuric acid:

$$SO_3\ (g) + H_2O\ (l) \longrightarrow H_2SO_4\ (l)$$

Sulfuric acid has numerous uses in the chemical industry – indeed the tonnage of it used annually gives a good indication of the extent of a country's chemical industry. These uses include manufacture of fertilizers (especially converting insoluble phosphate rock to soluble 'superphosphate'), polymers, detergents, paints and pigments. It is also widely used in the petrochemicals industry and in the industrial processing of metals. One of its minor, though possibly most familiar uses, is as the electrolyte in automobile batteries.

Exercise 7.2

1. The equilibrium constant for a reaction that occurs totally in the gas phase is given below. What is the chemical equation for this equilibrium?

$$K_c = \frac{[CO_2][CF_4]}{[COF_2]^2}$$

   A $CO_2\ (g) + CF_4\ (g) \rightleftharpoons COF_2\ (g)$
   B $CO_2\ (g) + CF_4\ (g) \rightleftharpoons 2\ COF_2\ (g)$
   C $2\ COF_2\ (g) \rightleftharpoons CO_2\ (g) + CF_4\ (g)$
   D $COF_2\ (g) \rightleftharpoons CO_2\ (g) + CF_4\ (g)$

2. Which one of the following will increase the rate at which a state of equilibrium is attained without affecting the position of equilibrium?

   A Increasing the temperature.
   B Increasing the pressure.
   C Decreasing the concentration of the products.
   D Adding a catalyst.

3. In the manufacture of methanol, hydrogen is reacted with carbon monoxide over a catalyst of zinc and chromium oxides and the following equilibrium is established:

$$2\ H_2\ (g) + CO\ (g) \rightleftharpoons CH_3OH\ (g)$$
$$\Delta H = -128.4\ \text{kJ mol}^{-1}$$

   Which one of the following changes would increase the percentage of carbon monoxide converted to methanol at equilibrium?

   A Decreasing the total pressure.
   B Increasing the temperature.
   C Increasing the proportion of hydrogen in the mixture of gases.
   D Increasing the surface area of the catalyst.

4. When heated in a sealed vessel, ammonium chloride is in equilibrium with ammonia and hydrogen chloride according to the equilibrium:

$$NH_4Cl\ (s) \rightleftharpoons NH_3\ (g) + HCl\ (g)$$

   Increasing the temperature increases the proportion of the ammonium chloride that is dissociated. The best explanation of this observation is that:

   A this increases the rate of both reactions, but the forward reaction is affected more than the reverse reaction.
   B this increases the rate of both reactions, but the reverse reaction is affected more than the forward reaction.
   C this increases the rate of the forward reaction, but decreases the rate of the reverse reaction.
   D this decreases the rate of both reactions, but the reverse reaction is affected more than the forward reaction.

5. When methane and steam are passed over a heated catalyst the equilibrium below is established.

$$CH_4\ (g) + H_2O\ (g) \rightleftharpoons CO\ (g) + 3\ H_2\ (g)$$

   Which one of the following will result in a change in the value of the equilibrium constant (K_c)?

   A Increasing the pressure.
   B Adding more methane (CH_4).
   C Decreasing the concentration of steam.
   D Increasing the temperature.

6. When 0.1 mol dm^{-3} aqueous solutions of silver nitrate and iron(II) nitrate are mixed, the following equilibrium is established:

$$Ag^{+}(aq) + Fe^{2+}(aq) \rightleftharpoons Fe^{3+}(aq) + Ag(s)$$

Which of the following changes would produce more silver?

A Adding some iron(III) nitrate solution.
B Adding more iron(II) nitrate solution.
C Removing some of the Ag^{+} ions by forming insoluble silver chloride.
D Increasing the total pressure.

7. In the conversion of nitrogen to ammonia using the Haber process, the main reason why the temperature is limited to about 450 °C is because

A a higher temperature would cause the catalyst to break down.
B a higher temperature would cause the reaction to occur too slowly.
C a higher temperature would decrease the amount of ammonia present at equilibrium.
D a higher temperature would cost too much money to maintain.

8. For each of the following equilibrium reactions, balance the equation with whole number coefficients and deduce its K_c expression:

a) $N_2(g) + H_2(g) \rightleftharpoons NH_3(g)$ (Haber process)

b) $SO_2(g) + O_2(g) \rightleftharpoons SO_3(g)$ (Contact process)

c) $NH_3(aq) + H_2O(l) \rightleftharpoons NH_4^{+}(aq) + OH^{-}(aq)$

d) $H_2O(l) \rightleftharpoons H^{+}(aq) + OH^{-}(aq)$

e) $NO(g) + Cl_2(g) \rightleftharpoons NOCl(g)$

f) $NH_3(g) + O_2(g) \rightleftharpoons H_2O(g) + NO(g)$

g) $CH_3NH_2(aq) + H_2O(l) \rightleftharpoons CH_3NH_3^{+}(aq) + OH^{-}(aq)$

h) $CH_3OH(l) + CH_3COOH(l) \rightleftharpoons CH_3COOCH_3(l) + H_2O(l)$

9. The central reaction in the Haber process is the equilibrium between nitrogen, hydrogen and ammonia.

a) Write a balanced equation for this equilibrium.
b) The enthalpy change in this reaction is −92.6 kJ mol^{-1} and the activation energy is +335 kJ mol^{-1}. Draw an energy level diagram for this equilibrium.
c) The reaction usually takes place in the presence of an iron catalyst. On the diagram from b), mark the reaction pathway for the catalysed reaction with a dotted line.
d) Would you expect the iron to be present as solid lumps or in a finely divided state? Explain why.
e) The reaction is usually carried out at a pressure well above atmospheric pressure. How would you expect this to affect the rate of reaction? Explain why it has this effect.

10. Nitrogen monoxide and oxygen react together in a reversible reaction to form nitrogen dioxide.

a) Describe, in terms of the rates of the reactions and the concentrations of the species present, the way in which equilibrium is established if nitrogen monoxide and oxygen are suddenly mixed in an empty flask.
b) Write a balanced equation for this equilibrium.
c) Nitrogen dioxide is brown, whereas nitrogen monoxide is colourless. If the oxygen is replaced with an equal volume of air, the mixture of gases becomes lighter coloured. Explain why this occurs.

11. For each of the following equilibria, state:

I whether change (i) would shift the position of equilibrium to the right or the left.
and
II how you could change the second factor (ii) so as to shift the position of equilibrium in the opposite direction.

a) $C(s) + H_2O(g) \rightleftharpoons CO(g) + H_2(g)$
Forward reaction endothermic

(i) increasing the total pressure.
(ii) changing the temperature.

b) $Br_2(aq) + H_2O(l) \rightleftharpoons HOBr(aq) + H^{+}(aq) + Br^{-}(aq)$

(i) adding potassium bromide.
(ii) changing the pH.

CORE

c) N_2O_4 (g) $\rightleftharpoons$ 2 NO_2 (g)
Forward reaction endothermic

(i) decreasing the temperature.
(ii) changing the total pressure.

d) CO (g) + Cl_2 (g) $\rightleftharpoons$ $COCl_2$ (g)
Forward reaction exothermic

(i) adding more chlorine.
(ii) changing the temperature.

e) NH_4HS (s) $\rightleftharpoons$ NH_3 (g) + H_2S (g)

(i) reducing the pressure.
(ii) changing the concentration of ammonia.

12. A gaseous mixture of hydrogen, iodine and hydrogen iodide are in equilibrium according to the equation:

$$H_2 (g) + I_2 (g) \rightleftharpoons 2\,HI (g) \qquad \Delta H = +56\ \text{kJ mol}^{-1}$$

State how the position of equilibrium will be affected by the following changes and explain your reasoning:

a) Decreasing the temperature.
b) Adding more hydrogen at constant pressure.
c) Increasing the total pressure.

13. A flask contains iodine monochloride, a brown liquid, iodine trichloride, a yellow solid, and chlorine gas in equilibrium according to the equation:

$$ICl (l) + Cl_2 (g) \rightleftharpoons ICl_3 (s)$$

a) If the volume of the flask was reduced so as to increase the total pressure, explain what you would expect to happen to the amounts of brown liquid and yellow solid?
b) When the flask is cooled in iced water the amount of yellow solid increases and there is less brown liquid. Explain what this shows about the equilibrium?

14. Sulfuric acid is manufactured by the reaction between sulfur trioxide and water. The sulfur trioxide is formed by the reaction of sulfur dioxide and oxygen from air in the presence of a catalyst. This is known as the Contact process and establishes an equilibrium in which the forward reaction is exothermic.

a) Write a balanced equation for the equilibrium.
b) What effect does the catalyst have upon:
i) the rate of the forward reaction?
ii) the rate of the reverse reaction?
iii) the proportion of sulfur dioxide converted to sulfur trioxide?
c) If a high pressure was used, what effect would this have on the relative proportions of sulfur dioxide and sulfur trioxide? Explain.
d) Much greater reaction rates could be achieved if the temperature was increased. Explain why this is not done.

CORE

HIGHER LEVEL

17.1 LIQUID-VAPOUR EQUILIBRIUM (AHL)

17.1.1 Describe the equilibrium established between a liquid and its own vapour and how it is affected by temperature changes.

17.1.2 Sketch graphs showing the relationship between vapour pressure and temperature and explain them in terms of the kinetic theory.

17.1.3 State and explain the relationship between enthalpy of vapourization, boiling point and intermolecular forces.

Consider an evacuated container with a layer of a volatile liquid in the bottom of it. Molecules of the liquid will escape from the surface and enter the vapour phase. These molecules in the vapour phase will collide with the walls of the container and exert a pressure. Some of the molecules will also strike the surface of the liquid and condense back into the liquid phase. Initially this rate of return will be low, but as more and more molecules escape into the vapour phase and the pressure increases, the rate of return also increases until it becomes equal to the rate at which the particles vapourise from the surface so that

Rate of vapourisation = Rate of condensation

At this point the system is in a state of dynamic equilibrium, similar to a chemical equilibrium, and the pressure exerted by the particles in the vapour phase is known as the **vapour pressure** of the liquid. Altering the surface area of the liquid affects both of the rates equally, so that it has no overall effect on the vapour pressure, though it will affect the time taken to reach equilibrium - the greater the surface area, the more rapidly equilibrium is achieved.

Molecules on the surface need a certain minimum amount of kinetic energy before they can escape from the attractive forces of the other surface molecules. This will depend on the strength of the intermolecular forces and is similar to the concept of activation energy for a chemical reaction. Vapourisation is an endothermic process, as it requires the overcoming of the attractive forces between the particles. The amount of energy required for this phase change is known as the enthalpy of vapourisation.

More precisely the **enthalpy of vapourisation** is the amount of energy required to convert one mole of the substance from the liquid to the gaseous state. Using water as an example, it is the enthalpy change associated with the transition:

$$H_2O\ (l) \longrightarrow H_2O\ (g)$$
$$\Delta H = +40.7\ \text{kJ mol}^{-1}\ \text{(at 373 K and 101.3 kPa)}$$

This energy is mainly required to overcome intermolecular forces, though some is required to do work against the atmosphere. When a substance boils, its temperature does not increase (there is no increase in kinetic energy), so that the energy absorbed is involved in increasing potential energy by overcoming attractive forces between the particles.

The stronger the forces between the particles, the greater the enthalpy of vapourisation, the lower the vapour pressure at a given temperature, and the higher the boiling point. This is illustrated by the data in Figure 710.

At a higher temperature, more molecules will have the required kinetic energy to escape into the vapour phase and the rate of vapourisation will increase (see Figure 711). This means that more molecules are required in the gas phase for the rate of condensation to equal the rate of vapourisation, hence an increase in temperature results in an increase in vapour pressure, as shown in Figure 711. A liquid will boil when its vapour pressure is equal to the pressure on the surface of the liquid, because this allows bubbles of vapour to form in the body of the liquid. The normal **boiling point** is the temperature at which the vapour pressure is equal to standard atmospheric pressure (101.3 kPa), as shown in Figure 711. A liquid will, however, boil at a lower temperature if the external pressure is reduced, as would be the case on top of a mountain. Similarly if the external pressure is increased, as in a pressure cooker, the boiling point of the liquid increases.

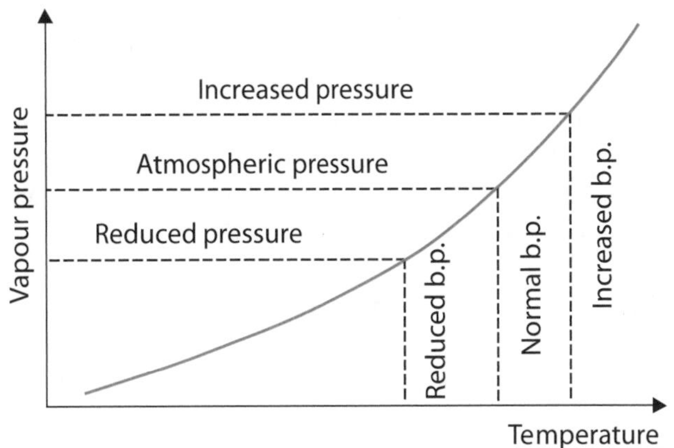

Figure 711 The relationship between temperature and vapour pressure showing the boiling point

Compound	Enthalpy of vapourisation / kJ mol^{-1}	Boiling point / K	Intermolecular forces
Methane	9.0	109	van der Waals' only
Methoxymethane	27.2	248	van der Waals' and dipole-dipole
Ethanol	38.6	352	van der Waals', dipole-dipole, and hydrogen bonds

Figure 710 Enthalpy of vapourisation and boiling point data of some compounds

AHL

17.2 THE EQUILIBRIUM LAW (AHL)

17.2.1 Solve homogeneous equilibrium problems using the expression for K_c.

AHL

A **homogeneous equilibrium** is one in which all the reactants and products are in the same phase. If there are two or more phases then it is a **heterogeneous equilibrium**. The concentrations, when substituted into the equilibrium constant formula, will only equal the equilibrium constant if the system is in fact at equilibrium. For other situations, when equilibrium is not present, the value produced by treating the concentrations in the same way as the equilibrium constant (sometimes referred to as the reaction quotient, Q_c) will indicate which way the reaction needs to shift in order to attain equilibrium. If $Q_c > K_c$, then the value of Q_c must fall, hence some products must be converted to reactants and the system must shift to the left (in the reverse direction) until $Q_c = K_c$ and equilibrium is established. Conversely if $Q_c < K_c$, then the system must shift to the right (in the forward direction) and some reactants must be converted to products until $Q_c = K_c$ and equilibrium is established. Consider the reaction:

$$CO_2\,(g) + H_2\,(g) \rightleftharpoons CO\,(g) + H_2O\,(g)$$

$K_c = 0.955$ at 1000 K

If equal amounts of the gases are mixed at 1000 K then $Q_c = 1$, which is greater than K_c at this temperature, so the system must shift to the left (in the reverse direction) to achieve equilibrium. In other words, some of the water and carbon monoxide will react to form carbon dioxide and hydrogen, altering the concentrations so that $Q_c = K_c$.

As with any mathematical expression, if all of the terms except one in the equilibrium expression are known, the unknown term may be calculated by substitution. This is best illustrated by means of examples:

Example

When a mixture initially containing 0.0200 mol dm^{-3} sulfur dioxide and an equal concentration of oxygen is allowed to reach equilibrium in a container of fixed volume at 1000 K, it is found that 80.0% of the sulfur dioxide is converted to sulfur trioxide. Calculate the value of the equilibrium constant at that temperature.

Solution

$$2\,SO_2\,(g) + O_2\,(g) \rightleftharpoons 2\,SO_3\,(g)$$

Assuming, for simplicity, a volume of 1 dm^3, then as 80% of the sulfur dioxide turns into the trioxide:

Equilibrium $[SO_3] = 0.0200 \times 0.800$

$= 0.0160$ mol dm^{-3}

Each sulfur trioxide molecule is formed from one sulfur dioxide molecule, so:

Equilibrium $[SO_2] = 0.0200 - 0.0160$

$= 0.0040$ mol dm^{-3}

Each sulfur trioxide molecule requires only half an oxygen molecule, so:

Equilibrium $[O_2] = 0.0200 - (½ \times 0.0160)$

$= 0.0120$ mol dm^{-3}

Substituting into the equilibrium constant expression, the value of the equilibrium constant may be calculated:

$$K_c = \frac{[SO_3]^2}{[SO_2]^2[O_2]}$$

$$= \frac{0.0160^2}{0.0040^2 \times 0.0120}$$

$= 1333$

$= 1330$ mol^{-1} dm^3 (3 s.f.)

Similarly if the equilibrium constant is known, then given appropriate information the equilibrium or starting concentration of one of the reactants may be found, the best technique usually being to substitute 'x' for the unknown quantity. In many cases though the resulting equation may contain powers of 'x' and hence require special techniques for their solution. This is not however the case with the example given below:

Example 2

In the gas phase at 730 K, the equilibrium constant for the reaction of hydrogen and iodine to form hydrogen iodide has a value of 490. If the initial concentration of iodine is 0.0200 mol dm^{-3}, what concentration of hydrogen is required for 90.0% of the iodine to be converted to hydrogen iodide?

Solution

$H_2\text{ (g)} + I_2\text{ (g)} \rightleftharpoons 2\text{ HI (g)}$

$$K_c = \frac{[HI]^2}{[H_2][I_2]}$$

Initial $[I_2]$ = 0.0200, so at equilibrium, if 90.0% converted, $[I_2]$ eq = (0.0200 – 0.0180) = 0.0020

Concentration of I_2 converted = 0.0200 – 0.00200

= 0.0180 mol dm^{-3}

∴ Concentration of HI formed = 2 × 0.0180 (1 mole of I_2 forms 2 moles of HI)

= 0.0360 mol dm^{-3}

If the initial concentration of $H_2 = x$,

then equilibrium concentration of H_2I_2

= $[H_2I_2]$ eq = x – 0.0180

Substituting:

$$490 = \frac{0.0360^2}{(x - 0.0180) \times 0.00200}$$

$$x - 0.0180 = \frac{0.0360^2}{490 \times 0.00200}$$

= 0.00132

x = 0.00132 + 0.0180

= 0.01932

= 0.0193 mol dm^{-3} (3 s.f.)

Exercise 17.2

1. At a particular temperature, a mixture of nitrogen monoxide and oxygen is allowed to reach equilibrium according to the equation:

   $2\text{ NO (g)} + O_2\text{ (g)} \rightleftharpoons 2\text{ NO}_2\text{ (g)}$

   The equilibrium concentrations of the gases are 0.03 mol dm^{-3} nitrogen monoxide; 0.04 mol dm^{-3} oxygen and 0.02 mol dm^{-3} nitrogen dioxide. What is the value of the equilibrium constant, K_c?

   A $\frac{0.3 \times 0.04}{0.02}$ mol dm^{-3}
   B $\frac{0.02}{0.03 \times 0.04}$ mol^{-1} dm^{3}
   C $\frac{0.02}{0.03 \times 0.04^2}$ mol^{-2} dm^{6}
   D $\frac{0.02^2}{0.03^2 \times 0.04}$ mol^{-1} dm^{3}

2. When 0.01 moles of iodine are added to 1 dm^{3} of 0.2 mol dm^{-3} aqueous potassium iodide, 99% is converted to the triiodide ion according to the equilibrium

   $I_2\text{ (aq)} + I^-\text{ (aq)} \rightleftharpoons I_3^-\text{ (aq)}$

   What is the approximate value of the equilibrium constant?

   A 500 mol^{-1} dm^{3}
   B 100 mol^{-1} dm^{3}
   C 2 mol^{-1} dm^{3}
   D 0.002 mol^{-1} dm^{3}

3. The equilibrium constant for the dissociation of hydrogen iodide into its elements, according to the equation below, at 900 K is 0.04.

   $2\text{ HI (g)} \rightleftharpoons H_2\text{ (g)} + I_2\text{ (g)}$

   If the equilibrium concentration of hydrogen iodide is 0.2 mol dm^{-3}, what is the approximate equilibrium concentration of iodine?

   A 0.3
   B 0.04
   C 0.008
   D 0.0016

4. When ammonium hydrogensulfide is heated it dissociates according to the equilibrium below. The value of K_c for this equilibrium at a particular temperature is 0.00001 $mol^2\ dm^{-6}$.

$$NH_4HS\ (s) \rightleftharpoons NH_3\ (g) + H_2S\ (g)$$

a) Explain the units of the equilibrium constant.
b) Calculate the concentration of ammonia at equilibrium.
c) If some ammonia gas was injected at constant pressure and temperature, how would this affect
   i the mass of solid present?
   ii the concentration of hydrogen sulfide?
   iii the value of K_c?

5. When nitrogen and hydrogen react together in the presence of a catalyst, they produce ammonia. The following table gives the percent of ammonia in the mixture when a 3:1 H_2:N_2 mixture reaches equilibrium under various conditions:

Temperature / °C \ Pressure / MPa	10	20
400	25%	36%
500	10%	17%

a) What do these data show about the equilibrium?
b) At 10 MPa and 400°C, the equilibrium concentrations of the species present are:
   $[N_2]$ = 0.335 mol dm^{-3},
   $[H_2]$ = 1.005 mol dm^{-3},
   $[NH_3]$ = 0.450 mol dm^{-3}.
   Calculate a value for the equilibrium constant and give appropriate units.

6. For the gaseous equilibrium:

$$CO\ (g) + Cl_2\ (g) \rightleftharpoons COCl_2\ (g)$$

a) Write the expression for the equilibrium constant K_c.
b) The concentrations of the various species at a particular temperature are given below. Calculate the value of the equilibrium constant K_c, giving appropriate units.
   [CO] = 0.800 mol dm^{-3};
   $[Cl_2]$ = 0.600 mol dm^{-3};
   $[COCl_2]$ = 0.200 mol dm^{-3}
c) If the pressure of the system is suddenly increased so that the volume halves, calculate the new concentrations.
d) If these are substituted into the equilibrium constant expression, what is the numerical result.
e) Is the system still at equilibrium? If not in which direction will the reaction proceed? How did you deduce this?
f) Is this consistent with Le Chatelier's principle? Explain.

EXTENSIONS

THE VAPOUR PRESSURE OF MIXTURES

If the system contains two components that do not mix (for example, water and trichloromethane), they will each exert their own vapour pressure, provided it is shaken so both come into contact with the vapour phase. In other words the total vapour pressure is the sum of the individual vapour pressures. The situation is just the same as if one side of the container contained one component and the other side the other component, because particles of a particular substance can only leave from, and return to their own surface.

If the system contains two substances that do mix, then both of them will have vapour pressures in the mixture that are lower than in the pure liquids. This is because there will be less molecules of each component near the surface, reducing the rate of escape, but all of the surface is available for particles in the gas phase to return to, hence the rate of return is unaffected by being a mixture. If both of the liquids are volatile, then the total vapour pressure is the sum of these reduced vapour pressures and this provides the basis for fractional distillation (see below). If however one of the components is non-volatile, as is usually the case for a solid dissolved in a liquid, then the total vapour pressure of the system will be reduced, as shown in Figure 712, and this is the basis for the elevation of boiling point and depression of freezing point.

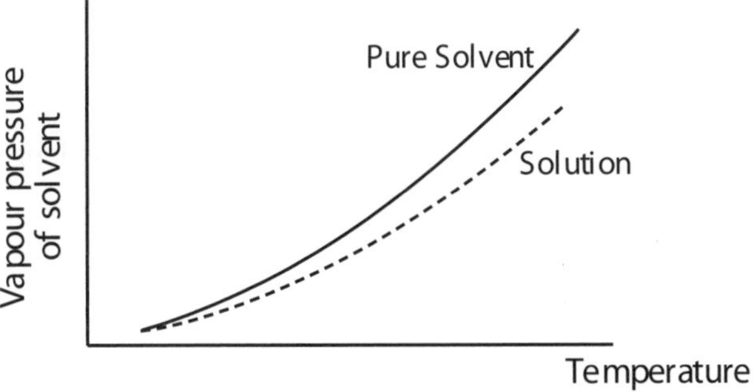

Figure 712 Illustrating the effect of a dissolved solid on the vapour pressure of a solvent

DISTILLATION AND FRACTIONAL DISTILLATION

A volatile liquid can be separated from a non–volatile solute by **simple distillation**. The apparatus for this is shown in Figure 713. The vapour from the heated flask passes over into the condenser, where it is cooled by the circulating cold water and turns back into a liquid, which is collected in the receiver. If necessary, to reduce thermal decomposition, the process can be carried out at a lower temperature by reducing the pressure in the apparatus so as to reduce the boiling point of the liquid (refer to Figure 711).

A mixture of two miscible, volatile liquids, will boil when the sum of the vapour pressures of the two components equals the external pressure. The vapour will always contain a greater proportion of the more volatile component than the liquid phase does. If the liquid contains an equal number of moles of two liquids, at the boiling point of the mixture, the more volatile component will be contributing more than 50% of the vapour pressure. For example the vapour above an equimolar mixture of benzene (b.p. = 353 K) and methylbenzene (b.p. = 384 K) will contain more than 50% benzene, but it is not possible to obtain pure benzene by simple distillation as there would still be significant amounts of methylbenzene vapour. Such a mixture could however be more completely separated by successive distillations – the greater the difference in boiling points the easier the separation.

Returning to the equimolar mixture of benzene and methylbenzene, the vapour pressures of the two components over the mixture at various temperatures are shown in Figure 714. At a particular temperature (~ 370 K) the total vapour pressure over the mixture equals atmospheric pressure and the mixture boils. The vapour evolved will contain the two components in the ratio of their vapour pressures at that temperature (~ 70% benzene and ~ 30% methylbenzene).

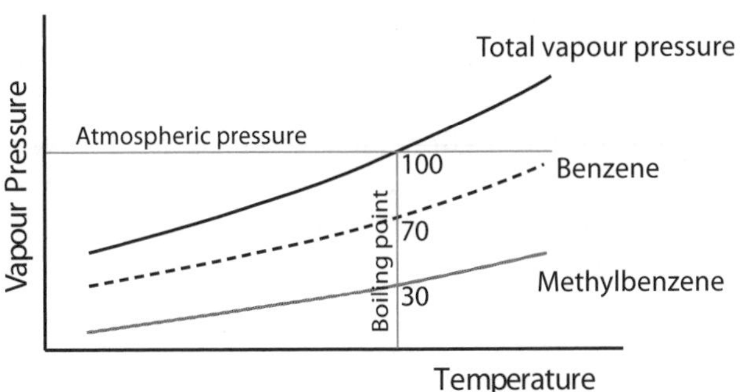

Figure 714 The vapour pressures in an equimolar benzene–methylbenzene mixture

EXTENSION

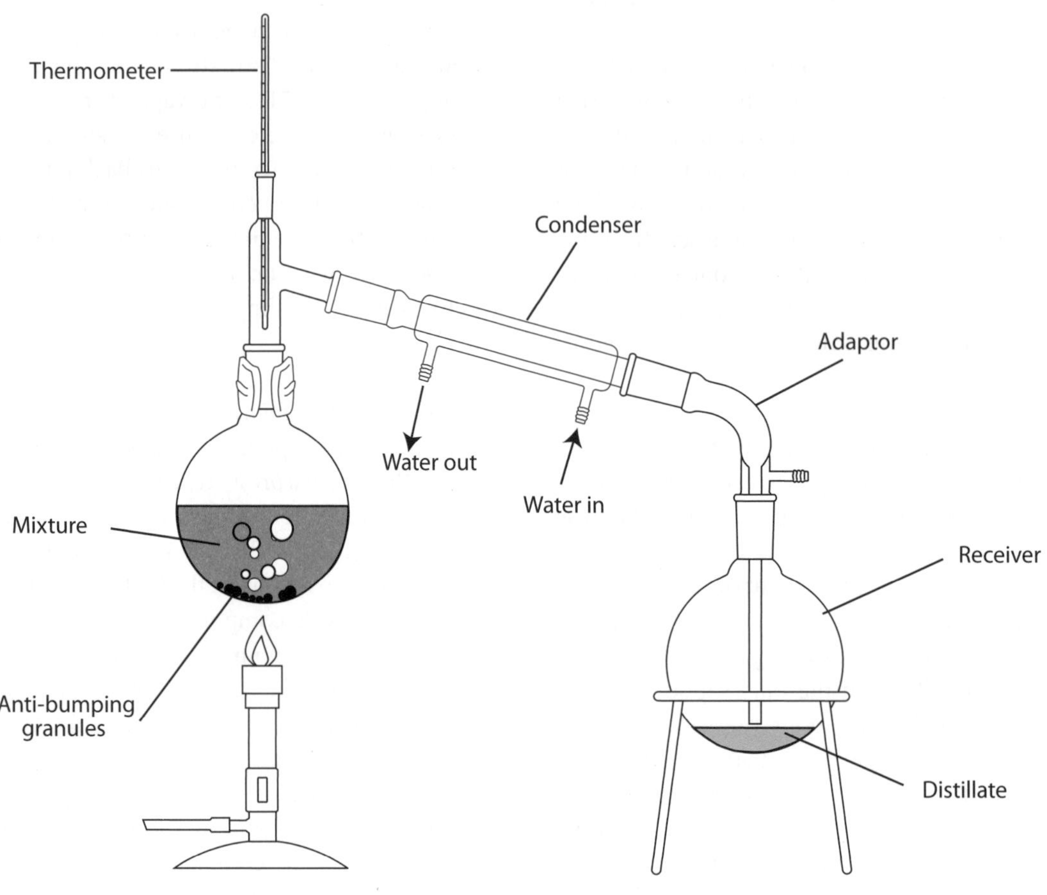

Figure 713 Typical simple distillation apparatus

EXTENSION

If this 70-30 mixture is now distilled, it will boil at a lower temperature (~ 365 K), as it is richer in the more volatile component, and the vapour that distils off will be even richer in benzene (~ 85% benzene and ~ 15% methylbenzene). This can again be distilled giving a product still richer in benzene and this process can be continued until the required degree of purity is obtained. This is best illustrated in the form of a boiling point composition graph for the system, shown in Figure 715, which indicates the boiling point of mixtures of differing compositions (liquid curve) and the composition of the vapour that will distil from this (vapour curve). The result of successive distillations can be seen by drawing lines (sometimes called 'tie lines') parallel to the axes, as shown in Figure 715:

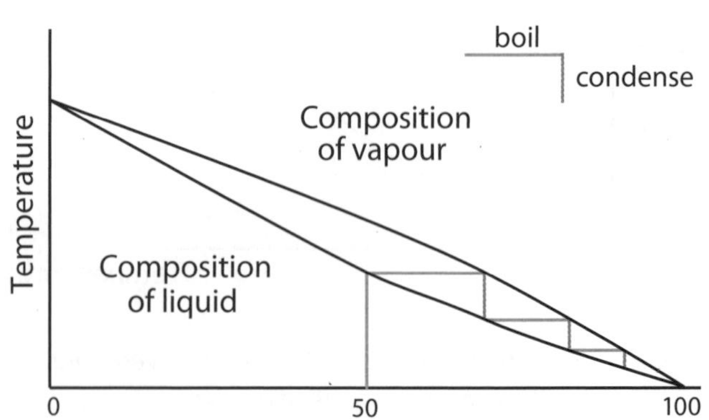

Figure 715 The boiling point–composition graph for benzene-methylbenzene mixtures

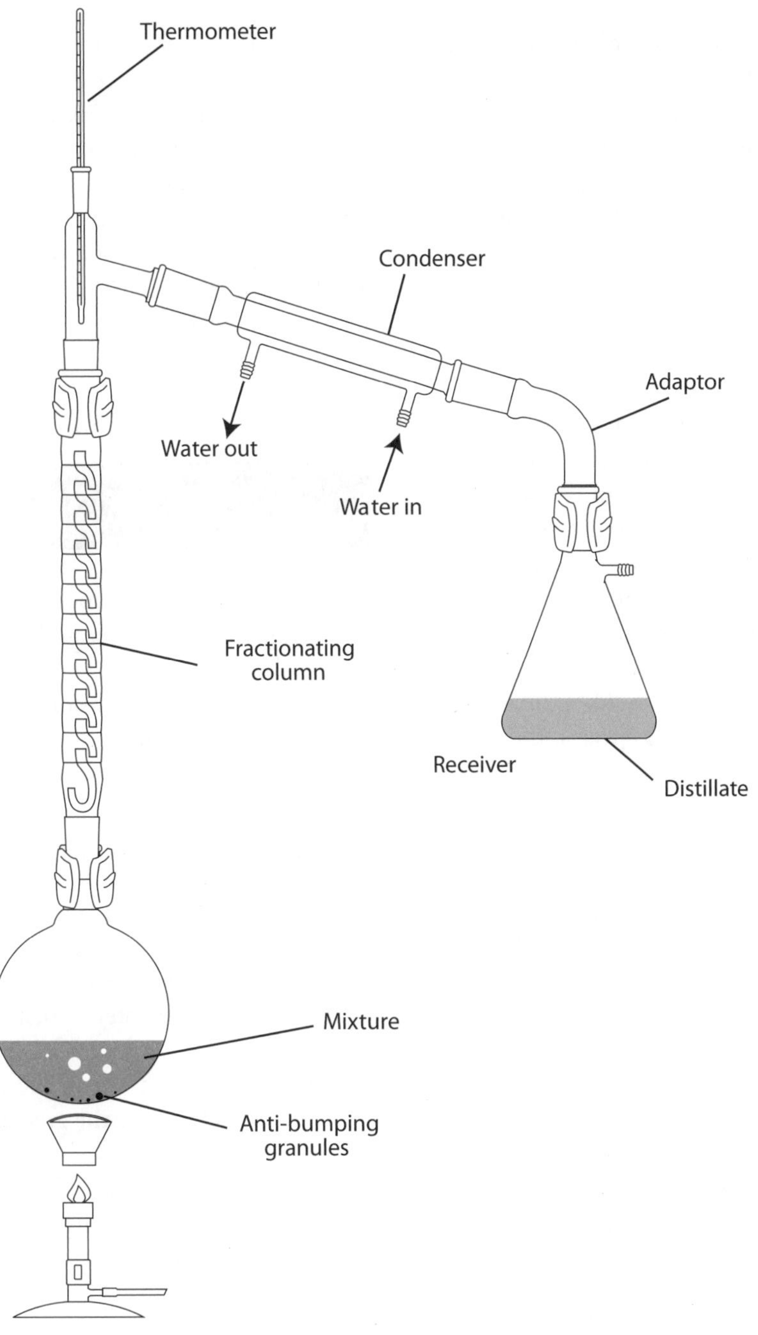

Figure 716 Typical fractional distillation apparatus

In **fractional distillation**, the vapour from the boiling liquid rises up the fractionating column, cools and condenses. It then runs down the column and meets hot vapours rising up, causing it to boil again. Thus as it rises up the column the liquid undergoes a number of vapourisation–condensation–vapourisation cycles, equivalent to having been distilled a number of times – the longer the column the more distillations. If a suitable column is used, the liquid distilling over will be a pure sample of the more volatile component of the mixture and eventually, in theory, the distillation flask will contain the less volatile component. Fractional distillation is carried out using apparatus similar to that shown in Figure 716. Fractional distillation is used in many industrial processes such as the separation of liquid air and of petroleum (refer to Chapter 14).

EXTENSION

RAOULT'S LAW AND DEVIATIONS FROM IDEALITY

The vapour pressure above a mixture of two miscible liquids is predicted by **Raoult's law**. This assumes that the forces between particles of the two components in the mixture (A–B forces) are identical to those present in the pure components (A–A and B–B forces), hence the vapour pressure of component A over the mixture (P_A) is equal to the vapour pressure of the pure component P^0_A multiplied by its mole fraction:

$$P_A = P^0_A \times \frac{\text{moles of A}}{\text{total moles}}$$

In many cases when the molecules only have weak van der Waals' forces between them, such as the cases of benzene and methylbenzene above, the situation approximates well to this ideal behaviour and the total vapour pressure varies in a linear manner with composition (see a in Figure 717). In other cases only minor deviations from ideality occur and the vapour pressure/composition graph is a smooth curve (see b in Figure 717). In some cases however, where strong inter-particle forces occur, as a result of hydrogen bonding or dissociation of one of the species, there are major deviations from ideality.

If the inter-particle forces in the mixture are weaker than those in the pure liquids, then it is easier for the particles to escape from the mixture, increasing the vapour pressure above the value predicted by Raoult's law (a positive deviation from Raoult's Law). In extreme cases of a **positive deviation from Raoult's Law**, the vapour pressure/composition graph will pass through a maximum, and as a result the boiling point/composition diagram will pass through a minimum (see c in Figure 717). In such cases separation of both components by fractional distillation is not possible because the liquid that distils over is not a pure component, but the mixture with the minimum boiling point. The mixture with this composition is known as an **azeotrope**. An example of this type of behaviour is a mixture of ethanol and water, where the azeotropic mixture (96% ethanol, 4% water) boils at a temperature of 78.2 °C, whereas the boiling point of pure ethanol is 78.5 °C.

If the inter-particle forces in the mixture are stronger than those in the pure liquids, then it is more difficult for the particles to escape from the mixture, decreasing the vapour pressure below the value predicted by Raoult's law (a negative deviation). In extreme cases of a **negative deviation from Raoult's Law** the vapour pressure/composition graph will pass through a minimum, and as a result the boiling point/composition diagram will pass through a maximum (see d in Figure 717). Again it is not possible to separate the mixture into the two components because the liquid that remains in the flask is the mixture with the maximum boiling point. This mixture is also known as an azeotrope. An example of this type of behaviour is a mixture of nitric acid and water, where the azeotropic mixture (68% nitric acid, 32% water) boils at a temperature of 121 °C, whereas the boiling point of pure nitric acid is 83 °C.

EXTENSION

Exercise

1. As the temperature increases, the vapour pressure of a liquid increases because

   A the intermolecular forces become weaker.
   B expansion causes the surface area of the liquid to increase.
   C a greater proportion of the molecules have the kinetic energy required to escape from the surface.
   D the number of molecules in the gas phase is constant, but they are moving at a greater velocity.

2. At 50 °C, which one of the following liquids would you expect to have the greatest vapour pressure?

   A Ethanol
   B Lubricating oil
   C Mercury
   D Water

3. Which one of the following does not affect the boiling point of a liquid?

   A The strength of the intermolecular forces.
   B Its surface area.
   C The external pressure.
   D The presence of dissolved impurities.

a) An ideal mixture

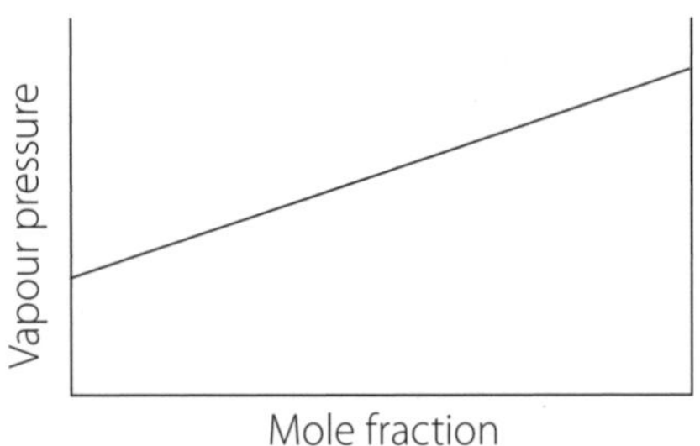

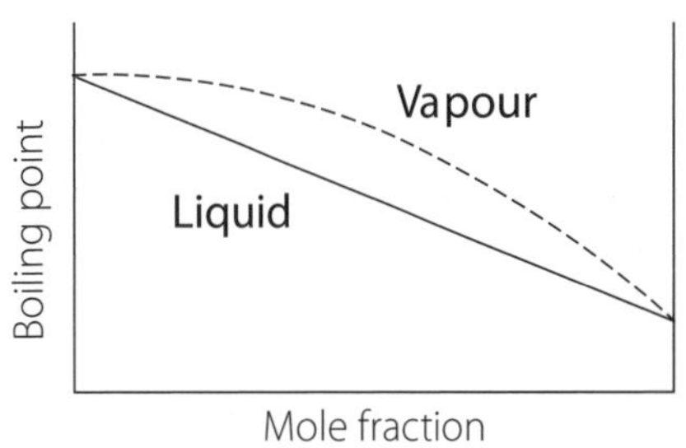

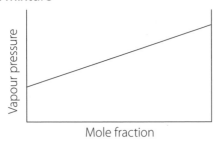

b) A slight positive deviation from Raoult's law

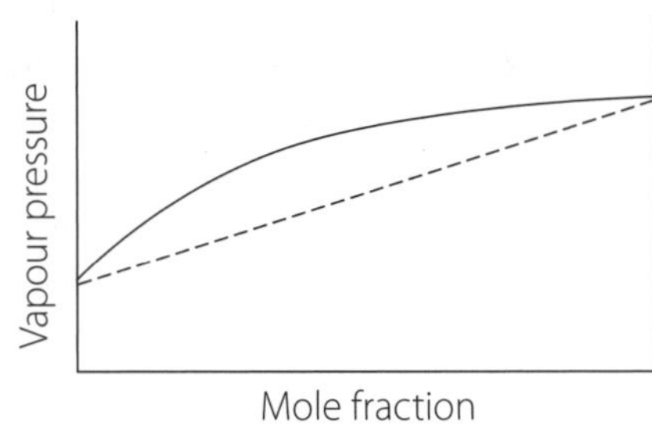

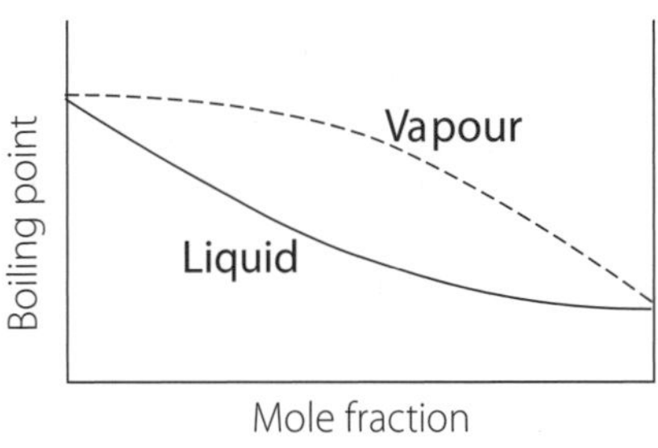

c) A major positive deviation from Raoult's law (e.g. ethanol-water)

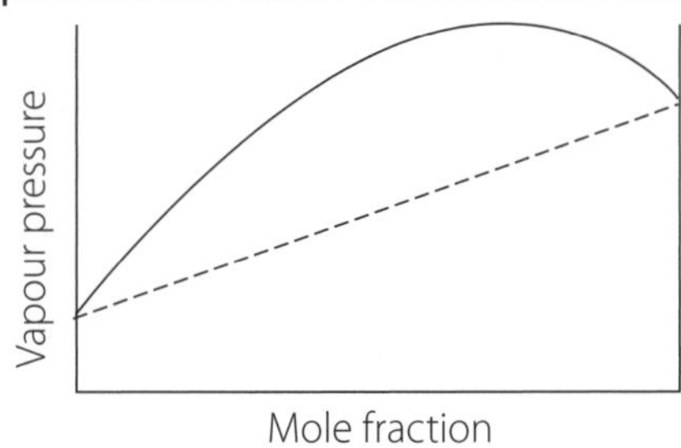

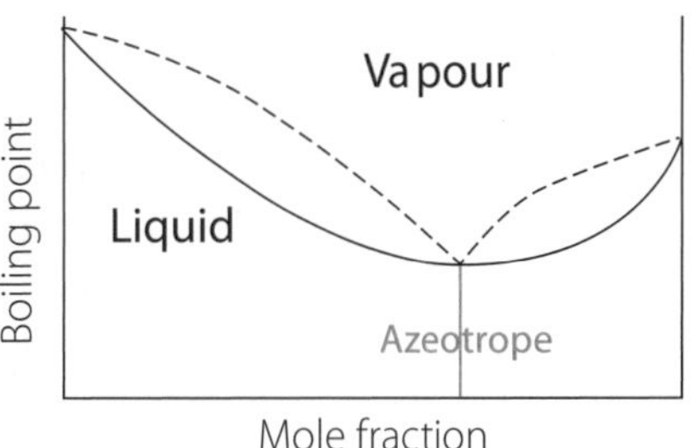

d) A major negative deviation from Raoult's law (e.g. nitric acid-water)

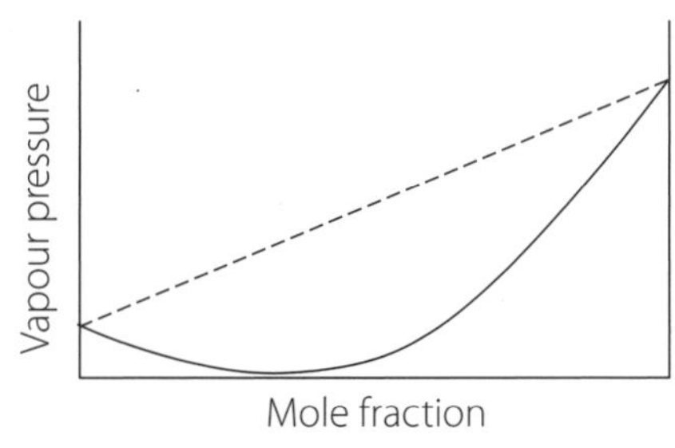

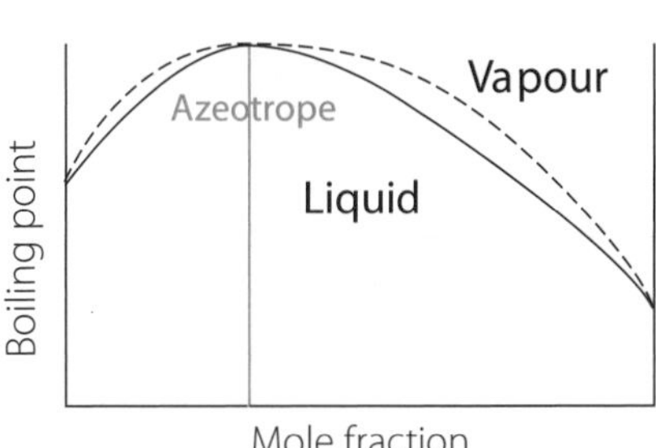

Figure 717 a, b, c, d Vapour pressure/composition and boiling point/composition graphs for ideal and non-ideal solutions

EXTENSION

4. A mixture containing equal numbers of moles of hexane (b.p. 69 °C) and cyclohexane (b.p. 81 °C) is heated.

   a) What conditions determine the temperature at which the liquid boils?
   b) What do the boiling points show about the relative strengths of the intermolecular forces in the two components?
   c) Would you expect this mixture to boil below 69 °C, between 69 °C and 81 °C, or above 81 °C? Explain why.
   d) How would you expect the composition of the vapour to compare with that of the liquid? Explain why this is so.
   e) If the vapour is condensed and then further distilled a number of times, what will happen to the proportions of the two components in the distillate?
   f) What separation technique depends on this principle?
   g) Give one industrial application of this separation method.

COLLIGATIVE PROPERTIES OF SOLUTIONS

EXTENSION

As was discussed previously (Section 7.4), the addition of a non–volatile solute to a solvent lowers its vapour pressure and this will affect both its **freezing point** and its **boiling point**. As a liquid boils when its vapour pressure is equal to the external pressure, by lowering the vapour pressure, a solute will increase the temperature required for this to occur, that is it elevates the boiling point, as shown in Figure 718.

At the freezing point of a substance the vapour pressure of both the liquid and the solid states must be equal. If this were not the case then, if both the liquid and solid were placed in an evacuated container at the freezing point, equilibrium would not exist. Normally when a solution freezes it is the pure solvent that separates from the solution, leaving the solute in the liquid phase. This means the vapour pressure of the solid state is unaffected, so lowering the vapour pressure of the liquid state means that it is not equal to that of the solid until a lower temperature, that is it depresses (lowers) the freezing point, as shown in Figure 718.

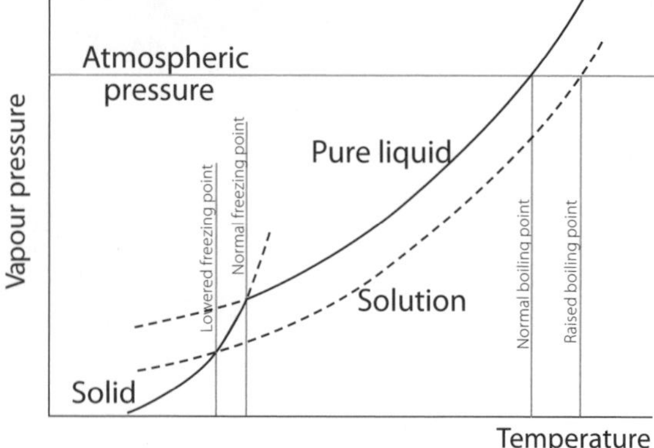

Figure 718 The effect of a non–volatile solute on freezing point and boiling point

An alternative explanation depends on the fact that when one phase is in equilibrium with another $\Delta G = 0$, that is, $\Delta H = T\Delta S$. Adding the non–volatile solute to the liquid phase increases the entropy of the liquid phase without affecting that of either the solid or vapour. This decreases ΔS for the phase change into the vapour (as the vapour has a greater entropy than the liquid $\Delta S = S_{vap} - S_{liq}$ gets smaller), hence a greater temperature is required for $T\Delta S$ to equal ΔH. It will however increase ΔS for the phase change from solid to liquid (in this case the solid has a lower entropy than the liquid so $\Delta S = S_{liq} - S_{sol}$ gets greater), so that it requires a lower temperature for $T\Delta S$ to equal ΔH.

The decrease in the vapour pressure of a particular solvent is proportional to the concentration of solute particles because they occupy spaces on the surface and hence reduce the surface available for solvent molecules to escape from. It is the concentration of such particles rather than the nature of the particles that is important, as a result in aqueous solution one mole of sodium chloride (which dissociates into Na^+ and Cl^-) will have twice the effect of one mole of sucrose (which does not dissociate) and aluminium sulfate will have five times the effect ($2 \times Al^{3+}$ and $3 \times SO_4^{2-}$). The magnitude of the effect varies from solvent to solvent, dependent mainly on its molar mass, but constants (**cryoscopic constants** for freezing and **ebullioscopic constants** for boiling) have been measured for most common solvents. These usually give the change in boiling/freezing point when one mole of particles is dissolved in 1 kg of the solvent, and if this is the case, the change in boiling/freezing point can be calculated using the formula:

$$\Delta T = K \times \frac{n \times m_{st}}{M_{st}} \times \frac{1000}{m_{sv}}$$

Where K is the relevant constant (units K mol^{-1} kg), n the number of particles the solute dissociates into, m_{st} the mass of the solute, m_{sv} the mass of the solvent (both masses in g) and M_{st} the molar mass of the solute.

Example

The freezing point depression constant for water is 1.86 K mol^{-1} kg. By how much will dissolving 5.00 g of sodium chloride in 100 g of water lower the freezing point?

Solution

$$\Delta T = K \times \frac{n \times m_{st}}{M_{st}} \times \frac{1000}{m_{sv}}$$

$$= 1.86 \times \frac{2 \times 5.00}{58.5} \times \frac{1000}{100}$$

$$= 3.18 \text{ K}$$

Because their magnitude is proportional to the number of moles of solute particles and is not dependent on the nature of these particles, reduction in vapour pressure, elevation of boiling point and depression of freezing point are all known as **colligative properties** of solutions. One other property that also varies in this way, and hence is also counted as a colligative property, is the **osmotic pressure** of a solution, discussed below. In all cases, the direct proportionality to the concentration of solute particles is only an approximation, the accuracy of which decreases as the concentration increases.

If a solvent and a solution are separated by a selectively permeable membrane (one that allows solvent molecules to pass through, but not solute particles) then, if the pressure on both sides of the membrane is equal, the rate at which solvent molecules pass into the solution will be greater than the rate at which they pass out of it. This is because on the solution side, some of the collisions between particles and the membrane involve solute particles that cannot pass through (making the pressure of the solvent less than the total pressure), whereas on the solvent side the pressure is totally generated by the collision of solvent molecules. The result is the net transfer of solvent molecules from the pure solvent to the solution – a process known as **osmosis**. The system may be brought into equilibrium and the transfer of solvent stopped by applying additional pressure to the solution side. The additional pressure required is known as the osmotic pressure. This is illustrated in Figure 719:

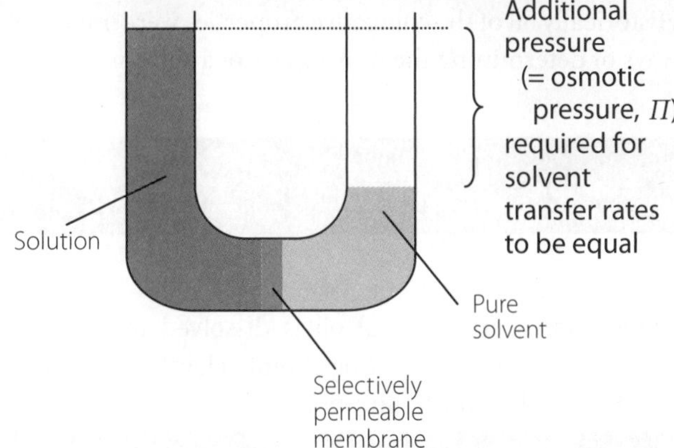

Figure 719 Osmotic pressure

The osmotic pressure of a solution may be calculated from the expression:

$$\Pi V = nRT$$

Where Π is the osmotic pressure in kPa, V the volume of solvent in dm^3, n the number of moles of solute particles, R the gas constant (8.314 J K^{-1} mol^{-1}) and T the absolute temperature.

Example

What is the osmotic pressure of a solution of 2.64 g of ammonium sulfate in 250 cm^3 of water at 300 K?

Solution

$$\text{Amount of ammonium sulfate} = \frac{m}{M} = \frac{2.64}{132} = 0.0200 \text{ moles}$$

$$\text{Amount of solute particles} = 3 \times 0.0200 = 0.0600 \text{ moles}$$

(as $(NH_4)_2SO_4$ dissociates into $2 \times NH_4^+$ and $1 \times SO_4^{2-}$)

$$\Pi = \frac{nRT}{V}$$

$$= \frac{0.0600 \times 8.314 \times 300}{0.250}$$

= 599 kPa (nearly six times atmospheric pressure!)

EXTENSION

Historically all of the colligative properties were important ways of determining the molar mass of a substance.

Example

When 1.00 g of a natural oil is dissolved in 50.0 g of tetrachloromethane (boiling point elevation constant 5.02 K mol^{-1} kg), the boiling point is increased by 0.500°C.

Solution

$$\Delta T = K \times \frac{n \times m_{st}}{M_{st}} \times \frac{1000}{m_{sv}}$$

$$= 5.02 \times \frac{1 \times 1.00}{M_{st}} \times \frac{1000}{50}$$

$$= 0.500$$

$$M_{st} = 5.02 \times \frac{1 \times 1.00}{0.500} \times \frac{1000}{50}$$

$$= 200.8 \text{ g mol}^{-1}$$

Exercise

1. Which one of the following is not a colligative property of a solution?

   A Vapour pressure
   B Elevation of boiling point
   C Depression of freezing point
   D Osmotic pressure

2. Which of the following will have approximately the same effect on the freezing point of water as 0.1 mole of sodium chloride?

   A 0.3 mole of sodium sulfate
   B 0.1 mole of glucose
   C 0.1 mole of copper(II) nitrate
   D 0.05 mole of aluminium chloride

3. When 1.50 g of naphthalene is dissolved in 50.0 g of cyclohexane (freezing point depression constant 20.1 K mol^{-1} kg), the freezing point is decreased by 4.70 °C. What is the molar mass of naphthalene?

4. When 0.0135 moles of a non-volatile solute is added to 20.0 g of a solvent in which it does not dissociate, the boiling point of the solvent increases by 1.20 °C. Calculate the ebullioscopic constant of the solvent, giving appropriate units.

5. When 5.00 g of a non–volatile solute of molar mass 150 g mol^{-1} is dissolved in 500 cm^3 of water at 25.0 °C, the osmotic pressure is found to be 330 kPa. What can you deduce about the substance from this information?

EXTENSION

OTHER EQUILIBRIUM CONSTANTS

In terms of partial pressures – K_p

The concentration of a gas is proportional to its **partial pressure** and it is sometime more convenient to write the equilibrium constant for a gas phase equilibrium in terms of this. This equilibrium constant is differentiated from that in terms of concentration by using the subscript '*p*' rather than the subscript '*c*'. Therefore for a general equilibrium

$$a\,A + b\,B + c\,C + \ldots \rightleftharpoons s\,S + t\,T + u\,U + \ldots$$

in which all the components are in the gas phase, the equilibrium constant in terms of partial pressures is given by

$$K_p = \frac{p(S)^s p(T)^t p(U)^u \ldots}{p(A)^a p(B)^b p(C)^c \ldots}$$

Where $p(A)$ represents the partial pressure of A, which can be calculated from the total pressure (P_{tot}) and the amount of A in the mixture using the expression:

$$p(A) = P_{tot} \times \frac{\text{moles of A}}{\text{total moles}}$$

For example in the equilibrium between ammonia and oxygen to give nitrogen monoxide and steam:

$$4\,NH_3\,(g) + 5\,O_2\,(g) \rightleftharpoons 4\,NO\,(g) + 6\,H_2O\,(g)$$

The equilibrium constant is given by

$$K_p = \frac{p(NO)^4 p(H_2O)^6}{p(NH_3)^4 p(O_2)^5} \quad Kpa$$

As with K_c, K_p does not have fixed units and they must be calculated in each case.

The concentration of a gas is linked to its partial pressure using the ideal gas equation:

$$[A] = \frac{n_a}{V} = \frac{p(A)}{RT}$$

This relationship can be used to inter–convert K_p and K_c values, by substituting in the relevant equation. This leads to $K_p = K_c(RT)^{\Delta n}$ where Δn is the change in the number of moles of gas.

It will have been noted by many students that the equilibrium constant and the free energy change for a reaction (ΔG) are both measures of the extent to which the reactants are converted to the products in a chemical reaction at equilibrium. It is not surprising therefore that the two quantities are linked. The exact relationship is:

$$\Delta G^{\ominus} = - RT\ln K_p$$

The solubility product – K_{sp}

[EXTENSION, but note that though not required in the Core or AHL sections of the IB syllabus, the solubility product is referred to in Section E12 of the Environmental Chemistry option, see Chapter 16.]

The **solubility product** is the name given to the equilibium constant (K_c) for an ionic solid in equilibrium with its aqueous ions (remembering that the concentrations of solids are omitted from such expressions). For example for a saturated solution of lead(II) chloride, the equilibrium and the solubility product is:

$$PbCl_2\ (s) \rightleftharpoons Pb^{2+}\ (aq) + 2\ Cl^-\ (aq)$$

$$K_{sp} = [Pb^{2+}][Cl^-]^2\ \text{mol}^3\ \text{dm}^{-9}$$

It is really only a useful concept for sparingly soluble electrolytes as concentrated ionic solutions exhibit significant deviations from ideal behaviour. The solubility product can be calculated from the solubility of a substance and vice versa.

Example

The solubility of lead(II) chloride at 298 K is 3.90×10^{-4} mol dm^{-3}, what is the solubility product for lead(II) chloride at this temperature?

Solution

From the equation above, each formula unit of lead(II) chloride forms one lead ion and two chloride ions, therefore:

$[Pb^{2+}] = 3.90 \times 10^{-4}$ mol dm^{-3} and
$[Cl^-] = 2 \times 3.90 \times 10^{-4}$
$= 7.80 \times 10^{-4}$ mol dm^{-3};
substituting:

$$K_{sp} = [Pb^{2+}] \times [Cl^-]^2$$
$$= 3.90 \times 10^{-4} \times (7.80 \times 10^{-4})^2$$
$$= 2.37 \times 10^{-10}\ \text{mol}^3\ \text{dm}^{-9}$$

Ions behave independently in solution and hence, in the above example, the chloride ions need not necessarily come from the lead(II) chloride, they could also come from some other solute, for example hydrochloric acid. This means that an ionic solid is significantly less soluble in a solution that already contains one of its component ions, than it is in pure water. This is known as the **common ion effect.**

Example

Calculate the solubility of lead(II) chloride, in g dm^{-3}, in 0.100 mol dm^{-3} hydrochloric acid at 298 K, given its solubility product determined above.

Solution

$[Cl^-] = 0.100$ mol dm^{-3}, (assuming any ions from the lead(II) chloride are negligible), therefore

$$K_{sp} = [Pb^{2+}] \times [Cl^-]^2$$
$$= [Pb^{2+}] \times (0.1)^2$$
$$(= 2.37 \times 10^{-10}\ \text{mol}^3\ \text{dm}^{-9})$$

$$[Pb^{2+}] = \frac{2.37 \times 10^{-10}}{0.0100}$$

$$= 2.37 \times 10^{-8}\ \text{mol dm}^{-3}$$

$$= [PbCl_2]\ \text{(note this is much less than in water)}$$

$$M_r(PbCl_2) = 278$$

$$m = n \times M_r$$
$$= 2.37 \times 10^{-8} \times 278$$
$$= 6.60 \times 10^{-6}\ \text{g dm}^{-3}$$

The solubility product may be used to predict whether a sparingly soluble salt will be precipitated under particular circumstances. The concentrations of the ions that would be present is calculated and then substituted into

EXTENSION

the solubility product expression. If the result of this is greater than the solubility product, then the solid will be precipitated.

Example

The solubility product for silver sulfate is 1.60×10^{-5} mol^3 dm^{-9}. Would silver sulfate be precipitated when 20.0 cm^3 of 0.0100 mol dm^{-3} aqueous silver nitrate is mixed with 30.0 cm^3 of 2.00 mol dm^{-3} sulfuric acid?

Solution

$$[Ag^+] = 0.01 \times \frac{20.0}{50.0}$$

$$= 0.004 \text{ mol dm}^{-3};$$

$$[SO_4^{2-}] = 2.00 \times \frac{30.0}{50.0}$$

$$= 1.20 \text{ mol dm}^{-3}$$

(Note the allowance made for the dilution effect of mixing solutions);

substituting:

$$K_{sp} = [Ag^+]^2 \times [SO_4^{2-}]$$

$$= (0.00400)^2 \times 1.20$$

$$= 1.92 \times 10^{-5} \text{ mol}^3 \text{ dm}^{-9}$$

This is just greater than the solubility product (1.60×10^{-5} mol^3 dm^{-9}), so a small quantity of solid silver sulfate would be precipitated.

EXTENSION

Exercise

1. For which one of the following would K_p and K_c have the same numerical value at the same temperature?

   A $2\ SO_2\ (g) + O_2\ (g) \rightleftharpoons 2\ SO_3\ (g)$
   B $C\ (s) + H_2O\ (g) \rightleftharpoons CO\ (g) + H_2\ (g)$
   C $N_2\ (g) + 3\ H_2\ (g) \rightleftharpoons 2\ NH_3\ (g)$
   D $H_2\ (g) + I_2\ (g) \rightleftharpoons 2\ HI\ (g)$

2. In which of the following solutions will silver chloride be least soluble?

   A 0.1 mol dm^{-3} sodium chloride
   B 0.1 mol dm^{-3} glucose
   C 0.1 mol dm^{-3} copper(II) nitrate
   D 0.1 mol dm^{-3} aluminium chloride

3. When air (assume 20% oxygen, 80% nitrogen) is heated to 2000 K at a pressure of 100 kPa, 3.0% of the oxygen is converted to nitrogen monoxide in the equilibrium:

   $$N_2\ (g) + O_2\ (g) \rightleftharpoons 2\ NO\ (g)$$

   Calculate the partial pressures of O_2, N_2 and NO at equilibrium.

4. The solubility of calcium sulfate is 6.34 g dm^{-3}.

   a) Calculate its solubility product, stating the units.
   b) If equal volumes of 0.1 mol dm^{-3} solutions of calcium chloride and sulfuric acid are mixed would you expect a precipitate of calcium sulfate to form. Explain your reasoning.

5. The solubility product of magnesium hydroxide is 2.0×10^{-11} mol^3 dm^{-9}.

   a) Calculate its solubility in g dm^{-3}.
   b) What is the concentration of hydroxide ions in a saturated solution?
   c) How many grams of the solid would dissolve in 50 cm^3 of water?
   d) How many grams would dissolve in 50 cm^3 of 0.010 mol dm^{-3} aqueous sodium hydroxide?
   e) Explain why the two values differ.

6. The solubility products of zinc carbonate and zinc hydroxide are:

   1.4×10^{-11} mol^2 dm^{-6} and
   2.0×10^{-17} mol^3 dm^{-9} respectively.

   a) Write chemical equations, including state symbols, for the two equations involved.
   b) Write solubility product expressions for these.
   c) Saturated aqueous solutions are made of these compounds. Which has the higher concentration of zinc ions?
   d) A solution containing zinc ions is added to a solution that is 0.10 mol dm^{-3} in both hydroxide and carbonate ions. Which solid will precipitate out first and what concentration of zinc ions would be required for this to occur? (Assume negligible change in total volume.)

ACIDS AND BASES

8.1 Theories of acids and bases

8.2 Properties of acids and bases

8.3 Strong and weak acids & bases

8.4 The pH scale

18.1 Calculations involving acids and bases (AHL)

18.2 Buffer solutions (AHL)

18.3 Salt hydrolysis (AHL)

18.4 Acid-base titrations (AHL)

18.5 Indicators (AHL)

8

8.1 THEORIES OF ACIDS AND BASES

8.1.1 Define *acids* and *bases* according to the Brønsted–Lowry and Lewis theories.

8.1.2 Deduce whether or not a species could act as a Brønsted–Lowry and/or a Lewis acid or base.

8.1.3 Deduce the formula of the conjugate acid (or base) of any Brønsted–Lowry base (or acid).

One of the first theories to explain the fact that all acids had similar reactions, was that of Arrhenius. This proposed that in aqueous solution all acids, to some extent (dependent on the strength of the acid), split up to form a hydrogen ion and an anion, i.e. for an acid HX:

$$HX\ (aq) \longrightarrow H^+\ (aq) + X^-\ (aq)$$

The hydrogen ion is hydrated, like all ions in aqueous solution, but some chemists prefer to show this reaction more explicitly with one water molecule forming a dative covalent bond to the hydrogen ion, to produce the H_3O^+ ion (the **hydronium ion**; also called hydroxonium ion and oxonium ion). In these terms the above equation becomes

$$HX\ (aq) + H_2O\ (l) \longrightarrow H_3O^+\ (aq) + X^-\ (aq)$$

This also emphasises the fact that water is not an inert solvent, but is necessary for acid–base activity. Indeed solutions of acids in many non–aqueous solvents do not show acidic properties. For example a solution of hydrogen chloride in methylbenzene does not dissociate and hence, for example, it will not react with magnesium. Invoking the hydronium ion is useful in discussing some aspects of acid–base theory, such as conjugate acid–base pairs, but apart from this the simpler terminology of the hydrated proton/hydrogen ion, H^+ (aq), will be adopted in this book.

The similar reactions of acids can be explained as all being reactions of the hydrogen ion and it is perhaps more accurate to write them as ionic equations, for example the reaction of an aqueous acid with magnesium can be written as:

$$Mg\ (s) + 2\ H^+\ (aq) \longrightarrow Mg^{2+}\ (aq) + H_2\ (g)$$

Bases were defined as substances that react with, and neutralise, acids to form water. Soluble bases (alkalis) form the hydroxide ion when dissolved in water, either because they are soluble and contain the hydroxide ion (as with NaOH), or because they react with water to produce one (as with ammonia, carbonates and hydrogen carbonates):

$$NaOH\ (aq) \longrightarrow Na^+\ (aq) + OH^-\ (aq)$$

$$NH_3\ (aq) + H_2O\ (l) \longrightarrow NH_4^+\ (aq) + OH^-\ (aq)$$

$$CO_3^{2-}\ (aq) + H_2O\ (l) \longrightarrow HCO_3^-\ (aq) + OH^-\ (aq)$$

$$HCO_3^-\ (aq) \longrightarrow CO_2\ (aq) + OH^-\ (aq)$$

Aqueous acids and alkalis contain ions that are free to move, which explains why they conduct electricity to some extent. If an acid and an alkali are mixed the hydrogen ions and hydroxide ions react exothermically to form water:

$$H^+\ (aq) + OH^-\ (aq) \longrightarrow H_2O\ (l)$$

This leaves the anion from the acid and the cation from the base in solution. If the water is then evaporated these combine to form a solid salt. For example if the acid were hydrochloric acid and the base sodium hydroxide:

$$Na^+\ (aq) + Cl^-\ (aq) \longrightarrow NaCl\ (s)$$

The usual contemporary definition of an acid is the **Brønsted-Lowry** definition, that an acid is a substance that acts as a donor of hydrogen ions (a hydrogen ion of course consists of just a proton, so acids are also often referred to as 'proton donors'). This means that when it dissolves in water it produces a solution containing hydrogen ions and hence fits with the Arrhenius definition, but extends this to other solvent systems so that reactions such as:

$$NH_4^+ + NH_2^- \longrightarrow 2\ NH_3$$

in a non–aqueous solvent (such as liquid ammonia) are also classified as acid–base reactions. According to the same definition, a base is a substance that acts as an acceptor of hydrogen ions ('proton acceptor').

For a species to act as an acid it must contain a hydrogen atom attached by a bond that is easily broken – in many cases this hydrogen is attached to an oxygen atom. For a substance to act as a base, it must have a non–bonding electron pair that can be used to form a bond to a hydrogen ion. Usually this lone pair is on an oxygen or nitrogen atom.

When an acid loses one hydrogen ion, the species produced is referred to as the conjugate base of the acid, for example, the **conjugate base** of H_2SO_4 is HSO_4^-. Similarly the species formed when a base gains one hydrogen ion is referred to as the **conjugate acid** of that base. The ammonium ion, NH_4^+, is therefore the conjugate acid of ammonia, NH_3. Acid–base reactions, which can be recognised because they involve the transfer of a hydrogen ion, therefore always involve two such acid–base pairs. Consider ethanoic acid dissolving in water in these terms:

$$\underset{\text{acid}}{CH_3COOH\ (aq)} + \underset{\text{base 2}}{H_2O\ (l)} \longrightarrow \underset{\text{acid 2}}{H_3O^+\ (aq)} + \underset{\text{base 1}}{CH_3COO^-\ (aq)}$$

It can be seen that the acid and its conjugate base in these two pairs (CH_3COOH / CH_3COO^- and H_3O^+ / H_2O) differ only in the loss of a single hydrogen ion.

If an acid is a strong acid (such as HCl), then its conjugate base (Cl^-) will be such a weak base that it can be considered non–basic so that the equilibrium below will lie fully to the right. As the strength of an acid (HB) decreases however the position of the equilibrium below shifts to the left, which is equivalent to an increase in the strength of its conjugate base (B^-). Eventually with a strong base (e.g. OH^-) the equilibrium lies so far to the left that the conjugate acid (H_2O) may be regarded as non–acidic:

Strong conjugate acid →

$$HB \rightleftharpoons H^+ + B^-$$

← Strong conjugate base

The relative strengths of some common acids and their conjugate bases is shown in Figure 801:

Some species, like the water molecule and the hydrogensulfate ion, can act as both acids and bases and are therefore described as **amphiprotic**:

$$H_3O^+ \Leftarrow \text{gain of } H^+ \Leftarrow \mathbf{H_2O} \Rightarrow \text{loss of } H^+ \Rightarrow OH^-$$

$$H_2SO_4 \Leftarrow \text{gain of } H^+ \Leftarrow \mathbf{HSO_4^-} \Rightarrow \text{loss of } H^+ \Rightarrow SO_4^{2-}$$

Most acids and bases only lose or gain one hydrogen ion and so are said to be **monoprotic**, but other acids and bases that can gain and that can lose more hydrogen ions and are said to be **polyprotic**. Sulfuric acid for example, is **diprotic** in aqueous solution because it can lose two hydrogen ions forming first the hydrogensulfate ion and then the sulfate ion:

$$H_2SO_4\ (aq) \longrightarrow H^+\ (aq) + HSO_4^-\ (aq) \rightleftharpoons 2\ H^+\ (aq) + SO_4^{2-}\ (aq)$$

Conjugate acid	pK_a/pK_b (See section 8.5)	Conjugate base
$HClO_4$	Strong acid	ClO_4^-
H_2SO_4	Strong acid	HSO_4^-
HCl	Strong acid	Cl^-
HNO_3	Strong acid	NO_3^-
H_2SO_3	1.8/12.2	HSO_3^-
• HSO_4^-	2.0/12.0	SO_4^{2-}
H_3PO_4	2.1/11.9	$H_2PO_4^-$
$ClCH_2COOH$	2.9/11.1	$ClCH_2COO^-$
HF	3.3/10.7	F^-
HNO_2	3.3/10.7	NO_2^-
$C_6H_5NH_3^+$	4.6/9.4	$C_6H_5NH_2$
CH_3COOH	4.8/9.2	CH_3COO^-
H_2CO_3	6.4/7.6	HCO_3^-
H_2S	7.1/6.9	HS^-
HSO_3^-	7.2/6.8	SO_3^{2-}
$H_2PO_4^-$	7.2/6.8	HPO_4^{2-}
HCN	9.3/4.7	CN^-
NH_4^+	9.3/4.7	NH_3
C_6H_5OH	9.9/4.1	$C_6H_5O^-$
HCO_3^-	10.3/3.7	CO_3^{2-}
HPO_4^{2-}	12.4/1.6	PO_4^{3-}
H_2O	strong base	HO^- (OH^-)
C_2H_5OH	strong base	$C_2H_5O^-$
NH_3	strong base	NH_2^-

Figure 801 The relative strengths of some acids and their conjugate bases

Similarly phosphoric(V) acid, found in cola drinks, is triprotic:

$$H_3PO_4\,(aq) \rightleftharpoons H^+\,(aq) + H_2PO_4^-\,(aq) \rightleftharpoons 2\,H^+\,(aq) + HPO_4^{2-}\,(aq) \rightleftharpoons 3\,H^+\,(aq) + PO_4^{3-}\,(aq)$$

Polyprotic acids and bases may be recognised because they form anions with more than one charge. Carbonic acid (aqueous carbon dioxide), for example, must be diprotic because it forms the carbonate ion, which has a charge of minus two (CO_3^{2-}).

When a base accepts a proton from an acid it forms a covalent bond to the proton, but this differs from most covalent bonds in that both of the electrons come from the base, as the proton has no electrons to contribute to the bond. Covalent bonds of this sort are known as 'dative' or 'co-ordinate' covalent bonds, but are identical to other covalent bonds in every way but the origin of the electrons. Dative bonds are indicated in structural formulae by an arrow, pointing in the direction that the electrons are donated, rather than a line.

Lewis therefore pointed out that an acid could be defined as 'a species that accepts a pair of electrons to form a dative bond'. All Brønsted–Lowry acids are in fact Lewis acids, for example when hydrogen chloride dissolves in water the water molecule forms a dative bond to the hydrogen ion to generate the hydronium ion:

$$Cl-H + :\underset{\displaystyle H}{\underset{|}{O}}-H \longrightarrow Cl:^- + H \leftarrow \underset{\displaystyle H}{\underset{|}{\overset{+}{O}}}-H$$

The term '**Lewis acid**' is however usually reserved for a species that is not also a Brønsted–Lowry acid. The substance that donates the electron pair to form the bond to these is known as a '**Lewis base**'. This extended the range of acid-base reactions beyond those involving the transfer of a hydrogen ion to include all reactions involving the formation of a dative bond.

A common example of a Lewis acid is boron trifluoride, in which boron has only six electrons in its valence shell. This reacts with ammonia (which acts as a Lewis base) to give a compound containing a dative bond (note the arrow in the structural formula), in which the lone pair from the nitrogen completes the valence shell of the boron:

CORE

$$F_3B + :NH_3 \longrightarrow F_3B \leftarrow NH_3$$

Other common Lewis acids are compounds of elements in group 3 of the periodic table, such as aluminium chloride ($AlCl_3$) in which the element forms three covalent bonds, leaving a vacancy for two electrons in the valence shell. Any species that can accept an electron pair into its incomplete valence shell (e.g. CH_3^+) is, however, capable of acting as a Lewis acid. Similarly any species with a non-bonding electron pair (all anions and indeed all molecules that are not hydrides of group 3 and group 4 elements) is capable of acting as a Lewis base. All interactions to form 'complex ions' are also Lewis acid–base reactions. In these the ligand acts as the Lewis base by donating a pair of electrons that is accepted by the central metal ion, which hence acts as a Lewis acid. For example:

$$\underset{\text{Lewis acid}}{Fe^{3+}(aq)} + \underset{\text{Lewis base}}{:SCN^-(aq)} \longrightarrow \underset{\text{complex ion}}{[FeSCN]^{2+}(aq)}$$

Several metal hydroxides such as $Zn(OH)_2$ and $Al(OH)_3$ are amphoteric. When these behave as acids the central metal ion acts as a Lewis acid and accepts a lone pair from the hydroxide ion, which acts as a Lewis base. For example

$$\underset{\text{Lewis acid}}{Al(OH)_3(s)} + \underset{\text{Lewis base}}{OH^-(aq)} \longrightarrow \underset{\text{anion from acid}}{Al(OH)_4^-(aq)}$$

TOK What is the relationship between depth and simplicity?

There is nothing that imparts energy quite like rivalry - if at a party last weekend your boy/girlfriend had been looking in an interested way at a member of the opposite sex, you might be taking a little more trouble over things this week. It's the same in science - if there is a rival theory on the block then people will start putting a lot more effort into research in this area, devising ingenious experiments that will support their pet theory or, more scientifically (you can never prove anything, only disprove it) undermine the alternative theory. In other word having differences of opinion raises interest and sharpens the focus on just what the differences are between the two approaches, maybe a little bit like the approach of a general election prompts you to look at the policy differences between the parties. Sometimes rival theories turn out to be complementary rather than in opposition to each other, as with the particle and wave theories of light where each describes a different aspect of the phenomena.

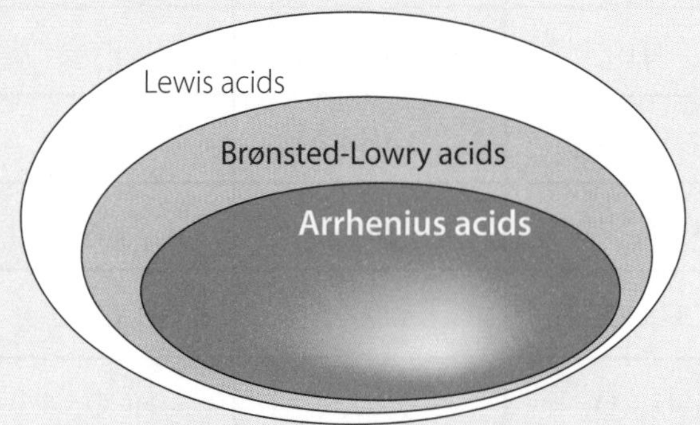

In the case of acid-base theories the relationship is one of generalisation, best indicated by the diagram shown. All Arrhenius acids are Brønsted-Lowry acids, and all of these are Lewis acids. Why don't we just have the Lewis definition; aren't the other ones obsolete? The answer is, not really. Almost all the acids we deal with are Arrhenius ones, because we work most of the time in aqueous solution. It is therefore a lot easier to interpret these reactions in terms of the reactions of H^+ (aq), rather than to spend time considering how electron-pair acceptance fits in to the picture. That is not to say that the other developments were a waste of time. The Brønsted-Lowry theory is the one that people most often use unless they specify otherwise. It has the advantages of focussing our attention on the reciprocity of the interaction (conjugates), as well as being nice and snappy ("proton donor" & "proton acceptor") – an aspect not to be underestimated. Lewis just pointed out that this is a subset of a much wider range of interactions that involve the formation of a dative bond. It can be useful at times to reflect on generalities, like there a variety of activities that you can only partake of above a certain age (drinking alcohol, driving, joining the army etc.), but it is sometimes more useful to have more specific knowledge, like knowing what the drinking age is before going into a bar.

Exercise 8.1

1. Which one of the following statements about acids is untrue?

   A Acids are proton donors.
   B Acids dissociate to form H^+ ions when dissolved in water.
   C Acids produce solutions with a pH greater than 7.
   D Acids will neutralise bases to form salts.

2. Which one of the following acids is diprotic?

   A H_3PO_4
   B CH_3COOH
   C H_2SO_4
   D HNO_3

3. In which one of the following reactions is the species in bold type behaving as a base?

   A $\mathbf{2\,NO}\,(g) + O_2\,(g) \rightleftharpoons 2\,NO_2\,(g)$
   B $\mathbf{CO_3^{2-}} + H^+ \rightleftharpoons HCO_3^-$
   C $\mathbf{NH_4^+} + H_2O \rightleftharpoons NH_3 + H_3O^+$
   D $\mathbf{Cu^{2+}} + 2\,OH^- \rightleftharpoons Cu(OH)_2$

4. Which one of the following is the conjugate base of the hydrogensulfite ion (HSO_3^-)?

   A H_2SO_3
   B $H_2SO_3^+$
   C SO_3^{2-}
   D SO_3^-

5. Which one of the following species, many of which are unstable, would you expect to be capable of acting as a base?

   A CH_4
   B $CH_3\bullet$
   C CH_3^+
   D CH_3^-

6. a) Give the conjugate acids of Cl^-; PO_4^{3-}; C_5H_5N; $H_3N{-}NH_2^+$; $^-OOC{-}COO^-$
   b) Give the conjugate bases of HNO_3; HI; HSO_4^-; NH_4^+; $HONH_3^+$
   c) From the species listed, select two species that are *amphiprotic.*
   d) Write the formula of another amphiprotic species and give its conjugate base and its conjugate acid.

7. In a mixture of concentrated nitric and sulfuric acids, the nitric acid acts as a base and the sulfuric acid as a monoprotic acid.

   a) Give the Brønsted–Lowry definition of
      i) an acid and
      ii) a base.
   b) Write an equation for this reaction and explain how your equation shows that the sulfuric acid is acting as an acid.
   c) On your equation link together with lines the two conjugate acid–base pairs.
   d) What is meant by the term '*conjugate*'?

8. In aqueous solution sulfuric acid and 'carbonic acid' (H_2CO_3) are both *diprotic* acids.

   a) Explain what is meant by *diprotic.*
   b) The hydrogencarbonate (bicarbonate) ion, HCO_3^- formed from 'carbonic acid' is described as being amphiprotic. Describe what you understand by this term and give the formulas of the species formed.
   c) Name another substance that is amphiprotic and write equations to illustrate this behaviour.

9. Anhydrous aluminium chloride can act as a *Lewis acid.* It will for example react with chloride ions in non-aqueous solution to form the complex ion $AlCl_4^-$.

   a) Explain what is meant by the term *Lewis acid.*
   b) Draw Lewis diagrams to represent the interaction between $AlCl_3$ (consider it to be a covalent molecule) and the chloride ion to form the complex ion.
   c) What kind of bond exists between the chloride ion and the aluminium? In what way does its formation differ from other covalent bonds?
   d) What shape would you predict for
      i) $AlCl_3$ and ii) $AlCl_4^-$?

10. For each of the following species, state whether it is most likely to behave as a Lewis acid or a Lewis base. Explain your answers.

    a) PH_3
    b) BCl_3
    c) H_2S
    d) SF_4
    e) Cu^{2+}

CORE

8.2 PROPERTIES OF ACIDS AND BASES

8.2.1 Outline the characteristic properties of acids and bases in aqueous solution.

Acids are corrosive chemicals with a sour taste (note: you should never taste chemicals as many are poisonous.). All **acids** have certain chemical characteristics in common:

- They form solutions with a pH < 7, so that indicators which change colour at about this pH give the same reaction with all acids, for example, they turn blue litmus red.
- They react with active metals (those above hydrogen in the reactivity series) to give a salt and hydrogen gas. For example, sulfuric acid reacts with magnesium to give magnesium sulfate and hydrogen:

$$\underset{\text{acid}}{H_2SO_4\,(aq)} + \underset{\text{metal}}{Mg\,(s)} \longrightarrow \underset{\text{salt}}{MgSO_4\,(aq)} + \underset{\text{hydrogen}}{H_2\,(g)}$$

- They react with bases, such as metal oxides and hydroxides to form a salt and water. For example, copper(II) oxide dissolves in nitric acid to form a solution of copper(II) nitrate and water:

$$\underset{\text{acid}}{2\,HNO_3\,(aq)} + \underset{\text{metal oxide}}{CuO\,(s)} \longrightarrow \underset{\text{salt}}{Cu(NO_3)_2\,(aq)} + \underset{\text{water}}{H_2O\,(l)}$$

  Phosphoric acid reacts with sodium hydroxide to form sodium phosphate and water:

$$\underset{\text{acid}}{H_3PO_4\,(aq)} + \underset{\text{metal hydroxide}}{3\,NaOH\,(aq)} \longrightarrow \underset{\text{salt}}{Na_3PO_4\,(aq)} + \underset{\text{water}}{3\,H_2O\,(l)}$$

- They react with metal carbonates and hydrogencarbonates to give a salt, water and carbon dioxide, which appears as effervescence (bubbles). For example, hydrochloric acid will react with zinc carbonate to form zinc chloride, water and carbon dioxide:

$$\underset{\text{acid}}{2\,HCl\,(aq)} + \underset{\text{metal carbonate}}{ZnCO_3\,(s)} \longrightarrow \underset{\text{salt}}{ZnCl_2\,(aq)} + \underset{\text{water}}{H_2O\,(l)} + \underset{\text{carbon dioxide}}{CO_2\,(g)}$$

  Ethanoic acid reacts with sodium hydrogencarbonate to form sodium ethanoate, water and carbon dioxide.

$$\underset{\text{acid}}{CH_3COOH\,(aq)} + \underset{\text{metal hydrogencarbonate}}{NaHCO_3\,(aq)} \longrightarrow \underset{\text{salt}}{NaCH_3COO\,(aq)} + \underset{\text{water}}{H_2O\,(l)} + \underset{\text{carbon dioxide}}{CO_2\,(g)}$$

Originally a **base** was considered to be any substance that reacted with an acid to neutralise it, but now the term has more precise meanings. The most common bases are the oxides, hydroxides and carbonates of metals, but a number of other compounds, such as ammonia and amines also act as bases. Solutions of bases, known as **alkalis** (for example aqueous sodium hydroxide), have a slippery feel and a bitter taste (though, again, you should never taste them). As with acids, all bases have certain chemical reactions in common:

- If they are soluble in water they give a solution with pH > 7, so that they will all have a similar effect on indicators that change colour at about this pH, for example, they turn red litmus blue.
- They react with acids to form a salt. For example, calcium oxide will react with hydrochloric acid to form calcium chloride and water:

$$\underset{\text{base}}{CaO\,(s)} + \underset{\text{acid}}{2\,HCl\,(aq)} \longrightarrow \underset{\text{salt}}{CaCl_2\,(aq)} + \underset{\text{water}}{H_2O\,(l)}$$

Exercise 8.2

1. Which one of the following substances would you **not** expect an acid to react with?

   A Blue litmus paper
   B Sodium carbonate
   C Magnesium ribbon
   D Silver chloride

2. When equal volumes of 2 mol dm^{-3} sulfuric acid and 2 mol dm^{-3} aqueous sodium hydroxide are mixed, how can you tell that they react?

   A A gas is evolved.
   B The mixture becomes warm.
   C The solution changes colour.
   D A solid precipitate is formed.

3. Write balanced equations for the following reactions:

   a) iron with dilute sulfuric acid.
   b) lead carbonate with nitric acid.
   c) zinc oxide with hydrochloric acid.
   d) calcium hydroxide with nitric acid.
   e) sodium hydrogencarbonate with sulfuric acid.
   f) potassium hydroxide with hydrochloric acid (write an ionic equation).

8.3 STRONG AND WEAK ACIDS & BASES

8.3.1 Distinguish between *strong* and *weak* acids and bases in terms of the extent of dissociation, reaction with water and electrical conductivity.

8.3.2 State whether a given acid or base is strong or weak.

8.2.3 Distinguish between strong and weak acids and bases, and determine the relative strengths of acids and bases, using experimental data.

Strong acids are those which are almost completely dissociated (ionised) in dilute aqueous solution:

$$HX\ (aq) \longrightarrow H^+\ (aq) + X^-\ (aq)$$

$\approx 0\%$ $\qquad$ $\approx 100\%$

This means that such solutions are good conductors of electricity, owing to the presence of mobile ions. Hydrochloric acid is a typical example of a strong acid:

$$HCl\ (aq) \longrightarrow H^+\ (aq) + Cl^-\ (aq)$$

Other common strong acids include sulfuric acid (H_2SO_4) and nitric acid (HNO_3).

$$H_2SO_4\ (aq) \longrightarrow H^+\ (aq) + HSO_4^-\ (aq)$$

$$HNO_3\ (aq) \longrightarrow H^+\ (aq) + NO_3^-\ (aq)$$

Generally speaking, in strong acids the hydrogen is bonded either to a more electronegative element (such as Cl, Br and I in HX), or to an oxygen bonded to a non-metal (as in H_2SO_4). In the binary hydrogen halides, the acid strength increases down the group: HI > HBr > HCl. Note that HF is a weak acid, contrary to expectations and unlike the other hydrogen halides. This is because, although HF is a highly polarized bond, it is also a very strong bond. Another factor is that the HF molecule, unlike the other hydrogen halides, can strongly hydrogen bond to water and this stabilises the undissociated molecule. In the oxyacids the strength of the acid increases with the electronegativity of the non-metal (H_2SO_4 is a strong acid, H_3PO_4 a weaker acid) and the number of oxygens present (HNO_3 is a strong acid, HNO_2 a weaker acid).

A weak acid is one which is only slightly dissociated into ions in dilute aqueous solution:

$$HA\ (aq) \rightleftharpoons H^+\ (aq) + A^-\ (aq)$$

$\approx 99\%$ $\qquad$ $\approx 1\%$

A typical example of a weak acid is ethanoic acid, where the **undissociated acid** is in equilibrium with the ions.

$$CH_3COOH\ (aq) \rightleftharpoons H^+\ (aq) + CH_3COO^-\ (aq)$$

Almost all organic acids are weak acids. Similarly aqueous carbon dioxide behaves as a weak acid:

$$CO_2\ (aq) + H_2O\ (l) \rightleftharpoons H^+\ (aq) + HCO_3^-\ (aq)$$

Other common inorganic weak acids are:

- aqueous sulfur dioxide (analogous to aqueous CO_2)
- hydrofluoric acid (HF, as noted previously)
- hydrocyanic acid (HCN)

Intermediate ions of polyprotic acids (e.g. HSO_4^-), cations formed by weak bases (such as NH_4^+) and the hydrated ions of small highly charged metal ions (e.g. Al^{3+} (aq)) also act as weak acids.

Strong and weak acids can be differentiated by comparing solutions of equal concentrations. The concentration of hydrogen ions in the solution of the weak acid will be considerably lower, giving rise to a number of differences that may be tested experimentally:

- A weak acid has a higher pH than a strong acid of equal concentration.
- Weak acids do not conduct electricity as well as strong acids of equal concentration, but they conduct electricity better than water.
- Weak acids react more slowly in typical acid reactions (such as those with a carbonate to give carbon dioxide or with an active metal to give hydrogen gas) than strong acids of equal concentration.

In the same way a strong base is one which is completely dissociated into ions in aqueous solution, like sodium hydroxide and barium hydroxide.

$$NaOH\ (aq) \longrightarrow Na^+\ (aq) + OH^-\ (aq)$$

$$Ba(OH)_2\ (aq) \longrightarrow Ba^{2+}\ (aq) + 2\ OH^-\ (aq)$$

With weak bases an equilibrium exists between the base and the hydroxide ions so that, for example, ammonia is only partially converted to the hydroxide ion in aqueous solution:

$$NH_3\ (aq) + H_2O\ (l) \rightleftharpoons NH_4^+\ (aq) + OH^-\ (aq)$$

The closely related amines, such as ethylamine ($C_2H_5NH_2$) also act as weak bases.

$$C_2H_5NH_2\ (aq) + H_2O\ (l) \rightleftharpoons C_2H_5NH_3^+\ (aq) + OH^-\ (aq)$$

The anions formed by weak acids (such as the carbonate ion, ethanoate and phosphate ions) also act as weak bases, for example:

$$CO_3^{2-}\ (aq) + H_2O\ (l) \rightleftharpoons HCO_3^-\ (aq) + OH^-\ (aq)$$

Methods for differentiating strong and weak bases are similar to those for strong and weak acids; for solutions of equal concentration a strong base will have a higher pH and a greater conductivity.

In chemistry care must be taken to use the terms strong and weak (meaning fully and partially dissociated) correctly and not as synonyms for concentrated and dilute (meaning containing a large or small number of moles in a given volume) as is done in everyday speech. The 'chemical' use of the term is also to be found, in 'strong electrolyte' and 'weak electrolyte'. The term **electrolyte** means forming ions in aqueous solution allowing it to conduct electricity. The term strong electrolyte refers to a substance that is completely converted to ions in aqueous solution (such as salts, strong acids and strong bases) whilst weak electrolyte refers to those only partially converted to ions (such as weak acids and bases). Note that only a very small fraction (< 1 in 10^8) of molecules in pure water is split up into ions, so it is a very weak electrolyte and hence a poor conductor of electricity.

Exercise 8.3

1. A weak acid is best described as one which

   A only contains a low concentration of the acid.
   B has a pH only slightly less than 7.
   C is only partially dissociated in aqueous solution.
   D reacts slowly with magnesium ribbon.

2. Which one of the following aqueous solutions would you expect to have a pH significantly different from the rest?

   A 0.001 mol dm^{-3} CO_2
   B 0.001 mol dm^{-3} HNO_3
   C 0.001 mol dm^{-3} H_2SO_4
   D 0.001 mol dm^{-3} HCl

3. Equal volumes of aqueous solutions of 0.1 mol dm^{-3} sodium hydroxide and 0.1 mol dm^{-3} ethylamine could be distinguished by three of the following methods. Which one would not work?

   A Comparing the volume of hydrochloric acid required for neutralisation.
   B Comparing the reading they give on a pH meter.
   C Comparing the electrical conductivities of the two solutions.
   D Comparing their effect on universal indicator paper.

4. Ammonia behaves as a weak base in aqueous solution.

   a) Write a balanced equation for the interaction of this substance with water and explain why it produces an alkaline solution.
   b) Using ammonia as an example, explain what is meant by the terms weak and base.
   c) Would you expect a 0.1 mol dm^{-3} solution of ammonia to have a higher or lower pH than a 0.1 mol dm^{-3} solution of sodium hydroxide? Explain.

5. Hydrochloric acid is a strong acid whereas ethanoic acid is a weak acid.

   a) Write equations that show the way in which these two acids interact with water and explain how they differ.
   b) If you had solutions of these two acids with concentrations of 1 mol dm^{-3}, explain how you would expect their electrical conductivities to compare?
   c) Using a chemical reaction, how could you tell which solution contained the strong acid and which the weak?

8.4 THE pH SCALE

8.4.1 Distinguish between aqueous solutions that are acidic, neutral or alkaline using the pH scale.

8.4.2 Identify which of two or more aqueous solutions is more acidic or basic, using pH values.

8.4.3 State that each change of one pH unit represents a 10-fold change in the hydrogen ion concentration [H^+ (aq)].

8.4.4 Deduce changes in [H^+ (aq)] when the pH of a solution changes by more than one pH unit.

pH is a measure of acidity of a solution on a scale that is usually thought of as going from 0 to 14, though for concentrated solutions of strong acids and bases it can extend beyond this range. At 25 °C the pH of water (a neutral liquid) is 7. If the pH of a solution is below 7 then the solution is acidic and if above 7 it is alkaline.

The lower the pH, the more acidic the solution; the higher the pH, the more basic the solution.

Water dissociates to a very slight extent to produce both hydrogen and hydroxide ions, so that in aqueous solutions an equilibrium exists between these ions and the undissociated water molecules:

$$H_2O\ (l) \rightleftharpoons H^+\ (aq) + OH^-\ (aq)$$

In pure water the concentration of hydrogen ions and hydroxide ions that results from this are equal, hence it is described as neutral. An acidic solution has an excess of hydrogen ions, whilst an alkaline solution has an excess of hydroxide ions.

In pure water at 25°C, the concentration of both hydrogen and hydroxide ions from the dissociation above is 10^{-7} mol dm^{-3}, in other words less than one molecule in 10 million is dissociated. The pH (which stands for **p**ower of **H**ydrogen) of a solution depends upon the concentration of hydrogen ions and is equal to power of 10 of the hydrogen ion concentration with the sign reversed. Hence the pH of water under these conditions is 7 as [H^+ (aq)] = 10^{-7} mol dm^{-3}.

If an acid is added so the concentration of hydrogen ions is increased by a factor of ten (for example, from 10^{-4} to 10^{-3} mol dm^{-3}) then the pH decreases by one unit (in this case 4 to 3). Adding a base to an aqueous solution will reduce the concentration of hydrogen ions by displacing the above equilibrium to the left, in accordance with **Le Chatelier's principle**. If the concentration of hydroxide ions is increased by a factor of ten (for example, from 10^{-6} to 10^{-5} mol dm^{-3}) the concentration of hydrogen ions will be decreased by a factor of ten (from 10^{-8} to 10^{-9} mol dm^{-3}) and the pH will increase by one unit (in this case from 8 to 9).

The pH of a solution can be determined either by using a pH meter, or by using universal indicator. This contains a number of indicators that change colour at different pH values, so that the colour of the mixture will vary continuously with the pH of the solution. The indicators used are chosen so that the colour changes occurs in a

pH	0	4	7	10	14
[H^+] (aq) [OH^-] (aq)	1 (× 10^0) 1 × 10^{-14}	1 × 10^{-4} 1 × 10^{-10}	1 × 10^{-7} 1 × 10^{-7}	1 × 10^{-10} 1 × 10^{-4}	1 × 10^{-14} 1 (× 10^0)
Universal Indicator	Red	Orange	Green	Blue	Purple
Description	Very Acidic	Slightly Acidic	Neutral	Slightly Basic	Very Basic
Common Example	Laboratory dilute acid	Vinegar, acid rain	Pure water	Milk of magnesia, household ammonia	Laboratory dilute alkali

Figure 802 The relationship between [H^+] (aq), [OH^-] (aq) and pH

'rainbow' sequence. The relationship between pH, [H^+], [OH^-], the colours that universal indicator turns and the acidity of the solution are given in Figure 802.

TOK Artificial and natural scales

Is the pH scale worthwhile? If you had some lemon juice what would be the advantages and disadvantages of saying it had a pH of 4 rather than saying it was quite acidic (as opposed to slightly acidic, or very acidic)? Certainly talking about pH might be really good if you wanted to show off to somebody, it might also be useful if you wanted to compare just how acidic the juices of different varieties of lemons were. Talking about the pH might however not be so helpful if you were really trying to explain something to your little sister or your old granddad, but they would probably understand "quite acidic".

Thinking about scales it is interesting to reflect on why a logarithmic scale is used rather than a linear one. Why isn't it just as easy to talk about the hydrogen ion concentration, rather than to introduce a totally new concept like pH? Probably it has to do with the fact that we feel more comfortable dealing with numbers similar to the number of fingers we have. We tend to try to avoid very small and very large numbers, unless the latter is associated with bank accounts.

Exercise 8.4

1. 10 cm^3 of an aqueous solution of a monoprotic strong acid is added to 90 cm^3 of water. This will cause the pH of the acid to

   A increase by ten.
   B increase by one.
   C decrease by one.
   D decrease by ten.

2. Approximately what pH would you expect for a 0.1 mol dm^{-3} solution of ethanoic acid?

   A 1
   B 3
   C 10
   D 13

3. What colour would you expect universal indicator paper to turn when dipped in aqueous 1 mol dm^{-3} sodium hydroxide?

   A Red
   B Orange
   C Green
   D Purple

4. Calculate the hydrogen ion concentration in aqueous solutions of the following pH:

   a) 3 b) 11 c) 0

5. Calculate the pH of the following aqueous solutions of strong acids:

   a) 10^{-4} mol dm^{-3} hydrochloric acid
   b) 0.01 mol dm^{-3} nitric acid
   c) 10^{-9} mol dm^{-3} sulfuric acid

6. 0.01 mol dm^{-3} ethanoic acid and 5×10^{-4} mol dm^{-3} hydrochloric acid both have a very similar effect on universal indicator. Explain why this is so.

7. A solution of nitric acid, which is a strong acid, contains 0.63 g of the pure acid in every 100 cm^3 of solution.

   a) What is the concentration of the nitric acid, in mol dm^{-3}?
   b) What is the pH of the solution?
   c) What will the concentration of hydroxide ions be in this solution?

   Nitrous acid, HNO_2, in contrast is a weak acid.

   d) Write an equation to show the equilibrium that exists in a solution of this acid.
   e) Would you expect a solution of nitrous acid, of equal concentration to that of the nitric acid calculated above, to have the same pH as the nitric acid, a higher pH or a lower pH. Explain.

8. The pH of 0.01 mol dm^{-3} hydrochloric acid is 2, the pH of 0.01 mol dm^{-3} sulfuric acid is 1.7 and the pH of 0.01mol dm^{-3} ethanoic acid is 3.4. Explain why these three acids, that all have the same concentrations, have different pH values.

HIGHER LEVEL

18.1 CALCULATIONS INVOLVING ACIDS & BASES (AHL)

18.1.1 State the expression for the ionic product constant of water (K_w).

18.1.2 Deduce [H^+ (aq)] and [OH^- (aq)] for water at different temperatures given K_w values.

18.1.3 Solve problems involving [H^+ (aq)], [OH^- (aq)], pH and pOH.

18.1.4 State the equation for the reaction of any weak acid or weak base with water, and hence deduce the expressions for K_a and K_b.

18.1.5 Solve problems involving solutions of weak acids and bases using the expressions:

$$K_a \times K_b = K_w$$

$$pK_a + pK_b = pK_w$$

$$pH + pOH = pK_w.$$

18.1.6 Identify the relative strengths of acids and bases using values of K_a, K_b, pK_a and pK_b.

In aqueous solutions molecular water is in equilibrium with hydrogen ions and hydroxide ions:

$$H_2O\ (l) \rightleftharpoons H^+\ (aq) + OH^-\ (aq)\ \ \Delta H = +57\ kJ\ mol^{-1}$$

In pure water at 25 °C (298 K) the concentration of hydrogen and hydroxide ions are both equal to 1.00×10^{-7} mol dm^{-3}. Hence in an aqueous solution at this temperature, the product of the concentrations of hydrogen and hydroxide ions is always 1.00×10^{-14} mol^2 dm^{-6}. This is known as the dissociation constant (or ionic product constant) of water and given the symbol K_w:

$$K_w = [H^+][OH^-]$$
$$= 1.00 \times 10^{-14}\ mol^2\ dm^{-6} \quad \text{at } 25\ °C\ (298\ K)$$

Because it involves breaking bonds, the forward reaction of this equilibrium is endothermic so that as the temperature is raised the equilibrium shifts to the right and the equilibrium constant increases. This means that

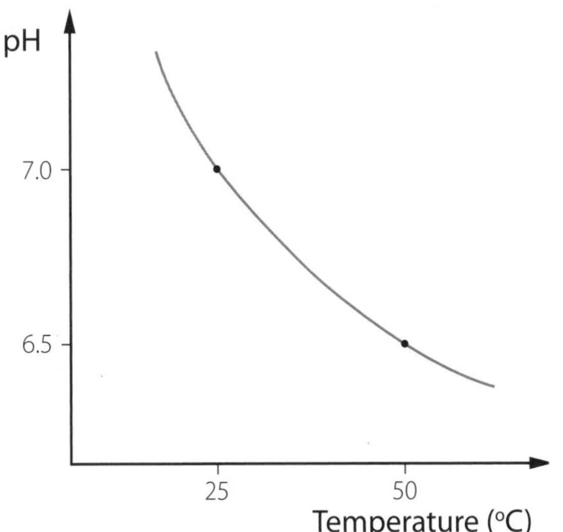

Figure 803 The effect of temperature on the pH of water

at higher temperatures $[H^+] > 10^{-7}$ mol dm^{-3}, so the pH of pure water is < 7, even though it is still neutral (i.e. $[H^+] = [OH^-]$). For example at 50 °C the concentration of both hydrogen and hydroxide ions increases to 3.05×10^{-7} mol dm^{-3} and the pH of pure, neutral water is 6.5. See Figure 803.

Substituting in the equation above, it can be seen that if the concentration of hydrogen ions in an aqueous solution is 1.00×10^{-4} mol dm^{-3} then the concentration of hydroxide ions will be

$$\left[\frac{1.00 \times 10^{-14}}{1.00 \times 10^{-4}}\right] = 1.00 \times 10^{-10}\ mol\ dm^{-3}.$$

The pH of a solution depends on the concentration of hydrogen ions in the solution and it is defined by the equation:

$$pH = -\log[H^+] \qquad (\text{hence } [H^+] = 10^{-pH})$$

This means that the pH of a solution in which $[H^+]$ is 1.00×10^{-5} mol dm^{-3} is 5.00. For non–integer values a calculator must be used, so if $[H^+]$ is 5.00×10^{-4} mol dm^{-3} then the pH is 3.30 and if the pH is 11.70, then $[H^+]$ is 2.00×10^{-12} mol dm^{-3}. This can be combined with the K_w expression above to calculate the pH of alkaline solutions. In a 0.00100 mol dm^{-3} solution of sodium hydroxide, the $[OH^-]$ is 1.00×10^{-3} mol dm^{-3}, so that $[H^+]$ will be 1.00×10^{-11} mol dm^{-3} hence the pH of the solution is 11.00. pOH is similarly defined as:

$$pOH = -\log[OH^-] \quad (\text{hence } [OH^-] = 10^{-pOH})$$

AHL

In a similar manner, pK_w is used for $-\log K_w$ (14.00 at 25 °C). Hence as $[H^+][OH^-] = K_w$:

$$pH + pOH = pK_w = 14.00$$

The pOH of a solution with a pH of 11.70 is therefore 2.30 (14.00 - 11.70).

Note that $[H^+]$ or $[OH^-]$ can never decrease to zero as an equilibrium is present between water and the $[H^+]$ and $[OH^-]$ ions.

Consider a weak acid in equilibrium with its ions in aqueous solution:

$$HA\ (aq) \rightleftharpoons H^+\ (aq) + A^-\ (aq)$$

for the general case or, in the specific case of ethanoic acid:

$$CH_3COOH\ (aq) \rightleftharpoons H^+\ (aq) + CH_3COO^-\ (aq)$$

The equilibrium constant for this reaction, known as the acid dissociation constant (K_a), is a measure of the strength of the acid – the greater its value the stronger the acid.

$$K_a = \frac{[H^+][A^-]}{[HA]}$$

so for ethanoic acid

$$K_a = \frac{[H^+][CH_3COO^-]}{[CH_3COOH]}\ \text{mol dm}^{-3}$$

The value of K_a is often expressed as a pK_a, the relationship being similar to that between $[H^+]$ and pH:

$$pK_a = -\log K_a \qquad (\text{hence } K_a = 10^{-pK_a})$$

The K_a of ethanoic acid, for example, is 1.74×10^{-5} mol dm^{-3} at 298 K, so that its pK_a is 4.76. The greater the pK_a value, the weaker the acid. Note that K_a, like K_w, varies with temperature and so calculations involving it only apply to a particular temperature.

The expression for the equilibrium constant above relates together the acid dissociation constant (which may be found from the pK_a), the concentration of the acid and the concentration of hydrogen ions/conjugate base (which must be equal in a solution of the acid and may therefore be found from the pH). Knowing any two of these quantities, the third may be found. Consider the equilibrium:

$$HA\ (aq) \rightleftharpoons H^+\ (aq) + A^-\ (aq)$$

	HA (aq)	H^+ (aq)	A^- (aq)
Initial Concentrations	a	0	0
Equilibrium concentrations	$a-x$	x	x

Substituting in the equilibrium expression:

$$K_a = \frac{[H^+][A^-]}{[HA]} = \frac{x \cdot x}{a-x} = \frac{x^2}{a-x}$$

Calculations involving this expression will often involve solving a quadratic equation, but in the case of a weak acid, because it is only slightly dissociated, $x \ll a$, so that $a-x$ is almost equal to a. Making this approximation the equation becomes:

$$K_a = \frac{x^2}{a-x} \approx \frac{x^2}{a}$$

This much simpler equation can be used in calculations. When the result has been obtained, the values of x and a can be checked to see if the approximation is valid. Note that a second assumption made is that $[H^+] = [A^-]$, in other words the H^+ from the dissociation of water molecules may be neglected, which can be checked when $[H^+]$ is known. It can generally be regarded as valid if pH < 6. A third assumption in these calculations is that the dissociation occurs at 25 °C.

Example 1

Calculating K_a

A 0.0100 mol dm^{-3} solution of a weak acid has a pH of 5.00. What is the dissociation constant of the acid?

Solution

If pH = 5.00, then $[H^+] = [A^-] = 1.00 \times 10^{-5}$ mol dm^{-3}.

$$K_a = \frac{x^2}{a-x} \approx \frac{x^2}{a} = \frac{(1.00 \times 10^{-5})^2}{0.0100} = 1.00 \times 10^{-8}\ \text{mol dm}^{-3}$$

Example 2

Calculating pH

Benzoic acid has a pK_a of 4.20. What is the pH of a 0.100 mol dm^{-3} solution of this acid?

Solution

If $pK_a = 4.20$, then $K_a = 10^{-4.20}$

$= 6.31 \times 10^{-5}$ mol dm^{-3}.

$$K_a = \frac{x^2}{a-x}$$
$$\approx \frac{x^2}{a}$$
$$= \frac{x^2}{0.10}$$
$$\therefore \frac{x^2}{0.10} = 6.31 \times 10^{-5}$$
$$x = \sqrt{6.31 \times 10^{-6}}$$
$$= 2.51 \times 10^{-3} \text{ mol dm}^{-3}$$
$$\text{pH} = -\log(2.51 \times 10^{-3})$$
$$= 2.6$$

Example 3

Calculating concentration

What concentration of hydrofluoric acid is required to give a solution of pH 2.00 and what percentage of the hydrofluoric acid is dissociated at this pH, if the dissociation constant of the acid is 6.76×10^{-4} mol dm^{-3}?

Solution

If pH = 2.00, $[H^+] = [F^-] = 1.00 \times 10^{-2}$ mol dm^{-3}.

$$K_a = \frac{x^2}{a-x}$$
$$\approx \frac{x^2}{a}$$
$$= \frac{(1.00 \times 10^{-2})^2}{a}$$
$$\therefore \frac{(1.00 \times 10^{-2})^2}{a} = 6.76 \times 10^{-4}$$
$$a = \frac{1.00 \times 10^{-4}}{6.76 \times 10^{-4}}$$
$$= 0.148 \text{ mol dm}^{-3}$$

$$\text{Percentage dissociation} = 100 \times \frac{1.00 \times 10^{-2}}{0.148}$$
$$= 6.76\%$$

Note that here the validity of the approximation is marginal as x is ≈ 7% of a. In this case solving the equation without the approximation is only slightly more difficult and gives a more accurate value for the concentration of 0.158 mol dm^{-3}.

When a weak base is dissolved in water, the equilibrium established can be dealt with in terms of the dissociation of its conjugate weak acid, using the equations above. Alternatively it can be considered in terms of the equilibrium between the base and water:

$$B\,(aq) + H_2O\,(l) \rightleftharpoons BH^+\,(aq) + OH^-\,(aq)$$

$$K_b = \frac{[BH^+][OH^-]}{[B]}$$

For this equilibrium making similar assumptions to those above for weak acids:

$$K_b = \frac{[BH^+][OH^-]}{[B]}$$
$$= \frac{y\ y}{b-y}$$
$$= \frac{y^2}{b-y}$$
$$\approx \frac{y^2}{b}$$

where K_b is known as the base dissociation constant. Similarly:

$$pK_b = -\log K_b$$

Calculations can be carried out using these equilibrium expressions in a similar manner to those for acids.

Example 4

A calculation involving a weak base

What is the pH of a 0.0500 mol dm^{-3} solution of ethylamine ($pK_b = 3.40$)?

Solution

$$pK_b = 3.40,$$
$$\therefore K_b = 10^{-3.40}$$
$$= 3.98 \times 10^{-4} \text{ mol dm}^{-3}$$

$$K_b = \frac{[BH^+][OH^-]}{[B]}$$
$$= \frac{y^2}{b-y}$$

AHL

$$\approx \frac{y^2}{b}$$

$$= \frac{y^2}{0.0500}$$

$$\frac{y^2}{0.0500} = 3.98 \times 10^{-4} \text{ mol dm}^{-3}$$

$$y^2 = 0.0500 \times 3.98 \times 10^{-4}$$
$$= 1.99 \times 10^{-5}$$
$$y = \sqrt{1.99 \times 10^{-5}}$$

$$[OH^-] = y$$
$$= \sqrt{1.99 \times 10^{-5}}$$
$$= 4.46 \times 10^{-3}$$

$$pOH = -\log[OH^-]$$
$$= -\log(4.46 \times 10^{-3})$$
$$= 2.40$$

$$pH = 14 - pOH$$
$$= 11.60$$

Consider a weak acid (HA) and its conjugate base (A^-). The equilibria established when they are added to water are:

$$HA\ (aq) \rightleftharpoons H^+\ (aq) + A^-\ (aq)$$

$$K_a = \frac{[H^+][A^-]}{[HA]}$$

$$A^-\ (aq) + H_2O\ (l) \rightleftharpoons HA\ (aq) + OH^-\ (aq)$$

$$K_b = \frac{[HA][OH^-]}{[A^-]}$$

Multiplying these two expressions:

$$K_a \times K_b = \frac{[H^+][A^-]}{[HA]} \times \frac{[HA][OH^-]}{[A^-]}$$
$$= [H^+][OH^-]$$
$$= K_w$$

Hence for any conjugate acid–base pair

$$K_a \times K_b = K_w = 10^{-14.00} \qquad \text{or} \qquad pK_a + pK_b = 14.00$$

This means that the stronger the acid (the greater K_a), the weaker the base (the smaller K_b) and vice versa, as may be seen in Figure 801.

Exercise 18.1

1. Hydrochloric acid is a strong acid. In a 0.01 mol dm^{-3} solution, what is the pH and the hydroxide ion concentration?

A	pH = 0.01	$[OH^-] = 0.01$ mol dm^{-3}
B	pH = 0.01	$[OH^-] = 12$ mol dm^{-3}
C	pH = 2	$[OH^-] = 0.01$ mol dm^{-3}
D	pH = 2	$[OH^-] = 10^{-12}$ mol dm^{-3}

2. Approximately what proportion of water molecules are dissociated into hydrogen ions and hydroxide ions?

   A One in 10^3
   B One in 10^6
   C One in 10^9
   D One in 10^{14}

3. A 0.01 mol dm^{-3} solution of a weak acid has a pH of 4. What is K_a for the acid?

   A 1×10^{-4} mol dm^{-3}
   B 1×10^{-5} mol dm^{-3}
   C 1×10^{-6} mol dm^{-3}
   D 1×10^{-8} mol dm^{-3}

4. The pK_b for a base is 5. What is the pH of a 0.1 mol dm^{-3} solution of the base?

   A 8
   B 9
   C 10
   D 11

5. Some weak acids and their pK_a values are given below. Which one of these acids will have the strongest conjugate base?

A	Methanoic acid	3.75
B	Bromoethanoic acid	2.90
C	Phenol	10.00
D	Methylpropanoic acid	4.85

6. a) What is the pH of a solution containing 0.0721 mol dm^{-3} hydrogen ions?
   b) What is the pH of a solution containing 4.6×10^{-9} mol dm^{-3} hydrogen ions?
   c) What is the concentration of hydrogen ions in a solution of pH 5.83?

d) What is the concentration of hydroxide ions in a solution of pH 11.64?

e) What is the pH of a solution containing 0.135 mol dm^{-3} hydroxide ions?

7. Sodium hydroxide is a strong base. In a 0.0010 mol dm^{-3} solution of this:

a) What would the hydroxide ion concentration be?

b) What would the hydrogen ion concentration be?

c) Would the pH be the same, greater or less for 0.0010 mol dm^{-3} solution of barium hydroxide? Why?

8. The K_a for 2–nitrophenol is 6.17×10^{-8} mol dm^{-3}. Use this information to calculate:

a) The pK_a of 2–nitrophenol.

b) The pH of a 0.020 mol dm^{-3} solution of 2–nitrophenol.

c) K_b for the conjugate base of 2–nitrophenol.

9. A 0.280 mol dm^{-3} solution of a weak acid has a pH of 4.67.

a) Calculate K_a for the acid.

b) Is it a stronger or weaker acid than ethanoic acid ($pK_a = 4.76$)?

c) What concentration of the acid would give a solution with a pH of exactly 5?

10. Hydrocyanic acid (HCN) is a very weak acid ($pK_a = 9.3$).

a) Write an equation for its interaction with water.

b) What would be the pH of a 0.010 mol dm^{-3} solution of this acid? How does this compare with the value that would be expected for a strong acid, such as hydrochloric acid, of a similar concentration?

c) In this solution, what percentage of the hydrogen cyanide is present as ions? If the solution were diluted, would this percentage increase or decrease?

d) What pH would you expect a 0.10 mol dm^{-3} solution of sodium cyanide (NaCN) to have?

18.2 BUFFER SOLUTIONS (AHL)

18.2.1 Describe the composition of a buffer solution and explain its action.

18.2.2 Solve problems involving the composition and pH of a specified buffer system.

If a small volume of a strong acid or base is added to water, then the pH of the water will change significantly; for example 0.1 cm^3 (≈2 drops) of 1 mol dm^{-3} hydrochloric acid added to a litre of water will change the pH from 7 to 4 (new $[H^+] = 1 \times 0.1/1000 = 10^{-4}$ mol dm^{-3}). If the acid were added to a mixture of a weak acid and its conjugate base rather than water, then the change in pH would be much less. Similarly, adding a small volume of a strong base to such a mixture has little effect on its pH. Such solutions, which resist a change of pH when a small amount of a strong acid or a strong base is added to them, are known as **buffer solutions**.

AHL

Consider the equilibrium in which there are significant amounts of both HA and its conjugate base A^-:

$$HA\ (aq) \rightleftharpoons H^+\ (aq) + A^-\ (aq)$$

If a small amount of a strong acid is added, the additional hydrogen ions displace the equilibrium to the left (Le Chatelier's principle) and the $[H^+]$ falls to near its original value, so that the effect of the added acid is minimised, and the pH is little changed. Similarly if a small amount of a strong base is added, the hydroxide ions react with the hydrogen ions to form water. The equilibrium is therefore displaced to the right until $[H^+]$ increases to near its original value, that is the effect of the added base is minimised and again the pH is little changed. In order to behave as an effective buffer the concentration of both the acid/base and its salt must be much greater than the strong acid/base added. The greater the concentration, the better the buffering action. For this reason a weak acid on its own would not act as a buffer (there is insufficient of the anion to react with added H^+) nor would a solution of its salt (there is insufficient of the undissociated acid to react with added OH^-).

A buffer therefore consists of a solution containing weak acid and its conjugate base or a weak base and its conjugate acid. Buffer solutions may be prepared in a number of ways. The simplest way is to mix solutions of the weak acid HA (for example ethanoic acid) and a salt of the weak acid (in this case an ethanoate, such as sodium ethanoate, which will provide ethanoate ions). Similarly solutions of a weak base (for example ammonia) and a salt of the weak base (in this case an ammonium salt, such as ammonium chloride) may be used. Alternatively, adding a little strong base to an excess of weak acid (adding sodium hydroxide to excess ethanoic acid), or a little strong acid to excess weak base (adding hydrochloric acid to excess ammonia) produces similar buffer solutions.

Consider the example of the acidic buffer consisting of ethanoic acid and ethanoate ions (from sodium ethanoate), which are in equilibrium:

$$CH_3COOH\ (aq) \rightleftharpoons CH_3COO^-\ (aq) + H^+\ (aq)$$

(i) If H^+ ions from a small amount of strong acid are added to the buffer, these will react with the conjugate base:

$$CH_3COO^-\ (aq) + H^+\ (aq) \longrightarrow CH_3COOH\ (aq)$$

(the reverse reaction of the above equilibrium)

The H^+ ions are therefore removed from the solution and the pH increases back to near its original level.

(ii) If OH^- ions from a small amount of strong base are added to the buffer, these react with the undissociated acid:

$$OH^-\ (aq) + CH_3COOH\ (aq) \longrightarrow H_2O\ (l) + CH_3COO^-\ (aq)$$

(the forward reaction of the above equilibrium)

The OH^- ions are therefore removed from the solution and the pH decreases back to near its original level.

Similarly consider the example of the basic buffer consisting of ammonia and ammonium ions (from ammonium chloride), which are in equilibrium:

$$NH_3\ (aq) + H_2O \rightleftharpoons NH_4^+\ (aq) + OH^-\ (aq)$$

(i) If H^+ ions from a small amount of strong acid are added to the buffer, these will react with the ammonia:

$$NH_3\ (aq) + H^+\ (aq) \longrightarrow NH_4^+\ (aq)$$

(the forward reaction of the above equilibrium)

The H^+ ions are therefore removed from the solution and the pH increases back to near its original level.

(ii) If OH^- ions from a small amount of strong base are added to the buffer, these react with the ammonium ions:

$$OH^-\ (aq) + NH_4^+\ (aq) \longrightarrow H_2O\ (l) + NH_3\ (aq)$$

(the reverse reaction of the above equilibrium)

The OH^- ions are therefore removed from the solution and the pH decreases back to near its original level.

One common example of a buffer solution is blood. It is vital that the pH of blood remains quite constant as enzymes only function effectively over a limited pH range. The buffering equilibrium is:

$$CO_2\ (aq) + H_2O\ (l) \rightleftharpoons H^+\ (aq) + HCO_3^-\ (aq)$$

The pH of blood (7.4) is relatively resistant to addition of small amounts of strong acid or strong base, thus, if 0.01 mol H^+ or 0.01 mol OH^- is added to 1.0 dm^3 blood, the pH changes by only 0.1 unit.

The concentration of hydrogen ions, and hence the pH, of buffer solutions may be calculated using the formula for the acid dissociation constant:

$$K_a = \frac{[H^+][A^-]}{[HA]}$$

This may be rearranged into the slightly more convenient form where [HA] is approximated to the concentration of the acid and $[A^-]$ to that of the conjugate base:

$$[H^+] = K_a \times \frac{[HA]}{[A^-]}$$

or, taking logarithms

$$pH = pK_a - \log\frac{[HA]}{[A^-]}$$

The pH of the buffer solution therefore depends on the K_a of the weak acid and also on the ratio of the concentrations of the acid and its conjugate base, so that a buffer solution of any desired pH can be prepared. Note that the dependence is only on the ratio of these concentrations and not on their actual values. This means that the pH of a buffer does not change when it is diluted, but it will be less effective as the amount of strong acid/base required to completely react with all of one of the buffer components decreases.

A buffer is most effective (an optimum buffer) when the concentration of acid and base are equal, and the pH is equal to the pK_a (4.74 for ethanoic acid / ethanoate ion; 7.20 for dihydrogenphosphate / hydrogenphosphate; 9.25 for ammonia / ammonium ion). It can however work reasonably effectively provided both components are present in reasonable concentrations, so in practice the effective buffer range of any weak acid/base is in the range $pK_a \pm 1$.

AHL

The pH of a buffer may be calculated knowing the K_a value of the acid and the concentrations of the conjugate acid and base. Similarly, if the composition of the buffer and its pH is known, then the dissociation constant of the acid may be found. The formula chosen for the calculation is a matter of personal preference, taking into consideration the data provided. Both are given in the example below.

Example

Solid sodium ethanoate is added to 0.200 mol dm^{-3} ethanoic acid until its concentration is 0.0500 mol dm^{-3}. Given that K_a for ethanoic acid is 1.74×10^{-5} mol dm^{-3}, and assuming no volume change on dissolving the solid, calculate the pH of the buffer solution formed.

Solution

$$[H^+] = K_a \times \frac{[HA]}{[A^-]}$$
$$= 1.74 \times 10^{-5} \times \frac{0.200}{0.05000}$$
$$= 6.96 \times 10^{-5} \text{ mol dm}^{-3}$$

$$pH = -\log[H^+]$$
$$= -\log(6.96 \times 10^{-5})$$
$$= 4.16$$

or

$$pH = pK_a - \log\frac{[HA]}{[A^-]}$$
$$= \log(1.74 \times 10^{-5}) - \log\left(\frac{0.200}{0.05000}\right)$$
$$= 4.76 - 0.6$$
$$= 4.16$$

Exercise 18.2

1. 10 cm^3 of each of the following solutions are prepared and divided equally between two test tubes. 10 drops of 1 mol dm^{-3} hydrochloric acid is added to one and 10 drops of 1 mol dm^{-3} aqueous sodium hydroxide to the other. For which solution will the difference in pH of the two solutions be least?

   A 0.1 mol dm^{-3} aqueous ethanoic acid mixed with an equal volume of 0.1 mol dm^{-3} aqueous sodium ethanoate.

   B 1 mol dm^{-3} aqueous ethanoic acid mixed with an equal volume of 1 mol dm^{-3} aqueous sodium ethanoate.

   C 0.1 mol dm^{-3} aqueous sodium hydroxide mixed with an equal volume of 0.1 mol dm^{-3} hydrochloric acid.

   D 1 mol dm^{-3} aqueous sodium hydroxide mixed with an equal volume of 1 mol dm^{-3} hydrochloric acid.

2. You wish to convert a solution containing X moles of hydrochloric acid into a buffer solution. Which one of the following should you add?

   A X moles of sodium hydroxide.
   B X moles of ammonia.
   C ½X moles of ammonia.
   D 2X moles of ammonia.

3. A solution that is 0.10 mol dm^{-3} in fluoroethanoic acid and 0.050 mol dm^{-3} in sodium fluoroethanoate has a pH of 3.0. What is the acid dissociation constant of fluoroethanoic acid?

   A 1×10^{-3} mol dm^{-3}
   B 5×10^{-4} mol dm^{-3}
   C 2×10^{-3} mol dm^{-3}
   D 5×10^{-3} mol dm^{-3}

AHL

4. A weak monoprotic acid (HA) has an acid dissociation constant of 4×10^{-5} mol dm^{-3}. Which one of the solutions containing the acid and its sodium salt (NaA) will have a pH of exactly 5?

   A [HA] = 0.25 mol dm^{-3}; [NaA] = 0.10 mol dm^{-3}

   B [HA] = 0.40 mol dm^{-3}; [NaA] = 0.10 mol dm^{-3}

   C [HA] = 0.10 mol dm^{-3}; [NaA] = 0.40 mol dm^{-3}

   D [HA] = 0.10 mol dm^{-3}; [NaA] = 0.25 mol dm^{-3}

5. An aqueous solution that is 0.10 mol dm^{-3} in ammonia and 0.10 mol dm^{-3} in ammonium chloride acts as a buffer solution with a pH of 9.3.

   a) Use the information given to calculate the base dissociation constant (K_b) of ammonia.

   b) A buffer with a pH of exactly 9.0 is required. Must more ammonia or more ammonium chloride be added to achieve this? Explain.

   c) Calculate the new concentration of the species whose concentration is increased to reduce the pH of the solution.

   d) Name two substances that could be mixed to produce a buffer solution of pH≈4.

6. An aqueous mixture of ammonia and ammonium chloride form a buffer solution with pH≈9.

   a) Explain what is meant by the term buffer solution?

   b) Describe what changes take place within the solution when a small volume of sulfuric acid is added. Repeat this for the addition of a small volume of aqueous sodium hydroxide.

AHL

18.3 SALT HYDROLYSIS (AHL)

18.3.1 Deduce whether salts form acidic, alkaline or neutral aqueous solutions.

A **salt** is an ionic compound comprised of cations (for example Na^+) from a base and anions (for example Cl^-) from an acid which are completely dissociated into ions in aqueous solution. Salts containing ions derived from weak acids or bases can affect the pH of their aqueous solutions, with cations being able to act as acids and anions as bases. The stronger the conjugate acid/base they are derived from, the weaker the acid–base activity of the ion (As $K_a \times K_b = K_w$, if K_a is very large then K_b for the conjugate base will be very small and vice versa). Therefore cations derived from strong bases, such as sodium hydroxide and barium hydroxide, have little acid–base activity and the same is true of the anions derived from strong acids, such as sulfuric, nitric and hydrochloric acids. Salts from a strong acid and a strong base, such as sodium chloride, therefore form neutral aqueous solutions.

If however the anion is derived from a weak acid, such as ethanoic acid, then the anion will act as a weak base so that a solution of the salt of a strong base and a weak acid, such as sodium ethanoate, will have a pH > 7:

$$CH_3COO^-\,(aq) + H_2O\,(l) \rightleftharpoons CH_3COOH\,(aq) + OH^-\,(aq)$$

Similarly if the cation is derived from a weak base, as is the case with ammonium salts, then the cation will act as a weak acid in aqueous solution, so that the pH of solutions of a weak base and a strong acid, such as ammonium chloride, is < 7:

$$NH_4^+\,(aq) \rightleftharpoons NH_3\,(aq) + H^+\,(aq)$$

With salts formed from a weak acid and a weak base the pH of the solution formed will reflect the relative strengths of the acid and base. In the case of ammonium ethanoate, for example, the solution is approximately neutral.

With small, highly charged hydrated cations (in which the metal ion has a high charge density), such as $[Al(H_2O)_6]^{3+}$, $[Fe(H_2O)_6]^{3+}$ and other transition metal ions, the electron attracting power of the ion weakens the O—H bonds in the water molecules bonded to it and stabilises the hydroxide ion. As a result these hydrated ions dissociate in aqueous solution and are quite acidic:

$$[Fe(H_2O)_6]^{3+}\,(aq) \rightleftharpoons [Fe(OH)(H_2O)_5]^{2+}\,(aq) + H^+\,(aq)$$

Exercise 18.3

1. Which one of the following salts would produce the most neutral aqueous solution?

   A NH_4NO_3
   B $FeCl_3$
   C Na_2SO_4
   D CH_3COOK

2. Many metal cations in aqueous solution interact with the water to make the solution acidic. Which combination of cation characteristics will lead to the most acidic solution?

   A Small size and low charge.
   B Small size and high charge.
   C Large size and low charge.
   D Large size and high charge.

3. Which one of the following solutions could you most easily distinguish from the others using universal indicator paper?

   A Aqueous ammonia
   B Aqueous sodium carbonate
   C Aqueous ammonium chloride
   D Aqueous calcium hydroxide

4. For each of the following salts, state whether you would expect them to form aqueous solutions that were neutral, slightly alkaline or slightly acidic and give reasons for your predictions.

   a) Ethylammonium sulfate
   b) Barium chloride
   c) Aluminium nitrate
   d) Sodium carbonate

18.4 ACID–BASE TITRATIONS (AHL)

18.4.1 Sketch the general shapes of graphs of pH against volume for titrations involving strong and weak acids and bases and explain their important features.

Consider gradually adding a 0.100 mol dm^{-3} strong monoprotic base, such as aqueous sodium hydroxide, to a 0.100 mol dm^{-3} strong monoprotic acid, such as hydrochloric acid. The pH will change from about 1 (obviously with a 0.0100 mol dm^{-3} strong monoprotic acid it would initially be pH 2 etc.), when the acid is in excess, to about 13 when the base is in excess. The change between these limits is not a gradual one, but is most rapid close to the **equivalence point** (when amount of acid = amount of base), as shown in Figure 804. When 90% of the required base has been added, 10% of the acid will remain and so its concentration, neglecting dilution effects, will be 0.010 mol dm^{-3} therefore the pH will be about 2. 99% of the way to the equivalence point, only 1% remains and the pH of the ≈0.001 mol dm^{-3} acid is about 3 and so on. After the equivalence point, 1% of excess base will give a hydroxide ion concentration of 0.001 mol dm^{-3} and a pH of 11. This means that there is a very rapid change of pH in the region of the equivalence point. This is centred around pH 7 as a salt of a strong acid and a strong base forms a neutral solution. Figure 804 shows the change in pH during the **titration** of a monobasic strong acid with a monobasic strong base of equal concentration.

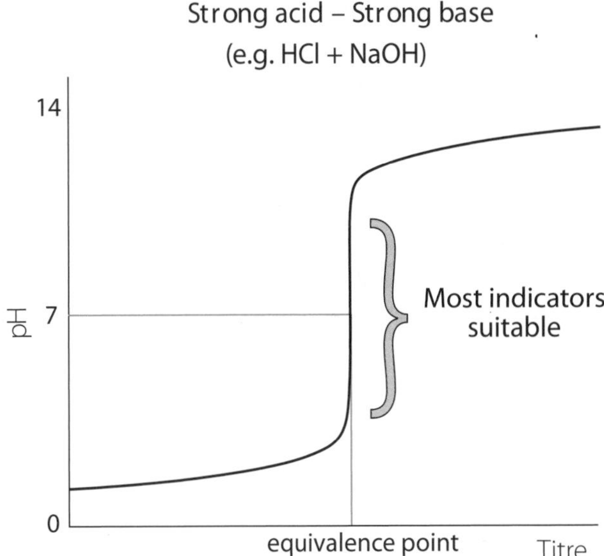

Figure 804 Strong acid - strong base

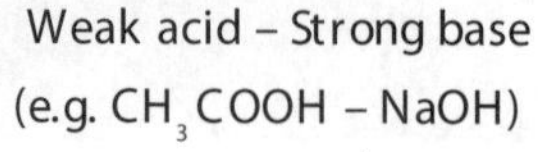

Consider the equivalent situation when a strong base is added to a weak acid (HA) as shown in Figure 805. The initial pH will be that of the weak acid and hence depends on both the concentration and pK_a, but will probably be in the range 3-5. As the base is a strong base, the final pH with excess alkali will still be about 13. As the strong base is added the reaction that occurs is

$$HA\ (aq) + OH^-\ (aq) \longrightarrow H_2O\ (l) + A^-\ (aq)$$

so that HA is gradually converted to A^-. This means that the pH gradually increases, as shown on the graph. This region where there are significant concentrations of both the weak acid (HA) and its conjugate base (A^-) is sometimes referred to as the buffering region because it is indeed a **buffer solution** and, as the low gradient in this region shows, adding small amounts of acid or alkali has little effect on the pH.

When half of the amount of base required to neutralise the acid has been added (the half-equivalence point), half of the weak acid (HA) will have been converted into its conjugate base (A^-), so that their concentrations are equal. At this point, known as the **"half-neutralisation" point**:

$$[HA] = [A^-]$$

$$\text{therefore as } [H^+] = K_a \times \frac{[HA]}{[A^-]}$$

$$K_a = [H^+] \quad \text{and} \quad pK_a = pH$$

This is the best way to determine the dissociation constant for a weak acid, as measuring the pH of a solution of known concentration is much more easily affected by imprecisions in making up the solution and trace impurities.

At the equivalence point, when all the acid is consumed the pH rapidly increases to that of the strong base. Note that at the equivalence point the pH of the solution is > 7, which corresponds to the fact that is an aqueous solution of a salt of a weak acid and strong base. Salts of this type form slightly alkaline solutions and knowing the K_a of the acid (or the K_b of the conjugate base) the precise pH can be calculated. Figure 805 shows the change in pH during the titration of a monobasic weak acid with a monobasic strong base of equal concentration.

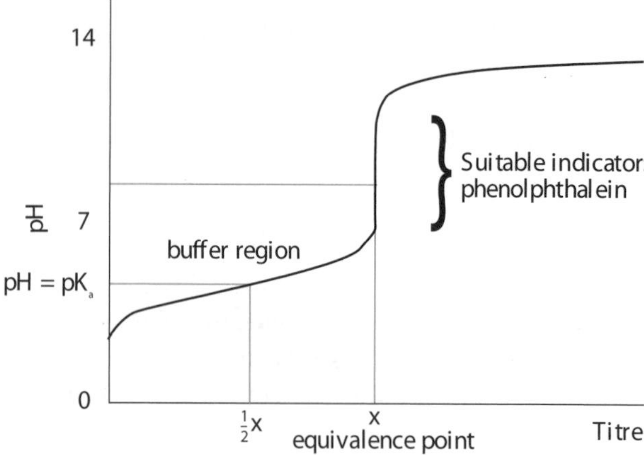

Figure 805 Weak acid – strong base

If the acid is a strong acid, but the base is a weak base, as shown in Figure 806, then as in the first case, the excess hydrogen ions from the strong acid ensure that the pH remains at about 1 until near the equivalence point, when all the base has been converted into its conjugate acid by the reaction:

$$B\ (aq) + H^+\ (aq) \longrightarrow BH^+\ (aq)$$

At the equivalence point the solution is the salt of a weak base and a strong acid, hence the pH of the solution is < 7 and the exact pH can be calculated knowing the K_b of the base, or the K_a of the conjugate acid.

As the concentration of free base starts to increase, the concentration of hydroxide ions, and hence the pH, is governed by the equation:

$$[OH^-] = K_b \times \frac{[B]}{[BH^+]}$$

There is therefore a gradual increase in pH as the concentration of the base increases and the solution is a buffer solution. When the total volume added is double that required to reach the equivalence point, then:

$$[B] = [BH^+]$$
$$\text{therefore } K_b = [OH^-]$$
$$\text{and } pK_b = pOH = 14 - pH$$

Again this, or half neutralising a weak base with a strong acid, which gives an equivalent solution, is the best way to determine the dissociation constant of a weak base. Figure 806 shows the change in pH during the titration of a monobasic strong acid with a monobasic weak base of equal concentration.

AHL

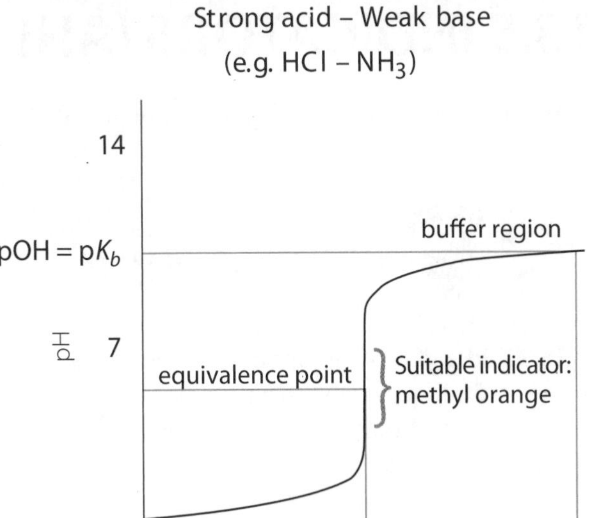

Figure 806 Strong acid – weak base

In a titration between a weak acid and a weak base, as shown in Figure 807, there is only a small change in pH at the equivalence point, making it difficult to detect. Figure 807 shows the change in pH during the titration of a monobasic weak acid with a monobasic weak base of equal concentration.

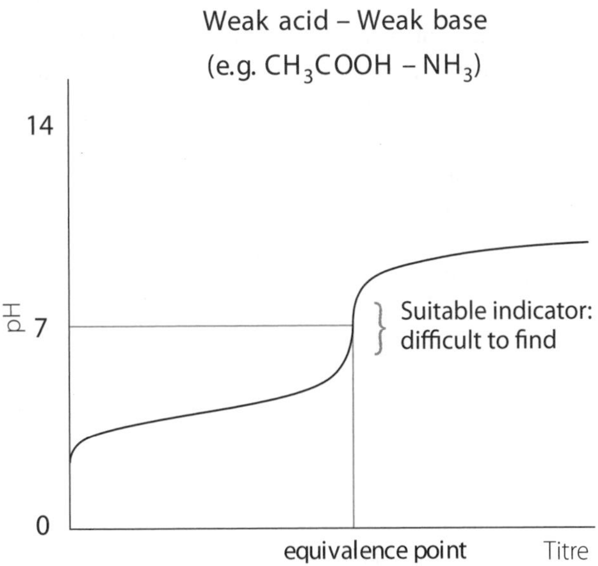

Figure 807 Weak acid – weak base

If in the titration the acid is added to a solution of the base, then the same considerations apply and the shapes of the pH curves are similar to those shown above, but reflected in a vertical line passing through the equivalence point.

Note that the volume at which the equivalence point occurs is not affected by the strength of the acid or base, it only depends on the stoichiometric ratio given by the balanced equation. If 25 cm^3 of alkali was needed to just neutralise a particular solution of hydrochloric acid, then the same volume would be required to neutralise the same volume of ethanoic acid of equal concentration. Double this volume (50 cm^3) would however be required to neutralise the same volume of sulfuric acid of equal concentration:

$$HCl\ (aq) + NaOH\ (aq) \longrightarrow NaCl\ (aq) + H_2O\ (l)$$

$$CH_3COOH\ (aq) + NaOH\ (aq) \longrightarrow NaCH_3COO\ (aq) + H_2O\ (l)$$

$$H_2SO_4\ (aq) + 2\ NaOH\ (aq) \longrightarrow Na_2SO_4\ (aq) + 2\ H_2O\ (l)$$

AHL

Exercise 18.4

1. 1 mol dm^{-3} nitric acid is being titrated with aqueous sodium hydroxide. When 99.9% of the acid has been neutralised, the pH of the solution, ignoring changes in the total volume, will be:

   A 3
   B 6
   C 6.900
   D 6.999

2. During the titration of a weak acid with a strong base, the pH of the solution will equal the pK_a of the weak acid

   A at the start of the titration.

   B when half the volume required to reach the end point has been added.

   C at the end point.

   D when twice the volume required to reach the end point has been added.

3. During the titration of a weak acid using a strong base, at the end point there will be a rapid change in pH between

   A 4 and 10
   B 3 and 7
   C 7 and 11
   D 6 and 8

4. When 20 cm^3 of a solution of aqueous ammonia is titrated with 0.20 mol dm^{-3} hydrochloric acid, 15 cm^3 of the acid were needed to reach the equivalence point.

   a) What is the concentration of the aqueous ammonia?

   b) Given that pK_a for the ammonium ion is 9.3, calculate the pH of the solution.
      i at the start.
      ii when 7.5 cm^3 of acid has been added.
      iii at the equivalence point.

   c) Bearing these values in mind, sketch the shape of the graph of pH against titre you would expect for this titration.

   d) Which section of this curve is known as the 'buffering region' and why is it so called?

   e) Identify two important ways in which the curve would differ if the titration were carried out with aqueous barium hydroxide of the same concentration as the ammonia.

AHL

18.5 INDICATORS (AHL)

18.5.1 Describe qualitatively the action of an acid-base indicator.

18.5.2 State and explain how the pH range of an acid-base indicator relates to its pK_a value.

18.5.3 Identify an appropriate indicator for a titration, given the equivalence point of the titration and the pH range of the indicator.

An **indicator** is a substance (often an organic dye) that has a different colour in acidic and alkaline solutions and hence can be used to detect the end point of a titration. This occurs because an indicator is a weak acid/base in which the two forms have different colours and are in equilibrium with each other:

$$HIn\,(aq) \rightleftharpoons H^+\,(aq) + In^-\,(aq)$$

For litmus: Red Blue

In the presence of an acid, the equilibrium is driven to the left (Le Chatelier's principle) so the indicator turns to the HIn form (red for litmus); whereas in the presence of a base the shift is to the right and the indicator changes into its In^- form (blue for litmus). The weak acid equilibrium is governed by the usual equation:

$$K_a = \frac{[H^+][In^-]}{[HIn]}$$

so rearranging this the ratio of the two coloured forms is given by:

$$\frac{[HIn]}{[In^-]} = \frac{[H^+]}{K_a}$$

The colour of the indicator therefore depends not only on the pH, and hence $[H^+]$, but also on the value of K_a, so that different indicators change colour over different pH ranges. Two of the most commonly met indicators are **methyl orange** and **phenolphthalein**, the characteristics of which are summarised in Figure 808.

When pH = pK_a, then the two coloured forms will have equal concentrations and the indicator will be in the middle of its colour change. If the concentration of one form (for example HIn) is ten times greater than that of the other form (In^-), then the colour of the indicator will

Property	Phenolphthalein	Methyl orange
pK_a	9.6	3.7
pH Range	8.3 to 10.0	3.1 to 4.4
Colour in acid	Colourless	Red
Colour in alkali	Pink	Yellow
Useful for	Titrations involving strong bases	Titrations involving strong acids

Figure 808 The properties of phenolphthalein and methyl orange

effectively be that of the predominant species. The pH of the solution at this point will be:

$$[H^+] = K_a \times \frac{[HIn]}{[In^-]}$$

$$= K_a \times \frac{10}{1}$$

$$= 10K_a$$

$$\text{or } pH = pK_a - 1$$

If $[In^-]$ were ten times greater than [HIn] then the result would be $pH = pK_a + 1$. Many indicators therefore change colour over a region of 2 pH units centred on the pK_a value, though this needs to be modified according the the relative intensities of the two colours, as is particularly obvious for phenolphthalein in the above table.

In order to be an effective indicator, the colour change (called the **end point**) must occur rapidly at the **equivalence point** (that is when the reagents have just reached their stoichiometric ratio). If a weak acid such as ethanoic acid is being used in a titration with a strong base, then phenolphthalein should be used as the indicator because the sudden change in pH at the equivalence point is from ≈ 7 to 10 (see Figure 805) and this corresponds to the range of phenolphthalein. Methyl orange conversely is used for titrations involving a weak base (ammonia or sodium carbonate) and a strong acid when the sudden pH change at the equivalence point is between ≈ 3 and 7 (see Figure 806). The pH change with a strong acid – strong base titration is so large at the end point that both indicators will perform satisfactorily (see Figure 804),

Exercise 18.5

1. For which one of the following titrations, would phenolphthalein not act as an appropriate indicator?

   A Nitric acid with sodium hydroxide.
   B Sulfuric acid with ammonia.
   C Ethanoic acid with barium hydroxide.
   D Hydrochloric acid with potassium hydroxide.

2. Hydrochloric acid (in the flask) is to be titrated with aqueous sodium carbonate (in the burette).

   a) Would you choose methyl orange or phenolphthalein for this titration?
   b) Explain the reasons for your choice.
   c) What colour change would you expect to see at the end point?
   d) Explain why the addition of too much indicator could lead to an inaccurate titration result.
   e) The laboratory has run out of both methyl orange and phenolphthalein. Below are listed some indicators that are available. Which would you use to replace your original choice? Explain your reasons.

Indicator	pK_a	Colour change
Bromophenol blue	4.0	Yellow to blue
Bromothymol blue	7.0	Yellow to blue
Thymol blue	8.9	Yellow to blue

3. 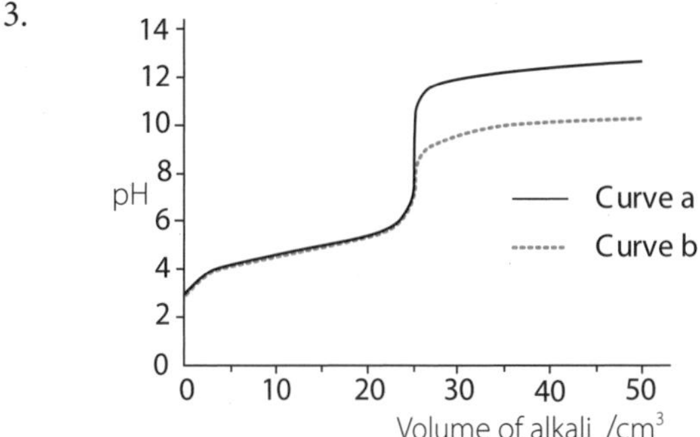

The graph shows the pH changes when 0.1 mol dm^{-3} ethanoic acid is titrated against 0.1 mol dm^{-3} aqueous sodium hydroxide (Curve a) and against 0.1 mol dm^{-3} aqueous ammonia (Curve b).

AHL

a) Why is the pH of 0.1 mol dm^{-3} ethanoic acid just under 3, when the pH of 0.1 mol dm^{-3} hydrochloric acid is 1?

b) Would methyl orange or phenolphthalein be a more appropriate indicator to detect the end point in the titration of 0.1 mol dm^{-3} ethanoic acid with 0.1 mol dm^{-3} aqueous sodium hydroxide (Curve a)?

c) No indicator is really suitable to detect the end point in the titration of 0.1 mol dm^{-3} ethanoic acid with 0.1 mol dm^{-3} aqueous ammonia (Curve b)? Explain why this is the case.

d) Explain how the above graph could be used to determine the base dissociation constant (K_b) of ammonia.

4.

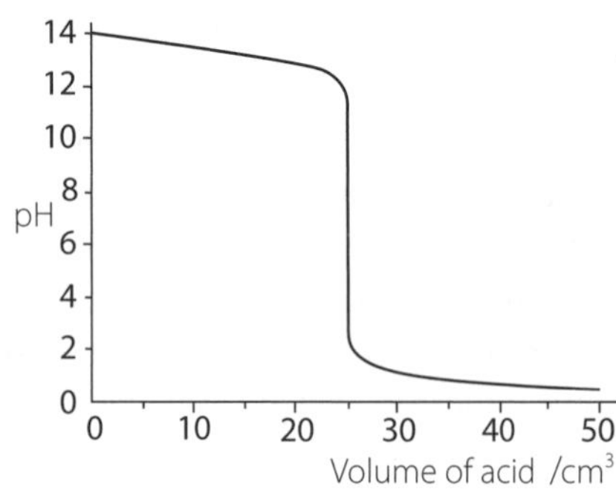

The diagram shows the variation in pH when 1 mol dm^{-3} hydrochloric acid is added to 20 cm^3 of 1 mol dm^{-3} aqueous sodium hydroxide.

a) Explain how and why the curve would differ in shape if the hydrochloric acid had been replaced by:
   i 1 mol dm^{-3} sulfuric acid.
   ii 1 mol dm^{-3} ethanoic acid.

b) Phenolphthalein and methyl orange are suggested as indicators for these three titrations. One would be appropriate for all three titrations, the other for only two of them. Explain this.

5. Hydrogen sulfide (H_2S) can act as a weak acid in aqueous solution.

a) What is the conjugate base of hydrogen sulfide?

b) Write an equation for the equilibrium that exists in an aqueous solution of hydrogen sulfide.

c) The solubility of hydrogen sulfide at room temperature and pressure is 3.4 g per litre. What is the concentration of this solution?
[A_r values: H – 1; S – 32].

d) The acid dissociation constant of hydrogen sulfide is 9.55×10^{-8} mol dm^{-3}. Calculate the pH of a saturated solution.

e) When 11.0 g of solid sodium hydrogensulfide (NaHS) is dissolved in a litre of this saturated solution, a buffer solution is formed. What is meant by the term buffer solution?

f) Describe, in terms of the effect on the equilibrium, what the result of adding a little aqueous sodium hydroxide to this solution would be.

g) What is the concentration of hydrogensulfide ions in the solution?
[A_r values: H – 1; Na – 23; S – 32]

h) Calculate the pH of the buffer solution that is formed.

i) What concentration of hydrogensulfide ions would be required to give a buffer of pH 3? Why would this not be a very effective buffer?

j) Bromothymol blue is an indicator that is yellow in acid and blue in alkali. It changes colour at about pH 7. Methyl yellow is an indicator that is red in acid and yellow in alkali, which changes colour at about pH 3.1. If a saturated solution of hydrogen sulfide is tested with each indicator, what colour will result in each case?

k) Explain how acid-base indicators work and why different indicators change colour at different pH values.

l) Which of these would be the more suitable for titrating hydrogen sulfide solution with aqueous sodium hydroxide? Explain why.

The sulfide ion S^{2-}, acts as a weak base in aqueous solution.

m) Write an equation for the equilibrium that is established in aqueous solution.

n) What term can be used to describe the behaviour of the hydrogensulfide ion in this equilibrium and those above?

o) A 0.100 mol dm^{-3} solution of sodium sulfide has a pH of 12.95. Calculate the concentration of hydroxide ions in this solution.

p) Use this to determine pK_a for the hydrogensulfide ion.

q) What two reagents could you add to sodium sulfide solution to prepare a buffer solution with a pH of 12.5?

OXIDATION & REDUCTION

9

CORE

9.1 Introduction to oxidation and reduction

9.2 Redox equations

Some common oxidising agents and reducing agents (EXT)

9.3 Reactivity

9.4 Voltaic cells

19.1 Standard electrode potentials (AHL)

9.5 Electrolytic cells

19.2 Electrolysis (AHL)

TOK Are oxidation numbers real?

I remember contemplating on the nature of reality back in Chapters 2 and 4, with regard to electrons and hybridization respectively. The implication always seems to be that reality is in some way desirable. Maybe my bank account might be a useful analogy to oxidation numbers? At the end of every month there is a number assigned to it, but as the month progresses this number gets smaller and the numbers assigned to the local supermarket, the petrol station, the government etc. all go up. Hardly any of it gets turned into bank notes for me to carry around and even then is a bank note any more real than the number printed on my bank statement. Isn't the fact that this piece of paper is worth $20 just another, very convenient, shared fiction? Along as we are all happy to share the belief that the figures on my bank statement and the number on my bank notes mean something then real or not these numbers, like oxidation numbers, are very useful and certainly a lot easier than pushing around wheelbarrows full of gold, or wearing a necklace of sea-shells with holes drilled in them. The whole thing is perhaps closely related to the philosophy of Charles Sanders Peirce, who developed the concept of "pragmatic truth" - that in which it was convenient for society to believe; in other words truth is more an attribute of a society than an attribute of the physical world. Are oxidation numbers useful? Certainly they are capable of giving us a definitive answer as to whether in a chemical change, a particular atom is oxidised, reduced, or neither, but is the change any more than "electron accounting" that helps us balance equations? F going to F^- is just a change of –1 whereas N going to N^{3-} is a change of –3, but the former is far more energetically favourable.

9.1 INTRODUCTION TO OXIDATION & REDUCTION

CORE

9.1.1 Define oxidation and reduction in terms of electron loss and gain.

9.1.2 Deduce the oxidation number of an element in a compound.

9.1.3 State the names of compounds using oxidation numbers.

9.1.4 Deduce whether an element undergoes oxidation or reduction in reactions using oxidation numbers.

Oxidation and reduction are most commonly defined in terms of the loss and gain of electrons. **Oxidation** is the loss of electrons, so if an iron(II) ion (Fe^{2+}) is converted to an iron(III) ion (Fe^{3+}), then the iron(II) ion has lost an electron and so has been oxidised.

$$Fe^{2+}(aq) \longrightarrow Fe^{3+}(aq) + e^-$$

Conversely **reduction** is the gain of electrons, so if hydrogen ions (H^+) are converted to hydrogen gas (H_2) the hydrogen ion has gained electrons and is therefore reduced.

$$2\,H^+(aq) + 2\,e^- \longrightarrow H_2(g)$$

Note that in these equations the charge as well as the numbers of atoms must balance.

A useful mnemonic (memory aid) for this is:

LEO *(the lion)* **goes GER**

Loss of **E**lectrons is **O**xidation;
Gain of **E**lectrons is **R**eduction.

Alternatively:

OILRIG
(**O**xidation **I**s **L**oss of electrons, **R**eduction **I**s **G**ain of electrons).

Consider the reaction between zinc and iodine:

$$Zn(s) + I_2(aq) \longrightarrow Zn^{2+}(aq) + 2\,I^-(aq)$$

In this the zinc atom loses two electrons to form the zinc ion and so is oxidised. The iodine molecule gains two electrons to form iodide ions and so is reduced. This is most clearly shown by splitting the overall equation into two 'half equations', i.e.

$$Zn(s) \longrightarrow Zn^{2+}(aq) + 2\,e^- \quad \&$$
$$I_2(aq) + 2\,e^- \longrightarrow 2\,I^-(aq)$$

The full equation can be produced by combining the appropriate half equations in such a way that the electrons cancel.

There are occasions when the atoms in the species change and so the definition above is difficult to apply. For example nitrogen is reduced in the conversion of nitrogen gas (N_2) to ammonia (NH_3), even though there is no obvious gain of electrons. Even worse, when nitrogen dioxide (NO_2) is converted to the nitrate ion (NO_3^-) it is oxidised even though it gains a negative charge (remember, the addition of electrons = reduction)! These problems are removed by the use of oxidation numbers.

The **oxidation number**, or oxidation state, of an atom is the charge which that atom would have if all covalent bonds were broken so that the more electronegative element kept all the electrons in the bond, hence the sign (+ or –) is always given. So for example in water the ions produced would be two H^+ and an O^{2-} hence in water the oxidation state of hydrogen is +1 and that of oxygen is –2.

In practice, rather than having to consider the breaking of every covalent bond in a molecule to find the oxidation number, it is easier to calculate this using a number of rules:

1. The total oxidation state of the atoms in a species is equal to the electrical charge it carries. Hence all elements in the elemental state have an oxidation state of zero, the total oxidation number of a neutral molecule is zero and that of ions is equal to the charge

2. Some elements almost always have the same oxidation state in their compounds, with a few exceptions. In order of decreasing numbers of exceptions:

   a) fluorine is –1 (no exceptions)

   b) hydrogen is +1 (except in the hydride ion, H^- where it is –1)

   c) oxygen is –2 (except +1 in hydrogen peroxide, H_2O_2, and related compounds)

d) the halogens (group 7 elements Cl, Br, & I) are –1 (except when bonded to oxygen or a halogen that is higher in the group)

Elements which commonly change their oxidation states are carbon, nitrogen, phosphorus, sulfur and the transition metals. The rules above are best illustrated by examples:

Hydrogen in H_2 is 0	In their elemental state the oxidation state of elements is always zero.
Iron in Fe^{2+} is +2	The total oxidation number is equal to the charge, and in this case there is only one element present.
Carbon in CH_4 is –4	There is no charge on CH_4, so the total must be zero. Hydrogen is +1, so that four hydrogens are +4. The carbon is therefore –4.
Sulfur in H_2SO_4 is +6	H_2SO_4 is a neutral molecule so he total is again zero. The four oxygens are –8 (–2 each) and the two hydrogens are +2 (+1 each) so that sulfur must be +6.
Phosphorus in PCl_4^+ is +5	The total is +1 (equal to the electrical charge). The four chlorines are –4 (–1 each) so phosphorus must be +5.
Iodine in IO_4^- is +7	The total is –1 (charge) and the four oxygens are –8 (–2 each) so that iodine must be +7. (Note that this is one of the exceptions mentioned in rule 2d.)

In terms of oxidation number, oxidation is an increase in oxidation number and reduction is a decrease in oxidation number. If the oxidation number does not change, then that element has not been oxidised or reduced. This covers the definition in terms of electrons, as well as many other cases.

Returning to the dilemmas at the start of the section it can be seen that in going from N_2 to NH_3, the oxidation number of nitrogen has decreased from 0 to –3, so it has been reduced. Similarly in going from NO_2 to NO_3^- the oxidation number has increased from +4 to +5 so it is an oxidation.

Consider the **redox** reaction (one in which **red**uction and **ox**idation occurs) below:

$$2\,MnO_4^-\,(aq) + 5\,SO_2\,(aq) + 2\,H_2O\,(l) \longrightarrow 2\,Mn^{2+}\,(aq) + 5\,SO_4^{2-}\,(aq) + 4\,H^+\,(aq)$$

In order to determine which elements have been oxidised and which reduced, the appropriate oxidation numbers must be calculated. If none of the elements change their oxidation number then the reaction is not a redox reaction. It is unusual for the oxidation state of hydrogen and oxygen to change (unless the reaction involves the elements or hydrogen peroxide). Application of the rules above to manganese and sulfur shows that:

Manganese is reduced as its oxidation number decreases: $MnO_4^- = +7$, $Mn^{2+} = +2$

Sulfur is oxidised as its oxidation number increases: $SO_2 = +4$, $SO_4^{2-} = +6$

For elements that have a variable oxidation number the oxidation state of the element in a particular compound is often signfied by the use of Roman numerals in the name, for example the permanganate(VII) ion and the manganese(II) ion in the above reaction. Another example would be iron(II) chloride for $FeCl_2$ and iron(III) chloride for $FeCl_3$.

In some cases a reaction can occur in which the same species is both oxidised and reduced. Reactions of this type are described as **disproportionation** (or self oxidation-reduction) reactions. An example would be the disproportionation of copper(I) ions in aqueous solution, when it is both oxidised to the copper(II) ion and simultaneously reduced to copper metal:

$$2\,Cu^+\,(aq) \longrightarrow Cu^{2+}\,(aq) + Cu\,(s)$$

$$+1 \qquad\qquad +2 \qquad\qquad 0$$

Commonly if there are a number of atoms of the same element in a species then they will all have the same oxidation number (for example chromium in $Cr_2O_7^{2-}$), but sometimes when they are in rather different environments, different atoms will have different oxidation numbers. Consider the two carbons in CH_3COOH. The normal calculation will give,the oxidation number of carbon as 0 [$2x + 4 + (2 \times -2) = 0$; thus $x = 0$]. This is the average oxidation number of the two carbon atoms in the molecule. In fact the oxidation number of the —CH_3 carbon is -3 and that of the —COOH carbon is +3 (imagine pulling apart the bonds). Another example is Fe_3O_4, a mixed oxide in which contains iron(II) and iron(III) ions in a 1:2 ratio and could be written as $FeO{\bullet}Fe_2O_3$.

TOK The changing language of chemistry

The language of chemistry, like all living languages undergoes continual change. I'm not quite old enough to have meaningfully used names like "spirit of hartshorn" and "muriatic acid" (old names for aqueous ammonia and hydrochloric acid respectively), but I was certainly aware of them. These old names were often related to where things came from; "spirit of hartshorn" is obvious and "muriatic acid" comes from *muria* – the Latin word for brine (saltwater). Sometimes they would also indicate relationships between things, as with the various vitriols; blue vitriol (copper(II) sulfate), green vitriol (iron(II) sulfate), oil of vitriol (concentrated sulfuric acid) etc. When I learnt my chemistry, in the 1960s we mainly used different endings and prefixes to indicate the "valency" (oxidation state) of metals or the amount of oxygen in an acid, or its salts. We therefore had ferrous chloride ($FeCl_2$) and ferric chloride ($FeCl_3$) and though it seemed to operate fairly effectively for simple cases, it couldn't cope with the multiple oxidation states of transition metals, hence the introduction of the Roman numeral oxidation number convention. This also helped with the nomenclature of acids and their salts, for example those involving hydrogen and chlorine:

Ending	Meaning	Example	Modern name	Formula
...ide	No oxygen	Sodium chloride	Sodium chloride	$NaCl$
Hypo......ite	Least oxygen	Sodium hypochlorite	Sodium chlorate(I)	$NaClO$
...ite	More oxygen	Sodium chlorite	Sodium chlorate(III)	$NaClO_2$
...ate	More oxygen	Sodium chlorate	Sodium chlorate(V)	$NaClO_3$
Per......ate	Most oxygen	Sodium perchlorate	Sodium chlorate(VII)	$NaClO_4$

In simpler cases the prefixes were left out, so with nitrogen for example there was just nitride (N^{3-}), nitrite (NO_2^-) and nitrate (NO_3^-). In organic chemistry the changes have been more noticeable with **IUPAC** names now being preferred to "trivial" names, but as always there is resistance to new ways, especially as the old names tended to be shorter! Biologists still talk of alanine rather than 2-aminopropanoic acid and industrial chemists would always refer to ethoxyethane as ether. Even the IBO retreated, for example from using the technically more correct alkanals to the more widely used aldehydes, on their syllabus and examination papers.

What is in a name? What is lost when a name is lost? I suppose that we are conditioned to think of older names as seeming more "quaint" and "poetic" than the new "sterile" systematic names. Both give us information, but it could probably be argued that knowing that formic acid is produced by ants (French - *formis*) is less important than knowing that methanoic acid is a carboxylic; Oops, alkanoic acid containing one carbon atom.

Exercise 9.1

1. Which one of the following reactions is not a redox reaction?

   A $CH_4 + 2\,O_2 \longrightarrow CO_2 + 2\,H_2O$
   B $CuO + H_2SO_4 \longrightarrow CuSO_4 + H_2O$
   C $2\,Al + Fe_2O_3 \longrightarrow Al_2O_3 + 2\,Fe$
   D $PbO + CO \longrightarrow Pb + CO_2$

2. In which one of the following reactions is the first reagent reduced?

   A $Fe + Pb(NO_3)_2 \longrightarrow Fe(NO_3)_2 + Pb$
   B $NaOH + HNO_3 \longrightarrow NaNO_3 + H_2O$
   C $H_2 + CuO \longrightarrow H_2O + Cu$
   D $CO_2 + C \longrightarrow 2CO$

3. In which of the following changes has the oxidation number of sulfur increased?

   A $H_2SO_4 \longrightarrow SO_2$
   B $H_2S \longrightarrow S_8$
   C $SO_2 \longrightarrow H_2S$
   D $SO_2 \longrightarrow S_8$

4. The three reactions below could all be used to prepare iron(II) sulfate:

   Reaction I $FeCl_2 + Ag_2SO_4 \longrightarrow FeSO_4 + 2\,AgCl$

   Reaction II $Fe_2(SO_4)_3 + SO_2 + 2\,H_2O \longrightarrow 2\,FeSO_4 + 2\,H_2SO_4$

   Reaction III $Fe + H_2SO_4 \longrightarrow FeSO_4 + H_2$

   Which of the following best summarises what is happening to the iron in each of these reactions?

	Reaction I	*Reaction II*	*Reaction III*
A	reduction	neither	neither
B	neither	oxidation	reduction
C	neither	reduction	oxidation
D	reduction	reduction	oxidation

5. In which one of the following reactions is the species in **bold** type acting as an oxidising agent?

   A $\mathbf{FeCl_3} + 3\,AgNO_3 \longrightarrow Fe(NO_3)_3 + 3\,AgCl$
   B $\mathbf{Fe} + 2\,Ag^+ \longrightarrow Fe^{2+} + 2\,Ag$
   C $2\,\mathbf{H^+} + Mg \longrightarrow Mg^{2+} + H_2$
   D $2\,\mathbf{Fe^{2+}} + Cl_2 \longrightarrow 2\,Fe^{3+} + 2\,Cl^-$

6. Give the oxidation number of the stated element in each of the following species:

   a) Iron in Fe^{2+}
   b) Phosphorus in P_4
   c) Silicon in SiO_2
   d) Sulfur in SCl_4
   e) Nitrogen in N_2O
   f) Carbon in CH_3OH
   g) Vanadium in VO^{2+}
   h) Bromine in BrO^-
   i) Iodine in IF_6^-
   j) Chromium in $Cr_2O_7^{2-}$

7. Give one example of the following:

   a) An iron compound with an oxidation state of +2.
   b) A nitrogen compound with an oxidation state of −3.
   c) A manganese compound with an oxidation state of +7.
   d) A carbon compound with an oxidation state of 0.
   e) A phosphorus compound with an oxidation state of +5.

8. For each of the following transformations, give the initial and final oxidation number of the element in **bold** type and hence state whether it has been oxidised, been reduced, or neither.

   a) $\mathbf{Cu}^{2+} \longrightarrow \mathbf{Cu}I$
   b) $\mathbf{N}O_2 \longrightarrow \mathbf{N}_2O_4$
   c) $\mathbf{P}H_3 \longrightarrow H\mathbf{P}O_2^{2-}$
   d) $\mathbf{C}H_3OH \longrightarrow H\mathbf{C}OOH$
   e) $\mathbf{S}_2O_3^{2-} \longrightarrow \mathbf{S}_4O_6^{2-}$

9. Hydrazine (N_2H_4) and dinitrogen tetroxide (N_2O_4) react violently to form nitrogen as a product from both reactants.

   a) Explain why this is considered to be a redox reaction stating, with reasons, what is being oxidised and what is being reduced.
   b) Write a balanced equation for this reaction.
   c) It has been suggested that this reaction is a very 'environmentally friendly' source of energy. Explain this.

10. In any redox reaction, the total increase in oxidation number must equal the total decrease in oxidation number. When ammonium dichromate(VI) is heated, it decomposes in a spectacular redox reaction.

a) Write the formula for ammonium dichromate(VI).
b) What is the significance of the (VI) in the name ammonium dichromate(VI)?
c) The chromium is reduced to chromium(III) oxide, a green powder. What is the **total** decrease in oxidation number of chromium in each ammonium dichromate(VI)?
d) What is the initial oxidation state of the nitrogen in the ammonium ion?
e) Taking into account the total number of nitrogens in ammonium dichromate(VI), by how much must the oxidation number of each nitrogen increase?
f) What must the final oxidation state of the nitrogen in the product be?
g) Suggest a substance containing nitrogen in this oxidation state.
h) What colour change would you see during this reaction?
i) The reaction gives out heat and a shower of sparks. What does this show about the reaction?

9.2 REDOX EQUATIONS

9.2.1 Deduce simple oxidation and reduction half-equations given the species involved in a redox reaction.

9.2.2 Deduce redox equations using half-equations.

9.2.3 Define the terms oxidizing agent and reducing agent.

9.2.4 Identify the oxidizing and reducing agents in redox equations.

With many substances, the oxidation or reduction that occurs during redox reactions in aqueous solution is independent of the particular **oxidant** or **reductant** that is causing the change. It is therefore convenient to write an equation for this change in terms of the loss or gain of electrons. For example, whenever the purple permanganate(VII) ion is reduced in acidic solution the almost colourless manganese(II) ion is formed, so the change occurring is:

$$MnO_4^- (aq) + 8\,H^+ (aq) + 5\,e^- \longrightarrow Mn^{2+} (aq) + 4\,H_2O\,(l)$$

These equations are known as **half equations** and for a redox reaction the half equations for the substance being oxidized and the substance being reduced can be combined in such a way that the electrons cancel out, so as to give a balanced equation for the redox reaction.

Half equations must balance in the same way as normal equations (with respect to number of atoms of each element and charge), the only difference being that they contain electrons. When constructing a half equation it is easiest to follow a sequence of steps. This will be illustrated using the half equation for the reduction of the orange dichromate(VI) ion to the green chromium(III) ion in acidic aqueous solutions, as an example:

$$Cr_2O_7^{2-} (aq) \longrightarrow Cr^{3+} (aq)$$

1) balance the number of atoms of the element being oxidized or reduced (in this case Cr is being reduced from +6 to +3) on the two sides:

$$Cr_2O_7^{2-} (aq) \longrightarrow 2\,Cr^{3+} (aq)$$

2) add water molecules to balance the number of oxygen atoms on the two sides:

$$Cr_2O_7^{2-} (aq) \longrightarrow 2\,Cr^{3+} (aq) + 7\,H_2O\,(l)$$

3) add hydrogen ions to balance the number of hydrogen atoms on the two sides:

$$Cr_2O_7^{2-} (aq) + 14\,H^+ (aq) \longrightarrow 2\,Cr^{3+} (aq) + 7\,H_2O\,(l)$$

4) add electrons so that the electrical charges on both sides balance:

$$Cr_2O_7^{2-} (aq) + 14\,H^+ (aq) + 6\,e^- \longrightarrow 2\,Cr^{3+} (aq) + 7\,H_2O\,(l)$$

Because this is a reduction, the electrons appear on the left hand side of the equation (GER) and their number is equal to the total change in oxidation number (two chromiums changing in oxidation state from +6 to +3 is a change in oxidation number of –6 (2 × –3) and hence requires a total of 6 electrons). In an oxidation, the electrons would appear on the right hand side of the equation (LEO). For example the half equation for the oxidation of iron(II) to iron(III) is:

$$Fe^{2+} (aq) \longrightarrow Fe^{3+} (aq) + e^-$$

To write a balanced equation for a redox reaction, the two half equations involved must be multiplied by suitable factors so that when added together the number of electrons lost by one equals the number gained by the other so that the electrons cancel. In the case of the oxidation of iron(II) to iron(III) by the reduction of dichromate(VI) to chromium(III), the equation for the oxidation of the iron(II) must be multiplied by six because six electrons are involved in the reduction of the dichromate(VI), so that the half equations involved become:

$$Cr_2O_7^{2-}\,(aq) + 14\,H^+\,(aq) + 6\,e^- \longrightarrow 2\,Cr^{3+}\,(aq) + 7\,H_2O\,(l)$$

$$6\,Fe^{2+}\,(aq) \longrightarrow 6\,Fe^{3+}\,(aq) + 6\,e^-$$

When added together, the electrons cancel and the final balanced equation is:

$$Cr_2O_7^{2-}\,(aq) + 14\,H^+\,(aq) + 6\,Fe^{2+}\,(aq) \longrightarrow 2\,Cr^{3+}\,(aq) + 7\,H_2O\,(l) + 6\,Fe^{3+}\,(aq)$$

In the example above, the dichromate(VI) ion is described as an oxidizing agent (or oxidant) as it oxidizes iron(II) to iron(III). Similarly the iron(II) ion is a reducing agent because it reduces the dichromate(VI) ion to the chromium(III) ion. Note that an oxidizing agent oxidizes another substance, but is itself reduced; conversely a reducing agent reduces another substance, but is itself oxidized in the process.

When balancing redox equations, sometimes it will then be necessary to cancel hydrogen ions and water molecules that appear on both sides of the equation. This is best illustrated by a second example – the half equation for the oxidation of sulfur dioxide to the sulfate ion is:

$$SO_2\,(aq) + 2\,H_2O\,(l) \longrightarrow SO_4^{2-}\,(aq) + 4\,H^+\,(aq) + 2\,e^-$$

If this is to be combined with the half equation for the reduction of the permanganate(VII) ion, given at the start of this section, then it is necessary to multiply the permanganate(VII) half equation by two and the sulfur dioxide half equation by five, so that both involve ten electrons:

$$2\,MnO_4^-\,(aq) + 16\,H^+\,(aq) + 10\,e^- \longrightarrow 2\,Mn^{2+}\,(aq) + 8\,H_2O\,(l)$$

$$5\,SO_2\,(aq) + 10\,H_2O\,(l) \longrightarrow 5\,SO_4^{2-}\,(aq) + 20\,H^+\,(aq) + 10\,e^-$$

When these are initially combined, the equation is:

$$2\,MnO_4^-\,(aq) + 16\,H^+\,(aq) + 5\,SO_2\,(aq) + 10\,H_2O\,(l) \longrightarrow 2\,Mn^{2+}\,(aq) + 8\,H_2O\,(l) + 5\,SO_4^{2-}\,(aq) + 20\,H^+\,(aq)$$

By cancelling the water molecules and hydrogen ions that appear on both sides, this simplifies to give the final balanced equation, which is:

$$2\,MnO_4^-\,(aq) + 5\,SO_2\,(aq) + 2\,H_2O\,(l) \longrightarrow 2\,Mn^{2+}\,(aq) + 5\,SO_4^{2-}\,(aq) + 4\,H^+\,(aq)$$

In this example, the permanganate(VII) ion is the oxidizing agent as it oxidizes sulfur in sulfur dioxide to sulfate (+4 to +6) and is itself reduced to the manganese(II) ion. On the other hand, sulfur dioxide is the reducing agent as it reduces manganese from the permanganate(VII) ion to the manganese(II) ion (+7 to +2) and is itself oxidized to sulfate.

Exercise 9.2

1. Which one of the following is the correct half equation for the iodate(V) ion in acidic solution changing to iodine?

   A $IO_3^- + 6\,H^+ \longrightarrow I + 3\,H_2O + 5\,e^-$
   B $IO_3^- + 6\,H^+ + 5\,e^- \longrightarrow I + 3\,H_2O$
   C $IO_3^- + 6\,H^+ + 5\,e^- \longrightarrow I_2 + 3\,H_2O$
   D $2\,IO_3^- + 12\,H^+ + 10\,e^- \longrightarrow I_2 + 6\,H_2O$

2. In the half equation for a substance acting as a reductant (reducing agent)

   A the oxidation number increases and the electrons are on the right hand side.
   B the oxidation number increases and the electrons are on the left hand side.
   C the oxidation number decreases and the electrons are on the right hand side.
   D the oxidation number decreases and the electrons are on the left hand side.

3. The overall equation for nitric acid oxidising iron(II) ions to iron(III) ions is

   $$HNO_3 + 3\,Fe^{2+} + 3\,H^+ \longrightarrow NO + 3\,Fe^{3+} + 2\,H_2O$$

   The half equation for the reduction of the nitric acid must therefore be

   A $HNO_3 + 4\,H^+ + 4\,e^- \longrightarrow NO + 2\,H_2O$
   B $HNO_3 + 3\,H^+ + 3\,e^- \longrightarrow NO + 2\,H_2O$
   C $HNO_3 + 3\,H^+ \longrightarrow NO + 2\,H_2O + 3\,e^-$
   D $HNO_3 + H^+ \longrightarrow NO + H_2O + e^-$

4. Write balanced half equations for the following changes:

   a) Zinc metal being oxidised to the zinc ion.
   b) Bromine being reduced to the bromide ion.
   c) Hydrogen sulfide being oxidised to sulfur.
   d) Nitric acid being reduced to nitrogen dioxide [nitrogen(IV) oxide].
   e) The vanadate(V) ion (VO_3^-) being reduced to the vanadium(III) ion.

5. Below are given some half equations for redox reactions. Combine these, as indicated, to produce balanced equations for the redox reactions involved.

   Equation I $Co^{3+} + e^- \longrightarrow Co^{2+}$

   Equation II $PbO_2 + 4\,H^+ + 2\,e^- \longrightarrow Pb^{2+} + 2\,H_2O$

   Equation III $ClO_3^- + 6\,H^+ + 6\,e^- \longrightarrow Cl^- + 3\,H_2O$

   Equation IV $Sn^{2+} \longrightarrow Sn^{4+} + 2\,e^-$

   Equation V $NO_2^- + H_2O \longrightarrow NO_3^- + 2\,H^+ + 2\,e^-$

   a) Equations II and IV.
   b) Equations I and IV.
   c) Equations II and V.
   d) Equations III and IV.
   e) Equations III and V.

6. Use the half equation method to write balanced equations for the following reactions:

   a) Magnesium reducing lead ions to lead metal.
   b) Sulfur dioxide being oxidised to sulfate through reducing iodine to iodide ions.
   c) Hydrogen peroxide oxidising iron(II) to iron(III) in acidic solution.
   d) Zinc reducing acidified dichromate(VI) ions to chromium(III).
   e) Acidified permanganate(VII) ions oxidising methanol to carbon dioxide and water.

7. A disproportionation reaction is one in which a single species is both oxidised and reduced in the same reaction. An example of this occurs when potassium chlorate(V) ($KClO_3$) is heated to just above its melting point. The chlorate ion is oxidised to the perchlorate [chlorate(VII)] ion (ClO_4^-) and reduced to the chloride ion (Cl^-).

   a) What is the oxidation state of the chlorine in these various species?
   b) Write a half equation for the oxidation of the chlorate(V) ion to the perchlorate(VII) ion in aqueous solution.
   c) Write a half equation for the reduction of the chlorate(V) ion to the chloride ion in acidic solution.
   d) Write a balanced chemical equation for the disproportionation of potassium chlorate(V).
   e) Why is there no need for the substances to be in aqueous solution for this reaction to occur?

8. If wine is left in an open bottle it often tastes 'vinegary' a few days later. This is because of the oxidation of the ethanol to ethanoic acid by atmospheric oxygen.

   a) Write the half equation for the oxidation of ethanol to ethanoic acid.
   b) What is the initial and final average oxidation number of the carbons in this change?
   c) Write the half equation for the reduction of oxygen in acidic solution.
   d) Combine these to produce an overall equation for the reaction.
   e) Normally, oxygen is a poor oxidant in aqueous solution. This change only occurs in the presence of bacteria which produce enzymes. Why is oxygen a poor oxidant and how do the enzymes affect this?

EXTENSION

SOME COMMON OXIDISING AGENTS AND REDUCING AGENTS

Some of the more common oxidising agents and reducing agents are given below along with their half equations and other characteristics.

OXIDISING AGENTS

Oxygen

Oxygen is not a very effective oxidant for substances in aqueous solution as a result of the high activation energy associated with breaking the O=O double bond. It will however oxidise many substances when they are heated in a stream of air or oxygen, the reaction being described as burning, or combustion, e.g.

$$2\,Mg\,(s) + O_2\,(g) \longrightarrow 2\,MgO\,(s)$$

Chlorine and the other halogens

Strong oxidants both in aqueous solution and when the substance is heated with the element. Going down Group 7 the halogens become less powerful oxidants. The usual colour change with bromine and iodine is from brown to colourless, though if iodide ions are completely oxidised to iodine it appears as a black solid. Using X as the symbol for the halogen, the half equation is:

$$X_2\,(aq) + 2e^- \longrightarrow 2\,X^-\,(aq)$$

Iron(III) ion

The yellow–brown iron(III) ion acts as a mild oxidant and is reduced to the pale green iron(II) ion. The oxidation state of the iron can best be demonstrated by adding aqueous sodium hydroxide and observing the colour of the precipitate.

$$Fe^{3+}\,(aq) + e^- \longrightarrow Fe^{2+}\,(aq)$$

Hydrogen peroxide

A moderate strength oxidant which in aqueous solution is reduced to water. The reactants and products are all colourless.

$$H_2O_2\,(aq) + 2\,H^+\,(aq) + 2\,e^- \longrightarrow 2\,H_2O\,(l)$$

[Note that very powerful oxidants, such as the permanganate(VII) ion can oxidise hydrogen peroxide to oxygen: $H_2O_2\,(aq) \longrightarrow O_2\,(g) + 2\,H^+\,(aq) + 2\,e^-$].

Manganate(VII) ion (Permanganate ion)

This very powerful oxidant is usually used in acidic solution when the purple permanganate(VII) ion is reduced to the almost colourless manganese(II) ion.

$$MnO_4^-\,(aq) + 8\,H^+\,(aq) + 5\,e^- \longrightarrow Mn^{2+}\,(aq) + 4\,H_2O\,(l)$$

At other pHs the product can be manganese(IV) oxide (a brown solid) or the manganate(VI) ion (a dark green solution).

Dichromate(VI) ion

This too is a powerful oxidant that is usually used in acidic solution. The orange dichromate(VI) ion is reduced to the green chromium(III) ion.

$$Cr_2O_7^{2-}\,(aq) + 14\,H^+\,(aq) + 6\,e^- \longrightarrow 2\,Cr^{3+}\,(aq) + 7\,H_2O\,(l)$$

REDUCING AGENTS

Hydrogen

This is not an effective reductant for aqueous solutions owing to a high activation energy. When passed over the heated oxides of metals below zinc in the reactivity series however, it reduces the oxide to the metal:

$$MO\,(s) + H_2\,(g) \longrightarrow M\,(s) + H_2O\,(g)$$

Carbon and carbon monoxide

Like hydrogen, activation energy considerations prevent being it effective in aqueous solution, but when heated with the oxide of zinc or metals lower in the reactivity series, they reduce the oxide to the metal:

$$2\,MO\,(s) + C\,(s) \longrightarrow M\,(s) + CO_2\,(g)$$

$$MO\,(s) + CO\,(s) \longrightarrow M\,(s) + CO_2\,(g)$$

These are very important reactions for obtaining metals from their ores.

Metals

The more reactive the metal the stronger it is as a reductant, so that metals such as magnesium, zinc and iron are very effective reductants. The metal is oxidised to the aqueous

EXTENSION

Oxidised form			Reduced form		
Permanganate(VII)	MnO_4^-	Purple	Manganese(II)	Mn^{2+}	Colourless
Dichromate(VI)	$Cr_2O_7^{2-}$	Orange	Chromium(III)	Cr^{3+}	Green
Iron(III)	Fe^{3+}	Red-brown	Iron(II)	Fe^{2+}	Pale green
Iodine	I_2	Brown, if excess I^-; blue-black if starch is present	Iodide	I^-	Colourless
Bromine	Br_2	Brown	Bromide	Br^-	Colourless

Figure 901 Colour changes in some common redox systems

cation, so that if this is **divalent**, using M as the symbol for the metal, the half equation is:

$$M\ (s) \longrightarrow M^{2+}\ (aq) + 2\ e^-$$

Iron(II) ion

The pale green iron(II) ion acts as a mild reductant in aqueous solution, being oxidised to the red–brown iron (III) ion:

$$Fe^{2+}\ (aq) \longrightarrow Fe^{3+}\ (aq) + e^-$$

Iodide ion

The colourless iodide ion acts as a mild reductant in aqueous solution, being oxidised to iodine, which appears as a brown solution if excess iodide is present:

$$2\ I^-\ (aq) \longrightarrow I_2\ (aq) + 2\ e^-$$

Thiosulfate ion

The thiosulfate ion is a mild reductant that reacts readily with iodine in aqueous solution according to the equation:

$$2\ S_2O_3^{2-}\ (aq) + I_2\ (aq) \longrightarrow S_4O_6^{2-}\ (aq) + 2\ I^-\ (aq)$$

Starch forms a very intense blue-black coloured complex with iodine and the sudden colour change from blue-black to colorless is used to determine the end point in redox titrations involving iodine.

Sulfur dioxide

Sulfur dioxide is a moderately powerful reductant in aqueous solution, being oxidised to the sulfate ion:

$$SO_2\ (aq) + 2\ H_2O\ (l) \longrightarrow SO_4^{2-}\ (aq) + 4\ H^+\ (aq) + 2\ e^-$$

The reactants and products are all colourless.

The colour changes that accompany some of these redox changes are summarised in Figure 901.

EXTENSION

Exercise

1. Which one of the following is least likely to oxidise iron(II) ions to iron(III) ions in aqueous solution?

   A Magnesium
   B Chlorine
   C Hydrogen peroxide
   D Dichromate(VI) ions

2. Which one of the following redox changes would not give rise to a change in colour of the solution?

   A Iron(II) being oxidised by acidified permanganate(VII).
   B Sulfur dioxide being oxidised by hydrogen peroxide.
   C Dichromate(VI) ions being reduced by zinc.
   D Iodide ions being oxidised by chlorine.

3. Which one of the reactions below, to reduce metal oxides, is least likely to occur?

   A $PbO + H_2 \longrightarrow Pb + H_2O$
   B $Fe_2O_3 + 2\ Al \longrightarrow Al_2O_3 + 2\ Fe$
   C $MgO + CO \longrightarrow Mg + CO_2$
   D $2\ CuO + C \longrightarrow 2\ Cu + CO_2$

4. The concentration of copper(II) ions in aqueous solution can be determined by adding an excess of potassium iodide, when the following reaction occurs:

   $$2\ Cu^{2+}\ (aq) + 4\ I^-\ (aq) \longrightarrow 2\ CuI\ (s) + I_2\ (aq)$$

   The iodine liberated is then titrated with standardised aqueous sodium thiosulfate.

a) In the above equation, what is the initial and final oxidation state of the copper.

b) Given that copper(I) iodide is a white solid, what colour change would be seen when the above reaction occurs?

c) Write a balanced equation for the reaction of iodine with sodium thiosulfate.

d) Calculate the initial and final average oxidation states of the sulfur in this reaction.

e) What indicator is usually used and what is the colour change at the end point?

f) In such a titration it is found that 20 cm^3 of an aqueous solution containing copper(II) sulfate required exactly 15 cm^3 of aqueous sodium thiosulfate of concentration 0.2 mol dm^3 to react with the iodine formed. What was the concentration of the copper(II) sulfate solution?

5. A 2.00 g iron nail is dissolved in excess sulfuric acid. The resulting solution is then titrated with 0.200 mol m^3 aqueous potassium permanganate(VII).

a) What colour change would occur at the end point of the titration?

b) What volume of aqueous potassium permanganate(VII) would be required if the nail were pure iron?

9.3 REACTIVITY

9.3.1 Deduce a reactivity series based upon the chemical behaviour of a group of oxidizing and reducing agents.

9.3.2 Deduce the feasibility of a redox reaction from a given reactivity series.

Usually a certain species will give a particular product as a result of gaining/losing electrons – this pair of species (for example Zn^{2+}/Zn) is referred to as a **redox couple**. (There are however a few exceptions, such as the permanganate(VII) ion where the product depends on other conditions such as the pH.) If one species in the couple is a powerful oxidising agent (has a great attraction for electrons) then it follows that the other half of the couple, that it forms when it has gained this electrons, will not readily give them up again, that is it will be a very weak reducing agent. This is similar to the relationship that exists between the strengths of a conjugate acid–base pair though in that case a hydrogen ion rather than an electron is being exchanged. This allows us to arrange redox pairs as a reactivity series in order of increasing oxidising/reducing power. A very simple **reactivity series**, showing some common metals and the halogens, is shown in Figure 902.

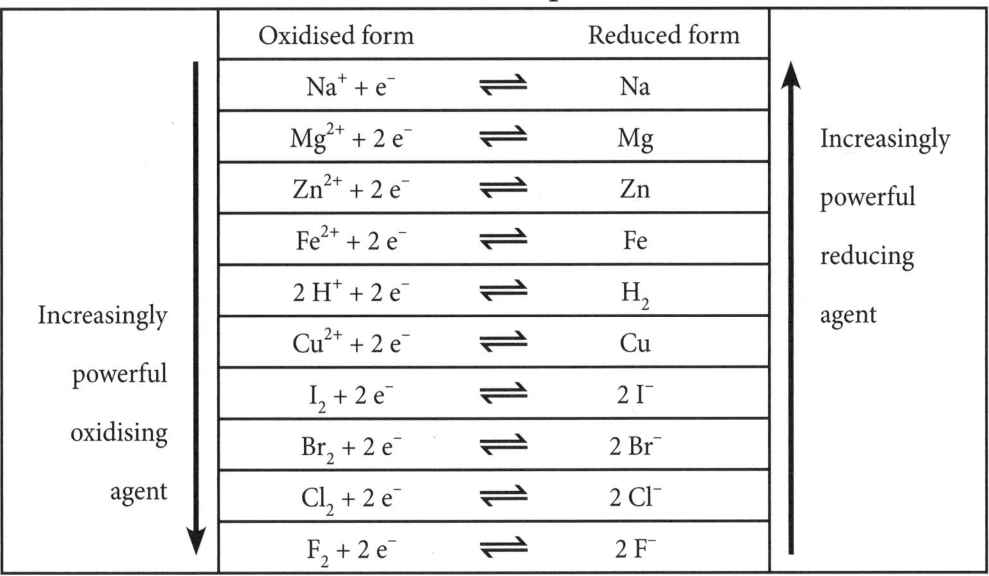

Redox Couple

Oxidised form		Reduced form
$Na^+ + e^-$	$\rightleftharpoons$	Na
$Mg^{2+} + 2e^-$	$\rightleftharpoons$	Mg
$Zn^{2+} + 2e^-$	$\rightleftharpoons$	Zn
$Fe^{2+} + 2e^-$	$\rightleftharpoons$	Fe
$2H^+ + 2e^-$	$\rightleftharpoons$	H_2
$Cu^{2+} + 2e^-$	$\rightleftharpoons$	Cu
$I_2 + 2e^-$	$\rightleftharpoons$	$2I^-$
$Br_2 + 2e^-$	$\rightleftharpoons$	$2Br^-$
$Cl_2 + 2e^-$	$\rightleftharpoons$	$2Cl^-$
$F_2 + 2e^-$	$\rightleftharpoons$	$2F^-$

Figure 902 A simple redox reactivity series

The gain of electrons to complete valence shells is behaviour that is typical of non–metals, hence non–metals tend to be oxidising agents and occur in the left hand column of the table. Going down the left hand column the elements become more reactive (note the relationship to the order of the elements in Group 7) so that an element lower in the table can oxidise the ion formed from an element higher in the table, but the reverse cannot occur. For example chlorine (Cl_2) attracts electrons more strongly than iodine (I_2), so that chlorine can oxidise iodide ions to iodine, but iodine cannot oxidise chloride ions to chlorine:

$$Cl_2\,(aq) + 2\,I^-\,(aq) \longrightarrow I_2\,(aq) + 2\,Cl^-\,(aq) \quad ☑$$

$$I_2\,(aq) + 2\,Cl^-\,(aq) \longrightarrow Cl_2\,(aq) + 2\,I^-\,(aq) \quad ☒$$

Conversely the loss of electrons to form empty valence shells is behaviour that is typical of metals, so metals behave as reductants and occur in the right hand column of the table. The most reactive metals are at the top and the reactivity decreases going down the table. A metal higher in the series will displace a metal lower in the series from its salts, but the reverse reaction cannot occur. For example zinc will displace copper from copper(II) salts (i.e. zinc is a powerful enough reductant to reduce copper ions to copper), but copper will not displace zinc from zinc salts (i.e. copper is not a powerful enough reductant to reduce zinc ions to zinc):

$$Zn\,(s) + Cu^{2+}\,(aq) \longrightarrow Cu\,(s) + Zn^{2+}\,(aq) \quad ☑$$

$$Cu\,(s) + Zn^{2+}\,(aq) \longrightarrow Zn\,(s) + Cu^{2+}\,(aq) \quad ☒$$

The above reactions of both the halogens and the metals are known as **displacement reactions**, because they involve are more reactive metal/non-metal displacing the less reactive one from its salt.

The position of a metal in the series relative to hydrogen can also be used to predict whether a metal will liberate hydrogen from dilute acids. Metals above hydrogen are powerful enough reducting agents to reduce hydrogen ions to hydrogen, for example magnesium:

$$Mg\,(s) + 2\,H^+\,(aq) \longrightarrow H_2\,(g) + Mg^{2+}\,(aq)$$

Metals below hydrogen, such as copper, are not strong enough reducing agents to reduce hydrogen ions and hence will not react with dilute acids.

Hence if zinc foil is dipped into aqueous copper sulfate, the zinc will acquire a reddish-brown coating of metallic copper and the blue colour of the solution will fade. See Figure 903

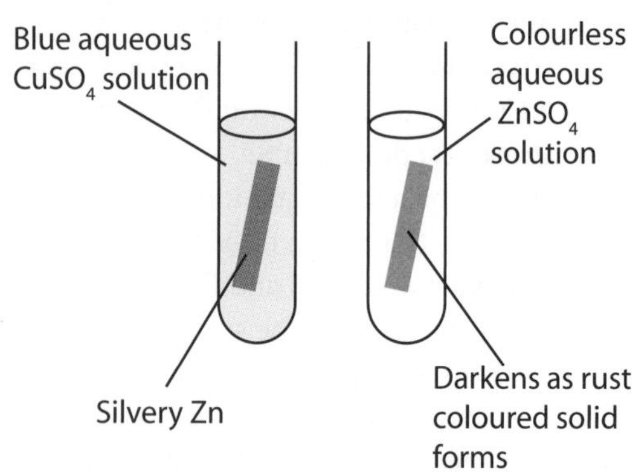

Figure 903 Reaction of metals and salts

Exercise 9.3

1. Which one of the following metals is the most powerful reductant (reducing agent)?

   A Copper
   B Magnesium
   C Iron
   D Zinc

2. In which one of the following would you expect a reaction to occur?

   A Copper placed in aqueous zinc chloride
   B Zinc placed in aqueous silver nitrate
   C Iron placed in aqueous magnesium sulfate
   D Magnesium placed in aqueous sodium chloride

3. Zinc reacts with dilute acids to liberate hydrogen. This is because

   A the zinc ion is a more powerful oxidising agent than the hydrogen ion.
   B the hydrogen ion is a more powerful oxidising agent than the zinc ion.
   C the zinc ion is a more powerful reducing agent than the hydrogen ion.
   D the hydrogen ion is a more powerful reducing agent than the zinc ion.

4. a) What would you observe when chlorine is bubbled through aqueous sodium bromide?

   b) What would you see when bromine is added to aqueous sodium chloride?

c) Interpret these results {in a) and b)} in terms of the reactions that occur and explain what this shows about the relative oxidising power of chlorine and bromine.

5. You have a sample of a metal M and an aqueous solution of its sulfate, MSO_4. Describe some simple experiments that you could do to try and determine the reactivity of M relative to other common metals such as copper, zinc and magnesium. Explain how you would interpret the results of these experiments.

9.4 VOLTAIC CELLS

9.4.1 Explain how a redox reaction is used to produce electricity in a Voltaic cell.

9.4.2 State that oxidation occurs at the negative electrode (anode) and reduction occurs at the positive electrode (cathode).

A **Voltaic** (Galvanic or electrochemical) **cell** is a device for converting chemical energy into electrical energy using a spontaneous redox reaction as a source of electrical energy and this is the basis of commercial **electrochemical cell**s (batteries). The opposite, which uses electrical energy to carry out a non-spontaneous redox reaction is known as electrolysis.

Consider a metal in contact with an aqueous solution of its ions. A redox equilibrium will be established and the metal will acquire an electrical charge:

$$M\,(s) \rightleftharpoons M^{n+}\,(aq) + n\,e^-$$

In the case of a reactive metal, the equilibrium will tend to the right, a little of the metal will dissolve and the remaining metal will become negatively charged because of the excess of electrons. The opposite may be true for an unreactive metal. It is not possible to measure these electrode potentials directly, but an electrical circuit can be constructed to compare the potentials of two such electrodes, using apparatus such as that illustrated in Figure 904.

The more reactive metal will always be the negative electrode and the greater the difference in reactivity of the metals, the greater the cell potential. A high resistance voltmeter connected between the metals will measure the potential difference between them. If however they are connected by a wire then this allows electrons to flow from the negative electrode (in this case the zinc) to the positive electrode (in this case the copper). At the negative electrode, the metal will slowly dissolve as these electrons are removed. In this case the reaction is:

$$Zn\,(s) \longrightarrow Zn^{2+}\,(aq) + 2\,e^-$$

Because electrons are lost from the negative electrode an oxidation reaction must occur to produce these electrons (LEO) and hence this is the anode, as oxidation always occurs at the anode. At the positive electrode, the electrons react with the metal ions to form a layer of the metal. In this case the reaction is:

$$Cu^{2+}\,(aq) + 2\,e^- \longrightarrow Cu\,(s)$$

As electrons flow to the positive electrode, a reduction reaction must occur to consume these electrons (GER)

CORE

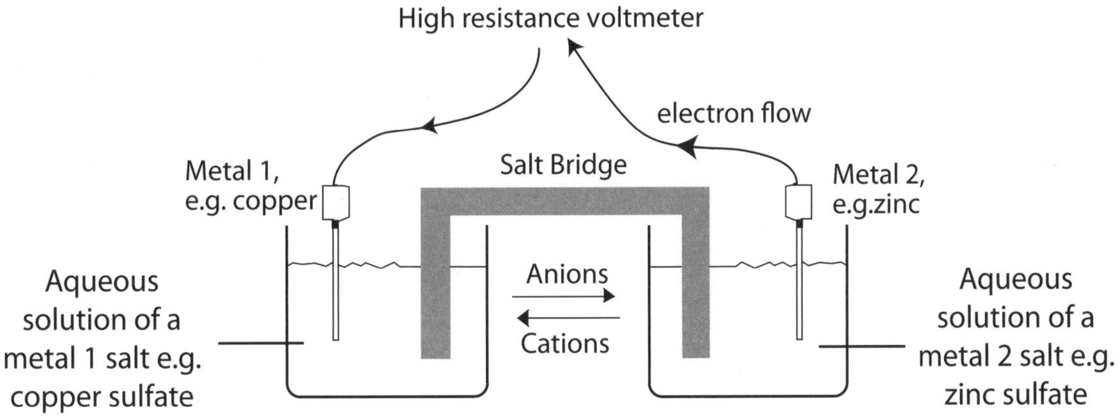

Figure 904 A typical Voltaic cell

and hence this is the cathode, as reduction always occurs at the cathode. Overall the cell reaction is:

$$Zn\ (s) + Cu^{2+}\ (aq) \longrightarrow Cu\ (s) + Zn^{2+}\ (aq)$$

Note that this is the same as the displacement reaction mentioned in the previous section, but in this case the energy produced in this spontaneous reaction is converted to electrical energy rather than heat. The cell will therefore continue to generate electricity until the zinc or the copper sulfate is all consumed.

The salt bridge in the electrochemical cell allows the movement of ions between the solutions, thus completing the circuit and maintaining electrical neutrality. This is frequently a piece of filter paper dipped in a solution of a strong electrolyte, such as potassium nitrate. At the right hand electrode in Figure 904 positive ions are being produced and at the left hand one they are being consumed. For this reason positive ions move from right to left in the salt bridge and negative ions from left to right.

Exercise 9.4

1. Two different metals are connected together in an electrochemical cell. Which of the following is true of the electrode made of the more reactive metal?

   A It will be the negative electrode and it will undergo oxidation.
   B It will be the negative electrode and it will undergo reduction.
   C It will be the positive electrode and it will undergo oxidation.
   D It will be the positive electrode and it will undergo reduction.

2. An electrochemical cell is capable of doing work. What is the source of the energy for this?

   A It comes from the thermal energy.
   B It comes from stored electrons.
   C It comes from an endothermic chemical reaction.
   D It comes from an exothermic chemical reaction.

3. An electrochemical cell is constructed using magnesium in aqueous magnesium sulphate and iron in aqueous iron(II) sulphate. What reactions would occur at the electrodes?

	Magnesium electrode	Iron electrode
A	$Mg\ (s) \longrightarrow Mg^{2+}\ (aq) + 2\ e^-$	$Fe\ (s) \longrightarrow Fe^{2+}\ (aq) + 2\ e^-$
B	$Mg\ (s) \longrightarrow Mg^{2+}\ (aq) + 2\ e^-$	$Fe^{2+}\ (aq) + 2\ e^- \longrightarrow Fe\ (s)$
C	$Mg^{2+}\ (aq) + 2\ e^- \longrightarrow Mg\ (s)$	$Fe\ (s) \longrightarrow Fe^{2+}\ (aq) + 2\ e^-$
D	$Mg^{2+}\ (aq) + 2\ e^- \longrightarrow Mg\ (s)$	$Fe^{2+}\ (aq) + 2\ e^- \longrightarrow Fe\ (s)$

4. (a) Draw a fully labelled diagram of an electrochemical cell using iron and copper as the two metals.

   (b) Show a wire connecting the two electrodes and mark on it the direction of electron flow.
   (c) Write half equations for the reactions that take place at the two electrodes.
   (d) State clearly which electrode is the anode and which the cathode.
   (e) Explain the function of the salt bridge.

5. You are intending to construct an electrochemical cell using two metals, chosen from copper, iron, magnesium and zinc, in aqueous solutions of their salts. Explain how you can use a reactivity series to choose the pair of metal that will produce the greatest potential difference for the cell and to predict which metal will be the anode and which the cathode.

HIGHER LEVEL

19.1 STANDARD ELECTRODE POTENTIALS (AHL)

19.1.1 Describe the standard hydrogen electrode.

19.1.2 Define the term standard electrode potential (E^{θ}).

19.1.3 Calculate cell potentials using standard electrode potentials.

19.1.4 Predict whether a reaction will be spontaneous using standard electrode potential values.

The potential of any two electrodes can be compared using the apparatus shown in Figure 904, and connecting the electrodes with a very high resistance voltmeter. (The high internal resistance of the cell means that the potential difference falls very rapidly if any current is allowed to flow, hence the need for a very high resistance voltmeter.) Conventionally electrode potentials are measured relative to the **standard hydrogen electrode** (SHE), which is defined as having a potential of zero. The potential differences of electrodes relative to this are known as standard electrode potentials (E^{θ}). Standard electrode potentials also refer to a temperature of 298K, normal atmospheric pressure (101.3 kPa) and the concentration of all solutions being 1 mol dm^{-3}. The construction of the standard hydrogen electrode is shown in Figure 906:

'Platinum black' is very finely divided platinum, which catalyses the electrode equilibrium:

$$2\,H^{+}\,(aq) + 2\,e^{-} \rightleftharpoons H_2\,(g)$$

Thus, the standard electrode potential of a half-cell, (also called standard reduction potential) is the **e.m.f.** of the half-cell when it is connected to the standard hydrogen electrode. If the half-cell is the positive terminal of the cell, then the sign of the standard electrode potential is positive (for example Ag^{+}/Ag is + 0.80 V); if however the half-cell is the negative terminal of the cell, then the sign of the standard electrode potential is negative (for example Zn^{2+}/Zn is – 0.76 V).

The electrode potential concept can be extended to redox couples that do not involve metals, for example iodine and the iodide ion. In this case the electrode consists of an inert metal, such as platinum, dipped into a solution containing both the oxidised and reduced form of the couple, so that the redox reaction can occur on the surface of the metal.

Reactive metals, that lose electrons easily have large negative electrode potentials (for example –2.71 V for Na^{+}/Na) and reactive non-metals, that gain electrons easily, have large positive electrode potentials (for example +2.87 V for $F_2/2\,F^{-}$). The greater the E^{θ}, the stronger the oxidising agent (on the left hand side of the equation as written below) and the weaker the reducting agent (on the right hand side). For example fluorine is a very powerful

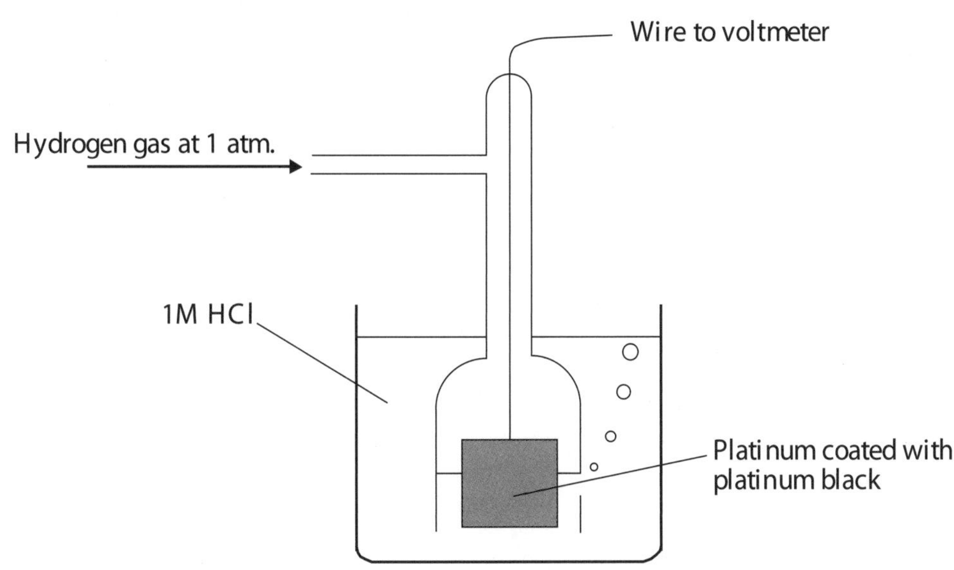

Figure 906 The standard hydrogen electrode

oxidising agent, but the fluoride ion is a very weak reducting agent. Conversely species with a very negative E^{θ} comprise weak oxidising agents and strong reducing agents. Electrode potentials are usually quoted for the oxidised form gaining electrons and being converted to the reduced form. Some species commonly involved in redox reactions and their E^{θ} values are given in Figure 907.

More powerful oxidizing agent ↓	**Half equation** In standard form: Oxidised + electrons ⇌ Reduced	E^{θ} in Volts	More powerful reducing agent ↑
	$Li^+ + e^- \rightleftharpoons Li$	–3.03	
	$K^+ + e^- \rightleftharpoons K$	–2.92	
	$Ca^{2+} + 2\,e^- \rightleftharpoons Ca$	–2.87	
	$Na^+ + e^- \rightleftharpoons Na$	–2.71	
	$Mg^{2+} + 2\,e^- \rightleftharpoons Mg$	–2.36	
	$Al^{3+} + 3\,e^- \rightleftharpoons Al$	–1.66	
	$Mn^{2+} + 2\,e^- \rightleftharpoons Mn$	–1.18	
	$H_2O + e^- \rightleftharpoons ½\,H_2 + OH^-$	–0.83	
	$Zn^{2+} + 2\,e^- \rightleftharpoons Zn$	–0.76	
	$Fe^{2+} + 2\,e^- \rightleftharpoons Fe$	–0.44	
	$Ni^{2+} + 2\,e^- \rightleftharpoons Ni$	–0.23	
	$Sn^{2+} + 2\,e^- \rightleftharpoons Sn$	–0.14	
	$Pb^{2+} + 2\,e^- \rightleftharpoons Pb$	–0.13	
	$H^+ + e^- \rightleftharpoons ½\,H_2$	0.00	
	$SO_4^{2-} + 4\,H^+ + 2\,e^- \rightleftharpoons SO_2 + 2\,H_2O$	+0.17	
	$Cu^{2+} + 2\,e^- \rightleftharpoons Cu$	+0.34	
	$½\,O_2 + H_2O + 2\,e^- \rightleftharpoons 2\,OH^-$	+0.40	
	$Cu^+ + e^- \rightleftharpoons Cu$	+0.52	
	$I_2\,(s) + 2\,e^- \rightleftharpoons 2\,I^-$	+0.54	
	$I_2\,(aq) + 2\,e^- \rightleftharpoons 2\,I^-$	+0.62	
	$Fe^{3+} + e^- \rightleftharpoons Fe^{2+}$	+0.77	
	$Ag^+ + e^- \rightleftharpoons Ag$	+0.80	
	$Br_2 + 2\,e^- \rightleftharpoons 2\,Br^-$	+1.09	
	$½\,O_2 + 2\,H^+ + 2\,e^- \rightleftharpoons H_2O$	+1.23	
	$Cr_2O_7^{2-} + 14\,H^+ + 6\,e^- \rightleftharpoons 2\,Cr^{3+} + 7\,H_2O$	+1.33	
	$Cl_2 + 2\,e^- \rightleftharpoons 2\,Cl^-$	+1.36	
	$MnO_4^- + 8\,H^+ + 5\,e^- \rightleftharpoons Mn^{2+} + 4\,H_2O$	+1.51	
	$F_2 + 2\,e^- \rightleftharpoons 2\,F^-$	+2.87	

Figure 907 The standard electrode potentials of common species in aqueous solution

Standard electrode potentials allow predictions to be made about which reactions can theoretically occur. For example chlorine is a more powerful oxidant than bromine, as it has a more positive E^{θ}, so chlorine could oxidise bromide to bromine (because it 'wants the electrons more'), but bromine could not oxidise chloride to chlorine. Similarly, considering zinc and copper, zinc is the more powerful reducing agent, so it can reduce copper(II) ions to copper, but copper could not reduce zinc(II) ions to zinc.

A more formal way of considering this is to calculate the **cell potential** that would be generated by a particular redox reaction, if the half reactions were combined in an electrolytic cell. Consider the question of whether acidified potassium dichromate(VI) will oxidise iron(II) to iron(III). The equation for the reaction can be produced by combining the two half equations. That for the iron(II)/iron(III), as well as being multiplied by six, needs to be reversed to give the required equation, so the sign of its electrode potential is changed – note that the fact that the iron(III)/iron(II) equation needed multiplying by a factor, does not affect the magnitude of the electrode potential. Thus, you must not multiply the E^{θ} values by coefficients in front of balanced equations.

Half equations:

$$Cr_2O_7^{2-} + 14\,H^+ + 6\,e^- \rightleftharpoons 2\,Cr^{3+} + 7\,H_2O \quad E^{\theta} = +1.33\text{ V}$$

$$6\,Fe^{2+} \rightleftharpoons 6\,Fe^{3+} + 6\,e^- \quad E^{\theta} = -0.77\text{ V}$$

Cell equation:

$$Cr_2O_7^{2-} + 14H^+ + 6Fe^{2+} \rightleftharpoons 2Cr^{3+} + 7H_2O + 6Fe^{3+} \quad E^{\theta}_{cell} = +0.56\text{ V}$$

The cell potential is calculated by adding the electrode potentials. If the cell potential is positive, as in the above case, then the reaction could occur spontaneously (meaning it is capable of doing work in the form of electrical energy), if negative then it could not. As a further example, consider whether copper metal can reduce hydrogen ions to hydrogen gas:

Half equations:

$$Cu \rightleftharpoons Cu^{2+} + 2\,e^- \quad E^{\theta} = -0.34\text{ V}$$

$$2\,H^+ + 2\,e^- \rightleftharpoons H_2 \quad E^{\theta} = 0.00\text{ V}$$

Cell equation:

$$Cu + 2\,H^+ \rightleftharpoons Cu^{2+} + H_2 \quad E^{\theta}_{cell} = -0.34\text{ V}$$

In this case the cell potential is negative so a spontaneous reaction cannot occur, which fits in with the experimental observation that copper does not dissolve in dilute acids. The reverse reaction (hydrogen reducing copper(II) ions to copper) is however spontaneous. In aqueous solution however the activation energy is too high, but it does occur if hydrogen is passed over heated copper(II) oxide.

It must be remembered that predictions made using electrode potentials give no indication of the activation energy and so even the most favourable reaction may not occur in practice if it has a very high activation energy. These predictions, made either by considering which species is the more powerful oxidant/reductant, or by calculating E_{cell}, only give predictions about the reaction under standard conditions (T = 298 K, P = 101.3 kPa, all concentrations 1 mol dm^{-3}). If the electrode potentials are quite close (< 0.2 V different) then an equilibrium rather than complete reaction will result. It may then be possible to produce some product from an unfavourable reaction by altering the conditions in accordance with Le Chatelier's principle.

EXTENSION

Predictions about whether a reaction can occur or not can also result from calculating free energy change for a reaction. There is actually a relationship between E^{θ}_{cell} and ΔG^{θ}:

$$\Delta G^{\theta} = -nFE^{\theta}_{cell}$$

Where n is the number of electrons transferred and F the Faraday constant (the charge on 1 mole of electrons = 96,500 C mol^{-1}). From this it can be seen that if E^{θ}_{cell} is positive then ΔG^{θ} will be negative so a spontaneous reaction is possible and *vice versa*. Using the above examples:

Iron(II)-dichromate(VI) E^{θ}cell = +0.56 V

$$\Delta G^{\theta} = -6 \times 96500 \times 0.56 = -324\text{ kJ mol}^{-1}$$

Copper - dilute acid E^{θ}cell = −0.34 V

$$\Delta G^{\theta} = -2 \times 96500 \times (-0.34) = +66\text{ kJ mol}^{-1}$$

The greater the value of E^{θ}cell, the more negative will be the value of ΔG^{θ} and the more spontaneous the reaction.

Consider the general equilibrium:

$$Ox + n\,e^- \rightleftharpoons Red$$

Increasing [Ox], or decreasing [Red] will shift the position of equilibrium to the right, reducing the number of electrons and hence making E^{θ} more positive. Similarly E^{θ} will become more negative if [Ox] is decreased or [Red] increased. In the case of metal/metal ion electrodes, the reduced form is the solid metal and so its concentration is fixed, the equilibrium being:

$$M^{n+} + n\,e^- \rightleftharpoons M$$

This means that increasing the concentration of the metal ions will make E^{θ} more positive and decreasing the concentration will make it more negative, and hence a better reducing agent. Consider a zinc-copper cell which is initially at standard conditions. The spontaneous reaction will be:

$$Zn\,(s) + Cu^{2+}\,(aq) \longrightarrow Zn^{2+}\,(aq) + Cu\,(s) \qquad E^{\theta}_{cell} = +1.10\text{ V.}$$

With time, $[Zn^{2+}]$ increases and so the zinc electrode becomes more positive. At the same time $[Cu^{2+}]$ decreases and so the copper electrode becomes more negative. As a result the cell potential decreases with time. Eventually the ratio $[Zn^{2+}]/[Cu^{2+}]$ becomes equal to K_c for the cell (= 10^{37}) and equilibrium is reached. As $\Delta G = 0$ at equilibrium, the voltage = 0 and the cell is 'dead'.

EXTENSION

The effect of concentration on the potential of a half-cell is quantified in the **Nernst equation**:

$$E = E^0 - \frac{RT}{nF}\ln\left(\frac{a_{Ox}}{a_{Red}}\right)$$

Where again n is the number of electrons transferred and F the Faraday constant (96,500 C mol^{-1}), R the gas constant (8.314 J mol^{-1} K^{-1}) and T the absolute temperature (in K).

To save drawing the apparatus used, the cell can be represented by a shorthand notation, called a cell diagram By convention this is written so that the oxidation half-reaction is placed on the left and the reduction half reaction placed on the right. A single vertical line (|) is placed between the metal and its ions and the salt bridge represented by two complete (||)or dashed (¦¦) lines. Taking the zinc-copper cell as an example:

Cell Diagram:

$$Zn\,(s)\,|\,Zn^{2+}\,(aq)\,¦¦\,Cu^{2+}\,(aq)\,|\,Cu\,(s) \quad E^{\theta}_{cell} = +\,1.10\text{V}$$

E^{θ}_{cell} is the difference between the two standard electrode potentials. The convention is to write E^{θ}_{cell} as (E^{θ}(right hand side) – E^{θ}(left hand side)); in this case (+0.34 – (–0.76)) = +1.10V. The positive sign of E^{θ}_{cell} indicates that the right hand (copper) electrode is the positive electrode.

Exercise

1. Which one of the following is not a condition for the standard hydrogen electrode?

   A The temperature must be 298K.
   B The pressure of hydrogen must be 101.3 kPa.
   C The concentration of hydrogen ions in solution must be 1 mol dm^{-3}.
   D The concentration of hydrogen gas in solution must be 1 mol dm^{-3}.

2. The standard electrode potentials of nickel and lead are:

   $Ni^{2+} + 2e^- \rightleftharpoons Ni \qquad E^{\theta} = -0.23$ V

   $Pb^{2+} + 2e^- \rightleftharpoons Pb \qquad E^{\theta} = -0.13$ V

   What is the cell potential for the reaction $Ni^{2+} + Pb \rightleftharpoons Ni + Pb^{2+}$?

   A +0.36 V
   B +0.1 V
   C –0.1 V
   D –0.36 V

3. A number of possible oxidising agents are suggested to oxidise bromide ions to bromine. Given the information below, which is the most likely to suceed?

   $\frac{1}{2}Br_2 + e^- \rightleftharpoons Br^- \qquad E^{\theta} = +1.09$ V

   A Iodate(V) ions
   ($2\,IO_3^- + 12\,H^+ + 10\,e^- \rightleftharpoons I_2 + 6\,H_2O$
   $E^{\theta} = +1.19$ V)
   B Copper ions
   ($Cu^{2+} + 2\,e^- \rightleftharpoons Cu$
   $E^{\theta} = +0.34$ V)
   C Phosphoric acid
   ($H_3PO_4 + 2\,H^+ + 2\,e^- \rightleftharpoons H_3PO_3 + H_2O$
   $E^{\theta} = -0.28$ V)
   D Hydrogen gas
   ($H_2 + 2\,e^- \rightleftharpoons 2\,H^-$
   $E^{\theta} = -2.25$ V)

4.

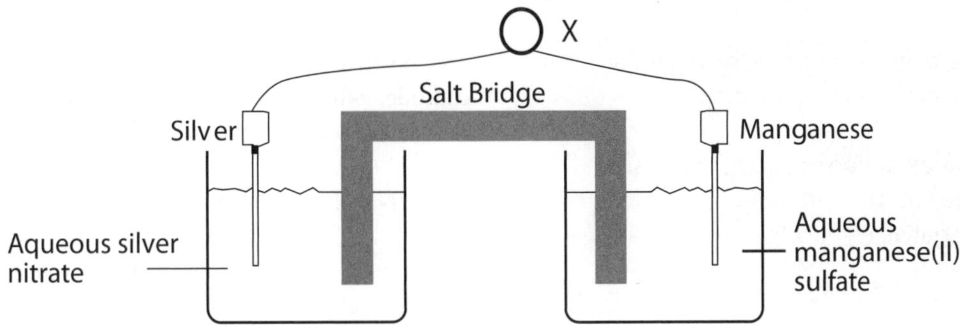

The apparatus above can be used to compare the electrode potentials of silver and manganese. According to reference sources, the standard electrode potentials of these metals are:

$Mn^{2+} + 2e^- \rightleftharpoons Mn$ $\quad E^\theta = -1.18$ V
$Ag^+ + e^- \rightleftharpoons Ag$ $\quad E^\theta = +0.80$ V

a) In order for the comparison to be of standard electrode potentials, what conditions must be imposed?

b) If the experiment was to determine the standard electrode potential of manganese, what must replace the silver/silver nitrate electrode?

c) What instrument is the instrument labelled '**X**' in the diagram?

d) What could be used as a 'salt bridge'?

e) Supposing the silver and manganese electrodes are joined directly with a wire:

i. In which direction will the electrons flow?

ii. Describe the changes that will take place at the silver electrode.

iii. Describe the changes that will take place at the manganese electrode.

iv. In what direction will the anions and cations in the salt bridge move?

f) Give the shorthand notation for the cell.

g) What would you expect the cell potential to be? (Ensure that the sign corresponds to your notation in f). What is the corresponding cell reaction?

h) Calculate ΔG^θ for this reaction and state what this indicates about the spontaneity of the reaction.

i) If the silver nitrate solution were diluted, would you expect the cell potential to increase or decrease? Explain your answer.

9.5 ELECTROLYTIC CELLS

9.5.1 Describe, using a diagram, the essential components of an electrolytic cell.

9.5.2 State that oxidation occurs at the positive electrode (anode) and reduction occurs at the negative electrode (cathode).

9.5.3 Describe how current is conducted in an electrolytic cell.

9.5.4 Deduce the products of the electrolysis of a molten salt.

In **electrolysis** electrical energy is used to bring about a non-spontaneous redox reaction. This is done by passing an electric current through a liquid containing ions, known as an **electrolyte**. In contrast to metals, the current in electrolytes is carried by the movement of ions rather than the movement of electrons. The solid conductors inserted into the liquid are called electrodes, the one with a positive charge is called the **anode** (because it attracts anions) and the one with the negative charge is called the **cathode.** When the anions reach the anode they lose electrons and are therefore oxidized (LEO). Similarly when the cations reach the cathode they gain electrons and are therefore reduced (GER). This process is illustrated in Figure 909.

Consider the electrolysis of molten sodium chloride. The negative chloride ions are attracted to the positive anode, where they lose electrons and are therefore oxidized to chlorine gas:

$$2\,Cl^{-}\,(l) \longrightarrow Cl_2\,(g) + 2\,e^{-}$$

The positive sodium ions are attracted to the negative cathode, where they gain electrons and are therefore reduced to sodium metal:

$$Na^{+}\,(l) + e^{-} \longrightarrow Na\,(l)$$

Electrolysis of a molten electrolyte is often used to obtain reactive metals from their ores.

Exercise 9.5

1. Which one of the following statements about electrolysis is correct?

   A Oxidation always occurs at the anode because oxygen is often evolved here.
   B Oxidation always occurs at the anode because it removes electrons from the electrolyte.
   C Oxidation always occurs at the cathode because hydrogen is often evolved here.
   D Oxidation always occurs at the cathode because it donates electrons to the electrolyte.

2. By what means is an electrical current carried in a molten salt?

   A By the movement of anions only.
   B By the movement of cations only.
   C By the movement of both anions and cations.
   D By the movement of electrons.

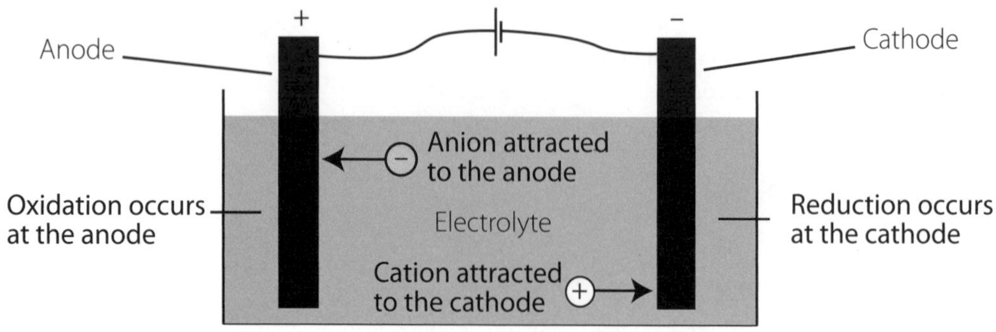

Figure 909 A diagrammatic representation of electrolysis

3. When molten lead(II) bromide is electrolysed,

   A the lead ions gain electrons at the anode to form lead.
   B the lead ions gain electrons at the cathode to form lead.
   C the lead ions lose electrons at the anode to form lead.
   D the lead ions lose electrons at the cathode to form lead.

4. This question concerns the passage of electricity through sodium chloride.

   a) Is the bonding in sodium chloride metallic, ionic or covalent?
   b) State whether the following would conduct electricity.
      i) Solid sodium chloride
      ii) Molten sodium chloride
      iii) Aqueous sodium chloride

   c) What names are given to the following?
      i) Passing an electric current through a liquid containing ions.
      ii) The liquid containing ions.
      iii) The solid conductors put into the liquid.

   d) A D.C. current is used and particular names are given to the solid conductors attached to the positive and negative terminals of the power supply. What are these names?
   e) Oxidation occurs on the surface of one of the solid conductors. Which one?

5. This question concerns the electrolysis of copper chloride.

   a) Solid copper chloride does not conduct electricity? Explain why.
   b) Give two ways in which it can be made to conduct.
   c) Write a balanced half equation for the reaction that occurs at the anode.
   d) What would be observed on the surface of this electrode?
   e) Write a balanced half equation for the reaction that occurs at the cathode.
   f) What would be observed on the surface of this electrode?
   g) Does e) represent an oxidation or a reduction reaction? Explain why.

HIGHER LEVEL

19.2 ELECTROLYSIS (AHL)

19.2.1 Predict and explain the products of electrolysis of aqueous solutions.

19.2.2 Determine the relative amounts of the products formed during electrolysis.

19.2.3 Describe the use of electrolysis in electroplating.

AHL

When a molten salt is electrolysed the cations are attracted to the cathode where they undergo reduction and the anions are attracted to the anode where they undergo oxidation. If the electrolyte is an aqueous solution, then the water present can also be oxidised or reduced. At the cathode, the water can be reduced to hydrogen gas and this will occur unless the electrolyte contains the ions of a metal low in the electrochemical series (with $E^{\theta} > 0$), such as silver and copper, or other easily reduced cations.

$$2\,H_2O\,(l) + 2\,e^- \longrightarrow H_2\,(g) + 2\,OH^-\,(aq)$$

Alternatively this can be regarded as the reduction of hydrogen ions produced from the dissociation of water:

$$2\,H^+\,(aq) + 2\,e^- \longrightarrow H_2\,(g)$$

Similarly at the anode the water can be oxidised to oxygen gas and this will occur unless the electrolyte contains easily oxidised anions, such as bromide and iodide ions, with $E^{\theta} < 1.23$ V, the E^{θ} for the oxygen/water half-cell.

$$2\,H_2O\,(l) \longrightarrow O_2\,(g) + 4\,H^+\,(aq) + 4\,e^-$$

Again this may regarded as the oxidation of hydroxide ions produced from the dissociation of water:

$$4\,OH^-\,(aq) \longrightarrow O_2\,(g) + 2\,H_2O\,(l) + 4\,e^-$$

Usually in electrolysis the electrodes are made from an inert conductor, such as graphite or platinum. If however the anode is made from a metal that is not inert, such as copper, then the anode itself may be oxidised and dissolve into the solution as the E^{θ} for this half cell (E^{θ} Cu^{2+}/Cu = +0.34 V) is less than that for the oxygen/water half-cell.

$$Cu\ (s) \longrightarrow Cu^{2+}\ (aq) + 2\ e^-$$

Hence, if aqueous copper sulfate is electrolysed between copper electrodes, copper is in effect transferred from the anode (which decreases in mass) to the cathode (which increases in mass). This process is used to purify copper for use as an electrical conductor. The cathode becomes coated in a layer of the metal, a process called electroplating. Similarly electrolysis of a solution containing silver ions (or the ions of some other easily reduced metal) will result in the metal being deposited on the cathode and this process is often used to electroplate less reactive metals on to cathodes made of more reactive metals, either for decoration or protection against corrosion.

AHL

When considering the products from the electrolysis of an aqueous solution the possible reactions:

Cathode - formation of the metal or formation of hydrogen,
Anode - formation of the non-metal, formation of oxygen or oxidation of the electrode,

must be considered and the most energetically favourable will take place. For the cathode this will be the one with the most positive; for the anode the one with the most negative electrode potential. For most common electrolytes:

Cathode - hydrogen is formed unless Cu^{2+} or Ag^+ are present,
Anode - oxygen is formed unless Br^- or I^- are present.

This is illustrated by the examples of the products from the electrolysis of aqueous solutions given in Figure 910.

Aqueous electrolyte	Product at the **cathode**	Product at the **anode**
Copper(II) bromide	Copper	Bromine
Sodium iodide	Hydrogen	Iodine
Silver nitrate	Silver	Oxygen
Potassium sulfate	Hydrogen	Oxygen
Copper sulfate	Copper	Copper(II) ions (if Cu anode)

Figure 910 The products from the electrolysis of some aqueous solutions

Pure water cannot of course be electrolysed because the concentration of ions is too low to allow it to conduct the current. If, however, an electrolyte producing ions that are the same as those of water, or less easily oxidised/reduced (such as aqueous sulfuric acid, aqueous sodium hydroxide or potassium sulfate - see Figure 909) is added, then hydrogen is produced at the cathode and oxygen at the anode. The volume of hydrogen produced at the cathode is twice that of oxygen produced at the anode because the production of one mole of oxygen gas requires twice the number of electrons that are needed for the production of one mole of hydrogen gas.

$$4\ H_2O\ (l) + 4\ e^- \longrightarrow 2\ H_2\ (g) + 4\ OH^-\ (aq)$$

4 moles of electrons produces two moles of H_2 gas

$$2\ H_2O\ (l) \longrightarrow O_2\ (g) + 4\ H^+\ (aq) + 4\ e^-$$

4 moles of electrons are given off when one mole of O_2 gas is produced

In effect the energy from the electric current is being used to split water into its component elements.

In some cases, when there is little difference in the ease of discharge of the ion and water, the concentration of the electrolyte may be the determining factor. The E^{θ} for the oxidation of chloride ions (+1.36 V) is not much greater than that for the oxidation of water (+1.23 V). In dilute aqueous sodium chloride for example, the major product of electrolysis at the anode is oxygen. If however a saturated solution of sodium chloride is used, then E^{θ} for the oxidation of chloride ions falls and the major product is chlorine. The electrolysis of sodium chloride, both molten and aqueous, is very important industrially and is covered in considerable detail in Section C.12.

The amount of product that results from electrolysis will depend upon:

- The number of electrons required to produce one mole of product.
- The magnitude of the **current** (the rate of flow of electrons).
- The time for which the current is passed.

For example if the same current is passed for the same time through an aqueous solution containing silver ions and an aqueous solution containing copper ions, then the amount of metal produced at the cathode of the silver cell would be twice as large as that produced in the copper cell, because the reduction of a silver ion requires one electron whereas the reduction of a copper ion requires two electrons:

$$Ag^+ + e^- \longrightarrow Ag \qquad Cu^{2+} + 2\ e^- \longrightarrow Cu$$

To produce the same amount of copper would require doubling the number of electrons passed, either by doubling the current or doubling the time it was passed for. The mass of product would of course also depend on the molar masses of the metals concerned.

EXTENSION

The amount of product can be calculated knowing the current and the time for which it is passed. The unit of electrical charge is the Coulomb (C). The number of Coulombs passed during electrolysis may be calculated by multiplying the current passing (in Amps) by the length of time for which it is passed (in seconds)

Charge (in Coulombs) = Current (in Amps) × Time (in secs)

The charge carried by one mole of electrons can be found by multiplying the charge on the electron (1.60×10^{-19} C) by the Avogadro constant (6.02×10^{23} mol^{-1}). The result (96500 C mol^{-1}) is known as the **Faraday constant.** Knowing the charge passed and this constant, the number of moles of electrons may be calculated:

$$\text{Amount of electrons} = \frac{\text{Charge passed (in C)}}{96\,500}$$

The amount of product formed can then be calculated from the balanced equation for the reaction at the electrode, which gives the ratio of the amount of electrons to the amount of product.

Example

Find the mass of copper produced at the cathode by passing a current of 3.00A through aqueous copper(II) sulfate for exactly 2 hours.

Solution

$$\begin{aligned}\text{Charge (in C)} &= \text{Current (in Amps)} \times \text{Time (in sec)}\\ &= 3.00 \times (2 \times 60 \times 60)\\ &= 21600 \text{ C}\end{aligned}$$

$$\begin{aligned}\text{Amount of electrons} &= \frac{\text{Charge passed (in C)}}{96\,500}\\ &= \frac{21\,600}{96\,500}\\ &= 0.2238 \text{ moles}\end{aligned}$$

$$Cu^{2+} + 2\,e^{-} \longrightarrow Cu$$

$$\begin{aligned}\text{Amount of Cu} &= \tfrac{1}{2} \text{ Moles of electrons}\\ &= \tfrac{1}{2} \times 0.2238\\ &= 0.1119 \text{ moles}\end{aligned}$$

$$\begin{aligned}\text{Mass of Cu} &= n \times M\\ &= 0.1119 \times 63.55\\ &= 7.11 \text{ g}\end{aligned}$$

Exercise 19.2

1. Which one of the following salts would give the same products irrespective of whether the molten salt or the aqueous solution is electrolysed?

   A Magnesium bromide
   B Copper(II) sulfate
   C Magnesium sulfate
   D Copper(II) bromide

2. An electric current is passed through two electrolysis cells in series. In the first, copper is deposited on the cathode from aqueous copper(II) sulfate. In the second, silver is deposited on the cathode from aqueous silver nitrate. After a certain length of time the mass of the copper cathode has increased by 1 g. Given that the relative atomic masses of silver and copper are 107.87 and 63.55 respectively, what will the increase in mass of the silver electrode be?

   A $\frac{2 \times 107.87}{63.55}$
   B $\frac{2 \times 63.55}{107.87}$
   C $\frac{107.87}{2 \times 63.55}$
   D $\frac{63.55}{2 \times 107.87}$

3. When an aqueous solution of a metal salt is electrolysed so that the metal is deposited on the cathode, which one of the following will not affect the increase in mass of the cathode, if the other variables are fixed?

   A The charge on the ion.
   B The molar mass of the metal.
   C The charge passed.
   D The potential difference applied.

4. With aqueous solutions containing ions, the water may be oxidised or reduced in preference to the ions present. Consider the electrolysis of a concentrated aqueous solution of calcium chloride.

   a) Which ion(s) will be attracted to the anode?

   b) Does oxidation or reduction occur at the anode?

   c) Which will be changed most easily, the ion from the calcium chloride or the water?

   d) Write a balanced equation for the reaction at the anode.

   e) What would be seen at the anode?

   f) Describe how diluting the electrolyte may affect the product at the anode

   g) Which ion(s) will travel to the cathode?

   h) Which ion will be changed most easily, the ion from the calcium chloride or the water?

   i) Write a balanced equation for the reaction at the cathode.

   j) What would be seen at the cathode?

   k) What would the aqueous solution eventually change into?

   l) As electrical energy is required for this change, what is the probable sign of $\Delta G^{\ominus}$ for the reaction?

EXTENSION

5. When aqueous copper(II) sulfate is electrolysed using copper electrodes, copper is transferred from the anode to the cathode. A current of 0.200 A is passed through such a cell for exactly 5 hours.

   a) The value of the Faraday constant is 96500 C mol^{-1}. What does the Faraday constant represent?

   b) What is the total charge passed through the cell?

   c) Given that the molar mass of copper is 63.55 g mol^{-1}, calculate the increase in mass of the cathode.

EXTENSION

ORGANIC CHEMISTRY

10.1 Introduction

20.1 Introduction (AHL)

10.2 Alkanes

10.3 Alkenes

10.4 Alcohols

10.5 Halogenoalkanes

10.6 Reaction pathways

20.5 Reaction pathways (AHL)

20.2 Nucleophilic substitution reactions (AHL)

20.3 Elimination reactions (AHL)

20.4 Condensation reactions (AHL)

20.6 Stereoisomerism (AHL)

10.1 INTRODUCTION

10.1.1 Describe the features of a homologous series.

10.1.2 Predict and explain the trends in boiling points of members of a homologous series.

10.1.13 Discuss the volatility and solubility in water of compounds containing the functional groups listed in AS 10.1.9.

Organic chemistry is the chemistry of carbon compounds (excluding compounds such as metal carbonates and oxides). Organic compounds constitute a major component of energy sources (petroleum, coal, natural gas), food (proteins, fats, carbohydrates, vitamins, enzymes, hormones, steroids), drugs (anaesthetics, antiseptics, antibiotics) and materials such as fibres, fabrics, plastics, paints, dyes, soaps, detergents, explosives etc.

Carbon is in group 4/14 of the periodic table and it always forms covalent bonds. As carbon has four electrons in its valence level (2,4 or $1s^2\ 2s^2\ 2p^2$) it forms four covalent bonds. When these are all single bonds, they have a tetrahedral arrangement. In organic molecules carbon always forms four bonds, oxygen two, hydrogen and the halogens one (refer Section 4.2)

Carbon atoms can combine with each other and with other atoms (especially H and O) to form millions of compounds. Compounds of this kind are the basis of all known life, hence the term 'organic'. The existence of such a large number of stable compounds is partly due to the strength and stability of the C—C and C—H bonds (348 and 412 kJ mol^{-1} respectively). The former ensure that carbon can form long chains (a process known as catenation) and rings of carbon atoms; the latter that these structures are relatively stable and unreactive. Multiple bonds can also be formed between carbon atoms, but the presence of these usually leads to an increase in chemical reactivity. Similarly **functional groups** containing other atoms, such as oxygen, nitrogen and the halogens, can be attached to the hydrocarbon chain and result in greater reactivity. The reactions of these functional groups are the dominant feature of organic chemistry. Organic compounds may therefore be usefully regarded as comprising a hydrocarbon skeleton to which **functional groups** are inserted and/or attached:

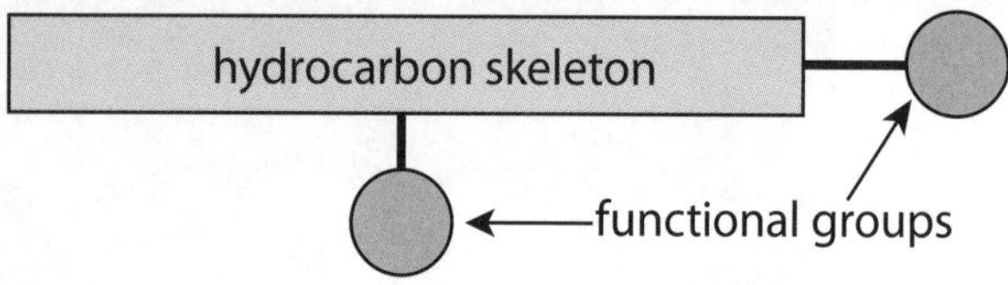

FIGURE 1001 Diagrammatic representation of an organic molecule

The ability of carbon atoms to form chains leads to the existence of a series of compounds that have the same functional group (and hence similar chemical properties) and only differ from each other by the presence of an additional carbon atom and its two associated hydrogen atoms in the molecule (which causes the physical properties to change in a regular manner). A series of compounds related in this way is said to form an **homologous series**. The alkanes are the simplest example of such a series, but others include the alkenes, the alcohols and the carboxylic acids. These series can be thought of as different 'families' of organic compounds. In these homologous series:

- successive compounds differ from each other by a $-CH_2-$ unit (known as a methylene group)
- the compounds can all be represented by a general formula (in the case of the alkanes C_nH_{2n+2}; if n = 3, then the formula is C_3H_8)
- the compounds have similar chemical properties
- successive compounds have physical properties that vary in a regular manner as the number of carbon atoms present increases.

The point about **chemical properties** is best illustrated by the sections that follow, on different homologous series. The changes in **physical properties** are a result of the changes that occur in the strength of van der Waals' forces with increasing molar mass and in some cases a change in molecular polarity. The simplest illustration of the effect of chain length on physical properties is the variation of the boiling point of the alkanes with the number of carbon atoms in the chain, as illustrated in Figure 1002.

This curve is initially quite steep because, for small molecules, the addition of an extra carbon has a proportionally larger effect on the molar mass (for example, from CH_4 to C_2H_6 there is an increase of 97.5%) and hence on the strength of the van der Waals' forces. As the length of the chain increases, the percentage change in molar mass becomes progressively smaller (there is a 10.9% increase in molar mass from C_9H_{20} to $C_{10}H_{22}$) and so the curve flattens. Similar regular variation would be found in graphs of other physical properties, such as density and viscosity, against the number of carbon atoms.

The physical properties, especially the melting and boiling point of a compound, depend on the intermolecular forces present. All other factors being unchanged, the greater the molar mass of a molecule the stronger the intermolecular forces, hence the trend in the boiling points of the alkanes illustrated below. Some functional groups (such as $>^{\delta+}C{=}O^{\delta-}$, in aldehydes and ketones, and the presence of halogens) give rise to polarity within molecules, and this results in dipole-dipole forces and hence slightly higher melting and boiling points than would otherwise be expected. Other functional groups, such as alcohol (—OH), carboxylic acid (—COOH), amine ($—NH_2$) and amide ($—CONH_2$) give rise to hydrogen bonding between the molecules. Compounds containing these tend to have significantly higher melting and boiling points than non-polar or polar organic compounds of similar molar masses.

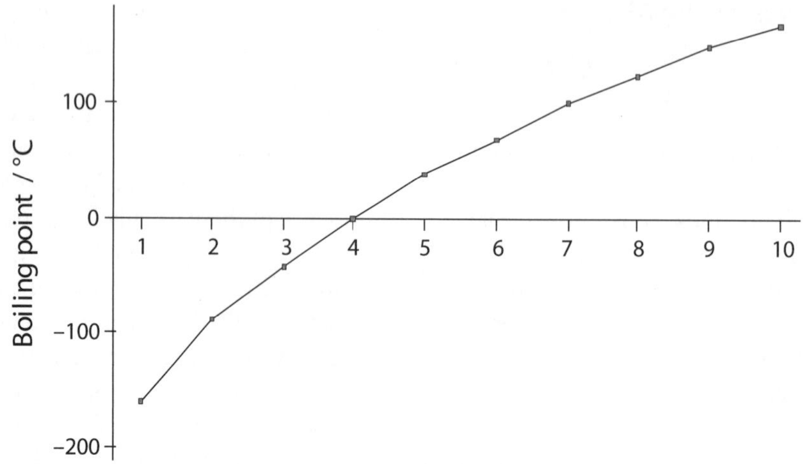

Figure 1002 Boiling points variations

These points are illustrated by the examples below:

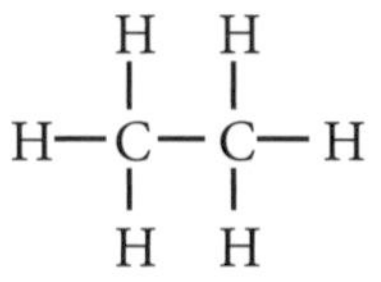

$$\begin{array}{ccccc} & H & & H & \\ & | & & | & \\ H- & C & - & C & -H \\ & | & & | & \\ & H & & H & \end{array}$$

Figure 1003 Ethane

$M_r = 30$ Non–polar b.p. = –89°C

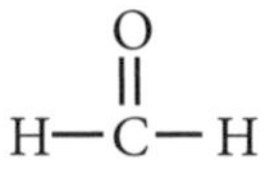

$$\begin{array}{ccc} & O & \\ & \| & \\ H- & C & -H \end{array}$$

Figure 1004 Methanal

$M_r = 30$ Polar b.p. = –21°C

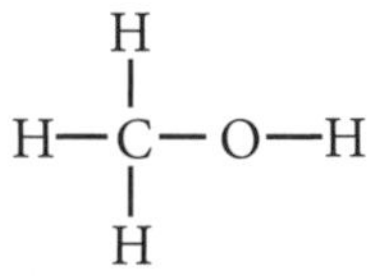

$$\begin{array}{ccc} & H & \\ & | & \\ H- & C & -O-H \\ & | & \\ & H & \end{array}$$

Figure 1005 Methanol

$M_r = 32$ Highly polar b.p. = 65°C

Most organic compounds are non–polar and hence tend to be insoluble in water owing to the strong hydrogen bonds between the water molecules. If however the functional groups can hydrogen bond to the water (that is those that hydrogen bond to themselves, plus those containing the >C=O group which can form hydrogen bonds to water), then the substance will be water soluble, as long as the hydrocarbon chain is relatively short. As the carbon chain increases there is a gradual decrease in the solubility as is the case with the alcohols. Thus, ethanol, CH_3CH_2OH, is water miscible (mixes in all proportions), but hexan-1-ol, $CH_3(CH_2)_5OH$, dissolves only slightly in water. Some functional groups interact with the water and hence affect the pH of the resulting solution. Carboxylic acids, for example behave as weak acids and so reduce the pH. Amines act as weak bases in a similar manner to ammonia and so increase the pH.

10.1.3 Distinguish between empirical, molecular and structural formulas.

In organic chemistry it is particularly important to distinguish carefully between **empirical formula, molecular formula, structural formula** and **full structural formula**. The full structural formula (also referred to as graphic formula and displayed formula) shows all the atoms and bonds. For example the full structural formula for butanoic acid is:

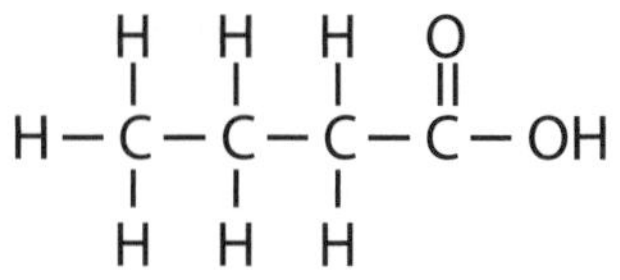

$$\begin{array}{ccccccccc} & H & & H & & H & & O & \\ & | & & | & & | & & \| & \\ H- & C & - & C & - & C & - & C & -OH \\ & | & & | & & | & & & \\ & H & & H & & H & & & \end{array}$$

Figure 1006 Structural formula for butanoic acid

A structural formula indicates in an unambiguous manner how the atoms are arranged in the molecule. A condensed structural formula, that can usually be written on a single line, is one in which the bonds are omitted, side chains put in brackets and repeated identical groups collected together. Again using butanoic acid as the example:

$CH_3CH_2CH_2COOH$ or $CH_3(CH_2)_2COOH$
condensed structural formula

As noted previously, the molecular formula gives the actual number of each type of atom in the molecule and the empirical formula the simplest whole number ratio of these. For butanoic acid these are:

$C_4H_8O_2$ molecular formula

C_2H_4O empirical formula

Note that an alkyl group (C_nH_{2n+1}, like an alkane with one H removed) can be represented by R. Thus alcohols (which contain the hydroxyl group —OH) can be represented as ROH. Similarly the benzene ring can be represented as ⏣ so that phenol (a benzene ring with an —OH attached) is represented as HO—⏣.

10.1.4 Describe structural isomers as compounds with the same molecular formula but with different arrangements of atoms.

Isomers are different compounds that have the same molecular formula. Different compounds have different physical properties (melting point, boiling point etc.). They may also have very different chemical properties depending on the type of isomerism present. Isomers may be divided into:

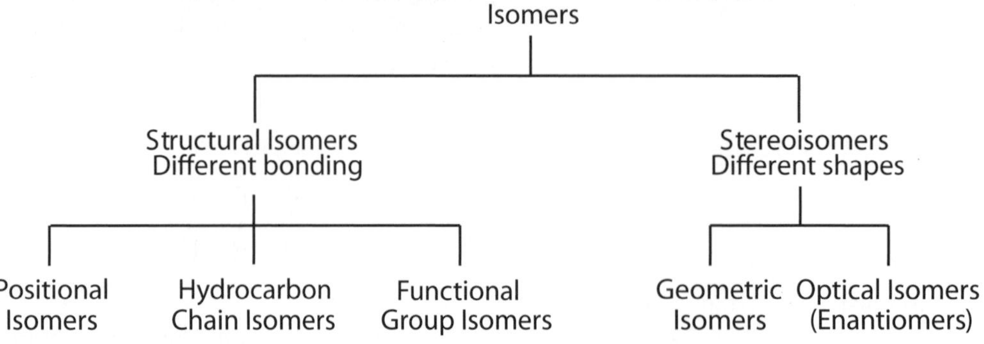

Figure 1007 The relationship of different types of isomers

- **structural isomers**, in which the atoms are joined in a different order so that they have different structural formulae.

and

- **stereoisomers**, in which the order that the atoms are joined together is the same, but the molecules have a different arrangement of atoms in space and hence different three dimensional shapes.

It is useful to subdivide structural isomers into positional isomers, hydrocarbon chain isomers and functional group isomers. Similarly stereoisomers can be divided into geometrical isomers and optical isomers (also called enantiomers) and these are dealt with in more detail later. The relationship between the different types of isomerism is illustrated in Figure 1007.

Positional isomers have the same hydrocarbon skeleton and the same functional group; it is just that the functional group is joined to a different part of the skeleton. A simple example of this type of isomerism is propan–1–ol and propan–2–ol:

$CH_3-CH_2-CH_2-OH$ $\quad$ $CH_3-CH(OH)-CH_3$

Propan-1-ol $\quad$ Propan-2-ol

Hydrocarbon chain isomers have, as the name would imply, different hydrocarbon skeletons that the functional group is attached to. Butane and methylpropane illustrate this type of isomerism:

$CH_3-CH_2-CH_2-CH_3$

$CH_3-CH_2-CH_2-CH_3$ $\quad$ $CH_3-CH(CH_3)-CH_3$

Butane $\quad$ Methylpropane

Because of their nature, some functional groups will usually have isomers containing another functional group. For example alcohols usually have an alkoxyalkane that is isomeric to them, hence ethanol has an isomer methoxymethane:

CH_3-CH_2-OH $\quad$ CH_3-O-CH_3

Ethanol $\quad$ Methoxymethane

Other common pairs of functional groups that display functional group isomerism with each other are:

Alkene and Cycloalkane

$H_5C_2(H)C=C(H)C_2H_5$ $\quad$ cyclo-$(CH_2)_6$

Hex-3-ene $\quad$ Cyclohexane

Aldehyde and Ketone

$H_3C-CH_2-C(H)=O$ $\quad$ $H_3C-C(=O)-CH_3$

Propanal $\quad$ Propanone

Carboxylic acid and Ester

$$H_3C-\overset{\overset{\Large O}{\|}}{C}-OH \qquad H_3C-O-C(=O)-H$$

Ethanoic Acid — Methyl methanoate

In the case of positional and hydrocarbon chain isomers the functional group, which usually dictates the reactivity of the molecule, is unchanged therefore they have quite similar chemical properties. With functional group isomerism the change in the functional group can have a profound effect on both the physical and chemical properties of the molecule. In the previous example ethanol is a liquid (at room temperature and pressure) that will react with sodium to release hydrogen. Sodium ethoxide is obtained as a white solid if excess ethanol is evaporated.

$$2\ C_2H_5OH\ (l) + 2\ Na\ (s) \longrightarrow 2C_2H_5O^-Na^+\ (eth) + H_2\ (g)$$

Methoxymethane (at room temperature and pressure) is a gas, since there is no hydrogen bonding, and it does not react with sodium because it has no hydroxyl group. Similarly methyl methanoate is a sweet smelling liquid that forms neutral solutions, whereas ethanoic acid has a sharp smell (vinegar) and forms acidic solutions.

TOK The importance of chemical models

The different types of formulas referred to in this chapter are certainly employed for different purposes. "Empirical" means "by experiment" and that's exactly what the empirical formula is – the result of a microanalysis experiment in which all of the carbon in the compound is converted into carbon dioxide and all the hydrogen into water, so the relative amounts of carbon, hydrogen and oxygen can be calculated, but on its own it is not of much further use. Combine it however with some information about how heavy each molecule is and we can then deduce some much more interesting information; how many atoms of each element are present in every molecule. That then allows us to test our theories of chemical bonding to work out the structural formulae showing how atoms can join together. Sometimes this can really stretch the mind and require creative thought, like Kekulé's dream.

This question also started me thinking about the words "formula" and "model" – do they mean the same thing and if not how do they differ? Both transfer information, but models (like the Bohr model of the atom) are also used to help with our "understanding" (whatever exactly that is) of the world and maybe that is a facet we do not seek in a formula. When I look, even at a full structural formula, I do not think that it helps my "understanding", it just conveys "information" about how the atoms are joined in the molecule and hence its probable shape. Now that leads us back to "models", though perhaps a slightly different use of the word – I'll leave you to judge. We get an even better idea of the shape using molecular models of different types. These are rather like different maps, each show some things clearly and other things less well, "Ball and stick" models for example give a clear idea of shape and what bonds are present, but the atoms always seem to be a long way apart. "Space filling" models more accurately reflect bond lengths as well as the different sizes of the atoms involved. Actually the concept of atomic size is an interesting one considering that we envisage the outer regions of an atom as just a cloud of electron density. How do we know where it ends? It's a bit like asking where does the Earth's atmosphere end; it doesn't really it just sort of fades away to nothing.

10.1.9 Deduce structural formulas for compounds containing up to six carbon atoms with one of the following functional groups: alcohol, aldehyde, ketone, carboxylic acid and halide.

10.1.10 Apply IUPAC rules for naming compounds containing up to six carbon atoms with one of the following functional groups: alcohol, aldehyde, ketone, carboxylic acid and halide.

10.1.11 Identify the following functional groups when present in structural formulas: amino (NH_2), benzene ring (⌬), esters (RCOOR).

10.1.12 Identify primary, secondary and tertiary carbon atoms in alcohols and halogenoalkanes.

THE IUPAC SYSTEM

There is a systematic scheme for naming organic compounds known as the **IUPAC** (International Union of Pure and Applied Chemists) system, but many compounds also have 'trivial' names used before the introduction of this system, hence a large number of organic compounds have two names. In this book IUPAC names will be used consistent with the names used in the IB syllabus.

From the point of view of IUPAC naming, organic compounds are considered to comprise a hydrocarbon 'backbone' to which side chains and functional groups are attached. The backbone is considered to be the longest continuous chain of carbon atoms in the molecule and this supplies the stem of the name. The first six of these are given in Figure 1008:

No. of C atoms	Stem	Side chain
1	meth	Methyl
2	eth	Ethyl
3	prop	Propyl
4	but	Butyl
5	pent	Pentyl
6	hex	Hexyl
Benzene ring	benz	Phenyl

Figure 1008 The naming of hydrocarbon chains

Note that it pays to inspect the formula carefully as the most obvious carbon chain is not always the longest one; $CH_3—CH(C_2H_5)—CH{=}CH_2$ has a principal chain 5 carbons long, not 4 carbons long as shown below:

H
$H_3C—C—CH{=}CH_2$
CH_2
CH_3

which is the same as

CH_3
$H_3C—CH_2—CH—CH{=}CH_2$

The prefix 'cyclo' can also be added to indicate that the carbon atoms are arranged in a ring. Hydrocarbon side chains may be attached to this longest chain and they are named in a similar manner. Another cyclic hydrocarbon structure that is often found in organic compounds is the **benzene ring**, C_6H_6, which in condensed formulas may be abbreviated to ⌬

If the compound is an alkane where no functional groups are present, the ending '-ane' is added to the stem. Hence:

$H_3C—CH_2—CH_3$

Propane

H_2C, CH_2, CH_2, CH_2, H_2C (ring)

Cyclopentane

CH_3
$H_3C—CH_2—CH—CH_3$

Methylbutane

Figure 1009

20.1 INTRODUCTION (AHL)

20.1.1 Deduce structural formulas for compounds containing up to six carbon atoms with one of the following functional groups: amine, amide, ester, nitrile.

20.1.2 Apply IUPAC rules for naming compounds containing up to six carbon atoms with one of the following functional groups: amine, amide, ester, nitrile.

The functional groups present in the molecule are indicated by prefixes or suffixes attached to the stem. These and a specific example of each class of compound are given in Figure 1010. In some cases a prefix is used if another **functional group** is already providing the ending; these alternatives are shown in brackets. There are also, in many cases, two ways of writing the functional group depending on whether a full structural formula or a condensed structural formula is being written. In formulas written

Name	Functional group	Prefix/suffix	Example
Alkane	None	-ane	CH_4; methane
Alkene	C=C	-ene	$CH_2=CH_2$; ethene
Alcohol	—O—H or —OH	-anol (or hydroxy-)	CH_3CH_2OH; ethanol
Aldehyde	$-\overset{O}{\overset{\parallel}{C}}-H$ or —CHO	-anal	CH_3CHO; ethanal
Ketone	$-\overset{O}{\overset{\parallel}{C}}-$ or CO	-anone	CH_3COCH_3; propanone
Carboxylic acid	$-\overset{O}{\overset{\parallel}{C}}-O-H$ or COOH	-anoic acid	CH_3COOH; ethanoic acid
Halogenoalkane (chloro, bromo, or iodoalkane)	X (i.e. Cl, Br, I)	Halogeno- (fluoro-, chloro-, bromo-, or iodo-)	CH_3CH_2Cl; chloroethane
Amine	$-\overset{H}{\overset{\vert}{N}}-H$ or NH_2	-ylamine (or amino-)	$CH_3CH_2NH_2$; ethylamine
Amide	$-\overset{O}{\overset{\parallel}{C}}-N\begin{smallmatrix}H\\H\end{smallmatrix}$ or $CONH_2$	-anamide	CH_3CONH_2; ethanamide
Ester	$R-\overset{O}{\overset{\parallel}{C}}-OR'$ or CO—O—	The naming of esters is covered in section 20.4,	$CH_3—CO—O—CH_3$ Methyl ethanoate
Nitrile	—C≡N or-CN	-anenitrile (or cyano-)	$CH_3—CN$ Ethanenitrile (cyanomethane)

Figure 1010 The naming of functional groups table (Note that the shaded groups are only required by Higher Level students).

AHL

this latter way, brackets are used to denote side chains, for example methylbutane would be $CH_3CH(CH_3)CH_2CH_3$.

The naming of esters is slightly different in that they are named as if they were salts of the carboxylic acid, as explained in Section 20.4.

- If there is more than one functional group or side chain present then a principal functional group defines the ending and the other functional groups and side chains are indicated as prefixes, arranged in alphabetical order:

  e.g. $HO—CH_2—CH(CH_3)—CHO$ is 3-hydroxy-2-methylpropanal ("h" comes before "m"; note CHO must be a terminal group and the COOH group is the same)

- A double or triple bond may be indicated by changing the first vowel in the ending.

  e.g. $HO\text{-}CH_2\text{-}C(CH_3)\text{=}CH\text{-}COOH$ is 4-hydroxy-3-methylbut-2-enoic acid

- If there are a number of identical side chains or substituents, then this is indicated by placing the prefixes di– (2), tri– (3), tetra– (4) immediately in front of the prefix/suffix.

  e.g. $Cl_3C—COOH$ is trichloroethanoic acid

- If there is more than one possible position for the side chain or functional group to attach itself, then this is indicated by numbers identifying the carbon atoms in the principal chain. If there is a functional group which must occur at the end of a carbon chain (such as COOH), then the carbon in this group is taken as the first carbon in the chain.

  e.g. $CH_3—CH_2—CHCl—COOH$ is 2-chlorobutanoic acid

  In other cases, the numbering starts from the end of the chain which gives the lowest sum of numbers for the substituents present.

  e.g. $CH_3—CH_2—CHC—CH_2—OH$ is 2-chlorobutan–1–ol, not 3-chlorobutan–4–ol

Note that numbering of a side chain or functional group is ignored when there are no alternatives. For example as the aldehyde CH_3CHO is propanal, not propan-1-al, similarly $(CH_3)_3CH$ is just methylpropane (the 2- numbering for methyl can be ignored as it can only be in the 2-position; if it were in the 1-position it would be butane). However, the name 'propanol' is ambiguous as it could be referring to propan-1-ol or propan-2-ol.

Comprehensive IUPAC nomenclature is a very complex subject, but this brief summary should enable you to cope with most of the compounds commonly encountered.

Organic compounds often contain functional groups bonded on to different types of carbon chains. These can often be usefully distinguished using the terms **primary, secondary** and **tertiary.** Primary means that the carbon that the functional group is joined to is bonded to only one other carbon atom, secondary means that it is bonded to two other carbon atoms and tertiary three other carbon atoms. This is illustrated in Figure 1011 where X represents the functional group.

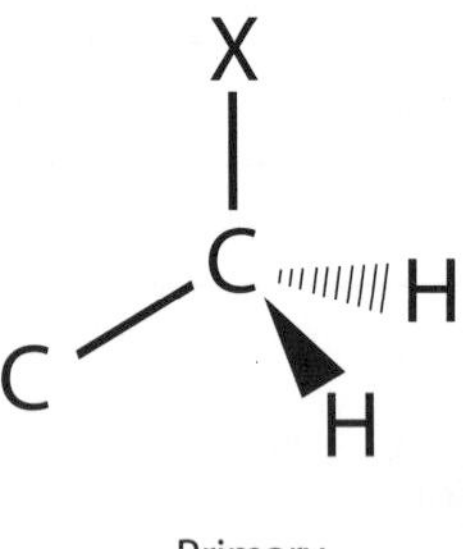

Primary

e.g. $CH_3CH_2CH_2\ CH_2Cl$

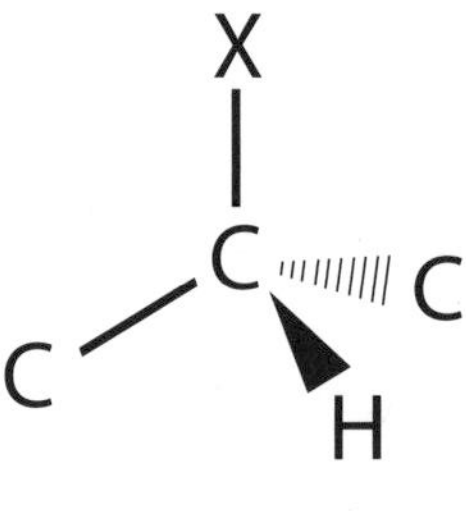

Secondary

e.g. $CH_3CH_2CHCl\ CH_3$

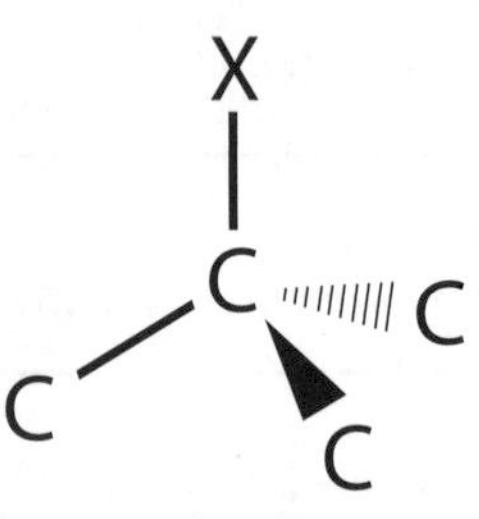

Tertiary

e.g. $(CH_3)_3CCl$

Figure 1011 Illustrating primary, secondary and tertiary structures

Exercise 20.1

1. Which of the following is correct about the number of bonds formed by atoms of different elements in organic compounds?

	Carbon	Hydrogen	Oxygen
A	4	2	2
B	4	1	2
C	4	1	3
D	3	2	3

2. The alcohols, methanol, ethanol, propanol, butanol etc., form a homologous series. This means that they:

   A have similar chemical properties, but gradually changing physical properties.
   B have similar physical properties, but gradually changing chemical properties.
   C have the same molecular formula, but different physical properties.
   D have similar physical properties and the same structural formula.

These structural formulae are required for questions 3 & 4:

$H_3C-CH_2-CH_3$
A

$H_3C-CH_2-CH_2-CH_2-CH_3$
B

$H_3C-CH_2-CH_2-CH_2-Br$
C

$H_3C-CH_2-CH_2-NH_2$
D

3. Which one of the above compounds would have the lowest boiling point?

4. Which one of the above compounds would be the most soluble in water?

5. Which one of the following lists the alkanes in order of decreasing boiling point?

   A Octane, Methane, Butane, Ethane
   B Methane, Ethane, Propane, Butane
   C Hexane, Octane, Propane, Methane
   D Hexane, Pentane, Propane, Ethane

6. Which one of the following formulae could represent more than one compound?

   A C_3H_8
   B $CH_3CH{=}CH_2$
   C $CH_3(CH_2)_3CH_3$
   D C_4H_{10}

7. How many isomers are there of the molecular formula C_3H_7Cl?

   A 2
   B 3
   C 4
   D 8

8. To which series of compounds does the molecule belong?

$$CH_3-CH_2-\overset{\overset{\Large O}{\|}}{C}-CH_3$$

   A Ketone
   B Alcohol
   C Carboxylic acid
   D Aldehyde

9. Which of the following is the structure of but-1-ylamine?

   A $CH_3-CH_2-CH_2-CH_2-CH_2-NH_2$
   B $CH_3-CH_2-CH_2-CH_2-NH_2$
   C $CH_3-CH_2-CH_2-CO-NH_2$
   D $CH_3-CH_2-CH_2-CH_2-CO-NH_2$

10. What is the correct name of $CH_3CHClCH_2CH_2CHO$?

   A 2-chlorobutanal
   B 4-chlorobutanal
   C 2-chloropentanal
   D 4-chloropentanal

11. The molecular formulae of a group of closely related molecules are given below.

CH_3NO_2; $C_2H_5NO_2$; $C_3H_7NO_2$; $C_4H_9NO_2$; $C_5H_{11}NO_2$

   a) What name is given to a group of compounds related in this way?

   b) Write a general formula for this group of compounds.

AHL

c) How would you expect the boiling points of these compounds to change with increasing numbers of carbon atoms? Explain.

d) Compared to alkanes of a similar molar mass, would you expect these compounds to be
i) more or less soluble in water.
ii) more or less volatile.
Explain your answers.

e) CH_3NO_2 can be reduced to CH_3NH_2 by reacting it with hydrogen over a nickel catalyst. What product would you expect when $C_5H_{11}NO_2$ was treated in the same way? On what do you base your prediction?

12. Draw structural formulae of the following compounds:

a) Pentane
b) 3–ethylhexane
c) Bromoethane
d) 2–methylbut–1–ene
e) 3.3–dichloro–2–methylbutanoic acid

13. The structural formula of 1–methoxybutane is

$CH_3—O—CH_2—CH_2—CH_2—CH_3$

Draw structural isomers of this compound that illustrate:

a) positional isomerism

b) hydrocarbon chain isomerism

c) functional group isomerism

14. Write abbreviated structural formulae and name all the structural isomers of the compound with molecular formula C_6H_{14}.

15. Name the following compounds:

a) $CH_3-C(CH_3)=CH_2$

b) $CH_3-CH_2-CH(CH_2-CH_3)-Cl$

c) $CH_3—CHI—CH_2—CH_2—OH$

d) $HO—C(CH_3)_2—CH_2—CH_2—COOH$

10.1.5 Deduce structural formulas for the isomers of the non-cyclic alkanes up to C_6.

10.1.6 Apply IUPAC rules for naming the isomers of the non-cyclic alkanes up to C_6.

Hydrocarbons are compounds containing only carbon and hydrogen. The simplest homologous series of this type is that comprising the straight chain **alkanes.** The first six members of this series, along with their names and structural formulae are given in Figure 1014.

No. of C atoms	Molecular Formula	Name	Structural formula
1	CH_4	Methane	H–C(H)(H)–H
2	C_2H_6	Ethane	H–C(H)(H)–C(H)(H)–H
3	C_3H_8	Propane	H–C(H)(H)–C(H)(H)–C(H)(H)–H
4	C_4H_{10}	Butane	H–C(H)(H)–C(H)(H)–C(H)(H)–C(H)(H)–H
5	C_5H_{12}	Pentane	H–C(H)(H)–C(H)(H)–C(H)(H)–C(H)(H)–C(H)(H)–H
6	C_6H_{14}	Hexane	H–C(H)(H)–C(H)(H)–C(H)(H)–C(H)(H)–C(H)(H)–C(H)(H)–H

Figure 1014 The straight chain alkanes

The compounds shown in Figure 1014 are known as the straight chain alkanes because isomers of these compounds exist in which the carbon atoms are not joined in a single chain. The simplest example of such **isomerism** is butane and methylpropane which both have the molecular formula C_4H_{10}. Similarly three isomers exist with the formula C_5H_{12}. The names and structural formulae of these compounds are shown in Figure 1015 below (Note that C_6H_{14} has 5 isomers).

C_4H_{10}

```
   H  H  H  H
   |  |  |  |
H—C—C—C—C—H
   |  |  |  |
   H  H  H  H
```

Butane

```
       H
       |
    H—C—H
   H   |   H
   |   |   |
H—C—C—C—H
   |   |   |
   H   H   H
```

Methylpropane

C_5H_{12}

```
   H  H  H  H  H
   |  |  |  |  |
H—C—C—C—C—C—H
   |  |  |  |  |
   H  H  H  H  H
```

Pentane

```
      H
      |
   H—C—H
   H  |  H  H
   |  |  |  |
H—C—C—C—C—H
   |  |  |  |
   H  H  H  H
```

Methylbutane

```
       H
       |
    H—C—H
   H   |   H
   |   |   |
H—C—C—C—H
   |   |   |
   H   |   H
    H—C—H
       |
       H
```

Dimethylpropane

Figure 1015 Isomers of C_4H_{10} and C_5H_{12}

10.2 ALKANES

10.2.1 Explain the low reactivity of alkanes in terms of bond enthalpies and bond polarity.

10.2.2 Describe, using equations, the complete and incomplete combustion of alkanes.

The most familiar reaction of the alkanes is **combustion**. Like almost all organic compounds, the alkanes are flammable and oxidise when burnt in the air to form carbon dioxide and water if sufficient oxygen is present. The combustion of organic compounds is a highly exothermic process and is one of the most common sources of energy in society. Equations for these reactions often involve quite large coefficients, but balancing them is easy provided the following procedure is adopted:

1. All carbon atoms are converted to carbon dioxide fixing this coefficient
2. All hydrogen atoms are converted to water, fixing a second coefficient
3. The number of oxygen molecules on the left must be adjusted to balance the oxygen

Consider applying this to the complete combustion of octane (C_8H_{18}), a major component of gasoline:

$$C_8H_{18} + O_2 \longrightarrow CO_2 + H_2O$$

1. There are 8 carbon atoms so these must form 8 carbon dioxide molecules.
2. There are 18 hydrogen atoms so these must form 9 water molecules.
3. There are now 25 oxygen atoms on the right hand side, requiring 12½ O_2 molecules.

The final equation is therefore:

$$C_8H_{18} + 12\tfrac{1}{2}\, O_2 \longrightarrow 8\, CO_2 + 9\, H_2O$$

This form is acceptable, but the '½' can be eliminated by doubling all the coefficients.

Gasoline and many other fuels very rarely burn in this way. If the supply of air/oxygen is limited, as is the case in an automobile engine, then **incomplete combustion** occurs, so some of the carbon in the fuel, rather than forming carbon dioxide, is converted to carbon monoxide (CO, a colourless, odourless, highly toxic gas) or the element carbon itself (hence black smoke). Note that the hydrogen is still converted to water. These products, along with other minor products of hydrocarbon combustion and the residue of the lead compounds still added to some gasolines, are a major source of air pollution in large cities. Many countries now require the installation of catalytic converters which ensure that the combustion process is more nearly complete. For more details of these pollution problems, refer to Option D.

10.2.3 Describe, using equations, the reactions of methane and ethane with chlorine and bromine.

10.2.4 Explain the reactions of methane and ethane with chlorine and bromine in terms of a free-radical mechanism.

Alkanes can also react with chlorine or bromine in a **substitution reaction**, to give an initial product in which one hydrogen atom is replaced by the halogen. Usually these reactions are brought about by exposure to ultraviolet light or sunlight, though they will also occur without light

CORE

TOK The importance of IUPAC names

Communicating what exactly we are talking about quickly and effectively is important in any subject, hence names. It also depend on who you are talking to. For example when you are talking to other people in your class "Charlie" is an effective way to refer to a particular individual. It is however not very specific. If you said "Charlie" to your mother for example she probably wouldn't know who you were talking about. To her "Charlie" is probably the name of the security guard at the hospital where she works. You would then have to go into a longer explanation – joined the school from Finland last term / has ginger hair / did a solo in the school concert / father drives a Ferrari etc. It's useful not to have to go through all of that each time you want to tell a friend about something that took place during the last lesson, so names have their uses and pitfalls. Chemistry has the same problems; names that are unique and universal. For example in one research group TCP might be trichlorophenol and in another it might be tetrachloropropyne. The IUPAC system tries to tidy this and goes one step further because it should allow us to draw the structure of an organic compound from its name. Is it worth it? Why don't we just draw the structure? In a few cases it might be quicker (compare HOOC-COOH with ethanedioic acid, 9:15 characters), but in most cases the reverse would be true and complex ring structures are really difficult to do in the middle of text! Nevertheless alanine is a lot simpler to write than 2-aminopropanoic acid and *p*-xylene is simpler than 1.4-dimethylbenzene, which is probably why IUPAC names have never really caught on with biochemists and industrial chemists.

An IUPAC equivalent with humans might be to have a system that looks at facial characteristics so you can draw somebody from their name? For example: {gender / hair colour / hair length / eye colour / nose / chin} - I'm sure my children used to have a game that was based on this idea – what was it called? Anyway, on this system I might be {male-brown-neck length-brown-medium-bearded} - though it would be strange to have to change your name if you altered your hairstyle! The advantage is you now have some idea what I look like, but it requires a lot more writing than "John" and it's hardly unique. How many characteristics would I have to list until my name was unique?

at very high temperatures. Taking ethane and chlorine as an example:

$$CH_3–CH_3\ (g) + Cl_2\ (g) \longrightarrow CH_3–CH_2–Cl\ (g) + HCl\ (g)$$

Note that the inorganic product is the hydrogen halide (in the above case HCl) and not hydrogen (H_2). These substitution reactions can replace more than one hydrogen, so that some of the chloroethane produced above will react with more chlorine to produce dichloroethanes. These substitutions also occur in a random manner so that the product will be a mixture of both 1.1-dichloroethane and 1.2-dichloroethane:

$$C_2H_5Cl\ (g) + Cl_2\ (g) \longrightarrow HCl\ (g) + C_2H_5Cl_2\ (g)$$
$$\text{(both } ClCH_2CH_2Cl \text{ and } CH_3CHCl_2\text{)}$$

Further substitution of hydrogen atoms by chlorine can take place eventually yielding, with a large excess of chlorine, hexachloroethane (C_2Cl_6)

The reaction of an alkane, such as methane, with a halogen is a **free radical chain reaction**. This process can be split up into three distinct stages, **initiation** which produces the radicals (reactive species with unpaired electrons), **propagation** which forms most of the product and in which the radicals are reformed (that is one radical is used up but another formed) and **termination** which consumes radicals. As a result the initiation stage occurring once can cause the propagation steps to occur many times before the radicals are consumed in a termination step. The details of such a process are given below using the reaction of methane with chlorine as an example.

$$Cl-Cl \longrightarrow Cl\cdot + \cdot Cl$$

Figure 1016 - Initiation

$$Cl\cdot + H-CH_3 \longrightarrow Cl-H + \cdot CH_3$$

$$\cdot CH_3 + Cl-Cl \longrightarrow CH_3-Cl + Cl\cdot$$

Figure 1017 - Propagation

$$Cl\cdot + \cdot Cl \longrightarrow Cl-Cl$$

$$Cl\cdot + \cdot CH_3 \longrightarrow CH_3-Cl$$

$$CH_3\cdot + CH_3\cdot \longrightarrow CH_3-CH_3$$

Figure 1018 - Termination

It is traces of this final product, ethane that give a clue as to the nature of the reaction mechanism. Note that the hydrogen atom (H•) does not occur at any stage in the mechanism. The mechanism of the reaction with ethane is very similar except that it involves the ethyl radical (CH_3CH_2•) rather than the methyl radical and traces of butane (C_4H_{10}) are found in the product from the combination of these in a termination step.

Bromine reacts in an almost identical manner to chlorine. Because of its brown colour the speed of reaction with bromine is easily followed and if a mixture of an alkane and bromine is placed in sunlight the brown colour slowly fades, but there is no reaction in the dark.

10.3 ALKENES

10.1.7 Deduce structural formulas for the isomers of the straight-chain alkenes up to C_6.

10.1.8 Apply IUPAC rules for naming the isomers of the straight-chain alkenes up to C_6.

The alkanes are said to be **saturated hydrocarbons** because they contain only single carbon-carbon bonds, those with multiple bonds are called **unsaturated hydrocarbons**. The simplest compounds of this type are the **alkenes**, which contain a carbon–carbon double bond. The **alkynes**, containing C≡C triple bonds, are also unsaturated hydrocarbons. The general formula for the alkene homologous series is C_nH_{2n} (note that this is also the general formula of the cycloalkanes) and the structural formulae and names of the simplest isomers of the first five members of the series are given in Figure 1019.

Though double bonds are stronger than single bonds, they are not twice as strong (C=C 612 kJ mol^{-1}, C—C 348 kJ mol^{-1}). This means that it is energetically favourable for a double bond to be converted into two single bonds. The activation energy for these reactions is also relatively low, owing to the high electron density in the double bond. This means that alkenes are considerably more reactive than alkanes and are an important starting point in the synthesis of other organic compounds. As a result alkenes, usually formed by the cracking of fractions of petroleum, are very important intermediates in the economically important **petrochemicals** industry.

No. of C atoms	Molecular formula	Name	Structural formula
2	C_2H_4	Ethene	$H_2C=CH_2$
3	C_3H_6	Propene	$H_2C=CH-CH_3$
4	C_4H_8	But-1-ene	$H_2C=CH-CH_2-CH_3$
5	C_5H_{10}	Pent-1-ene	$H_2C=CH-CH_2-CH_2-CH_3$
6	C_6H_{12}	Hex-1-ene	$H_2C=CH-CH_2-CH_2-CH_2-CH_3$

Figure 1019 Straight chain terminal alkenes

CORE

10.3.1 Describe, using equations, the reactions of alkenes with hydrogen and halogens.

10.3.2 Describe, using equations, the reactions of symmetrical alkenes with hydrogen halides and water.

10.3.3 Distinguish between alkanes and alkenes using bromine water.

10.3.4 Outline the polymerization of alkenes.

10.3.5 Outline the economic importance of the reactions of alkenes.

A reaction in which the double bond of an alkene is converted to a single bond and two new bonds are formed to the species it reacts with is known as an **addition reaction** and they are typical of alkenes and alkynes. A number of important addition reactions are illustrated in Figure 1020:

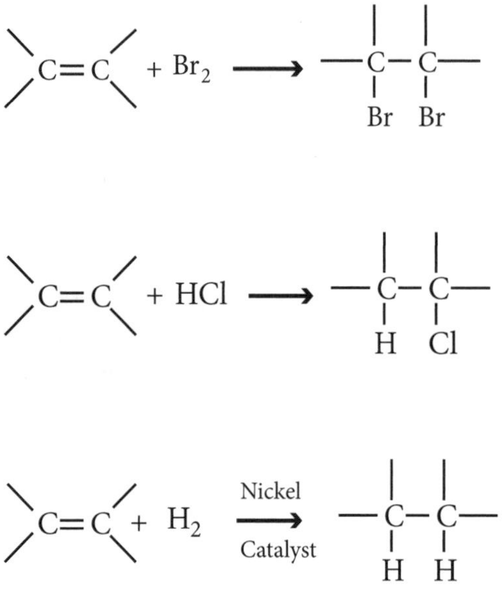

$$>C=C< + Br_2 \longrightarrow -\underset{Br}{\overset{|}{\underset{|}{C}}}-\underset{Br}{\overset{|}{\underset{|}{C}}}-$$

$$>C=C< + HCl \longrightarrow -\underset{H}{\overset{|}{\underset{|}{C}}}-\underset{Cl}{\overset{|}{\underset{|}{C}}}-$$

$$>C=C< + H_2 \xrightarrow[\text{Catalyst}]{\text{Nickel}} -\underset{H}{\overset{|}{\underset{|}{C}}}-\underset{H}{\overset{|}{\underset{|}{C}}}-$$

Figure 1020 Common addition reactions

The usual test for the presence of a carbon–carbon double or triple bond is to add bromine water to the compound. If a double or triple bond is present, the bromine water changes colour from yellow–brown to colourless. This reaction, shown in Figure 1020a, which also occurs with chlorine and iodine, takes place spontaneously at room temperature and pressure. A similar spontaneous reaction occurs between alkenes and hydrogen halides such as hydrogen chloride and this is shown in Figure 1020b. With hydrogen, the activation energy is slightly higher, but if a gaseous mixture of an alkene and hydrogen is passed over a heated nickel catalyst, an addition reaction to form an alkane occurs as shown in Figure 1020c. This reaction is the basis of the conversion of vegetable oils, which contain a number of C=C double bonds, into margarine, which has fewer double bonds and hence a higher melting point.

With water (in the form of superheated steam), the addition reaction is reversible. At a temperature of ~ 300°C and a high pressure (~7 atm) the equilibrium shown is driven to the right (Le Chatelier's principle) and this provides the basis for the industrial manufacture of ethanol. **Ethanol** is used in large quantities by industry both as a solvent and as an intermediate in the manufacture of other compounds, hence this is a very commercially important process. At atmospheric pressure the equilibrium lies to the left and alkenes are formed by the dehydration of alcohols. The reaction in both directions is catalysed by either acids (usually H_2SO_4 or H_3PO_4) or heated aluminium oxide, Al_2O_3.

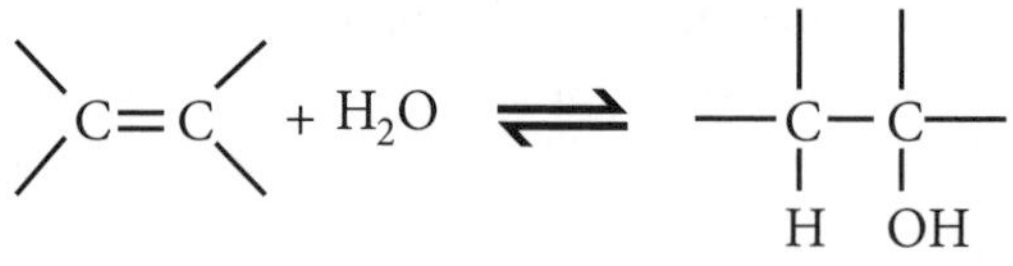

$$>C=C< + H_2O \rightleftharpoons -\underset{H}{\overset{|}{\underset{|}{C}}}-\underset{OH}{\overset{|}{\underset{|}{C}}}-$$

Polymers are long chain molecules that are formed by the joining together of a large number of repeating units, called **monomers**, by a process of **polymerisation**. Polymers, can be made artificially and these are usually referred to as plastics, but there are also a great number of naturally occurring polymers.

One type of polymerisation reaction is known as addition polymerisation. In this the monomers contain double bonds and in the addition reaction new bonds (shown coloured below) form between these monomer units. The simplest polymerisation reaction of this type is that of ethene when heated under pressure with a catalyst to form **polyethene**, commonly known as 'polythene'.

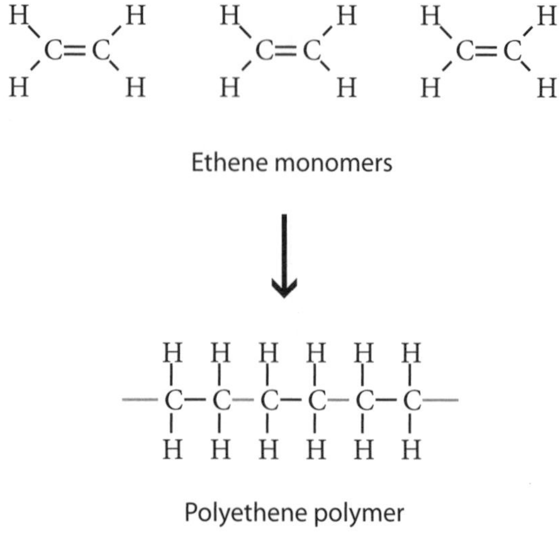

$$H_2C=CH_2 \quad H_2C=CH_2 \quad H_2C=CH_2$$

Ethene monomers

↓

$$-\underset{H}{\overset{H}{\underset{|}{\overset{|}{C}}}}-\underset{H}{\overset{H}{\underset{|}{\overset{|}{C}}}}-\underset{H}{\overset{H}{\underset{|}{\overset{|}{C}}}}-\underset{H}{\overset{H}{\underset{|}{\overset{|}{C}}}}-\underset{H}{\overset{H}{\underset{|}{\overset{|}{C}}}}-\underset{H}{\overset{H}{\underset{|}{\overset{|}{C}}}}-$$

Polyethene polymer

Figure 1021 The addition polymerisation of ethene to form polyethene

This may also be represented by the equation below in which the repeating unit is shown in square brackets.

$$n\ CH_2{=}CH_2 \longrightarrow [-CH_2-CH_2-]_n$$

Two other common addition polymers are poly(chloroethene), better known as **PVC** (short for its old name of PolyVinyl Chloride), formed by the polymerisation of chloroethene

$$n\ CH_2{=}CHCl \longrightarrow [-CH_2—CHCl-]_n$$

```
H      Cl    H      Cl    H      Cl
 \    /       \    /       \    /
  C=C          C=C          C=C
 /    \       /    \       /    \
H      H    H      H    H      H
```

Chloroethene monomers

↓

```
   H  Cl  H  Cl  H  Cl
   |  |   |  |   |  |
 — C— C— C— C— C— C—
   |  |   |  |   |  |
   H  H   H  H   H  H
```

Figure 1022 Polymerisation of chloroethene to form poly(chloroethene)

and **polypropene**, formed by the polymerisation of propene:

$$n\ CH_2{=}CHCH_3 \longrightarrow [-CH_2—CHCH_3-]_n$$

```
H      CH3   H      CH3   H      CH3
 \    /       \    /       \    /
  C=C          C=C          C=C
 /    \       /    \       /    \
H      H    H      H    H      H
```

Propene monomers

↓

```
   H  CH3 H  CH3 H  CH3
   |  |   |  |   |  |
 — C— C— C— C— C— C—
   |  |   |  |   |  |
   H  H   H  H   H  H
```

Polypropene polymer

Figure 1023 Polymerisation of propene to form polypropene

All of these polymers are produced in very high tonnages for the manufacture of a wide variety of products, hence these polymerisation reactions are economically very important. Polymers are discussed in greater detail in the Chemistry in Industry and Technology Option, Chapter 14.

CORE

Exercise 10.3

1. It is found that natural gas from a particular source decolourises bromine water. From this it can be concluded that

   A the gas contains some unsaturated hydrocarbons.
   B the gas contains only unsaturated hydrocarbons.
   C the gas is an alkene.
   D the gas contains some saturated hydrocarbons.

2. What is the formula of the organic product of the reaction between propene and bromine?

   A $Br—CH_2—CH{=}CH_2$
   B $CH_3—CH_2—CHBr_2$
   C $CH_3—CHBr—CH_2Br$
   D $Br—CH_2—CBr{=}CH_2$

3. Which one of the following molecular formulae does not represent an alkane?

   A C_3H_6
   B C_6H_{14}
   C C_8H_{18}
   D $C_{12}H_{26}$

4. When propane underoes complete combustion in air, for each mole of propane burnt, how many moles of oxygen are consumed and how many moles of water are formed?

	Moles of oxygen	Moles of water
A	3	8
B	5	8
C	3	4
D	5	4

5. Which one of the following would you not expect to find in the exhaust gases of a normal car?

   A Nitrogen
   B Hydrogen
   C Water vapour
   D Carbon monoxide

6. A free radical is any chemical species that:

   A is very reactive.
   B results from the breaking of a covalent bond.
   C is formed by the action of UV light on a molecule.
   D contains unpaired electrons.

7. a) Draw the structural formula of pent–2–ene.

   b) Write a balanced chemical equation for the complete combustion of pent–2–ene.

   c) What is produced during the reaction, other than the chemical products?

   d) If the supply of oxygen was reduced, what other chemical product might result from the combustion?

   e) Give one reason why the production of this substance is undesirable.

   f) Draw a structural isomer, other than pent-1-ene, and name the compound.

8. a) Name and write the structural formula of the organic product formed when ethene reacts with hydrogen bromide.

   b) To what class of reactions does this belong?

   c) What reagents and conditions are required for the conversion shown below?

   $$CH_3{-}CH{=}CH_2 \longrightarrow CH_3{-}CH_2{-}CH_3$$

   d) What test could you carry out on both the starting material and the product that would show that this reaction had occurred?

   e) What conditions are required for an alkene to react with steam?

   f) Name the alkene $CH_3{-}CH{=}CH{-}CH_3$.

   g) Write the structural formula of the product formed when this alkene reacts with steam.

9. Most plastics are polymers formed from monomers produced from crude oil.

   a) Explain what is meant by the terms in italics.

   b) Polythene, which may be produced by heating ethene ($CH_2{=}CH_2$) at a very high pressure, can be represented by the formula $[-CH_2CH_2-]_n$. Give the equivalent formulae for P.V.C. (polyvinyl chloride; polychloroethene) and also give the formula of the monomer that it is made from.

   c) Propene too can be polymerised to form the polymer "Polypropylene", used in ropes and knitwear. Write the structural formula of a section of "Polypropylene" containing three propene units.

10.4 ALCOHOLS

The simplest group of organic compounds containing oxygen are the **alcohols**, which contain the hydroxyl (—OH) group. The best known of this group of compounds is **ethanol** (C_2H_5OH), the 'alcohol' in alcoholic drinks. For the production of alcoholic drinks ethanol is formed by the fermentation of sugars such as glucose, a slow process requiring warm, anaerobic (meaning in the absence of oxygen) conditions:

$$C_6H_{12}O_6\,(aq) \longrightarrow 2\,C_2H_5OH\,(aq) + 2\,CO_2\,(g)$$

This reaction is brought about by enzymes (biochemical catalysts) produced by yeast (a microorganism) that grows in the fermenting liquid. This produces only ~15% ethanol, but pure ethanol may be produced by distillation. Ethanol for industrial purposes is usually produced by the addition reaction of ethene with steam over a phosphoric acid catalyst at high pressure. If an alcohol is passed over the acid catalyst or a heated aluminium oxide catalyst at atmospheric pressure it is dehydrated to an alkene:

$$C_2H_4\,(g) + H_2O\,(g) \underset{catalyst}{\overset{H_3PO_4\ or\ Al_2O_3}{\rightleftharpoons}} C_2H_5OH\,(g)$$

In the laboratory the dehydration reaction is more usually performed by heating the alcohol with a dehydrating agent such as concentrated sulfuric or phosphoric acid. Using ethanol as the example:

$$C_2H_5OH\,(l) \xrightarrow{excess\ H_2SO_4\ \approx 170\,^{\circ}C} C_2H_4\,(g) + H_2O\,(l)$$

The mechanism of this dehydration is discussed in more detail later on.

> 10.4.1 Describe, using equations, the complete combustion of alcohols.
>
> ©IBO 2007

Alcohols, like most other organic compounds, burn readily in air to form carbon dioxide and water, hence they are useful fuels. An equation for this reaction is given below, using ethanol as the example:

$$C_2H_5OH\,(l) + 3\,O_2\,(g) \longrightarrow 2\,CO_2\,(g) + 3\,H_2O\,(g)$$

As with all such combustion reactions, carbon monoxide or even carbon can be produced if the supply of air is restricted, hydrogen however is never a product of combustion.

> 10.4.2 Describe, using equations, the oxidation reactions of alcohols.
> 10.4.3 Determine the products formed by the oxidation of primary and secondary alcohols.
>
> ©IBO 2007

Alcohols may be subdivided into three classes according to the number of carbon atoms attached to the same carbon atom as the the hydroxyl group, -OH, group:

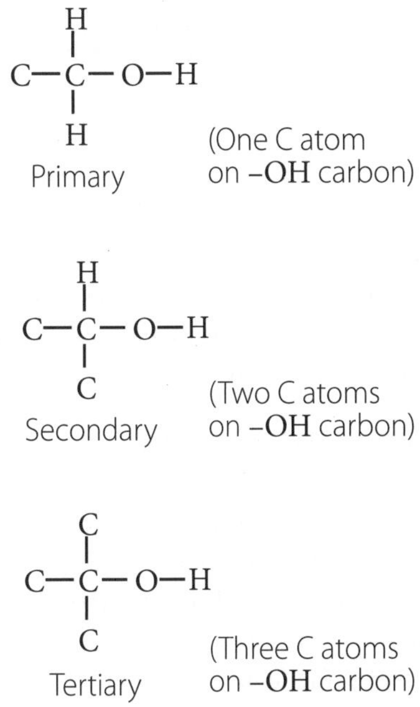

Figure 1024 Groups of alcohols (page 383)

The hydrogen atoms attached to the same carbon as the —OH group are readily **oxidised** and so these three classes of alcohols behave in rather different ways when they react with oxidising agents such as acidified potassium dichromate(VI). Tertiary alcohols do not have any reactive hydrogen atoms and are not readily oxidised. Secondary alcohols have one reactive hydrogen and so undergo one stage of oxidation to yield ketones. Primary alcohols have two readily oxidised hydrogen atoms and so the oxidation occurs in two stages producing firstly **aldehydes** and then, on further oxidation, carboxylic acids.This is summarised in Figure 1025.

Both aldehydes and alcohols are polar, however, alcohols have higher boiling points as these experience hydrogen bonding in addition to dipole-dipole forces. Thus, in practice to obtain the aldehyde, the alcohol is added to the boiling oxidising agent so that as soon as the more volatile aldehyde is formed, it **distils** off (see Figure 1026a) before it can be further oxidised. In order to obtain the carboxylic acid a more concentrated solution of the oxidising agent is used and the mixture is refluxed so that the aldehyde

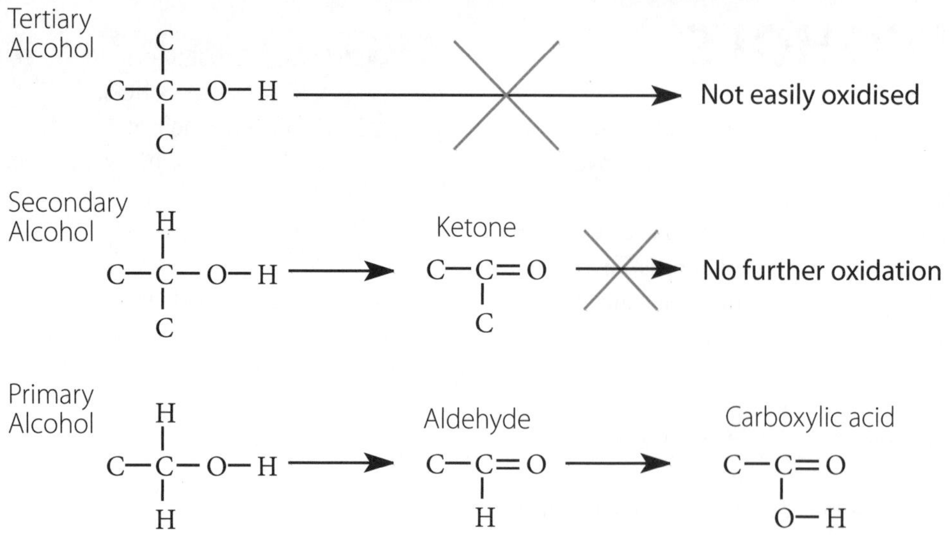

Tertiary Alcohol

$$\mathrm{C{-}\underset{C}{\overset{C}{C}}{-}O{-}H} \;\not\longrightarrow\; \text{Not easily oxidised}$$

Secondary Alcohol

$$\mathrm{C{-}\underset{C}{\overset{H}{C}}{-}O{-}H} \longrightarrow \underset{\text{Ketone}}{\mathrm{C{-}\underset{C}{C}{=}O}} \;\not\longrightarrow\; \text{No further oxidation}$$

Primary Alcohol

$$\mathrm{C{-}\underset{H}{\overset{H}{C}}{-}O{-}H} \longrightarrow \underset{\text{Aldehyde}}{\mathrm{C{-}\underset{H}{C}{=}O}} \longrightarrow \underset{\text{Carboxylic acid}}{\mathrm{C{-}\underset{O-H}{C}{=}O}}$$

Figure 1025 The oxidation of alcohols

cannot escape further oxidation (see Figure 11.8b). Heating under **reflux** allows us to carry out a reaction at the boiling point of the solvent without any loss of the solvent. The vapour from the boiling solvent turns back to a liquid in the vertical condenser and drips back into the flask (see Figure 1026b).

If dichromate(VI) is used as the oxidising agent, then the orange dichromate(VI) ion ($Cr_2O_7^{2-}$) undergoes a colour change to the green chromium(III) ion (Cr^{3+}). The balanced equation is rather complex (though writing one is a good test of understanding of half equations) and so in such reactions the convention has arisen to indicate the oxygen from the oxidising agent as an oxygen atom in square brackets. Hence the oxidation of ethanol to its final product, ethanoic acid, can be written as:

$$\underset{\text{ethanol}}{CH_3{-}CH_2{-}OH} + 2\,[O] \xrightarrow[Cr_2O_7^{2-}/H^+]{}$$

Intermediate stage

$$\underset{\text{ethanal}}{CH_3{-}CHO} + H_2O + [O] \longrightarrow$$

$$\underset{\text{ethanoic acid}}{CH_3{-}COOH} + H_2O$$

Other oxidising agents, such as the permanganate(VII) ion in acidified solution, may also be used, but care must be

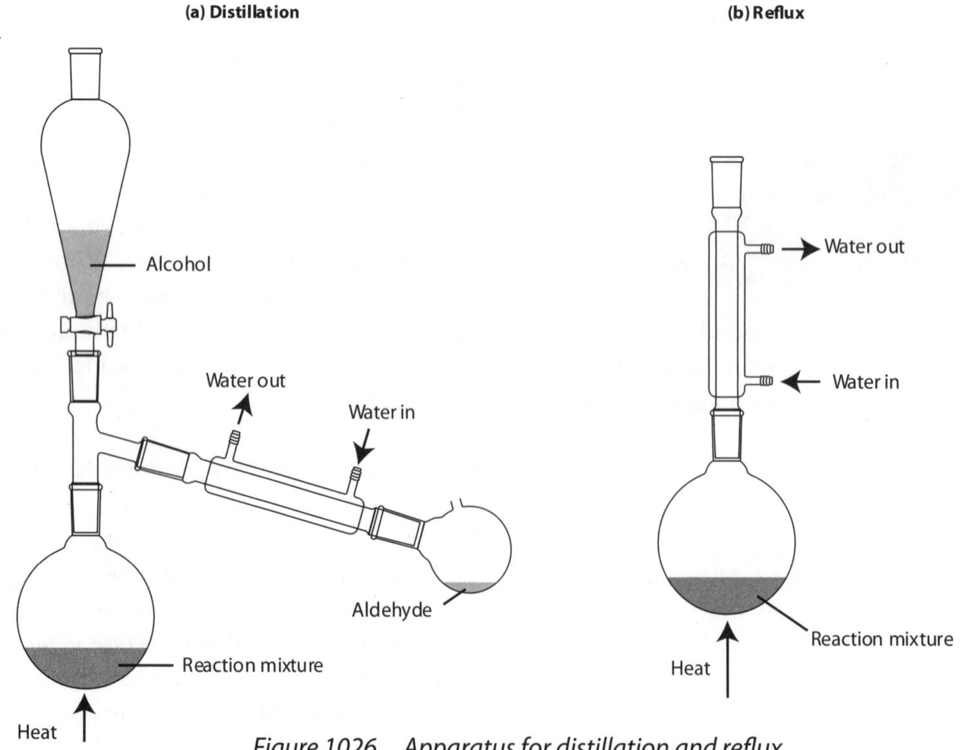

Figure 1026 Apparatus for distillation and reflux

taken as this more powerful reagent can also oxidise other functional groups (e.g. >C=C<). Ethanoic acid is also produced by bacterial oxidation when alcoholic drinks are left exposed to the air, producing vinegar. Carboxylic acids, as their name suggests, act as weak acids in aqueous solution.

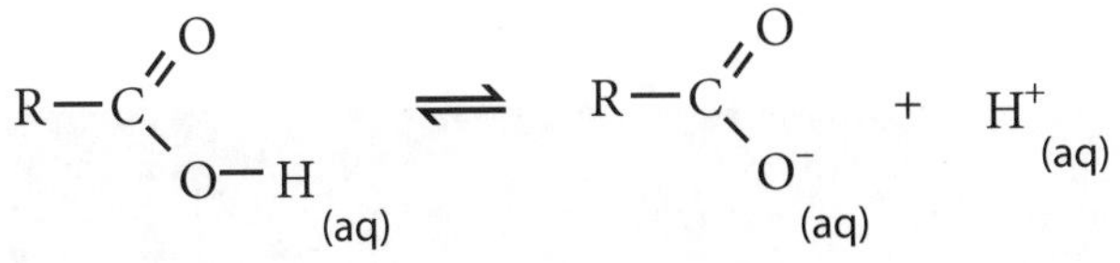

$$R{-}C(=O){-}O{-}H_{(aq)} \rightleftharpoons R{-}C(=O){-}O^-_{(aq)} + H^+_{(aq)}$$

FIgure 1027

Exercise 10.4

1. When ethanol is oxidised to ethanoic acid by heating with acidified potassium dichromate(VI):

   A the ethanol is reduced and the colour changes from orange to green.
   B the ethanol is reduced and the colour changes from green to orange.
   C the ethanol is oxidised and the colour changes from green to orange.
   D the ethanol is oxidised and the colour changes from orange to green.

2. When propan-1-ol is burnt in a plentiful supply of air, how many molecules of oxygen are consumed for each molecule of propanol?

   A 4½
   B 5
   C 9
   D 10

3. Propan-1-ol can be oxidised to propanoic acid in the same way as ethanol to ethanoic acid.

   a) What reagents would you use for this oxidation?
   b) What colour change would you expect to observe during the reaction?
   c) How would you expect the product to react with sodium carbonate?

10.5 HALOGENOALKANES

10.5.1 Describe, using equations, the substitution reactions of halogenoalkanes with sodium hydroxide.

10.5.2 Explain the substitution reactions of halogenoalkanes with sodium hydroxide in terms of S_N1 and S_N2 mechanisms.

CORE

In **halogenoalkanes**, the polarity of the carbon–halogen bond means that the carbon atom carries a slight positive charge. Because of this it is susceptible to attack by **nucleophiles** (reagents that attack at a centre of positive charge by donating an electron pair), and this means that halogenoalkanes are considerably more reactive than the alkanes, undergoing **nucleophilic substitution** reactions, in which the halogen atom is readily replaced by other atoms or groups of atoms. For example when they are warmed with an aqueous alkali halogenoalkanes undergo hydrolysis to form an alcohol:

$$R{-}X\ (l) + OH^-\ (aq) \longrightarrow R{-}OH\ (aq) + X^-\ (aq)$$

Warming 1-bromobutane with aqueous sodium hydroxide will therefore produce butan-1-ol:

$$C_4H_9{-}Br\ (l) + OH^-\ (aq) \longrightarrow C_4H_9{-}OH\ (aq) + Br^-\ (aq)$$

There are two distinct mechanisms by which nucleophilic substitution reactions occur. A mechanism is a model of how a reaction occurs through series of steps). The first of these is known as **S_N1**. In this mechanism there is a slow, rate determining, unimolecular (hence the 1), heterolytic fission of the carbon–halogen bond to yield an intermediate electron deficient carbocation. This then reacts rapidly with the hydroxide ion to yield the final product.

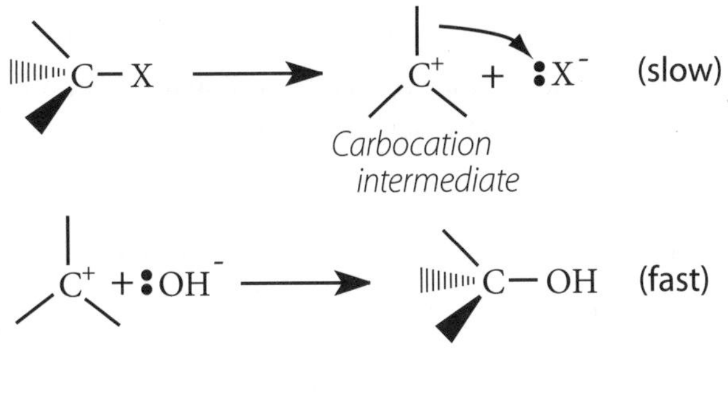

$$C{-}X \longrightarrow C^+ + :X^- \quad \text{(slow)}$$

Carbocation intermediate

$$C^+ + :OH^- \longrightarrow C{-}OH \quad \text{(fast)}$$

Figure 1028 Nucleophilic substitution by an S_N1 mechanism

Experimentally, the rate expression for this reaction is found to be:

$$\text{rate} = k\cdot[\text{R—X}]$$

that is it is first order with respect to halogenoalkane and independent of (zero order in) the concentration of the hydroxide ion.

The second mechanism is known as **S_N2**. In this mechanism, the bimolecular (hence the 2) attack of the hydroxide ion on the halogenoalkane molecule is rate determining. The reaction passes through a transition state (or activated complex) in which the bond to the hydroxide ion is starting to form at the same time as the bond to the halogen breaks, hence the substitution occurs in one concerted step:

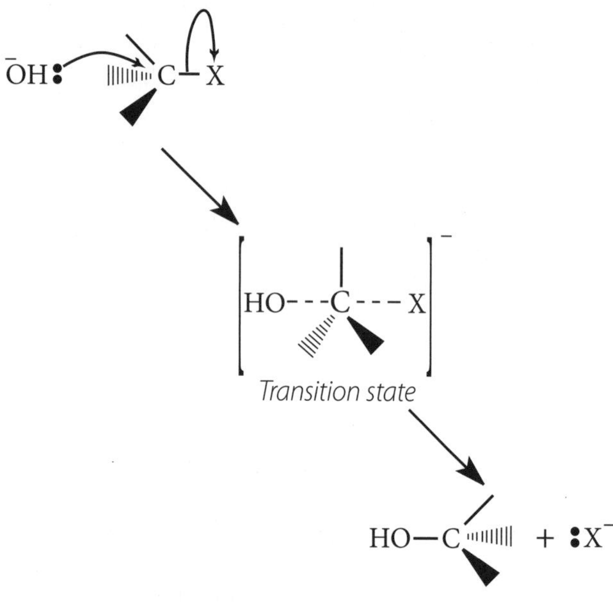

*Figure 1029 Nucleophilic substitution by a **S_N2** mechanism*

Reactions that occur by this mechanism are found to be first order with respect to both [RX] & [OH], hence second order overall:

$$\text{rate} = k[\text{R-X}]^1[\text{OH}]^1$$

Like alcohols, halogenoalkanes can be divided into primary, secondary and tertiary according to the number of groups bonded to the same carbon as the halogen:

H	H	C
C—C—X	C—C—X	C—C—X
H	C	C
Primary	*Secondary*	*Tertiary*

Figure 1030 Classes of halogenoalkanes

With primary halogenoalkanes (for example $CH_3CH_2CH_2CH_2Cl$) reaction with nucleophiles, such as the hydroxide ion, usually occurs by the **S_N2** mechanism, whereas with tertiary halogenoalkanes (for example $(CH_3)_3CCl$) it usually occurs by the **S_N1** mechanism. With secondary halogenoalkanes (such as $CH_3CH_2CHClCH_3$) both mechanisms can occur.

Exercise 10.5

1. When 2-iodopropane (CH_3CHICH_3) is warmed with aqueous potassium hydroxide the major organic product is:

   A CH_3COCH_3
   B $CH_3CH_2CH_2I$
   C $CH_3CH_2CH_2OH$
   D $CH_3CH(OH)CH_3$

2. Which one of the following compounds would be **most** likely to react with aqueous sodium hydroxide by an **S_N2** mechanism?

   A $CH_3CH_2CHBrCH_2CH_3$
   B $CH_3CH_2CH_2CH_2CH_2Br$
   C $CH_3C(CH_3)BrCH_2CH_3$
   D $CH_3CH_2CH_2CHBrCH_3$

3. Which one of the following is **not** true about a reaction between an aqueous alkali and a halogenoalkane that occurs by an **S_N1** mechanism?

   A The product will be an alcohol
   B The hydroxide ion bonds to the carbon at the same time as the halogen breaks free
   C The reaction occurs through the formation of a carbocation intermediate.
   D The mechanism involves the heterolytic fission of the carbon-halogen bond.

4. Write a balanced equation for the reaction between iodoethane and aqueous sodium hydroxide, then describe the mechanism of the reaction indicating the movements of the valence electrons.

5. Write the mechanism for the alkaline hydrolysis of 3-chloro-3-ethylpentane and use this to explain the meaning of the terms ***heterolyic fission*** and ***carbocation intermediate***.

10.6 REACTION PATHWAYS

10.6.1 Deduce reaction pathways given the starting materials and the product.

©IBO2007

Often in organic chemistry the desired product cannot be produced from the available starting material in a single step. In these cases the reaction must be carried out in a number of steps, referred to as the reaction pathway. For example if you wanted to convert 1-iodopropane into propanal you could not achieve this in a single step, so you must consider what substances can be easily converted to aldehydes (alcohols can) and whether you can form such a compound directly from the available starting material (in this case "yes"; if the answer is "no" then the pathway would involve more than 2 steps. The conversion can therefore be brought about by firstly hydrolysing 1-iodopropane to propan-1-ol and then oxidising this to propanal:

$$CH_3—CH_2—CH_2—I + OH^- \longrightarrow CH_3—CH_2—CH_2—OH + I^-$$

$$CH_3—CH_2—CH_2—OH + [O] \longrightarrow CH_3—CH_2—CHO + H_2O$$

It is also important to know the conditions required to bring these reactions about and this can be found either from the relevant sections of this chapter or from the summary table at the end of this section.

Another example of a conversion that cannot be directly carried out is be the preparation of butanone from but-2-ene. In the scheme in Figure 1031 the only reaction to produce a ketone is the oxidation of an alcohol. In fact it must be a secondary alcohol, as a primary alcohol gives an aldehyde then a carboxylic acid. Butanone must therefore be produced by the oxidation of butan-2-ol. This reaction can be brought about by heating the alcohol with acidified potassium dichromate(VI):

$$CH_3—CH_2—CH(OH)—CH_3\text{ (aq)} + [O] \xrightarrow{Cr_2O_7^{2-}/H^+} CH_3—CH_2—CO—CH_3\text{ (aq)} + H_2O\text{ (l)}$$

The scheme in Figure 1031 shows that it is possible to convert an alkene to an alcohol. This can be brought about by reacting the alkene with water in the presence of an acid catalyst, so that the reaction with but-2-ene will be:

$$CH_3—CH{=}CH—CH_3\text{ (g)} + H_2O\text{ (l)} \xrightarrow{H^+\ cat} CH_3—CH_2—CH(OH)—CH_3\text{ (aq)}$$

Note that it is important to use but-2-ene as but-1-ene could also produce some of the primary alcohol (butan-1-ol), which would oxidise to the aldehyde, not the ketone.

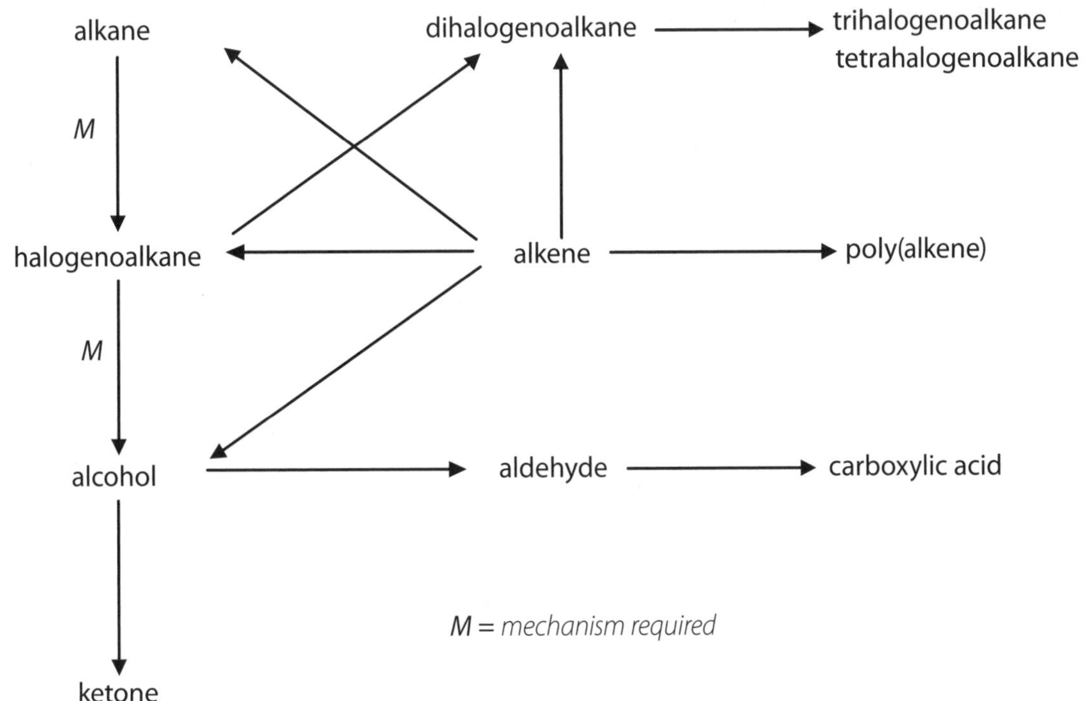

Figure 1031 Standard Level Reaction Pathways

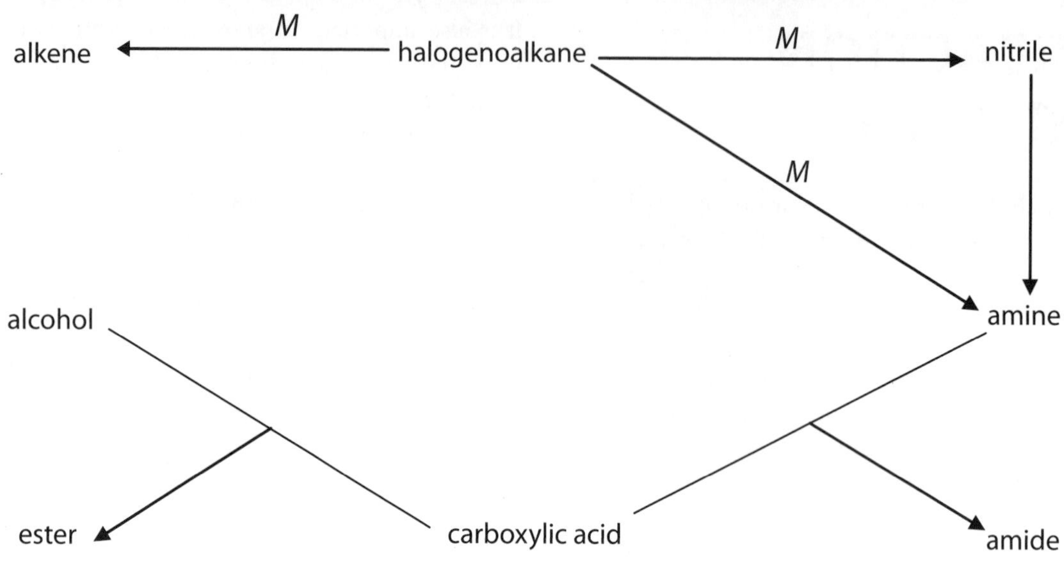

Figure 1032 Higher Level Reaction Pathways

AHL

HIGHER LEVEL

20.5 REACTION PATHWAYS (AHL)

20.5.1 Deduce reaction pathways given the starting materials and the product.

©IBO2007

An example of a more advanced conversion of this type would be the formation of ethylamine from ethene. Here the alkene could be converted to a halogenoalkane, which could then be converted to an amine, (refer to Figure 1032)

$$CH_2{=}CH_2\ (g) + HBr\ (g) \longrightarrow CH_3{-}CH_2{-}Br\ (g)$$

$$CH_3{-}CH_2{-}Br\ (l) + NH_3\ (aq) \longrightarrow CH_3{-}CH_2{-}NH_2\ (aq) + HBr\ (aq)$$

Again the conditions required to bring these reactions about and this can be found either from the relevant sections of this chapter or from the summary table provided.

Exercise 10.5

(* indicates HL question)

1. Which one of the following would be a suitable intermediate in the conversion of methane to methanol?

   A CH_3Cl
   B CH_2Cl_2
   C $CHCl_3$
   D CCl_4

2. An alkene can be converted to a ketone via

   A an aldehyde.
   B an alcohol.
   C a halogenoalkane.
   D an alkane.

3. Which one of the following cannot be produced by the oxidation of an alcohol?

   A An aldehyde.
   B A ketone.
   C A carboxylic acid.
   D An alkane.

4*. Which one two compounds can react to form an amide?

- A An alcohol and a carboxylic acid.
- B An amine and an alcohol.
- C A halogenoalkane and an amine.
- D An amine and a carboxylic acid.

5*. Which of the following reactions does not require a catalyst?

- A A nitrile reacting with hydrogen
- B An alcohol reacting with a carboxylic acid
- C A halogenoalkane reacting with aqueous sodium hydroxide
- D An alkene reacting with water.

6. Indicate by means of balanced equations how you could convert 2-chlorobutane to butanone. Give the reagents and conditions for the reactions that you give.

7*. Given just ethanol, how could you produce an ester? Name the ester and outline the reagents and conditions required for all of the reactions you describe.

HIGHER LEVEL

20.2 NUCLEOPHILIC SUBSTITUTION REACTIONS (AHL)

20.2.1 Explain why the hydroxide ion is a better nucleophile than water.

20.2.2 Describe and explain how the rate of nucleophilic substitution in halogenoalkanes by the hydroxide ion depends on the identity of the halogen.

20.2.3 Describe and explain how the rate of nucleophilic substitution in halogenoalkanes by the hydroxide ion depends on whether the halogenoalkane is primary, secondary or tertiary.

AHL

The reaction of **halogenoalkanes** with the hydroxide ion is just one example of a class of reactions known as **nucleophilic substitution** reactions. As outlined above these can occur by two different mechanisms, **S_N1** and **S_N2**. In the **S_N1** mechanism, the slow heterolytic fission of the carbon-halogen bond to form a carbocation intermediate is the rate determining step. The intermediate then reacts rapidly with the nucleophile (Nu^-) to form the final product. Note that the intermediate has a finite existence and occurs at a potential energy minimum on Figure 1033.

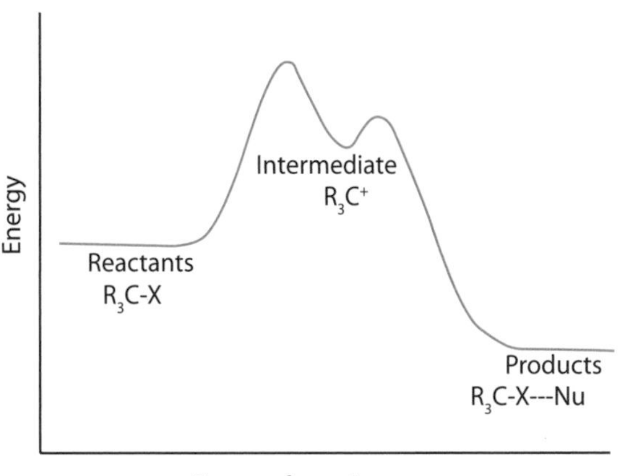

Figure 1033 Energy profile of a S_N1 reaction

In the S_N2 mechanism the breaking of the carbon-halogen bond occurs simultaneously with the formation of the new bond to the nucleophile. The point at which both are half completed is known as the transition state and it occurs at a potential energy maximum on the energy level diagram in Figure 1034.

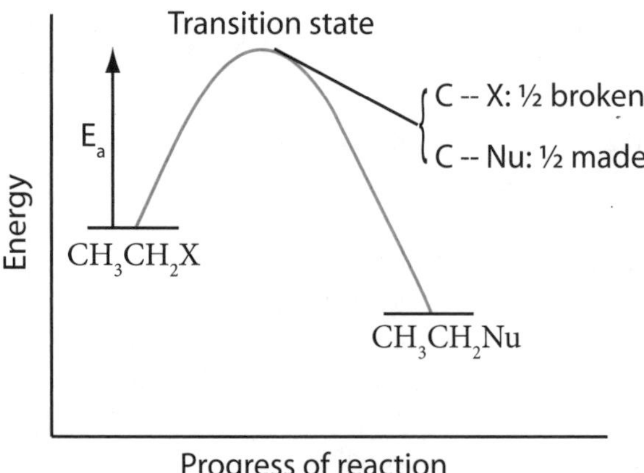

Figure 1034 Energy profile of a S_N2 reaction

The rate at which these reactions occur depends on the nature of both the nucleophile and the halogenoalkanes. For example some species are described as being stronger nucleophiles because they more readily attack a carbon with a partial positive charge. The hydroxide ion, for example, is a stronger nucleophile than the water molecule because it is negatively charged and hence attracted to the partial positive charge on the carbon attached to the halogen. As a result S_N2 hydrolysis reactions occur far more rapidly in aqueous alkali than in neutral solution.

The nature of the halogen also affects the rate of reaction. There are two factors. Firstly, as the halogen changes from chlorine to iodine, the polarity of the carbon–halogen bond decreases and this would be expected to decrease the rate of reaction going from chlorine to iodine because the partial positive charge on the carbon would become smaller. Secondly, the strength of the carbon–halogen bond decreases going from chlorine to iodine and it would be expected to have the opposite effect. In practice it is found that the rate of hydrolysis is greater for iodoalkanes than it is for chloroalkanes, implying that the bond strength is the dominant factor: see Figure 1035.

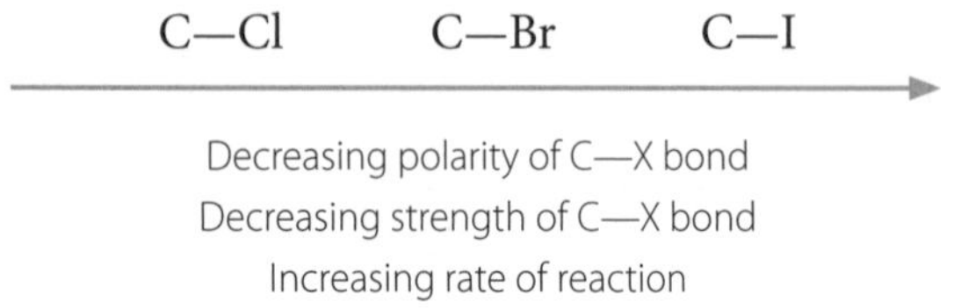

C—Cl   C—Br   C—I

→

Decreasing polarity of C—X bond
Decreasing strength of C—X bond
Increasing rate of reaction

Figure 1035 Effect of the halogen on the rate of nucleophilic substitution

Tertiary halogenoalkanes (R_3C—X) usually react by an S_N1 mechanism, whereas primary halogenoalkanes (RCH_2—X) usually react by an S_N2 mechanism. This is a result of a number of factors:

- Tertiary carbocations are relatively stable because of the inductive effect of the alkyl groups, which reduces the charge on the central carbon, so stabilising the carbocation intermediate required for S_N1.
- The change from tetrahedral to trigonal planar geometry when the carbocation is formed increases the bond angle from 109° to 120°. In tertiary halogenoalkanes this allows the alkyl groups to move further apart, so stabilising the carbocation by reducing steric stress.
- In the S_N2 mechanism, the nucleophile usually attacks the central carbon from the direction opposite to the halogen. In tertiary compounds bulky alkyl groups hinder such an attack.

Secondary halogenoalkanes (R_2CH—X) can react by either or both mechanisms. Because S_N1 reactions generally occur faster than S_N2 reactions it is found that, all other factors being equal, the rate of hydrolysis of halogenoalkanes decreases in the order

tertiary > secondary > primary.

Note that halogenated aromatic compounds, in which the halogen is bonded directly on to the benzene ring, are much less reactive than other halogenoalkanes. The main reasons for this are:

- the carbon-halogen bond is stronger and more difficult to break because one of the lone electron pairs on the halogen atom interacts with the delocalised σ-bond of the benzene ring giving the carbon-halogen bond partial double bond characteristics.
- attack from the opposite side to the carbon-halogen bond is blocked by the electron rich benzene ring.
- the partial charge on the carbon bonded to the halogen is reduced because of adjustments in the mobile electrons of the delocalised σ-bond.

20.2.4 Describe, using equations, the substitution reactions of halogenoalkanes with ammonia and potassium cyanide.

20.2.5 Explain the reactions of primary halogenoalkanes with ammonia and potassium cyanide in terms of the S_N2 mechanism.

20.2.6 Describe, using equations, the reduction of nitriles using hydrogen and a nickel catalyst.

Besides the hydroxide ion, a variety of other molecules and ions can behave as nucleophiles and participate in nucleophilic substitution reactions with halogenoalkanes. Two examples of these are the reaction with ammonia to form a **primary amine** and reaction with the cyanide ion to form a **nitrile**:

$$R—X\ (l) + NH_3\ (l) \longrightarrow R—NH_2\ (l) + HX\ (l)$$

With a primary halogenoalkane this will occur by an $\mathbf{S_N2}$ mechanism as shown in Figure 1036.

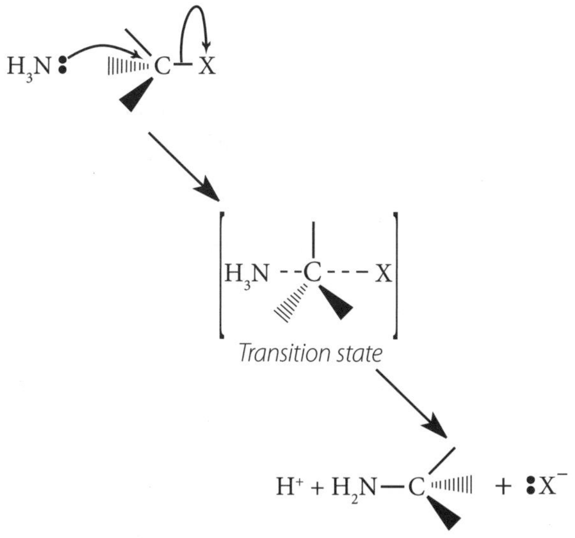

H₃N: C X

Transition state

$H^+ + H_2N—C + :X^-$

Figure 1036 The $\mathbf{S_N2}$ mechanism for the formation of a primary amine from a halogenoalkane

Note that the product above is the cation formed from the amine and it must lose a hydrogen ion to form the amine itself. Similarly the reaction of a primary halogenoalkane with the cyanide ion to form a nitrile will occur by an $\mathbf{S_N2}$ mechanism as shown in Figure 1037.

$$R—X\ (l) + C{\equiv}N^-\ (aq) \longrightarrow R—C{\equiv}N\ (l) + X^-\ (aq)$$

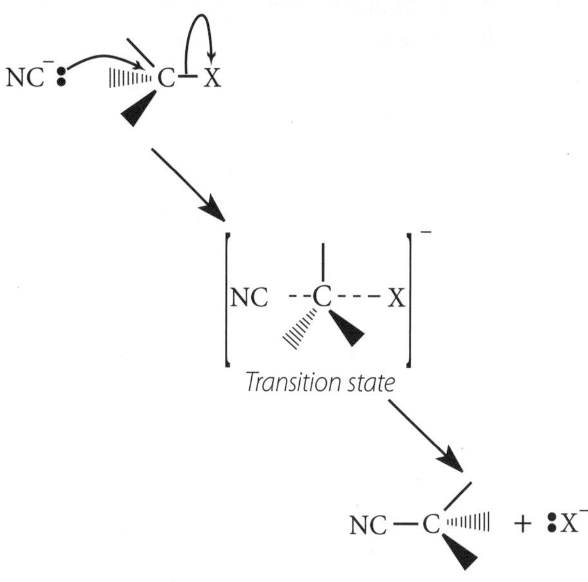

Figure 1037 The $\mathbf{S_N2}$ mechanism for the formation of a nitrile from a halogenoalkane

In forming this product a new carbon-carbon bond has been formed and hence it is a useful way to lengthen the hydrocarbon chain of a molecule. The triple bond in the nitrile may be readily reduced, using hydrogen and a nickel catalyst to form a primary amine, but note that this amine contains one more carbon atom than the one formed by direct reaction with ammonia.

$$R—C{\equiv}N\ (l) + 2\ H_2\ (g) \longrightarrow R—CH_2—NH_2\ (l)$$

AHL

Exercise 20.2

1. When a halogenoalkane reacts with ammonia, the product is:

   A a nitrile
   B an amine
   C a carboxylic acid
   D an amide

2. Which one of the following isomers would hydrolyse the most rapidly with aqueous sodium hydroxide?

   A $CH_3—CH(CH_3)—CH_2—Br$
   B $(CH_3)_3C—Br$
   C $CH_3—CH_2—CH_2—CH_2—Br$
   D $CH_3—CHBr—CH_2—CH_3$

3. Which one of the following does not undergo a nucleophilic substitution reaction with iodomethane?

A Ammonia
B Water
C Bromide
D Hydroxide

4. a) Write a balanced equation for the conversion of 1-chlorobutane to but-1-ylamine.

   b) What mechanism would this occur by?

   c) Draw this mechanism and use it to explain what is meant by the terms nucleophile and a transition state.

   d) Would you expect the reaction using 1-bromobutane to be more rapid or less rapid? Explain your reasoning.

5. a) Draw the structural formula of ethanenitrile and give the hybridisation of the two carbon atoms involved.

   b) Write a balanced equation for the formation of this compound from bromomethane and draw the mechanism for this reaction so as to show the movement of electrons.

   c) Ethanenitrile will react with hydrogen under suitable conditions. Write a balanced equation for this reaction, naming both the catalyst required and the product.

20.3 ELIMINATION REACTIONS (AHL)

20.3.1 Describe, using equations, the elimination of HBr from bromoalkanes.

20.3.2 Describe and explain the mechanism for the elimination of HBr from bromoalkanes.

When a bromoalkane is warmed with dilute aqueous alkali it undergoes a substitution reaction to produce the corresponding alcohol. If however it is added to a hot, concentrated solution of an alkali in ethanol it undergoes an **elimination reaction** to form an **alkene** as shown in Figure 1038.

In the case of the elimination reaction, the hydroxide ion reacts with the ethanol to produce the ethoxide ion as follows:

$$C_2H_5OH + OH^- \rightleftharpoons C_2H_5O^- + H_2O$$

This is a stronger base and weaker nucleophile than the hydroxide ion and so favours the elimination reaction, as does the higher temperature and concentration. The ethoxide ion acts as a base and removes the hydrogen ion from the carbon next to the halogen as shown in Figure 1039.

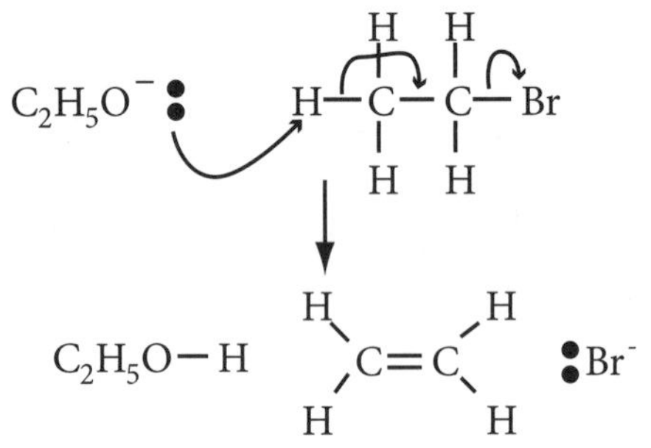

$C_2H_5O^-$: H–C(H)(H)–C(H)(H)–Br

↓

C_2H_5O–H $H_2C{=}CH_2$:Br^-

Figure 1039 Mechanism of the elimination reaction of a bromoalkane

The overall reaction is therefore the elimination of hydrogen bromide from the bromoalkane. Note that if the halogen is in the middle, rather than at the end of the hydrocarbon chain then the elimination can occur in more than one direction, hence a mixture of products may result. Hence, as shown in Figure 1040 below, two different alkenes are produced when 2-bromobutane is heated with alcoholic solution of potassium hydroxide:

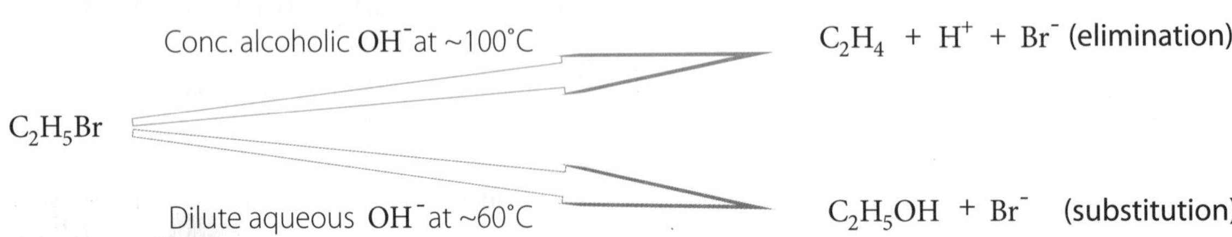

Figure 1038 The competition of elimination and substitution reactions in bromoalkanes

Exercise 20.3

1. When 1-bromobutane is added to the following solutions of potassium hydroxide, which would give the greatest yield of but-1-ene?

	Solvent	Concentration	Temperature
A	Ethanol	5 mol dm^{-3}	70°C
B	Ethanol	0.5 mol dm^{-3}	40°C
C	Water	5 mol dm^{-3}	40°C
D	Water	0.5 mol dm^{-3}	70°C

2. In the elimination reaction of 1-bromoethane to produce ethene, the hydroxide ion acts as:

   A a nucleophile.
   B an oxidising agent.
   C a reducing agent.
   D a base.

3. When 3-bromopentane undergoes an elimination reaction the product will be

   A pent-1-ene only.
   B pent-2-ene only.
   C a mixture of pent-1-ene and pent-2-ene.
   D a mixture of pent-1-ene and pentan-3-ol.

4. Explain how varying the reaction conditions can affect the product of the reaction between 1-bromopropane and sodium hydroxide.

5. 2-bromohexane is added to a concentrated boiling solution of potassium hydroxide in ethanol.

   a) What class of reactions does this belong to?

   b) Draw the mechanism by which this reaction occurs.

   c) Explain why two different products can be obtained and name these products.

   d) How would the product change if the halogenoalkane were warmed with dilute aqueous alkali?

20.4 CONDENSATION REACTIONS (AHL)

20.4.1 Describe, using equations, the reactions of alcohols with carboxylic acids to form esters, and state the uses of esters.

When **alcohols** are heated with **carboxylic acids** in the presence of concentrated sulfuric acid, they produce sweet smelling compounds called **esters**. Because of their aroma and taste, esters are often incorporated into artificial perfumes and flavours. They are also used as solvents and plasticisers. A simple reaction of this type is that of ethanol with ethanoic acid to form ethyl ethanoate:

$$CH_3-CO-OH + CH_3-CH_2-OH \underset{catalyst}{\overset{H_2SO_4}{\rightleftharpoons}} CH_3-CO-O-CH_2-CH_3 + H_2O$$

ethanoic acid ethanol

In these reactions, known as **esterification reactions**, the small amount of sulfuric acid has two functions. Firstly, and most importantly, the hydrogen ions act as a catalyst to increase the rate of the reaction and secondly it reacts with the water formed to shift the position of the equilibrium to the right hand side (Le Chatelier's principle) ensuring a good yield of product. Note that unlike the acid and alcohol, an ester does not contain an –OH group and so is much more limited in its ability to hydrogen bond to water molecules, hence esters tend to be insoluble in water.

It can be seen that the naming of esters is rather different from that of other organic compounds. They are named as if they were salts of the alcohol and the acid; the alcohol provides the first half of the name (alkyl) and the organic acid provides the second half of the name (alkanoate). In naming an ester it is important to remember that the –CO– group is part of the carboxylic acid. The molecule below is therefore methyl propanoate (not propyl methanoate), because it can be considered as being formed from methanol and propanoic acid.

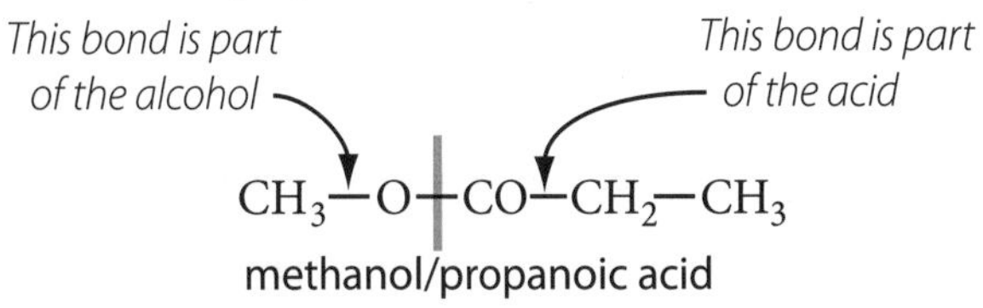
This bond is part of the alcohol
This bond is part of the acid
CH3–O–CO–CH2–CH3
methanol/propanoic acid

Figure 1041 Naming of an ester

AHL

20.4.2 Describe, using equations, the reactions of amines with carboxylic acids.

Ammonia and **primary amines** initially react with carboxylic acids to form a salt of the acid, but if this is heated it dehydrates to form an **amide**. If ethanoic acid is reacted with methylamine, and the initially formed methylammonium ethanoate is heated, then N-methylethanamide is formed:

$$CH_3—CO—OH\ (aq) + CH_3—NH_2\ (aq) \longrightarrow$$

Ethanoic acid, Methylamine

$$[CH_3—CO—O^-\ CH_3—NH_3^+\ (s)] \longrightarrow$$

methylammonium ethanoate

$$CH_3—CO—NH—CH_3\ (s) + H_2O\ (g)$$

N-methylethanamide

20.4.3 Deduce the structures of the polymers formed in the reactions of alcohols with carboxylic acids.

20.4.4 Deduce the structures of the polymers formed in the reactions of amines with carboxylic acids.

20.4.5 Outline the economic importance of condensation reactions.

The two reactions discussed above are made use of in **polymers** known as **condensation polymers**. In these polymers, two different functional groups are required and for each new bond between the monomer units (shown coloured below), a small molecule (often water) is produced. Each monomer must also have two functional groups. This can involve two different functional groups on the same monomer or more frequently, as in the examples below, two different monomers which have two identical groups on them. One group of condensation polymers are the **polyesters**, so called because the bonding depends on the reaction of an alcohol with a carboxylic acid to form an ester. The best known example of this polymer is **Terylene**, formed by the reaction of benzene–1.4–dicarboxylic acid with ethane–1.2–diol. as shown in Figure 1042(a)

The repeating unit in Terylene is therefore

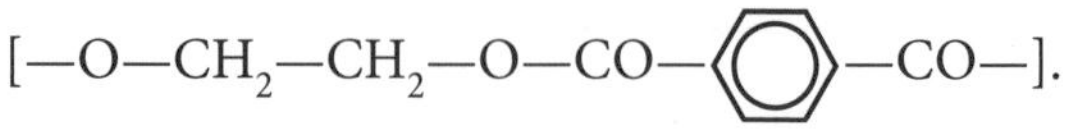

$$[—O—CH_2—CH_2—O—CO—C_6H_4—CO—].$$

Another group of condensation polymers is the **polyamides**, so called because the bonding depends on the reaction of an amine group with a carboxylic acid to form an amide. These polymers are better known as **nylon**, though there are actually a whole range of nylons. One of the most common is nylon 6.6, formed by the polymerisation of hexanedioic acid with hexane–1.6–diamine (See Figure 1042[b]).

The repeating unit in this is therefore

$$[HN\text{-}(CH_2)_6\text{-}NH\text{-}CO\text{-}(CH_2)_4\text{-}CO].$$

Both polyesters and nylons are used in large quantities for the production of fibres to convert into cloth for garments, hence the above reactions are of major economic importance in most developed countries.

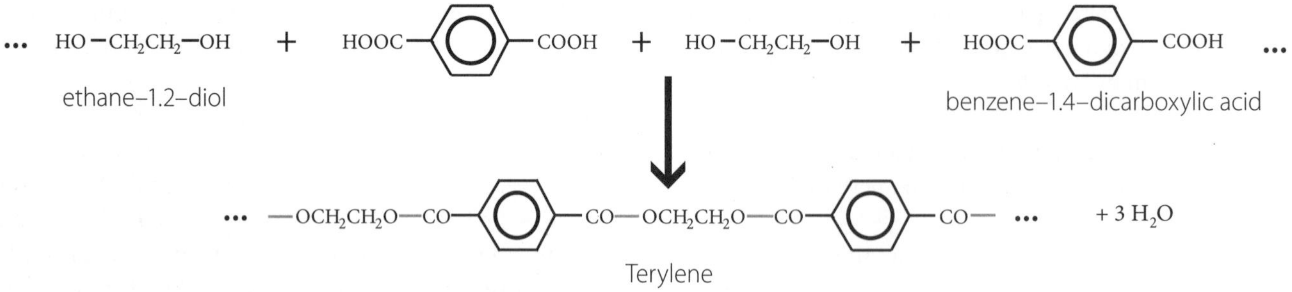

$$\ldots\ HO—CH_2CH_2—OH + HOOC—C_6H_4—COOH + HO—CH_2CH_2—OH + HOOC—C_6H_4—COOH\ \ldots$$

ethane–1.2–diol; benzene–1.4–dicarboxylic acid

$$\downarrow$$

$$\ldots\ —OCH_2CH_2O—CO—C_6H_4—CO—OCH_2CH_2O—CO—C_6H_4—CO—\ \ldots\quad + 3\ H_2O$$

Terylene

Figure 1042(a) The polymerisation reaction forming a polyester - Terylene

$$—H_2N—(CH_2)_6—NH_2 + HO—CO—(CH_2)_4—CO—OH + H_2N—(CH_2)_6—NH_2 + HO—CO—(CH_2)_4—CO—OH—$$

hexane–1.6–diamine; hexanedioic acid

$$\downarrow$$

$$\ldots—HN—(CH_2)_6—NH—CO—(CH_2)_4—CO—HN—(CH_2)_6—NH—CO—(CH_2)_4—CO—\ldots$$

$$+ H_2O \qquad + H_2O \qquad + H_2O$$

Figure 1042(b) The polymerisation reaction forming Nylon 6.6

Exercise 20.4

1. Which one of the following is not necessarily a characteristic of condensation polymers?

   A It involves two different monomers.
   B A small molecule is formed for each new bond between the monomers.
   C Each monomer must have two functional groups.
   D The reaction to form the bond between the monomers involves two different functional groups.

2. The molecule CH_3-CH_2-CH_2-O-CO-CH_3 is called

   A prop-1-yl methanoate.
   B prop-1-yl ethanoate.
   C ethyl propanoate.
   D methyl butanoate.

3. Which one of the following could not be a monomer for a condensation polymer?

   A HO–CO–CH_2–CH_2–CH_2–CO–OH
   B HO–⟨benzene ring⟩–CO–OH
   C HO–CO–CH_2–CH_2–CH_2–NH_2
   D CH_3–CH_2–CH_2–CO–NH_2

4. Write a balanced equation for the reaction that you would expect to occur when the initial product formed between butanoic acid and ethylamine is strongly heated and give the full structural formula of the organic product.

5. a) What reagents would you require to prepare a sample of methyl butanoate?

   b) Write a balanced equation for the reaction that occurs giving structural formulae for all organic compounds.

   c) Apart from the reactants what else would be required if the reaction were to produce a good yield of the product?

   d) Predict one property of methyl butanoate.

20.6 STEREOISOMERISM (AHL)

20.6.1 Describe stereoisomers as compounds with the same structural formula but with different arrangements of atoms in space.

20.6.2 Describe and explain geometrical isomerism in non-cyclic alkenes.

20.6.3 Describe and explain geometrical isomerism in C_3 and C_4 cycloalkanes.

20.6.4 Explain the difference in the physical and chemical properties of geometrical isomers.

Stereoisomers are molecules, in which the order that the atoms are joined in is the same (hence they are isomers with the same structural formula), but the molecules have a different arrangement of atoms in space and hence different three dimensional shapes. Stereoisomers can be sub-divided into **geometrical isomers** and **optical isomers** (or **enantiomers**).

GEOMETRIC ISOMERISM

It is possible for a molecule to rotate freely around a single (σ-)bond so that, for example, the two CH_3 groups in ethane can rotate relative to each other. Atoms joined by a double bond are however not free to rotate. This is because the π-bond in the double bond involves two regions of high electron density on opposite sides of σ–the bond, hence rotation would involve breaking this π–bond. As a consequence in a molecule containing a double bond, if the form produced by rotating one end of the bond by 180° is not identical to the original, then there can be two separate forms of the molecule. See Figure 1043.

```
Cl      Cl           Cl      H
  \    /               \    /
   C=C                  C=C
  /    \               /    \
H       H            H       Cl
```

cis–1.2–dichloroethene *trans*–1.2–dichloroethene

Figure 1043 Geometric isomerism in alkenes

AHL

These isomers are known as geometric isomers and the forms of 1.2-dichloroethene (ClCH=CHCl) is a typical example. The isomer in which the groups or substituents are on the same side of the double bond is known as the *cis*–isomer, the one with them on opposite sides is the *trans*–isomer.

Frequently, as in this case, the *cis*–isomer will be polar whilst the more symmetrical *trans*–isomer will not. This affects physical properties such as the boiling points, the *cis*–isomer above for example boils at 60°C, whereas the *trans*–isomer boils at 48°C. Thus, geometric isomers have different physical properties such as polarity (dipole moment), boiling point, melting point, and solubility, etc. They can therefore be separated by methods such as fractional distillation, chromatography, etc.

Usually the chemical properties are similar, but in some cases the proximity of the functional groups allows interaction in the *cis*–isomer more easily than in the *trans*–isomer. For example *cis*–butenedioic acid dehydrates at under 200°C to form the anhydride (see below), whilst the *trans*–isomer sublimes unchanged at ~200°C. Dehydration of the *trans*–isomer requires a much higher temperature so as to achieve the activation energy required for rotation about the double bond and hence the product has the same form as the *cis*–isomer as shown in Figure 1044

```
H—C—CO—OH
  ||
H—C—CO—OH

        ↘

      H—C—CO
        ||    \
        ||     O    +    H2O
        ||    /
      H—C—CO
```

Figure 1044 The dehydration reaction of butenedioic acid

Cycloalkanes also display geometrical isomerism because being part of a ring prevents rotation of carbon–carbon single bonds as well, so for example, 1.2 dichlorocyclopropane can exist as both *cis*– and *trans*–isomers:

cis–1.2 dichlorocyclopropane

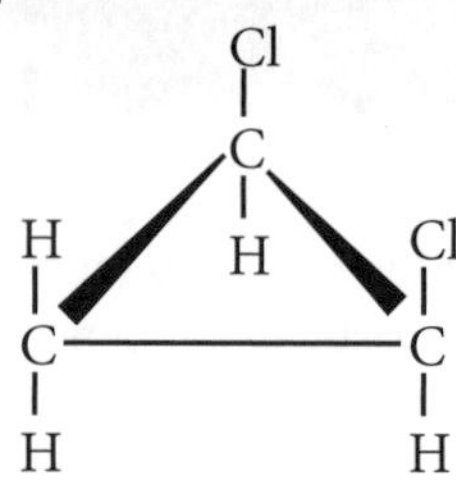

trans–1.2 dichlorocyclopropane

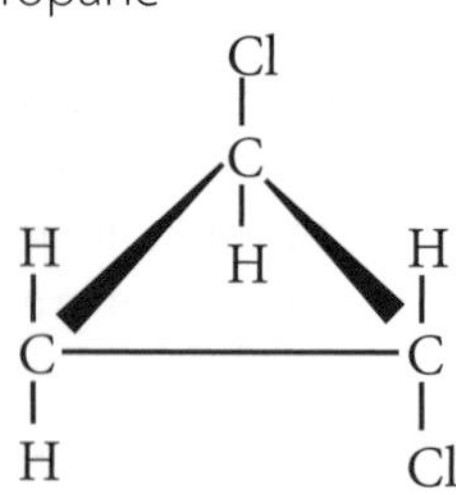

Figure 1045 Geometric isomerism in cycloalkanes

OPTICAL ISOMERISM

20.6.5 Describe and explain optical isomerism in simple organic molecules.

20.6.6 Outline the use of a polarimeter in distinguishing between optical isomers.

20.6.7 Compare the physical and chemical properties of enantiomers.

If a carbon atom has four different groups attached to it then there are two different ways in which these groups can be arranged around this carbon atom, which is known as an **asymmetric carbon atom**, or a **chiral centre** (from the Greek word for 'hand'). The two forms of such a chiral molecule, known as **optical isomers** (or enantiomers), are mirror images of each other, but cannot be superimposed on each other (like a pair of gloves). This is illustrated below using butan-2-ol as an example. The asymmetric carbon atom is marked with * in Figure 1046.

Note that all four groups must be different for this to occur so that propan-2-ol (CH_3-CHOH-CH_3) does not exist as a pair of optical isomers. Because these molecules are so similar, there is very little difference in their physical and chemical properties. In fact the only difference in the properties of these compounds is in their interaction with plane polarised light.

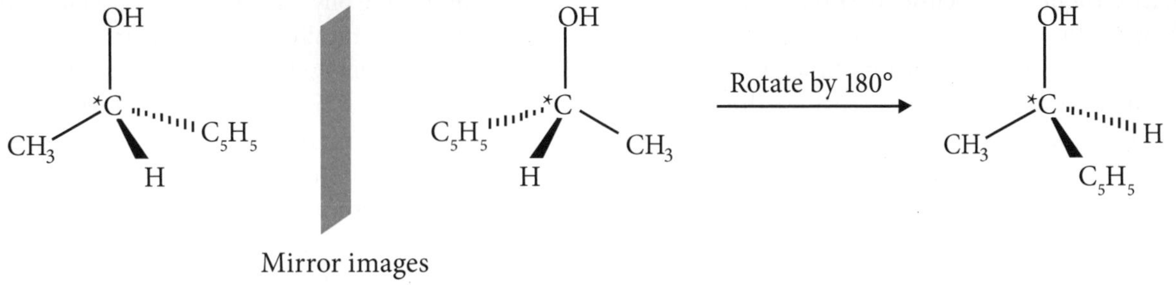

OH
*C
CH_3 C_5H_5
H

OH
*C
C_5H_5 CH_3
H

Rotate by 180°

OH
*C
CH_3 H
C_5H_5

Mirror images

Figure 1046 Optical isomerism

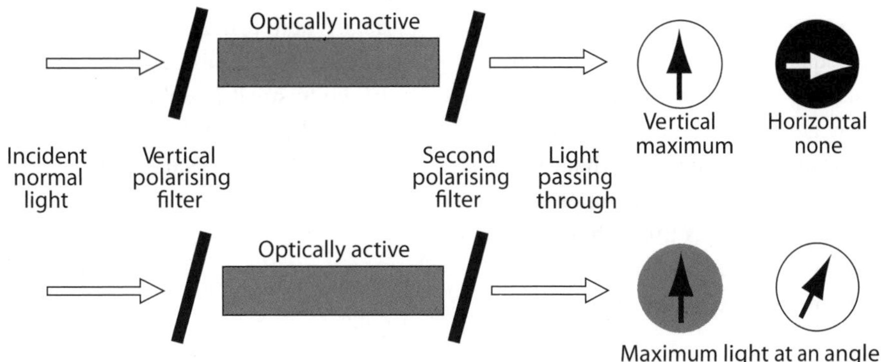

Figure 1047 Illustrating the effect of optically active compounds

AHL

TOK Belief or truth?

'The existence of optical isomers provided indirect evidence of a tetrahedrally bonded carbon atom. This is an example of the power of reasoning in allowing us access to the molecular scale. Do we know or believe those carbon atoms are tetrahedrally coordinated?' ©IBO2007

Knowledge and belief; the relationship between these is the basis of so many issues in TOK. One of the most common definitions of knowledge (though strongly challenged about 50 years ago by Edmund Gettier) is that knowledge is "Justified True Belief". Taking this as a starting point, the difference between knowledge and belief therefore lies in Truth and Justification. How do we know what is true? On truth test is "correspondence"; that something is true if it corresponds with reality, but can we consider atoms and molecules part of reality in the way that this book is? A second test is "coherence"; that something is true if it fits in, and does not contradict, other ideas we consider true. Now this might be a little more hopeful. What of justification? This is a far more personal thing. Even before the days of space flight, most people still accepted that the world was a sphere in spite of our observations, especially when in the middle of the ocean, that it looks pretty flat. This was because we accepted the many justifications for this, though inevitably there were still those who were not convinced.

I suppose that the strength of a justification lies in whether we can think of any alternatives to explain observations that we agree upon. In this case that there are two substances, identical in every way except for the effect they have on the plane of polarisation of polarised light. One explanation for this is the familiar one given in this chapter. The real test is to come up with an alternative explanation, which preferably also explains a few other phenomena as well (the way that relativity did), and does not contradict other evidence relating to the tetrahedral arrangement of bonds in carbon, such as x-ray diffraction data about the structure of diamond. In other words it's back to Popper again – our confidence in any theory depends only on our attempts to refute it (see TOK Box in Chapter 5). It probably follows that our knowledge of the universe is constrained only by our inability to imagine better theories than the ones we currently have.

Plane polarised light can be considered to be light in which the oscillation of the wave is restricted to one plane, say the vertical. This can be achieved by passing the light through a **polarising filter**. If the light is now passed through a second polarising filter orientated in the same direction (vertical) then there is virtually 100% transmission (see Figure 1045). If the second polarising filter has its axis at right angles to the first (horizontal) then no light will pass. A pure optical isomer placed between the two filters will rotate the plane of polarisation in one direction (say clockwise) so that maximum transmission is no longer when the second filter is aligned with the first one. The second optical isomer will rotate the plane of polarisation by exactly the same amount (assuming equal concentration), but in the opposite direction (anticlockwise). Substances that affect polarised light in this way are said to be **optically active**. An instrument containing two polarising filters that can be rotated relative to each other, separated by a compartment in which the plane polarise light passes through a liquid, allowing the angle through which the plane of polarisation is rotated is called a **polarimeter**. See Figure 1047.

Apart from this the physical properties of optical isomers are identical. Chemically, the behaviour of the optical isomers is identical unless the reaction also involves another pure optical isomer. Chemical reactions that produce an asymmetric (chiral) carbon atom in a molecule usually give rise to a mixture containing exactly equal amounts of the two optical isomers. Such a mixture is known as a **racemic mixture**. The effects of the two optical isomers in a racemic mixture cancel each other out and so it is not optically active. In contrast almost all natural products, produced by enzyme catalysed biochemical processes, result in just one pure optical isomer and hence produce optically active material. Natural turpentine (produced from pine tree resin) can, for example, be differentiated from white spirit (a substitute produced by the chemical industry) because turpentine is optically active and will rotate the plane of polarised light, whereas white spirit will not.

AHL

TOK The use of conventions in representing three-dimensional molecules in two dimensions

Conventions, and the extent that they are a result of cultural conditioning, is a fascinating subject. The diagrams in this book have to attempt to represent three-dimensional molecules through the two-dimensional medium of the page of the book. This is a problem that graphic artists also have to contend with and as a result they developed the technique of perspective. Our drawings have attempted to draw on some of these techniques, but added a few other little conventions, such as things with dotted lines being below the plane of the book and wedge shaped lines coming out of the page. Like so many things, the concept of perspective was well known to the Greeks, but was then lost to be rediscovered and thoroughly developed in the Renaissance period. It depends on the apparent diminution of size with distance and the resulting convergence of lines. If we show two human figures in a drawing, but one is much smaller than the other we can either assume the smaller one is further away from us, or that it represents a leprechaun or some other kind of diminutive human. Usually for us the former explanation is more convincing. A consequence of this is that the constant width of a road appears to be smaller the further away from us it goes, hence as it disappears towards the horizon the sides of the road appear to get closer together, meeting at the horizon (in theory an infinite distance away!). We have grown up with these tricks of the graphic artist and find it difficult when viewing a scene drawn using perspective, to imagine in any other way.

It is reported that when drawings incorporating perspective are shown to people of more 'primitive' cultures, they do not realise that some of the objects are supposed to be further away than others, in other words the appreciation of perspective is something that we develop by growing up in a culture where it is widely employed. Others however contest this say that the appreciation of perspective, even though not developed by all societies, is innate to humans rather than something that is culturally developed. Anyway I hope that you have all been exposed to enough Escher "impossible geometries" to be able to pick up the three-dimensional shapes that we are trying to represent.

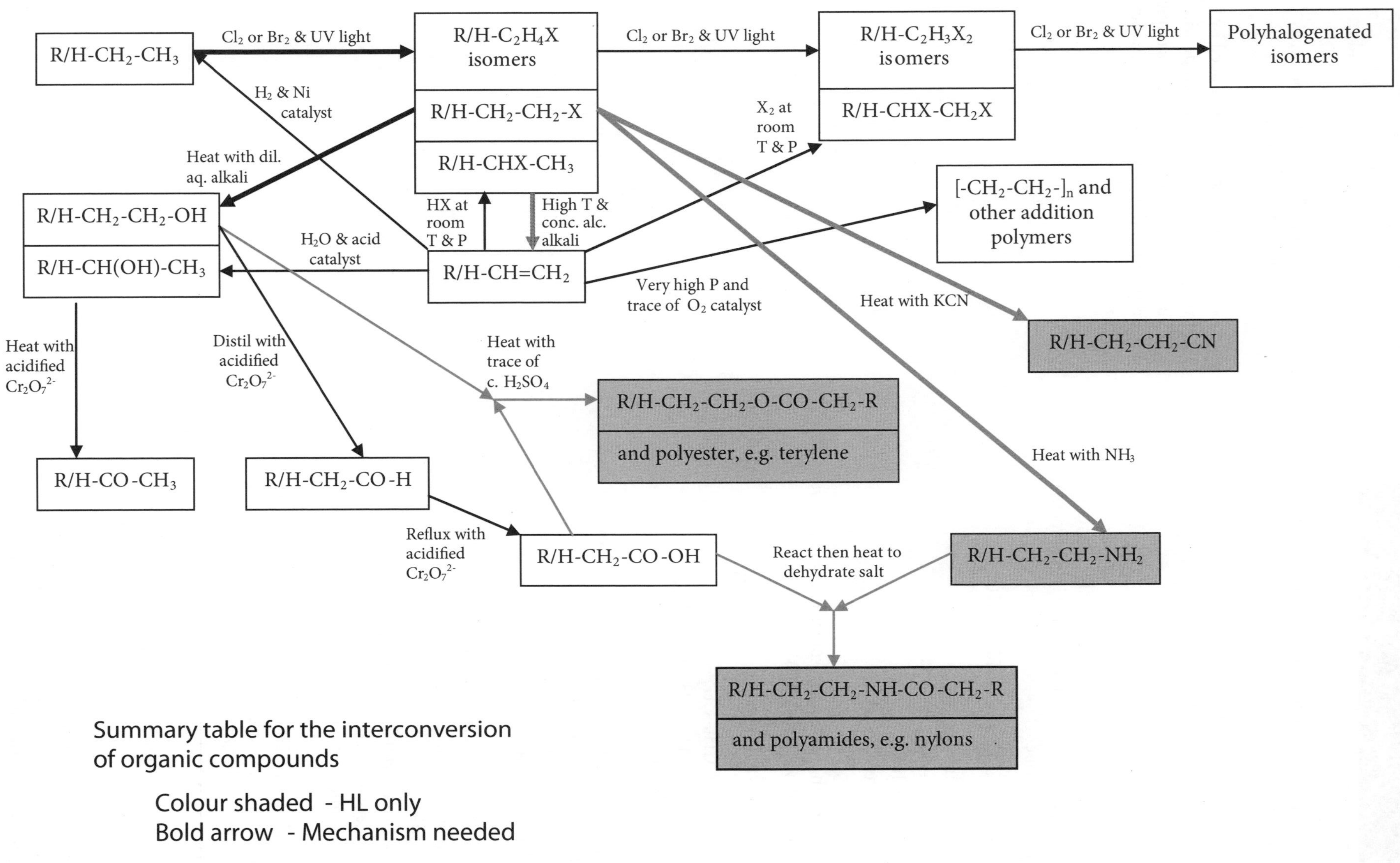

Figure 1048 A summary table for the interconversion of organic compounds

Exercise 20.6

1. Which one of the following compounds will exhibit geometrical isomerism?

   A $CH_3CH{=}CH_2$
   B $CH_3CCl{=}CH_2$
   C $CH_3CH{=}CHCl$
   D $CH_3CH{=}CCl_2$

2. Counting from the left hand end of the principal chain, which carbon atom in the following molecule is an asymmetric one?

   $ClCH_2{-}C(CH_3)_2{-}CHCl{-}CHCl_2$

   A The first
   B The second
   C The third
   D The fourth

3. Which one of the following isomeric alcohols can exist as a pair of optical isomers?

   A $CH_3{-}CH_2{-}CH_2{-}CH_2{-}OH$
   B $(CH_3)_2CH{-}CH_2{-}OH$
   C $CH_3{-}CH_2{-}CH(OH){-}CH_3$
   D $(CH_3)_3C{-}OH$

4. 3–bromopent–1–ene can exist in many isomeric forms. Draw a full structural formula of the molecule and then draw structural formulae of isomers that only differ from it in the manner given:

   a) A hydrocarbon chain isomer.
   b) An optical isomer (enantiomer).
   c) A positional isomer.
   d) An isomer which displays geometric isomerism.
   e) An isomer not containing a double bond.

5. Lactic acid [$CH_3CH(OH)COOH$] can either be extracted from sour milk, or it may be produced synthetically by the addition of water to propenoic acid ($CH_2{=}CHCOOH$).

   a) Explain what is meant by the terms 'optically active' and 'racemic mixture'.
   b) How would you expect samples from these two sources to differ.
   c) In practice, how could you determine whether a sample of lactic acid was of natural or synthetic origin?

6. a) Samples of 2–bromobutane may exhibit optical activity. Explain why.

   b) 2–bromobutane may be produced by the reaction of hydrogen bromide with but–2–ene. Would you expect a sample prepared in this way to be optically active? Explain why.

AHL

MEASUREMENT AND DATA PROCESSING

11.1 Uncertainty and error in measurement

11.2 Uncertainties in calculated results

11.3 Graphical techniques

CORE

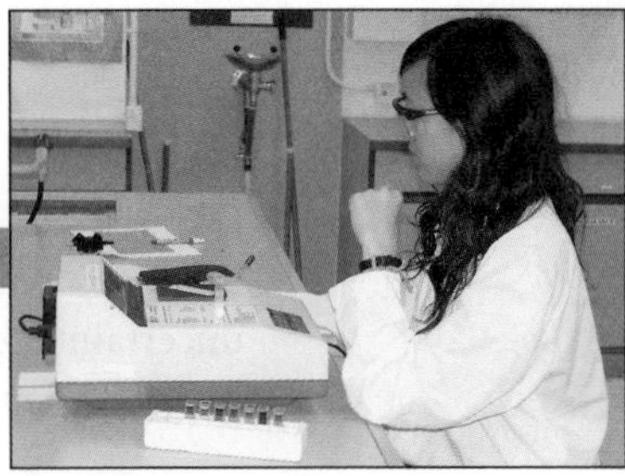

11.1 UNCERTAINTY & ERROR IN MEASUREMENT

11.1.1 Describe and give examples of random uncertainties and systematic errors.

11.1.2 Distinguish between precision and accuracy.

11.1.3 Describe how the effects of random uncertainties may be reduced.

11.1.4 State random uncertainty as an uncertainty range (±).

11.1.5 State the results of calculations to the appropriate number of significant figures.

In practical science, the results of experiments are never completely reliable as there are always **experimental errors** and **uncertainties** involved. It is therefore important, especially in quantitative work, to be able to assess the magnitude of these and their effect on the reliability of the final result. It is important to differentiate between the **accuracy** of a result and the **precision** of a result. The accuracy of the result is a **measure** of how close the result is to some accepted, or literature value for the quantity being determined. For example, an experiment that gives a value of 8.317 J mol^{-1} K^{-1} for the ideal gas constant (accepted value 8.314 J mol^{-1} K^{-1}) is obviously more accurate than one that gives a value of 8.103 J mol^{-1} K^{-1}. The accuracy is usually measured as the percentage deviation from the accepted value using the expression:

Percentage deviation =

$$\left|\frac{\text{Experimental value} - \text{Accepted value}}{\text{Accepted value}}\right| \times 100$$

It can be seen that the percentage deviation of the two values quoted for the (ideal) gas constant are 0.04% and 2.54% respectively:

$$\text{Percentage deviation} = \left|\frac{8.317 - 8.314}{8.314}\right| \times 100$$

= 0.03608
= 0.04 (*to 1 sig. fig. precision of top line*)

$$\text{Percentage deviation} = \left|\frac{8.103 - 8.314}{8.314}\right| \times 100$$

= 2.53788
= 2.54 (*to 3 sig. fig. precision of top line*)

The precision of the result is a measure of the certainty of the value determined, usually quoted as a ± value. Again, with regard to the gas constant, one group might quote a result of 8.34 ± 0.03 J mol^{-1} K^{-1}, whilst another group gives a value of 8.513 ± 0.006 J mol^{-1} K^{-1}. Whilst the result of the former group is the more accurate (i.e. closer to the accepted value), that of the latter group is the more precise (i.e. has the smallest uncertainty). The way that uncertainties are calculated is discussed extensively later in the chapter.

The relationship between accuracy and precision is illustrated in Figure 1101.

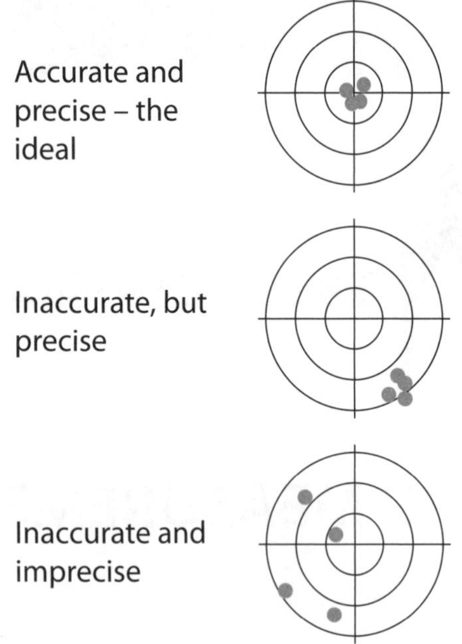

Figure 1101 The relationship between accuracy and precision

Random uncertainties make a **measurement** less precise, but not in any particular direction, in other words the actual value may be either greater or smaller than the value you record. Random uncertainties (or errors) arise mostly from inadequacies or limitations in the instrument. This may be a result of how precisely you can read a meter or scale of, for example, the burette in Figure 1102. We would probably take the reading as 43.6, but in so doing we are saying that it is nearer to 43.6 than it is to 43.5 or 43.7, in other words it is greater than 43.55 (had it been less we would have recorded it as 43.5) and smaller than 43.65 (had it been greater we would have recorded it as 43.7), hence we should record this value as 43.6 ± 0.05. See Figure 1102.

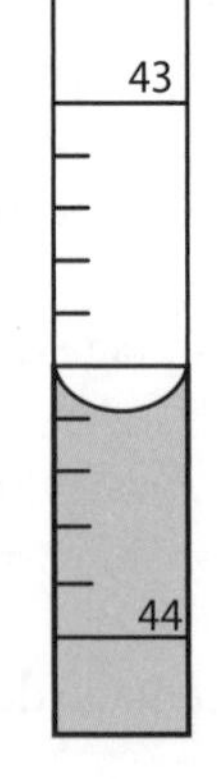

Figure 1102 A sample reading

Similarly if we are reading a digital instrument, such as a balance, then we should record the uncertainty as being half of the last digit. For example the reading **37.361** on a digital readout should be recorded as 37.361 ± 0.0005, assuming the readout is steady. If the reading is fluctuating, then you have to try to estimate the degree of certainty you feel you have in the value you record. If the last digit keeps going up or down by one, you may feel you can say the value is definitely greater than 37.359 and less than 37.363, so you record it as 37.361 ± 0.001.

In some cases, such as many thermometers, it is only possible to read a scale to the nearest 0.2 (that is, one would record 23.0, 23.2, 23.4 etc., but never an odd final digit such as 23.3). In this case the uncertainty would be ±0.1, because a reading of 23.2 means it is greater than 23.0, but less than 23.4.

Quantitative apparatus usually has a nominal random uncertainty which reflects the tolerances used in its manufacture. With volumetric apparatus it is possible to purchase both A-grade and B-grade apparatus. For example, with a 25 cm^3 bulb pipette the manufacturer's uncertainty for A-grade is ±0.03 cm^3, whereas for B-grade it is ±0.06 cm^3.

Large random uncertainties obviously decrease the precision of the values obtained and can also lead to inconsistent results if the procedure is repeated. If only one reading is taken, then a large random uncertainty can lead to an inaccurate result. Repeating experimental determinations should, however, increase the precision of the final result as the random variations statistically cancel out.

Systematic errors always affect a result in a particular direction and hence the accuracy of the experiment. They arise from flaws or defects in the instrument or from errors in the way that the measurement was taken. If, for example, a student takes the mass of an empty weighing bottle to calculate the mass of solid used, rather than re-weighing it after tipping the contents into a beaker, then this would be a systematic error because the mass of solid in the beaker will always be slightly less than the value the student uses (because some solid may have been left in the weighing bottle). It could never be higher. It is often difficult to allow for such errors quantitatively, but the direction in which it would affect the final result can always be determined. For example, in this case, if the solid were used to prepare a solution that was then titrated with a standard solution from a burette, then it might explain why the burette reading was less than the expected value, but it could not explain a higher reading. Often the order of magnitude is estimated. In this example, (assuming the mass taken was 10.000 g) 'solid left in the bottle' would not be able to explain why the titre was 10% less than expected – you would surely have noticed 1 g of remaining solid.).

Taking the initial reading of a burette when it was well above head height would also give rise to a systematic error. Parallax error, caused by not reading the scale perpendicularly would, in this case, give a value for the initial reading that was greater than the true reading. Hence the values obtained for the titre would be consistently lower than the true value. Another example of a systematic error would be to read the top rather than the bottom of the meniscus in measuring cylinders and pipettes, which would consistently deliver a smaller volume than that recorded. Errors in the calibration of instruments, for example pH meters, also lead to systematic errors. The most familiar systematic error is heat exchange to the surroundings which, in calorimetric experiments, inevitably leads to smaller temperature changes than would be observed in a perfectly insulated system.

A large systematic error can lead to the result being inaccurate and, if it is a variable systematic error (i.e. it always has an effect in a particular direction, but the size of the error varies), it can lead to inconsistent results.

If you are involved in calculations involving experimental data then these should be combined so as to reflect all of the uncertainties involved and that is covered in the next section. If, however, you are doing calculations involving data that you have been given, then it is important to quote the final result to a precision that reflects that of these data. The general rules to apply are:

- For multiplication and division, the result should have the same number of **significant figures** as the least precise piece of data.

- For addition and subtraction the result should not have more **decimal places** than the least precise piece of data.

Suppose you wish to calculate the formula of a fluoride of uranium given that 5.84 g of uranium produced 8.637 g of the fluoride and that the molar masses of uranium and fluorine are 238.03 and 19.00 g mol^{-1} respectively. If you were initially asked for the mass of fluorine present in the compound, this should be quoted as 2.80 g (rather than 2.797 g as there are only 2 d.p. in the mass data for uranium; note that the final zero in the mass of fluorine should be written as it is significant). The moles of uranium ($\frac{5.84}{238.03}$ = 0.0245347) should be quoted as 0.0245 as the mass of uranium is only known to 3 significant figures. Likewise, the moles of fluorine ($\frac{2.797}{19.00}$ = 0.1472105) should be quoted as 0.147 and the F:U ratio ($\frac{0.147...}{0.0245...}$= 6.0000937) as 6.00. It is good practice (especially with modern calculators) to keep intermediate results to the maximum precision (in the memory of the calculator) and then to round off the final result to the appropriate precision.

EXTENSION

Another factor related to experimental data is consistency. The **consistency** of a result is a measure of how reproducible the result is when the experiment is repeated. For example, the results of two groups for determining the value of the gas constant (literature value 8.314 J mol^{-1} K^{-1}) are given:

Group A – 8.537; 8.487; 8.598; 8.492; 8.472
Mean = 8.517 J mol^{-1} K^{-1} Range = 0.126

Group B – 8.13; 7.94; 8.44; 8.54; 8.22
Mean = 8.25 J mol^{-1} K^{-1} Range = 0.60

It can be seen that those obtained by Group A are far more consistent and more precise than those obtained by Group B, even though those of Group B are more accurate. The consistency is indicated by the range (maximum value – minimum value), though more sophisticated indicators, such as standard deviation, could be used to compare consistency. The uncertainty of a set of repeated measurements should reflect the consistency of the results. There are many statistical ways of estimating the uncertainty of repeated measurements, but probably one of the simplest is to divide the range of the results (X_{max} – X_{min}) by twice the square root of the number of readings taken (N):

$$\Delta X = \frac{X_{\text{max}} - X_{\text{min}}}{2\sqrt{N}}$$

Applying this, the results of Group A should be quoted as 8.517 ± 0.028 J mol^{-1} K^{-1} (or perhaps more correctly 8.52 ± 0.03 J mol^{-1} K^{-1}) and that of group B as 8.25 ± 0.13 J mol^{-1} K^{-1}. Note that the results obtained by Group B confirm the literature value (it is within the uncertainty) whereas those of Group A do not. Which group performed the better experiment?

Figure 1103 extends the relationship between accuracy and precision shown in Figure 1101 to include the concept of consistency.

EXTENSION

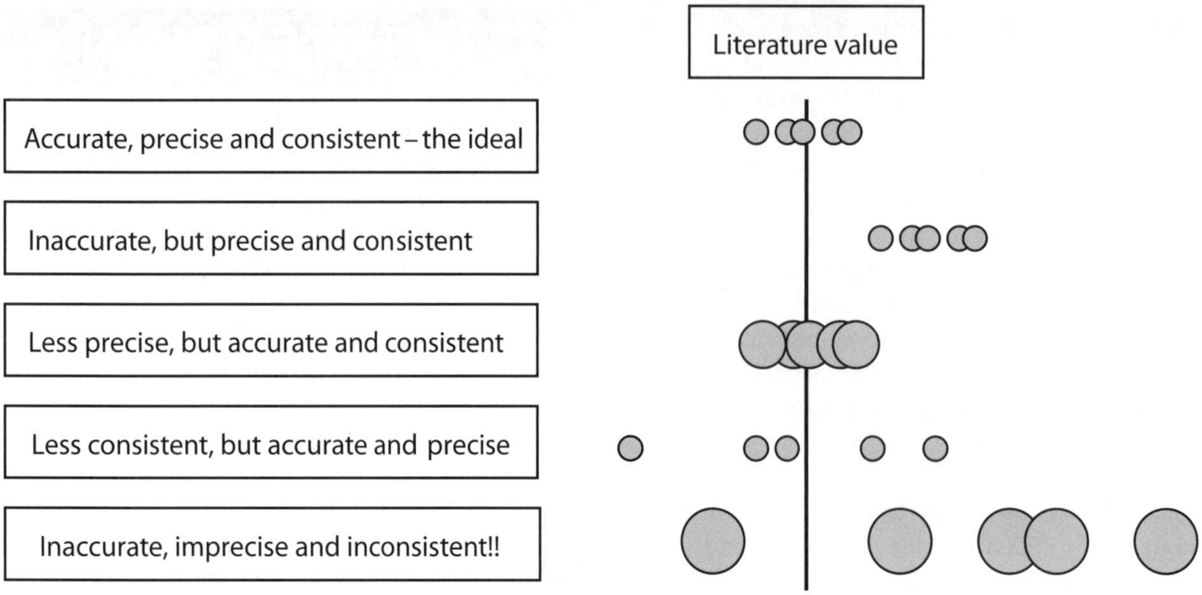

Literature value

Accurate, precise and consistent – the ideal

Inaccurate, but precise and consistent

Less precise, but accurate and consistent

Less consistent, but accurate and precise

Inaccurate, imprecise and inconsistent!!

Figure 1103 The relationship between accuracy, precision and consistency

11.2 UNCERTAINTIES IN CALCULATED RESULTS

11.2.1 State uncertainties as absolute and percentage uncertainties.

11.2.2 Determine the uncertainties in results.

The uncertainties in individual measurements can be combined to calculate the uncertainty in the final value of the quantity being determined. One way to estimate this would be to assume all the uncertainties were in the direction that would give the largest value of the final quantity (that is taking the largest possible number if the value is added or used to multiply and the smallest value if it is subtracted or used to divide) and recalculate the result with these data.

An alternative that is often easier to apply is to use the following simple rules:

- add **absolute** uncertainties when adding or subtracting numbers
- add **percentage** uncertainties when multiplying or dividing numbers
- [multiply **percentage** uncertainties by the exponential when raising to a power]

The **absolute uncertainty** is the **actual uncertainty** in the value, for example ±0.05 for a quantity that has the value 28.5 ± 0.05. The percentage uncertainty is the absolute uncertainty expressed as a percentage of the value. For example the percentage uncertainty of 28.5 ± 0.05 is ±0.18% ($100 \times \frac{0.05}{28.5}$). The third point is put in parentheses because it is a consequence of the second as $X^2 = X.X$. So applying the second rule the uncertainty of X^2 will be double the percentage uncertainty of X. Similarly the percentage uncertainty of $\sqrt{X}$ will be half the percentage uncertainty of X.

Suppose you want to calculate the value and uncertainty of X, where

$$X = A\,(B - C)$$

given the values:

$A = 123 \pm 0.5$; $B = 12.7 \pm 0.2$; $C = 4.3 \pm 0.1$

$$X = 123 \times (12.7 - 4.3)$$
$$= 1033.2$$
(note that this has not yet been rounded to an appropriate precision as the uncertainty has not been calculated)

Actual uncertainty in $(B - C)$ = ± 0.3 (add actual uncertainties, 0.2 + 0.1 = 0.3)

% uncertainty in A = 0.407% ($100 \times \frac{0.5}{123}$)

% uncertainty in $(B - C)$ = 3.571% ($100 \times \frac{0.3}{8.4}$)

% uncertainty in X = 3.978%
(add percentage uncertainties, 0.407 + 3.571)

Actual uncertainty in X = 41.1 ($1033.2 \times \frac{3.978}{100}$)

Therefore $X = 1033.2 \pm 41.1$

The usual practice is to only give the uncertainty to one significant figure and then to round off the value to a similar number of decimal places; hence the final; result should be quoted as

$$X = 1030 \pm 40$$

Note that, even though B and C were measured to greater precision, because they are subtracted they contribute much more to the final uncertainty than does A.

When using a literature value in calculations, assume its precision is limited to the number of digits given. For example, if the relative atomic mass of chlorine is given as 35.45 it should be taken as ±0.005. In some cases, however, the uncertainty of one quantity is much greater than that of all of the others, so the uncertainty of the final value can be considered to be due to only that factor and hence have the same percentage uncertainty. In these cases it is important to state that you are ignoring the minor uncertainties in other data. Consider a calorimetry experiment that gave the following results:

Initial temperature	21.6 ± 0.1°C
Final temperature	24.2 ± 0.1°C
Mass of water heated	200 ± 0.5 g
Amount of limiting reagent	0.0500 ± 0.00005 mol

Combined with the value below from a data book:

Specific heat capacity of water 4.183 ± 0.0005 J g^{-1} K^{-1}

It would be acceptable to state that the percentage uncertainty in the heat absorbed was being taken as being the same as the percentage uncertainty of the temperature change ($100 \times \frac{0.2}{2.6}$ = 7.7%) as this was so much larger than all the other quantities involved (±0.25%, 0.1% and 0.12% respectively for Δm and ±0.01% for s). The error analysis for the experiment would then be:

$\Delta T = 2.6 \pm 0.2$°C (in addition and subtraction, the uncertainties are added)

$$\% \text{ uncertainty} = 100 \times \frac{0.2}{2.6}$$

$$= 7.7\%$$

$$Q = m\,c\,\Delta T$$

$$= 200 \text{ g} \times 4.18 \text{ J g}^{-1} \times 2.6 \text{ °C}$$

$$= 2173.6 \text{ J}$$

$$\Delta H = -\frac{Q}{n}$$

$$= -\frac{2173.6}{0.0500}$$

$$= 43472 \text{ J mol}^{-1}$$

As the uncertainty in the temperature change is so much greater than that of the other quantities, the percentage uncertainty in the final result will be taken as 7.7%:

$$\text{Absolute uncertainty} = 43472 \times \frac{7.7}{100}$$

$$= 3347$$

So the final result should be quoted as

$$\Delta H = -43000 \pm 3000 \text{ J mol}^{-1}$$

$$= -43 \pm 3 \text{ kJ mol}^{-1}$$

Suppose the literature value for the enthalpy change was –45.6 kJ mol^{-1}, the percentage discrepancy would be:

$$\frac{45.6 - 43}{45.6} = 5.7\%$$

In this case the percentage discrepancy is smaller than the uncertainty in the experimental value (7.7%), hence the result of the experiment is in agreement with the literature value. The major errors in the experiment are therefore those related to the precision, especially that of the temperature change, and suggested improvements should therefore concentrate on improving this, may be by using a more precise thermometer (perhaps one that reads to ±0.01 °C, if available) or more likely by increasing the temperature change, perhaps by using more concentrated reagents. Note that there is little point in trying to reduce the uncertainties in other values (such as using a more precise balance to weigh the water so that Δm = ±0.05 g) until the uncertainty in the temperature has been significantly decreased.

If the literature value for the enthalpy change was –56.2 kJ mol^{-1}, the percentage discrepancy would be:

$$\frac{56.2 - 43}{56.2} \times 100 = 23.5\%$$

In this case the percentage discrepancy is much greater than could be accounted for by the uncertainties in the experimental value (7.7%), hence there must be some major systematic errors and the major focus of error analysis would now be to identify these. In this case, they would probably be factors such as heat loss to the surroundings, not taking into account the heat capacity of the calorimeter, assuming the heat capacity of the solution is equal to that of water etc. Improvements should then be suggested that minimise these such as covering the calorimeter to reduce heat loss, using Styrofoam calorimeter, measuring the heat capacity of the solutions used etc. The precision is poor, so suggesting ways to improve it would be appropriate, but this should not be the main focus.

TOK Why are graphs helpful in providing powerful interpretations of reality?

"Seeing is believing." I suppose this sums up better than anything else the extent to which we rely on vision to interpret the world and probably that is why we find graphs, and indeed diagrams in general, such a useful way of "getting a feel" for things. I suppose another relevant quotation would be "A picture's meaning can express 10,000 words" (apparently a more accurate literal translation than the usual one of the anonymous Chinese proverb). Diagrams and graphs provide us with a more concrete and less abstract experience. If we had the data table:

X	Y1	Y2
1	104.3	1.3
2	95.6	2.6
3	86.9	5.2
4	78.2	10.4
5	69.5	20.8
6	60.8	41.6
7	52.1	83.2
8	43.4	166.4

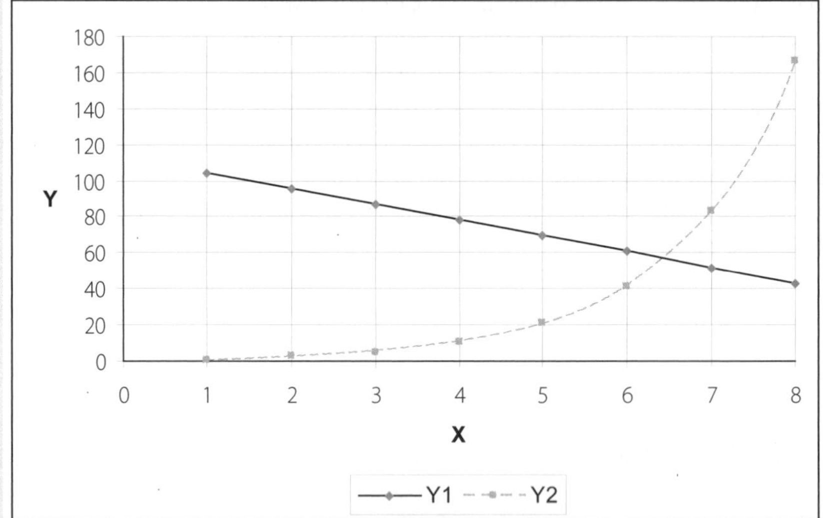

Given a little time we could probably work out that the numbers represented a linear decrease (Y1) and an exponential increase (Y2), but it is immediately obvious if we look at the graph. Maybe that is because one requires the use of the logic circuits in our brain (is the difference between 104.3 and 95.6, the same as between 78.2 and 69.5?), whereas the pictorial representation seems to by-pass this - we immediately see a recognisable, familiar pattern, like the face of an old friend.

11.3 GRAPHICAL TECHNIQUES

11.3.1 Sketch graphs to represent dependences and interpret graph behaviour.

11.3.2 Construct graphs from experimental data.

11.3.3 Draw best-fit lines through data points on a graph.

11.3.4 Determine the values of physical quantities from graphs.

Graphs are one of the most useful ways for interpreting scientific data because they allow for direct visual correlation between the data obtained and a particular scientific model or hypothesis. In its simplest form this involves organising data so that a linear graph is expected.

See Figures 1104 and 1105.

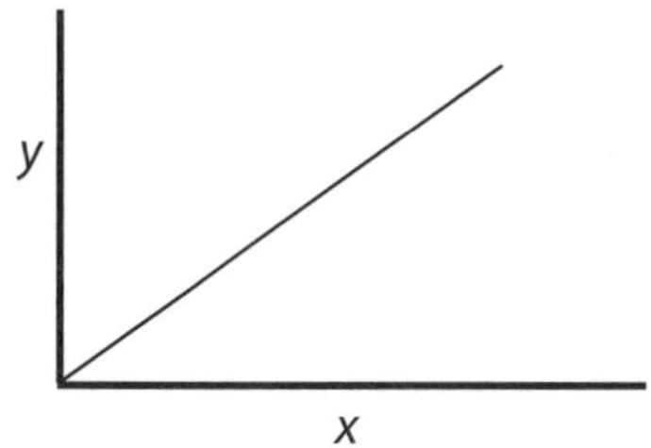

Figure 1104 Direct proportionality

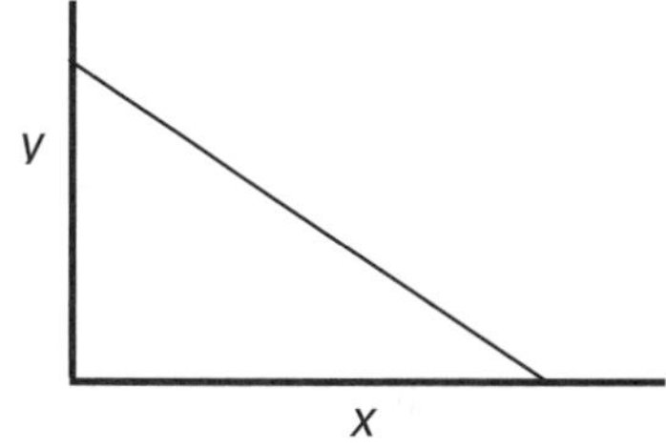

Figure 1105 A linear relationship

Sometimes it is possible to rearrange an equation that is not a linear relationship to give a modified equation that does have such a relationship. An example would be testing to see if the approximation of neglecting the effect of dissociation on the concentration of a weak acid is valid:

$$HA \rightleftharpoons H^+ + A^-$$

	HA	H^+	A^-
Initial Concentrations	a	0	0
Equilibrium concentrations	$a\text{-}x$	x	x

Substituting in the equilibrium expression:

$$K_a = \frac{[H^+].[A^-]}{[HA]} = \frac{x.x}{a-x} = \frac{x^2}{a-x} \approx \frac{x^2}{a}$$

$$K_a.a \approx x^2 \text{ so } x \approx \sqrt{K_a}\,.\,\sqrt{a}$$

Hence, if this approximation is valid, the $[H^+]$ (x) would be proportional to $\sqrt{[HA]}$ ($\sqrt{a}$) and this could be tested by drawing a graph of $[H^+]$ against $\sqrt{[HA]}$ and seeing if it was linear.

If manipulation cannot produce a linear function, sometimes there is an inverse proportionality or inverse linear relationship, which can be used to plot a graph that should give a straight line. See Figures 1106 and 1107.

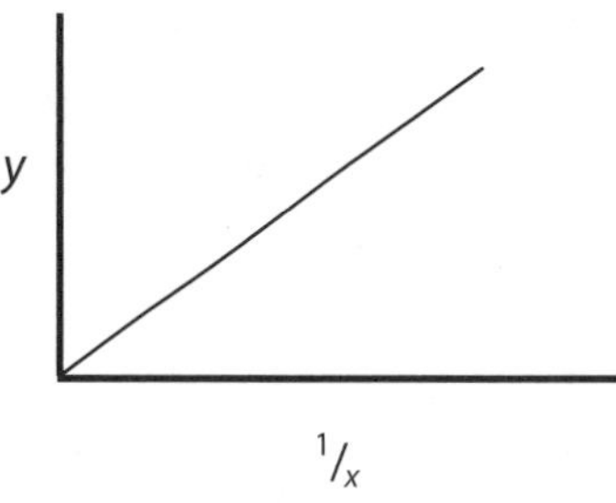

Figure 1106 Inverse proportionality

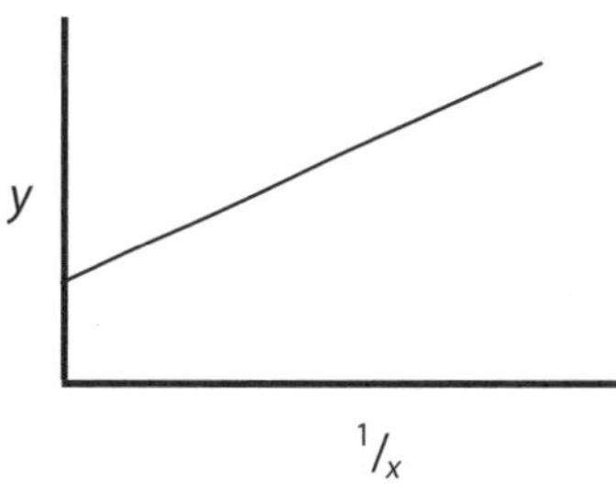

Figure 1107 Inverse linear relationship

If a buffer solution is made by taking a solution of a weak acid and dissolving a solid salt of that weak acid in it, then the dependence of $[H^+]$ on the amount of a solid salt added would be an inverse linear relationship:

$$K_a = \frac{[H^+].[A^-]}{[HA]} \text{ so } [H^+] = K_a.\frac{[HA]}{[A^-]}$$

This could be tested by seeing if a graph of $[H^+]$ against $\frac{1}{\text{mass of salt}}$ (as this will be proportional to $\frac{1}{[A^-]}$) was linear, assuming the volume and concentration of the acid are kept constant.

When drawing graphs it is usual to choose the axes so that the independent variable (frequently time) is plotted along the horizontal axis and the dependent variable on the vertical axis. The scale should be chosen so as to maximise the use of the graph area, taking into account any extrapolation of the data that may be required. A fairly simple scale should also be chosen (2, 4, 5, 8 or 10 squares equal to one unit) to facilitate the easy plotting of data. More complex scales (for example, 7 squares equal to one unit) may maximise the use of the graph area, but frequently lead to errors in the plotting of points.

Care must also be taken to have enough data points to ensure that the graph really is linear. For example it is questionable whether the data in Figure 1108 (a) really do represent a straight line rather than a curve, but the addition of extra data points, as shown in Figure 1108 (b), confirm that they do indeed describe a linear relationship, though if these points had been elsewhere, as in Figure 1108 (c), they could have indicated that the relationship is non-linear.

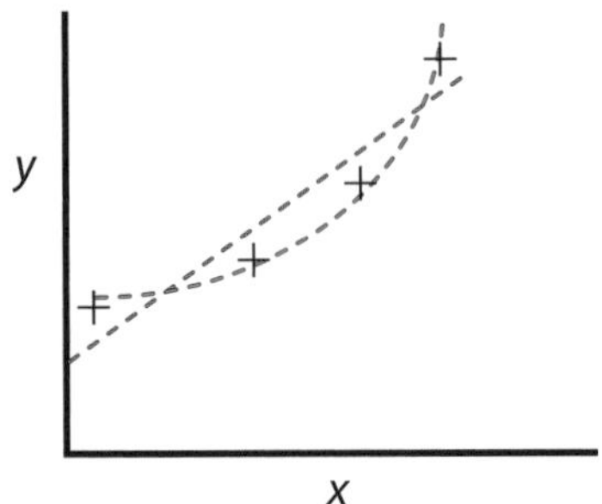

Figure 1108 (a)

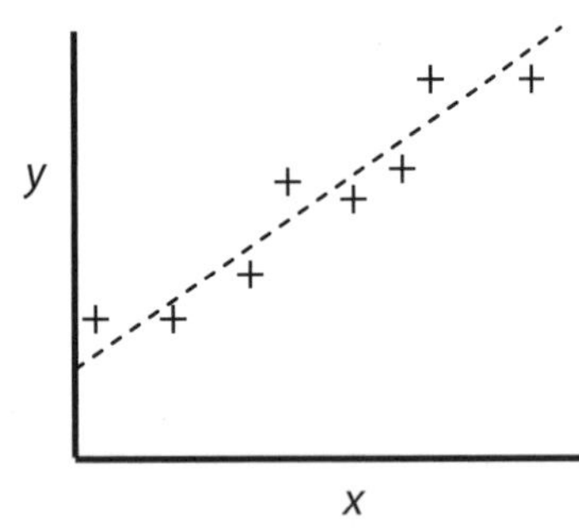

Figure 1108 (b)

Figure 1108 (c)

Graphs can be used to check the validity of a relationship, as in the examples above, or to determine some value from either the intercept (in which case the units are the same as those of the axis) or the gradient of the line (in which case the units are those of the vertical axis divided by those of the horizontal axis). Some of the more common graphs that are encountered in chemistry and their uses are considered:

Ideal gas law $P.V = n.R.T$

so $V = \frac{n.R.T}{P}$

or $P = \frac{n.R.T}{V}$

Where P is the pressure, V the volume, n the number of moles and T the absolute temperature of the gas sample. R is the ideal gas constant.

Most commonly P is plotted against $\left(\frac{1}{V}\right)$ at constant temperature (**Boyle-Mariotte Law**). A linear graph shows the validity of this relationship and, if the number of moles of gas can be determined (for example by knowing its mass) and the temperature is measured, then the value of the ideal gas constant (R) can be found from the gradient. See Figure 1109.

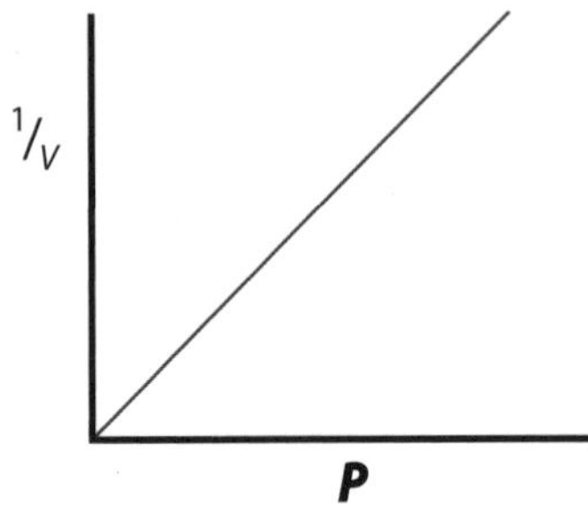

Figure 1109 Boyle's Law

Alternatively V can be plotted against T at constant pressure (**Charles's Law**). Again a linear graph shows the validity of this relationship and, if the number of moles of gas is known and the pressure is measured, then the value of the ideal gas constant (R) can be found from the gradient. The data can also be extrapolated back to $V = 0$ to find the value of absolute zero. See Figure 1110.

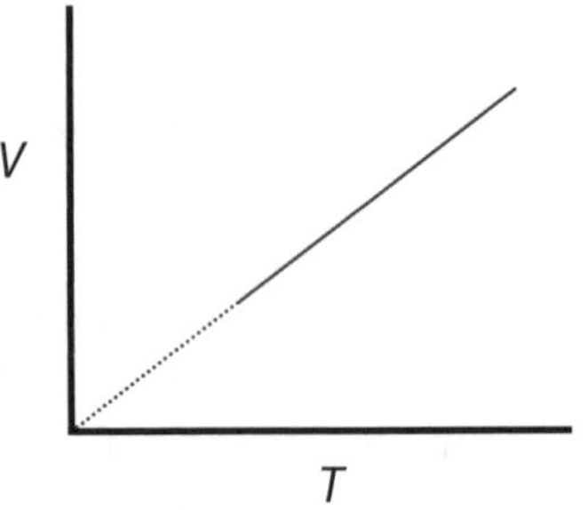

Figure 1110 Charles's Law

Cooling curves

Graphs of temperature versus time during and just after a chemical reaction

The portion of these graphs following the maximum temperature are often extrapolated backwards in order to estimate the temperature rise that might have occurred if the reaction had been instantaneous and hence involved no heat loss. A linear extrapolation is often used even though there is little theoretical justification for this. See Figure 1111.

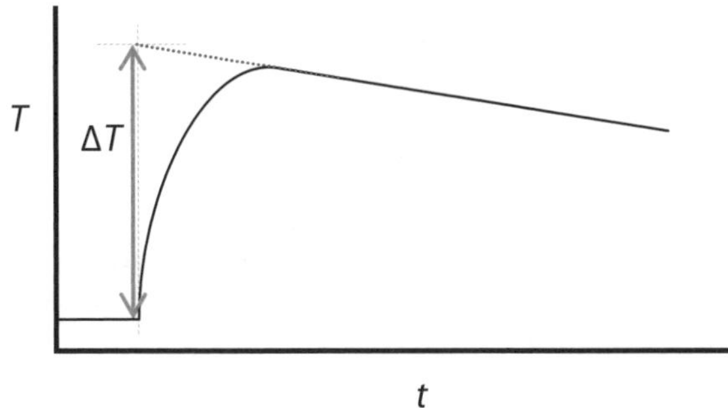

Figure 1111 A cooling curve

Reaction rate graphs

Graphs of concentration (or some property proportional to it) versus time

The gradient of a tangent to the line at any time (with the sign reversed if the concentration of a reactant is being followed) is proportional to the rate of reaction. The units of rate are therefore those of concentration divided by time (i.e. mol dm^{-3} s^{-1}). See Figure 1112.

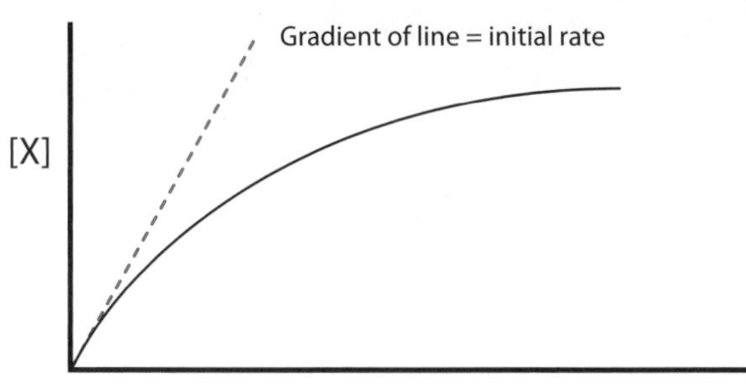

Figure 1112 A reaction rate curve

Reaction order graphs

Graphs of reaction rate versus concentration of one reactant (others constant).

The shape of the graph indicates the reaction order with respect to that reactant:

Zero order - linear horizontal line
1st order - linear
2nd order - curved upwards
See Figure 1113.

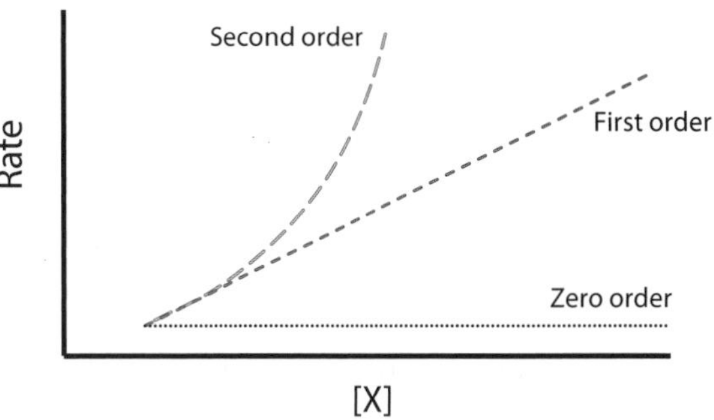

Figure 1113 A reaction order curve

Activation energy graphs

Graphs of the effect of temperature on reaction rate.

The Arrhenius relationship states:

$$k = Ae^{\left(\frac{-E_a}{RT}\right)}$$

Taking natural logarithms and rearranging:

$$\ln k = \ln A - \left(\frac{E_a}{R}\right)\left(\frac{1}{T}\right)$$

So a graph of ln(rate) (which is proportional to k if the concentrations remain constant) against $\frac{1}{T}$ (in Kelvin) is linear. The intercept is equal to ln$A$ and the gradient is equal to $-\frac{E_a}{R}$, so that knowing R the activation energy can be determined. See Figure 1114.

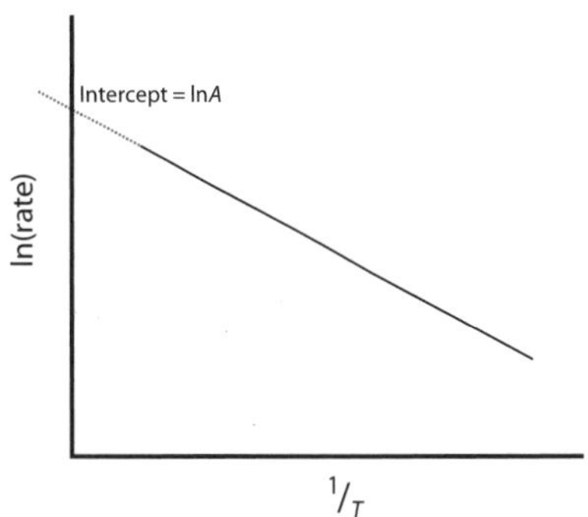

Figure 1114 An activation energy graph

CORE

Exercise 11.1

Four groups have done a calorimetric experiment to determine the enthalpy change of a reaction in aqueous solution, for which the literature value is 38.73 kJ mol^{-1}. The values found by the groups (in kJ mol^{-1}) were:

A 35.1 ± 0.3 B 36.5 ± 0.5
C 33.2 ± 0.1 D 34.7 ± 0.2

1. Which result is the most precise?

2. Which result is the most accurate?

3. Do you think the major problem is

   A Random error
   B Systematic error
   C Both are equally important
   D It is not possible to tell from the data given

4. If you were to repeat the experiment which of the following is most likely to be the improvement that would most improve the result?

   A Using a more precise thermometer.
   B Not assuming that the specific heat of the solution equalled that of water.
   C Using pipettes rather than measuring cylinders.
   D Improving the insulation of the calorimeter.

5. Which of the following is the best way to report the mean result of the group?

   A 34.875 ± 0.100 kJ mol^{-1}.
   B 34.9 ± 0.5 kJ mol^{-1}.
   C 34.9 ± 0.8 kJ mol^{-1}.
   D 35 ± 2 kJ mol^{-1}.

6. Repeating an experiment a number of times will lead to a decrease in:

   A the random error.
   B the systematic error.
   C both the random and the systematic error.
   D neither the random and the systematic error.

Exercise 11.2

1. Which result has the lowest absolute uncertainty?

   A 34.875 ± 0.017
   B 749 ± 5
   C 0.0004 ± 0.0001
   D 87500 ± 200

2. Which result has the lowest percentage uncertainty?

   A 34.875 ± 0.017
   B 749 ± 5
   C 0.0004 ± 0.0001
   D 87500 ± 200

3. If x = 749 ± 5 and y = 34.8 ± 0.7, which one of the following will have the greatest percentage uncertainty?

   A x + y
   B x - y
   C x/y
   D x.√y

4. Give the result and the absolute uncertainty, to the correct precision, of the following calculations:

   a) 20.1 ± 0.1 + 2.75 ± 0.05
   b) 115.4 ± 0.2 × 8.137 ± 0.001
   c) 0.572 ± 0.001 (17.6 0.2 - 114 ± 1)
   d) (1 - 0.276 ± 0.002)/0.024 ± 0.001
   e) 52800 ± 100/ √(17.2 ± 0.2 - 2.37 ± 0.01)

Exercise 11.3

1. Plot a graph of the following data. Construct the best straight line and use it to determine the value of the intercept and the gradient of the line.

x	1	2	3	4	5	6	7	8	9	10
y	7.6	10.7	13.2	17.1	19.8	23.0	25.7	28.7	32.9	35.4

2. Two variables, x and y, are related by the equation:

S x(T-y) = 5

where S and T are constants. Draw an appropriate graph to investigate whether the data below supports this and use it to find values for S and T.

x	1	2	3	4	5	6	7	8	9	10
y	2.52	3.78	4.11	4.35	4.52	4.59	4.62	4.71	4.73	4.74

MODERN ANALYTICAL CHEMISTRY

12

A1 Analytical techniques
A2 Principles of spectroscopy
A3 Infrared (IR) spectroscopy
A4 Mass spectrometry
A5 Nuclear magnetic resonance (NMR) spectroscopy
A9 Nuclear magnetic resonance (NMR) spectroscopy (HL)
A6 Atomic absorption (AA) spectroscopy
A7 Chromatography
A10 Chromatography (HL)
A8 Visible and ultraviolet spectroscopy (HL)

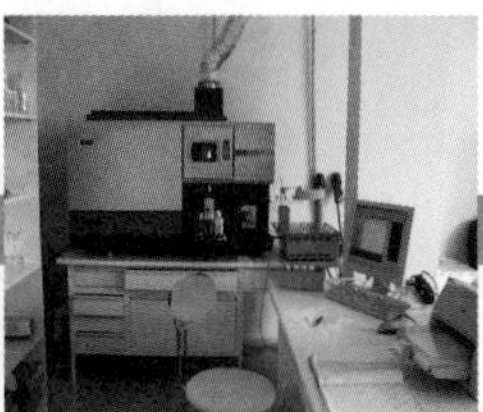

"Analytical chemistry techniques are widely used in today's society. Students should understand the chemical principles behind each analytical technique. This option builds on some of the key ideas in both physical and organic chemistry that were introduced in the core".

A1 ANALYTICAL TECHNIQUES

A1.1 State the reasons for using analytical techniques.

A1.2 State that the structure of a compound can be determined by using information from a variety of analytical techniques singularly or in combination.

Analytical chemistry involves qualitative and quantitative analysis of a sample to determine its chemical composition and structure. **Qualitative analysis** determines what components are present, for example, the presence of a forbidden colouring material in a processed food or the elements present in a compound. **Quantitative analysis** determines the amount of a particular substance in a mixture, for example the percentage of copper in brass or the amount of each element in a compound. **Structural analysis** is the determination of the structure of a pure substance, the way in which the atoms present are joined together and, in the case of large molecules, the way in which the molecule is arranged in three-dimensions as in the structure of a protein.

'Wet' chemical techniques involve observing characteristic chemical reactions, or the use of volumetric and gravimetric techniques. Analytical methods, on the other hand, are usually faster, more precise and easier to automate than 'wet' methods, and a combination of analytical techniques is often used to obtain complete structural information. Thus, whereas an IR spectrum shows the presence of organic functional groups such as carbonyl or hydroxyl groups, NMR is more diagnostic and can help determine molecular structure. GC-MS uses gas chromatography to separate a mixture of compounds followed by identification using mass spectroscopy.

A2 PRINCIPLES OF SPECTROSCOPY

A2.1 Describe the electromagnetic spectrum.

Many analytical techniques involve spectroscopy, i.e., the way in which the **absorption** or **emission** of **electromagnetic radiation** by substances varies with frequency. **Electromagnetic radiation** ranges from very high energy γ-rays through to low energy radio waves and beyond. A wave is characterized by its **wavelength** or **frequency**. The wavelength (λ, in units of distance, e.g.,

m) is the distance between successive peaks on the wave (Figure 1201). The frequency (f, in units of Hertz, Hz = s^{-1}) is the number of peaks that pass a fixed point every second. All electromagnetic waves travel at the same speed in a vacuum ($c = 3.00 \times 10^8$ m s^{-1}), and the relationship between frequency and wavelength:

Velocity of light = frequency × wavelength ($c = f\lambda$)

holds for ***all*** electromagnetic waves.

TOK How is the nature of the information carried by the electromagnetic spectrum limited by its wavelength?

Now this is a little bit different. In these things I'm used to discussing the boundaries between belief and knowledge, but maybe this one is more the boundary between TOK and Physics? I can think of a couple of ways in which this is true. Firstly there is the factor relevant to considering whether we could ever 'see' an atom. In order to see something, the electromagnetic waves have to be able to focus on an image of the object and this means that the wavelength of the waves has to be comparable to, or less than, the size of the object. Visible light has a much longer wavelength than the size of atoms so we can no more see atoms (until we develop γ-ray sensitive eyes) than we can take a family photo using radio waves.

Secondly there is the use of waves to transmit information. A constant wave transmits nothing, so to send a message it has to be altered in some way. The two most common ones are amplitude modulation (AM - altering how loud it is in a sound analogy) or frequency modulation (FM – altering how high pitched it is); these are illustrated below:

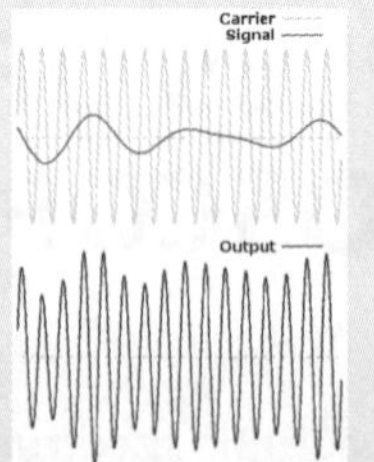

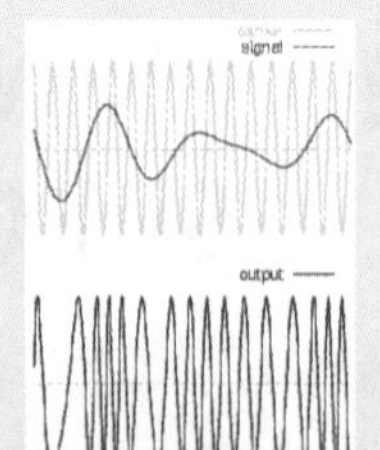

In both cases the signal is imposed on top of the 'carrier' wave, which must be of a shorter wavelength than the 'modulation' which carries the information, so that the shorter the wavelength, then the greater the range of frequencies available for transmitting information. I suppose it is going to be like that until we find a smarter way of sharing information.

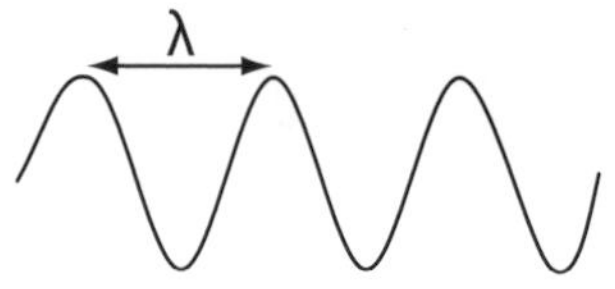

Figure 1201 An electromagnetic wave

Electromagnetic radiation also has a particle nature and each photon (particle of light) carries a quantum of energy. The energy of the quantum of radiation is related to the frequency of the radiation by the equation:

$E = \frac{hc}{\lambda}$ or $E = hf$
(where h = Planck's constant, 6.626×10^{-34} J s)

Example

If a molecule absorbs IR radiation of $\lambda = 900$ nm, calculate the energy absorbed per mole.

Solution

$$\Delta E = hf = \frac{hc}{\lambda} = \frac{6.63 \times 10^{-34}\,\text{J s} \times 3.00 \times 10^8\,\text{m s}^{-1}}{900 \times 10^{-9}\,\text{m}}$$

$= 2.21 \times 10^{-19}$ J per molecule

∴ Energy absorbed per mole

$= 2.21 \times 10^{-19}\,\text{J} \times 6.02 \times 10^{23} = 1.33 \times 10^5\,\text{J mol}^{-1} = 133\,\text{kJ mol}^{-1}$.

Thus high frequency (and hence short wavelength) radiation carries a great deal of energy and radiation of low frequency carries much less. A particle (atom, molecule or ion) can absorb a quantum of light and this will affect its state. The way in which its state is affected will depend on the amount of energy that the quantum carries:

- **γ-rays**, the highest frequency radiation, can bring about changes in the nucleus.
- **X-rays** cannot cause changes in the nucleus, but have enough energy to remove electrons in inner filled shells of atoms.
- **Ultraviolet** and **visible light** have enough energy to affect the valence electrons.

OPTION

- **Infrared** radiation, perceived as heat, can stimulate the vibrations of molecules.
- **Microwaves** affect the rotational state of molecules.
- **Radio waves** can alter the spin state of some nuclei when they are exposed to magnetic fields and are used in NMR spectroscopy.

Exposure to high intensities of any types of radiation can be harmful to health, but γ-rays, X-rays, and UV can break chemical bonds and initiate reactions; hence, they are harmful even at low intensities. UV radiation in sunlight with too much exposure causes sunburn. See Figure 1202 for more information about the electromagnetic spectrum, and the changes it causes.

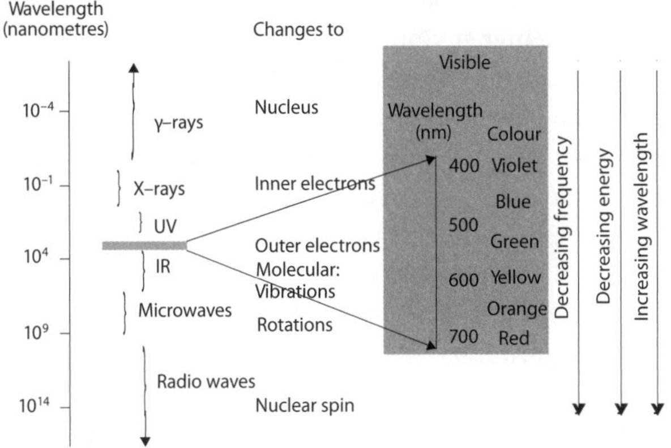

Figure 1202 The Electromagnetic Spectrum

A2.2 Distinguish between *absorption* and *emission* spectra and how each is produced.
© IBO 2007

In **emission spectroscopy** the frequency of the radiation emitted by excited particles dropping to a lower energy state is studied, e.g., the coloured light from a neon lamp is an emission process, as is the emission line spectrum of hydrogen see Figure 1203(a). In **absorption spectroscopy**, radiation of a wide range of frequencies is passed through the sample and the intensity of the radiation of various frequencies emerging on the other side is compared to that going in, to find out which frequencies are absorbed by the sample. Energy of particular frequencies is absorbed and used to enable a particle to move from a lower to a higher energy state, see Figure 1203(b). The red colour of red paint is the result of an absorption process because, of the wide range of frequencies in the white light shining on it, the paint absorbs the blue, green and yellow colours and it reflects the red light. Thus it is the absorption of light in the visible range that makes things coloured.

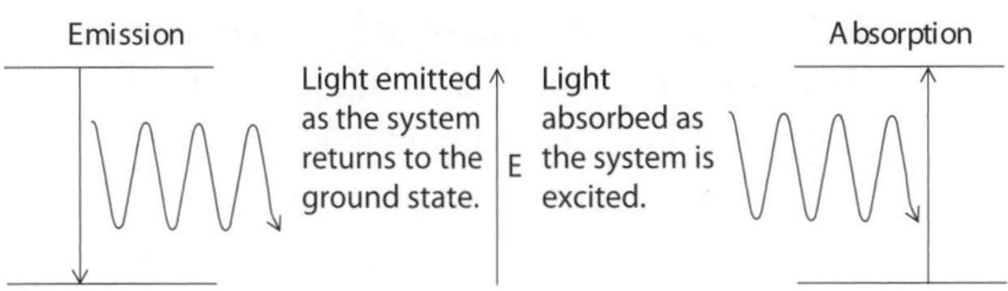

Figure 1203 (a) and (b) Emission and absorption spectroscopy

Exercise A2

1. Which of the following types of radiation has quanta of the highest energy?

   A X-rays
   B UV light
   C IR light
   D Microwaves

2. Green light has a wavelength of 500 nm. What is the frequency of this light?

   A 0.002 Hz
   B 3.31×10^{-31} Hz
   C 7.55×10^{35} Hz
   D 6.00×10^{14} Hz

3. Consider the following techniques:

   gas–liquid chromatography
   NMR spectroscopy
   mass spectrometry
   column chromatography
   IR spectroscopy
   UV–visible spectroscopy

   For each of the following problems, state which of the above techniques would be the most appropriate and justify your choice.

   a) Determining the concentration of an aqueous solution of copper(II) sulfate.
   b) Detecting the presence of 2–methylheptane in petrol.
   c) Whether a sample is propan–1–ol or propan–2–ol (assume no pure samples or data on these is available).
   d) Obtaining a pure sample of pure 4–nitrobenzene from a mixture with 2–nitrobenzene.
   e) Assessing the ^{16}O to ^{18}O ratio in a sample of ice from Antarctica.

OPTION

4. Modern analytical techniques have had a great impact in many other fields, but probably the greatest has been upon the medical sciences. Discuss three examples where three different techniques have contributed to the medical sciences and describe how their introduction has led to improvements.

A3 INFRARED SPECTROSCOPY

A3.1 Describe the operating principles of a double beam spectrometer

Many measurements in absorption spectroscopy employ **double-beam** instruments that allow the radiation passing through the sample to be compared with identical radiation that has not passed through the sample. The radiation from the source is split into two equal beams that pass along parallel paths. The sample is placed in one beam, whilst the second, known as the **reference**, is identical containing the same cell and solvent but without the substance being studied. The light from the source passes through a **monochromator**, which only allows radiation of a particular wavelength to pass through it. This **monochromatic light** (light of a single colour or single wavelength) then strikes a beam-splitter, which directs half of the radiation through the sample and the other half through the reference cell. The two beams are then recombined at the detector. The signals from the sample and reference beams are then compared electronically to see if the sample absorbs radiation of the frequency that the monochromator is set to and the output is sent to the recorder. As the spectrum of the sample is scanned, the frequency of the radiation that the monochromator transmits is varied and a graph of absorption against frequency (or wavelength or wavenumber) is drawn. Comparison of the spectrum of the unknown compound with a data bank enables its identification. The principle of the double-beam instrument (in UV-visible or infrared: they differ only in the source and detector) is illustrated in Figure 1204.

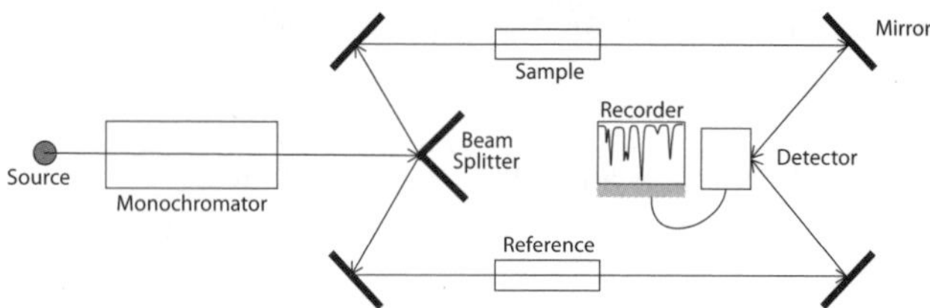

Figure 1204 A double-beam spectrometer

A.3.2 Describe how information from an IR spectrum can be used to identify bonds

The infrared region extends from about 600 cm^{-1} to 4000 cm^{-1}. A quantum of infrared radiation does not have sufficient energy to excite an electron to a higher energy level, but it does have sufficient energy to excite a molecule to a higher vibrational level. There are two types of vibrational motions that most molecules are capable of: stretching motions, where the bond lengths become longer then shorter, and bending motions, where the length of the bonds stays constant, but the angle between them increases and decreases. This latter kind of motion is, of course, not possible in diatomic molecules (such as H-Cl). The stretching and bending motions for water are shown in Figure 1205.

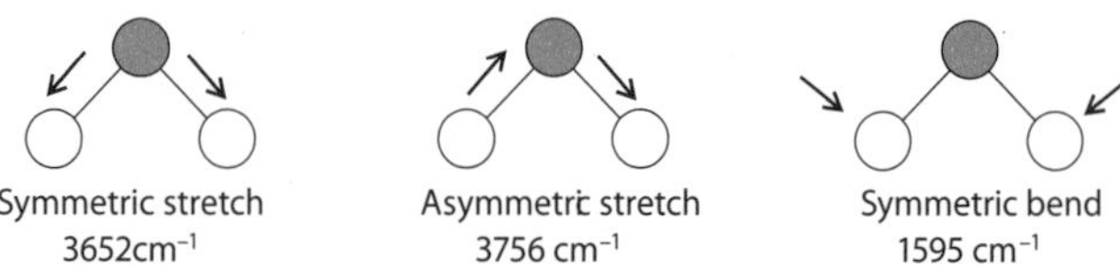

Figure 1205 The bending and stretching motions of water molecules

The 'wavenumbers' at which these motions absorb infrared radiation are shown under each mode. In infrared spectroscopy, the wavenumber (= 1/wavelength, units = cm^{-1}) is used rather than frequency. It is equal to the number of wave peaks in 1 cm of the wave. For example if infrared radiation has a wavelength of 2000 nm (0.002 cm) then its wavenumber = 1/0.002 = 500 cm^{-1}. The greater the wavenumber, the lower the wavelength, the higher the frequency and the greater the energy ($E = hf$). Note therefore that the stretching motions generally require more energy and therefore occur at a greater wavenumber than bending motions.

OPTION

A.3.3 Explain what occurs at a molecular level during the absorption of IR radiation by molecules.

In order to absorb infrared light, a vibrational motion must result in a change in the **dipole moment** of the molecule. Hence diatomic molecules with only one element such as H_2 and O_2 do not absorb infrared radiation. However hydrogen chloride is a polar molecule ($^{\delta+}H - Cl^{\delta-}$) and as the bond stretches, the distance between the atoms increases and so the dipole moment, which depends on both the partial charges and their separations, also increases. Hence the vibration of this bond absorbs infrared radiation of a particular wavenumber (2990 cm^{-1}).

All of the vibrations of water (see Figure 1205) lead to a change in dipole moment and hence to infrared absorption. In a symmetrical linear molecule, such as carbon dioxide, however, the symmetrical stretching mode does not change the dipole of the molecule (or, more precisely, it maintains the symmetry that leads to the molecule being non-polar) and hence it does not give rise to an infrared absorption, though other vibrations, such as the asymmetric stretch and the symmetric bend, do affect the dipole and thus absorb infrared radiation, as shown in Figure 1206.

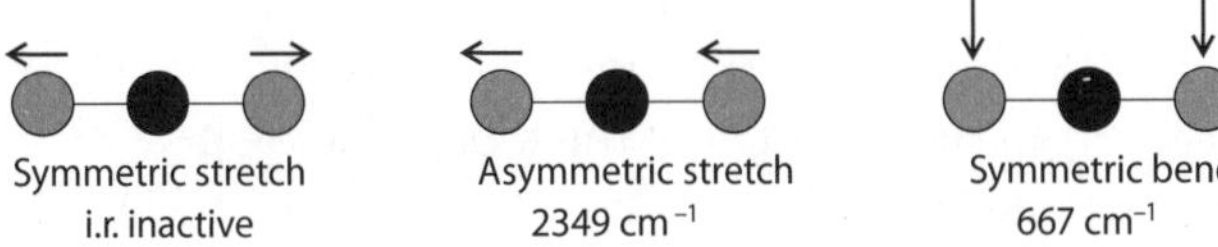

Figure 1206 The bending and stretching motions of carbon dioxide:

Likewise the symmetrical stretching mode of a symmetrical tetrahedral molecule is not infrared active, because it does not result in any change of the dipole of the molecule. Sulfur dioxide is non-linear (due to the effect of non-bonding e-pair) and similar in shape to water (bent). Hence, in contrast to carbon dioxide, even the symmetric stretch causes a change in dipole moment and is infrared active.

A.3.4 Analyse IR spectra of organic compounds *(up to three functional groups).*

The masses of atoms involved and the strength of the bond determines its infrared absorption frequencies, with heavier atoms and stronger bonds requiring more energy (see Figure 1207 and also the IBO Chemistry Data Book). Indeed a careful study of the infrared absorption frequency can be used to calculate the strength of the bond between two atoms.

Bond	Bond enthalpy / kJ mol^{-1}	Wavenumber / cm^{-1}
C – C	348	800 – 1200
C = C	612	1610 – 1680
C ≡ C	837	2070 – 2250
C – H	412	2840 – 3095

Figure 1207 Bond enthalpies and wavenumbers

With many bonds, the mass of the parts of the molecule attached by the bond (or at least the ratio of the mass of the lighter part to the rest, which is more important) tend not to vary too much and so absorptions involving that bond tend to be in a particular region of the infrared spectrum. Hence absorption of radiation of this frequency indicates the presence of this bond in a molecule. This is of particular use in deducing the structure of organic molecules. The precise wavenumber depends to some extent on the other groups present, so a range of frequencies is associated with that bond, as indicated in Figure 1208.

Bond; Organic molecules	Wavenumber / cm^{-1}
C – Cl: halogenoalkanes	700 – 800
C – O: alcohols, ethers, esters	1000 – 1300
C = C: alkenes	1610 – 1680
C = O: aldehydes, ketones, acids, esters	1680 – 1750
C ≡ C: alkynes	2070 – 2250
O – H: H-bonded in –COOH	2500 – 3300
C – H: alkanes, alkenes, arenes	2840 – 3095
O – H: H-bonded in alcohols, phenols	3230 – 3550
N – H: primary amines, RNH_2	3350 – 3500

Figure 1208 The IR absorption wavenumbers of some bonds

Particularly useful is the very strong absorption at 2550-3230 cm^{-1} due to the –OH group in alcohols and carboxylic acids, and the carbonyl group (>C=O) absorption found at 1680-1750 cm^{-1} in aldehydes, ketones, esters and carboxylic acids (see the spectrum of ethanoic acid in Figure 1209). Since the alcohol content of the breath is related to its content in the blood, infrared absorption due to C-H vibrations in the range 2840-3095 cm^{-1} is used in the 'intoximeter' to determine whether motorists have an illegal level of alcohol. (Note the 3250-3550 cm^{-1} peak due to O-H cannot be used since moisture in the breadth would also absorb in this region.) Absorption by >C=C< in the 1610-1680 cm^{-1} region can also be used to assess the degree of unsaturation present in vegetable oils.

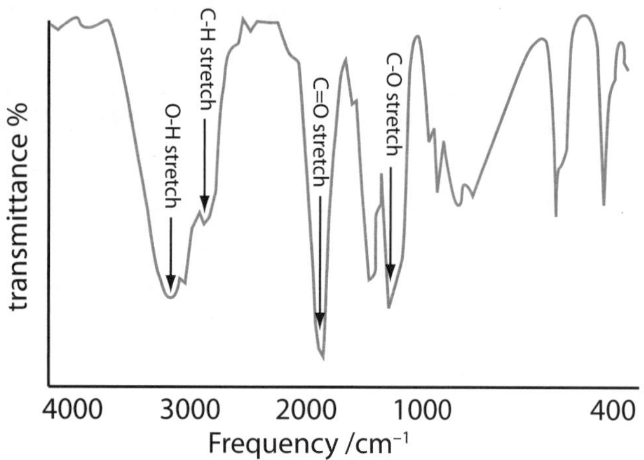

Figure 1209 IR Spectrum of ethanoic acid

Infrared spectra tend to be complex due to the large number of vibrations possible, hence an infrared spectrum, especially in the region 500 cm^{-1} to 1500 cm^{-1} (sometimes called the **'fingerprint' region**) is unique to that compound. This means that a comparison with standard spectra in a library can often be used to identify an unknown compound.

Exercise A3

1. A species has an infrared absorption at 2000 cm^{-1}. What is the wavelength of the light?

   A 2×10^5 m
   B 20 m
   C 5×10^{-2} m
   D 5×10^{-6} m

2. Consider the IR absorption spectrum of a compound, given below. Use a table of infrared absorption frequencies to assign two of the peaks. Also identify two groups that are not present in the compound.

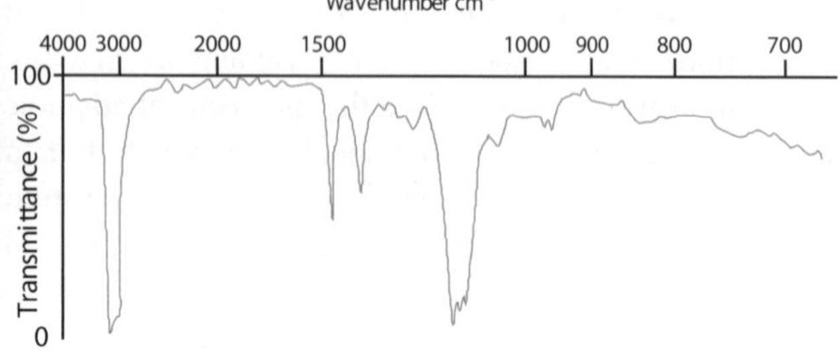

Explain why, given access to a library of IR spectra, this could be used to identify the compound.

3. Boron trifluoride, BF_3, is a trigonal planar molecule that absorbs radiation in the infrared region of the spectrum:

   a) What changes in the molecule lead to it absorbing in this spectral region?
   b) Not all changes of this type are infrared active. Explain why this is so.
   c) Use sketches to illustrate one that would be IR active and one that would not.

4. The positions of absorption bands in IR spectra are usually quoted in wavenumbers, with units of cm^{-1}. How is this related to the frequency of the radiation? Water absorbs radiation at 3652 cm^{-1}. Calculate the wavelength and frequency of this radiation?

A4 MASS SPECTROMETRY

A.4.1 Determine the molecular mass of a compound from the molecular ion peak.

In the **mass spectrometer**, gaseous molecules are converted to positive ions and these ions, after being accelerated through an electric field, are deflected by a magnetic field. The lower the mass of the ion, the greater the deflection and so, by varying the strength of the magnetic field, ions of differing mass can be brought to focus on the detector. The mass spectrum records the relative abundances of the fragments of different mass reaching the detector. To be more precise the **mass/charge (m/z) ratio** is measured, though as conditions are chosen to primarily generate singly charged ions, it is common just to refer to it as the 'mass'.

The inside of the mass spectrometer is at high vacuum so that the ions cannot collide. Hence, the ion with the greatest mass will usually correspond to a molecule that has only lost a single electron – the molecular ion. The mass of the molecular ion gives the relative molecular mass of the molecule. This can be combined with data from elemental analysis to calculate the molecular formula of the substance. In some modern instruments the relative molecular mass of the molecular ion can be found to such precision that, using the fact that relative atomic masses of isotopes are not precise integers (e.g. ^{16}O is 15.995), the molecular formula can be calculated directly as to this precision, for example, CO (M_r = 27.995) , N_2 (M_r = 28.0062) and C_2H_4 (M_r = 28.032) have different relative molecular masses.

A.4.2 Analyse fragmentation patterns in a mass spectrum to find the structure of a compound.
© IBO 2007

The excess energy from the impact of the electron forming the molecular ion will often cause it to break down, or 'fragment', inside the mass spectrometer giving rise to a '**fragmentation pattern**' of lower molecular mass ions. This fragmentation pattern can be used for 'fingerprint' purposes (see infrared spectra above), to allow the identification of the molecule by comparison with the spectra of known compounds from a library. The mass of the units that have broken off the molecule will frequently give clues as to the structure of the molecule. Sometimes only a hydrogen will break off, giving a peak at one mass number less than the main peak. If two fragments differ in mass by 15 then this probably corresponds to the loss of a methyl (CH_3–) group. Similarly a loss of 17 corresponds to the loss of HO-, 29 to the loss of C_2H_5– or H–CO–, 31 to the loss of CH_3–O– and 45 to the loss of –COOH. Figure 1211 shows the mass spectrum of butane and Figure 1212 that of propanoic acid with the molecular ion and some fragments labelled.

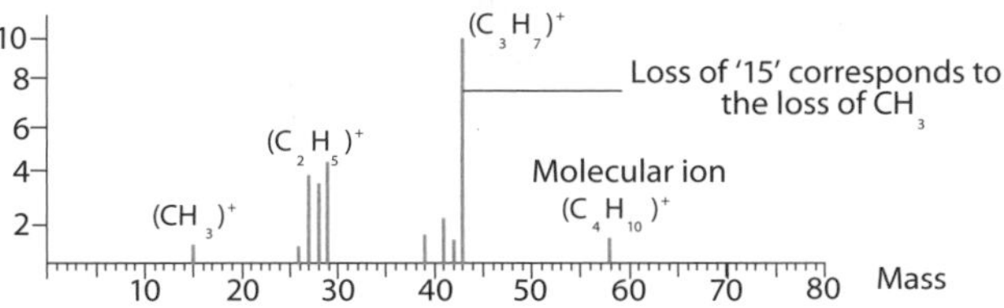

Figure 1211 The Mass spectrum of butane

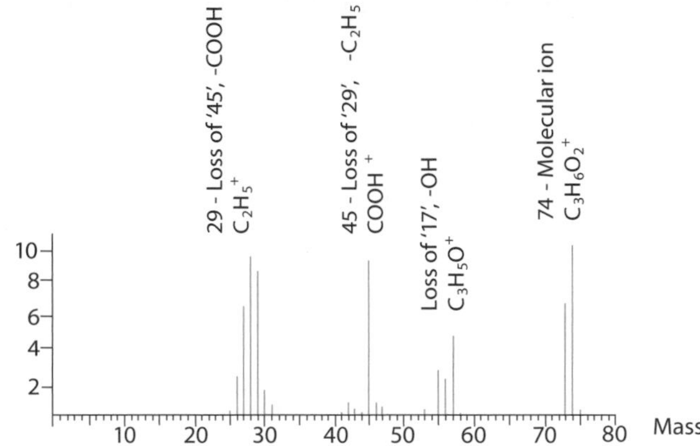

Figure 1212 The Mass spectrum of propanoic acid

Because of the possible places that bonds can break, the spectra of quite similar molecules can often be significantly different as shown in the mass spectra of the two isomers of octane below and the two propanols see Figure 1214:

Mass spectra can be produced from minute (as small as 10^{-6} g) samples. Besides determination of atomic and molar masses and organic structure, it can be used to detect the percentage of ^{14}C present in a sample in the process known as **radiocarbon dating** and in forensic science to determine the presence of small amounts of drugs and other substances of interest.

EXTENSION

A smaller peak is usually found in organic mass spectra at one mass number greater than the main peak. This is due to the presence in the compound of the isotope ^{13}C, which comprises about 1% of naturally occurring carbon. Its size, relative to the main peak, therefore depends on the number of carbon atoms in the molecule, because if there are six carbon atoms there is an approximately 6% chance (6 × 1%) of there being an atom ^{13}C of in the molecule. This peak can clearly be seen in Figure 1212.

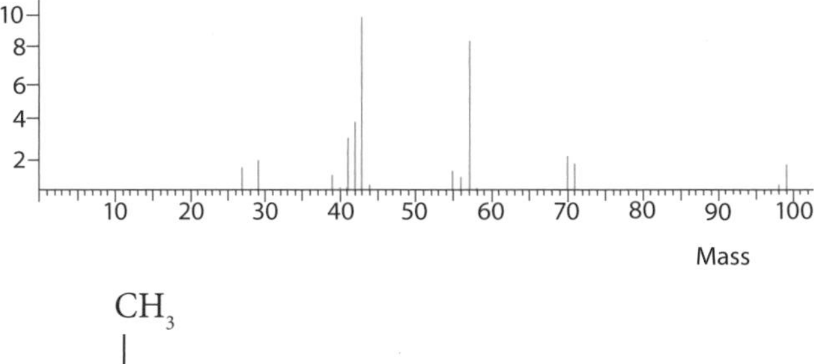

CH_3 (on C #2)
CH_3—CH-CH_2-CH_2-CH_2 -CH_2 -CH_3

2-methylheptane has a significant fragment at $(M_r - 15)^+ = 99$ due to easy loss of CH_3 at branch on C #2

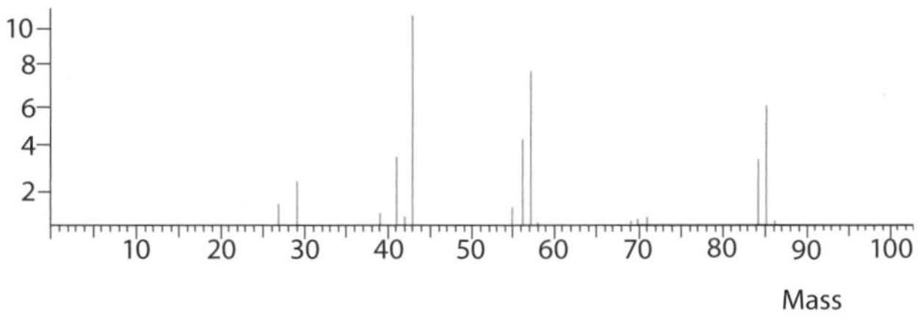

CH_3 (on C #3)
CH_3-CH_2—CH-CH_2-CH_2--CH_2-CH_3

3-methylheptane has a significant fragment at $(M_r - 29)^+ = 85$ due to easy loss of C_2H_5 at branch onC #3.

Figure 1213 (a) and (b) Comparing the mass spectra of two isomers of octane (C_8H_{18})

OPTION

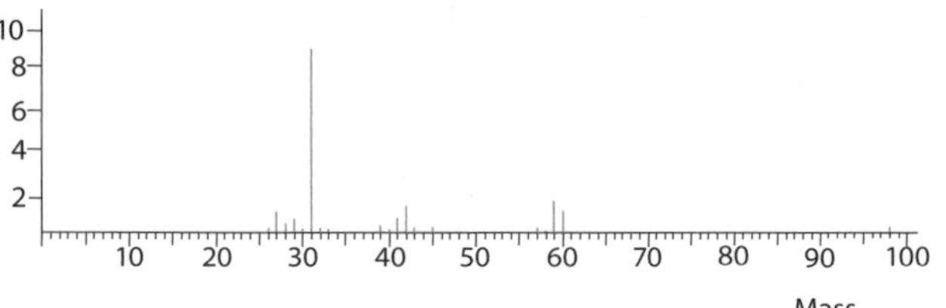

$CH_3-CH_2-CH_2-OH$

Only small peak at 45: $(M_r - 15)^+$: $(CH_2CH_2OH)^+$: due to loss of CH_3, as strong C-C bond to break.

Strong peak at 31: $(CH_2OH)^+$ from $(M_r - 29)^+$: due to loss of C_2H_5.; weaker C-C bond due to inductive effect of –OH.

Peak at 29 due to $(C_2H_5)^+$.

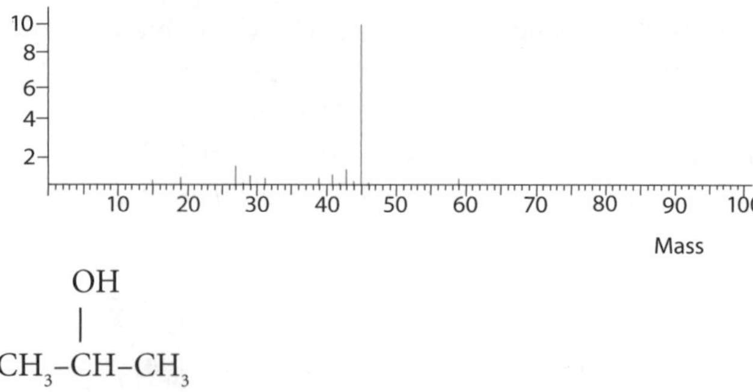

OH
|
$CH_3-CH-CH_3$

Strong peak at 45: $(M_r - 15)^+$: $(CH_3CHOH)^+$: due to loss of CH_3

No peak at 31: A peak at 31 requires loss of C_2H_5 $(M_r - 29)^+$and propan-2-ol has no C_2H_5 to lose.

Peak at 27 due to $(CH_3C)^+$.

Figure 1214 (a) and (b) Comparing the mass spectra of propan-1-ol and propan-2-ol (C_3H_7OH)

EXTENSION

Chlorine and bromine both comprise mixtures of isotopes with a mass difference of two (35 & 37 for Cl, 79 & 81 for Br). So in mass spectra involving these atoms there are two peaks two units apart. Their relative magnitudes reflect the natural abundances of the isotopes (3:1 ^{35}Cl: ^{37}Cl for chlorine, approximately equal abundances for bromine). If there are two halogen atoms present, then there will obviously be three peaks; in a ratio 9:6:1 for chlorine

$$\left(\frac{3}{4}\times\frac{3}{4}\right):2\left(\frac{3}{4}\times\frac{1}{4}\right):\left(\frac{1}{4}\times\frac{1}{4}\right)$$

and 1:2:1 for bromine. These can readily be observed in the mass spectrum of 2-chloropropane in Figure 1215 and of 1.2-dibromoethane in Figure 1216.

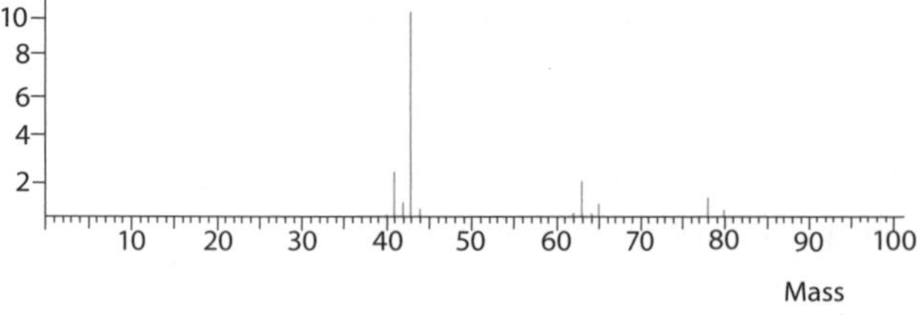

Figure 1215 The mass spectrum of 2-chloropropane

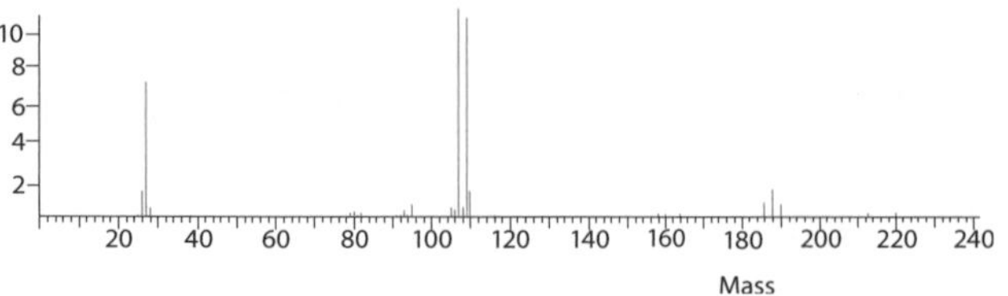

Figure 1216 The mass spectrum of 1.2-dibromoethane

Exercise

1. a) Determine the empirical formula of a hydrocarbon that contains 83.3% carbon by mass?

   b) Describe how you could use the mass spectrum to find the molecular formula of the compound. Outline how the mass spectrum could be used to confirm that it was indeed a hydrocarbon and not an oxygen/nitrogen containing molecule.

   c) Assume the molecular formula is C_5H_{12}. Consider the possible isomers and the way in which these might split up in a mass spectrometer to produce fragments around 55-57, 40-43 and 25-29. How might you attempt to deduce which isomer you had from the mass spectrum?

2. The mass spectrum below is that of a carboxylic acid.

   a) Identify the carboxylic acid in question.

   b) Give the formulae of the species that give rise to the peaks labelled A to F.

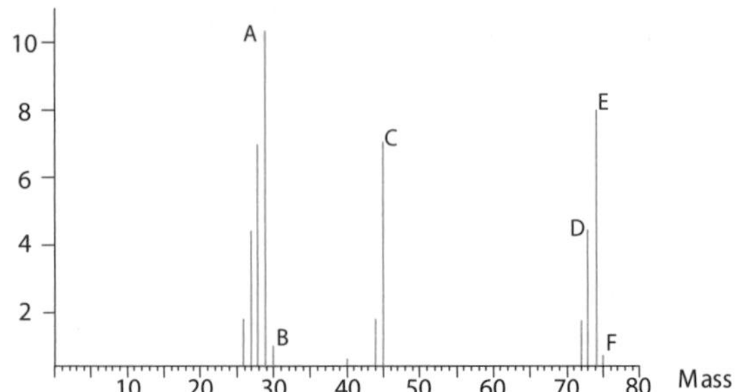

3. (Extension Question). When introduced into a mass spectrometer, dichloroethene gives a distinctive spectrum:

   a) What peaks would you expect to result from the molecular ion? Give the masses you would expect them to occur at and the relative intensities of these peaks.
   b) In what way might you expect the spectrum to reveal whether the dichloroethene is the 1.1 or a 1.2 isomer?
   c) There are two possible 1.2 isomers. Given pure samples of each how could you use a mass spectrometer to differentiate between them. Describe one simpler way of achieving this.

A5 NUCLEAR MAGNETIC RESONANCE (NMR) SPECTROSCOPY

A.5.1 Deduce the structure of a compound given information from its ¹H NMR spectrum *(splitting pattern not required at SL)*

Nuclear Magnetic Resonance (NMR) spectroscopy is arguably the most powerful single tool for investigating the structure of a molecule. It is found that, as a result of changes that occur in the nucleus (see Extension for further explanation), atoms with an odd mass number, when placed in a strong magnetic field, absorb radiation of radio frequency. The precise frequency varies slightly with the electron density around the nucleus and hence depends on its chemical environment. Most commonly this is applied to the hydrogen atoms in a molecule. The NMR spectrum indicates the bonding of all of the hydrogen atoms in the molecule and Figure 1218 gives the common bonding situations of hydrogen atoms in organic molecules and the region of the NMR spectrum (called the **chemical shift**, δ, and measured in ppm) that these absorb in.

Bonding situation (R – alkyl group, ⌬ – benzene ring)	Chemical shift, δ ppm
$R - CH_3$	0.9
$R - CH_2 - R$	1.3
$R_3C - H$	2.0
$CH_3 - CO - O - R$	2.0
$CH_3 - CO - R$	2.1
⌬$-CH_3$	2.3
$R - C{\equiv}C - H$	2.6
$R - CH_2 - F/Cl/Br/I$	3.2 – 3.7
$R - O - CH_3$	3.8
$R - CO - O - CH_2 - R$	4.1
⌬$-O - CO - CH_3$	4.0 – 4.2
$R - O - H$	0.5 – 6.5
$R - CH = CH_2$	4.9 – 5.9
⌬$-O - H$	7.0
⌬$-H$	7.3
$R - CO - H$	9.7
$R - CO - O - H$	11.5

Figure 1218 Characteristic ¹H NMR absorptions

From the relative intensities of the signals, the number of hydrogen atoms that are bonded in each of these environments can be determined. This is often displayed as an 'integration trace' (it integrates the area under the peak) in which the length of the vertical section at each peak is proportional to the number of hydrogen atoms in that chemical environment. Knowing the way in which all of the hydrogen atoms are bonded, along with the relative numbers of these (given by the integration trace), will frequently allow the structure of the molecule to be determined without reference to other techniques.

Figure 1219 below shows the low resolution NMR spectrum of ethanol with an interpretation of the various peaks in it. In high resolution spectra (Figure 1222) these broad peaks may appear as groups of separate sharp peaks.

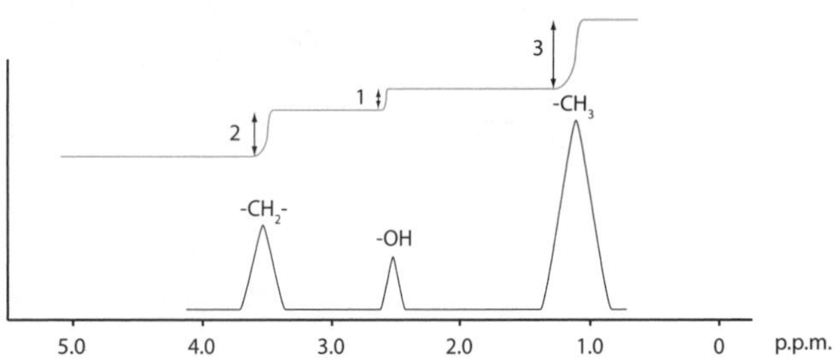

Figure 1219 The low resolution NMR spectrum of ethanol

OPTION

A.5.2 Outline how NMR is used in body scanners *(an important application of NMR Spectroscopy).*

The body scanner also operates on the principle of NMR spectroscopy. The main constituents of the body that contain hydrogen atoms, and hence produce signals, are water and lipids. Different parts of the body have different water-lipid ratios in the tissue and therefore absorb radio frequency radiation in different ways. The patient is placed in a strong magnetic field and as the scanner is moved around the body data about the absorption at various angles can be accumulated to allow a three–dimensional image of the various organs to be built up. The advantage of this technique, called **Magnetic Resonance Imaging** (MRI), in body scanning is obvious as radio waves are harmless. MRI is used to diagnose cancer, Multiple Sclerosis (MS) and other conditions Figures 1220 and 1221 show one of these machines and the image produced.

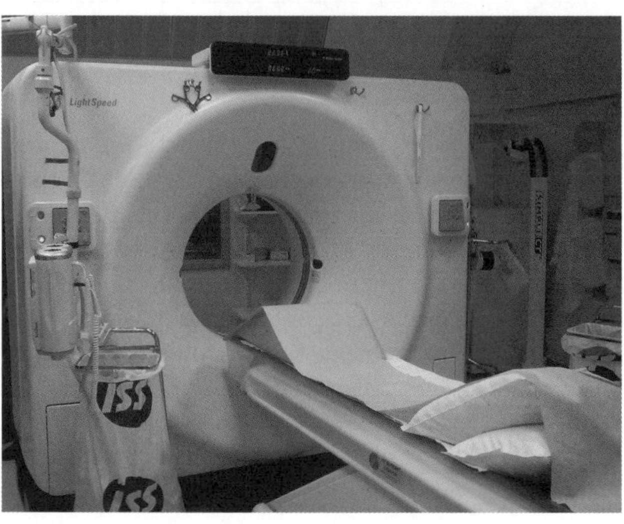

Figure 1220 A MRI body scanner

Figure 1221 The image produced by the scanner

A9 NMR SPECTROSCOPY [HL]

A.9.1 Explain the use of tetramethylsilane (TMS) as the reference standard.

It was seen above that when organic compounds are placed in an intense magnetic field, hydrogens in different 'chemical environments' absorb radio waves of slightly different frequencies. This 'chemical shift' (often given the symbol δ) is however very small – in the parts per million (ppm) range. The frequency of radiation is very dependent on the strength of the applied magnetic field and it is difficult to ensure that this remains constant to a comparable accuracy, which initially meant that it was difficult to obtain reproducible results. The problem is now overcome by mixing another substance with the sample and recording the frequency at which absorption occurs relative to this 'internal standard'. The substance chosen as the internal standard is **tetramethylsilane** (TMS) which has the formula $(CH_3)_4Si$. This has the advantage of being chemically inert, producing a single strong signal (as it has 12 hydrogens in identical chemical environments) and, because of the low electronegativity of silicon, it absorbs radiation of a frequency rather different from that of most other organic compounds. It does not interfere with their absorption signals. The chemical shift (in ppm) is then measured relative to this arbitrary standard being taken as 0 ppm.

A.9.2 Analyse ^{1}H NMR spectra.

One further complication is that the absorptions of hydrogen atoms on neighbouring carbon atoms interfere with each other and in a high resolution spectrum this leads to splitting of some absorptions into a number of closely grouped peaks. This is shown in Figure 1222 overleaf, for ethanol, in which some of the peaks are seen to split. The reason for this is that the precise frequency at which the absorption occurs is influenced by the direction of the magnetic field of any hydrogens attached to the neighbouring carbon atom. The signal of the CH_3– group in ethanol (δ = 1.1) is therefore affected by the alignment of the hydrogens of the $-CH_2-$ group. There are three combinations for this (↑↑, ↑↓ and ↓↑, or ↓↓) so the signal is split into three (a triplet) with an intensity ratio of 1:2:1

OPTION

(the same as the probabilities of the three states of the CH_2 hydrogens). Similarly the signal of the $-CH_2-$ group ($\delta = 3.8$) is split into a quartet by the possible alignments of the hydrogens in the CH_3- group (↑↑↑; ↑↑↓, ↑↓↑ & ↓↑↑; ↑↓↓, ↓↑↓ & ↓↓↑; ↓↓↓, hence a 1:3:3:1 ratio). The general rule is that the number of peaks is equal to the number of hydrogens on the neighbouring carbon plus one. The O–H signal is not split because the rapid exchange of this atom between ethanol molecules averages out the different possible spins.

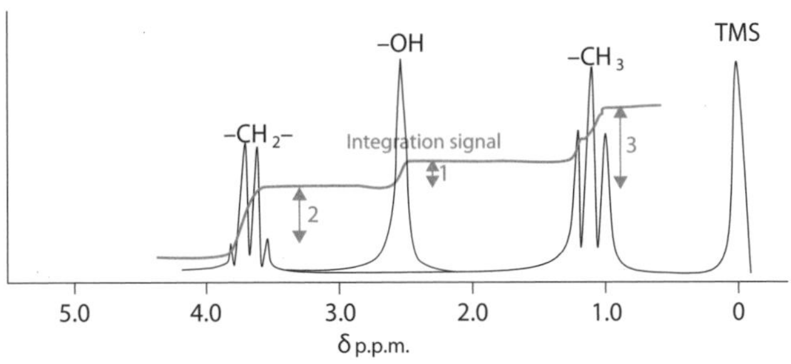

Figure 1222 High resolution NMR spectrum of ethanol with TMS reference

The strength of this technique is demonstrated by the very different spectra of the isomers of C_4H_9OH shown in Figure 1223 below.

You should be able to work out from the number of chemical environments and the ratio of hydrogen atoms in these, which spectrum belongs to which isomer [$(CH_3)_3COH$; $(CH_3)_2CHCH_2OH$; $CH_3CH(OH)CH_2CH_3$; $CH_3CH_2CH_2CH_2OH$]. The answer follows, can you also work out how the splitting of the peaks occurs?

(Answer (a) - butan-2-ol; (b) – 2-methylpropan-2-ol; (c) – butan-1-ol; (d) - 2-methylpropan-1-ol)

EXTENSION

Nucleons (protons and neutrons), like electrons have a property called **spin** which has a magnetic moment associated with it. In an external magnetic field they can either align themselves with or against the magnetic field. In many nuclei there is an even number of nucleons, which pair up (like electrons) and so their spins cancel each other out, so that the nucleus does not have an overall magnetic moment. Where there is an odd number of nucleons the nucleus has a net spin and magnetic moment. These have the same energy unless an external magnetic field is present in which case the magnetic field of the nucleus must either line up with the field (lower energy) or against the field (higher energy) – see Figure 1224a. The frequency corresponding to this small difference in energy ($\Delta E = hf$)

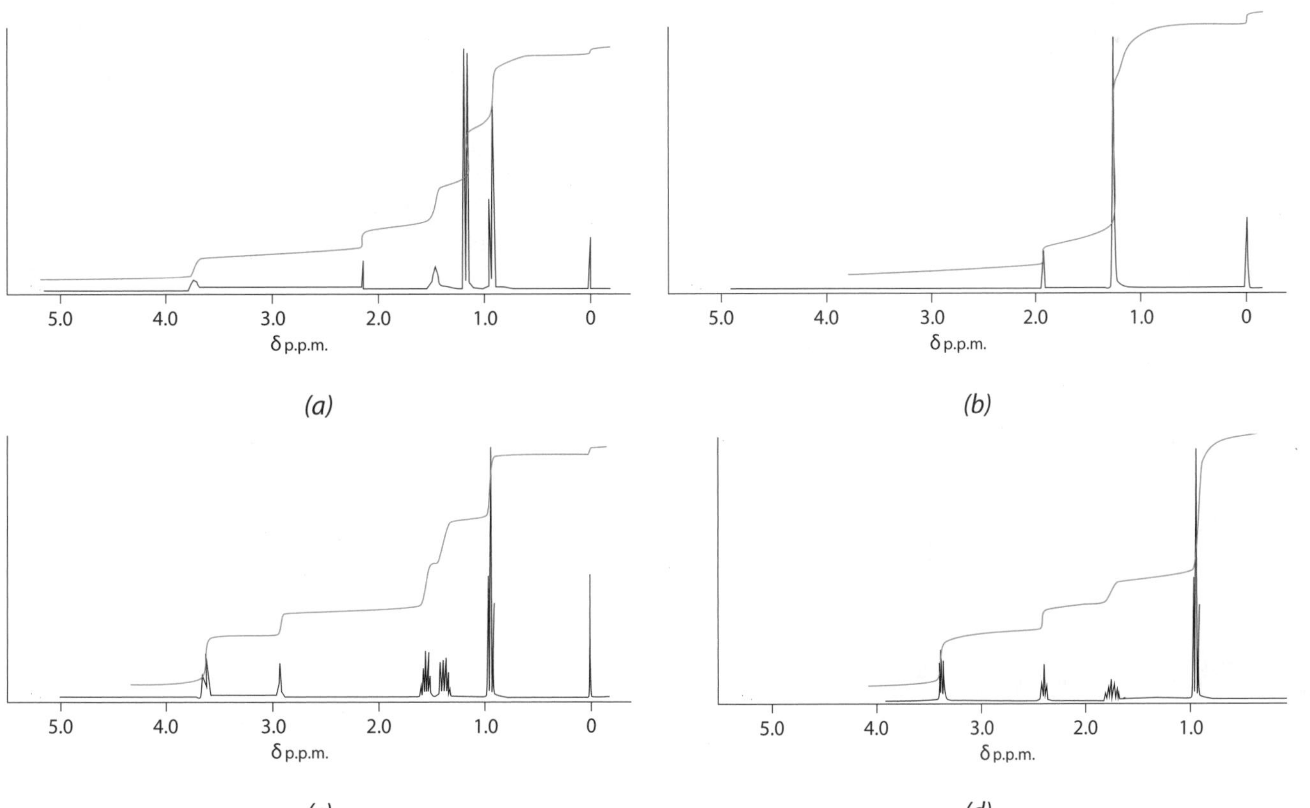

Figure 1223 (a), (b), (c) and (d) The NMR spectra of C_4H_9OH isomers

OPTION

falls in the radio waves frequency region. The nucleus can absorb radiation of just this frequency (in the radio frequency region) and the spin 'flips' to the higher energy orientation.

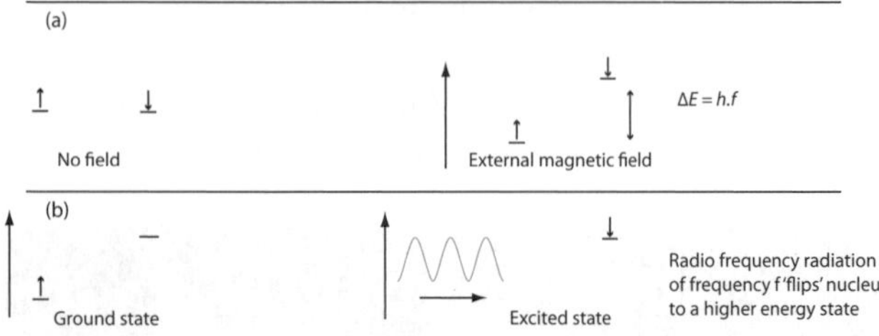

Figure 1224 The effect of a magnetic field on the spin states of a nucleus with residual spin and excitation by the absorption of radio frequency radiation

Useful nuclei with a non-zero magnetic moment are ^{1}H, ^{13}C, ^{19}F and ^{31}P. Such nuclei can therefore absorb radio frequency energy of the appropriate frequency and move ('flip') from the lower energy state to the higher energy state. An NMR spectrum is obtained by placing the sample in a cylindrical glass tube with a standard (TMS) in a strong magnetic field, often produced using superconducting magnets. The sample is surrounded by a radio frequency generator and receiver and the NMR spectrum is obtained by varying the strength of the magnetic field.

The reason for the chemical shift is that when electrons are in a magnetic field they orbit in such a way as to set up a magnetic field that opposes the applied field (**Lenz's law**). This means that the magnetic field experienced by the nucleus, and hence the precise frequency at which it absorbs radiation, depends on the electron density near to the nucleus and therefore on the chemical environment of the nucleus. For example, because chlorine is more electronegative than iodine, the hydrogen atom in H-Cl has less electrons near to it, so that it experiences a stronger magnetic field and will therefore absorb radiation of a higher frequency than the hydrogen atom in H-I. In molecules that have a number of hydrogens in different chemical environments, then each hydrogen will produce an absorption at a different frequency and the strength of the absorption will be proportional to the number of hydrogen atoms in that environment.

EXTENSION

Exercise

1. Use a table of chemical shifts to predict the absorptions that would occur (both the chemical shift in ppm and the relative intensity) in the NMR spectrum of 3–methylbutanal.

   There are a number of possible isomers of this compound. Name the isomer that would have the simplest NMR spectrum and describe the NMR spectrum that it would produce.

2. Identify the organic molecule responsible for the NMR spectrum shown below, explaining how you reach your conclusion, including reference to the splitting pattern.

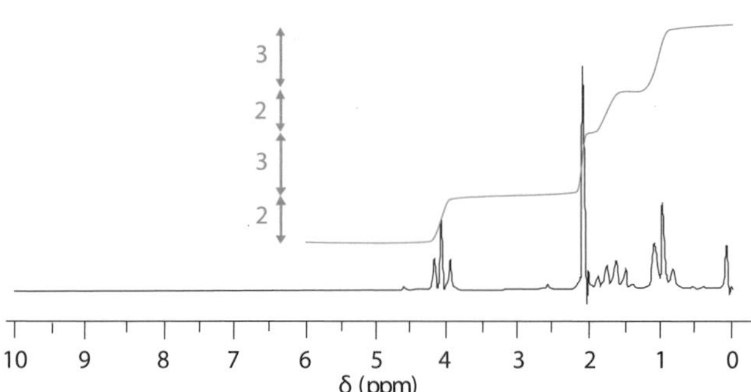

3. Explain why some atomic nuclei, such as ^{19}F, give rise to NMR spectra whilst others, such as ^{16}O do not. Explain why the nuclei of a particular isotope do not always absorb energy of exactly the same frequency.

A6 ATOMIC ABSORPTION (AA) SPECTROSCOPY

A.6.1 State the uses of Atomic Absorption spectroscopy.

Atomic absorption spectroscopy is a technique that is widely used for the detection of metal ions in samples. The technique can be used to detect metals in a wide variety of samples, such as water, blood, soil and food samples, for example:

- Aluminium in blood serum
- Calcium in blood serum, plants, soil samples, in water (for water hardness)
- Copper in copper-based alloys
- Chromium in sea water
- Iron in plants

It can be highly sensitive with detection levels in the parts per million range, though recent developments of the technique (such as graphite furnace AA spectroscopy) can operate at the parts per billion level. The technique also requires only very small samples, less than 1 drop of solution, to give reliable results. Another major strength of the technique is that it is not necessary to separate the metal from other components as it is highly selective and other components, such as other metal ions, do not interfere with it.

A.6.2 Describe the principles of atomic absorption.

The principles of atomic absorption are based on the fact that when metal atoms are excited by heat, the atoms absorb light. Each metal absorbs light of characteristic wavelength or frequency:

Metal	Zn	Fe	Cu	Ca	Na
Wavelength / nm	214	248	325	423	589

Figure 1226 Characteristic wavelengths absorbed by some metals

The non-excited vaporized metal atom absorbs its characteristic frequency from an external source and becomes excited, that is, it causes transition from the ground state to the excited state as shown in Figure 1227:

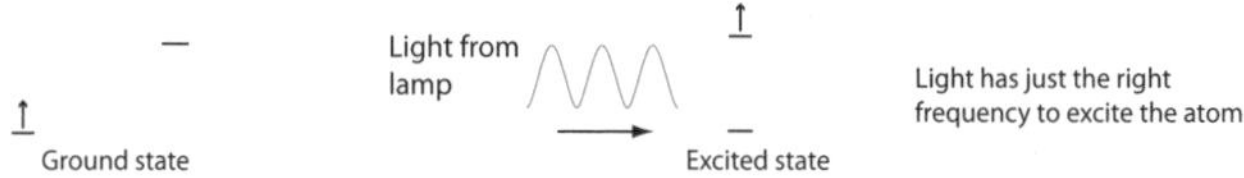

Figure 1227 Illustrating atomic absorption

The ratio of the intensity of the transmitted light to that of the incident light energy is proportional to the concentration of the metal atoms present. Thus, as the concentration goes up, the absorbance goes up, so that a calibration curve obtained by using standard solutions of known concentrations, can be used to determine the concentration of that metal in the unknown.

A.6.3 Describe the use of each of the following components of the Atomic Absorption spectrometer: fuel, atomizer, monochromatic light source, monochromatic detector, read-out.

Atomic absorption spectroscopy relies on the fact that metal atoms will absorb light of the same frequency as that emitted by excited atoms of that metal. For that reason if the intention is to analyse a sample for copper, then a lamp is used in which copper is excited so as to emit specific frequencies of light corresponding to the emission line spectrum of copper. Light from the lamp is then shone through a long, narrow, very hot flame (see Figure 1228, below), usually produced by burning a mixture of ethyne and oxygen, into which the sample is introduced. The light then passes through a monochromator, which acts like a prism to select just the frequency of light being used, then on to a sensitive detector. The detector measures the decrease in the intensity of that light which occurs when the sample is introduced into the flame. The technique relies on the fact that it is only atoms of that particular element that will absorb light of exactly the same frequency as that emitted by the lamp. If it is to be used for a different metal, then a different lamp containing that metal has to be used. Figure 1228 below shows a simple atomic absorption spectrophotometer:

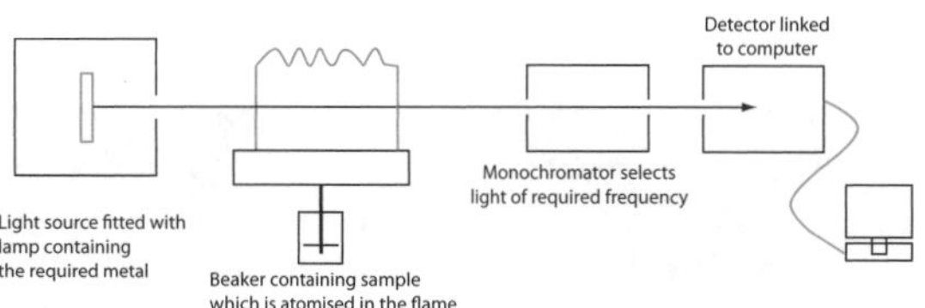

Figure 1228 A schematic diagram of an atomic absorption spectrometer

The sample is atomised into the flame. The simplest way of doing this is to atomise microscopic droplets of a solution into the gas supply to the flame. The heat of the flame firstly evaporates the solvent, then it causes the compound to split into individual atoms which absorb the light. The amount of light absorbed is proportional to the concentration of atoms of the metal in the flame and hence in the sample.

A.6.4 Determine the concentration of a solution from a calibration curve.

Atomic absorption spectroscopy can be used both for qualitative analysis, for example to detect the presence of lead in a gunshot residue, as well for as quantitative analysis to determine how much of the metal is present in the sample. The intensity of the absorption varies a little bit with conditions, such as the temperature of the flame and so therefore the instrument is usually calibrated using solutions of known concentration of the metal that is being detected. Using these data, a calibration curve can be drawn which may be used to find the concentration of the unknown. For example consider these data for the analysis of a sample of waste water for chromium at 358 nm. Figure 1229 illustrates how (a) data and (b) a calibration curve can be used to find the concentration of an unknown.

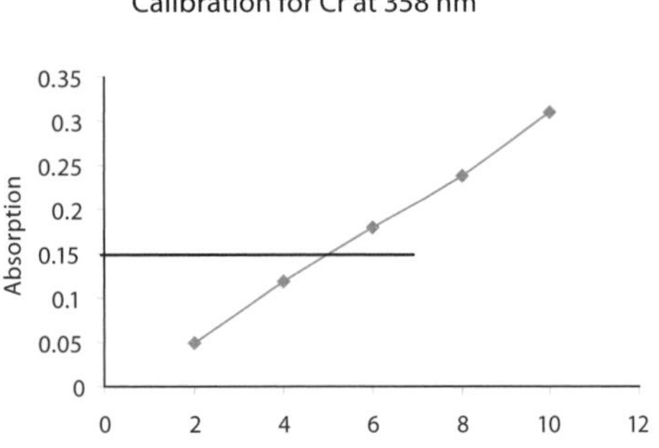

Figure 1229 (a) and (b)

It can be seen from Figure 1229 that the concentration of chromium in the unknown is approximately 5 ppm, though analysis of the data and calibration samples by a computer would yield a more precise result.

Exercise A6

1. Which of the following would be best detected using atomic absorption spectroscopy?

   A The presence of steroids in a urine sample from an athlete.
   B The concentration of mercury in the effluent from a brine electrolysis plant.
   C The presence of toxic carbon monoxide in gases from a mine.
   D The concentration of vitamin C in a sample of orange juice.

2. A 0.6230 g sample containing a compound of sodium is dissolved in water and diluted to 100 cm³ in a volumetric flask. It is analysed in an atomic absorption spectrometer using the 589 nm sodium line and shows an absorbance of 0.30. The following additional data was also obtained:

[Na] / mg dm³	0.00	0.50	1.00	1.50	2.00	2.50
Absorbance	0.00	0.10	0.26	0.36	0.46	0.62

   Draw a calibration curve in order to obtain the concentration in mg dm³ and percentage of sodium in the sample.

3 Lead is extracted from a sample of blood and analyzed at a 283 nm and gave an absorbance of 0.340 in an atomic absorption spectrometer. The following additional data was also obtained by the subsequent dilution of a standard solution of lead ions:

$[Pb^{2+}]$ / ppm	0.000	0.100	0.200	0.300	0.400	0.500
Absorbance	0.00	0.116	0.216	0.310	0.425	0.520

   Draw a calibration curve and determine the lead content of blood in ppm.

A7 CHROMATOGRAPHY

A7.1 State the reasons for using chromatography.

In chemistry, the concept of a pure substance (that is one that contains only one compound) is vital and so techniques that can identify whether a sample is a pure substance or a mixture, and separate mixtures of substances into their pure components are important. Most of these techniques are used for analytical purposes, that is to see what is present in the mixture (for example to see if a particular amino acid is present in the mixture from the hydrolysis of a protein), rather than to obtain a pure sample of one of the components of the mixture (for example to produce a sample of chlorophyll from the extract of a plant leaf).

Sometimes **chromatography**, as its name suggests, is used to separate coloured substances and the components can then be detected by their colour. More often it is used with colourless substances and in these cases a variety of special techniques must be used to detect the presence of the components of the mixture. These include the use of UV light if a fluorescent component is present, or a solution that makes a component visible by reacting with it, such as using ninhydrin solution to identify the presence of amino acids.

A7.2 Explain that all chromatographic techniques involve adsorption on a stationary phase and partition between a stationary and a mobile phase.

The term chromatography is used to describe a range of closely related techniques used to separate mixtures that involve the interaction of the components with two phases; a **stationary phase** that does not move and a **mobile phase** that moves through the stationary phase. The components are separated according to how much time the components spend in the different phases, as a result of the differences in their attractions for the stationary and mobile phases. Imagine a moving conveyor belt and a group of people standing together alongside it. The people all jump on to the conveyor belt, but one group (A) counts to five and then jumps off. When off, they count to ten and jump on again, then after five, off again and so on. The second group (B) count to ten when they jump on the conveyor and five when they jump off, ten when they are on again. After a minute or so, it is quite obvious that the people in group B will have travelled rather further than those in group A, so that the 'mixture' of people has been separated.

All chromatography depends on the relative tendencies of the different components to bond to the surface of the stationary phase, or to remain in the mobile phase. A component that bonds strongly to the stationary phase will not move very far, whereas one that bonds more strongly to the mobile phase will move faster. The separation between the stationary and mobile phases operates on the principle of partition or adsorption. Partition involves the way in which components of a mixture distribute themselves between two immiscible liquid phases, depending on their solubility in each phase, whilst adsorption involves the way a substance bonds to the surface of a solid stationary phase. The simplest chromatographic techniques are paper chromatography; thin–layer chromatography (TLC) and column chromatography. The way in which these are carried out, and the underlying theory of each, is described below.

A7.3 Outline the use of paper chromatography, thin-layer chromatography (TLC) and column chromatography:

Paper Chromatography

In **paper chromatography** a spot of the mixture is applied to absorbent paper, rather like filter paper. The end of this is then dipped in the solvent used to 'develop' the chromatogram. The solvent soaks up the paper by capillary action, moving past the spot where the mixture was applied and onwards. The components that bond strongly to the solvent will be carried along in the direction that the solvent is moving, whereas those that do not bond to it will remain almost stationary. Figure 1232 below shows one common arrangement for carrying out paper chromatography, though many others are possible.

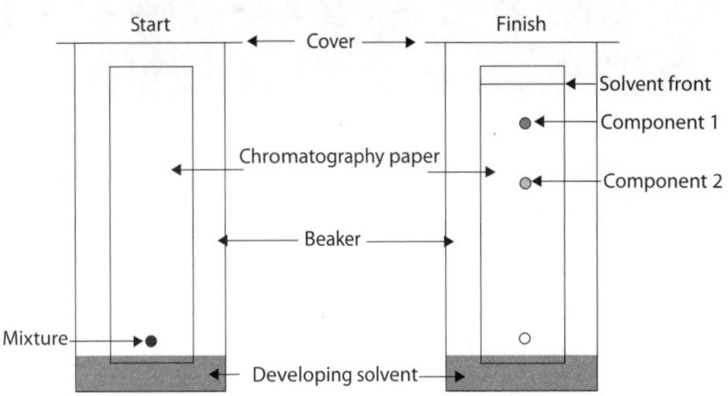

Figure 1232 Paper chromatography

In the above diagram, as the organic solvent soaks through the paper, Component 1 is very soluble in the solvent, which is the mobile phase, and only poorly in water held in the absorbent pores of the paper, which acts as the stationary phase. Component 1 has therefore moved almost as far as the solvent. Component 2, because of its different structure, bonds more strongly to the stationary aqueous phase and so does not move as far. This technique relies on the partition of the components of the mixture between a mobile non–aqueous phase and a stationary aqueous phase. Paper chromatography can be used to separate the coloured components of an ink, or the different amino acids from a mixture of amino acids.

Thin Layer Chromatography

Thin layer chromatography (TLC) is very similar in practice to paper chromatography. The physical arrangement being almost identical to that shown in the previous diagram. The difference is that the stationary phase is a thin layer, usually of silica (silicon dioxide, SiO_2) or alumina (aluminum oxide, Al_2O_3), on a glass or plastic support. This means that the separation is not the result of the partition of the components between two liquids, but it depends on the extent to which they bond to the surface of (i.e. are adsorbed by) the stationary oxide layer, which in turn mainly depends on the polarity of the substance. TLC is used to separate similar mixtures to paper chromatography, but because the particles in TLC are much finer than the pores in paper, it usually gives better separation.

In both paper and thin layer chromatography, components can be identified by their R_f value, where:

$$R_f = \frac{\text{Distance moved by component}}{\text{Distance moved by solvent}}$$

In the example in Figure 1232, the R_f value of component 1 is greater than that of component 2.

Example

Find the R_f value of the component shown on the paper chromatogram below:

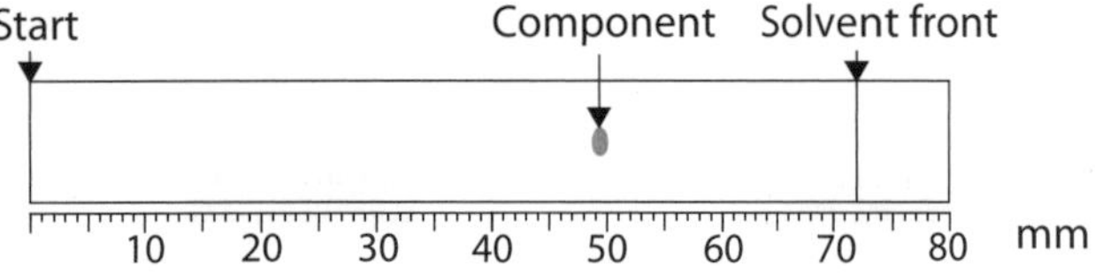

Figure 1233

Solution

$$R_f = \frac{\text{Distance moved by component}}{\text{Distance moved by solvent}} = \frac{49}{72} \approx 0.68$$

Column chromatography

The principle of **column chromatography** is very similar to thin layer chromatography, as the stationary phase is usually silica or alumina and separation depends on whether a component is strongly adsorbed onto the surface of this or remains dissolved in the mobile phase of solvent used to elute the column. The oxide powder is packed into a column with the solvent and the mixture applied at the top of the packing, as shown in Figure 1234. The solvent (also known as the **eluant**) is allowed to slowly drip out of the bottom of the column, controlled by a tap, and fresh solvent added at the top so that the packing never becomes dry. As the mixture moves down it will separate out into its components, as shown. This technique can be used to obtain a pure sample of the various components as they can be collected separately when they elute from the bottom of the column and the solvent evaporated. If the components are colourless, then separate fractions of the eluate (the solution leaving the column) must be collected and tested for the presence of the components of the mixture.

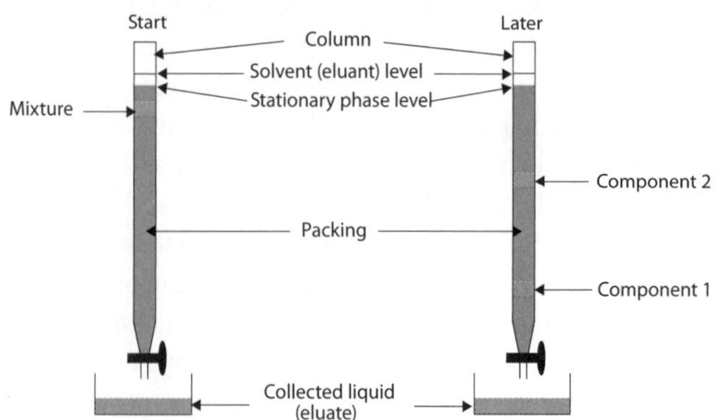

Figure 1234 An illustration of column chromatography

A10 Chromatography [HL]

A.10.1 Describe the techniques of gas-liquid chromatography (GLC) and high-performance liquid chromatography (HPLC).

Gas liquid chromatography

In **gas liquid chromatography** (GLC), the mobile phase is a gas and the stationary phase is packed into a very long (often a number of metres) thin column, that is coiled into a helix, see Figure 1235. There are various types of stationary phases that may be used. Sometimes the column is packed with an oxide (usually SiO_2 or Al_2O_3), or more frequently these days (HRGC - high resolution gas chromatography) a very thin column is coated on the inside with an oxide layer, and in these cases separation occurs because molecules of the mixture are adsorbed onto the surface of the oxide. Sometimes, the oxide will just be acting as a support for a high boiling point oil or wax. In this case separation depends on the partition of the components between the gas phase and solution in the oil.

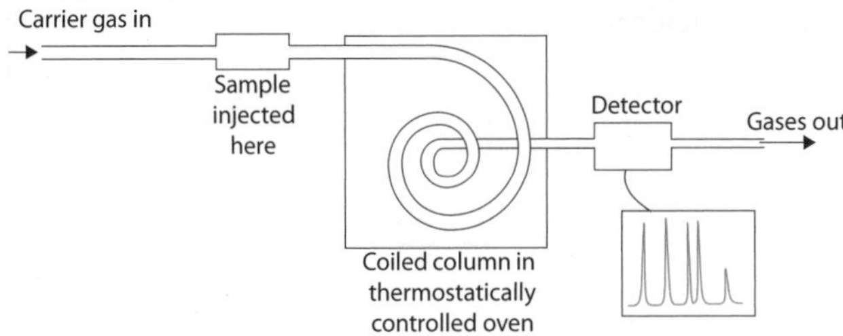

Figure 1235 Schematic diagram of gas chromatography

The mixture, which must vaporise at the temperature used, is usually injected, by means of a hypodermic syringe, into a steady gas flow at the start of the column. One great advantage of the technique is the very small samples required, of the order of a microlitre (1 μl = 10^{-6} dm^3). The rate at which the sample passes through the column can be controlled by the temperature and for this reason the column is housed in an oven. It is therefore important that samples used in GLC are thermally stable.

The components of the mixture are detected as they reach the end of the column, either by the effect they have on the thermal conductivity of the gas, or by the current that results from the ions formed when they are burnt in a flame. The results are shown as a graph of the detector signal against the time since the mixture was injected into the gas flow. The components can often be identified from the time taken for them to emerge from the column (called the **retention time**) and the area under the peak is proportional to the amount of the component in the mixture. Typical GLC chromatograms are shown in Figure 1236(a) and (b).

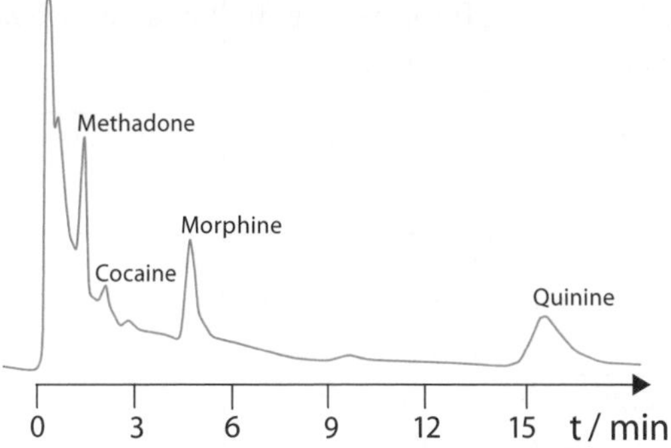

(a) typical glc to show the detection of drugs in a urine sample

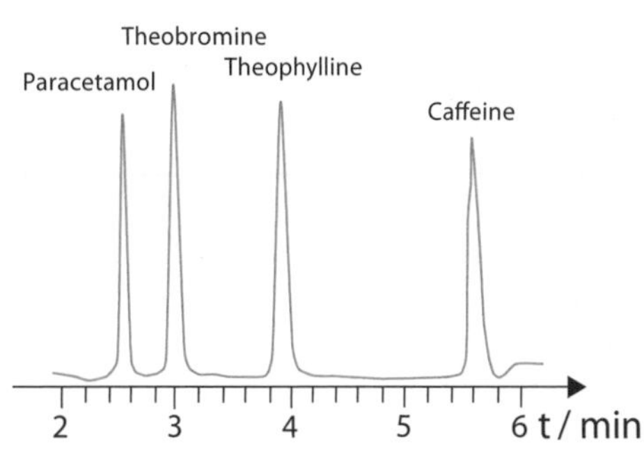

(b) typical hplc to show the components of a proprietary cold treatment

Figure 1236 Typical glc and hplc chromatograms

It can be seen that gas chromatography allows the number of components in a mixture to be identified and the relative amounts of these can be determined from the area under the peak. For more precise work, the system can be calibrated using samples of known concentration under identical conditions.

GLC is used to identify components that can vaporize without decomposition such as analysis of vegetable oil mixtures, analysis of gas mixtures from underground mines or from petrochemical works, analysis of components of fruit odours, detection of steroids or drugs in urine samples from athletes, and blood alcohol levels.

A very powerful technique **Gas Chromatography – Mass Spectrometry**, (GC–MS) involves coupling the output of the gas chromatography column to the input of the mass spectrometer. This means that each component is definitely identified as it elutes by means of its mass spectrum. This is particularly useful in food and drug testing as well as in forensic science.

Technique	Stationary Phase	Mobile Phase	Typical application
Paper chromatography	Trapped water in the paper	Organic solvent	Detection of amino acids in a mixture Testing food colours to see if they are single dyes or mixtures
Thin layer chromatography	Oxide coating	Organic solvent	Detection of amino acids in a mixture Testing food colours to see if they are single dyes or mixtures
Column chromatography	Oxide packing or ion exchange resin	Organic solvent	Preparative, e.g. separation of the chlorophylls and carotene in plant extract
Gas-liquid chromatography	Oxide or non-volatile liquid on the solid support	Gas	Analysis of vegetable oil mixtures Analysis of gas mixtures, especially from mines Analysis of components of fruit odours Detection of levels of alcohol in blood Detection of drugs in urine Detection of steroids
High Performance Liquid Chromatography	Oxide packing	Liquid	Analysis of sugars in fruit juices Analysis of additives in margarine Analysis of pesticide & herbicide residues Oil pollutants Alcohol in drinks

Figure 1237 Summary of some chromatographic techniques

HIGH PERFORMANCE LIQUID CHROMATOGRAPHY

The principle of **High Performance Liquid Chromatography** (HPLC) is basically very similar to gas chromatography except that the mobile phase is a liquid, forced under high pressure (up to 10^7 Pa) through a rather shorter column (usually 10–30 centimetres long), rather than a gas. Its advantage over gas chromatography lies in the fact that it can be used for non-volatile and ionic substances, as well as those that are not thermally stable enough for GLC. One of the major weaknesses of this technique is that the detector systems are less sensitive than those usually used in gas chromatography. The most commonly used detection system is the absorption of UV light, though there are a wide variety of other detector systems (e.g. fluorescence and conductivity) that find specialist use.

Usually (called 'normal phase') the packing is either a polar oxide (silicon dioxide or aluminium oxide), or an inert support coated with a thin layer of a polar liquid which acts as the stationary phase and a non–polar liquid is used as the mobile phase. In such a system, the less polar components elute before the more polar. The polarity of the phases can however be reversed ('reverse phase', i.e. a non-polar packing and a polar mobile phase) so that the more polar components elute first. A typical HPLC chromatogram is shown in Figure 1236(b).

HPLC is used for temperature-sensitive components and for chemicals that do not vaporize easily because of high boiling points or ease of decomposition, for example, in the analysis of oil pollutants in soil and water samples, analysis of antioxidants, sugars and vitamins in fruit juices and analysis of drugs in blood and urine.

A.10.2 Deduce which chromatographic technique is most appropriate for separating the components in a particular mixture

When facing an analytical problem it is important to select the correct technique. This will depend on what is required. Is it qualitative or quantitative? Are the components known or must they be identified? How much of the material is available (kilograms or micrograms?). How low are the concentrations of the substances to be detected (~0.01 mol dm^{-3} or 10^{-6} mol dm^{-3}). The choice also depends on the nature of the sample. Is it volatile? How polar is it? Is it thermally stable?

- For a stable, volatile sample, generally gas chromatography on a suitable column will offer the best solution.
- For a non-volatile or thermally unstable sample HPLC will often provide the solution.
- Column chromatography is most suitable for preparative purposes, whilst paper and thin layer techniques involve the minimum amount of apparatus, if all that is required is a simple qualitative check.

Some common applications of the different techniques are given in Figure 1237.

Exercise A10

1. Many chromatographic techniques are used to detect the presence of a particular substance. Column chromatography can however also be used as a preparative technique, i.e. to produce a sample of a substance. Explain how you would attempt to use this technique to produce pure samples of the different dyes comprising universal indicator.

2. (a) Describe the technique of paper chromatography to separate a mixture of dyes and explain the chemical principle behind it.
   (b) Define the term R_f. Describe how it could be determined for a component of a mixture and explain the significance of an R_f value of 0.0 and one of 1.0
   (c) Describe how you would detect the presence of an illegal substance added to a product with the food dye.

3. a) All chromatography depends upon a separation between two phases. What are these phases in the case of paper chromatography?

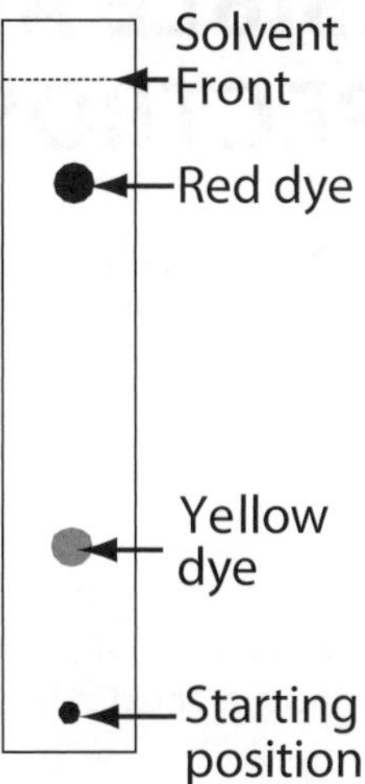

The paper chromatogram of an orange dye is illustrated. Explain the separation of the two components in terms of their relative affinities for the stationary and mobile phases.

b) Calculate the R_f values of the components.

c) Gas–liquid chromatography (GLC) and high performance liquid chromatography (HPLC) are both far more widely used than paper chromatography. Give at least two reasons why these techniques are preferred.

d) Give an example of a mixture for which GLC would give better results than HPLC and one for which the reverse is true. In each case state why that technique is to be preferred.

4. When a mixture of the four isomeric alcohols with the molecular formula C_4H_9OH is passed through a gas chromatography column they are separated with 2-methylpropan-2-ol eluting first and butan-1-ol eluting last.

a) What does this show about the relative attraction of butan-1-ol and 2-methylpropan-2-ol for the packing of the column? Explain how this leads to the separation of the two compounds.

b) How could the relative amounts of the four isomers in the mixture be found?

c) By what methods might the alkanols be detected as they elute from the column?

d) How would the time taken for the substances to elute be affected if the temperature of the column was increased?

A8 VISIBLE AND ULTRAVIOLET (UV-VIS) SPECTROSCOPY [HL]

Ultraviolet-visible spectroscopy, a very similar technique to infrared spectroscopy, but it uses UV and visible light instead of infrared, in the assaying of metal ions, organic structure determination and the detection of drug metabolites.

A.8.1 Describe the effect of different ligands on the splitting of the d orbitals in transition metal complexes

A.8.2 Describe the factors that affect the colour of transition metal complexes

The energy carried by a quantum of light in the UV (wavelengths between ~250 – 400 nm) and visible regions (wavelengths between ~400-700 nm) of the spectrum corresponds to the difference in energy between filled and unfilled electron orbitals in many ions and molecules. In many ions, for example sodium ions, the difference in energy between the highest filled orbital and the lowest unfilled orbital (i.e. the 2p and the 3s for Na^+) is quite large and so they only absorb very short wavelength UV light, hence their ions are colourless. In the transition metals, the difference in energy between filled and unfilled split d-orbitals is much smaller so that these ions in solution absorb energy in the far UV and visible regions, the latter being responsible for the fact that many of these ions are coloured. For example aqueous copper(II) ions appear blue in colour because they absorb light in the red and green regions of the visible spectrum; the colour observed being the complementary colour of the colours absorbed.

In transition metals, light can be absorbed because, even though in an isolated atom the d-orbitals are all of the same energy, when the atom is surrounded by charged or polar ligands the interaction of the different orbitals with the electric fields of these ligands varies and hence they have different energies. This usually causes the d-orbitals to split into two groups with three orbitals at a lower energy and two at a slightly higher energy.

The difference in energy between these two groups of orbitals is smaller than that between most electron orbitals and corresponds ($\Delta E = hf$) to light in the visible region of the spectrum. The exact difference in energy between the two groups of d-orbitals, and hence the colour of the light absorbed (remember the colour it appears is the complementary colour of the absorbed light) depends on a number of factors:

- the element being considered (especially the nuclear charge)
- the charge on the ion
- the ligands surrounding the ion
- the number and geometrical arrangement of the ligands.

The first point is easily illustrated by considering manganese(II), which has an almost colourless hexaaquo ion $[Mn(H_2O)_6]^{2+}$ and iron(III), which has a yellow-brown hexaaquo ion $[Fe(H_2O)_6]^{3+}$, even though they both have the same electronic structure [Ar] $3d^5$. This is a result of the differing charges on the two nuclei and the effect of this on the electron orbitals. An example of the second factor is the two oxidation states of iron, which have differing numbers of d-electrons and as a result $[Fe(H_2O)_6]^{2+}$ is pale green and $[Fe(H_2O)_6]^{3+}$ is yellow-brown. Here the nuclear charge is constant, but there is a difference in the electronic structures - [Ar] $3d^6$ and [Ar] $3d^5$ respectively.

Changing the identity of the ligand changes the degree of splitting depending on the electron density of the ligand and the extent to which it repels the electrons in the d-orbitals. The nature of the ligand is well illustrated by copper(II). With water there is the familiar pale blue colour of the hexaaqua ion, $[Cu(H_2O)_6]^{2+}$. If the ligands are gradually replaced by ammonia, to give for example $[Cu(NH_3)_4(H_2O)_2]^{2+}$, the colour deepens to a dark royal blue as the energy gap between the d-orbitals is increased. If the water ligands are gradually replaced by chloride ions the colour changes through green to the yellow of $[CuCl_4]^{2-}$ because chloride ions cause less splitting of the d-orbitals.

Obviously this last case also results from a change in the number and geometry of the ligands, which can lead to quite marked changes of colour. The hexaaqua ion of cobalt, $[Co(H_2O)_6]^{2+}$ is, for example, pale pink (i.e. blue, green and yellow light are weakly absorbed), but the tetrachloro ion, $[CoCl_4]^{2-}$ is dark blue (i.e green, yellow and red light are strongly absorbed).

OPTION

A.8.3 State that organic molecules containing a double bond absorb radiation.

A.8.4 Describe the effect of the conjugation of double bonds in organic molecules on the wavelength of the absorbed light.

A.8.5 Predict whether or not a particular molecule will absorb ultraviolet or visible radiation.

In the same way that atoms and ions have atomic orbitals, molecules have molecular orbitals, some of which are filled, others are unfilled. In simple molecules, such as water, as in simple ions, the difference in energy between the highest filled orbital and the lowest unfilled orbital is again quite large and so they too only absorb very short wavelength UV light and hence appear colourless. The difference in energy in molecules that have double bonds (i.e. C=C and C=O, structural elements known as '**chromophores**') is much less, especially if these are 'conjugated' (that is there are alternate double and single bonds), and/or involve extensive delocalised bonds (such as in a benzene ring). Molecules of this kind absorb light in the far UV and visible regions. For example 1,10–diphenyl–1,3,5,7,9–decapentene which, as shown below, has two benzene rings and an extensive chain of conjugated double bonds, is an orange colour because it absorbs blue and green light.

C_6H_5–CH=CH–CH=CH–CH=CH–CH=CH–CH=CH–C_6H_5

Figure 1239 The structure of 1,10-diphenyl-1,3,5,7,9-decapentene

If we examine the structures of a number of compounds to identify these structural elements, it is possible to predict to what extent these will absorb UV and visible light. Consider the following compounds:

2.3-dichloropentane contains only σ bonds and so will only absorb short wavelength UV light.	$CH_3CHClCHClCH_2CH_3$
Pent-3-enoic acid contains isolated double bonds (not alternate single and double bonds), hence no delocalization, so that it will only absorb in the mid UV region.	CH_3–CH=CH–CH_2–COOH (sp³ hybrid)
In pent-2-enoic acid the single and double bonds are alternate, hence the double bonds are conjugated, so the UV absorption will be at a longer wavelength.	CH_3–CH_2–CH=CH–COOH (Alternate double bonds)
It is only when there is an extended system of delocalised bonds and conjugated double bonds, as in the diazonium compound the absorption moves into the visible region to produce a coloured compound (in this case, red).	Azo dye (OH, N=N)

Note the difference in the structures of phenolphthalein given below. In acid solution, species I (Figure 1243), it is colourless as there is limited delocalisation due to the presence of the sp³ hybridised carbon. In alkaline solution, species II, there is extensive delocalisation possible due to the presence of the sp² hybridised carbon, and it is coloured pink.

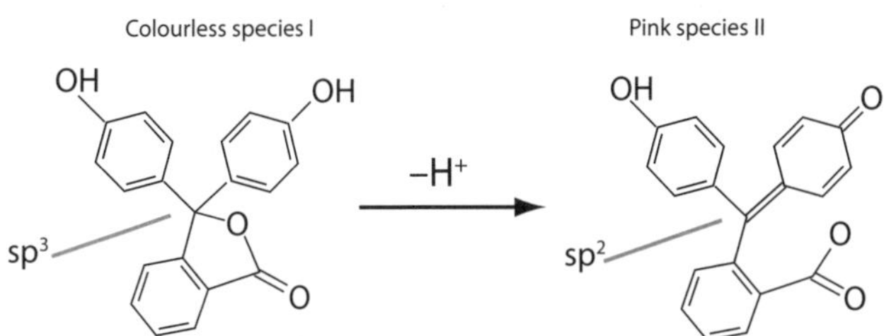

Figure 1243 The structures of phenolphthalein in acid and alkaline solution respectively

OPTION

Other substances that absorb visible light as a result of extended conjugated systems are (a) retinol (vital for vision) and (b) chlorophyll (vital for photosynthesis), the structures of which are shown in Figure 1244:

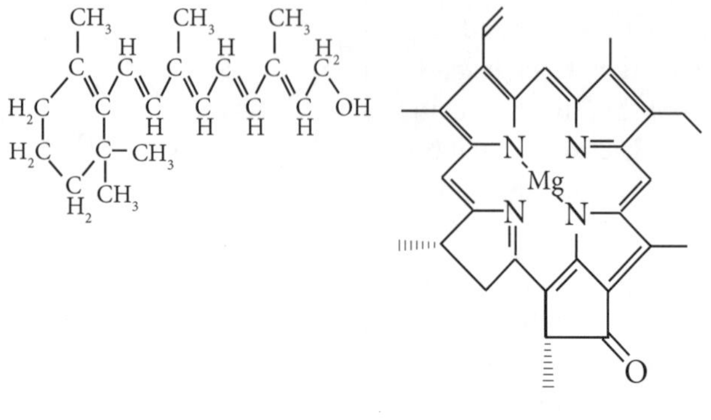

Figure 1244 (a) and (b) Some organic compounds that are coloured because they absorb visible light

Many drugs and their metabolites absorb light in the UV region so that UV/Vis spectrophotometry can also be used to detect and measure their concentrations. One other group of compounds for which the absorption of UV light is important is sun creams or sun blocks. Exposure to UV light damages the surface of the skin. If this occurs gently and in moderation then it results in the production of more melanin, a natural pigment, and a darkening of the skin – tanning. With excess exposure the damage to the skin can be severe (sun burn) and perhaps more seriously increases the risk of melanoma and other forms of skin cancer. To prevent this, sun blocks should be applied to the skin before long exposure to sunlight. These are compounds that strongly absorb UV light and as might be expected they have systems of extended conjugation. A typical example would be para-aminobenzoic acid (PABA) which is used as a 'sun-block' as shown in Figure 1245.

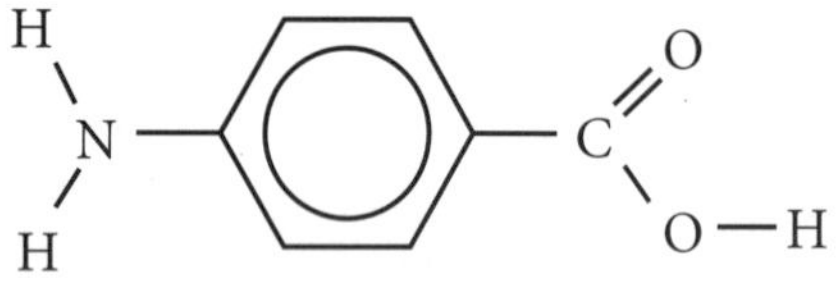

Figure 1245 The structure of para-aminobenzoic acid (PABA)

A.8.6 Determine the concentration of a solution from a calibration curve using the Beer–Lambert law.

The amount of light of a particular frequency which a solution absorbs will depend on the nature of the compound (which determines the molar extinction, or absorption, coefficient; ε), its concentration (c in mol dm^{-3}) and the distance the light passes through the solution (l, in cm). The intensity of the light (I) is found to decay exponentially as it passes through the solution, giving rise to a logarithmic relationship:

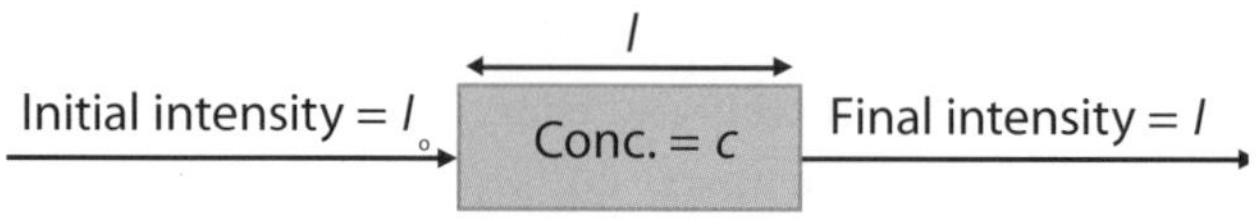

Initial intensity = I_0 | l | Conc. = c | Final intensity = I

Figure 1246 Intensity of light decays exponentially

$$I = I_0 10^{-\varepsilon cl}$$

Taking logarithms:

$$A = \log_{10}\left(\frac{I_0}{I}\right) = \varepsilon cl$$

This is known as the **Beer–Lambert law**, and A is known as the absorbance of the solution (note that because it is a logarithm, absorbance (A) does not have units.), the reading given directly by most UV/visible spectrophotometers, though some also give the percentage transmittance, T, where:

$$T = \frac{I_0}{I} \times 100$$

The molar extinction coefficient (ε) is a measure of how strongly the compound absorbs light. The larger the value of ε, the stronger the absorption – the permanganate ion (MnO_4^-) for example has a very large extinction coefficient. This relationship means that a graph of absorbance (A) against concentration (c) is linear, making it easy to use this technique to determine the concentration of a given species in a solution. The molar extinction coefficient (ε) may be found from the gradient, knowing the path length (l). It is equal to the logarithm of the fractional decrease in intensity of the monochromatic light as it passes through 1 cm of 1 mol dm^{-3} solution and therefore has units of dm^3 mol^{-1} cm^{-1}.

In fact the Beer-Lambert law only holds precisely for dilute solutions, so it is always best to produce a calibration curve, using solutions of known concentration, when using UV/Visible absorbance quantitatively. An example is the absorption of iodine in aqueous 0.10 mol dm^{-3} potassium iodide at 306 nm. The graph of absorbance against concentration as light passes through a 1 cm cell is shown in Figure 1247. As expected it is linear and from the gradient, the molar extinction coefficient may be determined as

$$\frac{2.3}{1 \times 0.015} = 153 \text{ dm}^3 \text{ mol}^{-1} \text{ cm}^{-1}$$

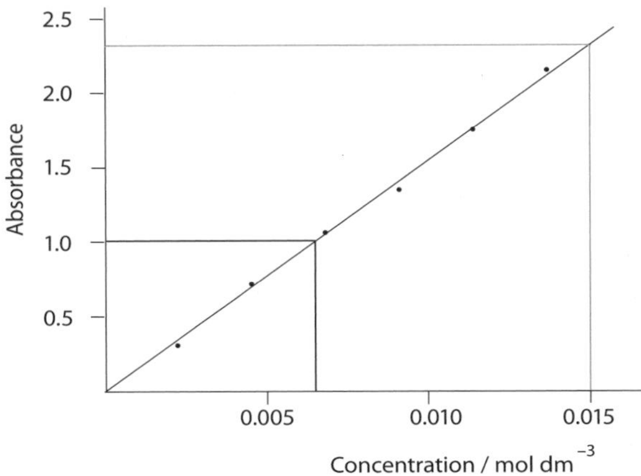

Figure 1247 The dependence of the absorption of iodine on concentration at 306 nm

If an unknown solution of iodine in 0.10 mol dm^{-3} potassium iodide had an absorbance of 1.0 at 306 nm its concentration can be read from the graph as 0.007 mol dm^{-3}.

Exercise A8

1. A 1×10^{-4} mol dm^{-3} solution of an organic compound in a 1 cm cell has an absorbance of 0.5 at a wavelength of 300 nm. What is the numerical value of its molar extinction coefficient at this wavelength.

   A 5×10^{-5}
   B 5×10^{3}
   C 2×10^{5}
   D 6.00×10^{-2}

2. At a particular wavelength the molar extinction coefficient of aqueous copper sulfate is 300 dm^3 mol^{-1} cm^{-1}. Approximately what percentage of the incident light of this wavelength will pass through a 0.010 mol dm^{-3} solution in a 1 cm cell?

   A 10%
   B 1%
   C 0.1%
   D 0.01%

3. (a) Transition metal ions tend to absorb light in the visible region of the spectrum. Explain why this occurs and why the precise colour may vary with the other species present.
   (b) In terms of the colours of light absorbed in this way, explain why aqueous nickel sulfate appears a green colour.
   (c) The intensity of green light passing through a particular sample of aqueous nickel sulfate is I_1. If the concentration of the salt is doubled, but all other factors are kept constant, how will the intensity of the light that now passes, I_2, be related to I_1? What changes must be made to the distance that the light passes through the solution in order to restore the intensity of the transmitted light to I_1?
   (d) Aqueous nickel(II) ions form a brightly coloured complex with an organic ligand. Various volumes of equimolar solutions of the two species are mixed and the absorbance recorded. Use the results below to derive the probable formula of the complex ion formed, explaining your method.

Volume of Ni^{2+} solution cm^3	Volume of ligand solution cm^3	Absorbance
0	10	0
2	8	1.27
4	6	1.71
6	4	1.26
8	2	0.63
10	0	0

4. Use the IB Data Booklet to find the structural fomula of a coloured organic compound and describe the features of its structure that result in it absorbing visible light.

OPTION

HUMAN BIOCHEMISTRY

B1 Energy
B2 Proteins
B3 Carbohydrates
B4 Lipids
B5 Micronutrients and macronutrients
B6 Hormones
B7 Enzymes (HL)
B8 Nucleic acids (HL)
B9 Respiration (HL)

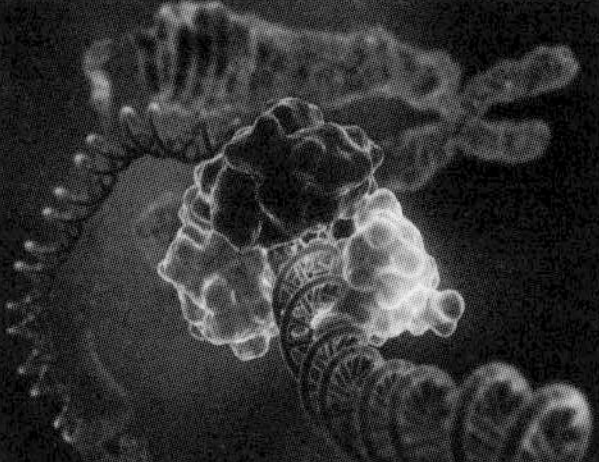

The aim of this option is to give students an understanding of the chemistry of important molecules found in the human body, and the need for a balanced and healthy diet. Although the role that these molecules play in the body should be appreciated, the emphasis is placed on their chemistry, and students who have not followed a course in biology will not be at a disadvantage. Students will not be required to memorize complex structures, but they will be expected to recognize functional groups and types of bonding within and between molecules. Structures of some important biological molecules are given in the *Chemistry data booklet*.

The human body requires certain substances to function and grow and good diet is essential to staying healthy. Food provides energy and replaces molecules used up by bodily processes. Nutrients are the food components which provide growth, energy and replacement of body tissue. They are generally divided into six groups, namely proteins, carbohydrates, lipids, micro- and macro-nutrients (including vitamins and minerals) and water. The human body requires different amounts of each nutrient for good health.

Water comprises about 70% of our body mass and is responsible for dissolving most of the chemicals in our system and transporting **nutrients** and waste. In order to create a balance between our intake and the amount of water we release through sweat, urine, faeces and respiration, humans generally require about one to one and a half litres of water daily in addition to that obtained from the food consumed.

B1 ENERGY

B.1.1 Calculate the energy value of a food from enthalpy of combustion data.

The oxidation of macro-nutrients fats, carbohydrates and proteins produces carbon dioxide, water and energy. The energy requirements of human beings depend on age, size, sex and daily activity. For adults with low activity levels, the recommended daily energy intake is about 10500 kJ (2500 kcal) for males and about 8000 kJ (1900 kcal) for females. Metabolism, the chemical reactions in living organisms, converts the food we eat into energy and produces various materials that our bodies require. Fats are used to store energy and make available about 37 kJ g^{-1} of energy, more energy than carbohydrates (the main source of energy) and proteins which make available about 17 kJ g^{-1}. The ratio of H:O atoms in lipids is higher, for example in palmitic acid, $C_{16}H_{32}O_2$, it is 16:1 compared with a 2:1 ratio in carbohydrates. Thus carbohydrates (and proteins) are more oxidized and produce less energy per gram.

The amount of energy stored in food, its calorific or energy value, can be found experimentally by completely burning different foods and using the energy released to raise the temperature of a fixed mass of water using an insulated food calorimeter. The energy content or value of a large apple is about 420 kJ. This means that if the apple was burnt in a food calorimeter, the energy produced on combustion would raise the temperature of 1 kg water

OPTION

by 100°C, assuming the calorimeter does not absorb any heat.

$\Delta H = mc\Delta T = 1000 \text{ g} \times 4.18 \text{ J g}^{-1} \text{°C}^{-1} \times 100 \times \text{°C} \approx 420 \text{ kJ}$

In calculations from experimental data however, any energy absorbed by the calorimeter must be taken into account.

Example

A large apple weighs 150 g. In a laboratory investigation, a 15.0 g sample of the apple, on complete combustion, raises the temperature of 200 g water in a glass container by 45.3 °C. Calculate the energy value of the whole apple. The heat capacity of the glass calorimeter = 89.1 J °C^{-1} and the specific heat of water = 4.18 J g^{-1} °C^{-1}.

Solution

Heat produced = heat absorbed by water + heat absorbed by calorimeter

$= (m \times c \times \Delta T)_{water} + (m \times c \times \Delta T)_{calorimeter}$

$= (200 \text{ g} \times 4.18 \text{ J g}^{-1} \text{°C}^{-1} \times 45.3 \text{ °C}) + (89.1 \text{ J °C}^{-1} \times 45.3 \text{ °C})$

$= (37871 + 4036)$ J

$= 41907$ J

= 41.9 kJ (produced by 15.0 g of apple)

Thus the energy value of the 150 g apple is 419 kJ.

Example

1.00 g cereal raises the temperature of 400 cm^3 water in an insulated food calorimeter from 23.7 °C to 33.4 °C. Calculate the energy value per gram of the cereal, assuming the heat capacity of the calorimeter is negligible and given the specific heat of water = 4.18 J g^{-1} C^{-1}.

Solution

Heat produced = heat absorbed by water

$= (m \times c \times \Delta T)_{water}$

$= [400 \text{ g} \times 4.18 \text{ J g}^{-1} \text{ C}^{-1} \times (33.4 - 23.7) \text{ °C}]$

= 16.2 kJ per gram of cereal.

The energy content of peanuts and proteins in eggs is about 24 kJ g^{-1}. A teaspoon of margarine releases about 420 kJ and the energy content of alcohol (ethanol) is about 29 kJ g^{-1}. The energy one consumes is expended through activity and the excess energy is stored as fat leading to weight gain. If a person eats less energy-containing food than the body needs, their stored fat is broken down for energy, resulting in weight loss.

B2 PROTEINS

Proteins are natural polymers, made up of C, H, O, N, (and sometimes S). Their primary use is to provide amino acids which are the building blocks of new proteins in the body. Amino acids are used to produce new proteins for growth and repair of body tissues as well as to make hormones, enzymes and antibodies. These can also be used as an energy source in the event of starvation. They make up 15% of our bodies and have molar masses of between 6000 to over 1,000,000 g mol^{-1}.

The variety of proteins that are important to human life are made of an assortment of some 20 α-amino acids. Out of some 20 amino acids, there are ten amino acids which our bodies cannot synthesize and cannot store in the same way they do fat, hence they must be found through food consumption. These are called **essential amino acids.** A protein which contains all ten of the amino acids we cannot synthesise and in a ratio similar to that which we need, is called a **complete protein**, such as casein from milk, cheese, eggs and soybeans. Most animal proteins such as those found in meat, fish and eggs are complete. Incomplete proteins include most plant proteins; wheat protein does not have lysine; rice protein does not contain lysine or threonine. Vegetarians can obtain all the proteins they require through a combination of legumes, such as peas, beans or corn, and grains as these serve to complement each other.

B.2.1 Draw the general formula of 2-amino acids.

Proteins are polymeric substances made up of long molecules formed by sequences of smaller nitrogen–containing units called amino acids. Amino acids are molecules that contain both a carboxyl group (–COOH) and an amino group (–NH_2).

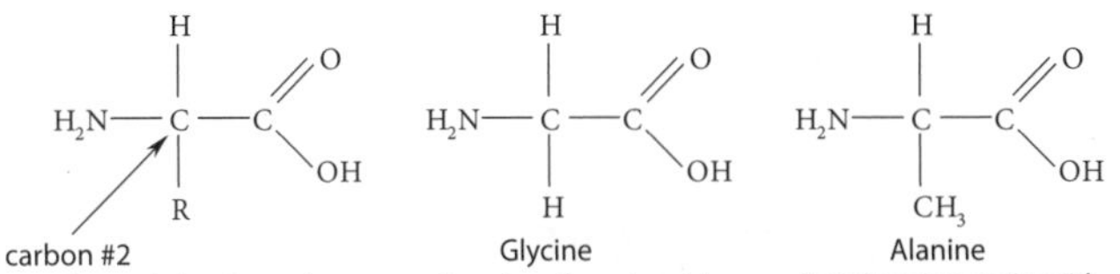

carbon #2
General structure of 2-amino acids

Glycine
2-aminoethanoic acid

Alanine
2-aminopropanoic acid

Figure 1301 General structural formula of 2-amino acid, glycine and alanine

The R group, called the side chain, can be hydrogen, an alkyl group or a complex substituent. All amino acids in natural proteins are **2-amino acids** (or **α-amino acids**), so called because the amino acid group is attached to the 2- or α–carbon atom, the one next to the carboxylic acid (–COOH) group. Amino acids have the ability to behave both as an acid and as a base in aqueous solution. In the simplest amino acid, glycine (IUPAC name 2-aminoethanoic acid), the methylene group (–CH_2–), is bonded to both an acidic carboxyl group (–COOH) and a basic amino group (–NH_2). If R is –CH_3, alanine is formed, (IUPAC name 2-aminopropanoic acid).

B.2.2 Describe the characteristic properties of 2-amino acids.

Amino acids are colorless, crystalline solids. These exist as **zwitterions** (dipolar ions) $H_3N^+CHRCOO^-$ which explains their relatively high melting points for organic compounds (for example, glycine has a melting point of 232 – 236°C), and why they are generally more soluble in water than in organic solvents.

Amino acids are amphoteric (capable of behaving as acids or bases); the majority of the amino acids contain one basic and one acidic group both of which can ionise in aqueous solution. As a base, the amine group accepts a proton from water:

$$H_2NCHRCOOH + H_2O \rightleftharpoons H_3N^+CHRCOOH + OH^-$$

At lower pH, the H^+ added reacts with OH^- present in the equilibrium and the forward reaction is favoured to replace some of the OH^- used up. Thus in a an acidic solution, the –NH_2 group is protonated.

As an acid, the carboxylic acid group donates a proton to water:

$$H_2NCHRCOOH + H_2O \rightleftharpoons H_2NCHRCOO^- + H_3O^+$$

At higher pH, the base added reacts with H_3O^+ present in the equilibrium and the forward reaction is favoured to replace some of the H_3O^+ used up. Thus in an alkaline solution, the carboxylic acid group donates a proton and is converted to the carboxylate ion.

A specific pH exists for each amino acid when the above two ionizations are identical (or balanced) and the amino acid exists only as zwitterions (dipolar ions): $H_3N^+CHRCOO^-$. This is called the **isoelectric point**, pI, of the amino acid, that is the pH at which the positive and negative charges are identical (or balanced), hence the molecule has no net charge and it shows no net migration in an electric field.

If the side chain, R also contains –NH_2 group, for example in lysine, then the number of –NH_2 groups > the number of –COOH groups, and it is a basic amino acid. If, on the other hand, the R group also contains a –COOH group, for example in aspartic acid, the number of –COOH groups > the number of –NH_2 groups, then it is an acidic amino acid. The presence of the basic side chains produces additional positively charged ions (NH_3^+) and the presence of acidic side chains produces additional negatively charged (COO^-) ions in the amino acids. Thus, how an amino acid behaves in the presence of an electric field depends very much on the relative numbers of these charged groups. This is affected by the acidity or basicity of the solution, that is, its pH.

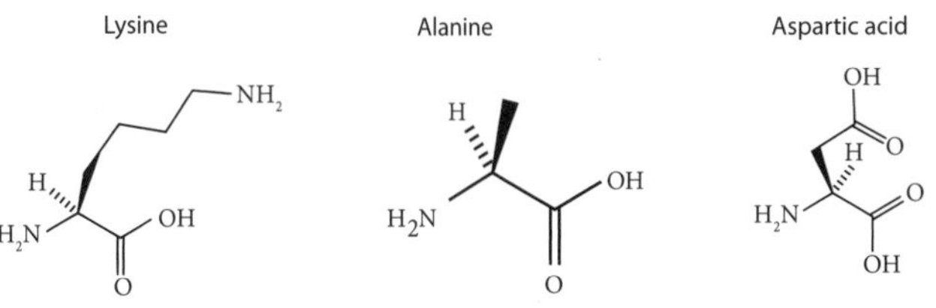

Figure 1302 The structures of some common amino acids

Their amphoteric nature makes it possible for the amino acids to act as buffers in aqueous solutions. Thus, when a strong acid, $H^+(aq)$, is added to an aqueous solution of an amino acid, the zwitterion accepts the proton, thus minimizing the effect of the acid added:

OPTION

$$H_3N^+{-}CH(R){-}COO^- + H^+ \rightleftharpoons H_3N^+{-}CH(R){-}COOH$$

Similarly, if a strong base OH^- (aq) is added, the zwitterion donates H^+ to neutralize the base to form water:

$$H_3N^+{-}CH(R){-}COO^- + OH^- \rightleftharpoons H_2N{-}CH(R){-}COO^- + H_2O$$

Within the 2-amino acids, when R ≠ H, the 2-carbon atom is chiral, the molecule is asymmetric and gives rise to two possible stereoisomers. These non-superimposable mirror images are called **enantiomers** (and exhibit optical activity). Thus, all amino acids, except glycine where R = H, can exist as a pair of enantiomers (the D or L forms).

> B.2.3 Describe the condensation reaction of 2-amino acids to form polypeptides.
>
> © IBO 2007

Since all amino acids have both a carboxyl group and an amino group, they are able to undergo condensation reactions to form substituted amides. For example, glycine and alanine can combine to form two possible dipeptides:

$$\underset{\text{Glycine}}{H_2N{-}CH_2{-}COOH} + \underset{\text{Alanine}}{H_2N{-}CH(CH_3){-}COOH} \xrightarrow{\text{enzyme}} H_2N{-}CH_2{-}CO{-}NH{-}CH(CH_3){-}COOH + H_2O$$

(peptide linkage: –CO–NH–)

$$\underset{\text{Alanine}}{H_2N{-}CH(CH_3){-}COOH} + \underset{\text{Glycine}}{H_2N{-}CH_2{-}COOH} \xrightarrow{\text{enzyme}} H_2N{-}CH(CH_3){-}CO{-}NH{-}CH_2{-}COOH + H_2O$$

The product, a **dipeptide**, is a substituted amide made up of two amino acids joined by a peptide bond or peptide linkage. Water is the other product formed in the enzyme controlled process. Note that two amino acids can give two different products depending which has the free amino and which the free carboxyl end. Similarly six different tripeptides can be formed using three different amino acids, if each amino acid is used only once (3 × 2 × 1). If a compound contains many of these peptide bonds it is considered to be a polypeptide which, after folding, becomes a protein. The 20 naturally occurring amino acids can hence undergo condensation reactions to produce a huge variety of proteins.

> B.2.4 Describe and explain the primary, secondary (α-helix and β-pleated sheets), tertiary and quaternary structure of proteins.
>
> © IBO 2007

As described previously amino acids can undergo condensation reactions in any sequence (order), thus making it possible to form an extremely large number of proteins. The structure of proteins can be broken down to four levels: primary, secondary, tertiary and quaternary structure.

Primary Structure

The **primary structure** is simply the sequence of amino acid residues that form the protein. This is indicated by using three-letter codes for the amino acids. A tripeptide containing the amino acids lysine, glycine and leucine would, for example, be lys–gly–leu in which, by convention, the terminal amino acid group of lysine is on the left and the terminal carboxylic acid group of leucine is on the right. Thus a different tripeptide leu–gly–lys consisting of the same three amino acids means the amino terminal group leucine is on the left and the acid terminal group lysine is on the right:

$$H_2N{-}\underset{R_1}{CH}{-}CO{-}NH{-}\underset{R_2}{CH}{-}CO{-}NH{-}\underset{R_3}{CH}{-}COOH$$

where R_1 is in leucine (containing the end group $-NH_2$), R_2 in glycine and R_3 in lysine (with the end group –COOH).

Each type of protein in a biological organism has its own unique primary sequence of amino acids. It is this sequence that gives the protein its ability to carry out its characteristic functions. Figure 1303 shows a typical primary structure with the amino end group tyrosine and carboxylic acid end group leucine.

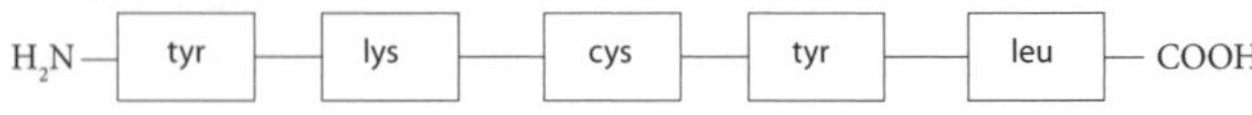

Figure 1303 A Primary structure

Secondary Structure

The **secondary structure** is the manner in which a polypeptide chain folds itself, due to intramolecular hydrogen bonding, in particular patterns that repeat themselves. This affects the arrangement in space of the polypeptide chain. Two features commonly found in a protein's secondary structure are referred to as an **α–helix** and a β-pleated sheet. In the α–helix structure, the peptide chain resembles a right handed spiral staircase or coiled spring; this shape is called a **helix**. This can make the protein elastic or sponge–like in fibrous proteins such as hair and wool. The α–helix maintains its shape through regular intramolecular hydrogen bonds. These are between the (δ–) oxygen of the carbonyl group (–C=O) and the (δ+) hydrogen of the –NH_2 group of the third peptide bond down the chain, that are in just the right position to interact. The H–bonding in the α–helix structure is parallel to the axis of the helix.

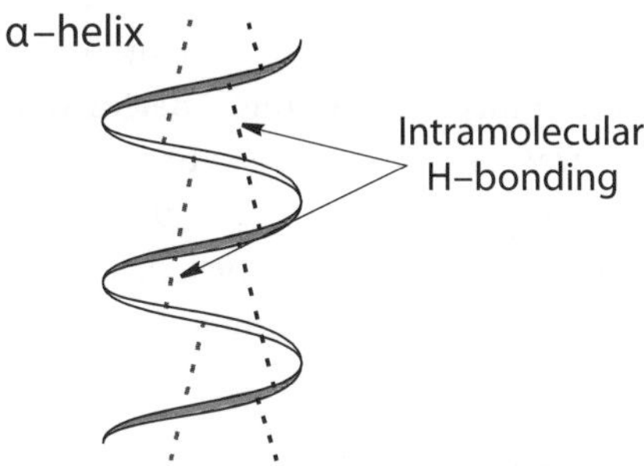

Figure 1304 The α-helix is a common secondary structure

In the **beta-pleated sheet** arrangement one, or more commonly several, different polypeptide chains are bound together by hydrogen bonds, (intramolecular if just one chain, or intermolecular if more than one) to create an orderly alignment of protein chains in which the direction of H–bonding is perpendicular to the sheet structure giving rise to a repeating, pleated pattern. Silk has this arrangement, making it flexible, but strong and resistant to stretching. If a particular part of a polypeptide chain does not exhibit a repeating pattern it is said to contain random coils.

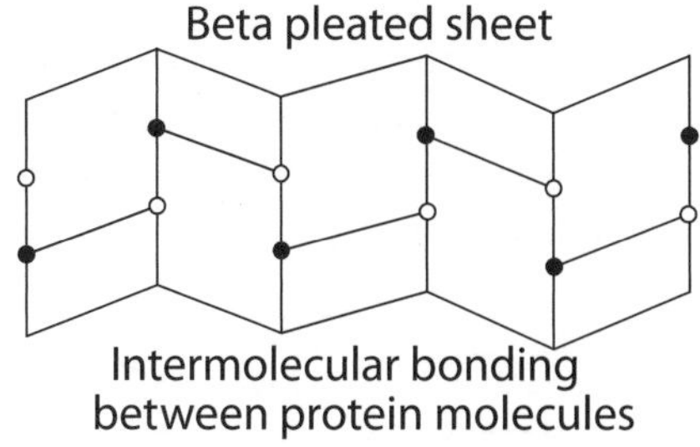

Figure 1305 The beta-pleated sheet is a secondary structures

Tertiary Structure

This is the folding or curling due to the interaction between the sequence of amino acids that maintains the three dimensional shape of the protein. The amino acid secondary structure in the helical, pleated or random coil form arranges itself to form the unique twisted or folded three dimensional shape of the protein.

In myoglobin about 70% of the amino acid sequence is α-helical secondary structure. The non-helical regions form a random coil and are a major factor that determines its tertirary structure. Refer to Figure 1306.

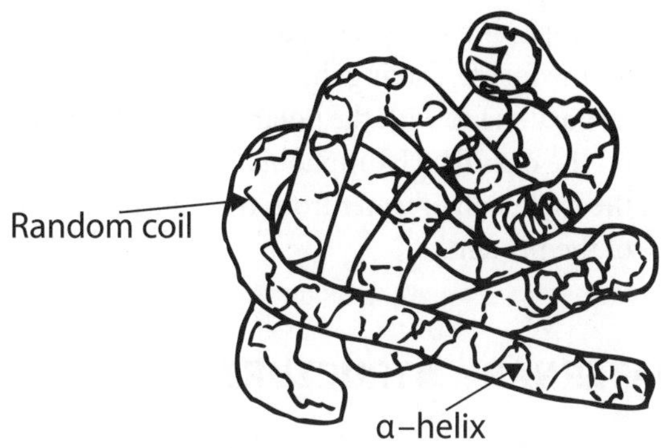

Figure 1306 The tertiary structure of myoglobin, a typical protein

There are four ways in which parts of the amino acid chains interact to stabilize their tertiary shapes.

These are:

(1) Covalent bonding, for example disulfide bridges can form between different parts of the protein when the –SH functional groups of two cysteine groups (cysteine is an aminoacid which has an -SH side-chain) link when oxidized under enzyme control:

$$\square\text{–S–H} + \text{H–S–}\square \xrightarrow{[O]} \square\text{–S–S–}\square + H_2O$$

For example, the **keratin proteins** in hair have a large number of cysteines connected by the disulfide bridges which hold the hair in its normal structure. In the artificial hair curling process, the –S–S– disulfide bridges on cysteine residues are reduced to the –S– H groups of cysteine:

$$\text{–S–S–} \xrightarrow{[2\ H]} \text{–S–H} + \text{H–S–}$$

On using a curler, hair is stretched and the –S–H groups are displaced. Then an oxidising agent is used to oxidize the curled hair to form new disulfide linkages to retain the new curls.

(2) Hydrogen bonding between -NH_2 and -COOH groups on the side chain.

OPTION

(3) Salt bridges (electrostatic attraction) between $-N^+H_3$ and $-COO^-$ groups.

(4) The R group side chain affects the 3–D structure of the resulting proteins depending on whether it is non-polar containing mostly C–H bonds and therefore hydrophobic or polar containing N–H and O–H bonds and therefore hydrophilic. Hydrophobic interactions occur when non-polar, hydrophobic side groups tend to clump together on the inside, forcing the protein chain into a tertiary shape with the polar parts of the molecule on the outside. Hydrophobic interactions involve the exclusion of water from the non-polar interior of the protein.

Quaternary Structure

This occurs only in proteins that are composed of more than one polypeptide chain which are held together by non-covalent bonds; these consist of hydrophobic interactions, hydrogen bonding and ionic bonds. When a protein consists of more than one polypeptide chain, each is called a subunit. The quaternary structure is how the polypeptide subunits are held together in a precise, more complex three-dimensional structural arrangement. An example is haemoglobin, which consists of two slightly different pairs of polypeptide chains grouped together to form the quaternary structure together with the haem co-factor (this binds the oxygen molecules reversibly).

Proteins can be denatured, that is they can lose their three dimensional structure and hence biological activity, in a number of ways. Denaturation affects the functioning of a protein because the exact shape is the key to the function of each of the numerous proteins in the body. The most common cause of denaturing is heat, as is the case when an egg is fried or boiled, which cause the breaking of hydrogen bonds. Other ways in which denaturing can occur include high energy ionising radiation, strong acids, bases and concentrated salt solutions (which can disrupt salt bridges) and, organic solvents and detergents (which can disrupt hydrophobic interactions).

B.2.5 Explain how proteins can be analysed by chromatography and electrophoresis.

A protein can be analyzed, that is, its amino acid residue composition can be determined by hydrolyzing the peptide bonds as shown in Figure 1307. With the lone electron pair on the nitrogen, the peptide linkage is a strong bond and complete acid hydrolysis usually requires the use of 6 mol dm^{-3} HCl solution at 110°C for several hours.

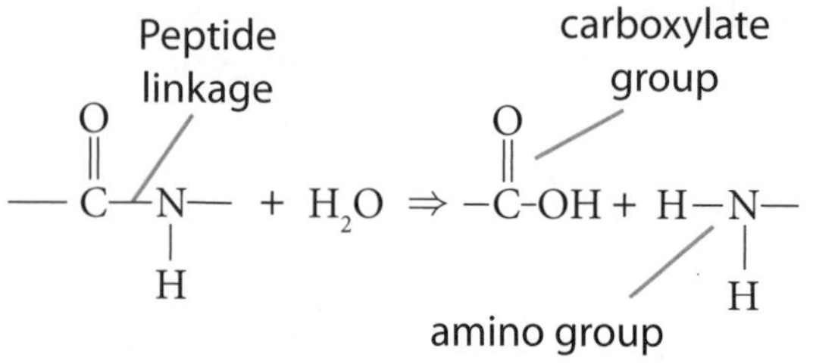

Peptide linkage
carboxylate group

$$—\overset{\overset{\displaystyle O}{\|}}{C}—\underset{\underset{\displaystyle H}{|}}{N}— + H_2O \Rightarrow —\overset{\overset{\displaystyle O}{\|}}{C}\text{-}OH + H—\underset{\underset{\displaystyle H}{|}}{N}—$$

amino group

Figure 1307 Hydrolysis of a peptide linkage

Hydrolysis of the peptide linkages produces individual amino acids which can be identified, and the amounts determined, using **high performance liquid chromatography** (hplc) since amino acids are not very volatile. In the laboratory, it is possible to identify individual amino acids using paper chromatography or electrophoresis, using known samples for comparison.

Chromatography

Chromatography is a very useful method for the separation of mixtures of substances which are otherwise not readily separated. Paper chromatography is suitable for the identification of components of a very small sample of mixture and is particularly suitable for separating hydrophilic substances such as amino acids. The relative solubility of different amino acids varies in the stationary phase (water, which is adsorbed on the cellulose paper), and the mobile phase (solvent). The principle of paper chromatography is the partition of solutes (the amino acids) between the two phases. Thus, amino acids with greater solubility in the eluting solvent will travel further in the direction of the solvent flow. Experimentally, a solution of the sample of the mixture of amino acids to be analyzed is placed as a spot on the surface of the chromatographic paper a couple of centimetres from the bottom, marked in pencil, and allowed to dry.

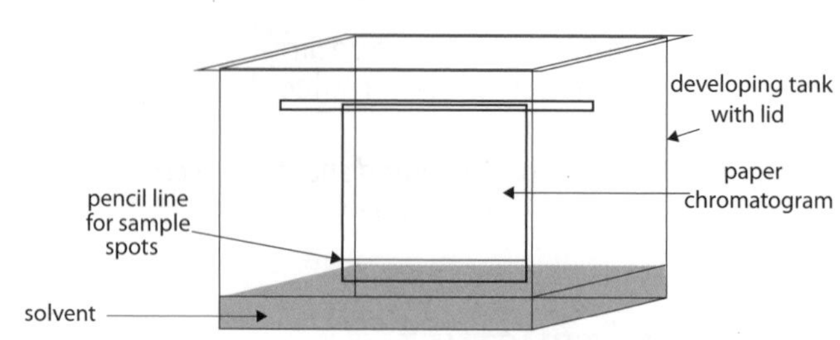

Figure 1308 One possible experimental arrangement for chromatography

The paper is placed vertically in a developing tank, the bottom of which contains about a ½ cm depth of the solvent. This is then covered and the solvent allowed to rise by capillary action. The components of the mixture move with the solvent at different rates depending on their solubility in the stationary and moving phases. Once the solvent nears the top of the paper it is removed, the solvent front is marked and the solvent allowed to evaporate. As the amino acids are colourless the plate must be developed by spraying it with a solution of ninhydrin. Glycine, for example, forms a blue/purple compound with ninhydrin, as do 19 of the 20 protein-derived α-amino acids (proline gives an orange color).

A number of spots will be found corresponding to the different amino acids in the protein. The amino acids can be identified by comparing the R_f values of the spots with those for pure amino acids developed at the same time, under the same conditions of solvent and temperature. R_f represents the 'Ratio of fronts' and refers to the ratio of the distance traveled by a compound (d_c) divided by the distance traveled by the solvent (d_s):

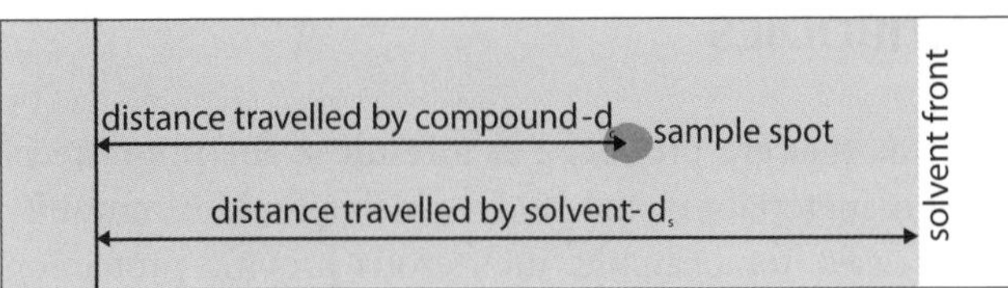

Figure 1309 Calculating the 'ratio of fronts' (R_f)

$$R_f = \frac{d_c}{d_s} = \frac{\text{distance travelled by compound}}{\text{distance travelled by solvent}}$$

Different substances have different R_f values under identical experimental conditions, so comparison of R_f values allows for the components of a mixture to be identified. If several components of a mixture have similar R_f values using a particular solvent, thus leading to incomplete separation, it is possible to repeat the experiment with a different solvent. One development of this is two–dimensional chromatography in which the sample spot is placed in one corner of a square piece of chromatography paper, the chromatogram is developed by eluting with one solvent system to allow partial separation. The paper is dried, turned at right angles from its original position and developed using a second solvent system (such as basic butan-2-ol/ammonia mixture if acidic butan-1-ol/ ethanoic acid was the first solvent) to achieve a more complete separation.

Electrophoresis and Isoelectric Points

Electrophoresis is the method of separating (similar sized) molecules on the basis of their electric charges. In order to analyse a protein using electrophoresis, the peptide bonds in the protein must first be hydrolysed to release the individual amino acids.

After a protein has been hydrolysed, each amino acid in the mixture produced has a different isoelectric point. This means that they can be separated using electrophoresis. Such a separation can be carried out using paper, cellulose acetate or other appropriate solid supports. The solid support is saturated with a buffer solution of known pH.

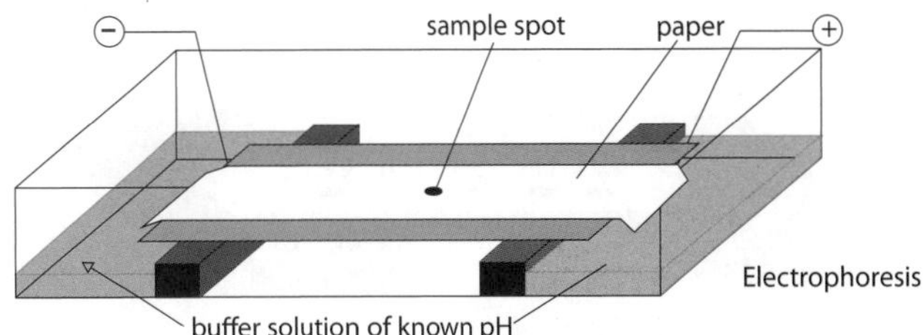

Figure 1310 Electrophoresis equipment

The sample consisting of a mixture of amino acids is applied to the centre of the paper. The electrodes and ends of the paper are placed in the buffered solution and a high electric potential is applied to the electrodes. Any amino acid at its isoelectric point does not move in either direction. However, amino acids with positive charges at that pH move to the cathode and amino acids with negative charges at that pH move to the anode. After sufficient separation is achieved, the paper strip is dried and sprayed with ninhydrin solution to make the components visible. The paper can then be compared with known samples. By repeating the process at different pH values the isoelectric points of the components can be determined, helping to identify individual amino acids. Figure 1311 lists the isoelectric points, pI, of some amino acids (see also the IB Chemistry Data Booklet Table 19, page 26):

Amino acid	Symbol	pI (pH units)
Cysteine	Cys	5.1
Glutamine	Gln	5.7
Glycine	Gly	6.0
Histidine	His	7.6
Lysine	Lys	9.7

Figure 1311 The iso-electric points of some common amino acids

At pH 6.0, glycine exists as the dipolar ion, H_3N^+–CH_2–COO^- and hence will not move if electrophoresis is carried out at this pH. If electrophoresis is carried out with glycine at pH = 7.0, the pH of the buffer is more basic than the isoelectric point of glycine (7.0 compared to 6.0), glycine will have a net negative charge because it largely exists as H_2N-CH_2-COO^- and it will migrate toward the positive electrode. However, if the electrophoresis is carried out at pH = 5.0, the pH of the buffer is more acidic than the isoelectric point of glycine (5.0 compared to 6.0), glycine will have a net positive charge (H_3N^+-CH_2-COOH) and will migrate towards the negative pole.

If electrophoresis of a mixture of the five amino acids listed in the previous table is carried out at a pH of 6.0, glycine will not move from the point of origin as it has a net charge of zero at its isoelectric point of 6.0.

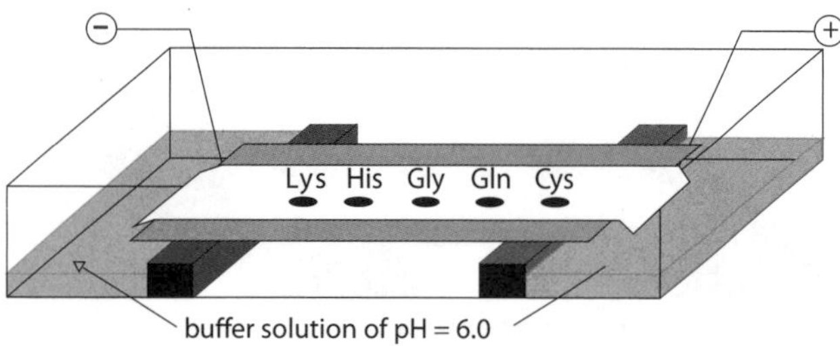

Figure 1312 Electrophoresis of a mixture of some common amino acids

Cysteine (pI = 5.1) and glutamine (pI = 5.7) will have negative charges because the buffer pH of 6.0 is more basic and will move to the positive pole. Histidine (pI = 7.6) and lysine (pI = 9.7) will have positive charges since the buffer of 6.0 is more acidic and they will move to the negative pole. Also, generally, the greater the difference between the pI and the pH, the faster the migration.

B.2.6 List the major functions of proteins in the body.

Proteins carry out many important functions in the body such as providing structure, and acting as enzymes (biological catalysts), hormones, immunoproteins (as antibodies in providing protection) and transportation proteins as well as acting as an energy source if carbohydrates and fats are not available.

Structural

Proteins such as collagen (found under the skin) and keratin (found in hair and nails) provide structure and strength.

Biological Catalysts

Enzymes, which are proteins, catalyze almost every chemical reaction in the human body without which reactions would occur much too slowly. Enzymes provide an alternate pathway for the reaction, thus lowering the activation energy and speeding up the reaction.

Hormones

Hormones such as insulin are important proteins in humans and animals.

Antibodies

Proteins that are produced as a result of the presence of foreign materials in the body which provide immunity to diseases, for example, interferons provide protection against viral infection.

Transport

Haemoglobin in the red blood cells carries oxygen from the lungs to the cells and to some extent, carbon dioxide from the cells to the lungs.

Energy

Proteins in the human body can be used to provide energy. Under starvation conditions, when supplies of carbohydrates and fats are insufficient, protein, from muscle, can be metabolised to provide energy.

B3 CARBOHYDRATES

Carbohydrates, empirical formula CH_2O, are the main energy source for our bodies and are vital to the synthesis of cells. They serve as food sources for living organisms and provide the structural support for plants. Many of the carbohydrates are large polymeric molecules made of simple sugars. Only plants synthesise carbohydrates. Important carbohydrates are: starch (a polysaccharide), lactose and sucrose (disaccharides) and glucose and fructose (monosaccharides). Glucose, molecular formula $C_6H_{12}O_6$, is found in all body cells and fructose, which has the same molecular formula as glucose, is found in fruits and honey.

Most carbohydrates (but not cellulose in humans) are changed to glucose, a simple sugar, as a result of digestion. Glucose is then carried by the blood to body cells, where it is oxidised during respiration. The energy available goes to physical activities, keeps the body warm and is used for repair and growth of cells. Excess carbohydrates are converted to fats and stored in the body.

Cellulose, another polysaccharide, is the major component of plant cells. It cannot be digested by humans who lack the enzyme cellulase to hydrolyse it. Cellulose though not a source of energy, is an important part of diet and is called fibre or roughage.

B.3.1 Describe the structural features of monosaccharides.

Monosaccharides, literally meaning 'one sugar', are the smallest molecular units of carbohydrates with the general formula $(CH_2O)_n$ where n = 3 to 9 and hence have the empirical formula CH_2O. Monosaccharides are aldehydes (alkanals) or ketones (alkanones) containing a carbonyl (>C=O) group and at least two hydroxyl (–OH) groups. Examples of monosaccharides are glucose, galactose and fructose. These three simple sugars contain six carbon atoms and are all examples of hexoses. Monosaccharides with five carbon atoms (such as ribose) are given the general name of pentoses. Pentoses and hexoses are the most common monosaccharides found in nature.

Monosaccharides and disaccharides have low molar masses, are sweet and readily soluble in water due to hydrogen bonding between water and the –OH groups. They form crystalline solids, due to intramolecular hydrogen bonding between the –OH groups. Since aldehydes are easily oxidized (to carboxylic acids), monosaccharides with aldehyde groups such as glucose are called reducing sugars.

B.3.2 Draw the straight–chain and ring structural formulas of glucose and fructose.

The straight chain formula of D–glucose containing the aldehyde group at C-1 is shown in the structure below:

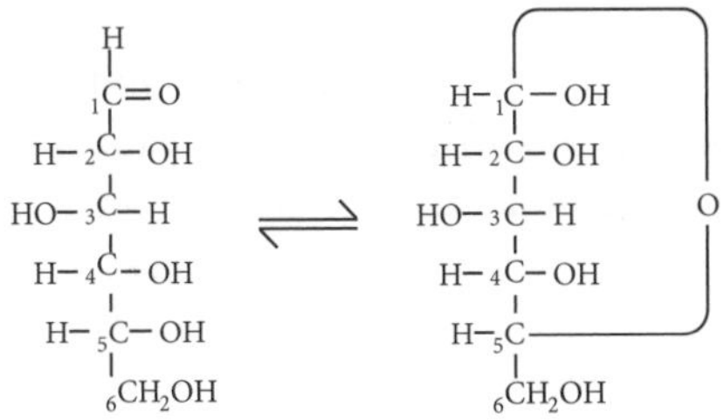

Figure 1313 Structures of glucose

The carbon atoms in glucose are numbered, starting with 1 at the carbonyl group. Note that there are four similar chiral (asymmetric) carbon atoms (C_2, C_3, C_4 and C_5) in the glucose molecule and thus several stereoisomers exist; C_1 and C_6 are not chiral.

Glucose is found almost exclusively in a ring or cyclic (hemiacetal) structure in aqueous solution (structure II). Because the intramolecular reaction between the aldehyde group on C-1 and the OH group on the C-5 atom produces a chiral carbon C-1 there are two possible ring structure isomers of glucose called α–D–glucose (where the –OH on C-1 is below the ring) and β–D–glucose (where the –OH group on C-1 is above the ring). (*Refer to Chapter 17, Option F Food Chemistry, for an explanation of D (and L) notation*). The only difference between the two is which side of the C-1 atom the –H and – OH are on (giving them different physical and chemical properties):

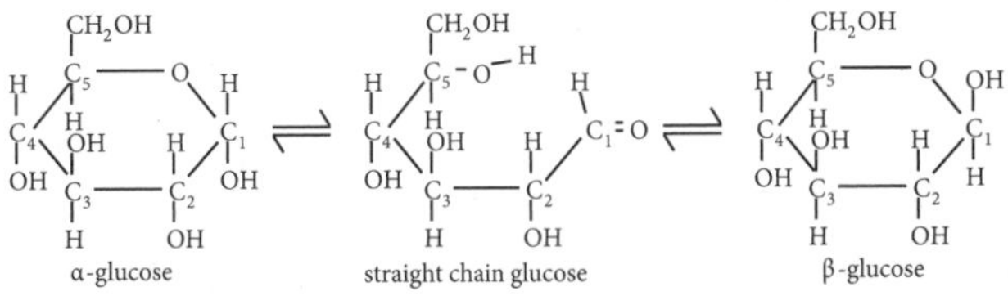

Figure 1314 The interconversion of α- and β-glucose

Fructose is an isomer of glucose but it is a ketose containing C=O in the C-2 position. It has the same configuration as straight chain glucose at C-3 to C-6 and differs only in the arrangement at C-1 and C-2. Fructose is capable of forming a six or a five membered ring:

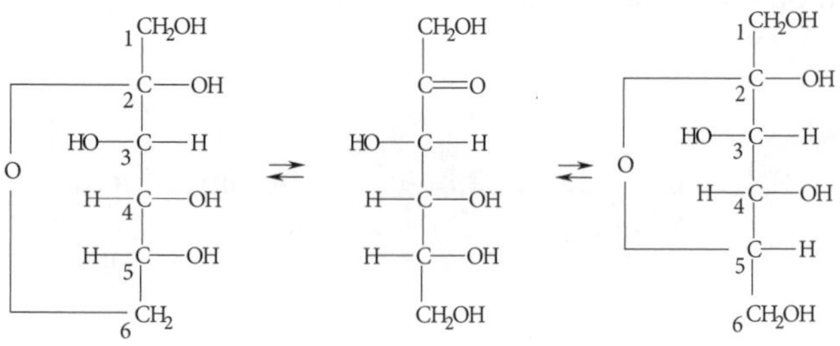

Figure 1315 Straight chain and cyclic structures of D- fructose

Similar to α- and β-glucose the two six-and five-membered ring structures of D-fructose, the only difference is which side of the C-2 atom the $-CH_2OH$ and – OH are on.

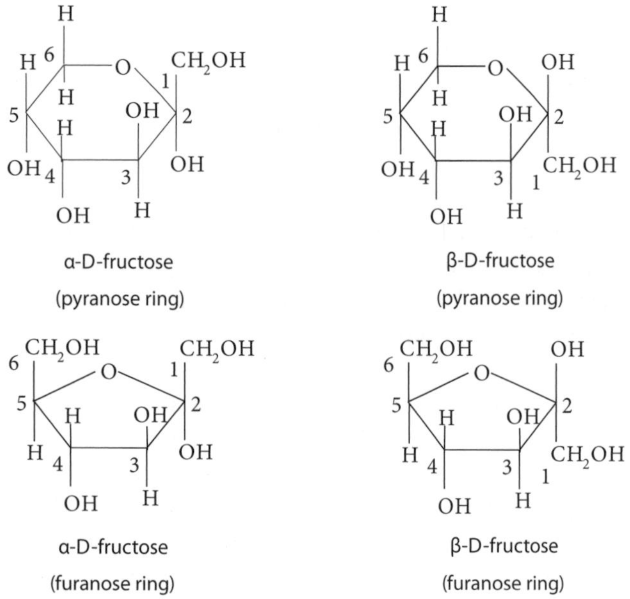

α-D-fructose (pyranose ring)

β-D-fructose (pyranose ring)

α-D-fructose (furanose ring)

β-D-fructose (furanose ring)

Figure 1316 Six-and five-membered D-fructose ring structures

B.3.3 Describe the condensation of monosaccharides to form disaccharides and polysaccharides.

When monosaccharides form disaccharides or when smaller polysaccharides form larger polysaccharides they do so through condensation reactions by eliminating a water molecule to form a C–O–C bond between the rings; this is called the glucoside (glycosidic) linkage. This normally forms between carbon atoms 1 and 4 of neighbouring units and is called a 1,4 or 1→ 4 bond. When a person digests sucrose, hydrolysis of the glucoside linkage takes place, (the reverse of the condensation reaction) and produces the two monosaccharides.

The following are some disaccharides formed from monosaccharides:

(i) β-glucose + β-galactose → lactose

(ii) α-glucose + α-glucose → maltose

(iii) α-glucose + β-fructose → sucrose (table sugar)

(i) Lactose contains β-1,4-glycoside linkages:

from β-D-galactose; from β-D-glucose; β-1,4-linkage

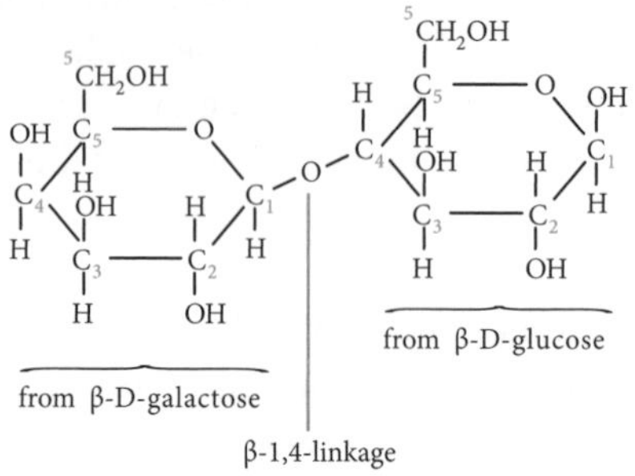

(ii) Maltose contains α-1,4-glycoside linkages:

from α-D-glucose; from α-D-glucose; α-1,4-linkage

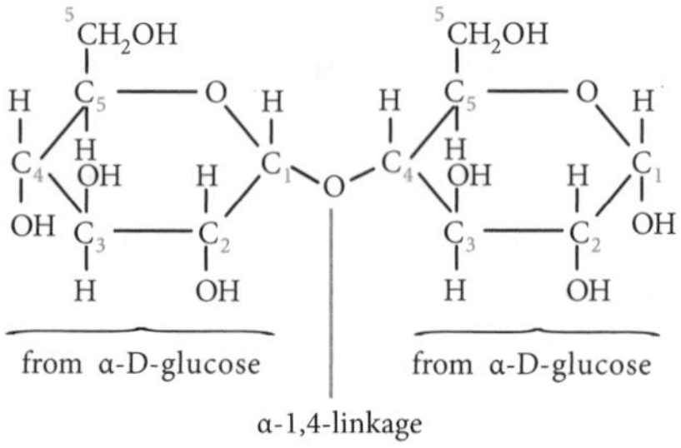

(iii) Sucrose contains α-1,2 -glycoside linkages:

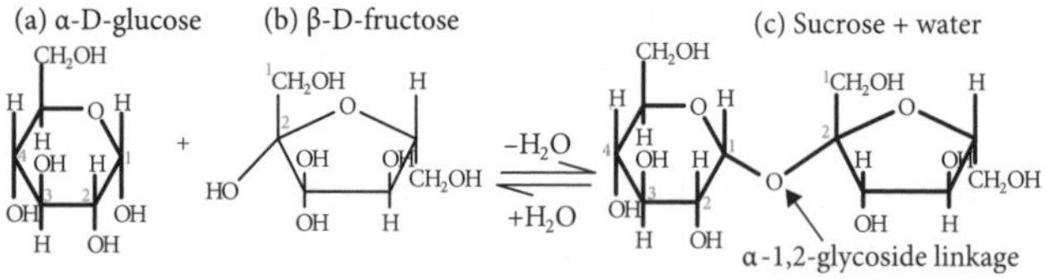

(a) α-D-glucose (b) β-D-fructose (c) Sucrose + water; $-H_2O$ / $+H_2O$; α-1,2-glycoside linkage

Polysaccharides are complex carbohydrates consisting of numerous monosaccharide units. These have large molar masses, are not sweet, are non–reducing and are generally insoluble or only slightly soluble in water. Starch is the polysaccharide by which plants store glucose for energy. Polysaccharides differ in the nature of their recurring monosaccharide units, the bonds connecting these, the length of their chains and the degree of branching. There are two forms of starch; both are polymers of α–glucose. Water soluble amylose (M_r = 10 000 – 50 000) has a straight chain structure consisting of long chains (thousands of monosaccharide units long) glucose joined by α–1,4 glycosidic linkages. Water insoluble amylopectin (M_r = 50 000 – 100 million) has these linkages as well as branches formed by α–1,6 glycosidic linkages on the glucose at which the branching occurs.

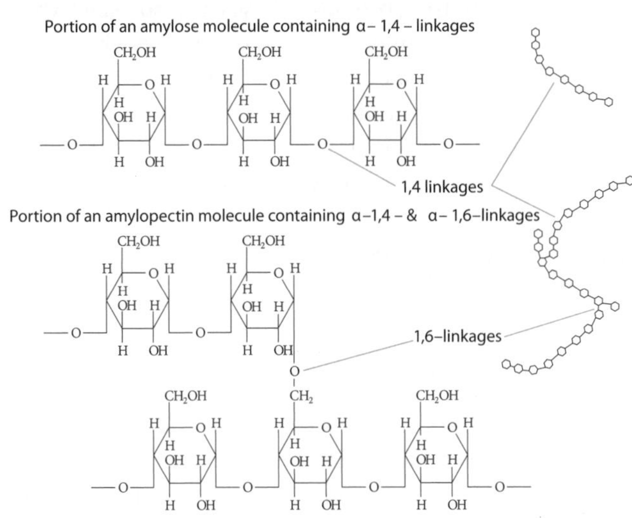

Figure 1317 Structure of amylose and amylopectin

Glycogen is made up of α-glucose and contains straight-chain α-1,4 glycosidic linkages as well as α-1,6 branching similar to amylopectin. The difference between glycogen and amylopectin is in the degree of branching: glycogen is more highly branched as the straight-chain component contains a smaller number of glucose units and branching occurs via α-1,6 linkage on the average every 8 to 12 glucose units.

Cellulose is made up of β-glucose units with all glycosidic linkages in the 1,4-positions, making it a linear polymer. This allows side by side alignment of cellulose chains resulting in extensive hydrogen bonding between them which gives it strength and rigidity, hence it is used as a structural component in plants. The extensive intermolecular hydrogen bonding also makes cellulose insoluble in water (as not enough water molecules can hydrogen bond with cellulose to separate the chains) and the length of the chains (M_r ~ 1 million) contributes to the lack of solubility.

> B.3.4 List the major functions of carbohydrates in the human body.
>
>

Functions of carbohydrates include:

- **Energy source:** Potatoes, bread, corn, rice and fruits contain carbohydrates, as do snack foods such as sweets, chips and soft drinks.

- **Energy reserve:** Animals use glycogen stored in the liver as their energy storage polysaccharide. Glycogen can be broken down by enzymes into glucose which can be transported by the blood to cells. Glucose and oxygen are the reactants necessary for aerobic cellular respiration which releases energy (see B9).

- **Precursor of other biologically important molecules:** Heparin which occurs in intestinal walls and is used as an anticoagulant is formed from carbohydrates. Carbohydrates are also found as components of nucleic acids.

> B.3.5 Compare the structural properties of starch and cellulose and explain why humans can digest starch but not cellulose.
>
>

As described earlier, both starch and cellulose are polymers of glucose units. Starch exists in two forms: amylose, which is a straight-chain polymer (α-1,4 linkage), and amylopectin, which is a branched structure with both α-1,4 and α-1,6 linkages. Cellulose on the other hand contains only β-1,4 linkage, which can be hydrolysed to glucose by the enzyme cellulase, which is absent in most animals, including mammals. Thus humans cannot digest cellulose. Cows and many other animals are able to digest cellulose in plants such as grass to produce glucose as a source of energy since they have bacteria in their alimentary canal that produce the cellulase enzyme.

> B3.6 State what is meant by the term dietary fibre.
>
>

Dietary fibre is mainly plant material that is part of fruits, grains and vegetables that the human body cannot digest as it is not hydrolysed by enzymes produced by the human digestive tract (but may be digested by bacteria in the gut). Examples include cellulose, hemicellulose (made of different sugar monomers unlike cellulose) lignin and pectin.

> B. 3.7 Describe the importance of a diet high in dietary fibre.
>
>

There are two types of dietary fibre. Water insoluble fibre, cellulose and lignin, present mainly in whole grain foods, fruits and vegetables. They absorb water, thus providing bulk and moving food through the digestive system.

Water soluble fibre includes pectins which undergo fermentation in the large intestine by bacteria to produce short-chain fatty acids such as propanoic and butanoic acids. These both have positive health effects such as stabilizing lipid and blood glucose levels (thus water soluble fibre may be helpful in the prevention of diabetes), and provide immune protection through stimulating the production of antibodies. Dietary fibre may be helpful in the prevention of other conditions as follows.

CONSTIPATION AND DIVERTICULOSIS

The large intestine (colon) makes, stores and eliminates stool (waste products). Low fibre diets lead to constipation due to the presence of hard stool that does not pass easily or frequently through the colon and requires effort. Pressure applied to move a stool along causes diverticulosis, the presence of bulges in the colon at weak places leading to abdominal pain. Diverticulosis is quite common in the western world where some diets consist of too much processed foods, which often lack fibre.

IRRITABLE BOWEL SYNDROME

Irritable Bowel Syndrome (IBS) refers to symptoms arising from the bowel not working as it normally should and includes constipation, bloating (feeling full), abdominal pain, etc. One way to decrease symptoms of IBS is to include more dietary fibre in the diet.

OBESITY

Regular intake of excess food leads to storage of energy in the fatty tissues. **Obesity** is excess body mass and leads to problems such as cardiovascular disease (involving heart and/or blood vessels), obesity related diabetes, breathing difficulties during sleep, etc. A high fibre diet leads to feeling full on a diet with reduced carbohydrates and fats, which then reduces weight gain.

CROHN'S DISEASE

This is an inflammatory bowel disease of the lower part small intestine and/or the large intestine. The cause of the disease is unknown; dietary fibre may be helpful in its prevention.

HAEMORRHOIDS

In this condition there are enlarged blood vessels in and around the rectum and anus that are swollen at weak points and can burst causing bleeding; these can also occur when the blood vessels get infected. Haemorrhoids can be caused by pressure in the abdomen as a result of constipation which can cause strain during bowel movements and by being obese or overweight. High fibre diet makes the bulk move through the large intestine more easily.

B4 LIPIDS

The term **lipid** does not suggest a particular chemical structure (unlike for example amino acids) but includes different structures. Lipids are substances found in living organisms that are defined in terms of their solubility: in general these are poorly soluble in water, but soluble in organic solvents which are non-polar or of low polarity. The very low solubility of lipids in water is due to large non-polar, hydrophobic ('water-hating') hydrocarbon chains present in such molecules with only a few hydrophilic polar groups. For this reason, lipids cannot dissolve in the bulk fluids of animal bodies whose chemistry is based upon water (the human body is around 70% water).

Lipids can be divided into several groups: triglycerides (fats and oils) such as tristearin, phospholipids (complex lipids containing phosphorus) such as lecithin and steroids such as cholesterol. 98% of lipids are triglycerides (glycerol esters) and 2% are complex lipids and cholesterol. Triglycerides (which are present in butter, cheese, meats, milk and nuts) contain carbon, hydrogen and oxygen (in a reduced form) with a low proportion of oxygen. For example, tristearin, a fat has the molecular formula $C_{57}H_{110}O_6$. Thus they are little oxidised and hence the most concentrated energy source (providing over twice as much energy per gram as carbohydrates).

Linoleic and linoeic acids are the two most vital fats since they cannot be synthesized in our bodies, but are necessary for its correct functioning.

B.4.1 Compare the composition of the three types of lipids found in the human body.

TRIGLYCERIDES (FATS AND OILS)

A triglyceride is formed from one molecule of glycerol (propan-1,2,3-triol, $CH_2(OH)CH(OH)CH_2OH$) and three fatty aliphatic acids (R–COOH, which can be the same or different fatty acids) which are carboxylic acids with long, straight, hydrocarbon chains. The fatty acids contain between 16 and 22 carbon atoms. If the triglyceride contains the same fatty acid (that is, $R_1 = R_2 = R_3$), then it is called a **simple triglyceride**. If the fatty acids are different (that is, $R_1 \neq R_2 \neq R_3$), then it is a **mixed triglyceride**.

Fats such as butter contain no unsaturation in the hydrocarbon chain whereas oils such as olive oil contain at least one C=C and are thus unsaturated. These are mono-unsaturated if there is one C=C and poly-unsaturated if there is more than one C=C bond. The arrangement around the double bonds is *cis,* meaning the alkyl groups across the C=C bond are on the same side. Triglycerides are un-ionised lipids (unlike phospholids that are ionised):

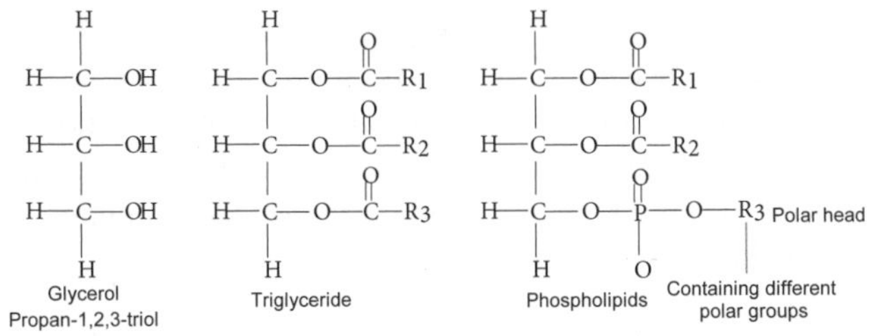

Figure 1318 Structures of glycerol, triglycerides and phospholipids

PHOSPHOLIPIDS

These are lipids that contain the phosphate group. They are formed from a backbone, such as glycerol with two fatty acids esterified onto it. The third carbon of glycerol is esterified with a phosphate group bonded to an alcohol derived from different polar groups (such as choline, ethanolamine). Thus, phospholipids are similar to triglycerides in their structure except that one fatty acid is replaced by a phosphate that contains a polar group. One example is lecithin which contains choline ($(CH_3)_3N^+CH_2CH_2OH$) as the side chain. The phospholipids are thus a source of choline for the production of acetylcoline, a nerve stimulus chemical transmitter:

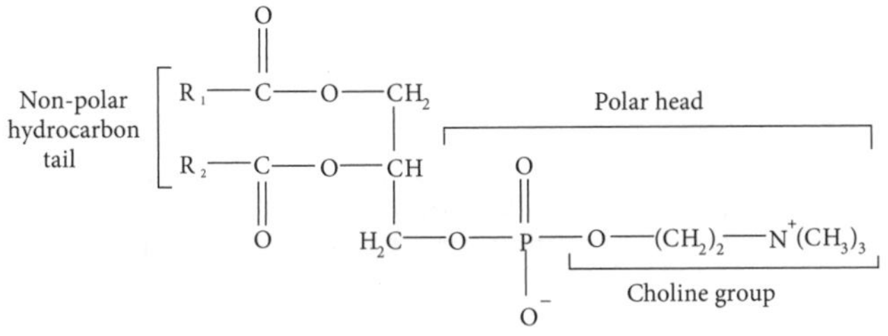

Figure 1319 Structure of lecithin

The R groups of the fatty acids are non-polar tails whereas the phosphate group is the polar head of the molecule. Such molecules are called **amphipathic.**

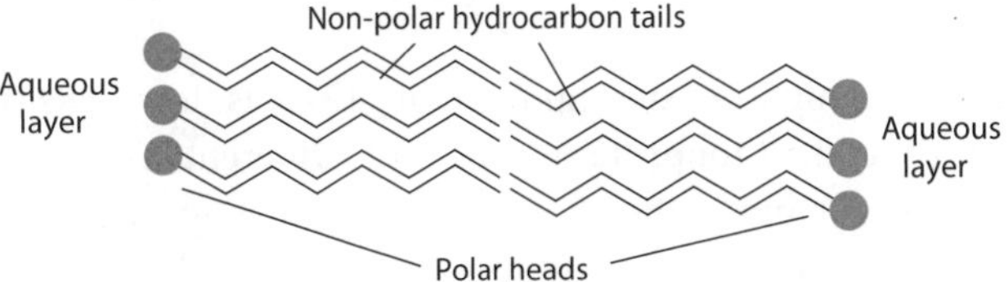

Figure 1320 Phospholipid bilayer structure

In water, phospholipids form a **bilayer** with the polar, hydrophilic heads facing the aqueous layer and the non-polar hydrocarbon tails lining up with each other. Phospholipids are a major part of all biomembranes that act as barriers around and inside a cell. Differences in the polar group and hydrocarbon tail (length of carbon chain and degree of unsaturation) determine the function and shape of the phospholipid.

Steroids (for example, cholesterol): The steroid skeleton is a characteristic molecular tetracyclic fused carbon ring structure consisting of three cyclohexane rings (labelled A, B and C) and a cyclopentane ring (labelled D), hence it is not related to the structures of fatty acids. The steroid skeleton can be modified in a large number of ways by attaching functional groups to it, one important example being **cholesterol** shown in Figure 1321.

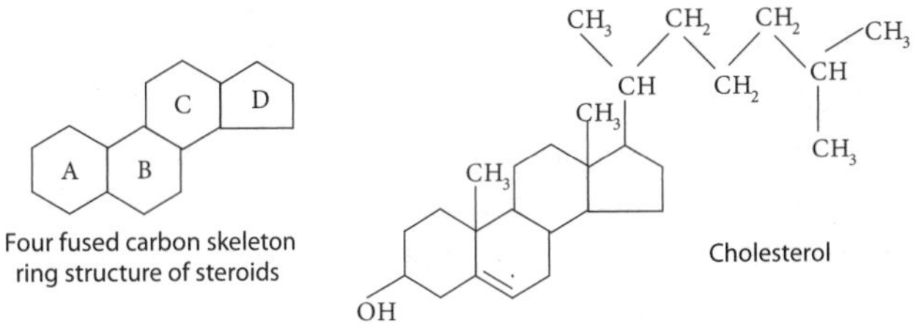

Figure 1321 The steroid structure showing cholsterol as a typical example

Cholesterol, $C_{27}H_{45}OH$, is the most abundant and important steroid in the body and belongs to the group of steroids called **sterols**. The steroid ring skeleton and hydrocarbon tail region are hydrophobic and hence fat-soluble, whilst the presence of the -OH group means it also has a hydrophilic, water-soluble, region and it is thus amphipathic. Cholesterol is produced primarily in the liver and is found in the bloodstream and body cells. It is present in foods like dairy products, eggs and meats but not in foods from plants. Steroids, such as sex hormones, and some vitamins, such as vitamin D, are synthesised from cholesterol.

B.4.2 Outline the difference between HDL and LDL cholesterol and outline its importance.

HDL is high-density lipoprotein; LDL is low-density lipoprotein. **Lipoproteins** are not different types of cholesterol but rather contain different proportions of lipid and proteins which transport cholesterol through the blood around the body. Lipoproteins are amphipathic: the protein part of a lipoprotein is water soluble whereas lipids such as cholesterol are not soluble in water. Since blood is mostly water, it is the protein part of a lipoprotein that forms an outer layer around cholesterol allowing it to be transported in the blood.

There are two main types of lipoproteins, HDL and LDL, which differ in composition and function. Their density is determined by the amount of proteins present in the molecule. HDLs consist of 40-55% protein and 45 to 60% lipid, whereas LDLs consist of 20-25% protein and 75 – 80% lipid, that is HDLs have a much higher percentage of proteins, about twice as much, as LDLs. HDLs thus prevent the build-up of cholesterol in the arteries. The lower percentage of lipids in HDLs means these can absorb more cholesterol and hence carry it away from the arteries, where it can build up narrowing the artery, to the liver where it is broken down for recycling and elimination.

LDLs carry cholesterol through the blood to the body to build and repair damaged tissues. However, LDLs contain a higher percentage of lipid cholesterol which tends to accumulate around damaged tissues. LDLs are thus associated with depositing cholesterol on arteries which leads to the formation of cholesterol plaque, a hard, thick substance. With time, the plaque leads to thickening of the arterial walls which narrow, leading to atherosclerosis and cardiovascular diseases.

B.4.3 Describe the difference in structure between saturated and unsaturated fats

Saturated and unsaturated fats are terms most commonly used in the context of nutrition. If the hydrocarbon chain has no double bonds present between carbon atoms (thus consisting of a maximum number of hydrogens bonded to the carbon atoms in the R groups) it is called a **saturated fat**. These are common in most animal fats (for example butter) and are usually solids at room temperature. The regular tetrahedral arrangement of carbon atoms in a saturated fat makes it possible for it to pack fairly closely together with parallel chains, (note that these are in fact triglycerides and not isolated single chains). Although weak van der Waals' forces are involved, the large surface area in the long R groups produce forces strong enough to make these solids at room temperature.

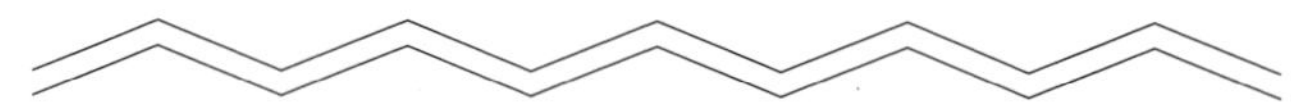

Figure 1322 Closely packed parallel chains of tetrahedral carbon atoms

An unsaturated fatty acid has one or more double bonds formed by the removal of hydrogen atoms. These include vegetable oils and are found to be liquids at room temperature. Most C=C double bonds in biological systems tend to have the *cis* arrangement. *Cis* and *trans* classification is based on the arrangement of the H atoms around the C=C double bond: *cis* contains the H on each carbon across the double bond on the same side; *trans* involves the H on the opposite side. The change in the bond angle to 120° at the C=C double bonds and the *cis* configuration prevents the oil molecules from packing closely together to solidify. The greater the number of C=C double bonds, the more difficult the close packing and the lower the melting points. Oils with one C=C double bond per fatty acid chain are called 'mono-unsaturated oils' and with more than one C=C double bond per fatty acid chain are called 'poly-unsaturated oils'. Most naturally occuring fats and oils have side chains containing a

Name	Formula	Structural Formula	Number of C atoms	Number of C=C bonds (degree of saturation)	Melting Point (°C)
Lauric acid	$C_{11}H_{23}COOH$	$CH_3(CH_2)_{10}COOH$	12	0 saturated	44
Myristic acid	$C_{13}H_{27}COOH$	$CH_3(CH_2)_{12}COOH$	14	0 saturated	58
Palmitic acid	$C_{15}H_{31}COOH$	$CH_3(CH_2)_{14}COOH$	16	0 saturated	63
Stearic acid	$C_{17}H_{35}COOH$	$CH_3(CH_2)_{16}COOH$	18	0 saturated	71
Oleic acid	$C_{17}H_{33}COOH$	$CH_3(CH_2)_7CH{=}CH(CH_2)_7COOH$	18	1 mono-unsaturated	16
Linoleic acid	$C_{17}H_{31}COOH$	$CH_3(CH_2)_4CH{=}CHCH_2CH{=}CH(CH_2)_7COOH$	18	2 poly-unsaturated	5

Figure 1323 Some Fatty Acids found in Dietary Fats and Oils

mixture of saturated, mono- and poly-unsaturated acids, which are classified according to the predominant type of unsaturation present.

Note the trend in the melting point of the first four acids listed, namely an increase with an increase in the length of the hydrocarbon chain (thus experiencing greater van der Waals' forces). The presence of one C=C double bond in oleic acid and two double bonds in linoleic acid, correspondingly decreases the melting points of these fatty acids due to the prevention of the close packing possible in the saturated fatty acids.

Unsaturated oils can be hydrogenated to solid, saturated fats by the reaction with hydrogen gas in the presence of nickel or platinum as a catalyst and heat.

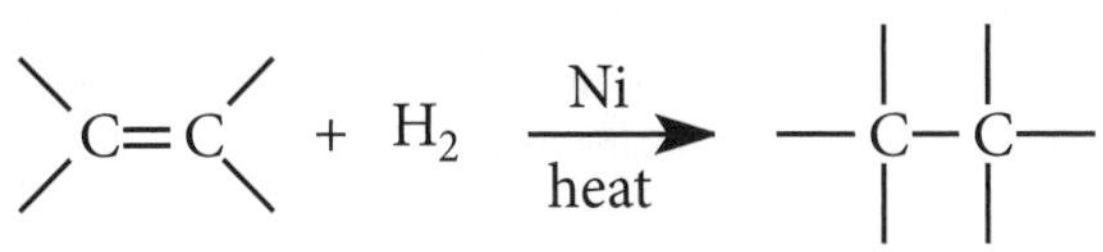

$$>C=C< + H_2 \xrightarrow[\text{heat}]{\text{Ni}} -\overset{|}{\underset{|}{C}}-\overset{|}{\underset{|}{C}}-$$

> B.4.4 Compare the structures of the two essential fatty acids linoleic (omega-6 fatty acid) and linolenic (omega-3 fatty acid) and state their importance.
>
>

A **fatty acid** is a long hydrocarbon chain carboxylic acid which has an acid group at one end and a methyl group at the other end. The human body is able to synthesize most of the fatty acids it requires, saturated or unsaturated. However, there are two essential fatty acids (EFAs) that our bodies cannot make and these must be present in our diets in order for the body to function properly. These are linoleic (omega-6 fatty acid) and linolenic (omega-3 fatty acid). Both contain 18-carbon chains. Linoleic acid contains two C=C double bonds in which the closest C=C bond to the end methyl group (labelled omega, the last letter of the Greek alphabet) is 6 carbon atoms away. Thus it is called omega-6 fatty acid. Linolenic acid contains 3 C=C double bonds with the closest C=C bond to the end methyl group 3 carbon atoms away and is called omega-3 fatty acid.

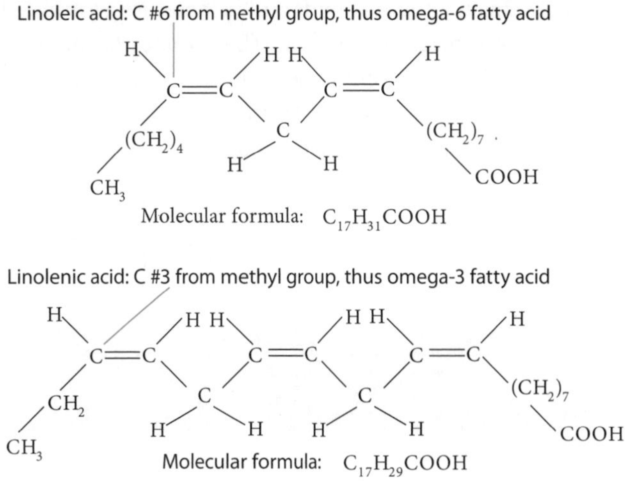

Linoleic acid: C #6 from methyl group, thus omega-6 fatty acid

$CH_3-(CH_2)_4-CH=CH-CH_2-CH=CH-(CH_2)_7-COOH$

Molecular formula: $C_{17}H_{31}COOH$

Linolenic acid: C #3 from methyl group, thus omega-3 fatty acid

$CH_3-CH_2-CH=CH-CH_2-CH=CH-CH_2-CH=CH-(CH_2)_7-COOH$

Molecular formula: $C_{17}H_{29}COOH$

Figure 1324 Structures of Linoleic and Linolenic acids

IMPORTANCE OF ESSENTIAL FATTY ACIDS

Lipids, including triglycerides and phospholipids are the primary structural components of body cell walls and membranes. Since most cells break down and are replaced, the **essential fatty acids** (EFAs) need to be part of the diet to manufacture the lipids. EFAs are precursors for important hormone-like chemicals, the prostaglandins and leukotrienes.

EFAs provide energy during lipid oxidation. Omega-3 is important for brain growth and development during pregnancy; EFAs promote good health, maintain healthy cholesterol levels, promote good circulation and support a healthy immune system. EFAs also elevate mood and reduce depression (a reason why people eat often when depressed). Lack of EFAs leads to lethargy, irritability, dry skin and reduced brain function amongst other symptoms.

> B.4.5 Define the term iodine number and calculate the number of C=C double bonds in an unsaturated fat/oil using addition reactions.
>
>

The **iodine index** or **iodine number** is the number of grams of iodine (in solution) that adds to 100 g of a triacylglyceride. Addition of iodine solution to an unsaturated molecule will cause the double bonds to break to form single–bonded carbon atoms. Since saturated and unsaturated fats and their products are colorless and iodine is colored, the reaction mixture of an unsaturated fat and iodine will turn from a red–violet to a colourless solution as the iodine is used up in the addition reaction. If a fat contains no double bonds and is therefore a saturated fat, it will not react with iodine. The number of moles of iodine reacting with one mole of fat hence indicates the number of double bonds present in the fat since each mole of double bond requires one mole of I_2:

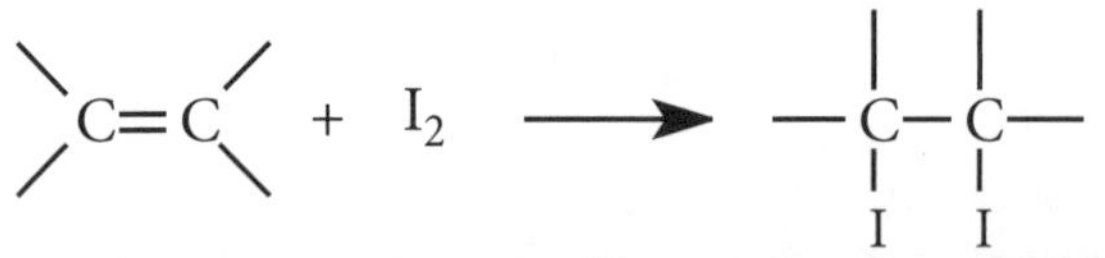

$$>C=C< + I_2 \longrightarrow -\underset{I}{\overset{|}{C}}-\underset{I}{\overset{|}{C}}-$$

Example

0.010 mol of linoleic acid reacts with 5.1 g iodine. Determine the number of double bonds present in the acid.

Solution

$$n_{I_2} = \frac{5.1 \text{ g}}{254 \text{ g mol}^{-1}} = 0.020 \text{ mol } I_2.$$

Therefore one mol of linoleic acid reacts with two moles of I_2 and it therefore contains two C=C double bonds.

Sunflower oil requires more drops of iodine solution for a red-violet colour to remain than peanut oil does. This is because the sunflower oil is more highly unsaturated (that is, it contains more C=C bonds per molecule of oil) than peanut oil.

Oil or Fat	Saturated fats	Mono Unsaturated fats	Poly Unsaturated fats	Iodine Number*
Butter fat	67%	29%	4%	30-38
Olive oil	15%	75%	10%	79-95
Peanut oil	18%	49%	33%	85-100
Sunflower oil	10%	13%	77%	119-138

Figure 1325 Iodine numbers and percentage fatty acid composition of common fats and oils

* Note that iodine numbers are often quoted as ranges because the fats and oils listed contain variable mixtures of triacylglycerols, whose composition varies according to the mixture of fats and oils in different samples of the foods. Thus, the more unsaturated oil has a higher iodine number.

Example

Calculate the iodine number of linoleic acid, $C_{17}H_{31}COOH$

Solution

$M_{(acid)} = 18(12.0) + 32(1.0) + 2(16.0) = 280 \text{ g mol}^{-1}$

$M_{(iodine)} = 2 \times 126.9 = 253.8 \text{ g mol}^{-1}$

Linoleic acid has 2 double bonds because its formula would require four more hydrogens to be that of the corresponding saturated fatty acid ($C_{17}H_{35}COOH$) and hence it reacts with 2 moles of I_2.

$\therefore$ 280 g of fat reacts with 2×253.8 g of I_2.

$\therefore$ 100 g of fat reacts with

$$\frac{2 \times 253.8}{280} \times 100 = 181 \text{ g of } I_2.$$

$\therefore I_2$ number = 181

B.4.6 Describe the condensation of glycerol and three fatty acid molecules to make a fat.

© IBO 2007

In a **condensation reaction** such as **esterification**, two molecules react (or link) together with the elimination of a small molecule such as water. Esters are formed from the condensation reaction of an organic acid and an alcohol in which the ester group (or linkage) connects the two molecules together. Fats and oils are a special type of ester in which the alcohol is glycerol (1,2,3–propantriol or propan-1,2,3-triol). Fats and oils are therefore esterified glycerol molecules:

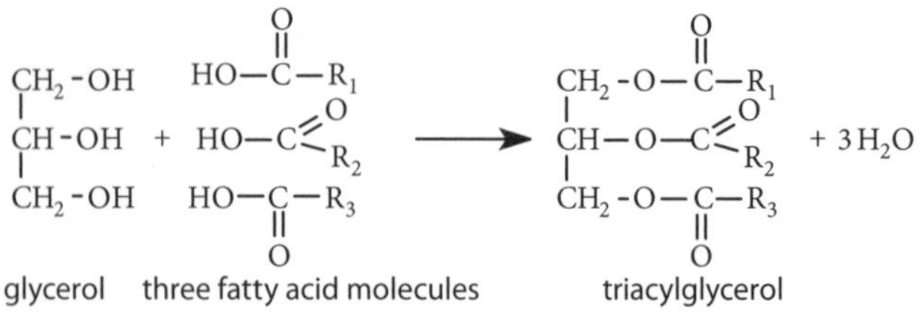

CH_2-OH / $CH-OH$ / CH_2-OH + $HO-C(=O)-R_1$ / $HO-C(=O)-R_2$ / $HO-C(=O)-R_3$ $\longrightarrow$ $CH_2-O-C(=O)-R_1$ / $CH-O-C(=O)-R_2$ / $CH_2-O-C(=O)-R_3$ + $3H_2O$

glycerol three fatty acid molecules triacylglycerol

Figure 1326 Formation of triacylglycerol

Since glycerol has three –OH groups, a single molecule of glycerol can have three acid molecules attached to it through ester bonds. Compounds with three acids attached to the glycerol are known as triglycerides or triacylglycerols where R_1, R_2 and R_3 are three fatty acid side chains.

Although the R group of the acid component varies, fats and oils have some features in common. They are almost always straight hydrocarbon chains without any branching present; they contain an even number of carbon atoms (as they are synthesised from a series of ethanoate ions by an enzyme catalysed reaction); they usually contain between 10 and 20 carbon atoms in the R group; besides the C=C bonds present in unsaturated fats, no other functional groups are present. Unsaturated fats almost invariably contain double bonds with the *cis* arrangement.

B.4.7 Describe the enzyme-catalysed hydrolysis of fats during digestion.

Hydrolysis of fats is the reverse of the esterification reaction. Hydrolysis is the splitting of a covalent bond by reaction with water. Hydrolysis of fats during digestion involves splitting the fats into their carboxylic acids and glycerol (propan-1,2,3-triol) catalysed by the enzyme lipase (since the uncatalysed reaction is too slow). The reaction tends to take place in steps via the formation of diglyceride and monoglyceride:

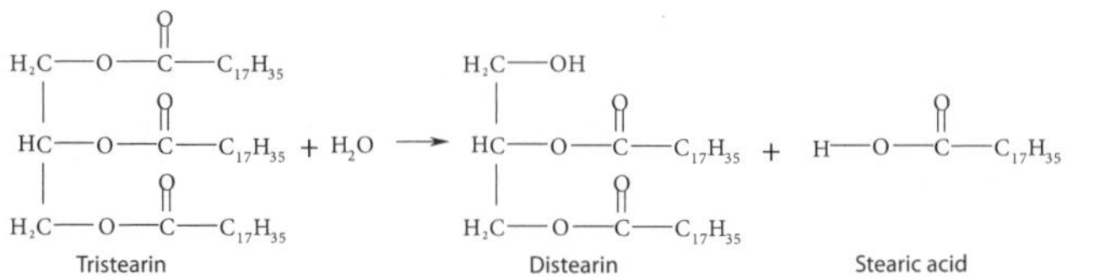

H₂C—O—C(=O)—C₁₇H₃₅ / HC—O—C(=O)—C₁₇H₃₅ / H₂C—O—C(=O)—C₁₇H₃₅ + H_2O → H₂C—OH / HC—O—C(=O)—C₁₇H₃₅ / H₂C—O—C(=O)—C₁₇H₃₅ + H—O—C(=O)—C₁₇H₃₅

Tristearin — Distearin — Stearic acid

Figure 1327 The hydrolysis of Tristearin

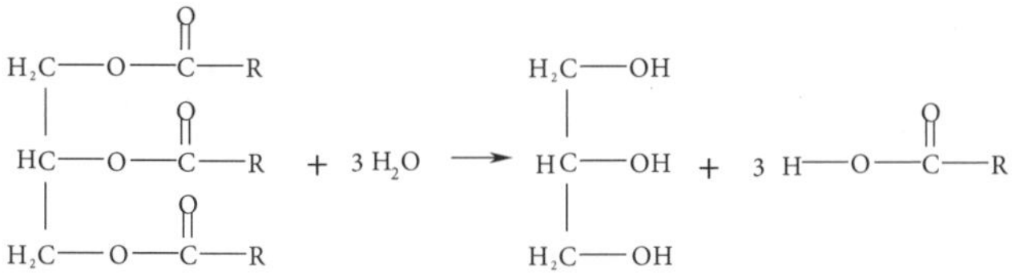

H₂C—O—C(=O)—R / HC—O—C(=O)—R / H₂C—O—C(=O)—R + 3 H_2O → H₂C—OH / HC—OH / H₂C—OH + 3 H—O—C(=O)—R

Simple triglyceride — Glycerol — Fatty acid

Figure 1328 Overall hydrolysis of a simple triglyceride

B.4.8 Explain the higher energy value of fats as compared to carbohydrates.

Fats have fewer oxygen atoms than carbohydrate molecules of corresponding molar masses, that is, these are less oxidized and thus more oxidation can take place. Therefore, more energy is released from the oxidation of fats compared with carbohydrates. Hence fats are much better biological fuels. Fats provide nearly twice as much energy (more kJ/g) as carbohydrates.

This can be illustrated by comparing the oxidation state of carbon in a unsaturated fatty acid (closely related to fats and oils) and a trisaccharide with the same number of carbon atoms, namely $C_{17}H_{31}COOH$ ($C_{18}H_{32}O_2$) and $C_{18}H_{32}O_{16}$: The 'average' oxidation number of carbon in the two compounds can be calculated since the sum of the oxidation numbers of the elements in a compound is equal to zero. Thus, if x is the oxidation of C, then:

(i) In the fatty acid: $18x + 32(+1) + 2(-2) = 0$ and $x = -28/18$

(ii) In the trisaccharide: $18x + 32(+1) + 16(-2) = 0$ and $x = 0$

Thus carbohydrates (polysaccharides) are in a more oxidized form compared with fats, where the carbon atoms are in a more reduced form. Oxidation (for example combustion) reactions are exothermic and release energy. A more oxidized molecule such as a carbohydrate will therefore produce less energy (as it is at a lower energy level) than fats (made up of fatty acids and glycerol) that are in a less oxidized state (or more reduced state) and produce more energy.

For the above two examples, the oxidation products would be:

$$C_{18}H_{32}O_2 + 25\,O_2 \rightarrow 18\,CO_2 + 16\,H_2O$$

$$C_{18}H_{32}O_{16} + 18\,O_2 \rightarrow 18\,CO_2 + 16\,H_2O$$

The two reactions form the same products in the same amounts meaning the same number of bonds are formed (bond formation is exothermic). The difference in the change in energy for the two reactions must then depend on the energy required to break the bonds in the two reactants.

Although fewer oxygen molecules are being broken in the second reaction, more strong O–H bonds are present in

OPTION

$C_{18}H_{32}O_{16}$ (requiring more energy; in the gaseous state it would be 463 kJ mol^{-1}) compared with $C_{18}H_{32}O_2$ that has many more weak C–H bonds (requiring less energy; in the gaseous state it would be 412 kJ mol^{-1}). The net result is that fats produce more energy than carbohydrates.

B.4.9 Describe the important roles of lipids in the body and the negative effects that they can have on health.

Important roles of lipids in the body include

Energy storage

Lipids, such as fats are a very efficient way for the body to store energy. Hydrolysis of a fat produces glycerol plus the corresponding fatty acids present in the fat. The fatty acids are oxidized to produce large amounts of energy. Lipids provide energy storage primarily in the form of triacylglycerols in which fatty acids are the major components.

Insulation and protection of organs

Fats are stored in adipose tissue which provides insulation that is important for regulating the internal temperature of the body as well as providing a protective covering for some parts of the body.

Steroid hormones

Lipids serve as precursors to steroids (such as estrogen and testosterone), cholesterol and vitamins (such as vitamin D).

Structural components of cell membranes

Phospholipids arranged in a bilayer form a stable boundary between two aqueous components, such that the hydrophilic parts face water molecules and protect the hydrophobic parts that face towards each other and away from the aqueous environment. Cell membranes are made mostly of phospholipids.

Omega-3 poly-unsaturated fatty acids

These fatty acids are present in fish oil and are thought to reduce the risk of cardiovascular disease.

Poly-unsaturated fats

These may lower levels of LDL, the low density lipoproteins associated with cholesterol deposits on artery walls.

Negative effects include

Increased risk of heart disease

From elevated levels of LDL cholesterol and *trans*-fatty acids; the major source of LDL cholesterol is saturated fats, in particular lauric (containing 12 carbon atoms, $CH_3(CH_2)_{10}COOH$), myristic (C_{14}; $CH_3(CH_2)_{12}COOH$) and palmitic (C_{16}; $CH_3(CH_2)_{14}COOH$) acids.

Obesity

When we eat more than we metabolise, this leads to fat being deposited on the abdomen, hips and buttocks, eventually leading to obesity.

B5 MICRONUTRIENTS AND MACRONUTRIENTS

Nutrients in food have specific roles in metabolism in the human body. **Micronutrients** such as vitamins and trace minerals are required in very small amounts. Vitamins are organic compounds required for metabolism, to protect health and for proper growth in children. Vitamins also assist in the formation of hormones, blood cells, nervous system chemicals and genetic material. They generally act as catalysts, combining with proteins to create enzymes that regulate changes inside body cells and produce hundreds of important chemical reactions throughout the body. Without vitamins, many of these reactions would slow down or cease.

Minerals are the very small amounts of inorganic ions required by the body for strong bones and teeth (Ca, Mg and P) and for the formation of hormones, enzymes and in the maintaining of fluid levels in the body.

B.5.1 Outline the difference between micronutrients and macronutrients.

Micronutrients are substances required in very small daily amounts (mg or μg), that mainly function as a co-factor of enzymes (<0.005% body weight) and are essential for proper cell function. Like water, micronutrients do not produce energy. Examples include vitamins and trace minerals (Fe, Cu, F, Zn, I, Se, Mn, Mo, Cr, Co, B). Minerals and most vitamins except vitamin D are not synthesized by the body and must be taken in the diet.

Macronutrients are chemical substances that are required in relatively large amounts (>0.005% body weight). Examples include proteins, fats, carbohydrates and minerals (Na, Mg, K, Ca, P, S, Cl). Macronutrients such as carbohydrates, fats and proteins supply energy and are required for growth and maintainance of the body. They are therefore required in the diet in large amounts as are some minerals.

B.5.2 Compare the structures of retinol (vitamin A), calciferol (vitamin D) and ascorbic acid (vitamin C).

B.5.3 Deduce whether a vitamin is water or fat soluble from its structure.

Various vitamins are not chemically related and most differ in their structures and physiological actions. Vitamins such as A, D, E and K contain long hydrocarbon groups which make these vitamins more fat-soluble in organic non-polar or slightly polar solvents. The fat–soluble vitamins are generally consumed along with fat–containing foods and because they can be stored in the body's fat, they do not have to be consumed every day. The water–soluble vitamins, the eight B vitamins and vitamin C, cannot be stored and must be consumed frequently, preferably every day (with the exception of some B vitamins). Vitamin C, for example, contains highly polar OH groups which are capable of extensive hydrogen bonding with water, making it water soluble (see Figure 1331).

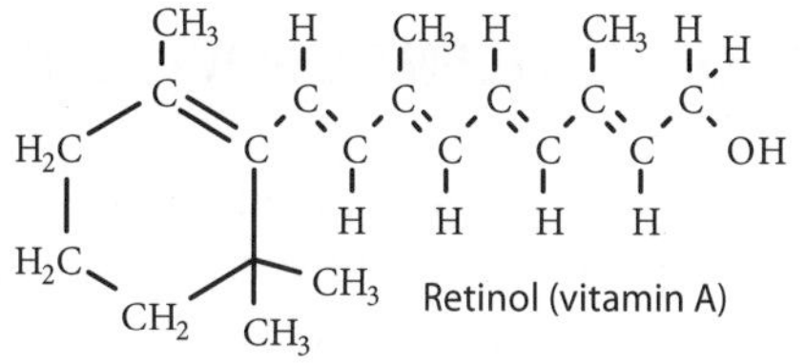

Retinol (vitamin A)

Figure 1329 Structure of Vitamin A

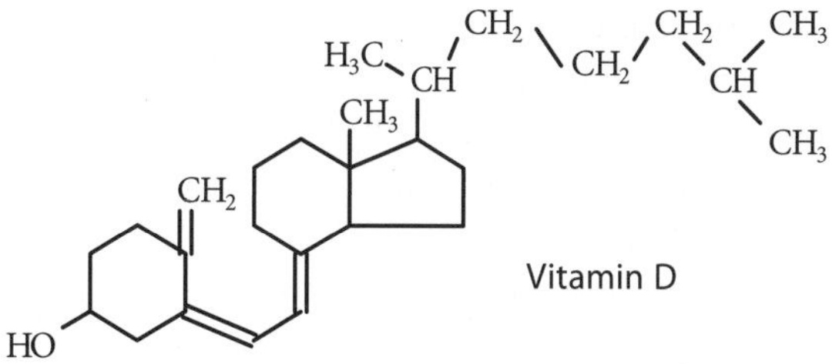

Vitamin D

Figure 1330 Structure of Vitamin D

Vitamin A (retinol) contains a long carbon chain, with a conjugated system of alternate double and single bonds, and one –OH group (see Figure 1329). It is a fat soluble primary alcohol and is light sensitive because it contains many conjugated double bonds. Vitamin A is required for the production of rhodopsin (light sensitive material in the rods of the retina). It is the active material in the process where light impulses change the conformations of the molecules. This is the specific arrangement of atoms, assuming that there is free rotation around a single bond. **Conformers** are isomers that differ only in rotation around a single bond. The changed conformation of the molecules eventually results in a nerve impulse, which is translated in the cortex of the brain as vision.

Vitamin C (ascorbic acid) has a five-membered ring containing an oxygen atom and overall contains 4 hydroxyl groups (-OH), a C=C alkene and a C=O carbonyl group (see Figure 1331).

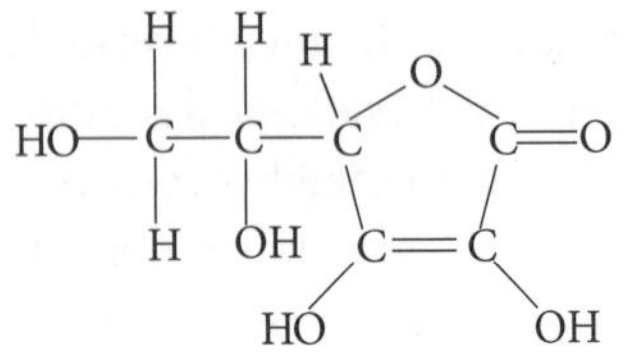

```
      H   H   H
      |   |    \   O
HO—C—C—C         C=O
      |   |        \  /
      H  OH   C=C
              /      \
           HO        OH
```

Figure 1331 Structure of vitamin C

> B.5.4 Discuss the causes and effects of nutrient deficiencies in different countries and suggest solutions.
>
>

Causes of nutrient deficiencies

Deficiences in micro- and macronutrients in the diet such as carbohydrates, proteins, vitamins and minerals that are essential for growth and development leads to malnutrition. In the developed world, income disparities, lack of economic opportunities and poor eating habits (particularly in children and the aged) are important reasons for malnutrition. In the developing and third world, poverty, limited food supply and famine are the key reasons. Lack of safe drinking water, proper sanitation and lack of good hygiene lead to the spread of infectious diseases leading to malnutrition. Also, lack of health services and poor literacy rates contribute to the problem. It is estimated that one third of African children and about half of South Asian children are under-weight or malnourished.

Examples of micro-nutrient deficiencies and their effects

- Iron deficiency causes anaemia, a blood disorder, characterised by a deficiency of red blood cells. Heme is a complex of iron in haemoglobin, the oxygen transport protein. Due to anaemia, insufficient oxygen is carried to the cells, leading to fatigue.
- Iodine deficiency causes goitre which is swelling in the neck due to enlarged thyroid gland.
- Retinol (vitamin A) deficiency may cause xerophthalmia (dry eyes) due to failure to produce tears; an early deficiency symptom of vitamin A is night blindness (difficulty in adapting to darkness).
- Niacin (vitamin B3) deficiency causes pellagra; deficiency symptoms include diarrhea, dementia (mental disorder) and skin rash (dermatitis).
- Thiamin (vitamin B1) deficiency causes beriberi which affects the muscles, heart, nerves etc.
- Ascorbic acid (vitamin C) deficiency causes scurvy, first noticed in sailors on long voyages. Scurvy is identified by bleeding lesions on the legs and thighs and soft, rotten gums.
- Calciferol (vitamin D) deficiency causes rickets, the malformation and softening of bones. Vitamin D is necessary for normal bone formation and for the retention of calcium and phosphorus in the body. Vitamin D absorbs calcium ions into the blood stream and, in the presence of phosphorus, makes it possible for the calcium ions to be added to the bones and teeth. Thus vitamin D protects the teeth and bones against the effects of low calcium intake by making effective use of calcium and phosphorus.

Examples of macronutrient deficiencies and their effects

- **Protein deficiency** produces marasmus and kwashiorkor. Marasmus is severe protein and calorie deficiency in children under one year of age. It results in growth retardation and wasting; victims are emaciated (gaunt) and body mass may be as little as 20% of normal mass. Kwashiorkor is malnutrition from insufficient protein in the diet and occurs in children over 18 months old.

Protein deficiency leads to edema (swelling), fatigue, decreased immunity, lethargy, muscle weakness, slow growth and development, weight loss, etc.
- Lack of calcium produces osteoporosis.
- Lack of sodium ions produces cramps.

Solutions to micronutrient deficiencies

A balanced diet provides all the vitamin and micronutrient requirements of humans; however it is common to add vitamins to foods, such as vitamin A to margarine, vitamin B to flour, vitamin C to juices and vitamin D to milk. Diets high in fruits and vegetables tend to meet many of the requirements. Balanced vegetarian diets should include essential nutrients. Such diets tend to be lower in cholesterol and saturated fats with lower risks of diabetes, coronary disease, high blood pressure and obesity.

Solutions to vitamin deficiency include:

- providing food rations that are composed of fresh vitamin- and mineral-rich foods (brown rice, whole grains, fruits and vegetables for vitamin B1, fish, poultry, nuts, cereals for vitamin B3, fruits and green vegetables for Vitamin A and C, milk and milk products for calcium, etc.)
- adding nutrients missing in commonly consumed foods, such as salt fortified with iodine
- genetic modification of food so that foods contain essential nutrients that would not be naturally present
- providing nutritional supplements for many of the vitamins and minerals
- providing selenium supplements to people eating foods grown in selenium-poor soil
- eating iron rich foods such as green leafy vegetables, red meat, whole grain, etc. or taking iron containing supplements.

B6 HORMONES

B.6.1 Outline the production and function of hormones in the body.

Hormones are chemical messengers that are produced by the body's endocrine glands (many of which are controlled by the pituitary gland which in turn is controlled by the hypothalamus). Hormones are released directly into the bloodstream, and then pass to distant receptor sites such as an organ, tissue or cells where they are absorbed and exert a specific effect. Hormones perform a variety of different functions and vary greatly in their chemical composition and structure. Hormones generally have a negative feedback mechanism whereby a high level of the hormone inhibits its own production. Hormones are effective in minute amounts and only target cells that are equipped to respond to them. Hence, a hormone can affect different target cells in different ways.

Negative feedback mechanism – an example

The increased blood glucose level caused by eating and digesting a chocolate bar results in the production of insulin. This stimulates the body cells to take up glucose, as does the liver, which stores it as glycogen and the blood glucose level is lowered. Skipping a meal lowers blood glucose level and the cells in the pancreas produce glucagon. This stimulates the liver to convert glycogen to glucose and release it into blood. The blood glucose level increases. As a result of this **negative feedback mechanism**, the blood glucose level remains around the optimum level (controlled by the hypothalamus).

B.6.2 Compare the structures of cholesterol and the sex hormones.

Steroids are a family of polycyclic ring structure chemicals containing a common carbon molecular framework (or backbone). The ring structure consists of 17 carbon atoms arranged as 3 cyclohexane rings fused together with a cyclopentane ring on one extremity. The presence of various functional groups such as the methyl and hydroxyl groups results in hormones that give rise to a variety of physiological functions ranging from sexual

Hormone	Production Location	Derived from	Role in the Body
ADH, anti-diuretic hormone (note: caffeine and alcohol reduce ADH production and are diuretics)	Pituitary gland located at the base of the brain	Amino acids; 9 amino acid peptide	ADH is released when the body has lost water. It stimulates the absorption of water back into the blood in the kidneys and preserves water in the body through a reduction in the formation of urine and subsequent loss of water.
Aldosterone, a steroid hormone	Adrenal gland which rests on top of both kidneys	Cholesterol	Regulates the concentration of electrolyte ions (mostly Na^+ and K^+) in the blood and body fluids.
Adrenalin or epinephrine; a stimulant related to amphetamine	Adrenal gland which rests on top of both kidneys	The amino acid tyrosine	Responsible for flight or fight response characterized by goose bumps, increased heart rate/output and blood pressure. Affects rate of glucagon release into the liver and release of glucose by liver into the blood.
Thyroxine, an iodine containing amino acid.	Thyroid gland, located in the neck	Small molecule from amino acids	Responsible for basal metabolic rate in vertebrates: essential for regulating metabolism.
Insulin, a protein of 51 amino acids	Pancreas, located at back of abdomen	Protein	Regulates blood sugar levels. Decreases blood glucose level; increases glucose and amino acid uptake and use by cells.
Sex hormones 1. Androgens, principally testosterone	Principally the testes (the ovaries produce very small amounts)	Cholesterol	Responsible for development and maintenance of the male reproductive system as well as secondary sexual characteristics.
2. Estrogen, principally estradiol	Principally the ovaries		Play a similar role in females; responsible for sexual development; regulate changes in uterus and ovaries for menstrual and reproductive cycles.
3. Progestins including progesterone	Principally the ovaries		

Figure 1332 Hormones and their roles

characteristics (by estrogen and testosterone) to cell membrane components (by cholesterol).

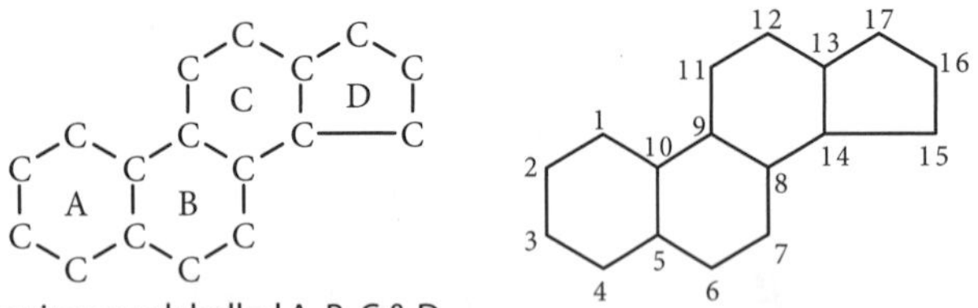

The rings are labelled A, B, C & D.

Figure 1333 Polycyclic ring structure of steroids

Sex hormones such as **androgens** (male sex hormones), estrogens (female sex hormones) and progestins (present in the male and female body) have a similar polycyclic structure to cholesterol. However, the functional groups on the sex hormones are different from those found on cholesterol and these slight differences in their molecular structures give rise to totally different functions.

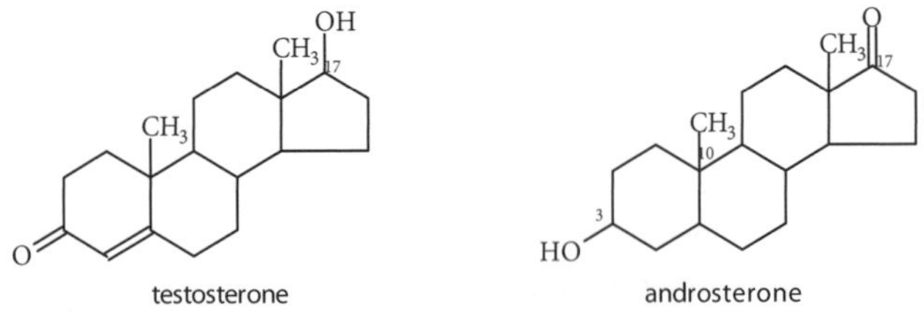

Figure 1334 Structures of testosterone and androsterone

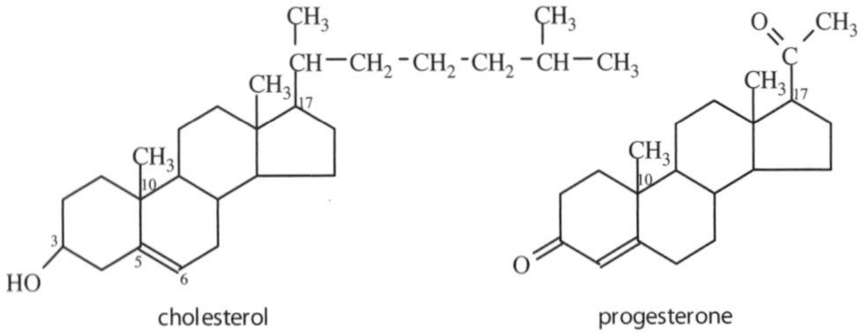

Figure 1335 Structures of cholesterol and progesterone

For example, the only difference between testosterone and progesterone is the presence of the –OH group on C–17 of the steroid framework for testosterone, compared to the presence of the methyl alkanone on progesterone. Similarly, the difference between cholesterol and androsterone is the presence of a C=C bond between C–5 and C–6 (in the second ring) and a longer chain R group on C–17 in cholesterol, compared to just the C=O on C–17 of the framework. Note that besides the common framework, both these molecules contain the secondary –OH group on C–3 as well as the methyl groups on C–10 and C–13 atoms.

B.6.3 Describe the mode of action of oral contraceptives.

During pregnancy, progesterone prevents ovulation; estrogen prevents irregular flow during a menstrual cycle. Thus, the most popular version of **oral contraceptive** (the pill) combines a synthetic progesterone and estrogen. The two hormones act to stop the release of follicle stimulating hormone (FSH) and luteinizing hormone (LH) by the pituitary. This results in the ovaries not being stimulated and thus inhibits ovulation. In effect, the female reproductive system is fooled because the drug mimics the action of progesterone in a pregnant woman and ovulation is stopped.

Problems with the use of progesterone such as rapid breakdown by the liver and side effects has led to the use of progesterone-like synthetic chemicals such as norethynodrel and norethindrone combined with an estrogen-like compound to prevent irregular menstrual flow. The molecular framework of the synthetic chemicals in such pills is the same as progesterone, but the $-COCH_3$ group on the D ring is replaced by the –OH and –C≡CH on C17. The presence of these groups seems to cause the synthetic steroids to tightly bind to their receptor sites. Thus, the rapid breakdown by the liver no longer takes place, making it possible to administer the pill orally.

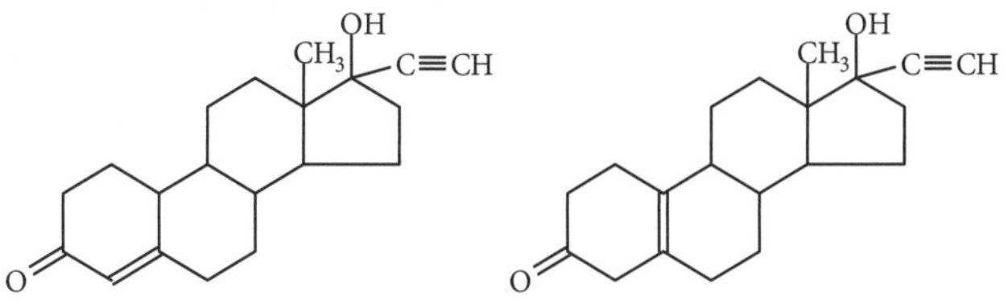

OH
CH_3 C≡CH
O
Norethindrone

OH
CH_3 C≡CH
O
Norethynodrel

Figure 1336 Structures of norethindrone and norethynodrel

A second type of oral contraceptive is called the minipill. It contains progestin only (a progesterone–like synthetic chemical). It changes the composition of the cervical mucous from the mucous membrane, thereby preventing the sperm from entering the uterus. This variation of the pill can be inserted underneath the skin and will slow-release the progestin for a period of up to 5 years.

B.6.4 Outline the use and abuse of steroids.

Besides the development of male secondary sexual characteristics, testosterone promotes muscle growth. Such anabolic (meaning 'building up') steroids are effective ways to increase muscle mass. Thus for patients suffering from long, debilitating illnesses such as cancer, testosterone-like steroids, which cause minimal side effects, can be used to stimulate muscle growth and increase muscle mass and help such patients recover their body weight. However, athletes have been known to abuse such drugs. Both male and female athletes stand to improve their performances by using these substances. Testosterone is more prevalent in men and is principally responsible for muscle build-up. Women who use anabolic steroids have much to gain because, initially, there is a low concentration of testosterone present in their bodies.

Taking large doses of anabolic steroids causes harmful side effects. In males, the effects of aging are observed including impotence, baldness, problems in urinating, smaller testes, etc. In women, steroids affect secondary sex characteristics, build up of muscles and the growth of facial hair. Both men and women can also develop violent tempers, increased aggressive behavior as well as an increased risk of diseases such as liver tumors, high blood pressure and heart attacks. As a result, anabolic steroids are strictly forbidden at international athletic competitions. Competitors are given random urine tests (to detect steroids and other banned drugs) and winners are often required to undergo compulsory urine tests for such banned substances.

B7 ENZYMES (HL)

B.7.1 Describe the characteristics of biological catalysts (enzymes).

© IBO 2007

B.7.2 Compare inorganic catalysts and biological catalysts (enzymes).

© IBO 2007

Enzymes are protein biological catalysts that speed up the rate of reactions in the body. A **catalyst** does not alter the enthalpy or free energy change of a reaction. Thus it does not change the position of an equilibrium reaction or the equilibrium constant; it only speeds up the reaction so the equilibrium is reached faster. Thus, a catalyst cannot make a reaction take place that would not usually take place without the catalyst. Rather the same equilibrium position is reached but much faster with an enzyme. A catalyst increases the rate of a reaction by providing an alternate reaction pathway with a lower activation energy without being used up or chemically changed. See Figure 1337. Catalysts can be divided into inorganic and biological (or organic) catalysts called **enzymes**. See also Chapter 6.

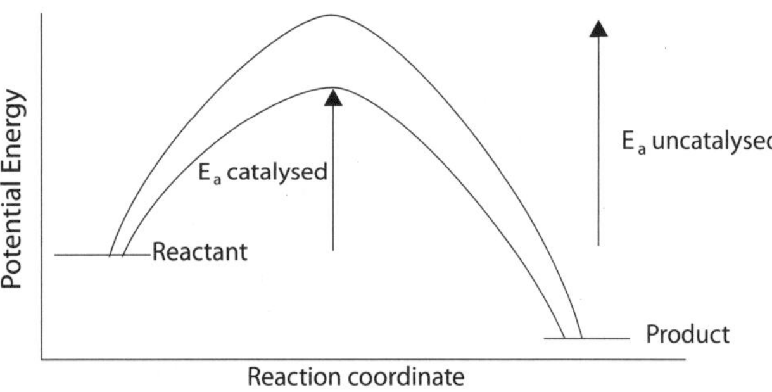

Figure 1337 Activation energy

Enzymes are proteins which have four levels of structure. It is their tertiary and quaternary structures which determine if the enzyme can act properly. This is because of the 'lock & key' nature of their action – the shape of the enzyme allows the substrate (i.e. the substance on which it acts) to bond to its surface, but will not bond to, or affect, other substances that have a different shape. When a protein denatures due to its environment, the tertiary and quaternary structures are altered. For example, the hydrophobic regions in the core of the tertiary structure may be affected when the protein is placed in an organic solvent such as ether. Chemicals can also disrupt the hydrogen bonds, ionic bonds and the disulfide bridges in the tertiary and quarternary structures.

The active site is usually a pocket or a grove on the surface of the protein, formed by only a few of the enzyme's amino-acid residues, into which the substrate molecule fits. An enzyme can distinguish its substrate from closely related compounds. Hence, enzymes are very specific, each of them catalyzing only one particular reaction. The active site is not rigid as it can change its shape slightly so as to allow a better fit for the substrate. This is called an '**induced fit**'. The enzyme E reacts with the substrate at the active site by weak interactions such as hydrogen bonds and ionic interactions to form the enzyme-substrate complex, ES, which then decomposes to form the product and the free enzyme is regenerated. Thus, when bound, the catalytic action of the enzyme converts the substrate to the product of the reaction which is then released by the enzyme, leaving the active site free for another substrate molecule to bind to it.

For example, the enzyme urease catalyzes only the hydrolysis of urea but not other amides. Where stereoisomers exist, an enzyme that is effective with one enantiomer is found to be ineffective with the mirror image enantiomer. Sometimes a reaction can be catalysed by an enzyme and by inorganic catalysts. For example the decomposition of hydrogen peroxide can be brought about by the enzyme catalase, or by various inorganic catalysts such as manganese(IV) oxide.

An enzyme is highly efficient. Enzymes operate under fairly mild conditions of temperature and pH. The efficiency of an enzyme can be seen from the biological synthesis of ammonia that requires only the enzyme **nitrogenase**. The industrial synthesis of ammonia by the Haber process requires the inorganic catalyst Fe as well as pressures of 200 to 1000 atmospheres and a temperature of about 500°C. Similarly, the enzyme catalase decomposes hydrogen peroxide much more efficiently than inorganic catalysts such as MnO_2. Enzymes are extremely effective biological catalysts increasing some rates of reactions by factors as much as 10^8 to 10^{20}.

Most enzymes are protein molecules and enzymatic reactions take place in aqueous solution in biological organisms. Inorganic catalysts can be surface metal catalysts such as Ni or Fe where gas phase heterogeneous reactions occur or these can be homogeneous catalysts where the catalyst and the reactant are in the same phase, as in the case of sulfuric acid in esterification reactions.

Inorganic catalysts are not temperature sensitive; enzymes are. Like all reactions, the rate of an enzyme catalyzed reaction increases with temperature, but excess heating denatures the enzymes, that is, the complex enzyme molecules can be easily destroyed by heat and this leads to a decrease in the reaction rate as the active sites are no longer available. Hence proteins have an optimum temperature at which they operate most efficiently. Enzymes also work optimally in a narrow pH range.

This topic can lead to a good investigation to compare the effect of inorganic catalysts such as MnO_2, $FeCl_3$ and Zn with enzyme catalase from pieces of apple, banana, beef liver or potato on the decomposition of hydrogen peroxide. This can be done by observing the rate of production of oxygen gas compared with a standard where no catalyst is added.

B.7.3 Describe the relationship between substrate concentration and enzyme activity.

If the concentration of an enzyme is increased, while all other factors such as temperature, pH and substrate concentration are held constant, the reaction rate (velocity) is found in most cases to be first order with respect to enzyme concentration. That is, the rate is directly proportional to the enzyme concentration when the concentration of the enzyme is much less than the substrate concentration.

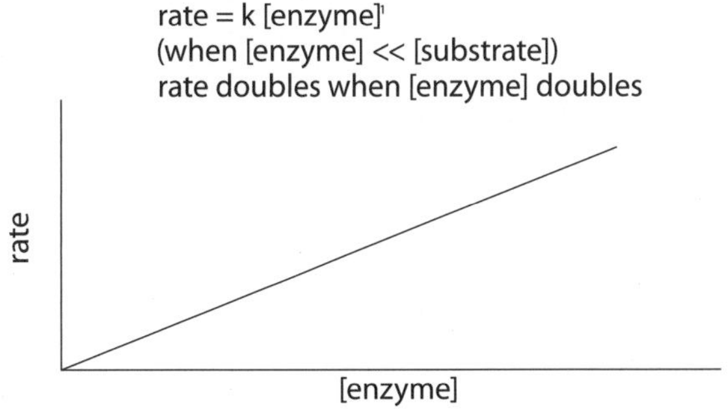

Figure 1338 The effect of enzyme concentration on reaction rate

Substrates bind to an enzyme's active site to form an enzyme–substrate complex. Once the reaction is finished, the product leaves and the enzyme binds to another substrate molecule. At very low substrate concentrations, the rate generally increases in a linear fashion because the active sites of the enzyme molecules have not been used up. Increasing substrate concentration involves more enzyme molecules and the conversion of substrate to product proceeds at a faster rate (velocity).

However, a hyperbolic dependence is observed at higher substrate concentrations as shown in Figure 1339. This is because, once the concentration reaches a particular point, all the active sites are engaged and the rate will not speed up anymore at that enzyme concentration. Eventually the enzyme saturation point is reached by the substrate at V_{max}, the maximum rate (velocity) and the reaction becomes zero order with respect to the substrate concentration. At this point, the enzyme is saturated and the rate (velocity) of the reaction is dependent on the rate at which the substrate is converted to the product and leaves the active site. Here, the only method of increasing the rate (velocity) is to increase the enzyme concentration. The variation of rate with substrate concentration when temperature and pH are constant are shown in Figure 1339.

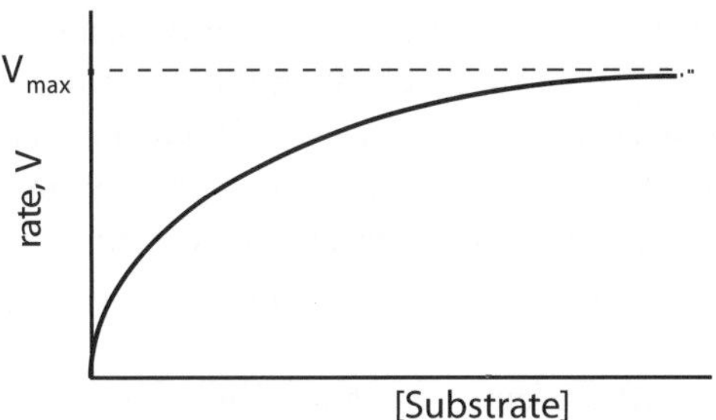

Figure 1339 Variation of rate with [substrate]

B. 7.4 Determine V_{max} and the value of the Michaelis constant (K_m) by graphical means and explain its significance.

The saturation effect led two scientists, Michaelis and Menten, to derive a theory of enzyme kinetics. Here the enzyme E reacts with the substrate S to form ES, the enzyme-substrate complex, which then decomposes to form the product P and the free enzyme E is generated.

$$E + S \underset{k_2}{\overset{k_1}{\rightleftharpoons}} ES \xrightarrow[k_3]{} P + E$$

In the first equilibrium equation, k_1 is the rate constant of the forward reaction and k_2 is the rate constant of the reverse reaction. k_3 is the rate constant for the second forward reaction. The rate constant of the second reverse reaction is ignored since it is usually too small compared with k_1, k_2 and k_3.

Applying the principles of kinetics, the **Michaelis–Menten equation** can be derived which provides a means of analyzing enzyme-catalyzed reactions in terms of their rate constants:

V_{max} is the maximum velocity (reaction rate) of the enzyme reaction, that is when the enzyme is fully saturated. [S] is

OPTION

$$\text{Rate} = \frac{V_{max}[S]}{K_m + [S]}$$

the substrate concentration and K_m, the Michaelis constant (a function of three or more rate constants), in the above equation it is equal to:

$$\frac{k_2 + k_3}{k_1}$$

The Michaelis–Menten equation accounts for the hyperbolic relationship between the rate, v, and the substrate concentration. Note that, in that curve, it is difficult to obtain an accurate value of V_{max} by extrapolation due to the hyperbolic nature of the line. Also, if [S] is much less than K_m, then in the equation the denominator ≈ K_m and the equation reduces to $v \approx V_{max}$ [S]/ K_m or v α [S]. This accounts for the linear dependence of velocity (rate), v, on [S] at very low substrate concentrations. If [S] >> K_m. Then the denominator in the rate equation ≈ [S], and $v = V_{max}$.

The Michaelis–Menten equation gives the quantitative relationship between the rate of enzyme reaction, v, and the substrate concentration, [S], if either V_{max}, the maximum velocity, or K_m is known. To understand the significance of the constant, K_m, consider half the maximum velocity, that is, $v = ½V_{max}$:

According to the Michaelis–Menten equation:

$$\text{rate} = v = \frac{V_{max}[S]}{K_m + [S]}; \text{ if } v = \frac{1}{2}V_{max}, \text{ then}$$

$$\frac{1}{2} = \frac{[S]}{K_m + [S]}$$

$$K_m + [S] = 2[S]$$

$$\therefore K_m = [S] \text{ when } v = \frac{1}{2}V_{max}$$

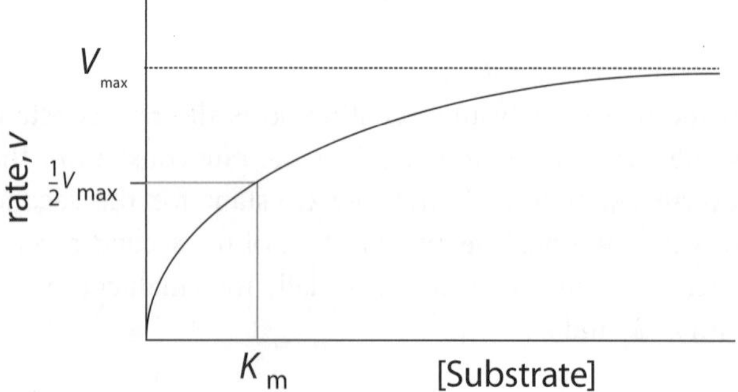

Figure 1340 Determination of K_m from rate versus [substrate] graph

Thus K_m is equal to the substrate concentration when the velocity (rate) is equal to half the maximal value. Units of K_m are the same as the units of [S], namely mol dm^{-3}. K_m is an experimentally determined quantity; it is independent of the enzyme concentration [E], though its value varies with the chosen substrate, temperature and pH. Note that the higher the K_m value, the lower the enzyme activity, i.e. K_m is inversely proportional to enzyme activity because a lower value of K_m means a more efficient enzyme. That is, with a given substrate concentration, there is a higher reaction velocity (rate) relative to V_{max}.

The 'double reciprocal' (**Lineweaver–Burke**) plot of reciprocal of substrate concentration versus reciprocal of initial velocity (rate) allows the accurate determination of V_{max}, unlike the velocity (rate) versus [substrate] plot where the determination of the V_{max} value is uncertain due to its asymptotic approach. This involves the rearrangement of the Michaelis–Menten Equation:

$$\text{Rate} = \frac{V_{max}[S]}{K_m + [S]}$$

Taking the inverse of both sides:

$$\frac{1}{v} = \frac{K_m + [S]}{V_{max}[S]}$$

$$= \frac{K_m}{V_{max}[S]} + \frac{[S]}{V_{max}[S]}$$

$$= \left[\frac{K_m}{V_{max}} \times \frac{1}{[S]}\right] + \frac{1}{V_{max}}$$

(***y*** = ***mx*** + ***c*** is a straight line equation)

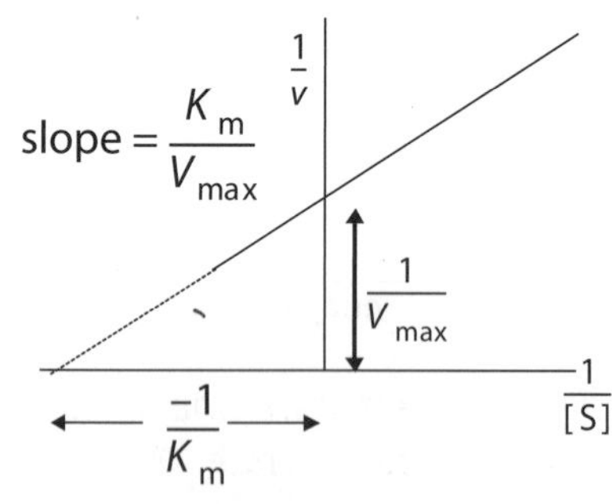

Figure 1341 The Lineweaver-Burke plot

Thus a graph of $\frac{1}{v}$ against $\frac{1}{[S]}$ is a straight line with slope $= \frac{K_m}{V_{max}}$ and its intercept is equal to $\frac{1}{V_{max}}$.

Also, extrapolating the line, when $\frac{1}{v} = 0$, then $\frac{1}{[S]} = \frac{-1}{K_m}$.

OPTION

B.7.5 Describe the mechanism of enzyme action, including enzyme substrate complex, active site and induced fit model.

The complex structure of enzymes requires specific shape with active sites for interaction with a reactant called a substrate. The active site is usually a pocket or a groove on the surface of the protein, formed by only a few of the enzyme's amino-acid residues, into which the substrate molecule fits. This site is not rigid and it can change its shape slightly so as to allow a better fit for the substrate. This is called an **induced fit**. The enzyme E reacts with the substrate at the active site by weak interactions such as hydrogen bonds and ionic interactions to form the enzyme-substrate complex, ES, which then decomposes to form the product and the free enzyme is regenerated. Thus, when bound, the catalytic action of the enzyme converts the substrate to the product of the reaction which is then released by the enzyme, leaving the active site free for another substrate molecule to bind to it. Refer back to 7.1 and 7.2.

B.7.6 Compare competitive inhibition and non-competitive inhibition.

Particular chemicals inhibit the action of specific enzymes. If the **inhibitor** attaches to the enzyme by covalent bonds, inhibition is irreversible and usually involves the destruction or permanent modification of the enzyme structure. If it attaches by weak interactions, the inhibition is reversible and can be treated quantitatively by using the Michaelis–Menten equation.

There are two major types of reversible inhibition: competitive and non–competitive. Inhibitors that resemble the normal substrate molecule and compete for the enzyme's active site are called **competitive inhibitors**. These reduce the activity of the enzyme because they block the substrate from entering the active site. If inhibition is competitive, an increase of substrate concentration can reduce the impact of the inhibitor.

Consider the enzyme succinate dehydrogenase which catalyzes the reduction (namely the removal of two H atoms) from the two $-CH_2$ groups of the succinate ion:

$$\underset{\text{succinate ion}}{^{-}OOC-CH_2-CH_2-COO^{-}} + X \overset{\text{enzyme}}{\rightleftharpoons} {}^{-}OOC-CH=CH-COO^{-} + H_2X$$

The malonate ion, $^{-}OOC-CH_2-COO^{-}$, which also has two ionized groups, resembles the succinate ion in structure and hence inhibits the action of the enzyme because both compete for the same site. If the concentration of the succinate ion is increased, the amount of inhibition by the malonate ion is reduced.

Competitive inhibition is recognized in the Lineweaver–Burke double reciprocal plots of $1/v$ versus $1/[S]$ at various inhibitor concentrations. In such a case, V_{max} remains the same and is not affected by the competitive inhibitor, I. This is because at any inhibitor concentration, it is still possible to reach the same maximum velocity (that is full enzyme activity) at a substrate concentration, however high.

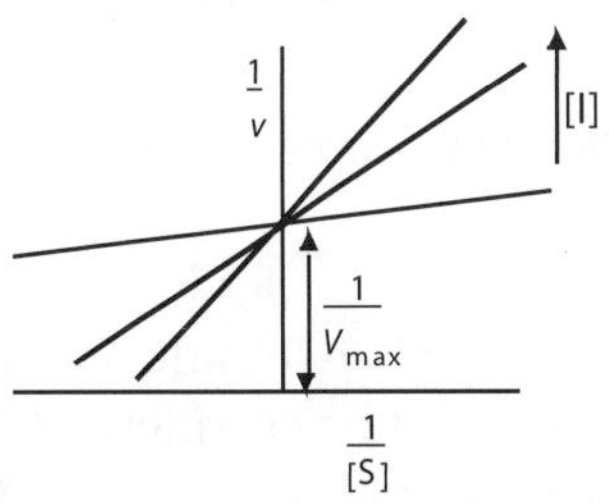

Figure 1342 Competitive inhibition

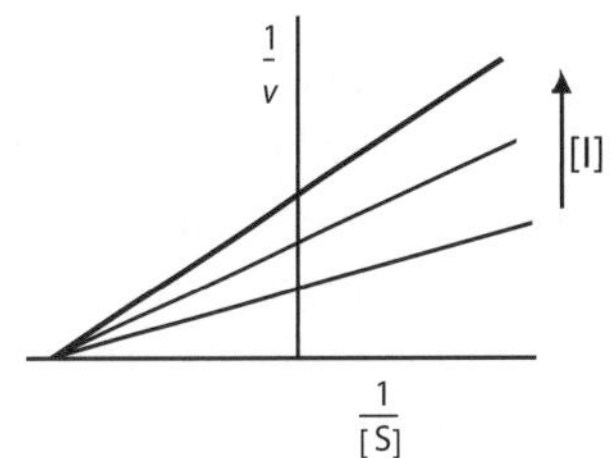

Figure 1343 Non-competitive inhibition

Non–competitive inhibitors impede enzymatic reactions by binding to a part of the enzyme away from the active site, which causes the enzyme to alter its shape, reducing its effectiveness. The inhibitor, I, may bind to the free enzyme, E (to give EI), to the enzyme–substrate complex ES (to give ESI) or to both, making the enzyme inactive.

$$E + I \; EI; \; ES + I \rightleftharpoons ESI$$

Consider the reversible action of a heavy metal ion Hg^{2+} on the –SH group of the cysteine residue which is essential for enzyme catalytic activity:

OPTION

$$2\ E\text{–}S\text{–}H + Hg^{2+} \rightleftharpoons E\text{–}S\text{–}Hg\text{–}S\text{–}E + 2H^+$$

The enzyme is inhibited non-competitively by the formation of the –S–Hg–S– linkage. Thus, one would expect V_{max} to be decreased by the inhibitor as the active enzyme concentration is decreased and the velocity cannot be increased by increasing the substrate concentration. Thus in the double reciprocal graphs of $1/v$ against $1/[S]$, the slopes do not have the same intercept on the $1/v$ axis. The higher the inhibitor concentration, the lower the velocity v, the larger the $1/v$ value and therefore the greater the intercept as shown above. Thus the hyperbolic curves for the rate of reaction versus substrate concentration are shown in Figure 1344.

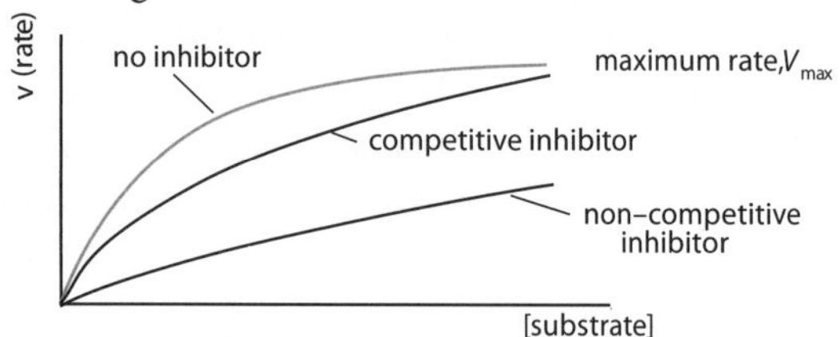

Figure 1344 Effect of substrate concentration on inhibitors

B.7.7 State and explain the effects of heavy metal ions, temperature changes and pH changes on enzyme activity.

If in any way the enzyme changes its shape or arrangement, the substrate will no longer be able to bind to the active site and the enzyme is rendered non-functional. This **denaturation** can take place when the surrounding environment changes even slightly. This may be brought about in several ways such as a variation in temperature or pH of the solution, or by the presence of heavy metal ions such as Hg^{2+}.

Each enzyme has conditions under which it works optimally as that environment favours the most active conformation for the enzyme. Temperature increases enzymatic reaction rates up to a certain point as the substrates collide with active sites more frequently as the molecules move faster. However, the speed of the reaction drops sharply when the temperature reaches a certain point. Here, the thermal agitation of the enzyme disrupts the hydrogen bonds, ionic bonds and other non–covalent interactions that stabilize its active structure. If the three-dimensional structure is changed as a result of temperature, the enzyme activity is affected. All enzymes have an optimum temperature at which they are not yet denatured and the substrates collide fastest with the enzyme. In humans, enzymes have an optimum temperature of about 37°C, about the same as the internal body temperature. Above this temperature, the change in the enzyme structure affects the active site (usually irreversibly) and the rate drops sharply. Refer to Figure 1345. The optimum temperature is often called **critical temperature** in industrial applications of enzymes.

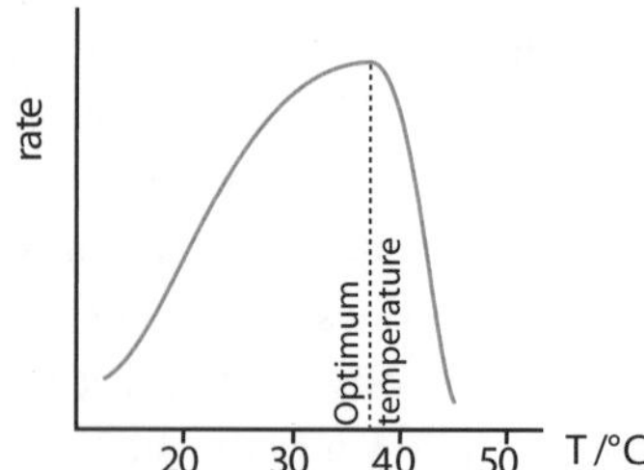

Figure 1345 Rate of reaction versus temperature

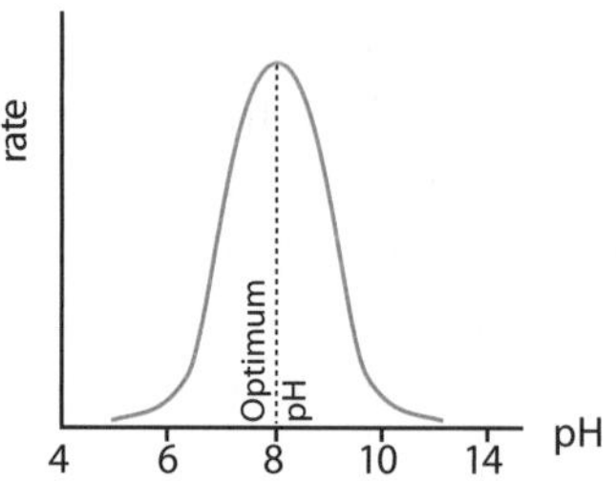

Figure 1346 Rate of reaction versus pH

Proteins contain groups such as $-NH_2$ and –COOH and are susceptible to pH changes. Extreme changes in pH values denature such ionisable enzymes rendering them ineffective, hence at low or high pH values, the enzyme is irreversibly denatured and the rate (v) drops sharply. Within a narrow pH range, the enzyme structure changes reversibly and each such enzyme works optimally at a particular pH. Thus the maximal rate for the enzyme chymotrypsin occurs around pH 8 and for pepsin this occurs at pH 2. If however an enzyme is acting on an electrically neutral substrate molecule such as sucrose, or where the charge plays no role in the catalyzed reaction, changes in pH have little effect on the rate (v) of the reaction. For example the enzyme invertase, which catalyzes the hydrolysis of the sucrose molecule, has a constant rate (v) in the pH range 3.3 to 7.5.

Heavy metal ions can also disrupt the active sites of some enzymes. When a heavy metal ion is present at the active site, substitution of a different metal ion for the original ion can cause the enzyme to malfunction and lose its activity. This is particularly evident where heavy metal ions can bind or chelate to the –S–H groups in proteins to form a –S–M–S– type arrangement.

Uses of enzymes in biotechnology

Biotechnology is the application and harnessing of microorganisms (such as bacteria, viruses and fungi) or biological processes to produce desired and useful substances (such as insulin) and facilitate industrial processes. **Fermentation** is an example of microbial biotechnology. Brewing, baking and the manufacture of cheese all involve the fermentation process. The manufacture of wine, for example, involves the fermentation of grape juice, a rich source of glucose, by wild yeasts present on grape skin. The process produces an alcohol content of 8 to 15% by volume (which is high enough to kill the yeast).

Similarly, the fermentation of sugar by yeast is the basis for the production of other alcoholic drinks:

$$\underset{\text{Starch}}{2\,(C_6H_{10}O_5)_n} + n\,H_2O \xrightarrow{\text{diatstase in malt}} \underset{\text{maltose}}{n\,C_{12}H_{22}O_{11}}$$

$$\underset{\text{Maltose}}{C_{12}H_{22}O_{11}} + H_2O \xrightarrow{\text{maltase}} \underset{\text{glucose}}{2\,C_6H_{12}O_6}$$

$$\underset{\text{Glucose}}{C_6H_{12}O_6} \xrightarrow{\text{zymase}} \underset{\text{ethanol}}{2\,C_2H_5OH} + 2\,CO_2$$

Better brewing through improving yeast and large scale production are the results of biotechnology. The genes responsible for the yeast enzymes have been cloned and bacteria have been used in the large scale production of the yeast enzymes needed.

Genetic engineering involves the manipulation of genes. It is the term used to describe the modern techniques in molecular biology where genes can be removed from one type of cell and placed in another, altering a cell's genetic content and potential. **Genetic engineering** has revolutionized the process of biotechnology and has given rise to the manufacture of important products such as new antibiotics, insulin and biological detergents. Transfer of human insulin genes into yeast or bacteria has made large scale production of human insulin possible in bioreactor vessels (much as in brewing).

Lipolase, an enzyme which is a constituent of biological detergents, consists of fat-digesting (splitting) enzymes. Scientists at Novo Nordisk in Japan have created lipolase by taking a gene coding from a particular species of fungus and transferring it to another microbe, *aspergillus*, that produces enzymes in very high yields. As a result, enzymes are widely used in the soap and detergent industry. Such biological detergents' main environmental benefits are that they save energy (a reduction in washing temperature from 60°C to 40°C). They are rapidly biodegradable, thus leaving no harmful residues, and produce no negative impact on sewage treatment processes and pose no risk to aquatic life.

Similarly scientists working in South America have discovered an enzyme which breaks the glucose chains in cellulose by hydrolysis only when a strand of cellulose comes loose. Thus this has found ready application in detergents used to clean cellulose cotton in which the enzyme is able to break bonds holding loose fibers, making the fabric appear new.

Other applications of genetic engineering have found their way into medicine. **Interferons** are natural anti-viral proteins that can be used against viral infections. Genes cloned in yeasts are used to produce such proteins and extensive research is under way in this area. The Hepatitis B vaccine has been genetically engineered and research is continuing into finding vaccines for AIDS and malaria.

B8 NUCLEIC ACIDS

B.8.1 Describe the structure of nucleotides and their condensation polymers (nucleic acids or polynucleotides).

B.8.2 Distinguish between the structures of DNA and RNA.

A **nucleic acid** is a polymer chain of repeating nucleotides which consist of a phosphate group, a pentose sugar and an organic nitrogenous base. Thus, nucleic acids are high molar mass polymers of fairly simple composition involving only a few different nucleotide bases compared with proteins which are made of some 20 different amino acids. Genetically, the most important components of nucleotides are the nitrogenous bases, since the sequence of the bases in DNA (deoxyribonucleic acid) and RNA (ribonucleic acid) polymer molecules are the key to the storage of genetic information.

There are five nitrogenous bases that are incorporated as part of naturally occurring nucleotides. These may be classified into two groups, the purines and the pyrimidines. Adenine (A) and guanine (G) are purines, which have a double ringed structure and cytosine (C), thymine (T) and uracil (U) are pyrimidines with a single ringed structure. The base thymine is present predominantly in DNA nucleotides (and rarely in RNA, for example, in transfer RNA) while uracil, rather than thymine, is found

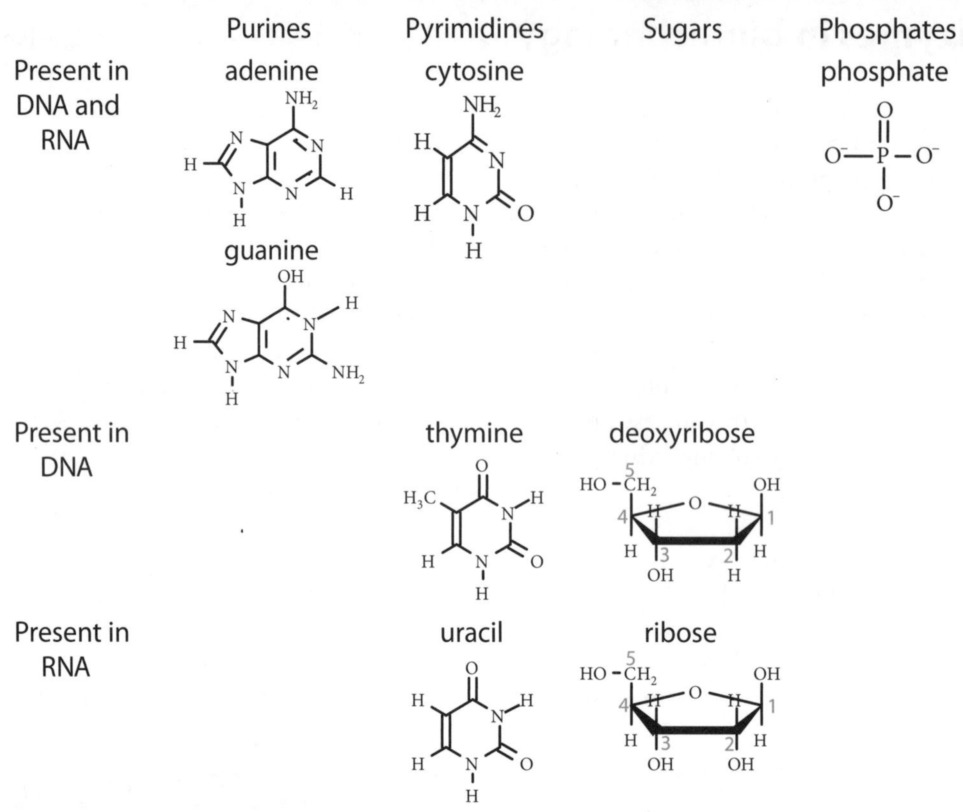

Figure 1347 Components of nucleic acids

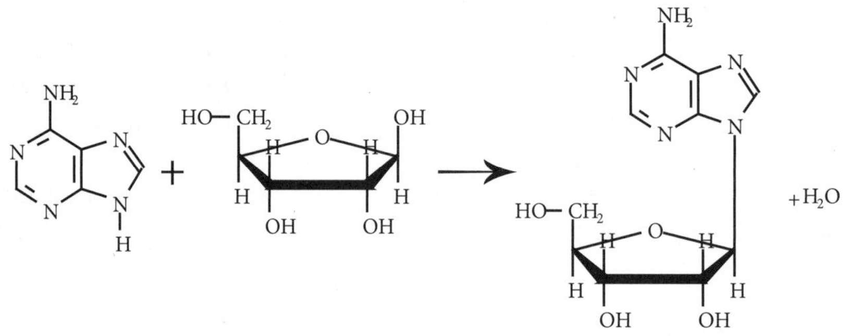

Figure 1348 Condensation reaction of adenine with ribose

in RNA nucleotides. Thymine differs from uracil only in the presence of a $-CH_3$ group on the C–5 position.

There are two forms of pentose that may make up a nucleoside. As the name implies, the sugars are either ribose (corectly called D-ribose) found in RNA or deoxyribose (2-deoxy-D-ribose) found in DNA nucleotides (stereochemistry is crucial to nucleic acid structures). These sugars differ only in that the hydroxyl group on the C–2 of ribose is replaced by a hydrogen atom in deoxyribose and lacks an oxygen atom on C–2. Thus deoxysugars, like deoxyribose, do not fit the empirical formula, CH_2O, generally given for carbohydrates.

A nitrogenous base together with a pentose sugar form a nucleoside. The condensation reaction occurs through the hydrogen atom present on a N atom of the base combining with the hydroxyl group on the C–1 of the sugar to release water and form a covalent N–C bond between the sugar and the base.

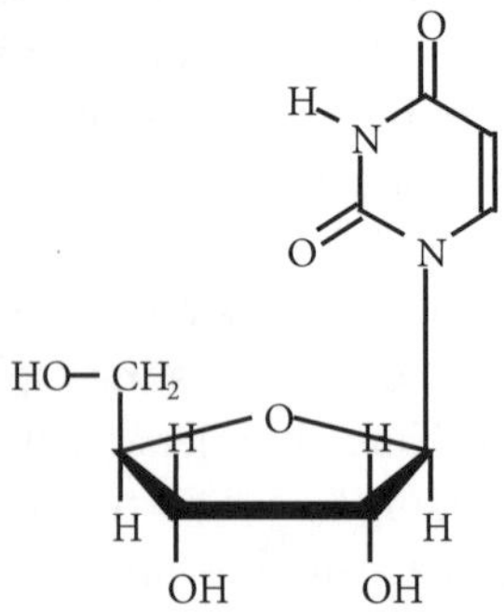

Figure 1349 Nucleoside from uracil and ribose

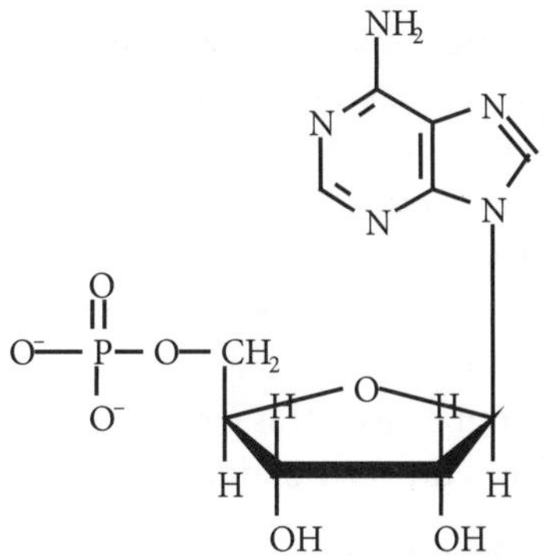

Figure 1350 A nucleotide

A nucleoside combines with a phosphate group to produce a nucleotide. The phosphate group HPO_4^{2-} is an ionized form of phosphoric acid, H_3PO_4 - the reason both DNA and RNA are acidic in aqueous solution. Again, a condensation reaction bonds the $-CH_2OH$ of a nucleoside to the phosphate group, with the hydroxyl group on the C–5 of the sugar reacting with a hydrogen from the phosphate group to release water and form a covalent bond. The bonded phosphate group has a charge of negative two, making the entire nucleotide negatively charged.

Note that a nucleoside is made up from a base and a sugar molecule, a nucleotide from a base, a sugar and an ionised phosphate group and a nucleic acid is a polymer of nucleotides.

A nucleic acid polymer consists of a chain of nucleotides formed by enzyme catalysed condensation reactions. The phosphate of one nucleotide combines with the hydroxyl group on the C–3 of the sugar on another nucleotide, releasing water and forming a bond. As the polymerization continues, a backbone of alternating sugar and phosphate groups is formed with the nitrogenous bases emerging from this backbone.

The sequence of these bases is important in the storage of genetic information. At one end of a nucleic acid chain is a nucleotide that does not have another nucleotide attached to its phosphate group and at the other an unbonded sugar. Figure 1351 shows the regularity of the sugar phosphate 'backbone' of DNA.

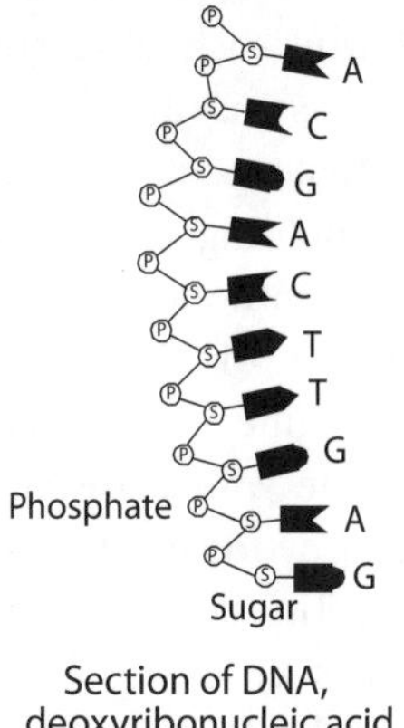

Figure 1351 Section of DNA

B.8.3 Explain the double helical structure of DNA.

DNA has a secondary structure that results in the formation of a **double helix** that consists of two strands of nucleic acid that interact through intermolecular hydrogen bonding between the bases attached to the strands to form a double helix. The organic bases are located between the two backbones of sugar and phosphate groups. The structure of DNA shows that adenine (A) and thymine (T) only occur opposite each other and the same applies to cytosine (C) and guanine (G), see Figure 1353. Part of the reason for this is that only the combination of a purine and a pyrimidine give a similar distance between the two backbones of DNA, since a purine is double ringed and a pyrimidine is single ringed, as shown in Figure 1353.

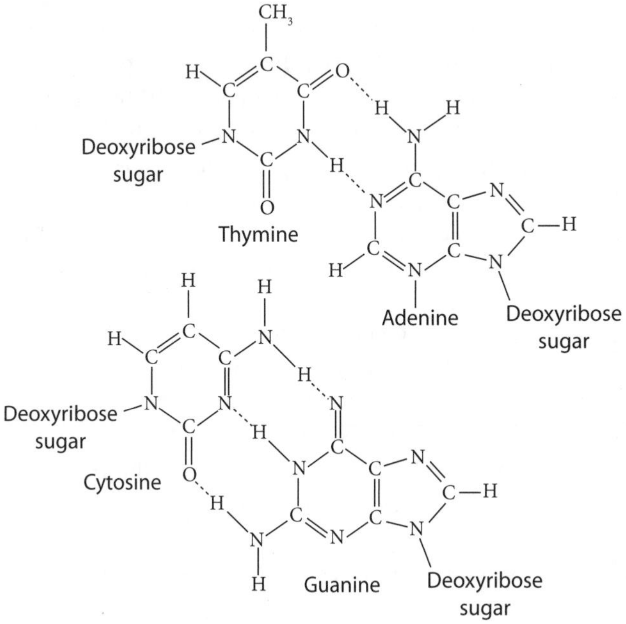

Figure 1353 Hydrogen bonding in Thymine-Adenine and Cytosine-Guanine base pairs

The major reason why each base combines only with one other type of base is due to the intermolecular hydrogen bonding that occurs between them and this is the major factor holding the double-stranded DNA molecule together. Adenine forms two hydrogen bonds with thymine because of their molecular geometry and cytosine and guanine form three hydrogen bonds. The pairing of adenine with cytosine and thymine and guanine do not form hydrogen bonds strong enough to hold DNA together. The double helix is also stabilised by other interactions such as dipole-dipole hydrophobic interactions and van der Waals' forces between the base pairs. In order to minimize the electrostatic repulsions between negatively charged phosphate residues, the sugar-phosphate backbone adopts a helical configuration.

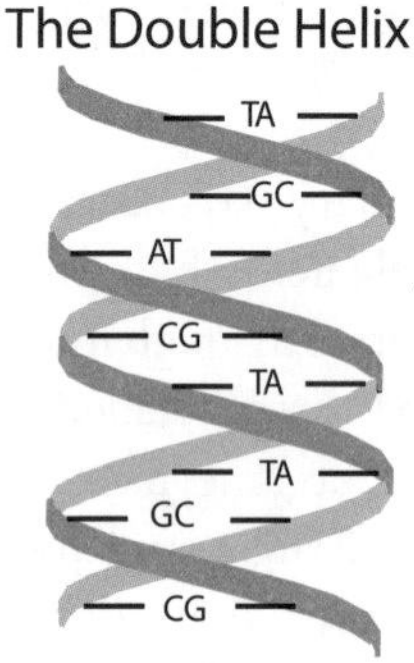

Figure 1354 The DNA double helix

The hydrogen bonding between the bases and the twisting of the sugar–phosphate backbone result in DNA's secondary structure taking the form of a double stranded, helical shape with a 'ladder' of bases spanning the gap between the two strands. The fact that each organic base on a strand has only one possible complement on the other (A & T and C & G; called **complementary base pairs**) is essential to the passing on of genetic information from one cell to the next. This pairing is based entirely on intermolecular hydrogen bonding.

B.8.4 Describe the role of DNA as the repository of genetic information, and explain its role in protein synthesis.

The role of DNA is to reproduce itself and carry the information which encodes the proteins (including the enzymes) in any organism. DNA carries the genetic information that defines any organism. A gene is a section of a DNA molecule that codes for a protein. A gene contains many nucleotides with a specific sequence of the four bases A, C, G and T in the required order to produce a specific protein. That is, the sequence of the organic bases in each gene specifies the linear amino acid sequence of a polypeptide chain (or of an RNA molecule). An organism's characteristic properties are determined by its DNA. All cells in one organism have exactly the same DNA with

TOK What are the implications of the molecular basis of life?

Now this one probably deserves a book, or even a series of books, with one volume devoted to each field of knowledge. About the best I can do in the confines of this tiny box that I've been given is generate a few random thoughts, mainly related to our mental pre-programming, assuming that our brains are as different as our bodies and that this affects the way we think about things (are these both fair assumptions?).

- Suppose we know somebody has a genetic tendency to violence or criminal acts, will we keep that person under extra surveillance? If your answer is "No", then what are your reasons? What if you could detect this during the first weeks of pregnancy?
- Should we allow people to choose their own jobs? If I have an excellent mind for a teacher, wouldn't it be a waste to allow me to work as a check-out operative at a supermarket (and *vice-versa* - equally culpable). Does this mean that we would get paid different amounts on the basis of our mental construction?
- Suppose two artists produce equally brilliant work, but we know one has the perfect brain for artistic creativity (are either of these two assumptions possible?), whereas the other has a brain totally unsuited to this, but ideal for flipping burgers. Would knowing this affect the way in which we viewed their work?
- What about religions that postulate a soul or reincarnation? Do they assume that there is a part of DNA responsible for this (maybe divine influence affects which bits come from each parent and hence constructs the required physical/mental incarnation) or do they assume that it is passed on in some other way?

OPTION

the same sequence of base pairs; different species contain different DNA molecules. Also, genetic information is passed on to the offspring of an organism through the transfer of DNA. Therefore, when new organisms are produced or cells divide, DNA must be accurately copied or replicated. The complementary base pairs allow this process to occur easily.

If a DNA sequence is damaged, for example by ultraviolet (UV) light or X-rays, it may produce little or no protein, or a different mutant protein or damaged DNA may be produced. The production of damaged DNA can lead to disease, for example, the uncontrolled growth of cells (cancer). In other cases, a changed base sequence may give rise to a non-harmful genetic change such as different hair or eye color.

Instructions for protein synthesis are encoded in DNA. DNA contains four nucleotides, but some twenty amino acids which are involved in the synthesis of proteins. Clearly one nucleotide base could not denote a particular amino acid as this would only specify four of the twenty amino acids. Similarly, two nucleotides would not be sufficient as the four bases would specify only $4^2 = 16$ amino acids (e.g. AA, AG, AC, AT, GC, GT, GA, GG, etc.). A three nucleotide sequence with four bases can produce a total of $4^3 = 64$ combinations of triplets to specify all the amino acids, where many of the amino acids are encoded by more than one triplet. For example, AAA and AAG both specify the amino acid lysine. The triplet code AUG signals the start of a protein chain whereas three other triplets specify the end of the protein chain. A three nucleotide sequence, called a triplet code or codon, codes for a specific amino acid in the polypeptide chain. Thus the sequence of nucleotides in DNA determines the precise arrangement of amino acids in proteins. Proteins are not made directly from the genetic information stored in the DNA in the cell nucleus. The transfer of genetic information involves transcription from DNA to messenger RNA (mRNA) and translation from mRNA to protein synthesis by transfer RNA (tRNA).

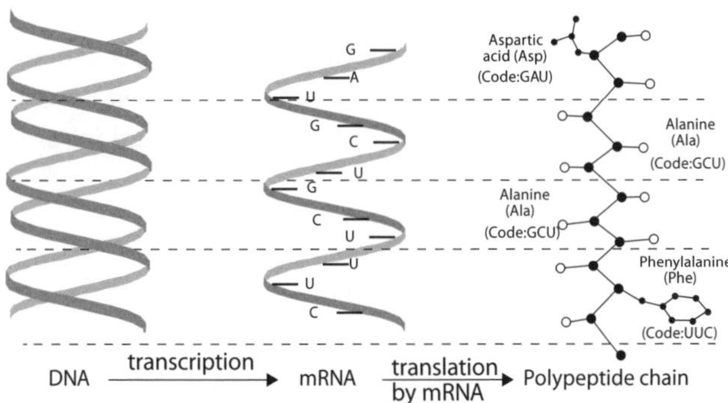

Figure 1355 Transcription and translation

B.8.5 Outline the steps involved in DNA profiling and state its use.

One of the many useful applications of DNA technology is **DNA profiling**, which involves the production of a genetic 'fingerprint'. The key to DNA profiling is that all cells from an organism must create the same DNA profile. If the process is carried out extensively enough it is possible to produce a profile of sufficient detail that would make it almost impossible for any other organisms to have the same profile. A DNA profile may be obtained by two methods, both of which require a small amount of cellular material and involve observing the number of different pieces a molecule of DNA can be split into and the sizes of these pieces.

The first method depends on the use of **restriction enzymes**, which have the ability to find a certain sequence of usually four to eight base-pairs and to cut the molecule of DNA at or near to those sequences. Therefore, if a section of DNA is chosen that varies considerably from person to person, then each person will have this section of DNA cut into different lengths as the restriction sequences will occur at different points in each person's DNA. This method has low sensitivity.

Another more sensitive method of obtaining a unique combination of DNA sizes is through examining a section of DNA called VNTR (variable number of tandem repeats). The exact function of these parts of DNA is not known, but they consist of a short sequence of base pairs repeated many times, with the number of repeats varying from person to person. These fragments of DNA can be analysed through the use of an enzyme catalyzed reaction which copies the required section of DNA millions of times, even if the initial sample is very small. Depending on the number of repeats on the VNTR site, different sizes of DNA fragments are produced. Many people will have the same number of repeats at one VNTR site, but if numerous sites are chosen then some of these will vary in length and a DNA profile can be created that is unique.

Once a unique combination of DNA fragments of different sizes is created, **gel electrophoresis** is used to make an observable DNA profile. A thin plate of electrically conducting gel is set up, a negative potential is applied at one end of the plate and a positive potential at the other. A solution of the various DNA fragments is placed on the plate near to the negative end. Since DNA has negatively charged phosphate groups it is attracted to the positively charged end. As the fragments of DNA move, the smaller fragments move more quickly through the gel than the larger ones. A fluorescent dye is added which makes the DNA glow in UV light. A photograph can then be taken of the number and position of the bands of DNA that appear in the gel.

DNA profiling is mainly used to identify people. This is especially useful in helping to solve crimes, as any cells left behind at the scene of a crime in the form of blood, semen, saliva or hair roots can be used to provide a DNA sample. DNA profiles can be made from the suspect's DNA and compared to the DNA profile connected with the scene of the crime. DNA profiling can also be used in paternity cases, especially the VNTR method, since all of the child's different VNTR lengths must come only from those that are present in the mother or the father.

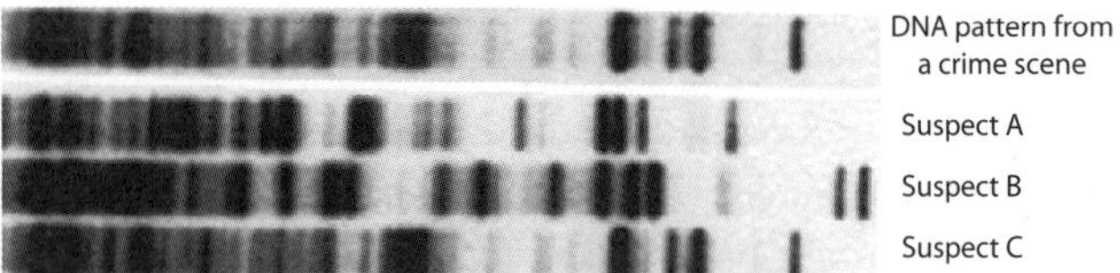

Figure 1356 Using DNA to solve a crime and implicate suspect C

B9 RESPIRATION (HL)

B.9.1 Compare aerobic and anaerobic respiration of glucose in terms of oxidation/reduction and energy released.

Digestion breaks down proteins to amino acids, fats to fatty acids (and glycerol) and carbohydrates to simple sugars such as glucose. Cellular respiration involves complex sequence of metabolic chemical reactions in a cell involving enzymes that convert energy from glucose (but occasionally also amino acids and fatty acids) into chemical energy. Sugars undergo glycolysis (breakdown of glucose) as the first stage in cellular respiration in which a glucose molecule, $C_6H_{12}O_6$ splits into two pyruvic acid molecules each with three carbon atoms. Pyruvic acid is a weak acid and dissociates to form pyruvate ions:

$C_3H_4O_3 \rightleftharpoons C_3H_3O_3^- + H^+$ (*Note: some sources use the term pyruvic acid and pyruvate interchangeably*).

Pyruvic acid: $CH_3COCOOH$ ($C_3H_4O_3$)

Pyruvate ion: CH_3COCOO^- ($C_3H_3O_3^-$)

Figure 1357 Structures of pyruvic acid and pyruvate ions

The formation of smaller molecules from larger ones during metabolism is also called **catabolism**. In glucose this involves removal of hydrogen atoms and is achieved by hydrogen carrier species such as nicotinamide adenine dinucleotide, NAD^+ to form NADH: Thus the conversion of glucose to pyruvate is summarised by the equation:

$$C_6H_{12}O_6 + 2\,NAD^+ \rightarrow 2\,C_3H_3O_3^- + 2\,NADH + 4\,H^+ + \text{energy}$$

This process is **anaerobic** (the opposite of **aerobic**) respiration since it occurs in the absence of air, meaning 'without oxygen'. In this reaction, there are now fewer H atoms present per carbon in the product compared with the reactant; thus carbon experiences an increase in oxidation number and is oxidized. NAD^+, on the other hand, gains electrons and is reduced:

$$NAD^+ + H^+ + 2e^- \rightarrow NADH$$

Aerobic (also called oxidative) respiration requires air in which molecular oxygen is the oxidizing agent (electron acceptor) and a fuel molecule is the reducing agent (the electron donor). Once glucose is converted into the pyruvate ion, aerobic oxidation takes place in which oxygen converts pyruvate ion to carbon dioxide and water, reforming the NAD^+:

$$2CH_3COCOO^- + 2NADH + 4H^+ + 6O_2 \rightarrow 6CO_2 + 6H_2O + 2NAD^+$$

Overall redox reaction: $C_6H_{12}O_6 + 6O_2 \rightarrow 6CO_2 + 6H_2O$; $\Delta H^\circ = -2820\ \text{kJ mol}^{-1}$

Overall, in aerobic oxidation, the carbon atoms in glucose are oxidized to form CO_2 and oxygen is reduced to form water. The two redox half equations for the reactions are:

Oxidation ½-reaction (Ox. No. of C increases):

$$C_6H_{12}O_6 + 6\,H_2O \rightarrow 6\,CO_2 + 24\,H^+ + 24\,e^-$$

Reduction ½-reaction (Ox. No. of O decreases):

$$6\,O_2 + 24H^+ + 24\,e^- \rightarrow 12\,H_2O$$

In this reaction the 'average' oxidation number of C in glucose ($6x + 12(+1) + 6(-2) = 0$; $x = 0$) increases from 0 to + 4 in CO_2. That is, there is a loss of 4 e^- per carbon atom which is oxidized. The molecular oxygen is the electron acceptor; it accepts 2 e^- per oxygen atom and is reduced; in H_2O. Its oxidation number is –2. Overall, energy is produced by the oxidation reaction since glucose (and also amino acids and fatty acids) contain a larger number of C–C and C–H bonds which are not as strong (bond enthalpies respectively of 348 and 412 kJ mol^{-1} in the gaseous state) compared with C=O and O–H bonds (743 and 463 kJ mol^{-1} respectively) in the products. Thus less energy is required to break the weaker reactant bonds and more energy is produced in making stronger product bonds; the net result is an exothermic reaction.

When the supply of oxygen is insufficent, aerobic respiration cannot occur and under such circumstances, the pyruvate ion is reduced to the lactate ion:

$$CH_3COCOO^- + NADH + H^+ \rightarrow CH_3CHOHCOO^- + NAD^+ + \text{energy}$$

The respective reduction and oxidation half-reactions are:

$$2e^- + 2H^+ + CH_3COCOO^- \rightarrow CH_3CHOHCOO^-$$

$$NADH + H^+ \rightarrow NAD^+ + 2e^- + 2H^+$$

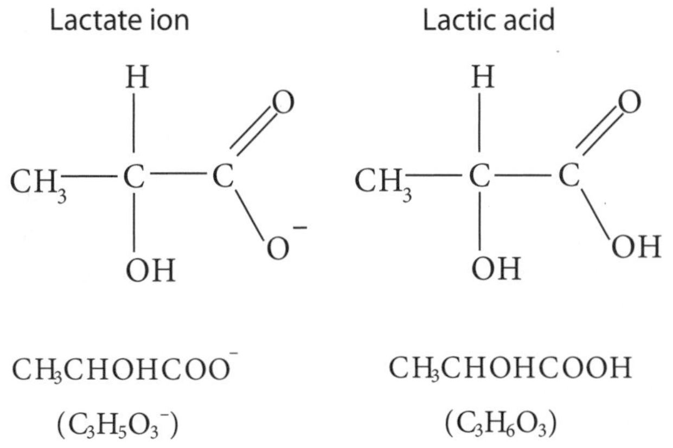

Lactate ion | Lactic acid

$CH_3CHOHCOO^-$ $(C_3H_5O_3^-)$ | $CH_3CHOHCOOH$ $(C_3H_6O_3)$

Fig 1358 Structures of lactate ion and lactic acid

This is known as **anaerobic respiration** and during strenuous exercise, which requires oxygen faster than it can be delivered by the blood stream, anaerobic respiration occurs, causing the build up of lactic acid in muscle cells. This happens for a limited time only in the human body as the increase in lactic acid decreases the pH in the muscle causing pain. If oxygen is again available, lactic acid can be oxidized to carbon dioxide and water. The overall reaction and the respective reduction and oxidation half-reactions are:

$$C_3H_6O_3 + 3\,O_2 \rightarrow 3\,CO_2 + 3\,H_2O + \text{energy}$$

$$3\,O_2 + 12\,e^- + 12\,H^+ \rightarrow 6\,H_2O$$

$$C_3H_6O_3 + 3\,H_2O \rightarrow 3\,CO_2 + 12\,e^- + 12\,H^+$$

Whereas pyruvate ions are converted to lactate ions in anaerobic respiration in humans, yeast converts pyruvate ions to ethanol and carbon dioxide.

$$2\,CH_3COCOO^- + 2\,NADH + 4\,H^+ \xrightarrow{Yeast} 2\,C_2H_5OH + 2\,CO_2 + 2\,NAD^+$$

Thus, in the presence of yeast as catalyst, overall conversion of sugar takes place to alcohol.

$$\text{Overall reaction: } C_6H_{12}O_6 \xrightarrow{Yeast} 2C_2H_5OH + 2CO_2$$

In this reaction, the 'average' oxidation number of carbon in the reactant decreases from 0 ($6x + 12(+1) + 6(-2) = 0$; $x = 0$) to –2 in the reactant ethanol ($2x + 6(+1) + (-2) = 0$; $x = -2$) and increases to +4 in CO_2. Thus the glucose is reduced to ethanol and oxidized to carbon dioxide.

B.9.2: Outline the role of copper ions in electron transport and iron ions in oxygen transport.

METAL IONS IN BIOLOGICAL SYSTEMS

Metal ions found in the diet are essential to biological systems. Different metal ions fulfil different roles in the body due to their differences in charge density, redox properties and complex ion formation. Iron was the first trace metal ion found to be essential in the human diet. Other first row transition metals such as copper and cobalt are also required in trace amounts by the human body. Iron is present in the haemoglobin molecule of red blood cells so that iron deficiency produces anemia and causes fatigue as cells are deprived of oxygen. Copper deficiencies have been known to give rise to bone disease and cobalt is a vital component of vitamin B12. Transition metal ions are important in biological systems because they have the ability to form complex ions and also to exist in multiple oxidation states and hence catalyse redox reactions.

In haemoglobin for example coordinate covalent bonding takes place between the lone electron pairs on the nitrogen containing bases and the iron ion, which has a charge because of the presence of lone electron pairs on the nitrogen of the bases and the high charge density (charge

OPTION

to size ratio) of the transition metal ions. Consequently coordinate covalent bonding takes place where the metal ion is the electron pair acceptor (Lewis base) and the nitrogen on the base, the electron pair donor (the Lewis base). This is an example of a complex ion formation in which the species containing the nitrogen donor atoms surrounding the metal ion is called a **multidentate ligand**:

structure of heme group of haemoglobin

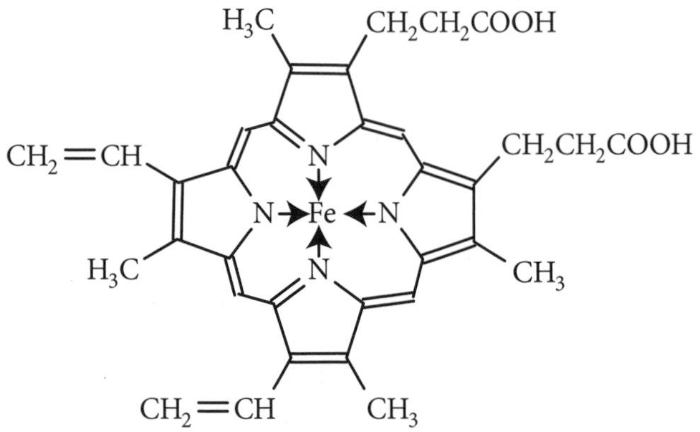

H_3C CH_2CH_2COOH $CH_2{=}CH$ N CH_2CH_2COOH N→Fe←N H_3C N CH_3 $CH_2{=}CH$ CH_3

Figure 1359 The structure of the heme group of hemoglobin

Macro-nutrients such as proteins, fats and carbohydrates undergo a series of redox reactions involving gain and loss of electrons in the mitochondria inside cells. **Cytochromes** are part of the electron transfer chain which generates **adenosine triphosphate** (ATP), a form of short term stored chemical energy. Cytochromes are iron and copper containing proteins that carry energetic electrons to produce ATP. Living organisms use ATP to transfer useful energy ($\Delta G°$ is negative) from exothermic reactions, such as oxidation of carbohydrates and fats to biosynthetic reactions and other endothermic processes that require energy. The energy produced in the oxidation of food is stored in the form of ATP (the 'energy currency'). ATP (and water) is made by the addition of **adenosine diphosphate** (ADP) to phosphate ion and this reaction is endothermic. The reverse reaction, hydrolysis of ATP to ADP is exothermic and provides the energy for the cell to function. The sequence of such reactions in the oxidation of glucose ensures there is controlled slow release of energy.

$$ATP \rightleftharpoons ADP + P + \Delta G$$

The iron atoms of the cytochromes undergo one-electron oxidation-reduction reactions during aerobic respiration between iron(II) and iron(III) oxidation states and the copper between copper(I) and copper(II):

$$Fe^{2+} \rightleftharpoons Fe^{3+} + e^-; Cu^{1+} \rightleftharpoons Cu^{2+} + e^-$$

Reduced co-enzymes such as NADH (nicotinamide adenine dinucleotide) carry hydrogen ions and electrons from the metal ions which serve as intermediates to form water and produce energy:

$$4e^- + 4\,H^+_{(aq)} + O_{2\,(g)} \rightleftharpoons 2\,H_2O_{(l)} + \text{energy}$$

This exothermic reaction is carried out in many steps involving a number of enzymes. Copper in the cytochrome oxidase is the terminal electron carrier in the **electron transport chain** (also called the respiratory chain) which converts oxygen to water and the energy produced is used to form ATP.

Haemoglobin is the best known oxygen transport protein. It bonds to oxygen in the lungs in order to transport it via the blood to tissues throughout the body. Heme is a complex of iron in a hydrophobic environment due to the non-polar side chains that surround it. This environment makes it possible for the oxygen to bind with the Fe^{2+} reversibly without oxidising the metal to Fe^{3+}.

The iron in haemoglobin bonds to oxygen to form oxy-haemoglobin. This carries oxygen to the cells where it releases the oxygen, picks up some of the carbon dioxide and returns the CO_2 to the lungs where it is released. Most of the carbon dioxide in the circulatory system is transported as carbonic acid, i.e. as hydrogen carbonate and hydrogen ions, and is eventually exhaled through the lungs:

$$CO_2\,(g) + H_2O\,(l) \rightleftharpoons H^+(aq) + HCO_3^-(aq)$$

Iron deficiency causes anemia (shortage of red blood cells) and, as a result, insufficient oxygen is carried to the cells, leading to fatigue. Species such as carbon monoxide, CO, bind tightly with Fe(II) and block its ability to pick up oxygen. This interferes with oxygen transport, depriving the body cells of vital oxygen. The heart must pump at a greater rate and if sufficient oxygen cannot be supplied, the animal can die by asphyxiation. Since the reactions of haemoglobin with both O_2 and CO are reversible, excess amounts of oxygen can eventually displace the CO and the effect of CO metabolic poisoning can be reversed to some extent.

OPTION B: HUMAN BIOCHEMISTRY QUESTIONS

B1 Energy

1. 1,00 g of roasted peanut is heated electrically and burned in a supply of oxygen in a food calorimeter. The heat produced increases the temperature of the water and calorimeter by 6.60°C. Given the 'water equivalent' of the calorimeter and water is equal to 532 g, calculate the energy content of the peanut in kJ per g.

B2 Proteins

2. Describe the structural feature that distinguishes glycine from alanine.

3. Draw the condensation reaction of two molecules of alanine to form the dipeptide. Name and describe the covalent bond (linkage) that connects the two amino acids.

4. (i) Using symbols, write the combinations of tripeptides that can be formed from alanine (Ala) and glycine (Gly).

(ii) Thus deduce the number of different tripeptides that can be formed using three different amino acids.

(iii) Determine the number of tripeptides if three different amino acids are present only once in each tripeptide.

5. Outline two experimental procedures that can be used to analyse the amino acids present in a tripeptide. Describe and explain how each method can identify the individual amino acids.

6. Draw the structure of aspartic acid from the Data Booklet. Given that the isoelectric point of aspartic acid = 2.8, draw the structure of the species present in solution and explain your reasoning. Deduce the structure of the species at pH = 1.0 and 11.0 and explain your reasoning.

7. Describe and explain how the primary, secondary (α-helix and β-pleated sheets), tertiary and quaternary structure of proteins differ.

8. List the major functions of proteins in the body.

B3 Carbohydrates

9. State the empirical formula of a monosaccharide and identify two functional groups present in monosaccharides.

10. Identify the structural characteristics present in the formula of straight chain glucose, and state the type of isomerism it exhibits.

11. Two common ring structures of glucose are called α-glucose and β-glucose. Describe any differences between the two structures.

12. Maltose is a disaccharide that contains two glucose rings in a 1→ 4 linkage. Describe the type of reaction and the linkage that leads to the formation of maltose, and meaning of the expression: 1→ 4. Write a balanced equation for the reaction, given glucose has the formula: $C_6H_{12}O_6$. Describe what happens when one consumes maltose.

13. Describe the similarity and difference(s) between the structure of amylose and amylopectin.

14. Based on the structures of the disaccharides maltose and sucrose and the polysaccharide starch, deduce the names of the monosaccharides they are formed from.

15. Explain why monosaccharides and disaccharides are water soluble.

16. Describe the difference between amylopectin and glycogen.

B4 Lipids

17. Explain the relationship between iodine number and unsaturation in a fat or an oil.

OPTION

18. Linolenic acid has the formula: $C_{17}H_{29}COOH$. 2.78 g of the fatty acid requires 7.62 g iodine. Determine the number of double bonds present in the acid.

19. Compare the composition of the three types of lipids found in the human body, triglycerides (fats and oils), phospholipid (lecithin) and steroids (cholesterol).

20. Describe the structural similarities and any differences between a fat and an oil and explain why they differ in their melting points.

21. (a) Predict and explain whether stearic acid, $C_{17}H_{35}COOH$, relative molecular mass 284, is a solid or liquid at room temperature.

(b) Oleic acid, $C_{17}H_{33}COOH$, of a similar relative molecular mass, is a liquid at room temperature. Suggest a reason why this is the case.

(c) Linoleic acid, $C_{17}H_{31}COOH$, of a similar relative molecular mass, is a liquid with a lower melting point than oleic acid. Suggest a reason why this is the case.

22. Explain why triglycerides are a concentrated energy source providing more energy per gram than carbohydrates.

B5 Micro- and macro-nutrients

23. Define the term 'micronutrient' and give two examples.

24. Define the term 'macronutrient' and give two examples.

25. Study the structure of vitamin D in the Data Booklet. Identify two functional groups present in the molecule. Deduce whether it is fat or water soluble and explain your reasoning.

26. Study the structure of vitamin C in the Data Booklet. Identify two functional groups present in the molecule. Deduce whether it is fat or water soluble and explain your reasoning.

B6 Hormones

27. Outline the production and function of hormones in the body.

28. Study the structures of the two sex hormones oestradiol and testosterone given in the Data Booklet. List the differences between the two structures and suggest how the two hormones could be distinguished in a school laboratory.

[HL] B7 Enzymes

29. List the function of an enzyme and describe the characteristics of enzymes.

30. The enzyme urease decomposes urea in living systems.

(i) Outline the mechanism of the reaction of the enzyme, E with the substrate, S.

(ii) Sketch a graph of the velocity, *V*, of the reaction (on the *y*-axis) against the concentration of urea (on the *x*-axis).

(iii) Describe and explain the shape of the graph. Clearly show the value of V_{max} on the sketch and explain its significance.

(iv) From the sketch you have drawn, show the value of the Michaelis constant (K_m) and explain its significance.

(v) Describe the relationship between K_m value and enzyme activity.

31. Explain why enzyme activity is affected even when there is a slight change in its shape.

32. State and explain the effect of the following factors on enzyme activity:

(i) the presence of heavy-metal ions

(ii) temperature changes, and

(iii) pH changes.

[HL] B8Nucleic acids

33. (i) Describe the structure of nucleotides and list the bases involved.

(ii) State the reaction that leads to the formation of nucleic acids from nucleotides.

(iii) Describe how nucleotides link to form polynucleotides.

(iv) Describe the structure of nucleic acids (polynucleotides).

(v) State two differences between the chemical composition of the nucleic acids DNA and RNA.

34. The structure of DNA shows that adenine (A) and thymine (T) only occur opposite each other and the same applies to cytosine (C) and guanine (G). Use the structures of the bases in the Data Booklet to illustrate why this is the case, and identify the force of attraction that leads to it.

35. (i) Describe the basis of DNA profiling.

(ii) Outline the steps involved in DNA profiling.

(iii) Describe one method used to obtain a genetic fringerprint.

(iv) State and explain the uses of DNA profiling.

[HL] B9 Respiration

36. (a) Distinguish between aerobic and anaerobic respiration.

(b) Identify the oxidizing and reducing agent in the aerobic oxidation of glucose

(c) Write the oxidation and reduction half-reactions and the overall reaction for the aerobic oxidation of glucose.

(d) In terms of bond energies, explain why the aerobic oxidation of glucose is an exothermic process.

(e) Deduce the type of respiration that takes place during strenuous exercise. Explain your reasoning and describe its consequence. Describe the products formed if additional oxygen is then available.

37. Outline the role of copper ions in electron transport and iron ions in oxygen transport.

Outline the role d-block metal ions play in:

(i) electron transport and

(ii) oxygen transport.

For each process, state the biological molecule, the metal ion present in it and describe how the molecule functions giving relevant equation(s).

CHEMISTRY IN INDUSTRY AND TECHNOLOGY

14

C1 Iron, steel and aluminium

C2 The oil industry

C3 Addition polymers

C4 Catalysts

C5 Fuel cells and rechargeable batteries

C6 Liquid crystals

C7 Nanotechnology

C8 Condensation polymers (HL)

C9 Mechanisms in the organic chemicals industry (HL)

C10 Silicon and photovoltaic cells (HL)

C11 Liquid crystals (HL)

C12 The chlor–alkali industry (HL)

As one of the most important roles of chemistry is to make forms of matter that have never existed before, it plays a central role in any material revolution. The Industrial Revolution of the 18th century was the result of the large-scale extraction of iron, but the material revolution continues the development of new materials with structures and properties that serve the technologies of today. The consideration of how the materials benefit society makes this option particularly relevant to aim 8 (raising awareness of the moral, ethical, social, economic and environmental implications of using science and technology).

INTRODUCTION

The chemical industry can take raw materials and turn them into much more valuable products such as sulfuric acid, ammonia, ethene, sodium hydroxide, and chlorine amongst others. Technology is used extensively in the chemical industry to produce biofuels or manufacture polymers with different properties. The importance of chemistry in industry and technology rests on the food, clothes, medicines and the great variety of consumer articles that it produces. One sign of the economic development of a country is the state of its chemical industry. For example, the commercialization of the Haber process likely prolonged World War I by at least one year. Almost a century later, "the emerging fields of nanoscience and nanotechnology are leading to unprecedented understanding and control over the fundamental building blocks of all physical things. This is likely to change the way almost everything - from vaccines to computers to automobile tires to objects not yet imagined - is designed and made."

(quoted from: Nanotechnology shaping the world atom by atom, National Science and Technology Council Report, September 1999, Washington, D.C.)

OPTION

C1 IRON, STEEL AND ALUMINIUM

C.1.1 State the main sources of iron.

The main sources of iron include iron ores and scrap iron. Iron ores are mined as oxides, Fe_2O_3, (haematite), Fe_3O_4, ($FeO{\cdot}Fe_2O_3$, magnetite, a mixed oxide) and the sulfide FeS_2, (iron pyrites). The latter is roasted in air to form the oxide and sulfur dioxide.

$$4\,FeS_2\,(s) + 11\,O_2\,(g) \longrightarrow 2\,Fe_2O_3\,(s) + 8\,SO_2\,(g)$$

C1.2 Describe and explain the reactions that occur in the blast furnace.

A mixture of the raw materials limestone (calcium carbonate, $CaCO_3$), coke (C) and iron ore (for example iron(III) oxide, Fe_2O_3) is fed into the blast furnace from the top (called the hopper), see Figure 1401. The mixture is called 'solid charge'. A large volume of air is introduced under pressure near the bottom of the furnace where coke is oxidized exothermically to carbon dioxide as follows:

$$C\,(s) + O_2\,(g) \longrightarrow CO_2\,(g) + heat$$

The furnace is at about 2200 K temperature in this lower region. Higher up the furnace, carbon dioxide reacts with coke to form carbon monoxide. This reaction is endothermic, with the furnace in this region cooling to 1400 K:

$$CO_2\,(g) + C\,(s) + heat \rightarrow 2\,CO\,(g)$$

If natural gas methane, CH_4 is injected with the hot air, incomplete combustion can occur to form carbon monoxide and less coke is required:

$$2\,CH_4\,(g) + O_2\,(g) \longrightarrow 2\,CO\,(g) + 4\,H_2\,(g)$$

It is carbon monoxide that plays the largest part in the reduction of the ore towards the top of the furnace. Iron oxides are reduced exothermically:

$$Fe_2O_3\,(s) + 3\,CO\,(g) \longrightarrow 2\,Fe\,(l) + 3\,CO_2\,(g) + heat$$

$$Fe_3O_4\,(s) + 4\,CO\,(g) \longrightarrow 3\,Fe\,(l) + 4\,CO_2\,(g) + heat$$

If methane is injected, the hydrogen gas produced on partial oxidation can also act as a reducing agent:

$$Fe_3O_4\,(s) + 4\,H_2\,(g) \longrightarrow 3\,Fe\,(l) + 4\,H_2O\,(g)$$

Coke can also reduce the oxide, for example:

$$Fe_2O_3\,(s) + 3\,C\,(s) \longrightarrow 2\,Fe\,(l) + 3\,CO\,(g)$$

The iron produced sinks to the bottom of the furnace where the temperature is high enough to keep it molten. At the same time, because of the high temperature, the limestone in the charge decomposes to form calcium oxide and carbon dioxide:

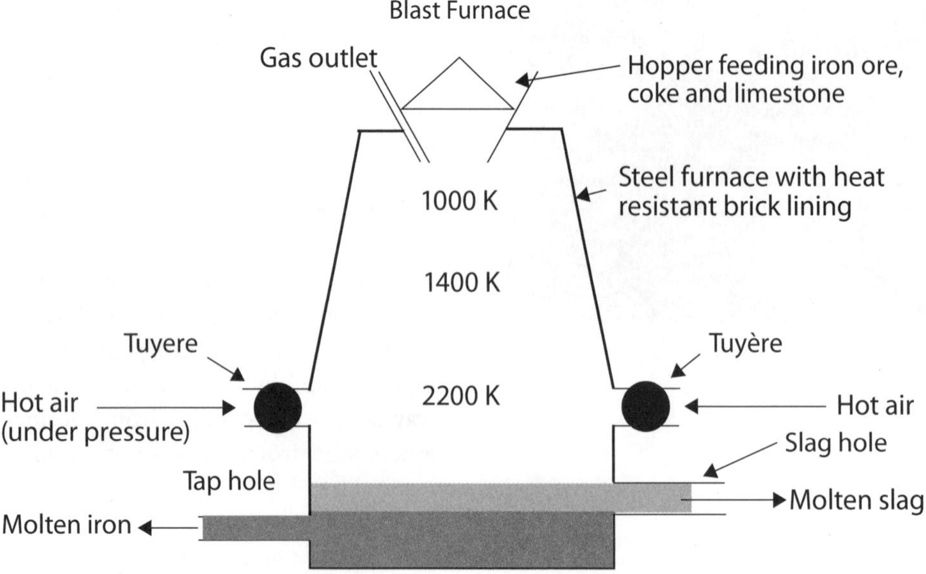

Figure 1401 Blast Furnace

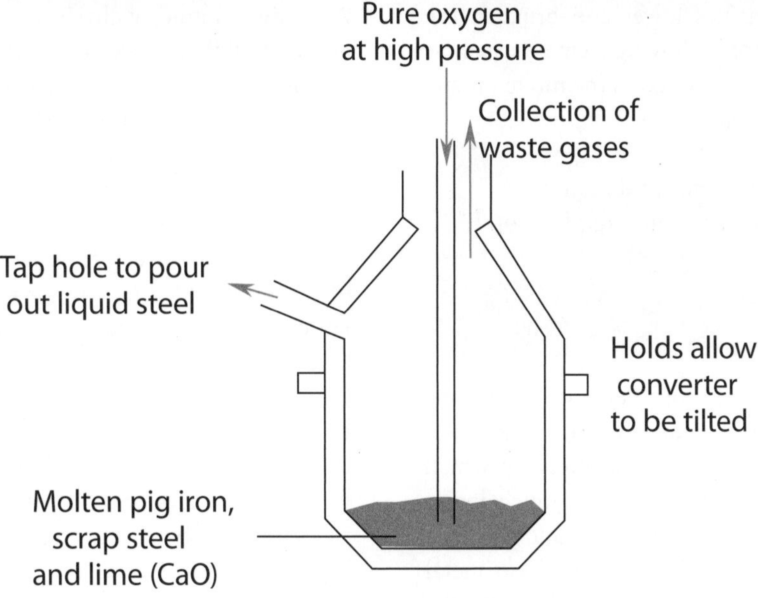

Figure 1402 A basic oxygen converter

$$\text{heat} + CaCO_3\ (s) \longrightarrow CaO\ (s) + CO_2\ (g)$$

The highly basic calcium oxide combines with the acidic silicon(IV) oxide present as sand in the impure ore and the amphoteric aluminium oxide (which can behave as an acid or a base). These impurities in the ore form a molten slag of calcium silicate(IV) and calcium aluminate(III), which trickles down the stack:

$$CaO\ (s) + SiO_2\ (s) \longrightarrow CaSiO_3\ (l)$$

$$CaO\ (s) + Al_2O_3\ (s) \longrightarrow CaAl_2O_4\ (l)$$

The molten iron, called pig iron, is impure and not so strong. It contains about 4 – 5% carbon, 1 – 2% silicon and smaller amounts of elements such as manganese, phosphorus and sulfur. The more dense pig iron lies at the bottom of the furnace and the lighter slag forms an immiscible layer above it; the molten iron and slag are tapped off every few hours. Slag is used for road making and in the manufacture of cement. A furnace can operate continuously for several years before it needs relining. See Figure 1401.

C.1.3 Describe and explain the conversion of iron into steel using the basic oxygen converter.

THE BASIC OXYGEN PROCESS

The most common method of making steel is to blast pure oxygen through the impure molten iron. Scrap steel is placed in the converter (see Figure 1402), which is then tilted and molten pig iron is transferred from the blast furnace. The oxygen and powdered calcium oxide (lime) are blown onto the surface of the metal at high pressure through water cooled pipes. The oxygen penetrates into the molten iron and oxidizes the impurities rapidly. Acidic oxides of carbon, sulfur, phosphorous and silicon are formed, which escape from the melt as gases or combine with lime to form slag:

$$C + O_2 \longrightarrow CO_2$$

$$S + O_2 \longrightarrow SO_2$$

$$4P + 5\ O_2 \longrightarrow P_4O_{10}$$

$$Si + O_2 \longrightarrow SiO_2$$

$$SiO_2 + CaO \longrightarrow CaSiO_3\ (\text{slag})$$

Slag forms a layer above the crude steel (containing less than 1.5% carbon) and remains behind as liquid steel which is poured off. The oxidation of the impurities is an exothermic process and the heat evolved as the impurities are oxidized keeps the contents of the furnace in a molten state, despite a rise in the melting point as impurities

OPTION

are removed (recall: impurities lower and broaden the melting point of a substance). Alloying elements such as manganese and cobalt are then added to the molten metal to form alloys with specific properties.

C.1.4 Describe alloys as a homogeneous mixture of metals or a mixture of a metal and non-metal.

An **alloy** is a mixture of two or more elements at least one of which is a metal; thus it is a homogeneous mixture of metals or a mixture of a metal and non-metal in which the metal, called the base metal, is in the much larger amount resulting in metallic properties. The alloy is made by mixing the alloying element(s) with the base metal when molten and allowing the mixture to cool to form the alloy.

C.1.5 Explain how alloying can modify the properties of metals.

Metals contain a lattice of cations in a sea of electrons with an orderly arrangement of the atoms and with no rigid or directional bonds present in the metallic crystal structure (unlike, for example, in covalent macromolecular structures). As a result, metal layers are able to slide over each other when a stress is applied to it and are soft, ductile and malleable – properties typical of metals. The presence of another element, with differently sized atoms/cations, modifies the micro-structure of the base metal by disrupting the regular, repeating lattice, see Figure 1453. This now makes it difficult for one layer to slide over another. With atoms such as carbon, which are very much smaller than the metal cations, they can fit into the holes of the metal lattice disrupting the bonding between metal atoms and again impacting on the structure.

Alloying can modify physical properties such as hardness and malleability, as well as engineering properties such as tensile strength and chemical properties such as resistance to corrosion. For example, stainless steel and bronze are stronger and more corrosion resistant than their base metals iron and copper respectively. Addition of different amounts of metals to steel changes its hardness, resistance to oxidation and strength. Similarly when a low percentage of carbon is added to iron, there is less disruption in the lattice structure of the base metal. The steel can still be bent and shaped and thus used to make automobiles. As the percentage of carbon is increased, the disruption in the crystal lattice increases, the layers experience greater difficulty in sliding over each other and a stronger steel is formed that can be used to build bridges. Further increase in carbon (to about 1%) makes steel very hard and it can be used in drill bits. If the amount of carbon becomes higher still, to about 4% as in pig iron, it is so difficult for the layers to slide over each other that it becomes brittle and of little use for construction.

C.1.6 Describe the effects of heat treatment of steel.

Steel obtained from the basic oxygen converter (see Figure 1452) may not have the desired properties and often requires further heat (or mechanical) treatments. These lead to changes at the micro-crystal structure level that result in the desired effect. Thermal treatments include annealing, quenching and tempering:

Annealing is the process of slowly heating steel and holding it at a particular temperature (sometimes about half its melting point) to modify crystal structure, and then cooling it. The rate of heating and cooling and the temperature it is raised to depend on the type of steel and the desired properties. Annealing is used to soften steel (that is make it more ductile and malleable), remove

Stress applied to metallic structure

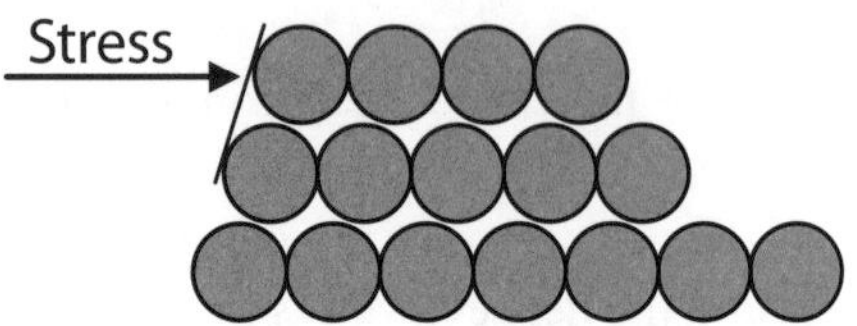

Layers are able to slide over each other when a stress is applied

Larger element disrupts regular metal lattice structure

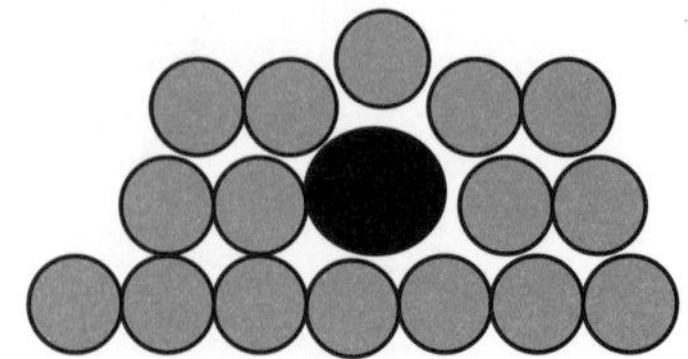

Figure 1403 How alloying can modify the properties of metals

OPTION

stress caused by uneven heating or mechanical treatment, change its electrical or other physical properties as well as remove trapped gases (which if not removed, weaken the steel making it susceptible to cracking).

Quenching refers to rapid cooling and involves the sudden immersion of hot metal in cold water or oil. Quenching allows the crystal structure which is stable at high temperatures to exist at low temperatures. These crystal structures tend to be harder than those stable at room temperature since the alloying elements are trapped within the crystal lattice making the sliding of layers very difficult. For example, carbon steel (containing nearly 1% carbon) is used for the production of cutting tools.

If the quenched steel is too brittle, it has to be made more ductile through a heat treatment called **tempering** which leads to a loss of some hardness but which makes the steel less brittle. Tempering is the process of re-heating hardened steel to certain temperatures (in the 200 °C to 600 °C range) depending on the type of steel and then cooling it (and is done subsequent to quenching). Tempering allows some of the carbon atoms to diffuse to form a different structure, making the steel softer and more ductile.

C.1.7 Describe the properties and uses of iron and steel.

Iron is a shiny, soft, ductile, malleable metal of high strength which can be shaped into objects. Iron rusts to form hydrated iron(III) oxide which crumbles easily:

$$4\,Fe\,(s) + 3\,O_2\,(g) + x\,H_2O\,(l) \longrightarrow 2\,Fe_2O_3\,.\,x\,H_2O\,(s)$$

Unlike aluminium oxide, rust is porous, allowing oxygen and water to penetrate it and continue the corrosion process.

Uses of iron include tin cans (mild steel coated with a layer of tin), ornamental gates, bridges, reinforcing concrete with steel and use as a catalyst in the Haber process. Most iron produced is used to make steel. Many different steels are made, with different properties for different uses. The amount of carbon and the alloying metals mixed with the iron largely determine the nature of the steel such as its tensile strength and other useful mechanical properties. Small amounts of elements such as manganese, are added to give desirable qualities such as toughness so that it can be used as tool steel. The presence of chromium as an additive to steel inhibits rusting and produces stainless steel. It also contains some nickel; formation of a coating of chromium(III) oxide, Cr_2O_3 prevents the iron from rusting. Other important steel alloys, their properties and some uses are given in Figure 1404.

C.1.8 Describe and explain the production of aluminium by electrolysis of alumina in molten cryolite.

Aluminium is obtained industrially by the electrolysis of molten aluminium oxide, Al_2O_3. This is obtained from bauxite, impure hydrated aluminium oxide, $Al_2O_3{\cdot}xH_2O$. The main impurities in bauxite are iron(III) oxide, Fe_2O_3 and silicon(IV) oxide, SiO_2. The amphoteric nature of Al_2O_3 is an essential feature on which its purification is based. When the impure bauxite is treated with hot concentrated sodium hydroxide, silicon(IV) oxide and aluminum oxide dissolve:

$$SiO_2\,(aq) + 2\,NaOH\,(aq) \longrightarrow H_2O\,(l) + Na_2SiO_3\,(aq)$$
sodium silicate

$$Al_2O_3\,(s) + 2\,NaOH\,(aq) \longrightarrow H_2O\,(l) + 2\,NaAlO_2\,(aq)$$
sodium aluminate

Iron + other metals	Important Properties	Some uses
Titanium steel	Withstands high temperatures	Gas turbines, spacecraft
Chromium steel	Hard	Ball bearings
Cobalt steel	High magnetic permeability	Magnets
Manganese steel (10 - 18% Mn)	Tough tool steel; resistant to wear	Earthmoving machinery, railway lines
Stainless steel containing about 20% chromium and 10% nickel	Non-rusting	Cutlery, sinks, car accessories, surgical instruments

Figure 1404 Properties and uses of some iron alloys

OPTION

Iron(III) oxide and other basic materials remain insoluble and are removed by filtration. The solution is diluted and seeded with solid sodium hydroxide to reverse the reaction and precipitate aluminium hydroxide (sodium silicate stays in solution):

$$2H_2O(l) + NaAlO_2(aq) \longrightarrow Al(OH)_3(s) + NaOH(aq)$$

Finally, the aluminium hydroxide is heated to obtain pure aluminium oxide:

$$2\ Al(OH)_3\ (s) \longrightarrow Al_2O_3\ (s) + 3\ H_2O\ (g)$$

Figure 1405 summarizes the treatment of impure bauxite to obtain pure aluminium oxide.

Aluminium is so reactive that it is obtained by electrolysis of molten salts, requiring high temperatures to maintain the molten state. The melting point of Al_2O_3 is > 2000 °C (the cation Al^{3+} and the anion O^{2-} both have high charge densities due to their relatively small sizes and large charges, leading to very strong electrostatic interactions, high lattice energy and a very high melting point; in addition there is a high degree of covalent character to the bonding so the molten substance is also a poor conductor). Alumina is mixed with molten cryolite, Na_3AlF_6, as a solvent which lowers the melting point to about 900 °C and improves the conductivity. The electrolyte is maintained at this temperature by the current through it and thus the process is energy intensive. The mixture of cryolite and alumina is electrolyzed in a cell with graphite (carbon) positive electrodes (anodes) and a graphite cell lining that serves as the negative electrode (cathode), see Figure 1406. As the electrolysis takes place, molten aluminium (melting point 660 °C) sinks to the bottom of the cell and is run off into molds.

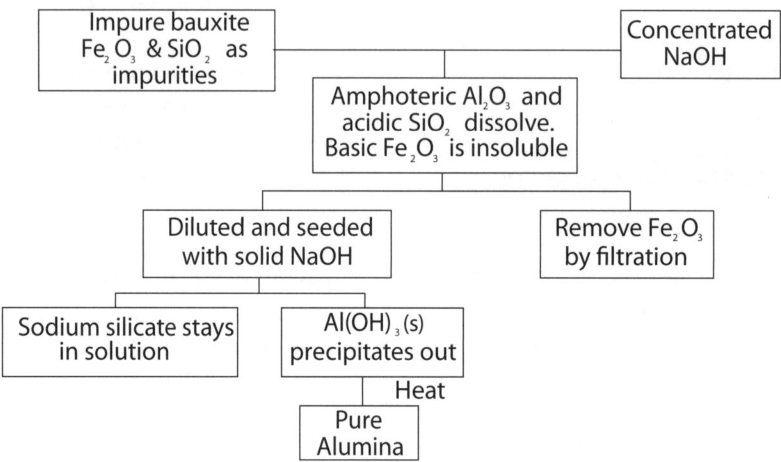

Figure 1405 Treatment of impure bauxite to obtain pure Al_2O_3

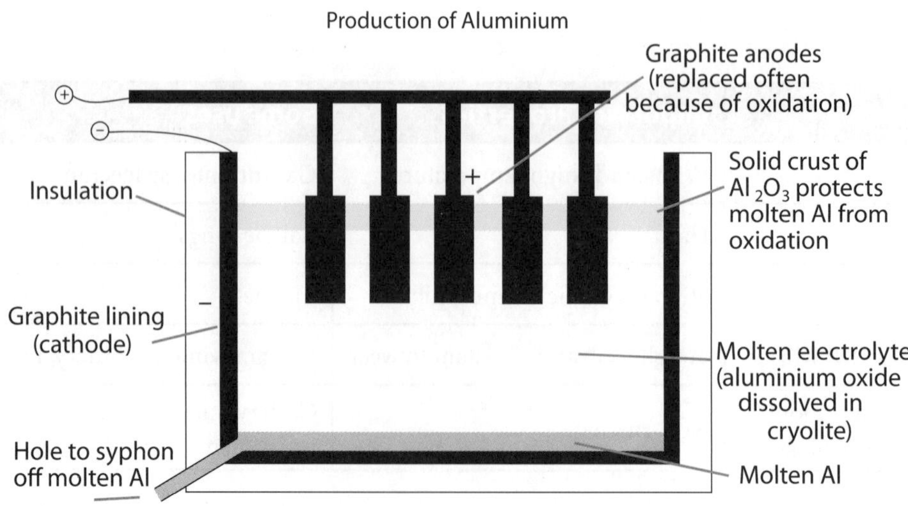

Figure 1406 Production of Aluminium

OPTION

(–) electrode half reaction (cathodic reduction; molten aluminium produced):

$$Al^{3+} (l) + 3 e^- \longrightarrow Al (l)$$

(+) electrode half reaction (anodic oxidation; oxygen gas evolved):

$$2 O^{2-} (l) \longrightarrow O_2 (g) + 4 e^-$$

The overall reaction is:

$$4 Al^{3+} (l) + 6 O^{2-} (l) \longrightarrow 4 Al (l) + 3 O_2 (g)$$

The O_2 produced reacts with the graphite positive electrodes (anodes) to form oxides of carbon:

$$C (s) + O_2 (g) \longrightarrow CO_2 (g)$$

Thus the anodes gradually burn away and are replaced regularly. Every ton of aluminium requires half a ton of carbon.

C.1.9 Describe the main properties and uses of aluminium and its alloys.

The position of aluminium in the electrochemical series and its electrode potential suggest it should react with oxygen to form its oxide and react with dilute acids to produce hydrogen:

$$Al^{3+} (aq) + 3e^- \longrightarrow Al (s); \quad E^\theta = -1.66 \text{ V}$$

$$H^+ (aq) + e^- \longrightarrow \tfrac{1}{2} H_2 (g); \quad E^\theta = 0.00 \text{ V}$$

The high chemical reactivity of the element is offset by rapid formation of a very thin, hard, non-porous film of aluminium oxide, Al_2O_3, over the surface, which protects the metal from further oxidation by oxygen or moisture (iron, on the other hand, forms a porous oxide rust layer allowing further rusting to continue underneath the rusted surface).

Aluminum is a light-weight, corrosion resistant metal with good electrical and thermal conductivity; it is also a versatile, malleable metal that can be made into a variety of shapes. Many of its alloys are very strong. Hence, aluminum is an excellent choice when a strong, but lightweight, metal is required. It is used both as a structural and decorative metal and as an electrical conductor in high voltage transmission lines.

Most of the uses of aluminum such as saucepans, aircraft and vehicle bodywork are possible because of the protective oxide coating. The thickness of the oxide layer can be increased by an electrolytic proces known as **anodizing**. This is done by making aluminium the anode during the electrolysis of sulfuric acid. Water is oxidized to oxygen at the anode:

$$2 H_2O (l) \longrightarrow O_2 (g) + 4 H^+ (aq) + 4 e^-$$

Oxygen combines with the aluminium and thickens the oxide layer, thus protecting it even further. The electrolytic anodizing process can be carried out in the presence of dyes which are absorbed by the oxide layer, thus coloring the anodized material to make it suitable for different uses such as window frames, kettles and drink cans. Light-weight aluminum alloys for different needs are made by the addition of elements such as copper, magnesium, manganese, silicon and zinc amongst others as shown in Figure 1407.

Aluminum alloy with:	Properties	Uses
Copper	Increased strength	Automobiles
Iron and silicon	Increased strength; heat resistant	Foil
Up to 12% silicon	Lowers the melting range	Welding
Magnesium	Hardened alloy; corrosion resistant	Marine work
Zinc (with smaller amounts of Mg, Cu and Cr)	High strength	Airplane frames

Figure 1407 Properies and uses of some aluminium alloys

C.1.10 Discuss the environmental impact of iron and aluminium production.

All of the processes in steel making, from the blast furnace to the final heat treatment and the production of aluminium by electrolysis use tremendous quantities of energy. In the production of a ton of steel, approximately one ton of coal is consumed and a ton of slag produced! About ten times more energy is needed to produce a ton of aluminium than to produce a ton of steel. The environmental effects of mining the ore depend on the extraction method used as well as the geographic area in which the ore is found. The mined areas can leave scars on the landscape unless the mining company decides to revegetate the area. The waste products of mining, '**tailings**', and the metal wastes from these can be very damaging to the environment. The purification of bauxite produces considerable waste of iron(III) oxide, the disposal of which, as it is a vivid colour, can result in visual pollution.

Recycled aluminium from aluminium cans requires approximately 5% of the energy needed to produce the metal from the ore. Thus, recycling is essential because it saves money, energy and fuels; it saves the environment and the reserves of materials and it reduces the problem of waste disposal. However, recycling is not always economically feasible as it can be labor intensive to collect, sort and process. The higher the value of the material, the more economical it is to recycle. Thus, virtually all gold is recycled, but only about half of the aluminium produced is recycled and a still lesser percentage of scrap iron and steel is recycled.

C2 THE OIL INDUSTRY

C.2.1 Compare the use of oil as an energy source and as a chemical feedstock.

By supplying a large part of the world's energy needs, crude oil has become the most important modern raw material. Although only about 10% of the refined products of crude oil are used as **chemical feedstock**, the raw materials required for an industrial process to produce petrochemicals, it is still the most significant source of organic chemicals. By itself, crude oil is not a very useful resource. However, it consists of a mixture of very useful hydrocarbons which are sources of energy such as petrol and other fuels for transport and oil heating systems.

Petrochemicals are organic compounds found in, or derived from, petroleum and are used in the manufacture of products other than fuels. Examples include polymers, drugs, cosmetics, paints, fertilizers, pesticides, detergents and dyes. Fractional distillation of crude oil produces lubricating oils, wax candles, ointments, polishes and chemicals which, in turn, are used to produce fibers, agricultural chemicals, synthetic rubber and solvents. Benzene from crude oil is converted to aminobenzene used in the preparation of drugs and dyestuffs; methylbenzene is nitrated to produce TNT and also to produce polyurethane foams for upholstery, insulation and flotation devices.

C.2.2 Compare catalytic cracking, thermal cracking and steam cracking.

The petroleum fractions with 1 to 12 carbon atoms in the molecule are in greater demand than other fractions. **Cracking** is the breaking up of larger, less useful, hydrocarbon fractions into shorter chain, more useful alkanes and alkenes which are used as fuels and petrochemical feedstock. Thus, cracking is a critically important process in the oil industry. Cracking can be achieved under different conditions of temperature, pressure and the presence or absence of a catalyst, steam or hydrogen gas. Thermal cracking is also called **pyrolysis**. For example, the presence of a catalyst reduces the temperature at which cracking occurs. In the absence of a catalyst, higher temperature (and pressure) is required. Steam cracking requires pre-heating and vapourising

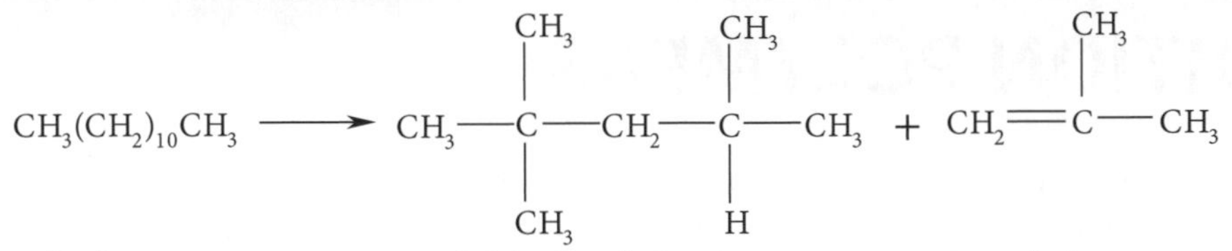

$$CH_3(CH_2)_{10}CH_3 \longrightarrow CH_3-C(CH_3)_2-CH_2-CH(CH_3)-CH_3 + CH_2=C(CH_3)-CH_3$$

Dodecane → 2,2,4-trimethylpentane + 2-methylpropene

Figure 1408 The thermal cracking of dodecane

the feedstock and mixing it with steam at still higher temperatures to form low molar mass alkenes.

The smaller alkanes are more easily vaporized and are more useful fuels. Cracking can also produce more branched hydrocarbons that are better as fuels as they have higher **octane numbers** and thus cause less **knocking** in the automobile engine. The alkenes are feedstock for other petrochemicals and form polymers with extensive uses. Use of different feedstocks, temperatures and catalysts produce different products, see Figure 1409.

*The powdered catalyst in catalytic cracking is treated to give it fluid-like characteristics for greater contact with the reactants. As a result of the decomposition of hydrocarbons, carbon deposits on the catalyst reduce its activity. From time to time air is passed through the reactor so the coke is burnt off to regenerate the catalyst. The combustion of coke produces energy which is used for further cracking.

	Catalytic cracking (Cat cracking)	Thermal cracking Pyrolysis; breaking using heat	Steam cracking
Feedstock: reactant molecules	Gas oil: 14 – 20 carbon chain liquids (250 – 350 °C boiling point range)	Kerosene: 10 – 16 carbon chain liquids (190 – 250 °C boiling point range)	Naphtha: 5 – 10 carbon chain liquids (40 – 190 °C boiling point range)
Reaction conditions	Lower temperatures of about 500 °C Moderately low pressures Catalyst: Powdered zeolite (aluminum silicate)'*'; historically silica and alumina used Short contact time	Moderate temperature range: 500 – 750 °C High pressure of about 70 atm. No catalyst Longer contact time	Higher temperature range: 800 – 900 °C Moderately low pressures No catalyst Very short contact time
Mechanism of reaction	Ionic intermediate; catalyst behaves as an electron pair acceptor forming carbocations	Free radicals formed; C—C bonds break so each atom has one unpaired electron	Free radicals formed; C—C bonds break so each atom has one unpaired electron
Products example	$C_{16}H_{34} \longrightarrow C_8H_{18} + C_8H_{16}$ Branched alkanes and alkenes	$C_{12}H_{26} \longrightarrow C_8H_{18} + C_4H_8$ Branched alkanes and alkenes	$C_6H_{14} \longrightarrow C_3H_6 + C_3H_8$ $C_4H_{10} \longrightarrow 2\,C_2H_4 + H_2$ Alkanes and alkenes (+ hydrogen)
Uses of products	High grade gasoline (branched chain alkanes increase fuel octane rating)	Lighter fractions used as fuel	Low molar mass alkenes used in polymer manufacture; hydrogen used in hydrocracking

Figure 1409 Comparison of different methods of cracking

OPTION

C3 ADDITION POLYMERS

Polymers are long chain macromolecules made by joining together many smaller repeating units called **monomers.** **Polyethene**, a typical addition polymer, is a giant molecule made of hundreds of thousands of ethene monomers joined together to make a long chain polymer, polyethene, represented by $-(C_2H_4)_n-$. The empirical formula for polyethene is CH_2, just as it is for ethene.

$$nCH_2=CH_2 \longrightarrow -(C_2H_4)_n-$$

This is an example of addition polymerization in which all the monomer's atoms are present in the polymer, a double bond is converted to a single bond and two extra single bonds are formed. Other alkenes can also undergo polymerisation (see FIgure 1410), the general equation for these reactions is:

$$nCHX=CH_2 \longrightarrow -(CHX-CH_2)_n$$

> C.3.1 Describe and explain how the properties of polymers depend on their structural features.
>
>

The greater the average chain length, the greater are the intermolecular forces and hence higher the strength and melting point of a polymer. Besides chain length and IMFs, three other structural features are generally important in determining the properties of addition polymers:

1. Branching: Depending on reaction conditions, polyethene can be made either as a high-density polyethene (HDPE) or low-density polyethene (LDPE) polymer. HDPE has little branching. Thus it is a 'linear' polymer in which the carbon backbone of the chain takes up a zig-zag pattern due to the tetrahedral structure for carbon bonded to four other atoms. Such a 'straight' chain polymer can pack closer together. Thus, it is strong and quite rigid with a comparatively high melting point (about 135 °C) and is used for making rigid articles such as buckets, milk bottle crates, disposable syringes, etc. However, in the low density polymer, side chains are present off the main chain. The presence of branches in LDPE limits how close polymer chains can come to each other, thus lowering intermolecular forces, leading to lower density and melting point (about 100 °C). LDPE is used to make plastic bags, wrappers, squeeze bottles, plastic bowls, etc.

2. Orientation (or position) of the alkyl groups along a polymer backbone chain: Different properties arise from the stereochemistry of the polymer chains. For example polypropene is made by the polymerisation of propene as shown in Figure 1411.

$$n\,CH_2=CH-CH_3 \longrightarrow \left[CH_2-\underset{CH_3}{\overset{H}{C}} \right]_n$$

Figue 1411 The formation of polypropene

The carbon atoms in the polymer backbone are arranged in a in a zig-zag manner (with tetrahedral angles) as shown in Figure 1412.

X in $CHX = CH_2$	Monomer	Polymer
H	Ethene	Poly(ethene)
CH_3	Propene	Poly(propene)
C_6H_5	Phenylethene	Poly(phenylethene), also called polystyrene
If X and H atoms replaced by F	Tetrafluoroethene	Poly(tetrafluoroethene); commercial name: Teflon

Figure 1410 Examples of addition polymerization of $CHX=CH_2$

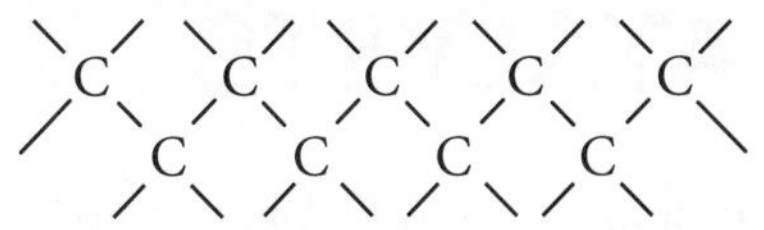

Figure 1412 The arrangement of the carbon 'backbone'

The hydrogen atom and the methyl side chain (—CH_3) can appear on either side of the backbone. If the methyl groups are all on the same side and the hydrogen atoms on the opposite side, that is the methyl groups are ordered with the same orientation, the polymer is said to be **isotactic**. Refer to Figure 1413. Polymers with regular isotactic arrangements can pack more closely with stronger intermolecular forces. Thus these polymers are tough and are used to make fibres, ropes, carpets and automobile bumpers. If the arrangement is random, that is without any order to the orientation of the methyl groups (which is the more likely), the polymer is called **atactic**. Refer to Figure 1413. Polymer chains in atactic polypropylene cannot pack as closely and are not held very tightly making polypropylene soft and flexible, with a low melting point and not very strong. It is, for example, used in making sealants and water-proofing materials.

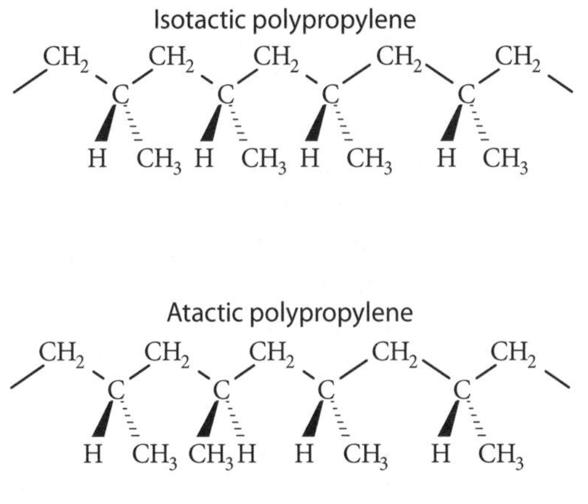

Isotactic polypropylene

Atactic polypropylene

Figure 1413 Isotactic and atactic arrangements

> C.3.2 Describe ways of modifying the properties of addition polymers.
>
> © IBO 2007

Plasticizers in polyvinyl chloride: The stronger dipole-dipole intermolecular forces between chains in the polymer polyvinyl chloride (PVC) lead to a rigid plastic. Plasticizers are small molecules added to a polymer. These reduce IMFs and allow polymer chains to slide over each other, producing a softer plastic. Medical products such as blood bags and intravenous drip tubes tend to be made of polyvinyl chloride containing a (diethylhexyl phthlate) plasticizer. A 10% concentration of the plasticizer produces a semi-rigid PVC and higher concentrations produce the more flexible polymers.

Volatile hydrocarbons in the formation of expanded polystyrene: This involves the polymerisation of styrene in the presence of a volatile hydrocarbon of low boiling point such as pentane, C_5H_{12}. This produces polystyrene containing the volatile hydrocarbon which, as it vaporises, causes the polystyrene to expand to several times its original size and hence have a reduced density. These expanded polystyrenes are very good thermal insulators and are used, for example, in making disposable coffee cups.

> C.3.3 Discuss the advantages and disadvantages of polymer use.
>
> © IBO 2007

Polymers are light, impermeable to water and can be pigmented, giving rise to articles with a wide variety of attractive colors. Since weak van der Waals' forces exist between polymer chains, most polymers become soft and melt on heating so they can be molded to form thin films and sheets as well as rods and tubes. Polymers contain strong covalent bonds within the polymer chains making them resistant to chemical reactions and they also generally have good electrical insulation properties. The advantage of polymers is that they can be specially made to exhibit different properties such as:

- Strength and high density: Examples include HDPE, rigid PVC, polystyrene.
- Flexibility and low density: Examples include LDPE, flexible PVC.
- Insulators: Polymers such as expanded polystyrene, and polytetrafluoroethene (PTFE) are excellent examples.

Disadvantages of plastics: The source of most synthetic polymers is petroleum, a non-renewable resource, so using plastics further depletes this. Other disadvantages include the volume occupied by plastics in landfills. These can have a substantial environmental impact as non-degradable materials collect and toxic fumes, caused by the burning plastics are released. Some other disadvantages appear under disposal of plastics.

Disposal of plastics is of key importance since currently a great deal of it ends up in landfills. There are four possible approaches to reducing this:

INCINERATION

Buried plastics represent a high energy content in landfills. Products of complete combustion of plastics are primarily carbon dioxide and water and can lead to a large reduction in plastic waste while producing useful energy. However, incineration does present problems namely: (i) carbon dioxide produced is a greenhouse gas, (ii) chlorinated polymers such as PVCs produce hydrogen chloride on combustion, leading to acid rain, (iii) if the incineration temperature is not high enough, toxic chemicals such as dioxins are formed and (iv) some printed plastic contains heavy metals such as lead and cadmium, which are toxic. Also, polyurethane foams produce toxic vapours (hydrogen cyanide and nitriles) when burnt.

BIODEGRADABILITY

The use of bacteria and fungi to break down plastics: Microorganisms are able to break down natural polymers such as cellulose and starch into simpler molecules using enzymes. Thus, starch can be incorporated into a plastic to make it biodegradable. The question of biodegradability is complicated by the fact that landfills are often lined to stop leaching into the water table. Unfortunately, such covering produces anaerobic (oxygen-free) environments where biodegradation by aerobic micro-organisms occurs very slowly or cannot take place.

RECYCLING

Recycling can reduce the amount of new plastics manufactured. The amount of plastic recycled ranges from very little to as much as 50% depending on government policies. There is a clear increase in the recycling of plastic bottles made of PET (**p**oly**e**thylene **t**erephthlate) which is easy to melt and reuse. This is true of any polymer that is not extensively cross-linked. The molten polymer can either be used in the manufacture of new products if the waste is made of similar monomers or it can be used to make plastic of lower quality with appropriate uses such as cheap plastic lumber. However, the sorting of plastic waste can be quite labour intensive.

CONSERVATION

As a society we have become voluminous users of plastics which are made from a non-renewable resource. Conservation, recycling and minimal use of plastics should be a key strategy in extending the life of non-renewable resources (Reduce, Reuse, Recycle).

C4 CATALYSTS

C.4.1: Compare the modes of action of homogeneous and heterogeneous catalysts.

C.4.2: Outline the advantages and disadvantages of homogeneous and heterogeneous catalysts.

C.4.3: Discuss the factors in choosing a catalyst for a process.

Catalysts are of vital importance in biochemistry (known as enzymes which are protein based), environmental chemistry (such as platinum and rhodium based catalytic converters), and industrial chemistry. Examples include iron in the manufacture of ammonia, vanadium(V) oxide in the Contact process for the manufacture of sulphuric acid, Zeigler-Natta organometallic catalysts in the production of high density polyethene, powder silica/alumina in catalytic cracking, nickel in the hydrogenation of vegetable oils to manufacture margarine amongst many others.

As discussed in Chapter 5, a catalyst is a substance that increases the rate of a chemical reaction without being chemically changed. It is usually required in small amounts and is not used up in the reaction (inhibitors or negative catalysts decrease the reaction rate). A catalyst speeds up a reaction by lowering the activation energy of a reaction involving different transition state(s) and providing an alternate path for it to occur (like a tunnel through a mountain) See Figure 1414 (a) and (b). With lower activation energy, a larger number of particles can now react successfully. However, ΔH of the reaction is not affected (it remains the same); neither is the position of equilibrium; a catalyst increases the rate of both the forward and reverse reactions equally.

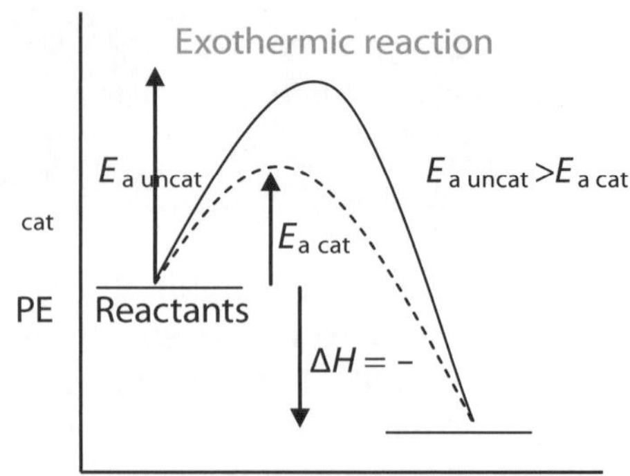

Figure 1414 (a) Exothermic reactions

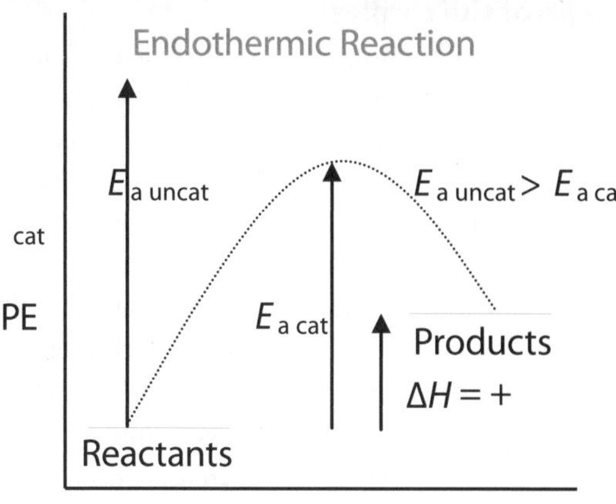

Figure 1414 (b) Endothermic reactions

The effect of a catalyst can also be shown on a Maxwell-Boltzmann distribution curve: In the presence of a catalyst, activation energy, E_a is lowered via an alternate pathway. Many more particles now have the minimum energy to react and rate increases. Refer to Figure 1415.

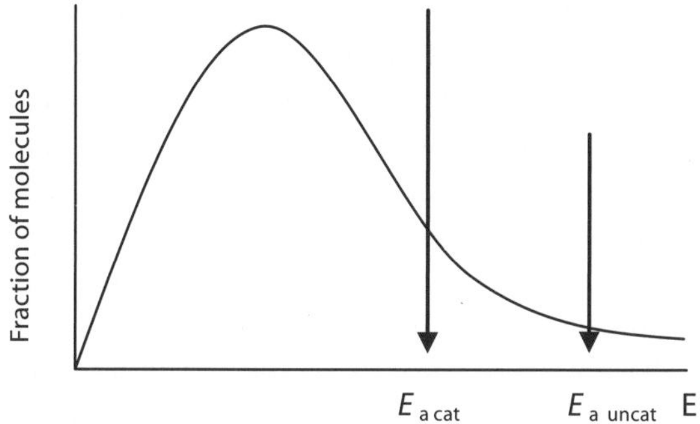

Figure 1415 A Maxwell-Boltzmann distribution curve

Catalysts can react at the surface or participate in the reaction. In surface catalysts such as nickel in the hydrogenation of alkenes, the surface of the catalyst provides active sites on which the reaction can occur with reduced activation energy. d block metals such as iron and nickel behave as surface catalysts. Intermediate catalysts such as aluminium chloride, $AlCl_3$, used in the halogenation and alkylation of benzene react with a reactant to form an intermediate ($AlCl_4^-$) and are regenerated at the end of the reaction.

Catalysts can be classified as homogeneous or heterogeneous catalysts:

In **homogeneous catalysis**, the reactants and the catalyst are in the same phase; the catalyst allows the reaction to take place by a different mechanism, with lower E_a, thus increasing reaction rate. In this process the catalyst reacts in a step of the mechanism and is regenerated at a later step. An example in aqueous solution is the reaction between $S_2O_8^{2-}$ (aq) and I^- (aq) in the presence of Fe^{2+} (aq) as a catalyst:

$$S_2O_8^{2-}\,(aq) + 2\,I^-\,(aq) \longrightarrow 2\,SO_4^{2-}\,(aq) + I_2\,(aq)$$

Fe^{2+} (aq) behaves as an intermediate catalyst: it is oxidized to Fe^{3+} (aq) and reduced to Fe^{2+} (aq) in the subsequent step:

$$S_2O_8^{2-}\,(aq) + 2\,Fe^{2+}\,(aq) \longrightarrow 2\,SO_4^{2-}\,(aq) + 2\,Fe^{3+}\,(aq)$$

$$2\,I^-\,(aq) + 2\,Fe^{3+}\,(aq) \longrightarrow 2\,Fe^{2+}\,(aq) + I_2\,(aq)$$

Another example is the formation of esters (sweet smelling compounds) used in the perfume and food industry (such as the smell of bananas, peaches, perfumes) that use concentrated sulfuric acid, H_2SO_4, as a catalyst:

$$CH_3COOH\,(aq) + C_2H_5OH\,(aq) \overset{H^+\,(aq)}{\rightleftharpoons} CH_3COOC_2H_5\,(aq) + H_2O\,(l)$$

Ethanoic acid + ethanol $\overset{H^+\,(aq)}{\rightleftharpoons}$ ethyl ethanoate + water

The forward reaction is the acid-catalysed formation of the ester, and the reverse reaction is the acid-catalysed hydrolysis of the ester; both are examples of homogeneous catalysis.

In **heterogeneous catalysis**, the reactants and the catalyst are in different phases, typically a solid catalyst with the reactants being in the gas or liquid phase where the catalyst provides the reactive surface upon which the reaction can take place. Examples include:

1. The **Contact Process**: Production of SO_3 for the manufacture of sulfuric acid, the 'king' of chemicals:

$$2\,SO_2\,(g) + O_2\,(g) \overset{V_2O_5\,(s)}{\rightleftharpoons} 2\,SO_3\,(g)$$

2. The **Haber Process**: Production of ammonia for manufacture of fertilizers, explosives (TNT), etc.

$$N_2\,(g) + 3\,H_2\,(g) \overset{Fe\,(s)}{\rightleftharpoons} 2\,NH_3\,(g)$$

3. Hydrogenation of an alkene containing C=C bonds (an example of an addition reaction):

$$C_2H_4\,(g) + H_2\,(g) \overset{Ni\,(s)}{\longrightarrow} C_2H_6\,(g)$$

OPTION

This type of reaction is used in the food industry to produce partially saturated compounds, for example, margarine.

Enzymes have some characteristics of both homogeneous and heterogeneous catalysts. Like homogeneous catalysts most enzymes occur in the same phase as the reactants, but like heterogeneous catalysts the reactants bind to an active site on the surface of the enzyme molecule. Enzymes are unique in that these are very specific, efficient and work best at body temperature. Enzymes can catalyse only one particular reaction unlike inorganic catalysts such as alumina, which catalyses many reactions. Enzymes differ from inorganic catalysts in their incredibly higher catalytic activity. In mammals and birds respiration occurs at 37 °C and requires numerous steps, each one catalysed. In the lab, the reaction occurs above 600 °C.

Modes Of Action Of Homogeneous And Heterogeneous Catalysts

Ability to form a range of oxidation states by transition metal compounds

Transition metal ions exhibit relatively stable multiple oxidation states by gaining or losing electrons in redox reactions. An example of homogeneous catalysis is the role of Iron(II)/(III) in speeding up the slow reaction between acidified hydrogen peroxide and iodide ions. The iron(II) is oxidised by the peroxide to iron(III) which is then reduced by the iodide ions to regenerate iron(II):

$$H_2O_2\,(aq) + 2H^+\,(aq) + 2Fe^{2+}\,(aq) \longrightarrow 2H_2O\,(l) + 2Fe^{3+}\,(aq)$$

$$2\,I^-\,(aq) + 2\,Fe^{3+}\,(aq) \longrightarrow I_2\,(s) + 2\,Fe^{2+}\,(aq)$$

These reactions occur more rapidly because both have lower activation energies than the reaction without the use of the catalyst.

An example of a heterogeneous catalyst involving change in oxidation number of the transition metal ion catalyst is the use of vanadium(V) oxide in the Contact process. In the first step, sulfur dioxide is oxidised to sulfur trioxide and the vanadium(V) is reduced to V(IV); subsequently, V(IV) is oxidised by oxygen to regenerate the catalyst:

$$SO_2\,(g) + V_2O_5\,(s) \longrightarrow SO_3\,(g) + V_2O_4\,(s)\ (\text{or } 2\,VO_2)$$

$$V_2O_4\,(s) + \tfrac{1}{2}O_2\,(g) \longrightarrow V_2O_5\,(s)$$

The shape of the catalyst

Enzymes are very complex in structure. The three dimensional shape of the globular protein molecules is crucial to the catalytic activity of enzymes. Enzymes and substrates are only effective if they have specific three–dimensional shapes which complement one another (the lock and key model). If the enzyme changes its shape or arrangement, the substrate will no longer be able to bind to the active site and the enzyme is rendered non-functional. This **denaturation** can take place when the surrounding environment changes even slightly. This may be brought about in several ways such as a variation in the temperature or pH of the solution, or by the presence of heavy metal ions (see Chaper 13, Section B 7.7).

For example, an increase in temperature increases enzymatic reaction rates up to a certain point as the substrates collide with active sites more frequently as the molecules move faster. However, the speed of the reaction drops sharply when the temperature reaches a certain point. Here, the thermal agitation of the enzyme disrupts the hydrogen bonds, ionic bonds and other non–covalent interactions that stabilize its active structure. If the three–dimensional structure is changed as a result of temperature, the enzyme activity is affected. All enzymes have an optimum temperature at which they are not yet denatured and the substrates collide fastest with the enzyme. In humans, enzymes have an optimum temperature of about 37 °C, about the same as the internal body temperature. Beyond this temperature, the change in the enzyme structure affects the active site (usually irreversibly) and the rate drops sharply. Figure 1416 shows the variation of reaction rate with temperature when the substrate concentration and pH and other factors are held constant.

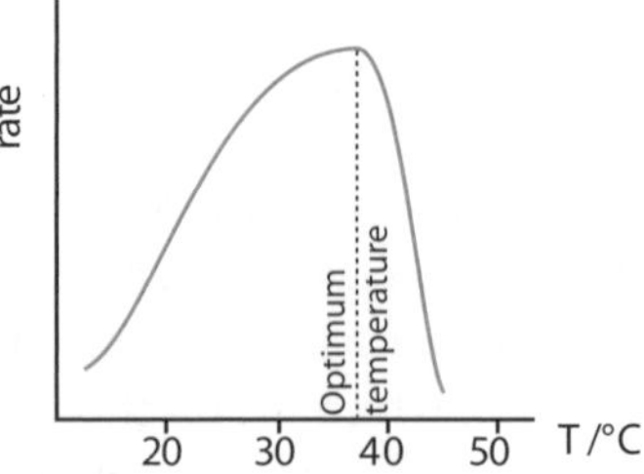

Figure 1416 The effect of temperature on enzyme activity

Proteins contain groups such as $—NH_2$ and —COOH and are susceptible to pH changes. Extreme changes in pH values denature such ionisable enzymes rendering them ineffective. At low or high pH values, the enzyme is irreversibly denatured and the rate drops sharply. Within a narrow pH range, the enzyme structure changes reversibly and each such enzyme works optimally at a specific pH. Thus the maximum rate for the enzyme chymotrypsin occurs around pH 8 and for pepsin this occurs at pH

	Homogeneous catalysts	Heterogeneous catalysts
Advantages	High activity as all the catalyst is exposed to the reactants High selectivity for single product as the catalyst has unique active sites	Solid catalysts are easy to remove and recover from products by filtration Long catalytic life
Disadvantages	Difficult to recover from reaction mixture for reuse	Only effective on the surface – hence most of the solid is not used; also, any coating on surface reduces activity

Figure 1418 Advantages and disadvantages of various catalysts

2. However, the enzyme invertase which catalyzes the hydrolysis of the neutral sucrose molecule has a constant rate in the pH range 3.3 to 7.5. Thus, if an enzyme is acting on an electrically neutral substrate molecule, or where the charge plays no role in the catalyzed reaction, changes in pH have little effect on the rate of this reaction. Figure 1417 shows the variation of reaction rate with pH when the substrate concentration, temperature and other factors are held constant.

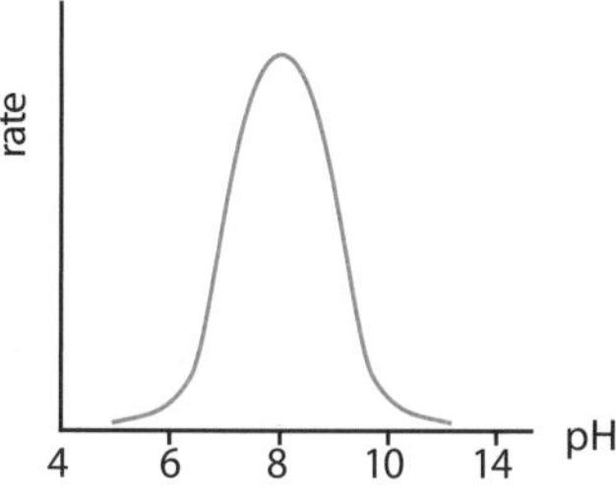

Figure 1417 The effect of pH on enzyme activity

Heavy metal ions can also disrupt some enzyme activity. When a heavy metal ion is present at the active site, substitution of a different metal ion for the original ion causes the enzyme to malfunction and denature, particularly where heavy metal ions can bind or chelate to the –S–H groups in proteins to form –S–M–S– type arrangement (see, also Chapter 13 Option B).

Availability of active sites

The region of the catalyst which binds to one or more reactants is called the **active site**. For enzymes the lock and key model illustrates how the substrate molecule binds reversibly to the active site to form the enzyme-substrate complex (in which the substrate forms weak bonds), the reaction is catalysed to form the enzyme-product complex and the products leave to make the active sites available for further catalytic activity. Refer also to Option B.

Heterogeneous catalysts contain active sites that are able to adsorb one or more reactants onto it to facilitate the reaction and reduce the activation energy. Adsorption is an increase in the concentration of one substance, the reactant, at the surface of another, the catalyst (it is different to absorption). Consider the hydrogenation of an alkene at the surface of nickel catalyst: on adsorption, the electron pair that holds the two hydrogen nuclei together in hydrogen and the electron pair in alkene forming the π bond of the double bond are attracted to the catalyst. This weakens the H—H bond and the C=C double bond making the reaction between the two faster. Once the product is formed it has weaker attraction for the active site and leaves, freeing the active site to adsorb other reactant molecules to its surface.

Good heterogeneous surface catalysts such as nickel, platinum and rhodium adsorb the reactants(s) sufficiently to lower the activation energy for reaction to take place but do not adsorb the product molecule which is released, allowing the process to continue. Metals such as silver adsorb reactant molecules too weakly (or tungsten which adsorbs too strongly) to be useful as surface catalysts. Figure 1418 shows the advantages and disadvantages of homogeneous and heterogeneous catalysts.

Factors In Selecting A Catalyst

Selectivity

Enzymes are highly selective and catalyse only one type of reaction. Good selectivity means only the desired product is produced and unwanted by-products are not formed. If a catalyst leads to unwanted products, it exhibits poor selectivity. Zeolites are examples of solid catalysts with regular molecular size porous holes (also called pores and channels). Zeolites are more selective as only molecules of the specific size can enter the holes and only products of size smaller than the holes can exit.

A good example of a zeolite catalyst in action is to compare the methylation of methylbenzene using $AlCl_3$ or zeolite as a catalyst. Since the methyl group is ortho, para (2,4-) directing (see Option G.10), the products are 1,2- and 1,4-dimethylbenzene. When $AlCl_3$ is used, the 1,2-isomer is formed in the larger amount as there are two ortho positions on benzene, but only one para position. A small amount of 1,3-isomer is also formed. However, using zeolite of specific sized pores, the product is almost entirely the 1,4-isomer since the other two isomers have a larger cross-section than the diameter of the pores.

1,2-dimethylbenzene

CH_3

CH_3

1,3-dimethylbenzene

CH_3

CH_3

1,4-dimethylbenzene

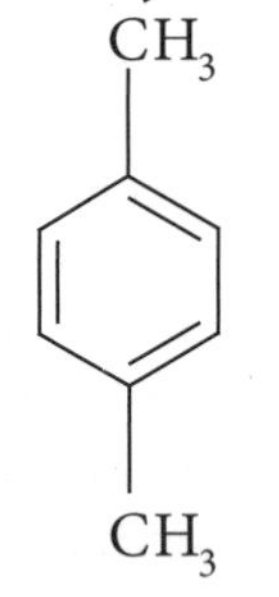

Figure 1419 The use of zeolite catalyst

Efficacy (or effectiveness)

This tells us how rapidly the catalyst forms the desired product. For example, zeolites expose a much larger surface area to reactants producing greater efficacy than $AlCl_3$. Hydrogen peroxide is decomposed by a variety of catalysts including manganese(IV) oxide, silver, platinum and iodide ion as well as the enzyme catalase. The enzyme, which contains iron at its active site, is, however, the most effective.

Ability to work under mild/severe conditions

One of the disadvantages of enzymes is that they work under narrow temperature and pH ranges and are easily denatured beyond these ranges. On the other hand, heterogeneous catalysts such as iron are effective under vastly different conditions of temperature and pressure, for example in the Haber process.

Environmental impact

Catalysts are in great demand with estimates of 80% of all chemical industries using catalysts. This raises the concern over their environmental impact. For example, the demand for the platinum group elements (platinum, rhodium, palladium) used in catalytic converters since the 1970s has increased greatly. Some of these metals are lost to the environment and raise the issue of potential health risks since, although cisplatin and other platinum based drugs are used in the treatment of cancer, these exhibit severe side effects and toxicity to living cells. Disposal of spent catalysts is a concern though the cost of the platinum group of elements makes a convincing argument for recycling. Also, research is providing new catalysts in place of acid catalysts to reduce environmental impact.

Catalyst poisoning

A catalyst can be poisoned or rendered ineffective. The efficiency of a catalyst usually decreases with time as it becomes inactive due to impurities in the reaction mixture, side reactions, or if its active surface becomes coated and unavailable for activity such as the coke coating on alumina or silica in catalytic cracking. The coke can, however, be burnt off to regenerate the catalyst. Enzymes denature by the effect of temperature, pH and heavy metal ions such as Hg^{2+} and Pb^{2+} if their structures are altered.

C5 FUEL CELLS AND RECHARGEABLE BATTERIES

C.5.1 Describe how a hydrogen–oxygen fuel cell works.

A **fuel cell** is a device that converts the chemical energy of fuels directly into electrical energy. Normally fuels are burnt converting chemical energy to heat which can be converted to electricity by generating steam to turn turbines. This is a highly inefficient method; fuel cells lead to a much more efficient conversion of chemical energy directly into electrical energy to generate power.

In a hydrogen-oxygen fuel cell, the negative electrode (anode) is made of porous carbon impregnated with the catalyst Pd or Pt; the positive electrode (cathode) is also made of porous carbon containing the catalyst Pt. These electrodes are separated by aqueous hydroxide electrolyte (KOH or NaOH) and the oxidation of hydrogen gas by oxygen gas takes place in a controlled manner.

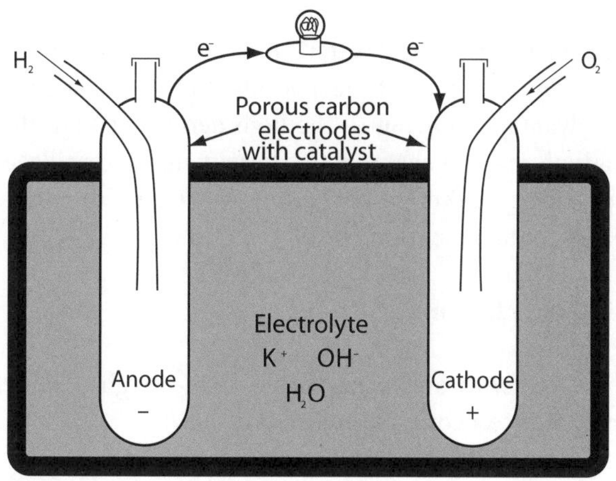

Figure 1420 Hydrogen-oxygen fuel cell

The oxidation process leads to the loss of electrons by the hydrogen gas, H_2 at the negative electrode (anode). The electrons flow out of the fuel cell and back to the positive electrode (cathode), via an external circuit to reduce the oxygen gas, O_2 to hydroxide ions, OH^-. Most commonly, the reactions take place in basic solution:

(–) anode oxidation half reaction:
$$2\,H_2\,(g) + 4\,OH^-\,(aq) \longrightarrow 4\,H_2O\,(l) + 4\,e^-$$

(+) cathode reduction half reaction:
$$O_2\,(g) + 2\,H_2O\,(l) + 4\,e^- \longrightarrow 4\,OH^-\,(aq)$$

Overall reaction:
$$2\,H_2\,(g) + O_2\,(g) \longrightarrow 2\,H_2O\,(l)$$

The net result is the oxidation of H_2 at the (–) anode electrode and and the reduction of O_2 at the (+) cathode electrode.

Half reactions in acidic conditions are also possible:

(–) anode oxidation half reaction:
$$2\,H_2\,(g) \longrightarrow 4\,H^+\,(aq) + 4\,e^-$$

(+) cathode reduction half reaction:
$$O_2\,(g) + 4\,H^+\,(aq) + 4\,e^- \longrightarrow 2\,H_2O\,(l)$$

Advantages and disadvantages of fuel cells: Fuel cells are highly efficient (70-80%) since they convert the chemical energy of the fuels directly to electrical energy. Thus these greatly reduce thermal pollution, as well as being less polluting in general as water is the product, so there is no release of greenhouse gases from the combustion of fossil fuels, though note that if electrolysis of water is used as a source of hydrogen gas for the fuel cell, the power for the electrolysis may well have come from fossil fuel plants. Fuel cells also tend to be light weight. On the other hand, fuel cells can experience technical problems ranging from leaks to corrosion and catalytic failures. The dangers of storing and transporting hydrogen gas also have to be considered. Fuel cells are used in the space program. These usually operate at about 70-140 °C, generate about 0.9 V and the water produced can be purified and used for drinking. Some fuel cells are used for commercial production of electricity in Japan. A great deal of research has taken place to make fuel cells for the auto industry in order to reduce the dependence on non-renewable fuel. Also, the production of carbon dioxide greenhouse gas is reduced and less is released into the environment. A combination of fuel cell and electrically powered hybrid solutions are also being developed.

C.5.2 Describe the workings of rechargeable batteries.

Rechargeable batteries are examples of secondary cells. These electrochemical cells are reversible, and can be recharged; the reactant concentration can be restored by applying an external source of electricity in the opposite direction.

Lead-acid storage battery

These are used in automobiles and are an important example of rechargeable batteries. They use lead plates (in practice an alloy) and moderately concentrated sulfuric acid as the electrolyte (see Figure 1421). The lead reacts with the acid to produce a coat of lead(II) sulfate on both electrodes. When the battery is charged up, at the electrode into which electrons flow, the lead(II) sulfate is reduced to lead metal (oxidation state = 0):

$$PbSO_4\,(s) + 2\,e^- \longrightarrow Pb\,(s) + SO_4^{2-}\,(aq)$$

and at the electrode that loses electrons the lead(II) sulfate is oxidised to lead(IV) oxide:

$$PbSO_4\,(s) + 2\,H_2O\,(l) \longrightarrow PbO_2\,(s) + 4\,H^+\,(aq) + SO_4^{2-}\,(aq) + 2\,e^-$$

This removes water and produces sulfuric acid, so the concentration of the acid electrolyte increases.

When the battery is used to power an external load these reactions are reversed, so at the electrode that behaves as the negative terminal, the lead anode is oxidised to lead(II) sulfate:

$$Pb\,(s) + SO_4^{2-}\,(aq) \longrightarrow PbSO_4\,(s) + 2\,e^-$$

At the electrode that acts as the positive terminal, the lead(IV) oxide cathode is reduced to lead(II) sulfate

$$PbO_2\,(s) + 4\,H^+\,(aq) + SO_4^{2-}\,(aq) + 2\,e^- \longrightarrow PbSO_4\,(s) + 2\,H_2O\,(l)$$

The overall reaction for the discharging process is:

$$Pb\,(s) + PbO_2\,(s) + 2\,H_2SO_4\,(aq) \longrightarrow 2\,PbSO_4\,(s) + 2\,H_2O\,(l)$$

This consumes sulfuric acid so the concentration of the acid decreases. Thus, the state of a battery can be determined from the density of the electrolyte solution using a hydrometer.

The battery is charged by the alternator while under operation in an automobile; a flat battery can be charged by a battery charger and the reverse reaction takes place:

$$2\,PbSO_4\,(s) + 2\,H_2O\,(l) \rightleftharpoons Pb\,(s) + PbO_2\,(s) + 2\,H_2SO_4\,(aq)$$

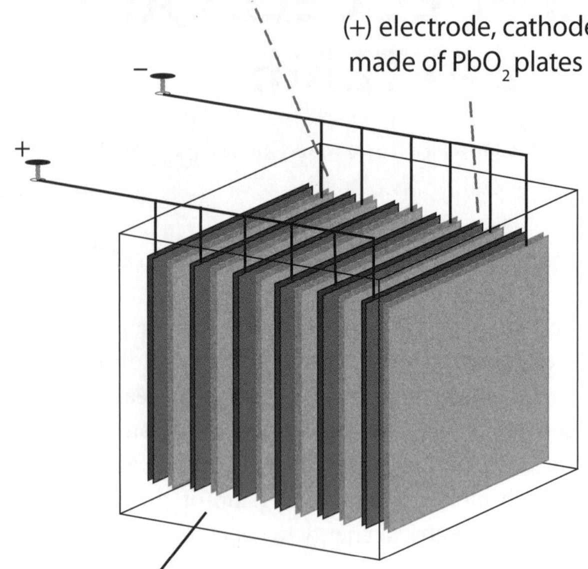

Figure 1421 The lead-acid storage battery

The voltage produced per cell is 2V. Thus, for a 12V car battery, six 2V cells are arranged in series. This produces 12 volts but internal resistance also increases, thus producing less current than six single cells.

Advantages of lead acid battery: It can deliver large amounts of energy for short time periods and is rechargeable. Disadvantages: Owing to the high density of lead, there is a high mass to charge ratio (heavy) and acid spillage is a possibility, although car batteries now tend to come in sealed containers.

Nickel–Cadmium ('NiCad') Batteries

These batteries are rechargeable, light-weight dry cells that produce a constant potential of 1.4V:

At the negative cadmium electrode (the anode), an oxidation half reaction takes place in the presence of hydroxide ions and Cd is oxidized to Cd^{2+}:

$$Cd\,(s) + 2\,OH^-\,(aq) \longrightarrow Cd(OH)_2\,(s) + 2\,e^-$$

At the positive nickel electrode (the cathode), a reduction half reaction occurs where Ni^{3+} in NiO(OH) is reduced to Ni^{2+}:

$$e^- + NiO(OH)\,(s) + H_2O\,(l) \longrightarrow Ni(OH)_2\,(s) + OH^-\,(aq)$$

OPTION

The overall reaction is:

$$Cd\ (s) + 2\ NiO(OH)\ (s) + 2\ H_2O\ (l) \longrightarrow Cd(OH)_2\ (s) + 2\ Ni(OH)_2\ (s)$$

Oxidation numbers:

0 +3

+2 +2

Cadmium is being oxidized from 0 to +2; nickel is reduced from +3 to +2. Insoluble hydroxides of cadmium and nickel deposit on the electrodes and half reactions are easily reversed during charging. The reducing agent cadmium and oxidizing agent NiO(OH) are regenerated on recharging:

$$Cd(OH)_2\ (s) + 2\ Ni(OH)_2\ (s) \longrightarrow Cd\ (s) + 2\ NiO(OH)\ (s) + 2\ H_2O\ (l)$$

A Ni-Cd battery experiences the 'memory" effect which occurs when it is charged after being incompletely discharged (this happens as a result of unreactive surface formed on the electrodes that stops reactions during recharging). It is thus best to completely discharge the battery before being re-charged. The nickel and cadmium are more expensive, produce a lower voltage, but have longer life than lead-acid accumulators. Cadmium is toxic to many life forms and there are environmental concerns about the disposal of toxic cadmium containing batteries.

C.5.3 Discuss the similarities and differences between fuel cells and rechargeable batteries.

Figure 1422 gives the similarities and differences between fuel cells and rechargeable batteries.

Fuel cells and rechargeable batteries

Similarities	Differences
Both devices convert chemical energy directly into electrical energy using spontaneous redox reactions. Both have similar modes of operation, namely, negative anode electrodes where an oxidation half-reaction takes place and positive cathode electrodes where a reduction half-reaction takes place.	Fuel cells are energy conversion devices whereas rechargeable batteries are energy storage devices. Fuel cells require a constant supply of reactants (an example of an open system) and produce electrical energy only as long as fuel is made available to the cell. Batteries on the other hand have stored chemical energy in a closed system and provide power until the stored chemicals are used up. Batteries can be recharged; this uses electrical energy to carry out the reverse reaction. Recharging takes a battery out of operation. A fuel cell, on the other hand, does not need recharging like a battery. Rather, it can have a continuous supply of fuel (by replacing empty fuel containers with full ones) providing longer operating life. The electrodes in fuel cells are made of inert materials (such as porous carbon impregnated with platinum and palladium as a catalyst) which allow the movement of hydrogen, oxygen and water. Fuel cells are currently more expensive than rechargeable batteries.

Figure 1422 Comparing fuel cells and rechargeable batteries

Lithium-ion battery

The very high activity of lithium metal means an oxide layer forms over the metal easily reducing the contact with the electrolyte in a battery. This is overcome in the lithium-ion battery which contains no metal and involves the movement of lithium ions between the negative anode and the positive cathode electrodes through the electrolyte, a lithium salt in an organic solvent. Such cells use carbon graphite as the negative electrode (anode). Lithium ions can enter (insert) into the graphite lattice with an approximate LiC_6 composition. The positive electrode (cathode) is a metal compound, for example of formula MO_2, such as manganese(IV) oxide (MnO_2), cobalt(IV) oxide (CoO_2) or nickel(IV) oxide (NiO_2). Oxidation occurs at the negative electrode (anodic oxidation):

$$LiC_6 \longrightarrow Li^+ + 6\,C + e^-$$

Lithium ions in solution enter the oxide positive electrode where reduction occurs (cathodic reduction):

$$Li^+ + e^- + MnO_2 \longrightarrow LiMnO_2$$

The net result is the movement of lithium ions from the negative anode to the positive cathode: The overall reaction is:

$$LiC_6 + MnO_2 \longrightarrow 6\,C + LiMnO_2$$

It is the difference in the free energy of lithium between LiC_6 and $LiMnO_2$ that powers the cell. The electrodes are called insertion electrodes as small lithium ions can be inserted (and removed) into the electrode lattice. On recharging, the reverse reaction takes place. The lithium-ion battery does not suffer from the 'memory' effect that Ni-Cd batteries do.

OPTION

C6 LIQUID CRYSTALS

C.6.1 Describe the meaning of the term liquid crystals.

C.6.2 Distinguish between *thermotropic* and *lyotropic* liquid crystals.

C6.3 Describe the liquid-crystal state in terms of the arrangement of the molecules and explain thermotropic behaviour.

C.6.4 Outline the principles of the liquid-crystal display device.

C.6.5 Discuss the properties needed for a substance to be used in liquid-crystal displays.

LIQUID CRYSTALS

The states of matter depend on the mobility of particles and typically include solid, liquid and gas which depend on temperature. For example, 'water' is ice below 0 °C, water between 0 and 100 °C and water vapour above 100 °C (at 1 atmosphere pressure). In solids, particles have an orderly, three dimensional arrangement in which molecules are fixed in position and orientation (pointing in the same direction) and are arranged in a repeating pattern to give a particular crystal lattice. In liquids, the molecules are free to move about randomly and can change their orientation (typically, liquids occupy a little more space than solids; water and ice are an exception due to hydrogen bonding in ice that gives rise to holes in the crystal structure). Ordinary liquids are called **isotropic** (meaning independent of direction) as the molecules are randomly arranged, have no orientation order and exhibit no long range order. The distribution of the particles is such that, overall, ordinary liquids have the same physical properties such as optical, magnetic and electrical properties when viewed from any direction.

On the other hand, some substances exist in what is called the *mesophase* (meso meaning between), sometimes called the 'fourth state'. For example, cholesterol myristate is a solid below 71 °C and a clear liquid above 86 °C. In between, it exists as a cloudy liquid. Such liquid crystals (LCs) have some order but also some ability to flow, namely these are in a phase with order between that of a liquid and a solid. There is a degree of orientation of molecules in LCs like a solid, but molecules also move to different positions, that is, a loss of order in the position takes place similar to a liquid, thus the apparent contradiction in the name: 'liquid crystal' (LC).

LCs are fluids that have physical properties (such as electrical, optical and elasticity) that are dependent on the molecular orientation relative to some fixed axis in the material, making them unique in their properties and uses.

Elongated, moderate size organic molecules tend to form liquid crystals that orient on their longer axis, although liquid crystals are not restricted to elongated molecules; disc-like and banana-shaped molecules of liquid crystals are also possible. One example of an elongated organic liquid LC is called MBBA in which the benzene rings form a planar skeleton as shown in Figure 1423.

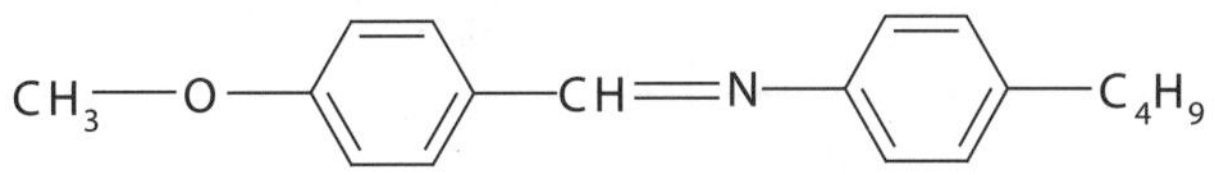

$CH_3—O—C_6H_4—CH{=}N—C_6H_4—C_4H_9$

Figure 1423 Structural formula of MBBA

Examples of LCs include biological materials such as cell membranes (for example, phospholipids), aqueous polymeric DNA solutions, some viruses such as the tobacco mosaic virus, the solution extruded by a spider to form silk threads, micelles such as soap solution, colloidal solutions, graphite and cellulose amongst others. Note that liquid crystal materials may not always be in the liquid phase just as water is not always in the liquid phase.

Thermotropic and lyotropic lcs

Thermotropic LC materials are pure substances that occur as LCs over a certain temperature range between the solid and liquid phases such as the example of cholesterol myristate given previously. At the temperature below the range, the substance forms a solid crystal; above the temperature range, it turns into the liquid phase. The biphenyl nitriles (cyanobiphenyls) are common examples of thermotropic LCs, for example 5CB, which is crystalline below 18 °C, an isotropic liquid above 36 °C and LC between the two temperatures. See Figure 1424.

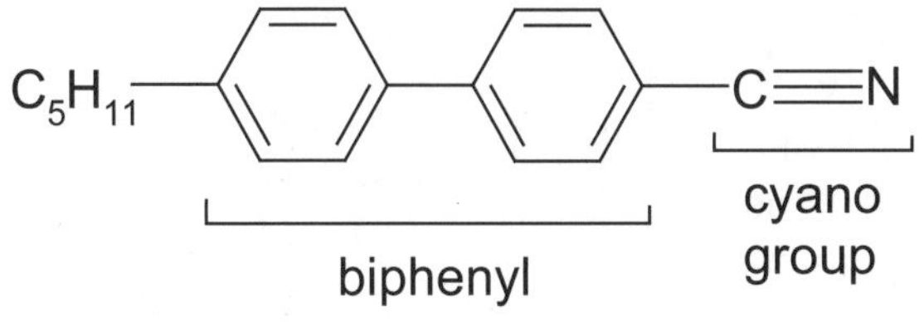

$C_5H_{11}—C_6H_4—C_6H_4—C{\equiv}N$

biphenyl

cyano group

Figure 1424 A thermotropic LC

Lyotropic LCs, on the other hand, are solutions that show the liquid crystal state at certain concentrations, that is as a function of the concentration of the molecules, such as soap or detergent, in a solvent such as water (in this case leading to the formation of micelles LC example). Above a certain soap concentration, a LC phase is formed in which the the carbon chain hydrophobic tail of the soap molecules point away from the polar water while the hydrophilic soap components point toward the water.

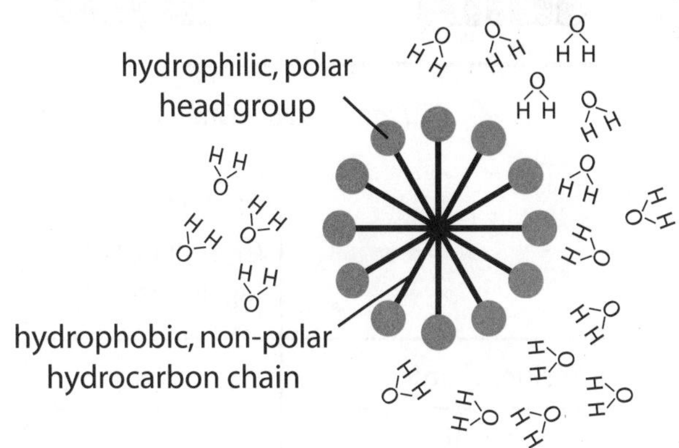

Figure 1425 A lyotropic LC

Thermotropic behaviour in terms of arrangement of molecules in LC state:

In the crystalline solid, the rod-shaped molecules are fixed in position and direction: these are parallel, arranged in layers and the layers positioned one over the other (as shown in Figure 1426) in a three-dimentional arrangement. The intermolecular forces present in a solid lattice of a LC are different in various directions. As the solid crystal is heated, first the weak forces are overcome; the heating disturbs the precise order of molecules giving rise to random arrangement in some direction, but the stronger forces are still at play and this provides regular arrangement in other directions. In **smectic LCs**, layers still exist (the molecules are still arranged in layers) with movement within layers so that the molecules are roughly parallel. See Figure 1426.

Further heating disrupts the long range positional order to form **nematic LCs** in which the layer arrangement no longer exists. See Figure 1426. In nematic LCs, the rod-shaped molecules are distributed randomly but, on average, point in the same direction; this is typically used in LCDs. On still further heating, the increased thermal agitation disrupts this directional order until it is lost when the isotropic (normal) liquid phase is formed with loss of directional order as well. It is the ability of molecules in a LC to point in a particular axis, called the director, that is its distinguishing feature:

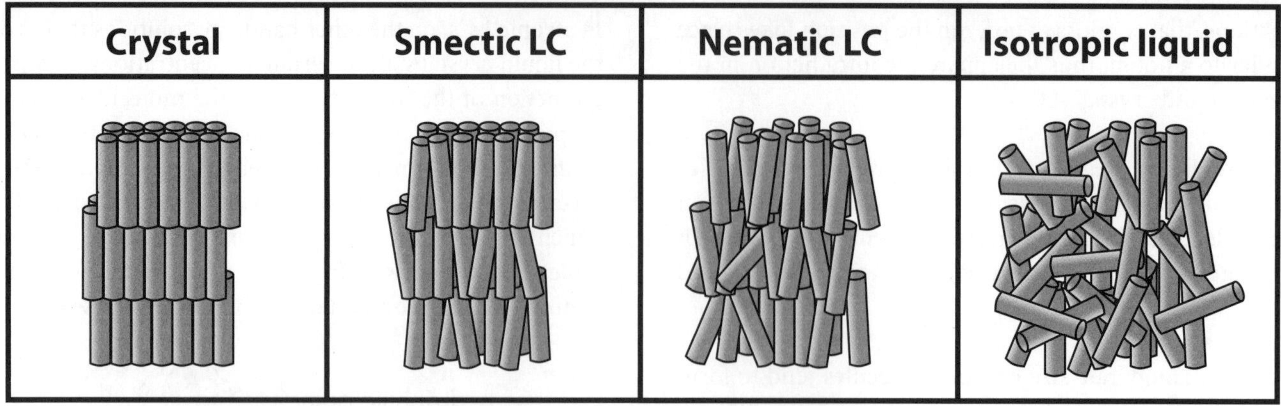

Figure 1426 Order in crystals, smectic LC, nematic LC and isotropic liquids

	Crystalline Solid: highly ordered	Liquid Crystal		Isotropic Liquid: No long range order
		Smectic	Nematic	
Positional order	Yes	Some	No	No
Directional (orientational) order	Yes	Yes	Yes	No

Figure 1427 A comparison of LC forms for positional and directional order

Principles of liquid-crystal display devices

A polarizer allows light in which the electric field vibrates in only one direction to pass through as shown in Figure 1428 (a) and (b) at right.

In crossed polarizers, where one polarizer is perpendicular to the other one in its direction of propagation, no light transmission takes place after the second polarizer, as shown in Figure 1429.

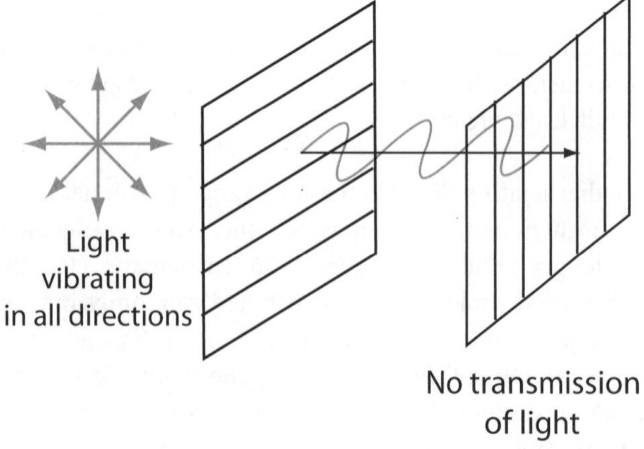

Figure 1429 The principle of cross-polarization

a) Polarizer in the *x* direction

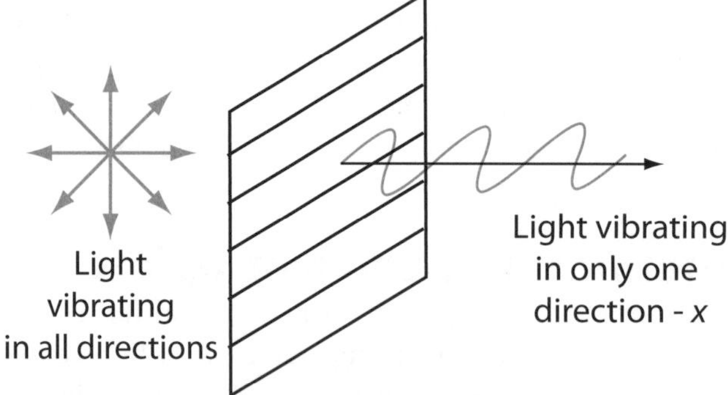

b) Polarizer in the *z* direction

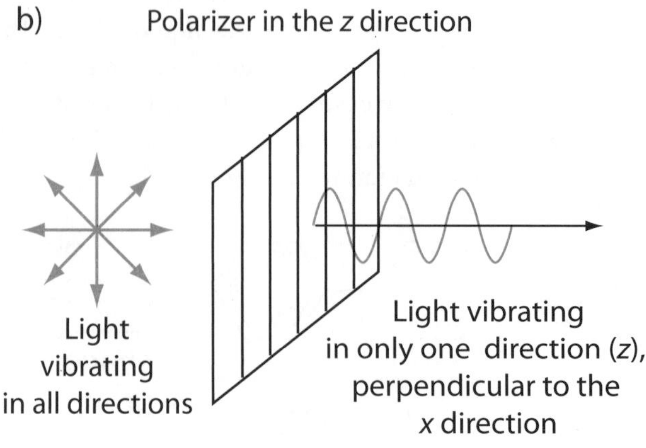

Figure 1428 (a) and (b) The principle of a polarizer

OPTION

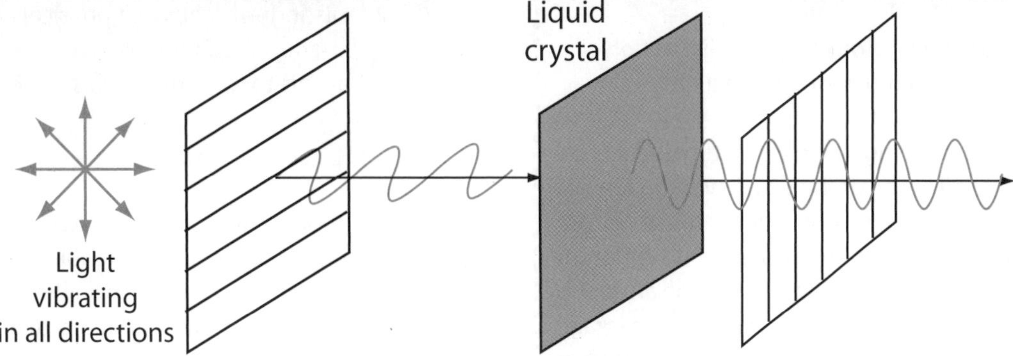

Figure 1430 The use of an LC with a polarizer

If, however, a liquid crystal is placed between the above two crossed polarizers, transmission of light can occur after the second polarizer as shown in Figure 1430.

This suggests that a LC is able to rotate or twist the plane of polarization of the light propagating through it. As stated earlier, it is the ability of molecules in a LC to point in a particular axis, its director, that allows LC molecules to transmit light depending on the orientation of the molecules. The orientation of the polar LC molecules can be controlled by the application of a small voltage across a thin film of the material. The areas of the display that are light and dark can be controlled in this way.

LCDs use very little electrical power and are thus ideal for use in battery operated electronic devices such as calculators, radios, digital watches, laptop notebooks, mobile phones, flat panel displays (LCD TVs), etc. leading to a multi-billion dollar industry.

Properties needed for a substance to be used in liquid-crystal displays:

The earliest LC materials, the cyanobiphenyls were found to be ideal for use in LCDs because these molecules possess a number of important properties: Their chemical stability means they do not decompose in the instruments; they are operational at room temperature and the LC phase is stable over a wide and suitable temperature range (for example, from about –10 °C to 60 °C). Additionally, the materials have dipoles (polar or easily polarizable). This is essential as the application of an electrical field leads to a change in the orientation of the molecules. Also, LCs must have a rapid switching speed between orientations so there is no lag when a small voltage is applied, that is, they must have a fast response time to the applied electric field.

C7 NANOTECHNOLOGY

C.7.1 Define the term nanotechnology.

C.7.2 Distinguish between physical and chemical techniques in manipulating atoms to form molecules.

C.7.3 Describe the structure and properties of carbon nanotubes.

C.7.4 Discuss some of the implications of nanotechnology.

"Nanotechnology has given us the tools … to play with the ultimate toy box of nature – atoms and molecules. Everything is made from it… The possibilities to create new things appear limitless."

Horst Stormer (Nobel laureate)

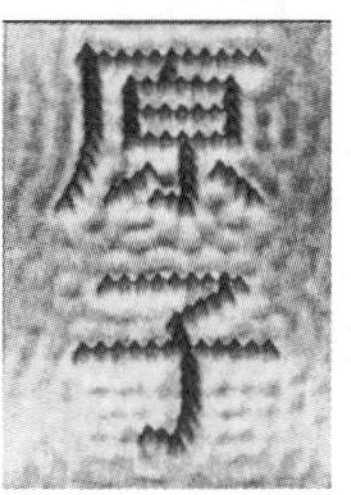

Figure 1431 Atomic art?

Figure 1431 shows the Japanese Kanji, which means 'atom', written literally with atoms, each just a few nanometres across.

TOK Does technology blur the distinction between simulation and reality?

The scanning tunnelling microscope turns electrical signals generated as the probe turns over the sample into an image. Does the way it does this vary from machine to machine? In other words do different machines give the same image? Even if the answer is "yes" then surely the signals are turned into an image according to some model – is this reality? If not then I suppose we could ask which image is the correct image? There are almost certainly features they have in common, like the arrangement and spacing of the atoms, but this at present only reinforces data we have from other techniques such as X-ray diffraction, using which we have been able to construct 3D models. So does being able to "see" atoms actually make us more certain of the atomic model, because it allows a simulated direct visual display? Compared to other things the effect of the scanning tunnelling microscope on blurring simulation and reality is probably pretty trivial. What do you think?

Nanotechnology involves measurements in the nanometre scale, namely 10^{-12} m range which is the size of a group of atoms; DNA molecules are about 2.5 nm wide, the smallest bacterium is about 200 nm wide whereas human hair is about 100,000 nm wide. **Nanoparticles** often have physical and chemical properties that are quite different and novel since a large proportion of the small group of atoms are at the surface, that is they have a large surface area to volume ratio compared to bulk matter. For example, gold is known for its chemical inertness. However, at the nanoscale it is reactive, catalytic and its melting point is much lower (in fact a liquid at about room temperature) compared to the macroscale element. Particles of gold can also appear red, blue or gold, depending on their size. Thus at nanoscale, properties do not depend only on composition and structure of the matter as they do at the macroscale.

Definition of the term nanotechnology: "Nanotechnology involves research and technology development at the 1 nm to 100 nm range. (It) creates and uses structures that have novel properties because of their small size. Nanotechnology builds on the ability to control or manipulate at the atomic scale."

(Definition from IBO Guide as quoted from the Nanotechnology Initiative.)

OPTION

C.7.2 Distinguish between physical and chemical techniques in manipulating atoms to form molecules.

Scanning probe microscopes (such as the scanning tunnelling microscopes, STMs) are able to move individual atoms one atom at a time, or allow the controlled deposition of single atomic or molecular layers one on top of another. Metals can be vaporized and atomic layer deposition leads to nanoparticles when cooled. These are examples of physical techniques which allow atoms to be manipulated and positioned to specific requirements. On the other hand, chemical techniques position atoms in molecules using chemical reactions. Thus whereas a STM can be used to move a carbon monoxide molecule to an iron atom, a voltage can be used to chemically bind these together. Similarly, a voltage activated platinum-rhodium tip on a STM can catalyse the homolytic fission of hydrogen gas and deposit the hydrogen atoms across a C=C alkene double bond placed on a surface. The result is selective hydrogenation of the double bond.

C.7.3 Describe the structure and properties of carbon nanotubes.

A carbon nanotube (CNT) is made of rolled graphite (graphene) along an axis consisting of carbon hexagons and closed at the ends by hemispherical (half-size) fullerene-like caps or domes requiring carbon pentagons to close the structure at the ends. Nanotubes are hollow cylinders made of carbon atoms and can be one atom thick (single-wall carbon nanotubes - typically about 1 nm wide, but wider ones can be formed) or multi-walled carbon nanotubes consisting of concentric nanotubes with a smaller one in a larger one, like a set of Russian matryoshka dolls. Typically the sides of the tubes contain hexagons, the caps hexagons and pentagons. The latter are rather more susceptible to chemical reactions and the reactivity allows particles of metals, metal oxides, metal salts amongst others to be inserted into the nanotubes. Figure 1432 shows a single-walled carbon nanotube

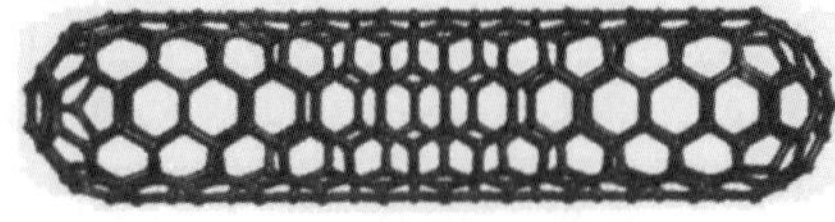

Figure 1432 A single-walled carbon nanotube

The structure of a nanotube determines its properties such as electrical and thermal conductivity. Whereas graphite is soft and somewhat malleable, CNTs are structurally rigid and extremely strong, many times stronger than steel. Like graphite, carbon atoms are bonded by strong covalent bonds with sp^2 hybridization along the nanotube length. They also exhibit unique electrical properties, and can act either as excellent electrical conductors or semiconductors depending on the length and multi-walls present. The narrower the diameter of the nanotube, the less it behaves like graphite. As the diameter gets wider, the more its bulk properties are similar to those of graphite; this is typical of the nanoscale materials mentioned earlier.

C.7.4 Discuss some of the implications of nanotechnology.

Possible applications

Currentapplicationsincludeinvisiblesuncreenscomprising titanium or zinc oxides, bacteriocidal bandages with silver nanoparticles, production of spill-proof, water repellent and wrinkle free garments (requiring infrequent cold water cleaning), heterogeneous catalysis and microcircuits, amongst many others. Progress in nanotechnology research and development is rapid as governments, research institutions and industry are investing heavily in it. Potential uses range from development of vaccines and drugs to faster, cheaper and more powerful electronics with much higher storage capacities, to light weight, longer lasting materials for construction, transportation and everyday uses that require less energy and resources and cause less pollution.

Nanomedicine and bionanotechnology are examples of new multidisciplinary fields with developments in, for example, drug delivery methods. If drugs can be targeted just to cancer cells in the correct dosage, the benefit would be tremendous to society in terms of reduced costs and fewer possible side effects. Similarly the possibility of using nano-amounts as catalysts in catalytic converters, fuel cells, oil refineries and chemical industries can go a long way to reducing pollution. Incredible possibilities are being suggested for nanotechnology – no doubt it will lead to beautiful successes and spectacular failures. It certainly has lead to "Nano-Buzz" and "Nano-Hype".

Heath and environment effects and concerns

It is possible that the combination of small size and distinctive properties may pose environmental and or health risks. The small size means it is easy to inhale nanoparticles. For example, the ultra thin soot particles from industrial activity are known to have adverse effects on the respiratory system of humans. What about possible cancer causing risks if nanoparticles can change the genetic makeup of cells? Will nanoparticles be able to cross the blood-brain barrier and if they can, what will the effects be? What about the use of metal oxide nanoparticles in sunscreens, is there any potential hazard as a result of absorption through the skin? Nanoparticles have been found to be harmful to animals. If these can enter the lymphatic system, the body's immune system, by passing through the skin's top layer, there could be health concerns.

Toxicity concerns

The field of **nanotoxicology** is concerned with various apsects of the toxicity of nanoparticles, since such materials have properties quite different from their macro counterparts. For example, an inert material may become very reactive at the nanoscale and the current standards of toxicity for that substance may no longer apply. Thus a determination of the harmful effects of nanoparticles to humans and the environment presents a great challenge since there are many variables involved such a size, shape, surface area to volume ratio etc. Nanoparticles tend to aggregate and the properties of these nanoclusters tends to be different from nanoparticles, further complicating toxicity issues. The website www.nanotoxicity.php makes several references to the toxicity of nanotubes and this is an area that requires more research and data in order to establish toxicity standards. As more data is available, nanotechnology will require international regulations and restrictions on the production and use of harmful products.

Responsibilities of industries

If nanotechnology does not require heavy industry, scarce natural resources and massive capital, it has the potential for exponential growth of manufacturing systems leading to fast acceleration in manufacture and improvement of products and use of inexpensive raw materials (as much smaller amounts will be required). The responsibility of industries to rise to the challenges posed by nanotechnologies will require working to the highest ethical and social standards while balancing between global and self interest.

Ethical and political issues

The implications of nanotechnology are many and these have given rise to new interdisciplinary areas of study ranging from nanoethics (the ethical and social uses in developing nanotechnology, for example the military uses such as cheaper, more powerful weapons) to nanopolitics, (such as the need for public education, for informed debate and for public involvement in policy discussions). The nano-divide is the concern of the increase in the gap between the poor and the rich; could nanotechnology help reduce the divide by making smaller and cheaper technology available to a larger number of people around the world? Nanotechnology is still at an early stage and the science behind it is not fully understood. It is of global importance and successful use of nanotechnology for the benefit of humans will require a joint effort by governments, industry, academia and businesses from around the world.

TOK Science versus Politics

Who should determine priorities in the funding of research?

Can anything ever be 'values free'? As humans we inevitably have values and cannot help regarding everything in the light of these values. These values of course are the fundamentals of moral judgements and differ from person to person. There are various moral codes such as Utilitarianism, "Might is right", "Do unto others as you would have them do to you", "Cultural relativism".

I suppose, pragmatically, the basic principle guiding research has to be "He who pays the piper calls the tune". If you don't want any money to do it, then you can probably research into what you like – as long as it's legal. Again I don't think there is much question about this with regard to private research institutions; if ICI is paying for the research then nobody questions them telling their scientists what to investigate. With research that takes place in state institutions then it is not quite clear who is paying the piper. Sometimes industrial companies will sponsor a research worker and again probably they have the right to direct that research, but what about the others? Maybe there shouldn't be any others, maybe those who are likely to profit should pay like industry does, but who then would be likely to profit? In the short term, shall we pay for better mapping of the Earth's magnetic field by an expensive satellite? It might never get done even though in the long term there could be lots of benefits, generally impossible to predict at the outset. The laser is a good example of a discovery that has transformed so many things and which came out of some "blue sky" research. I suspect we (at least if you are a taxpayer) are the "payers". Maybe I have 10 minutes of a scientist's time as a result of what I pay in taxes – I wonder what I'm going to get him/her to do? Not a problem, the government, in its wisdom, as well as taking our money away from us in taxes because it knows better how to spend it, also relieves us of the burden of research decisions. Once upon a time academics were trusted just to research into whatever they found interesting. Nowadays money is a little tighter, so that usually they have to submit proposals to research councils who award funding. Unfortunately that means that many spend as much time writing research proposals and going through all the involved "follow up", as they do actually carrying out any research! Who are on these research councils anyway? Usually it is other scientists in a similar field who, supposedly, have the expertise to decide which projects deserve support and which do not. But what should their decisions rest on – something that looks likely to "pay off" in 5-years or something that, just possibly, might revolutionise everything 50 years down the track? Somebody who is working in a prestigious university, somebody who has published a lot of academic papers (though maybe of dubious interest) recently, the guy who bought you a beer in the bar at the last conference? Lack of funding might even be a stimulus; I think it was Ernest Rutherford who said "Our request for funding hasn't been granted, so we'll have to think instead".

HIGHER LEVEL

C8 CONDENSATION POLYMERS (HL)

C.8.1 Distinguish between *addition* and *condensation* polymers in terms of their structures.

C.8.2 Describe how condensation polymers are formed from their monomers.

C.8.3 Describe and explain how the properties of polymers depend on their structural features.

C.8.4 Describe ways of modifying the properties of polymers.

C.8.5 Discuss the advantages and disadvantages of polymer use.

There are two main types of polymers - addition and condensation polymers.

In **addition polymerization**, monomers are unsaturated organic compounds such as ethene, $CH_2{=}CH_2$ and chloroethene $CH_2{=}CHCl$ (vinyl chloride). Monomer units add together without the elimination of any atoms to form the polymer. Addition takes place across the double bond. After polymerization, the double bond is converted to a single bond. Typically, a single monomer is involved (see also C.3)

In **condensation polymerization**, the monomer units have two reacting sites on them for polymerization to take place such as dicarboxylic acids, diols and diamines (called bifunctional monomers). These undergo condensation reactions to produce a larger molecule with the elimination of a smaller molecule such as water. Typically two monomers are involved, though there are examples of condensation polymers (such as nylon-6) which only involve a single monomer with different functional groups at the two ends of it. Butanedioic acid, ethane-1,2-diol and 1,2-diaminoethane are examples of bifunctional monomers as shown in Figure 1433.

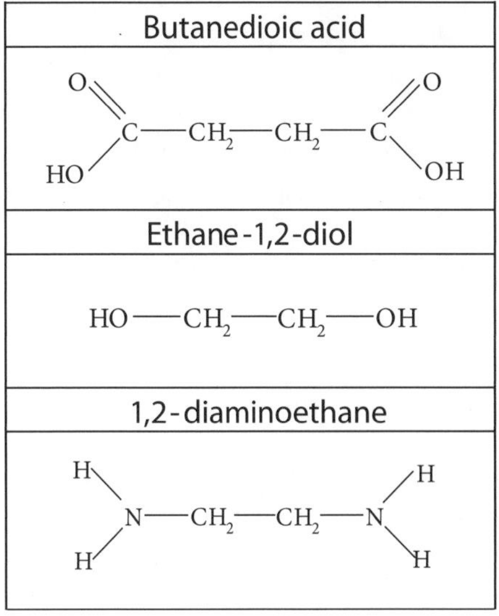

Figure 1433 Examples of bi-functional monomers

Thus, the repeating unit of the polymer made from the condensation of the two monomers butanedioic acid and ethane-1,2-diol is shown in Figure 1434.

$$\left[-C(=O)-CH_2-CH_2-C(=O)-O-CH_2-CH_2-O- \right]_n$$

From butanedioic acid From ethane-1,2-diol

Figure 1434 The repeating unit

EXAMPLES OF CONDENSATION POLYMERS

Phenol-methanal plastics

The —OH group on the phenol is 2,4-directing. Thus, the intial reaction between phenol and methanal involves substitution at both the 2- and 4-positions on the benzene ring as shown in Figure 1435.

OPTION

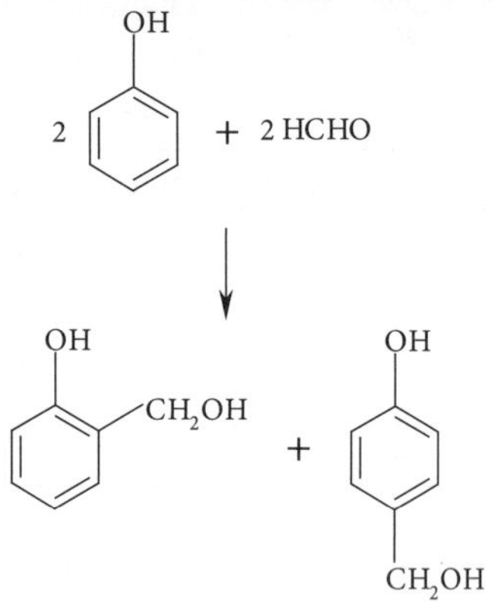

Figure 1435

It is the reaction of the substituted products from the above reaction with phenol that undergo condensation with the elimination of water, as shown in Figure 1436.

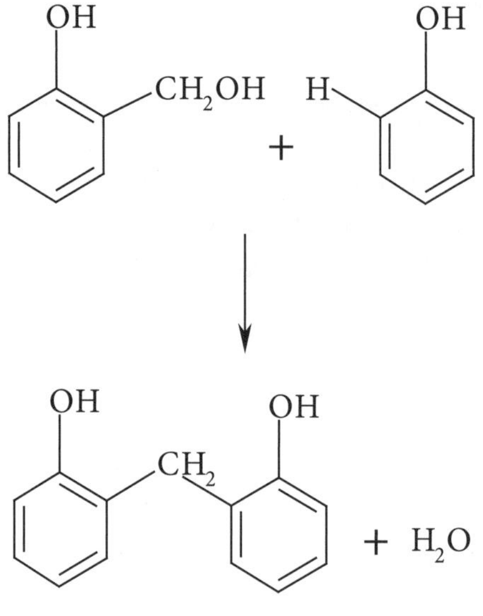

Figure 1436

Subsequent condensation reactions with hydrogen on the 2- and 4-positions produce the phenol-methanal plastic (commercially called Bakelite) with extensive cross-links. As shown in Figure 1437.

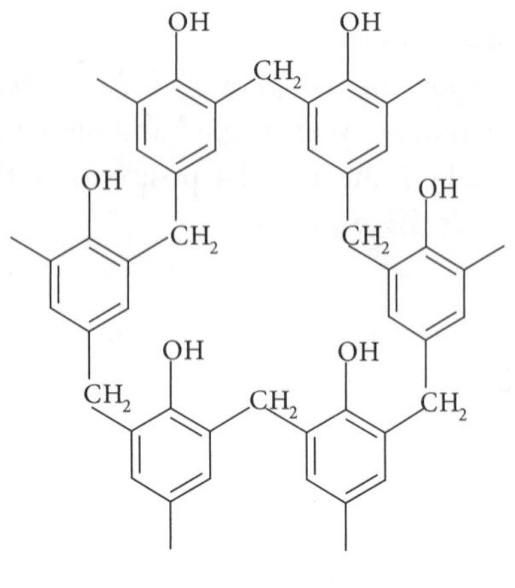

Figure 1437 Structure of bakelite

Polyurethanes

Polyurethanes are used extensively in making polyurethane fibres and foams. Polyurethane is made by the reaction of di-isocyanates in which an oxygen atom is bonded to the cyano group at either end of the carbon chain containing monomer: OCN—(carbon chain)—NCO. The other bifunctional monomer for the condensation reaction is a diol, for example, ethane-1,2-diol as shown in Figure 1438 (a).

Polyethylene terephthalate (PET)

PET is the polymer of choice in the blow-moulded bottling industry because unlike glass it is light weight and does not shatter. It is a polyester made by the condensation of benzene-1,4-dicarboxylic acid (called terephthalic acid) with ethane-1,2-diol (called ethylene glycol) – hence the name of the polymer: polyethylene terephthalate, PET. (Figure 1438 (b)).

FACTORS DETERMINING THE PROPERTIES OF CONDENSATION POLYMERS

Chain length

The greater the average chain length, the greater are the intermolecular forces and hence the higher the strength and melting point.

The way groups are arranged or orientated along a polymer backbone chain

Different properties can arise from different stereochemistries of polymers. **Kevlar** is an excellent example of a condensation polymer where the trans orientation of the chain allows it to be a straight chain polymer with close approach between chains, allowing strong hydrogen bonding between them, which gives it great strength. The cis-orientation however produces bent chains and does not allow close approach for strong bonding between chains (see Figure 1448).

Cross–linking

In **cross-linked polymers**, two different chains are connected by short lengths of another chain which in some cases may be only two or three atoms long. A cross-linked polymer is found to be more rigid than a linear or branched polymer. The amount of cross–linking determines how rigid the final structure becomes. A good example of this is the vulcanization of rubber. Natural rubber is a soft, sticky substance which hardens to a useless material unless it is treated with sulfur, or some other chemical. Rubber is built from isoprene (2–methyl–1,3–butadiene) monomers. When rubber is heated with sulfur it maintains its spring for longer periods of time than natural rubber. The sulfur atoms create strong covalent links between the chains so that treated rubber retains the shape into which it was molded. This led to the development of rubber tires and the use of rubber in hoses, shoes and balls.

OPTION

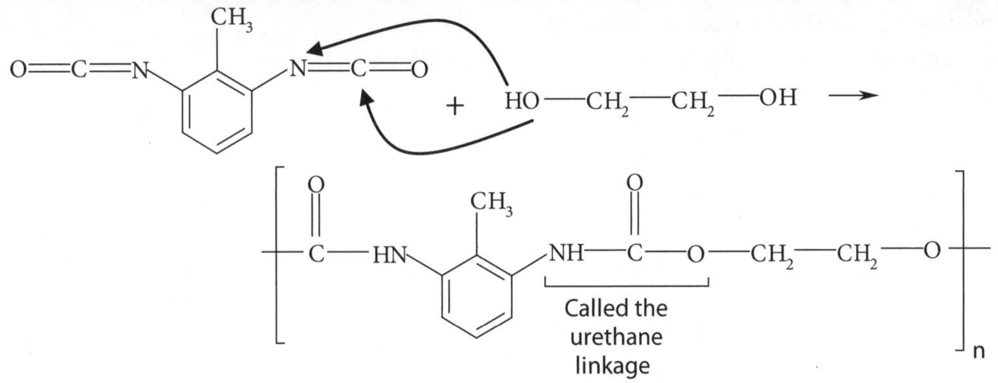

Called the urethane linkage

Figure 1438 (a) The urethane linkage

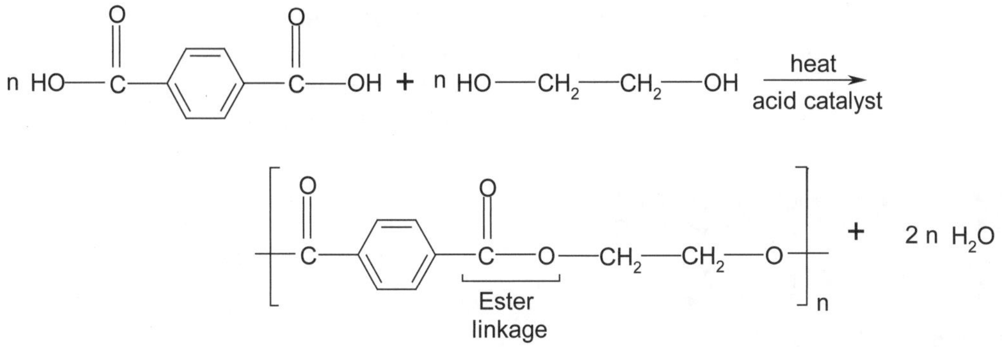

Ester linkage

Figure 1438 (b) The ester linkage in the polymer PET

The phenol-methanal plastic (see Figure 1437) is an example of a polymer where the benzene ring is bonded to CH_2 in three positions with extensive 3-D cross-links that produce rigid plastics with high melting points which are high enough that it undergoes decomposition before melting (that is, a thermosetting rather than a thermoplastic polymer). Thus phenol-methanal plastics are excellent electrical insulators, non-flammable and chemically inert. These plastics are used in electrical plugs, sockets, switches, casings for electronic equipment, etc.

WAYS OF MODIFYING THE PROPERTIES OF POLYMERS

Air in the manufacture of polyurethane foams

A 'blowing agent' such as air produces a polyurethane foam that is soft and has a low density. Such foams are used as cushioning materials for furniture. More often, in the case of polyurethane, water is used to produce the foaming agent carbon dioxide since the isocyanate group reacts with water to produce CO_2.

$$—NCO + H_2O \longrightarrow —NH_2 + CO_2$$

Doping a polymer

A polymer such as polyethyne, made by the polymerization of ethyne, can produce two types of polymers: one containing the cis-arrangment in the polymer chain containing the C=C double bond and the other containing the trans-arrangement. It is found that the trans-polymer is not an insulator like polyethene, but more like a semi-conductor because of the presence of the conjugated system of alternate C—C single and C=C double bonds. Addition of the oxidant iodine as vapour increases the level of conductivity to that of metals. Thus doping polyethyne with iodine vapour produces an organic polymer that can conduct electricity.

Blending of polyester fibres

For example, a blend of aromatic polyamide with polyester fibre produces a flame-resistant garment material. Similarly, soft blended polyester fibres are used to manufacture comfortable mattress pads, and polyblend fibres can produce strong and durable fabric materials. Blending of polyester fibres with particular molecular groups or charges (such as sulfonic acid radical or anionically modified nylon) make these materials easy to dye due to a strong attraction for dyes with the opposite electrical charge (called the affinity method of dyeing).

Advantages and disadvantages of condensation polymer use

Advantages of plastics: Plastics can be engineered easily with unique properties such as excellent heat and electrical insulation. Thermoplastics such as polyurethanes become soft and melt on heating; they can be moulded, are excellent insulators and are unreactive. Rigid polyurethanes have high tensile strength and are used as insulators in building panels. Polyurethane can be made flexible by adding a blowing agent which is used as foam material for furniture. Polyurethane is used to make fabric that stretches for use in exercise clothing. Phenol-methanal plastics are cross-linked by covalent bonding, hence they are chemically inert, act as electrical and thermal insulators and are non-flammable. Also, they have high density and high strength with numerous applications including use as electric switches, electronic casings, utensil handles, etc. Some plastics such as PET can be recycled. Plastics are durable and can stand up to a variety of environmental conditions without falling apart (the lack of degradability is also a disadvantage).

C9 MECHANISMS IN THE ORGANIC CHEMICALS INDUSTRY (HL)

C.9.1 Describe the free-radical mechanism involved in the manufacture of low-density polyethene.

C.9.2 Outline the use of Ziegler–Natta catalysts in the manufacture of high-density polyethene.

A **free-radical mechanism** is involved in the manufacture of LDPE: recall the addition polymerization to form polyethene from ethene:

$$n\mathrm{CH_2{=}CH_2} \longrightarrow -(\mathrm{CH_2{-}CH_2})n-$$

The weaker π-bond in each ethene breaks to give the two stronger σ bonds at the end of the molecule to form the macromolecular polymer. Evidence from kinetic studies of polymerization reactions is, however, necessary to elucidate the mechanisms for such reactions. Low density polyethene is made at very high pressure (≈1500 atm), a temperature of about 200 °C and in the presence of organic peroxides which are a source of free radicals. See Figure 1439.

$$n\mathrm{CH_2{=}CH_2} \xrightarrow[\text{peroxides}]{200°\mathrm{C};\ 1500\ \mathrm{atm}} -(\mathrm{CH_2{-}CH_2})_n-$$

low density polyethene

Figure 1439

A free radical mechanism involves initiation, propagation and termination steps; also, peroxides contain a very weak O—O bond in the R—O—O—R functional group.

MECHANISM

Initiating step

Peroxides decompose to form alkoxy free radicals as the O—O covalent bond in the peroxide is broken. This is shown in Figure 1440.

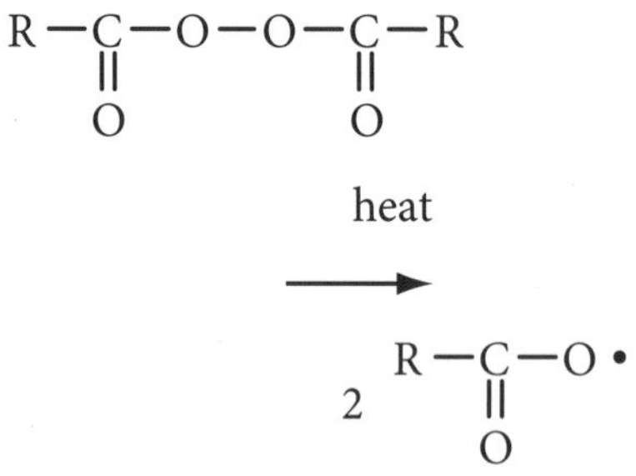

$$\mathrm{R{-}C({=}O){-}O{-}O{-}C({=}O){-}R} \xrightarrow{\text{heat}} 2\ \mathrm{R{-}C({=}O){-}O\bullet}$$

Figure 1440 Formation of alloxy free radicals

Propagating step

The alkoxy free radicals react with the alkene to produce a longer alkyl free radical:

$$\mathrm{RO\bullet + CH_2{=}CH_2 \longrightarrow R{-}O{-}CH_2{-}CH_2\bullet}$$

The chains add successive ethene units to produce longer free radicals:

$$\mathrm{R{-}O{-}CH_2{-}CH_2\bullet + CH_2{=}CH_2 \longrightarrow R{-}O{-}CH_2{-}CH_2{-}CH_2{-}CH_2\bullet}$$

Also the following reaction takes place that leads to chain branching:

$$\mathrm{R{-}O{-}CH_2{-}CH_2{-}CH_2{-}CH_2{-}O{-}R + \bullet O{-}R \longrightarrow \bullet R{-}O{-}CH_2{-}\dot{C}H{-}CH_2{-}CH_2{-}O{-}R + R{-}O{-}H}$$

It is this branching that gives polyethene its low density as the chains cannot pack very closely, giving it a comparatively low melting point.

OPTION

Terminating step

The free radicals either combine to form a longer chain molecule or the transfer of a hydrogen atom occurs to form a combination of an alkane and alkene:

$$2\,R{-}O{-}CH_2{-}CH_2{-}CH_2{-}CH_2\bullet \longrightarrow (R{-}O{-}CH_2{-}CH_2{-}CH_2{-}CH_2)_2{-}$$

or

$$2\,R{-}O{-}CH_2{-}CH_2{-}CH_2{-}CH_2\bullet \longrightarrow R{-}O{-}CH_2{-}CH{=}CH{-}CH_3 + R{-}O{-}CH_2{-}CH_2{-}CH_2{-}CH_3$$

The use of **Ziegler-Natta catalysts** in the manufacture of HDPE: High-density polyethene is formed at much lower pressures (5-7 atm) and lower temperatures (about 75°) in the presence of special catalysts. The Ziegler-Natta catalysts used in the production of high-density polymers are not soluble in alkane solvents. The reaction mixture is thus a heterogeneous one and polymerization takes place at the surface of the catalyst which is a suspension of titanium (III) or (IV) chloride and an alkyl-aluminium compound. As a result the process is also called **coordination polymerization** (because of the coordination/bonding between the unsaturated reactive center of the monomer and the transition metal). This polymerization uses an ionic mechanism.

The typical compounds used as catalysts are: titanium(IV) chloride, $TiCl_4$, and triethylaluminium, $(C_2H_5)_3Al$ in which the aluminium is electron deficient. They react together to give an organotitanium compound $Ti{-}CH_2{-}CH_3$ which is believed to play a key role in which the Ti—C bond is quite polar. The titanium is the site for the coordination with the alkene. Bonding between the partially positive metal and the alkene's π bond develops. This is followed by insertion of the alkene into the hydrocarbon chain bonded to the titanium atom. See Figure 1441.

$$Ti^{\delta+}{-}CH_2{-}CH_3 \quad CH_2{=}CH_2$$

$$Ti^{\delta+}{-}CH_2{-}CH_2{-}CH_2{-}CH_3 \quad CH_2{=}CH_2$$

Figure 1441 Formation of the growing hydrocarbon chain attached to the catalyst:

The polymerization produces linear, regular arrangements of groups along the chains with no branching of the polymer chain, which fit together much better in a crystal structure. These rigid high density polymers thus have stronger van der Waals' forces and higher melting point than LDPE.

C10 SILICON AND PHOTOVOLTAIC CELLS (HL)

C.10.1 Describe the doping of silicon to produce p-type and n-type semiconductors.

C.10.2 Describe how sunlight interacts with semiconductors.

Silicon is the most important element used in the semiconductor industry without which it would be impossible for the industry to exist. Silicon contains 4 valence electrons. As each atom forms four tetrahedrally directed covalent bonds to other silicon atoms, a macromolecular crystal structure in three dimensions is built up. Carbon in the form of diamond, with a similar tetrahedral structure to silicon, is a non-conductor of electricity. Carbon is smaller than silicon in size and all valence electrons are held tightly by forming strong covalent C-C bonds in three dimensions, making diamond extremely hard. Because of the larger bond length in silicon, electrons are not as tightly held allowing it to be a semiconductor. Semiconductors are a special class of materials which have an electrical resistance between those of electrical conductors and electrical insulators and are better conductors under certain circumstances. For example, they conduct electricity better as the temperature rises.

According to **band theory**, in giant non-ionic structures the valence atomic orbitals interact to give allowed electron energy bands. If these bands are completely filled (as in diamond) then electrons cannot move within the solid and it is an insulator. If the band is only partially filled (as in copper) then electrons can move throughout the structure and it is an electrical conductor. Silicon is a semiconductor because, even though it has a filled lower electron band, it has unfilled bands at a level that electrons can reach by thermal excitation. As the temperature increases, more electrons can move into the conduction band and hence the conductivity increases with temperature, unlike metals.

"Doping" a semiconductor with a trace of another element can increase conductivity. If a trace of an element from group 5/15 of the periodic table is added to the silicon (for example phosphorus) then the extra electrons have to go into the upper unfilled band and this increases the conductivity. This is known as an n-type semiconductor (n for negative as the current is carried by negative electrons). Conversely if the doping element is from group 3/13 (for example boron), then there are gaps or "holes" in the filled band and this too enhances conductivity. A doped semiconductor of this type is known as a p-type semiconductor (p for positive as the current is carried by positive holes).

Doping of silicon to produce n-type and p-type semiconductors

Doping is the incorporation of minute amounts of impurities within the crystal lattice of silicon so as to increase its conductivity. Typically, doping of semiconductors is carried out by adding certain substances to molten silicon. This can be done by exposing the semiconductor to the vapor of the substance which is added in the furnace. The chosen substance is added in carefully controlled amounts to bring its content up to only a few parts per million. The atoms of the added substance are therefore well spaced out in the semiconductor so that its crystal structure is not weakened. The process is called doping and the added substances are called **dopants**. In surface doping, a solid silicon surface is exposed to the vapour of the dopant.

There are two types of doped semiconductors: **n–type** and **p–type**. In n–type semiconductors, the dopants are Group V (or 15) elements, such as arsenic and antimony which have 5 electrons in the outer shell. When an arsenic dopant atom replaces an atom of silicon in the structure, it uses four of its five valence electrons to form covalent bonds with silicon atoms. The fifth electron is supplied to the material, creating a negative charge. These are called n–type semiconductors. The added atoms are called **donor atoms** because they donate electrons to the material. The addition of donor atoms leaves the crystal uncharged overall because the additional electrons are associated with additional positive charges on the donor nuclei. See Figure 1442

In p–type semiconductors, the dopants are Group III (or 13) elements, such as boron (B), gallium (Ga), or indium (In), which have three electrons in the outer shell. When a boron atom replaces a silicon atom, it forms three electron pair bonds with three silicon atoms, but the fourth bond is incomplete as it has only one electron. The vacancy is called an **electron hole** and is positively charged, producing a p–type semiconductor. The added atoms are called **acceptor atoms** because they can accept electrons to fill the holes in the bonds.

A typical solar (phòto–voltaic) cell consists of two layers of almost pure silicon; one has a trace of arsenic (n–type) and the other a trace of boron (p–type). The n–type has atoms with an extra electron which is relatively free to move whereas the p–type layer has atoms short of an electron. When the two layers are placed together, the extra electrons from the n–type move to the p–type layer giving the p-type a net negative charge at its junction with the p-type. This means that electrons can therefore move from the p-type to n-type but the negative charge on the p-type prevents them moving the other way around. This therefore operates as a **diode**. When sunlight strikes such a surface, the sun's energy is able to give electrons the energy to move, but because of the diode, they can only move from the p-type to the n–type layer. If an external circuit is present, the electron can flow back through it from the n-type layer to the p–type layer.

The advantages of solar cells are many. These include no moving parts, no liquids and no corrosive chemicals. They generate electricity as long as the sun is shining. The disadvantages include the need for large surfaces, the fact that pure silicon is very expensive and that the solar cells only work when the sun is shining and produce low power outputs.

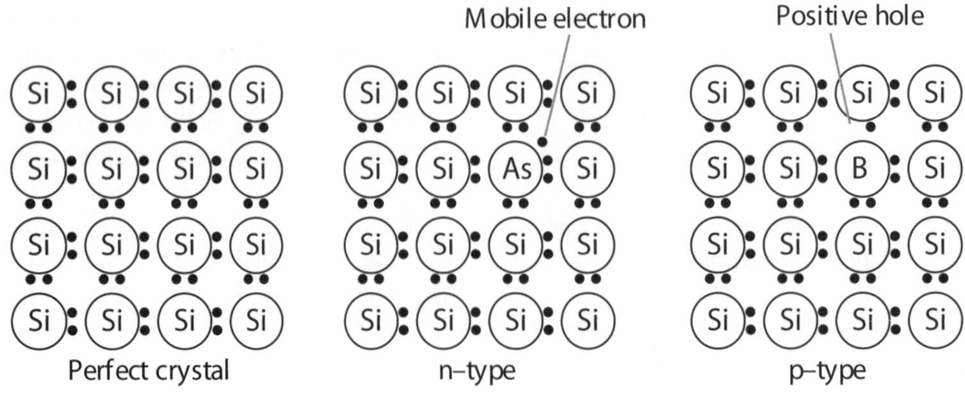

Figure 1442 Structure of semi-conductors

C11 LIQUID CRYSTALS (HL)

C.11.1 Identify molecules that are likely to show liquid-crystal properties, and explain their liquid-crystal behaviour on a molecular level.

C.11.2 Describe and explain in molecular terms the workings of a twisted nematic liquid crystal.

C.11.3 Describe the liquid-crystal properties of Kevlar, and explain its strength and its solubility in concentrated sulfuric acid.

Molecules that show LC properties, and their LC behaviour on a molecular level:

A mixture of cyanobiphenyls (biphenyl nitriles) that operate over a wide enough temperature range are used in LCDs. See Figure 1443

C_5H_{11}–(biphenyl)–C≡N (biphenyl; cyano group)

C_5H_{11}–O–(biphenyl)–C≡N

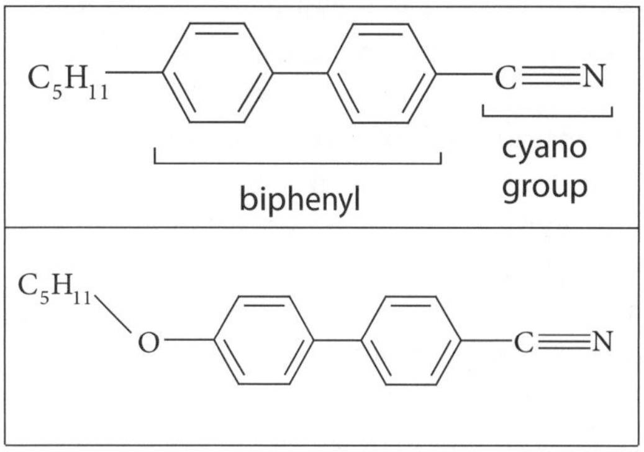

Figure 1443 Examples of cyanobiphenyls

These molecules have three key chemical/structural features

- The polar cyano (nitrile) group allows an electric field to control the orientation of the molecules as well as creating strong intermolecular forces for the molecules to be oriented in the same direction.
- The biphenyl groups contain two planar benzene rings bonded by a single covalent bond. These are chemically stable, make the molecule rod-like and rigid.
- The long hydrocarbon chain affects the melting point as the molecules cannot pack together as closely and can maintain the LC phase. The size and shape of the alkyl group can be changed to alter the melting range.

The workings of a twisted nematic liquid crystal

Many common **liquid crystal displays** (LCDs) use twisted nematic liquid crystals, TNLCs. A TNLC is naturally twisted and can be untwisted depending on the voltage

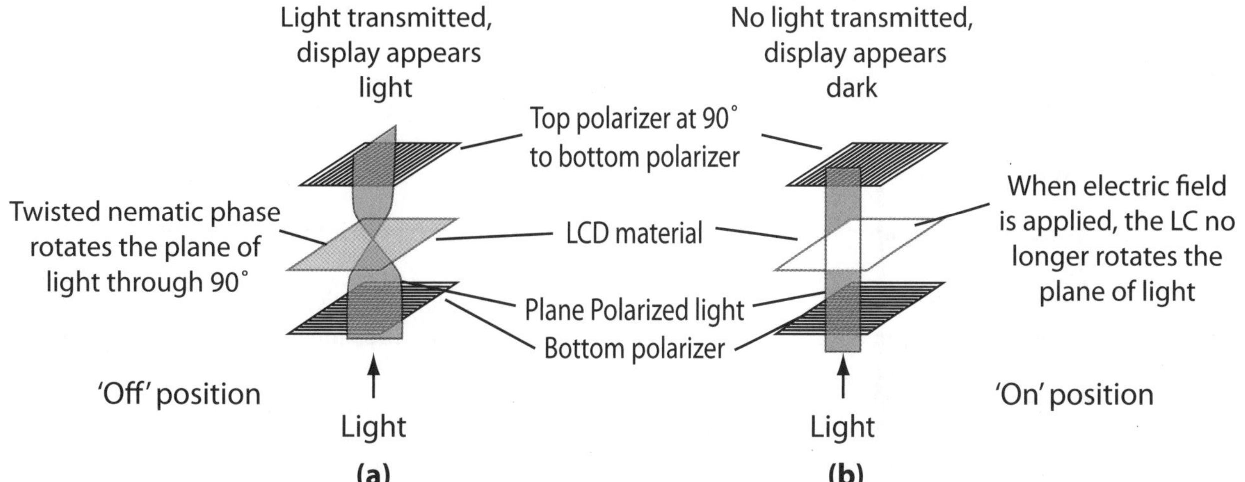

Figure 1444 (a), (b) How an LCD works

applied. That is, its effect on polarized light is influenced by an electric current. An LCD contains a collection of pixels (tiny sections containing single points in an LCD image) which can be controlled using an electric field. The principle behind the TNLC display is that the twisting or rotation of polarized light by the TNLC molecules can be removed by the application of an appropriate amount of voltage.

An LCD is made of multiple layers consisting of glass sheets coated with transparent indium tin oxide (ITO). A metal oxide film above and below which act as electrodes that apply the voltage to untwist the LC. In between, an LCD contains an LC material placed between a pair of crossed polarizers that are perpendicular to each other. These can be made by creating scratches on glass (or transparent plastic) plates at 90° to each other. The LC molecules in contact with the glass line up with the scratches, and molecules form a twisted arrangement between the plates due to intermolecular forces.

Light vibrating in the plane of the first polarizer passes through. When it comes in contact with the TNLC molecules, it is rotated by the molecules through 90° as it passes through the LC film. Since the second polarizer is at 90° to the first one, the polarized light emerging from the LC is aligned with the scratches. Light will pass through the film and the pixel will appear bright when no electric field applied to it (thus called the 'off' position) as shown in Figure 1444 (a).

If a voltage is applied across the film, the polar molecules align with the electric field and the twisted structure is lost. Plane-polarized light is no longer rotated, and so the pixel appears dark as in Figure 1444 (b). Thus regions in which an electric field of sufficient magnitude is applied appear dark. If the electric field is switched off, the twist is re-established and bright light pixel appears. For example, the numbers on a calculator are based on seven sections; applying voltages to different sections produce different numbers, for example if sections 1, 3, 4, 5 and 7 are in the on position, the number 2 appears whereas sections 1, 3, 4, 6, and 7 in the on position gives the number 3 as shown in Figure 1445.

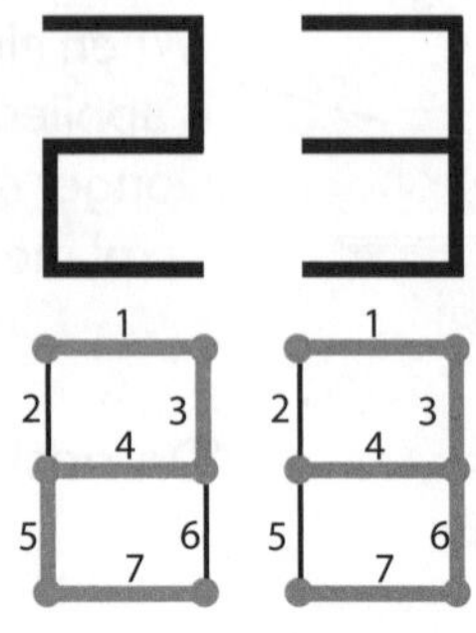

Figure 1445 An LCD display

Liquid-crystal properties of Kevlar, its strength and its solubility in concentrated sulfuric acid

Kevlar is a rod-like polyaromatic amide. It is a condensation polymer of 1,4-diaminobenzene and 1,4-benzenedicarboxylic acid with the repeating unit as shown in Figure 1446.

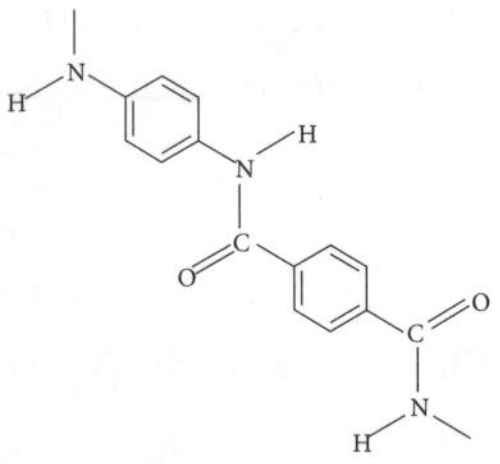

Figure 1446 The repeating unit of Kevlar

Kevlar is a very strong, light-weight synthetic fibre spun like a spider's web in which the trans-polymer chains are arranged parallel to each other. The carbon-based polymer does not corrode and is several times stronger than steel! Thus it has many uses including in bullet-proof vests and radial tyres. Kevlar's strength comes from the strong intermolecular hydrogen bonding between the polar amide groups in the adjacent chains. This is due to the attraction of the highly electronegative oxygen atom in one chain and the tiny partially positive hydrogen atom bonded to the highly electronegative nitrogen atom on the other chain, shown by dashed lines in the structure below. The strength also comes from the interaction that results from the arrangement of the π bonds in the benzene rings in the adjacent chains. See Figure 1447.

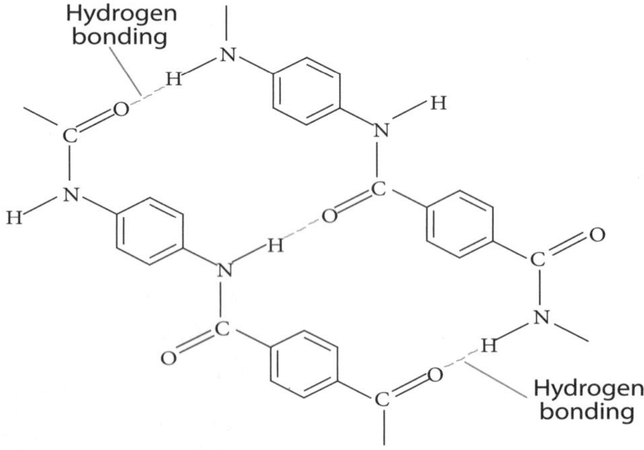

Figure 1447 The structure of Kevlar

These interactions give rise to a highly ordered and strong polymer, of unidirectional orientation and structural rigidity, which is resistant to dilute acids and bases. However, Kevlar degrades on exposure to concentrated sulphuric acid as the hydrogen bonds can be broken between the chains by the protonation of the oxygen and the nitrogen atoms. Hydrolysis of the amide linkage takes place to form a lyotropic liquid crystal solution in moderate concentration of the acid containing rigid rod-shaped molecules due to the linked benzene rings. The long range order (the alignment of the molecules) is maintained depending on the concentration of LC molecules in the concentrated acid solution.

Molecular Modelling

Kevlar is a good example of a polymer that can be studied through molecular modelling which involves making and visualizing large molecules in three dimensions using computer simulations. A quick look at the chain structure of Kevlar suggests that its cis-arrangement (conformation) around the amide group will lead to bent chains which will not line up to form strong interactions between the chains; the trans arrangement, on the other hand, will be able to. Also, on making a 3-D structure, the instability of the cis arrangement becomes clear as it reveals that there is not enough space for the hydrogen atoms on the adjacent benzene rings on the 2-positions to fit within the narrow space between the two rings. See Figure 1448.

a) Cis conformation

Cis arrangement around amide group; organic groups on the same side

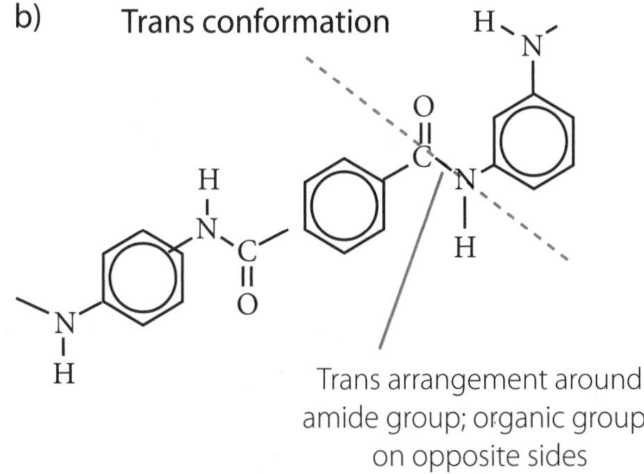

Figure 1448 (a) and (b) Cis and Trans conformations

Molecular modelling has become an important tool in the hands of chemists in many branches of the subject ranging from the study of biologically important molecules to drug research. Numerous resources are available on the subject, including on the world wide web (www).

C12 THE CHLOR–ALKALI INDUSTRY (HL)

C.12.1 Discuss the production of chlorine by the electrolysis of sodium chloride.

The **chlor–alkali industry** is the name given to a group of related industries that produce chlorine, sodium hydroxide and sodium carbonate. These chemicals are used in huge quantities in many different chemical processes. Chlorine and sodium hydroxide are made from the electrolysis of brine solution (salt water; aqueous sodium chloride) by various commercial methods including mercury, diaphragm and membrane cells which produce hydrogen gas as a useful by product.

The mercury cell process: Brine is continuously passed into a cell that has positive graphite electrodes, the anodes where chloride ions are discharged in preference to the hydroxide ions in water (because of the much higher concentration of chloride ions present). A moving layer of mercury acts as the negative electrode, the cathode where sodium ions are discharged in preference to water or hydrogen ions. Although sodium is higher than hydrogen in the activity series, sodium's discharge is due to the use of mercury as the negative cathode where sodium reacts with the mercury, making a liquid alloy known as an amalgam (Na/Hg (l)). The reduction half reaction is:

$$Na^+ (aq) + e^- + Hg (l) \longrightarrow Na/Hg (l)$$

The amalgam travels out of the cell into a chamber containing water. It is at this stage that sodium hydroxide solution and hydrogen gas are produced:

$$2 Na/Hg (l) + 2 H_2O (l) \longrightarrow 2 Na^+ (aq) + 2 OH^- (aq) + 2 Hg (l) + H_2 (g)$$

This is catalysed by the presence of steel grids. The mercury is then recycled to the electrolysis cell.

OPTION

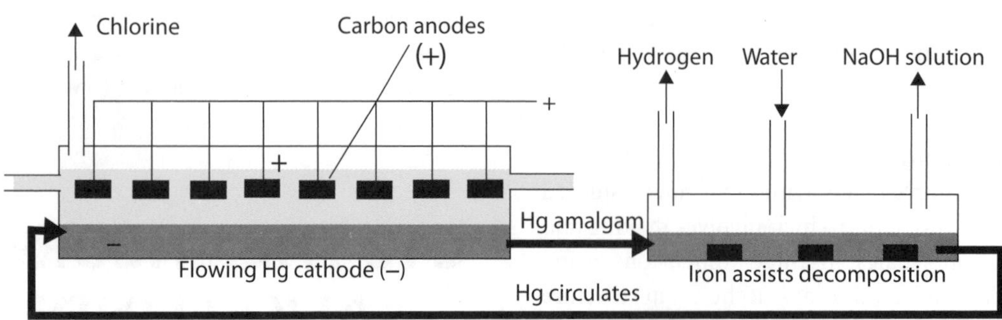

Figure 1449 The mercury cell

Oxidation takes place at the positive graphite electrode, the anode to form chlorine gas:

$$2\,Cl^- \longrightarrow Cl_2\,(aq) + 2\,e^-$$

The overall equation for the reactions taking place is:

$$2\,NaCl\,(aq) + 2\,H_2O\,(l) \longrightarrow 2\,NaOH\,(aq) + H_2\,(g) + Cl_2\,(g)$$

The chlorine gas produced by the oxidation of chloride ions at the (+) graphite anode electrode is slightly impure owing to it being mixed with water vapor. The latter is removed by drying the gas with concentrated sulfuric acid. See Figure 1449.

Diaphragm and membrane cell process: In a diaphragm cell, the positive electrode, the anode, and the negative electrode, the cathode, are in two compartments separated by a diaphragm. Diaphragms were made of asbestos. Asbestos fibres, however, scar lung tissue and cause asbestosis. Membrane cells, on the other hand, use ion-selective membrane technology which does not use asbestos; an organic flouropolymer, similar to PTFE, is used instead as a membrane in these cells. The positive anode is made from titanium, sometimes with a coating of platinum, and the negative cathode is made from steel. See Figure 1450.

In the (+) anode compartment, chlorine is given off by the oxidation of chloride ions:

$$2\,Cl^-\,(aq) \longrightarrow Cl_2\,(g) + 2\,e^-$$

In the (-) cathode compartment, water is reduced to hydrogen gas and hydroxide ions are formed:

$$2\,H_2O\,(l) + 2\,e^- \rightarrow 2\,OH^-\,(aq) + H_2\,(g)$$

The overall result is that the brine loses its chloride ions and becomes richer in hydroxide ions as a result of electrolysis:

$$2\,NaCl\,(aq) + 2\,H_2O\,(l) \longrightarrow Cl_2\,(g) + H_2\,(g) + 2\,NaOH\,(aq)$$

Several reactions, however, can occur unless the separation of the electrolytes in the two compartments is effective. In

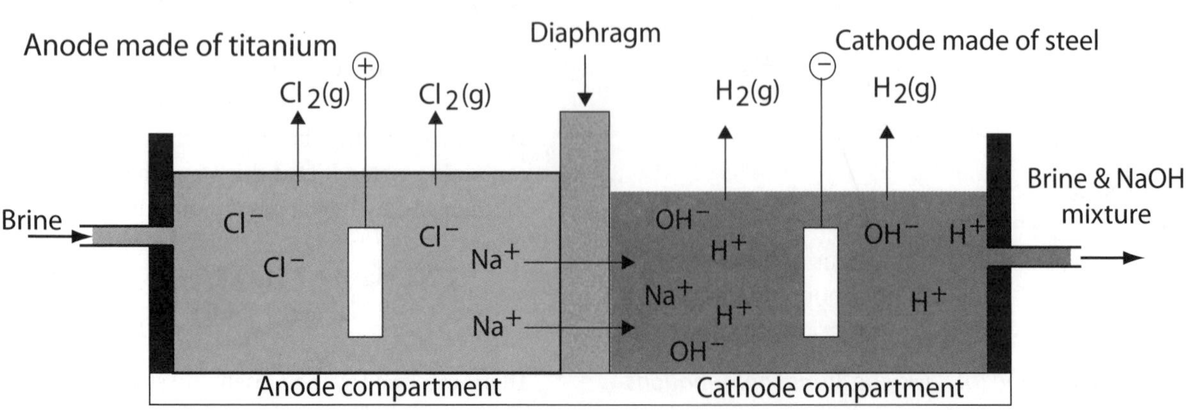

Figure 1450 The diaphragm cell

the cold, chlorine reacts with hydroxide ions to produce chlorate(I) ions, ClO^- ions:

$$Cl_2\,(aq) + 2\,OH^-\,(aq) \longrightarrow Cl^-\,(aq) + ClO^-\,(aq) + H_2O\,(l)$$

In some cells however this is promoted because the product is liquid bleach. Also if hydroxide ions reach the (+) anode, these can be discharged. If this happens, oxygen is given off due to oxidation of hydroxide ions.

$$4\,OH^-\,(aq) \longrightarrow 2\,H_2O\,(l) + O_2\,(g) + 4\,e^-$$

A similar reaction occurs if the concentration of the chloride ions falls too low so that water is oxidised at the (+) anode:

$$2\,H_2O\,(l) \longrightarrow O_2\,(g) + 4H^+\,(aq) + 4\,e^-$$

These contaminate the chlorine and makes the isolation of pure chlorine more difficult. To avoid these problems, the brine in the (+) anode compartment is kept at a slightly higher pressure than in the (-) cathode compartment. This makes it less likely that the solution around the (-) cathode will reach the (+) anode.

In membrane cells the membrane only allows cations to pass and, because of its structure, it is impermeable to anions. This prevents the anions in the two compartments from mixing, whilst allowing cations to move between them, thus keeping the current flowing.

C.12.2 Outline some important uses of the products of this process.

Electrolysis of an aqueous solution of sodium chloride produces three very important chemicals, chlorine gas, hydrogen gas and sodium hydroxide. Their uses are outlined in Figure 1451.

C.12.3 Discuss the environmental impact of the processes used for the electrolysis of sodium chloride.

The amount of mercury escaping around a mercury cell plant is always controlled and minimised, but almost inevitably some mercury enters the environment. Mercury reacts with many organic molecules to form organo–mercury compounds. Intake of organo-mercury compounds results in a sickness called Minamata disease (because it was first identified in this Japanese town). Mercury is converted to methyl–mercury ions by bacterial action which can enter the food chain and end up in fish, leading to biological magnification when fish is the main diet for people. Methyl–mercury compounds can form strong covalent bonds to sulfur atoms in the —SH groups present in the cysteine units in some proteins, thus seriously altering their properties. Mercury poisoning can cause inflammation of gums, nausea, diarrhoea, kidney failure, blindness, damage to the brain and damage to the central nervous system.

Some uses of chlorine	Some uses of sodium hydroxide	Some uses of hydrogen
Manufacture of solvents	Manufacture of inorganic chemicals	Hydrogenation of unsaturated oils - margarine
PVC manufacture	Manufacture of organic chemicals	HCl manufacture
Bleaching paper products	Paper products - converting wood to pulp	Future potential use in fuel cells
Disinfecting drinking and swimming pool water	Aluminium industry	
Production of inorganic chemicals	Soap manufacture	

Figure 1451 Some important uses of products

OPTION

Minamata disease has been largely responsible for the replacement of the mercury cell by the diaphragm cell. However, the use of an asbestos diaphragm presents problems of its own as it has been identified as causing respiratory tract cancer and asbestosis. Thus asbestos is no longer the only diaphragm material and is replaced with an organic polymer instead as a membrane in these cells.

Amongst its many uses, chlorine is used in the manufacture of chlorine-containing solvents and CFCs. Besides their use as solvents, they are used as aerosol propellants, refrigerants in automobiles, home and commercial air conditioners, in refrigerators and freezers and in fire extinguishers. It is the high strength of the C–Cl (and the C–F) bonds that makes these molecules stable. This and their low densities make it possible for the substances to reach the upper atmosphere without decomposing. This is where a major concern arises because of the interference of CFCs with the ozone layer. The presence of CFCs and other gases have been found to be responsible for the destruction of ozone in the ozone layer. As a result of the Montreal Protocol, the use of chlorinated solvents has been greatly curtailed.

Chlorine is also used in large quantities in the production of chlorine containing polymers, such as PVC. Other major uses of chlorine are to kill bacteria in the treatment of drinking water and as a bleach.

Sodium hydroxide has many uses as a general alkali in the chemical industry, for example in the purification of bauxite in the production of aluminium. Large quantities are also used in the treatment of woodpulp for paper making.

OPTION C: CHEM IN IND & TECH QUESTIONS

C1 Iron, steel and aluminium

1. (a) Different chemical methods are used to extract aluminium and iron. State a method for the extract each metal, briefly describe the chemical principle behind each method and explain your reasoning.

(b) (i) State the main sources of iron.

(ii) Using appropriate equations, state two reasons why coke is used in the manufacture of iron.

(iii) State two other chemicals required in a blast furnace. One of the chemicals added leads to the formation of iron, the other to slag. Write relevant equations for the formation of iron and slag and suggest three possible uses for slag.

(iv) With the help of two equations, outline how addition of methane to the pre-heated air in a blast furnace forms the reducing agent that also forms iron.

(v) State and explain one serious environmental problem associated with the production of iron.

2. (a) (i) State the main aluminum ore.

(ii) Write the formula of cryolite and explain why it is used in the manufacture of aluminum.

(iii) State the main impurities in the aluminium ore and describe how the impurities are removed.

(iv) Write equations for half-reaction at the positive anode and negative cathode, and the over all reaction during the manufacture of aluminium.

(b) Explain the effect of the product on the positive anode and how the effect is addressed.

3 (a) (i) State the name given to the molten iron formed in a blast furnace.

(ii) Name the two major impurities in the molten iron.

(b) Describe and explain the conversion of iron into steel using the basic oxygen converter.

(c) (i) State the meaning of the term *alloy* and describe how an alloy may be made.

(ii) Explain how alloying can modify the structure of a metal and state properties it can affect.

(iii) Steel obtained from the basic oxygen converter may not have the desired properties and often requires further heat treatments. Describe the three common heat treatment processes used in the making of steel.

(iv) Describe the main properties and uses of aluminum and its alloys.

(d) (i) Discuss the environmental impact of iron and aluminum production.

(ii) Suggest two reasons why it is advisable to recycle aluminium.

C2 The oil industry

4. (a) (i) Compare the use of oil as an energy source and as a chemical feedstock and suggest why it is better to search for new energy sources.

(ii) Define the term *cracking* as it is applied to the oil industry.

(iii) Cracking can be achieved under different conditions of temperature, pressure the presence or absence of a catalyst, and steam. State and compare the conditions used in catalytic cracking, thermal cracking and steam cracking, giving appropriate equations. State the use of products from each of the cracking processes listed above.

C3 Addition polymers

5. (a) (i) Define the term *polymer*.

(ii) At the molecular level, describe what happens in addition polymerization and give the name and formula of a organic compound other than ethene that undergoes addition polymerization.

(b) Describe and explain how the physical properties of an addition polymer depend on the structural features listed below and state the type of polymer that arises as a result:

(i) branching, and

(ii) orientation (or position) of the alkyl groups along a polymer backbone chain:

(iii) State conditions under which low-density and high-density polyethylene is formed.

(c) Discuss the advantages and disadvantages of polymer use.

C4 Catalysts

6. (a) (i) Define the term *catalyst*, explain its effect on the rate of the forward and reverse reactions and on the activation energy, change in enthalpy and position of equilibrium of the reaction.

(ii) Outline the advantages and disadvantages of industrial catalysts.

(b) Compare the modes of action of homogeneous and heterogeneous catalysts and give an example of a chemical reaction for each.

(c) Outline the advantages and disadvantages of homogeneous and heterogeneous catalysts.

7. (a) Describe how enzymes have some characteristics of both homogeneous and heterogeneous catalysts. Describe how enzymes are unique and how they differ from inorganic catalysts.

(b) Describe the modes of action of homogeneous and heterogeneous catalysts in terms of:

(i) ability to form a range of oxidation states by transition metal compounds.

(ii) the shape of the catalyst, and

(iii) availability of active sites.

8. Outline factors involved in selecting a catalyst and give an example of each.

C5 Fuel cells and rechargeable batteries

9. (a) Define the term *fuel cell* and explain why fuel cells are more efficient than the ways in which electricity is normally produced.

(b) State the electrodes and the electrolyte in a hydrogen–oxygen fuel cell and describe how it works in (i) an acidic and (ii) a basic condition. Write balanced equations to show the chemical reactions taking place at the electrodes in each case.

(c) List the advantages and disadvantages of fuel cells.

10. (a) Write balanced equations for the reaction at each electrode taking place in the following batteries:

(i) lead-acid

(ii) NiCad, and

(iii) Lithium ion.

(b) Discuss two similarities and two differences between fuel cells and rechargeable batteries.

C6 Liquid crystals

11. (a) Describe the meaning of the term liquid crystals.

(b) Distinguish between *thermotropic* and *lyotropic* liquid crystals.

(c) Use an example to describe the liquid-crystal state in terms of the arrangement of the molecules and explain *thermotropic* behaviour and explain the terms *smectic* and *nematic* LCs.

12. (a) Outline the principles of the liquid-crystal display device.

(b) Discuss the properties needed for a substance to be used in liquid-crystal displays.

C7 Nanotechnology

13. (a) Define the term nanotechnology.

(b) Distinguish between physical and chemical techniques in manipulating atoms to form molecules.

(c) Describe the structure and properties of carbon nanotubes.

(d) Discuss some of the implications of nanotechnology including possible and potential uses. Include examples of new multidisciplinary fields, potential health and environmental effects, toxicity concerns and potential ethical and political issues.

[HL] C8 Condensation polymers

14. (a) Distinguish between addition and condensation polymers in terms of their structures.

(b) Describe and explain how the properties of polymers depend on their structural features.

(c) Describe ways of modifying the properties of polymers.

(d) Discuss the advantages and disadvantages of condensation polymer use.

[HL] C9 Mechanisms in the organic chemicals industry

15. (i) State the conditions used in the manufacture of low density polyethene.

(ii) State the three steps common to free-radical mechanisms and describe this mechanism in terms of the movement of electrons involved in the manufacture of low-density polyethene.

(iii) State the conditions used in the manufacture of high density polyethene.

(iv) Outline the use of Ziegler–Natta catalysts in the manufacture of high-density polyethene.

[HL] C10 Silicon and photovoltaic cells

16. (a) List the number of valence electrons in silicon and suggest why it is a semiconductor.

(b) Describe the doping of silicon to produce p-type and n-type semiconductors.

(c) Describe how sunlight interacts with semiconductors.

[HL] C11 Liquid crystals

17. (a) Identify molecules that are likely to show liquid-crystal properties, and explain their liquid-crystal behaviour on a molecular level.

(b) Describe and explain in molecular terms the workings of a twisted nematic liquid crystal.

(c) Describe the liquid-crystal properties of Kevlar, and explain its strength and its solubility in concentrated sulfuric acid.

[HL] C12 The chlor-alkali industry

18. Discuss the production of chlorine by the electrolysis of sodium chloride, write the appropriate half equations and the equation for the overall reaction and explain why it is important to keep the products apart.

19. Describe the mercury cell process for the manufacture of chlorine, write equations for reactions at the electrodes and the overall reaction and outline the advantage and disadvantage of this method.

20. Describe the diaphragm cell process for the manufacture of chlorine, write equations for reactions at the electrodes and the overall reaction and outline the advantage and disadvantage of this method.

21. Outline some important uses of the products of the electrolysis of sodium chloride process.

MEDICINES AND DRUGS

D1 Pharmaceutical products
D2 Antacids
D3 Analgesics
D4 Depressants
D5 Stimulants
D6 Antibacterials
D7 Antivirals
D8 Drug action (HL)
D9 Drug design (HL)
D10 Mind altering drugs (HL)

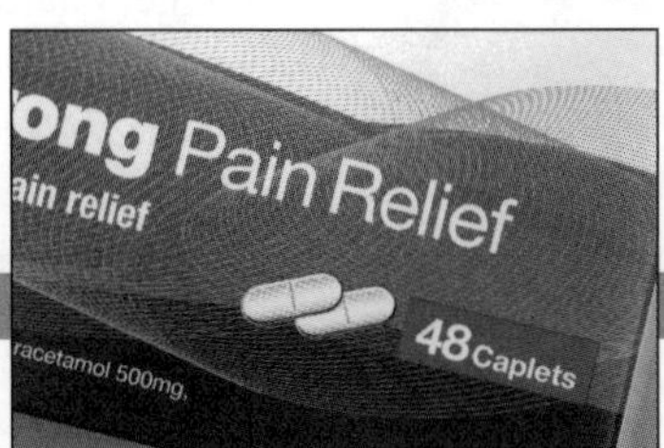

The aim of this option is to give students an understanding of how medicines and drugs can influence the functioning of the body. Students should be able to recognize the fundamental structures and relevant functional groups of several classes of drugs and medicines (as listed in this option or in topic 10), and should be able to distinguish between them. Memorizing of complex formulas is not required. Throughout the option, the contribution that science has made (and continues to make) towards maintaining and improving the health and well-being of the world's population should be stressed.

PUBLISHER'S NOTE

This chapter gives general information about drugs. The dosages described are examples only and are not to be interpreted as in an way definitive instructions about medicinal use.

All drugs have dangers and should only be used under the supervision of properly qualified professionals and according to the laws of the country you are in at the time.

D1 PHARMACEUTICAL PRODUCTS

D.1.1 List the effects of medicines and drugs on the functioning of the body.

The treatment of diseases by use of chemicals is called **chemotherapy**. A **drug** is any substance, natural or synthetic, used for its effects on bodily processes and is often defined as any substance taken to change the way in which the body or the mind functions. The drug may be naturally produced such as salicylic acid which was isolated from willow bark, or morphine from the opium poppy. It may be semi-synthetic such as aspirin which can be formed from salicylic acid. Or it may be totally synthetic, such as the opiate demerol. The definitions of drugs and medicines vary across cultures. In some countries the terms drug and medicine are interchangeable. In others, drugs are considered harmful and medicines or pharmaceuticals (which lead to an improvement in health) beneficial, though the terms harmful and benficial are open to debate. Generally a drug or medicine is any chemical which does one or more of the following:

- alters incoming sensory sensations
- alters moods or emotions
- alters physiological states, including consciousness, activity level or co-ordination.

Drugs:

- may or may not come from doctors or drug stores/pharmacies
- may or may not have beneficial medicinal properties

- may come from plants or fungi or may be manufactured in laboratories, ; some may also come from genetically modified bacteria, blood serum from mammals and other sources
- can be legal or illegal
- can be helpful or harmful.

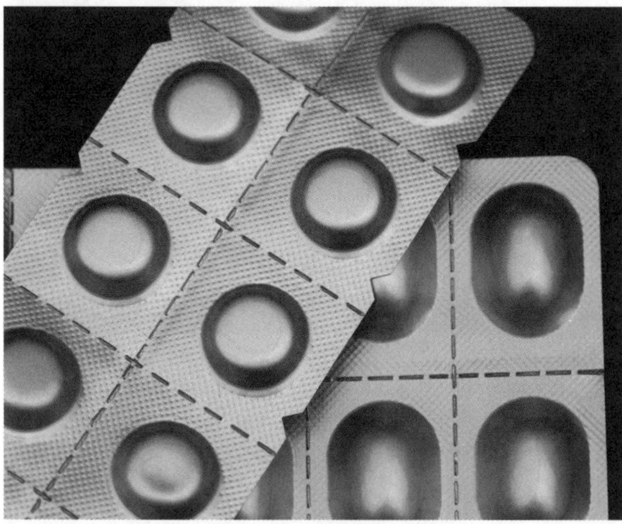

Figure 1501 Blister packed drugs

Drugs are divided into categories depending on their effects. These include infection fighters (antiseptics, antibiotics, antivirals), those affecting body chemistry or metabolism (hormones, vitamins), and those affecting the central nervous system (CNS) including the brain (stimulants, depressants, analgesics, anaesthetics).

The body's natural healing processes

White blood cells, which are produced in the bone marrow, are one line of defence the body uses to fight infections that may come from the air, food or water. The application of chemical knowledge to medicine has made it possible to develop medicines that augment the body's natural processes that combat diseases. This approach has increased the life expectancy of human beings over the decades.

Placebo Effect

Pharmacology is the scientific study of the interactions of drugs with the different cells found in the body. The **placebo effect** refers to a pharmacologically inert substance that produces a significant reaction because of what an individual expects, desires or is told will happen.

A **placebo** is an inert substance used as a control in an experiment, or given to patients for its probable beneficial effects (i.e. a 'fake' therapy without any side effects). Why a 'sugar pill' should be effective is not completely known, but does suggest the importance of the body's natural healing processes. The word placebo comes from the Latin "to please". Researchers have found asthmatics dilated their own airways when told they were inhaling asthma medicine. The action of placebos implies the power of suggestion, and some believe the placebo effect to be psychological, namely what counts is the reality present in the brain. This can have a biochemical effect on the body, presumably via the endocrine and immune systems. This means that a person's mental attitude may be very important in determining whether he or she recovers from injury or illness. It is thought that the placebo effect triggers natural healing processes in the body.

D.1.2 Outline the stages involved in research, development and testing of new pharmaceutical products.

Research, Development and Testing of new drugs

This is a lengthy, very costly process which is rigidly controlled by governments in many countries. In most countries, drugs must be subjected to thorough laboratory and clinical studies that demonstrate their usefulness and safety. Before studies on humans are permitted, the drugs are extensively tested on animals and cell cultures. These include establishment of the range of effective doses, the doses at which side effects occur and the lethal doses in various animals. Because of differences between species of animals, at least three different species are tested to determine an LD_{50} value. An LD_{50} (**lethal dose** in 50% of the population) value is used to indicate the dose of a given toxic substance in mg per kg body mass that kills 50% of the laboratory animals under study such as rats, mice and guinea pigs. The smaller the value of LD_{50}, the more toxic the substance. Since different species react differently to various poisons, any application of such data based on animal studies to human beings must be used with caution. Thus, studies are often carried out with different animals before such extrapolation is made.

If a drug is found to be safe when given to animals, it may be taken to initial clinical trials (phase 1) on volunteers as well as on patients with 50% receiving a placebo. This is aimed at establishing the drug's safety, dose range, and possible problems and side effects (see D.1.4) for further study.

Using animals and humans for drug testing raises ethical issues (a good TOK discussion point): testing animals is a concern for those who believe that animals should have the same rights as humans. Ethical concerns arise when human volunteers such as those from a prison population or those who volunteer for financial reasons are used.

If phase 1 indicates safety, a drug is subjected to thorough clinical evaluation (phase 2) to eliminate variables such as response and investigator bias. Statistical validation is critical at this stage. Finally if the drug looks promising, it enters human studies with extended clinical evaluation (phase 3). Most new drugs never get approval for marketing. Most drugs on the legitimate market have reasonable risk/benefit ratios. No drug is completely without risk, but most legal drugs should be relatively safe.

According to *Gary Becker*, a Nobel laureate, drug research and development is so expensive that by 2002, much of the US $ 800 million cost of a new drug went for trials proving its efficacy.

Thalidomide is an example of what can go wrong. It was marketed outside North America in the late 1950s and early 60s. It was first introduced in (the then West) Germany in 1957, and was prescribed to pregnant women to treat morning sickness. However, its use resulted in the birth of thousands of deformed babies because thalidomide prevented the proper growth of the fetus. Thalidomide is now approved in several countries including Brazil, Mexico and the US to treat the painful, disfiguring skin sores associated with leprosy, and to prevent and control the return of these skin sores. However, the medicine comes with special warnings about the risks of severe birth defects or death to an unborn baby. Birth defects include babies with no arms and legs, short arms and legs, missing bones and intestinal abnormalities.

D.1.3 Describe the different methods of administering drugs.

METHODS OF ADMINISTRATION

Transporting a drug into the body is a complex process. Administration of a drug involves introducing a drug into the blood stream. The entire blood volume (approximately 6 litres) circulates in the body about once a minute and drugs are fairly evenly distributed throughout the blood. There are several ways of administering a drug: each has advantages and disadvantages. Also, different effects can be seen depending on the route of administration. The four main methods are: oral, parenteral by injection (which may be intraveneous, intramuscular or subcutaneous), inhalation and rectal.

Oral (by mouth)

This is very convenient. However the effect is variable since the rate of absorption is influenced by, for example, drug concentration and stomach content. Absorption takes place along the entire gastrointestinal tract from the mouth to the intestine. The percentage absorption of a drug in the stomach is generally small, except for alcohol, about one third of which is is absorbed. For most drugs taken orally, the primary site of absorption is the small intestine which is also the site of absorption of digested food. A drug that is difficult to dissolve will be absorbed slowly. Time release capsules have various coatings to ensure gradual release of

TOK Should scientists be held morally responsible when drugs have adverse effects?

Firstly is this the same question about scientists being morally responsible for anything they discover that, like the invention of gunpowder, has brought misfortune to some people. Scientists always have the option of not telling anybody about a discovery they have made. On the plus side nobody will be harmed, but equally nobody will benefit and they will not get the kudos for the discovery. Also, somebody else, more unscrupulous, might come up with the same idea in a few month's time. Initially at any rate, the direction in which it is developed might be controlled. I don't know of any instances where people have not told us of their discoveries (think about it.). Actually that is clever, not quite accurate – I seem to recall that after his death, somebody sorting through Gauss' papers found that he had developed a lot of the theory of non-Euclidean geometry, but had not published it for fear of ridicule.

Whilst in the case of drugs the above is obviously true, perhaps in some ways they are a little different. Let's assume that this refers to drugs developed with the intention of fighting disease, rather than the replacement for Ecstasy, so that the underlying motivation is a worthy one. (I will leave you to discuss whether developing a successor to Ecstasy could display positive motives). In building a new road bridge we know there is a distinct possibility that somebody will die whilst building it, and an even higher possibility that some day there will be a fatal crash on it. Nevertheless, provided we take reasonable precautions to guard against both we go ahead because the potential good well outweighs the potential ill.

the drug over time. The form in which a drug is available, as a tablet or in liquid form, and whether it is taken on an empty stomach or with food determines the rate at which the drug is absorbed.

Parenteral (by injection)

a. Beneath the skin (subcutaneous route): Drug absorption is slower than intravenous (directly into a vein). Dental injections are often subcutaneous. The method is also common with illegal drug users. (see Figure 1502)

b. Into muscles (intramuscular): This method is used if immediate response is not required or when a large volume of drug needs to be injected. The method is relatively safe and easy provided a blood vessel is not accidentally penetrated. Many vaccination injections, for example for overseas travel, are intramuscular.

c. Directly into the blood stream (intravenous). This is the most practical; the drug is introduced by injection into a vein and distributed around the body within about a minute, so the effect is virtually instantaneous. An advantage is that it is possible to administer precise amounts of the drug since concentration is not affected by stomach acid or content. However, once administered, the drug cannot be retrieved as it can be (to some extent) with oral administration.

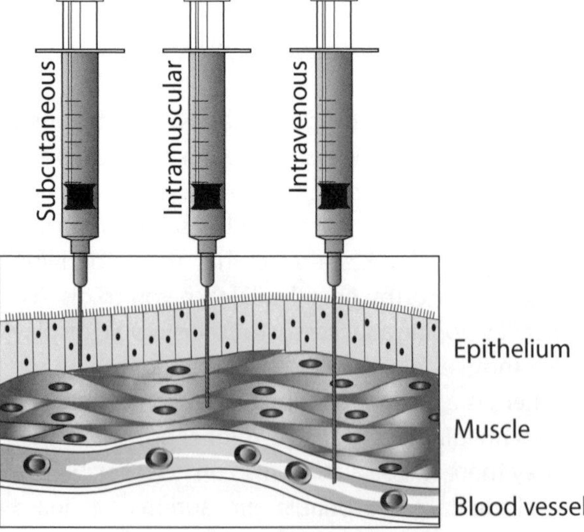

Figure 1502 Methods of drug injection

Inhalation (by breathing in)

Administration is rapid because of the extensive network of blood vessels in the lungs. Drugs can be administered by this route to produce a systemic effect (such as general anaesthesia) in which the drug is absorbed into the blood stream to produce an effect in the brain and the whole body. Patients suffering from asthma achieve quick relief from the use of drugs such as Ventolin® that dilate the respiratory tract.

Rectal (via the rectum)

This method of administration is very effective when patients experience nausea or vomiting or are unable to take medicine orally before or after surgery. Drugs that are pH sensitive and which may be destroyed by the stomach's acidity may be delivered rectally. A drug capable of systemic effect - one that affects any part of the body – can be inserted into the rectum in the form of suppositories. The drug is then absorbed into the bloodstream. Suppositories for the relief of haemorrhoids (enlarged and painful blood vessels in or around the anus) are used for local effect.

Except for intravenous injections, a drug must be transported across the blood vessels, which contain a fatty or lipid layer. Drugs which dissolve readily in fats are therefore more easily absorbed. Drugs can be absorbed into the bloodstream, from a region of high to low drug concentration, by osmosis. The capillaries of the brain are denser and prevent diffusion of many substances into the neurons of the brain - this is called the **blood-brain barrier** and is very important. For example, penicillins do not pass this barrier. This is fortunate since they cause convulsions if injected directly into the brain. Psychoactive drugs have to pass into the brain as these drugs alter behaviour or change consciousness.

Termination of a drug's action takes place when it is broken down by the liver and eliminated by the kidneys. Half-life is the time required for half the drug to be eliminated. For example, the half life of cocaine is a few minutes, but marijuana can be detected up to 28 days after use - it is absorbed by fatty tissue, and bound to it, making diffusion into the blood stream a very slow process.

D.1.4 Discuss the terms therapeutic window, tolerance, and side effects.

THERAPEUTIC WINDOW

This is a measure of the relative margin of safety of the drug for a particular treatment (for a typical population). Quantitatively, it is given as a ratio of the lethal dose (LD_{50}) to the therapeutic dose of the drug (ED_{50}) where LD_{50} is the lethal dose for 50% of the population and ED_{50} is the effective dose for 50% of the population.

If the effective dose is small and the lethal dose is large, then a wide therapeutic window exists since in this case the toxicity occurs at higher concentrations, well above the dose required to achieve the maximum desired effect. On the other hand, when the therapeutic window is narrow, small doses must often be administered for successful treatment.

A toxic substance (poison) is a chemical that is dangerous or causes illness or death (lethal effect) in small amounts. An example is the nerve gas sarin used in the Tokyo subway incident which was found to be extremely toxic in minute quantities. Substances such as nicotine can be moderately toxic to animals, whereas water is considered almost completely non-toxic. The lethal dose for a toxic substance varies from chemical to chemical and from one individual and/or species to another.

Drugs can be considered hazardous when they pose risks to the physical, mental, or social well-being of the user. Drugs can lead to dependence and or tolerance and usually have side effects:

TOLERANCE

Tolerance means that, over time and with regular use, a user needs increasing amounts of a drug to get the same physiological effect. For example, long term use of opiates can lead to tolerance. Tolerance increases the health hazards of any drug simply because the amount taken increases over time. Tolerance also increases the risk of a dangerous fatal overdose for two reasons:

- Firstly, with some drugs, the body does not necessarily develop tolerance to the harmful effects of the drug. Long-term barbiturate users, for example, become tolerant to the drug's sedative effect, but not to its side effect on breathing. If the drug is used for too long a time, the dose people need to fall asleep or calm their nerves may be more than enough to stop their breathing.
- Secondly, if a drug user has not taken the drug in a long time, the expected tolerance may actually have decreased. So after a long period of abstinence, the size of dose the user had previously become accustomed to may actually be enough to cause an overdose.

SIDE EFFECTS

The desired effect of a drug is considered to be the main effect; the unwanted responses are considered side effects. This happens because no drug exerts a single effect; usually several different body functions are altered. To achieve the main effect, the side effects must be tolerated, which is possible if they are minor but may be limiting if they are more serious. The distinction between main and side effects is relative and depends on the purpose of the drug, e.g. morphine. If pain relieving properties are sought, the intestinal constipation induced is an undesirable side effect. However, it may also be used to treat diarrhoea, so constipation induced is the main effect and any relief of pain is a side effect.

No drug is free of toxic effects; often these may be trivial but can also be serious. Allergies are caused by the over-reaction of the immune system due to sensitivity to foreign substances and tend to be harmless in most but not all cases. Allergies to drugs may take many forms from mild skin rashes to fatal shock caused by such drugs as penicillin. Because drugs are concentrated, metabolized and excreted by the liver and kidney, damage to these is not uncommon. For example, alcohol causes liver damage and the thalidomide tragedy dramatically illustrated that drugs may adversely influence fetal development.

DEPENDENCE

Some people use drugs because they have become physically or psychologically dependent on them. When an individual continues to use a certain drug because s/he does not feel 'right' without it, that person can be said to be drug-dependent.

Physical Dependence

Physical dependence occurs when a drug user's body becomes so accustomed to a drug that it can only function normally if the drug is present. Without the drug, the user may experience a variety of physical symptoms ranging from mild discomfort to convulsions. These symptoms, some of which can be fatal, are referred to as 'withdrawal'. Not all drugs produce physical dependence. Physical dependence is a form of drug addiction. For example, long term use of opiates can lead to physical dependence.

Psychological Dependence

Psychological dependence exists when a drug is so central to a person's thoughts, emotions, and activities that it is extremely difficult to stop using it, or even stop thinking about it. Psychological dependence is marked by an intense craving for the drug and its effects. Like physical dependence, psychological dependence is a form of drug addiction (see Sections D.3.4, D.4.2, D 5.5).

D2 ANTACIDS

D.2.1 State and explain how excess acidity in the stomach can be reduced by the use of different bases.

The walls of the human stomach contain cells which secrete gastric juices containing hydrochloric acid. The normal pH of gastric juices is in the 1.0 – 3.0 range. The purposes of this acidic solution are:

- to suppress growth of harmful bacteria, and
- to help in digestion by hydrolysing proteins to amino acids.

Over-eating or eating certain types of food, or stress (worrying) stimulates excess acid production, causing discomfort, called indigestion, a term often used to describe any form of abdominal discomfort that occurs after meals. Excess acid can eventually eat away the protective mucus layer that lines the stomach, causing painful ulcers. An **antacid** is a remedy for excess stomach acidity. Antacids are bases, usually, metal oxides, hydroxides, carbonates or hydrogen carbonates (bicarbonates) that neutralize excess acid in the stomach to adjust the stomach pH to the desired level. Thus they relieve indigestion and allow damage done by excess acid to the stomach lining to repair itself.

The active ingredients in 'over-the-counter' antacids include aluminium hydroxide $Al(OH)_3$, magnesium hydroxide $Mg(OH)_2$, calcium carbonate $CaCO_3$, and sodium hydrogen carbonate $NaHCO_3$ (see Figure 1503). The antacids are often combined with chemicals called alginates (extracted primarily from brown seaweeds) that produce a neutralising layer that prevents acid reflux. That is, they prevent acid in the stomach from rising into the oesophagus and causing 'heartburn'. Similarly anti–foaming agents such as dimethicone are added that reduce the surface tension of gas bubbles, causing them to coalesce (come together), producing a defoaming action.

Tums®	$CaCO_3$, $MgCO_3$, $MgSi_3O_8$ (magnesium trisilicate) for the treatment of ulcers and gastritis.
Rotaids®	$AlNa(OH)_2CO_3$.
Maalox®	$Mg(OH)_2$, $Al(OH)_3$.
Alka Seltzer®	$NaHCO_3$, citric acid, aspirin. The solid hydrogen carbonate and citric acid react in water ('pop pop fizz fizz') to release carbon dioxide which induces belching and aids in the removal of air in the stomach, thus relieving discomfort.
Milk of Magnesia®	$Mg(OH)_2$ (or $MgO/Mg(OH)_2$mixture).
Amphogel®	$Al(OH)_3$.
Di-Gel®	$CaCO_3$.

Figure 1503 Active ingredients of some commercial antacids

ACTION OF ANTACIDS

1. Magnesium oxide

$$MgO\ (s) + 2\ HCl\ (aq) \longrightarrow MgCl_2\ (aq) + H_2O\ (l)$$

2. Magnesium hydroxide

$$Mg(OH)_2\ (aq) + 2\ HCl\ (aq) \longrightarrow MgCl_2\ (aq) + 2\ H_2O\ (l)$$

3. Aluminium hydroxide

$$Al(OH)_3\ (s) + 3\ HCl\ (aq) \longrightarrow AlCl_3\ (aq) + 3\ H_2O\ (l)$$

4. Calcium carbonate

$$CaCO_3\ (s) + 2HCl\ (aq) \longrightarrow CaCl_2\ (aq) + H_2O\ (l) + CO_2\ (g)$$

5. Sodium hydrogen carbonate

$$NaHCO_3\ (aq) + HCl\ (aq) \longrightarrow NaCl\ (aq) + H_2O\ (l) + CO_2\ (g)$$

6. Magnesium trisilicate

$$Mg_2Si_3O_8\,(s) + 4\,HCl\,(aq) \longrightarrow 3\,SiO_2\,(s) + 2\,H_2O\,(l) + 2\,MgCl_2\,(aq)$$

SIDE EFFECTS OF ANTACIDS

Aluminium hydroxide may cause constipation or irregularity. Aluminium ions can also prevent uptake of phosphate ions, due to precipitation of aluminium phosphate. They bind to certain drugs because of their large charge density due to their small ionic radius and high charge. Magnesium hydroxide has laxative properties. Calcium carbonate may result in kidney stones and sodium ions may lead to hypertension. Very low antacid doses barely decrease stomach acidity to normal and high doses carry it too far, causing a basic stomach. This also causes discomfort and is often mistaken as being due to an acidic stomach so one takes more antacid making the stomach still more basic, causing more indigestion. This condition is called alkalosis (a rise in the pH of blood). For example, excessive use of sodium hydrogen carbonate may lead to alkalosis and fluid retention ('bloating'). Repeated use of calcium carbonate as an antacid may lead to excessive amounts of calcium ions being absorbed into the body.

Example

Two solid antacid products containing the same mass of different active ingredients are on sale for the same price. One contains sodium bicarbonate, the other calcium carbonate as the active ingredient. Deduce which one is a better buy and explain your reasoning.

Solution

Determine which one neutralizes more stomach acid; assume 1.00 g active ingredient:

$$n(NaHCO_3)\text{: } \frac{1.00}{23.0 + 1.0 + 12.0 + 3 \times 16.0} = \frac{1.00}{84.0}$$

$$= 0.0119 \text{ mol}$$

$$n(CaCO_3)\text{: } \frac{1.00}{40.1 + 12.0 + 3 \times 16.0} = \frac{1.00}{100.1} = 0.00999 \text{ mol}$$

Write balanced chemical equations for the two active ingredients with HCl to determine the amount of HCl in moles neutralized by each antacid:

$$NaHCO_3\,(s) + HCl\,(aq) \longrightarrow NaCl\,(aq) + H_2O\,(l) + CO_2\,(g)$$

$$n\,(HCl) = n\,(NaHCO_3) = 0.0119 \text{ mol}$$

$$CaCO_3\,(s) + 2HCl\,(aq) \longrightarrow CaCl_2\,(aq) + H_2O\,(l) + CO_2\,(g)$$

$$n\,(HCl) = 2 \times n\,(CaCO_3) = 2 \times 0.00999 = 0.0200\ (> 0.0119)$$

For the same mass, calcium carbonate neutralizes a greater amount of stomach acid than sodium bicarbonate, and is thus a better buy.

TOK How does perception affect our way of knowing?

Why is it that when I have a headache I usually ignore it, but my wife will usually pop a couple of Paracetamols and get rid of it? Probably, if you asked her, she would tell you that it's because I'm a stupid masochist and maybe she has a point. In all kinds of perception we differ in our sensitivities, but to what point? Do I have less pain cells? Do my cells generate lower output voltages? Do my nerves conduct the signal less efficiently? Is the part of my brain where they end up less responsive? Have I got so many things whizzing round my mind that I don't notice? Was I brought up by people telling me "big boy's don't cry if they're hurt" and that eventually led to conditioning? There are so many points on the chain where things could differ – it's not just like the needle on a light meter.

How does this affect perception as a way of knowing? Well it would be unwise to rely on absolutes. My "loud noise" might not be a loud noise to somebody else, depending on where they spend their Saturday nights, but we would most likely agree that the plane currently going overhead is louder than the music coming from my stereo – it's a lot safer to stick to comparatives. I remember being told that women have a greater ability than men to differentiate between shades of colour. I wonder if that is because they have different eyes, different brains, or have just developed this ability more as they grew up?

D3 ANALGESICS

D.3.1 Describe and explain the different ways in which analgesics prevent pain.

Pain has been described as 'an unpleasant sensory and emotional experience associated with actual or potential tissue damage'. Pain receptors in our bodies are nerves that transmit pain. These are free nerve endings located in various body tissues that respond to thermal, mechanical and chemical stimuli. When stimulated, these pain receptors generate an impulse. Pain results from interaction between various impulses arriving at the spinal cord and the brain. When tissues become injured, they release chemicals called prostaglandins and leukotrienes that make the pain receptors more sensitive. Sensitized receptors react to even gentle stimuli, causing pain.

Different people have different tolerance for, and perception of, pain – some will find a pail of water too hot, others not so hot. Some can walk on burning charcoal with ease, others not. Some react to a injection needle with much pain, others with little irritation.

Analgesics are drugs that relieve pain without causing loss of consciousness. These include:

- mild analgesics used for relief of mild pain (and frequently fever) – examples include aspirin (ASA, acetyl salicylic acid), acetaminophen (metabolic byproduct of phenacetin) also sold as tylenol, paracetamol, etc. phenacetin, ibuprofen (sold as Actiprofen®, Advil®, MotrinIB®, Medipren® etc), NSAIDS (non-steroidal anti-inflammatory drugs). These mild analgesics are considered non-addictive
- strong opiates used for the relief of very severe pain include the narcotics morphine, heroin (also called diacetylmorphine or diamorphine) and codeine. These are controlled substances that are addictive
- local anaesthetics (pain killers in localised areas) include lidocaine and procaine used in dentistry
- general anaesthetics act on the brain and produce reversible unconsciousness as well as insentivity to pain.

Mild analgesics, such as aspirin, work by indirectly blocking the enzyme-controlled synthesis of prostaglandins. Among their many effects are the constricting of blood vessels. This helps increase the body temperature because less heat can escape from the tissues into the blood. Prostaglandins also have a direct effect on the body's heat regulating centre (the hypothalamus), which produces fever. These chemicals also increase the permeability of capillaries, allowing water to pass out of the capillaries into nearby tissues, thus causing swelling and pain. By lowering the concentration of prostaglandins, mild analgesics reduce pain, fever and inflammation.

Chemical painkillers such as endorphins and enkephalins are produced naturally in the body. Enkephalins are the natural opiates found in the part of the brain and the spinal cord that transmit pain impulses. These are able to bind to neuro-receptors in the brain and produce relief from pain. The temporary loss of pain immediately after an injury is associated with the production of these chemicals. Similarly strong analgesics (opiates) work by temporarily binding to the opiate receptor sites in the brain, preventing the transmission of pain impulses without depressing the central nervous system.

This mechanism of action of aspirin - acting on inflammed tissues and the associated nerves - is in contrast to the action of morphine, a very powerful painkiller, that acts directly on the brain.

D 3.2 Describe the use of derivatives of salicylic acid as mild analgesics and compare the advantages and disadvantages of using aspirin and paracetamol (acetaminophen).

USES OF THE DERIVATIVES OF SALICYLIC ACID

- as a mild analgesic for minor aches and pains, to relieve headaches, sunburn pain and the pain of arthritis
- as an anti-pyretic to reduce fever
- as an anti-inflammatory agent when there is swelling from injuries
- as an anti-platelet agent in the prevention of abnormal blood clotting and as an anti clotting agent after heart surgery. Aspirin's anti-clotting ability results from the fact that it inhibits the production of prostaglandins. These are hormone-like fatty acids that cause blood platelets to stick together and clot. Moderate doses of ASA have been found to be useful in preventing the recurrence of heart attacks. It has thus been called a 'miracle drug' by heart disease patients.

Disadvantages of aspirin

- due to its acidic nature in aqueous solution, aspirin can cause stomach upset and internal bleeding; it can cause ulceration and aggravate existing peptic ulcers
- there is a risk of developing severe gastrointestinal bleeding following the use of alcohol
- about 0.5% who take aspirin (and 3-5% asthmatics) are allergic to it, leading to skin rashes, respiratory difficulty, and even shock
- aspirin is one of the most frequent causes of accidental poisoning in infants.
- There is a small but significant correlation between the use of aspirin and the development of Reye's syndrome in children who take ASA for chicken pox or flu-like symptoms. Reye's syndrome is a potentially fatal liver and brain disorder that can result in coma, brain damage and death.

Aspirin Substitutes

As a result of allergic reactions to aspirin, or for people who experience upset stomachs, substitutes exist. These include phenacetin and acetaminophen, called paracetamol in some countries.

$C_2H_5-O-C_6H_4-N(H)-C(=O)-CH_3$ Phenacetin

Acetaminophen $HO-C_6H_4-N(H)-C(=O)-CH_3$

Figure 1507 Aspirin substitutes

Acetaminophen is the metabolic byproduct of phenacetin and is the active ingredient of many over-the-counter (OTC) drugs.

Uses of acetaminophen

- like aspirin it is an anti-pyretic and reduces fever
- as an analgesic to reduce mild pain.

Unlike aspirin, acetaminophen does not upset the stomach or cause internal bleeding. It is not, however, an effective anti-inflammatory drug. It is a very safe drug when used in the correct dose but can, very rarely, cause side effects such as blood disorders and kidney damage. It is the preferred treatment for patients with aspirin allergy, ulcers or clotting disorders. It should not be taken with alcohol, nor by patients with kidney or liver disease. An overdose (>20 tablets) can cause serious liver damage, brain damage, coma and even death.

Ibuprofen has many of the same effects as aspirin but seems to cause fewer stomach problems. Unlike acetaminophen, it is an anti-inflammatory drug. It is effective in low doses and has a wide margin of safety. Besides being implicated in kidney problems in large doses, its other side effects are similar to those of ASA.

D.3.3 Compare the structures of morphine, codeine and diamorphine (heroin, a semi-synthetic opiate).

D.3.4 Discuss the advantages and disadvantages of using morphine and its derivatives as strong analgesics.

STRONG ANALGESICS

Morphine, diethanoyls morphine (heroin) and codeine

These are refered to as 'opiates', 'narcotics' or 'narcotic analgesics' that are prescribed for the relief of strong pain. The term 'opiate' refers to any natural or synthetic drug that exerts actions on the body similar to those induced by morphine – the major pain relieving substance obtained from the seeds of the opium poppy plant. 'Narcotic' is a term generally used for drugs that have both a narcotic (sleep inducing) and analgesic (pain relieving) action.

Morphine is the principal **alkaloid** (nitrogen containing organic compound) and makes up about 10% by mass of raw opium. Codeine is about 0.5% by mass of raw opium. Heroin is usually synthesised by functional group modification to the structure of morphine where the two –OH groups on morphine are effectively replaced by two ester (CH_3COO-) groups (see Figure 1508). Heroin is thus a semi-synthetic drug.

OPTION

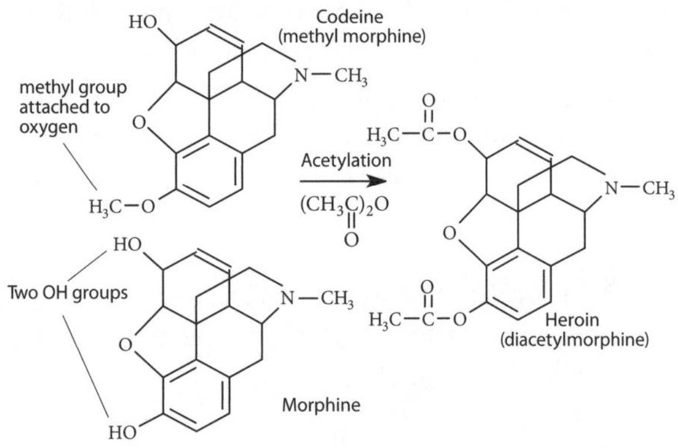

Figure 1508 The chemical strucure of some opiates

Besides having the same carbon skeleton, morphine contains two –OH groups. Codeine contains one –OH and one $-OCH_3$ group and heroin contains two ethanoyl (also called acetyl) groups, CH_3COO-. Thus functional group modifications to the structure of morphine result in the semi-synthetic drugs heroin and codeine (also prepared semi-synthetically because of its very small percentage in raw opium).

Advantages and disadvantages of opiates

Pharmacological effects

Opiates exert major effects on:

- the central nervous system
- the eye and
- the gastrointestinal tract (the digestive system)

The prime medical uses of opiates

- as a strong analgesic in the relief of severe pain caused by injury, chronic disease such as cancer, prior to and recovery from surgery etc. Heroin is more potent and codeine less potent than morphine
- in the treatment of diarrhoea by producing a constipating effect
- to relieve coughing by suppressing the 'cough centre' situated in the brain stem.

Psychological effects of opiates

Opiates produce analgesia, drowsiness, mood changes and mental clouding. Some individuals experience anxiety, fear, lethargy, sedation, lack of concern, inability to concentrate, nausea and vomiting. Also, users feel a relief from emotional and psychological pain.

Tolerance and dependence

Tolerance appears due both to the induction of drug metabolising enzymes in the liver and the adaptation of neurons in the brain to the presence of the drug. Cross tolerance – drug users who become tolerant to one opiate will also exhibit a tolerance to all other natural or synthetic opiates, e.g. tolerance to morphine will also lead to tolerance of heroin but not to alcohol or barbiturates which are sedatives (or hypnotics).

Physical Dependence is a state in which people do not function properly without a drug. Withdrawal is experienced when the drug is not regularly administered. Symptoms include restlessness, sweating, fever, chills, vomiting, increased rate of respiration, cramping, diarrhoea, unbearable aches and pains. The magnitude of these withdrawal symptoms depend on the dose, frequency of drug administration, the duration of the drug dependence and the opiate used.

The opiates are extremely potent and valuable drugs for the treatment of pain. But they also have the capacity to induce a state of euphoria and relief from psychological pain, which can lead to a strong compulsion to misuse them. The opiates induce profound tolerance and physiological dependence, the consequencies of which are important both medically and sociologically as the user is difficult to treat and must frequently resort to crime to support the habit and reach a source of supply.

Usual short - term effects	Typical long - term effects
Sedation and stupor; relief from pain.	Loss of appetite; malnutrition, constipation.
Euphoria; impaired functioning and coordination, and temporary impotence.	Risk of dangerous infections (hepatitis, AIDS) due to shared needles.
Reduced tension, worry and fear.	Withdrawal illness, loss of job, crime.
Reduced coughing reflex.	Sterility.
Occasional death from overdose.	Diversion of energy and money.

Figure 1509 Summary of the effects of narcotics

Several totally synthetic opiates, including demerol (meperidine), methadone (dolophine) and fentanyl (sublimaze), exhibit effects like those of opiates but are produced in the laboratory. Demerol is a synthetic morphine derivative. Methadone blocks the euphoric high of heroin and is used in the treatment of heroin addicts in certain countries where it is a legal drug. The opiates are addictive, heroin being the more addictive of the three. Codeine is often replaced by dextromethorphan, a synthetic non-narcotic medication.

D4 DEPRESSANTS

D.4.1 Describe the effects of depressants.

Depressants

(sometimes called 'downers')

Depressants (tranquilizers, sedatives and hypnotics) calm and relax (that is depress) the central nervous system by interfering with nerve impulse transmission. These slow down the activity of the brain and other organs such as the heart. They reduce the rate of breathing and in general dull emotional responses. At low doses a depressant may exert little or no effect. At moderate doses the compound may induce sedation (soothing, reduction of anxiety). At higher doses it may induce sleep and at extremely high doses it may cause death. Depressants are often described as anti-depressants because they relieve depression.

Tranquilizers

Examples include alcohol, valium and librium. These have the property of reducing nervous tension and anxiety but do not produce sleep in normal doses. Librium and valium (diazepam) are two common benzodiazepine tranquilizers used widely for relieving anxiety and tension and are safer than barbiturates.

Sedatives

Examples are certain **barbiturates** (a class of drugs that are depressants). Sedatives can cause soothing of distress, again without producing sleep in normal doses. The main difference between a tranquilizer and a sedative is one of degree of action. Tranquilizers are mild in their action compared to sedatives.

Hypnotics

An example is chloral hydrate. **Hypnotics** are a class of drug that produces sleep. Note that phenobarbital (a barbiturate) can behave as a sedative or a hypnotic depending on the dose.

Figure 1510 shows how increasing the dose of a depressant affects behavior.

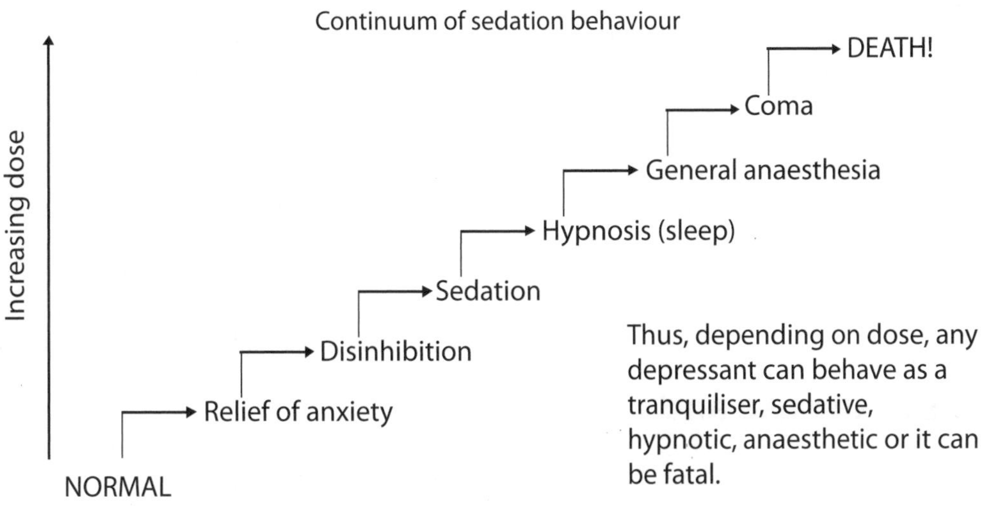

Figure 1510 How depressants affect behaviour

OPTION

B.4.2 Discuss the social and physiological effects of the use and abuse of ethanol.

B.4.4 Describe the synergistic effects of ethanol with other drugs.

ETHANOL (C_2H_5OH)

$$C_2H_5—\ddot{O}^{\delta-}—H^{\delta+}$$

Figure 1511 The chemical structure of ethanol

The presence of a tiny hydrogen atom attached to a highly electronegative oxygen atom makes it possible for ethanol, alcohol in alcoholic drinks, to form hydrogen bonds with water. Ethanol is also fat soluble as it is a relatively small organic molecule. Thus it readily penetrates cell and tissue membranes and is therefore completely and easily absorbed from the entire gastrointestinal tract.

About 30 to 50 milligrams (mg) per 100 cm^3 of blood leads to mild intoxication resulting in a sense of euphoria (great happiness). In people who have not developed tolerance to ethanol, silly behaviour is observed. Once the concentration of ethanol has reached 100 mg per 100 cm^3, most people suffer neurological problems resulting in slurred speech and staggering. Aggressive and dangerous behaviour is also common, even in experienced drinkers. At concentrations of 200 mg per 100 cm^3 blood, vision and movement are difficult and at 400 mg per 100 cm^3 of blood, coma and death are likely. Alcoholism is medically defined as a disease. It is often progressive and frequently fatal. It often appears to run in families and has recently been established to have a strong genetic component in some people. It seems to be related to the levels of specific enzymes inside the body.

There are few current medical uses for alcohol. It is used as a solvent in tincture of iodine (an antiseptic) and in antiseptics such as mouthwashes. In North America and Europe it is estimated to be used by at least 80% of the adult population.

OPTION

Social effects of the use and abuse of alcohol

The major social costs from alcohol use and abuse are due to sickness and death associated with drinking (see short and long term effects). These costs consist of hospital treatment as well as lost productivity due to ill health and death. It is estimated that in countries such as the US, Australia, Europe, Japan, etc. over 80% of all alcohol-induced costs are borne by society. Other costs attributed to alcohol include crime, motor traffic related costs and the pain and suffering felt by crime and accident victims and their families. Research in the US shows that there is considerable evidence that offenders are often affected by alcohol when committing violent crimes.

Physiological effects of the use and abuse of alcohol

Alcoholism is a disease which involves a psychological addiction characterised by an inability to control intake, that is a craving or compulsion to drink and inability to stop drinking, as well as physical addiction. Genetic factors may also be involved. Alcohol abuse involves a pattern of drinking associated with failure to fulfil major obligations (at work, school or home), drinking while driving, operating machinery, participating in dangerous situations, physically harming someone or on-going problems in relationships. Physical dependence involves withdrawal symptoms such as nausea, sweating, anxiety, increased blood pressure when alcohol use is stopped. Tolerance involves the need for increasing amounts of the drug to feel the same effects.

Short–term effects

As a central nervous system depressant, alcohol reduces tension, anxiety and inhibitions. The extent to which the CNS function is impaired is directly proportional to the concentration of alcohol in the blood. In moderate amounts, a user experiences euphoria, sociability, talkativeness, feeling of relaxation, increased self confidence and decreased inhibitions. Small blood vessels in the skin get dilated, leading to a feeling of warmth. As the amount of alcohol consumed increases, loss of judgement, impairment of perception, memory and comprehension takes place and driving accidents are more likely due to increased reaction time. With increased consumption, violent or aggressive behaviour is possible, as is slurred speech, dizziness, double vision, loss of balance, nausea and vomiting. At high alcohol concentration, loss of consciousness may follow as well as death from respiratory arrest.

Long–term effects

These include cirrhosis (due to scar tissue) and cancer of the liver, coronary heart disease, high blood pressure, strokes, gastritis (inflammation of the stomach) and peptic ulcers. Long term heavy drinking leads to physical dependence and tolerance. Alcoholics often suffer from anxiety and depression and poor eating habits. Excess drinking by pregnant women can lead to miscarriage, low birth mass and fetal abnormalities including poor development in infants. Fetal Alcohol Syndrome refers to physical and mental birth defects resulting from a woman drinking too much alcohol during pregnancy.

Synergistic effects

Synergetic effect takes place when the combination of two drugs is more harmful than either drug taken alone. Alcohol produces a synergic effect with other drugs whose performance is enhanced many more times with alcohol than without, sometimes leading to devastating effects. For example, alcohol taken with sedatives like sleeping pills and barbiturates that affect the central nervous system can produce increased risk of heavy sedation even leading to coma and death. Alcohol taken with aspirin increases the risk of stomach bleeding.

When alcohol is used with cocaine, a substance called cocaethylene is formed, which may extend and enhance the cocaine 'high'. However, cocaethylene is far more toxic than cocaine and alcohol used separately and causes severe vasoconstriction (narrowing of blood vessels leading to a rise in blood pressure) and arythmogenecity (an irregular heart beat). Similarly, alcohol can be fatal when taken with benzodiapenes, such as mogadon and valium. In these cases the combination of drugs suppresses the actions of the nervous system.

D.4.3 Describe and explain the techniques used for the detection of ethanol in the breath and in the blood or urine.

The **Blood Alcohol Concentration** (BAC) is the mass in grams of ethanol per 100 cm^3 of blood. In some countries this is listed as a percentage. For example, in many countries a 0.08% blood alcohol level (equal to 80mg alcohol per 100 cm^3 of blood) is the legal limit for driving cars.

Ethanol passes from the stomach into the blood stream, and since it is sufficiently volatile, it passes into the lungs where an equilibrium is established at the body's temperature.

$$C_2H_5OH_{(blood)} \rightleftharpoons C_2H_5OH_{(vapour)}$$

and the concentration of ethanol in the lungs will depend on the concentration of ethanol in the blood. The concentration of alcohol decreases with time as it is metabolized in the liver.

BREATHALYSER TEST

The roadside breathalyser test done by law enforcement officers involves a redox reaction in which acidified potassium dichromate(VI), $K_2Cr_2O_7$ is used as the oxidising agent. It oxidises any alcohol in the breath to ethanoic acid, CH_3COOH. The orange Cr(VI) is reduced to green Cr(III) with the gain of three electrons per Cr. The two half reactions and the overall reaction are:

$$Cr_2O_7^{2-} + 14\,H^+ + 6\,e^- \longrightarrow 2\,Cr^{3+} + 7\,H_2O:$$
reduction half reaction

$$C_2H_5OH + H_2O \longrightarrow CH_3COOH + 4\,e^- + 4\,H^+:$$
oxidation half reaction

$$2\,Cr_2O_7^{2-} + 3\,C_2H_5OH + 16\,H^+ \longrightarrow 4\,Cr^{3+} + 3\,CH_3COOH + 11\,H_2O$$

The redox reaction, involving transfer of electrons generates, an e.m.f. that is converted to a signal in the breathalyser device to indicate the BAC in the sample of breath. Such devices generally suffer from inaccuracy and unreliability when used in legal cases. More accurate analysis is carried out by gas liquid chromatography (glc) and infra-red spectroscopy.

Gas Liquid Chromatography

Very small samples of gases and volatile liquids such as ethanol can be separated from breath as well as from samples of blood and urine and identified using gas liquid chromatography (glc).

Glc uses a stationary phase such as a non-volatile liquid or solid support and a mobile phase such as an inert carrier gas, for example nitrogen, N_2. The components of the breath including carbon dioxide, water vapour and alcohol vapour are partitioned between the mobile and stationary phases depending on their boiling points. Thus the components move through a column of the solid phase at differing speeds and exit after intervals of time depending on the substance. These can then be detected and recorded by a detector that can identify the changes in the composition of the carrier gas as it comes out of the column.

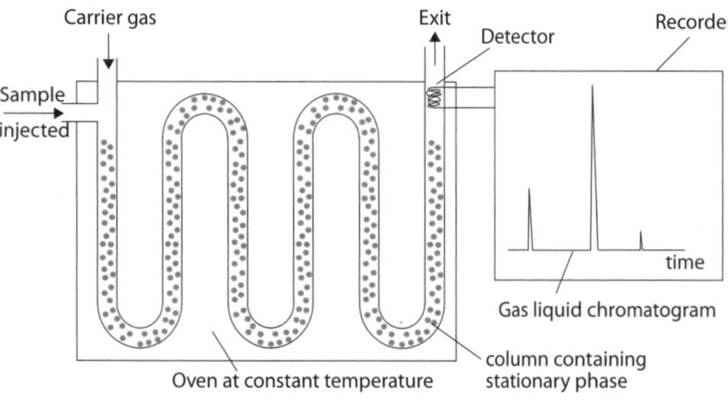

Figure 1512 A gas liquid chromatogram

A **gas liquid chromatogram** (Figure 1512) displays the time taken for each component to pass through the column, called the retention time. A standard ethanol sample is first passed through the column under certain conditions such as the same carrier gas at the same flow rate, the same stationary phase and a constant temperature, to determine its retention time. The sample of breadth, urine or blood is then introduced under all the same conditions, and the ethanol is identified by comparing the retention times. Glc not only identifies the compound, but the area under the peak represents the amount of the compound, thus allowing law enforcement officers to determine accurately the blood alcohol concentration (BAC). Not only can alcohol be detected and measured, other drugs can be detected and measured at the same time. Gas chromatography, unlike the Intoximeter (see below), is able to distinguish between ethanol and propanone (found in the breadth of diabetics).

Infra-red Spectroscopy

Use of Infra-red Spectroscopy to detect alcohol levels:

Infra-red (IR) energy is not sufficiently large to excite an electron to a higher energy level, but is sufficient to cause vibrational motions which depend on the mass of the atoms and the length/strength of the bonds within the molecule.

An infra-red spectrum is therefore characteristic of the bonds or functional groups present in a compound and can act as a 'finger print' to identify it.

IR spectra use the wavenumber scale where the wavenumber = $\frac{1}{\text{wavelength}}$. The units are cm^{-1} and the IR range is from 667 to 4000 cm^{-1}. The presence of the C-H bond in alcohol is detected at 2950 cm^{-1} on an IR spectrum (Figure 1513), whereas the O–H shows an absorption at 3340 cm^{-1}. However, since water vapour is also present in the breath, the O–H peak cannot be used for the detection of any alcohol and instead the IR absorption at 2950 cm^{-1} is used to detect the presence of the C–H group.

Police use the Intoximeter to confirm a road side breathalyser test. This is an IR spectrophotometer in which the IR radiation is passed through the breath sample. If alcohol is present, the frequencies are absorbed by the sample depending on the bands present (such as C–H and O–H) and the rest of the radiation is transmitted. The detector compares the intensity of IR radiation through the sample with the intensity through air. The recorder then produces the IR spectrum as % transmittance (the amount of radiation through the sample) against wavenumber (Figure 1514). However, the Intoximeter does not distinguish between ethanol and propanone which is often present in the breadth of a diabetic patient.

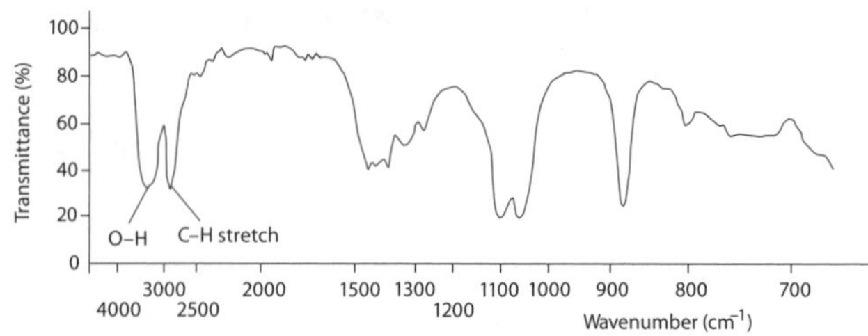

Figure 1513 The spectrum of ethanol showing the C–H stretch used for detection.

OPTION

A simplified schematic diagram of a double-beam IR spectrophotometer

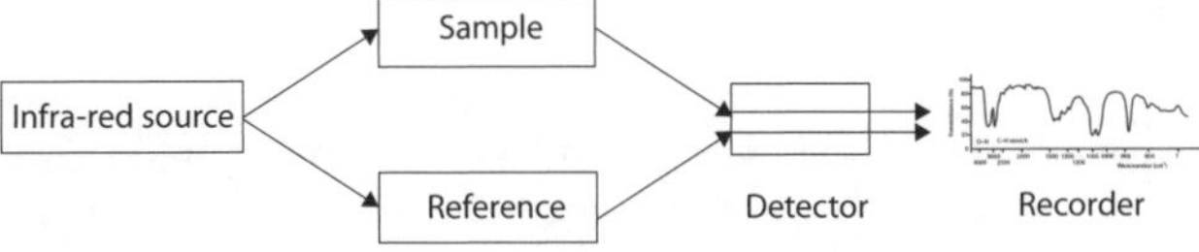

Figure 1514 Double beam IR spectrophotometer

Similar to glc, the size of the peak at 2950 cm^{-1} depends on the amount of radiation absorbed by the breath sample. This depends on the amount of alcohol present, thus allowing accurate determination of the blood alcohol concentration (BAC).

D.4.5 Identify other commonly used depressants and describe their structures.

© IBO 2007

Valium® is a sedative drug. It is the most prescribed drug in the world and is used in the relief of anxiety and tension. It is believed to function by inhibiting nerve transmission by interacting with neurotransmitters. Nitrazepam (Mogadon®, a common sleeping pill) is a hypnotic drug that induces sleep and it is also used to control seizures and infantile spasms.

Valium® and Mogadon® are synthetic drugs known as benzodiazepines. Both have a common structure consiting of a phenyl (C_6H_5) group, a fused benzene ring with a seven membered heterocyclic ring consisting of two nitrogen atoms, one of which is a secondary amine. On the fused benzene ring, valium contains Cl whereas Mogadon® contains the NO_2 group.

Prozac® (Fluoxetine hydrochloride) is an anti-depressant drug that is used to treat mental depression and is thought to work by increasing the activity of serotonin, a neurotransmitter, in the brain. The chemical structure of Prozac® is unlike that of Valium® or Mogadon®. Prozac® contains the amine group which can react with HCl to produce fluoxetine hydrochloride which is water soluble.

Diazepam

Nitrazepam

Prozac®

Figure 1515 Structures of some common depressants

D5 STIMULANTS

D.5.1 List the physiological effects of stimulants.

© IBO 2007

Stimulants (also called 'uppers') are chemicals that stimulate the brain and the central nervous system by increasing the state of mental alertness. Their effect is opposite to the depressants ('downers'). Stimulants cause increased alertness and wakefulness (and in many cases decrease appetite and are therefore used as diet pills). Amphetamines, nicotine and caffeine are all examples of stimulants.

D.5.2 Compare amphetamines and adrenaline (epinephrine).

© IBO 2007

The hormone Adrenaline (epinephrine) is a natural stimulant produced in the adrenal gland. It is transported through the blood stream and affects the part of the nervous system that controls the heart and breathing rates, pupil dilation and sweating. Adrenaline is released in response to anxiety, exercise or fear and is responsible for the 'flight or fight' syndrome.

Amphetamines have chemical structures similar to the hormone adrenaline, and both derive from the phenylethylamine structure ($CH_3CH_2NH_2$ is ethylamine. See Figure 1516.:

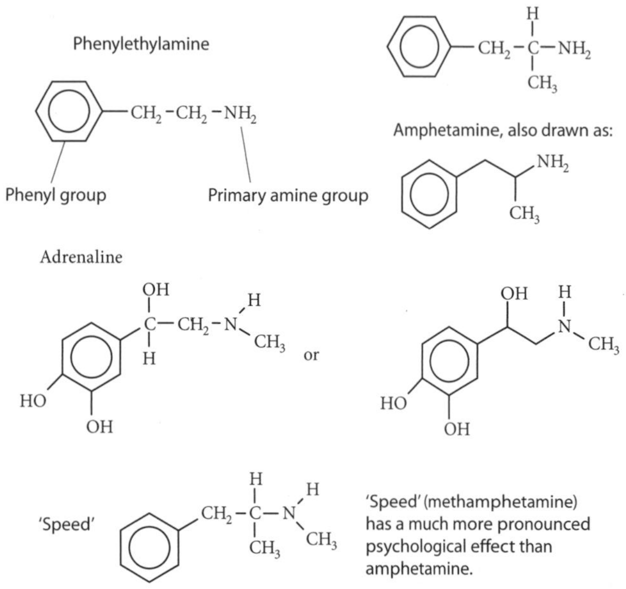

Phenylethylamine

$-CH_2-CH_2-NH_2$

Phenyl group

Primary amine group

$-CH_2-C(H)(CH_3)-NH_2$

Amphetamine, also drawn as:

NH_2 CH_3

Adrenaline

OH H $C-CH_2-N$ CH_3 H HO OH or OH H N CH_3 HO OH

'Speed'

H H CH_2-C-N CH_3 CH_3

'Speed' (methamphetamine) has a much more pronounced psychological effect than amphetamine.

Figure 1516 Strucures of amphetamines and adrenaline

Amphetamines mimic the effects of the hormone adrenaline and are known as sympathomimetic drugs; these are drugs whose actions resemble that of the stimulated sympathetic nerves which are part of the nervous system that, for example, cause arteries to contract. They do this by constricting the arteries, increasing sweat production etc. Amphetamines are strong stimulants and act on the central nervous system, mainly the brain. Medical uses of amphetamines include treatment of mild depression, narcolepsy (tendency to fall asleep) and asthma (because these drugs cause broncodilation). Amphetamines increase the heart rate, blood pressure, respiration, wakefulness, restlessness and insomnia. A temporary elevation of mood is produced followed by fatigue, irritability and depression. Amphetamines allow the body to use reserve energy, just like adrenalin. However, use may be followed by sudden exhaustion leading to blackout or collapse.

Ecstasy is an example of a designer drug made illegally by modifying amphetamine structure to avoid existing laws regarding drugs that alter brain function. It has a structure similar to the stimulant methamphetamine and the hallucinogen mescaline. Like many designer drugs, it is more potent than amphetamine and can be fatal even after one dose.

D.5.3 Discuss the short- and long-term effects of nicotine consumption.

Nicotine is a nitrogen containing alkaloid found in tobacco leaves and cigarette smoke is a source of nicotine, a mild stimulant. In fact the effect as a stimulant is rather transient and short-lived. The initial response is followed by depression, which encourages frequent use.

Short term effects of nicotine

Nicotine increases heart rate and blood pressure and constricts the blood vessels. This puts stress on the heart since it is forced to pump blood harder than normal. This accounts for the greater long-term incidence of heart problems for smokers. Besides causing mild stimulating effects, nicotine reduces urine output.

Long term effects of nicotine

The ability of nicotine to constrict blood vessels stresses the heart, forcing it to pump harder. This increases the risk of heart disease and coronary thrombosis (formation of blood clots) since it may also cause a rise in fatty acids in the bloodstream. Smoking also produces carbon monoxide which inhibits the ability of the blood to carry oxygen, thus placing more stress on the heart. As a stimulant, it may produce excess acidity in the stomach, thus increasing the risk of peptic ulcers. In addition to nicotine, cigarette smoke contains many other toxic chemicals.

Medical evidence indicates that smoking causes:

- lung cancer
- cancers of the larynx and mouth
- heart and blood vessel disease
- emphysema (a chronic lung condition marked by loss of elasticity of the air sacs or alveoli, causing breathing difficulties)
- chronic bronchitis (inflammation of the bronchial tubes)
- air pollution and
- fires (50% of fires in Canada are caused by careless smoking).

Yellow stained fingers and teeth and bad breath are common amongst regular smokers.

It is much easier to become dependent on nicotine than on alcohol or barbiturates. Nicotine produces psychological dependence and builds up tolerance. Many heavy smokers experience physical dependence as well. People who give up smoking can experience withdrawal symptoms such as weight gain, nausea, insomnia, irritability, fatigue, inability to concentrate as well as depression and a craving for cigarettes.

D.5.4 Describe the effects of caffeine and compare its structure with that of nicotine.

Caffeine, an alkaloid, is found in tea, coffee and soft drinks. Caffeine exerts its central nervous system stimulant action by working inside nerve cells to increase their rates of cellular metabolism. This means that the rate at which energy is made available from respiration is increased. Caffeine stimulates the central nervous system, heart, kidneys, lungs and arteries supplying blood to the heart and brain. In moderate doses, caffeine enhances alertness, well-being, energy, motivation and concentration. Thus sustained intellectual effort is made possible. However physical coordination and timing may be adversely affected by higher doses. In small amounts, caffeine is considered relatively harmless. When consumed in large amounts, it can cause sleeplessness. Because it stimulates the kidneys, caffeine is a weak diuretic (a drug that increases the flow of urine).

Caffeine leads to some tolerance, but no physical addiction. It can lead to minor psychological addiction ('morning grouch' symptoms). Because of its ability to stimulate respiration, it finds a medical use to stimulate breathing especially in new born babies with respiratory problems. Caffeine is a vasoconstrictor – it can cause constriction of blood vessels. Since migrane headaches are related to the dilation of blood vessels in the head, caffeine has a potential use in reducing migranes.

Caffeine is a heterocyclic compound in which one or more carbon atoms in the ring are replaced by another atom, nitrogen. Like nicotine it contains a tertiary amine group - in which three organic substituents are attached to nitrogen, fitting the general formula R_3N (See Figure 1517):

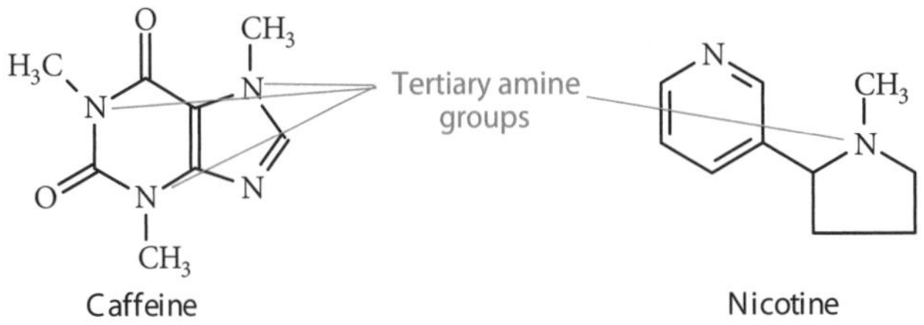

Figure 1517 Structure of caffeine and nicotine

TOK What part does serendipity play in scientific discoveries?

There's a saying, (at least in my part of the world), that people make their own luck and that is probably true with regard to serendipity, the art of making fortunate discoveries by chance, in science. Take the discovery of the nucleus of the atom. Marsden was a very junior research assistant and only 1 in 2000 α-particles were being deflected through an angle of more than 180° by the gold foil. How easy would it have been to have ignored these ("Detector seems to be playing up.") and to have produced the expected result? How many times have we done exactly that. In some circumstances it is not just enough to have the courage to double check whether unexpected results that challenge the paradigm are genuine. It also probably needs a little bit of lateral thinking to realise the significance of the interesting observation. Probably that is what differentiated Fleming from Florey and Chain. Fleming revived his observation after over a decade; the latter pair could see the possibility that this discovery could lead to drugs to fight bacterial infections. Even though they did not make a fortune through their discovery, they got the Nobel prize. Actually, just by coincidence, I'm writing this in the suburb of Florey, in Canberra, Australia, named after the great man. Nowadays a degree of business acumen helps as well – I remember a professor telling me how one of his students showed him a compound that was yellow, but went purple when air was let into the apparatus, then went yellow again as the pressure was reduced. There is now a piece of apparatus for the small scale extraction of pure oxygen from air based on this principle, patented in the name of the professor.

D6 ANTIBACTERIALS

D.6.1 Outline the historical development of penicillins.

D.6.2 Explain how penicillins work and discuss the effects of modifying the side-chain.

D.6.3 Discuss and explain the importance of patient compliance and the effect of penicillin overprescription.

Antibacterials (called antibiotics in many countries) are drugs that inhibit the growth of, or kill, microorganisms that cause infectious diseases. These drugs are selective; they act against infecting bacteria much more than they act against human cells. Many diseases can be traced to microorganisms that invade the body and this is the basis of the germ theory of diseases. Microorganisms are usually single celled life forms that are capable of independent life given an adequate supply of nutrients. Infectious diseases occur when the body's natural defences are ineffective, for example when it has no natural immunity to the infection or there are too many microorganisms for the body's immune system to overcome, or when the organism evolves rapidly.

There are two main types of infectious agents; bacteria and viruses. **Bacteria** are single-celled organisms that can damage body tissue. However, not all bacteria are harmful, and some are helpful, such as those in the human digestive tract. Since antibiotics are ineffective against normal body cells, they cannot combat viral infection. Antibodies produced by the body's defence mechanism protect the body against infection. When bacteria multiply faster than they can be neutralised by the body's defences they produce infectious disease. Antibiotics aid white blood cells by preventing bacteria from multiplying, either by inhibiting cell division (bacteriostatic drugs) or by directly killing bacteria (bacteriocidal drugs).

Examples of bacterial infections include: tetanus, tuberculosis (TB), cholera, typhoid fever, syphilis, gonorrhea. Viral infections include: influenza, the common cold, hepatitis, measles and AIDS.

Historical Developments of Penicillins

In the 1890s scientists found that certain fungi killed bacteria. In an experiment, mice were introduced to disease-causing bacteria. Some were also exposed to one of these fungi. Mice exposed only to the bacteria died whereas mice exposed to both the bacteria and the fungus lived. These results were however largely ignored. In 1928 similar observations were made by *Alexander Fleming*, a bacteriologist working at St Mary's Hospital in Paddington, England. *Fleming* was working with a bacterium called *staphylococcus aureus* that causes boils and other types of infection. In one of the cultures in a petri dish whose lid had been left off, he found mould (mold) growing, but no bacteria around the mould. He concluded that the mould (*penicillium notatum*) must have inhibited bacterial growth by producing a compound that he called penicillin. However *Fleming* gave up the project after he found it difficult to isolate and purify the active ingredient in the mould.

In 1940, *Florey* and *Chain*, working at Oxford University renewed the research. They injected mice with deadly bacteria; some mice received penicillin and survived. In 1941, penicillin was used for the first time on a human being, a London policeman who had serious blood poisoning from a cut. The effect of penicillin was immediately favourable. In 1941 a massive development program was started in the U.S. where scientists at the Bureau of Agricultural Chemistry in Peoria, Illinois grew strains of penicillin mould in a medium of corn-steep liquor in large fermentation tanks. By 1943 penicillin was available clinically and by 1945 enough supply was present for everyone needing it, thus saving thousands of lives during World War II. In 1945, *Fleming*, *Florey* and *Chain* received the Nobel Prize for medicine for their work on penicillin.

Structure of penicillins and modifications of the side chain

The first penicillin used was penicillin G: after its structure was determined by X-ray crystallography, other penicillins were made. Since penicillin G is deactivated by stomach acid it had to be injected. Acid resistant penicillins such as penicillin V (phenoxymethylpenicillin) were developed by keeping the basic penicillin structure, but modifying the side chains. Also, bacteria were able to deactivate penicillin G by synthesising an enzyme, penicillinase, thus requiring the production of a number of synthetic penicillins by modifying the side chain which results in penicillins that are more resistant to the penicillinase enzyme. The structural feature common to all the penicillins is 6-APA, 6- aminopenicillanic acid (see Figure 1518). On its own, this has little effect on the bacterial growth. However, if an extra side-chain is added to its NH_2 amino group, active penicillin is created:

6-aminopenicillanic acid

Penicillin structure with side chain

Amino group

Side-chain

When R = C_6H_5-CH_2-: benzyl penicillin or penicillin G; not acid resistant.
When R = C_6H_5-CH_2-CH_2-: penicillin V; acid resistant.
When R = C_6H_5–C—C— cloxacillin; acid and penicillinase resistant.

Figure 1518 Structure of penicillins

Broad and narrow spectrum antibiotics

A broad spectrum antibiotic is one which is effective against a wide variety of bacteria, whereas a narrow spectrum antibiotic is effective against only certain types of bacteria. Most penicillins (and the sulfa drugs) are examples of narrow spectrum antibiotics. (Ampicillin on the other hand is a broad-spectrum antibiotic). Tetracyclines are examples of broad spectrum antibiotics – compounds of the tetracycline family get their names from their four-ring structures. Aureomycin® and Terramycin®, both tetracycline antibiotics, are examples of broad spectrum antibiotics; the suffix 'mycin' is used for antibiotics obtained from soil fungi. Repeated use of broad–spectrum antibiotics may wipe out harmless as well as helpful bacteria in the alimentary canal including the oesophagus, stomach and in particular the large intestines. Also, the destroyed bacteria may be replaced by harmful strains.

Working of the Penicillins

Cell walls of some bacteria are composed of largely different polysaccharides. The cell wall in the bacteria protects and supports the delicate cell structure and components enclosed within it. The cell wall layers are reinforced by a series of three dimensional chemical cross-links connecting one layer to another. Penicillins interfere with this cross link formation, thus weakening the cell walls. The cells can burst easily and the bacteria die. This is why penicillins are called bacteriocidal drugs (See Figure 1519).

Note that the cells of animals do not have 'cell walls'. They have external cell membranes which are different in composition and are therefore not affected by penicillin. Thus penicillin can destroy some bacteria without harming human cells. Penicillins are bacteriocides that destroy bacteria by interferring with cell wall construction. The bacteria can produce the molecular components of their cell walls, but in the presence of penicillin, cannot put them together. Thus it is unable to hold its size and shape. Water enters by osmosis, the cell expands and bursts, killing the bacterium.

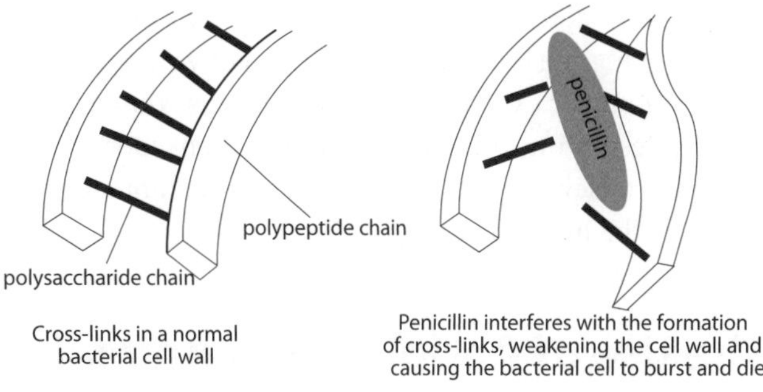

Figure 1519 The mechanism of action of penicillin

Effects of over prescription of Penicillins

Penicillins have had great value in controlling a large number of infectious diseases. However, over prescription can produce several disadvantages.

1. Penicillins are usually safe except for a small percentage of the population (about 10%) who experience allergic reactions and suffer side effects ranging from fever and body rash to occasionally shock and death. Repeated use can sometimes lead to allergic reaction.

2. Antibiotics, if used repeatedly, may wipe-out harmless bacteria and helpful ones in the alimentary canal (this is the food canal, or gut, including the oesophagus stomach and intestines). Also, the destroyed bacteria may be replaced by more harmful bacteria.

3. Another serious problem is that of genetic resistance. As antibiotics are used extensively, a few organisms survive and pass on their resistance to succeeding generations. For example typhoid, gonorrhoea, TB and other diseases all have strains that are now resistant to many antibiotics.

A microorganism may also become resistant as a result of mutation. The mutated strain may be able to reproduce on a large scale, with very serious consequences. A mutated strain may develop an enzyme that changes an antibiotic into a harmless substance. Thus continuing research is needed to develop new antibiotics. This is why antibiotics are considered miracle drugs in constant need of renewal. The prime rule for the use of antibiotics is that they should be used only when no other treatment can significantly reduce suffering or save life.

However, we live in a world where antibiotics are often misused and abused. Strict adherence to a recommended treatment regime is necessary for the effective treatment of an infection. For example, bacteria that cause tuberculosis (TB) by destroying lung tissues require patient cooperation in the use of several anti-TB drugs used in combination to ovecome the infection.

The Use of Antibiotics in Animal Feedstock

Antibiotics are used as supplements in animal feedstock for the control of animal diseases and to increase the rate of growth of animals. Feedstock can contain plant and animal pathogens which can be a danger to animal and human health. Thus antibiotics are used in the production of meat and poultry to control these bacteria and hence to increase productivity.

However, routine exposure of bacteria to small amounts of antibiotics allows naturally drug-resistant bacteria to survive, reproduce and spread. Thus, humans may be exposed to drug-resistant salmonella, *E.Coli* etc. that are not killed by the antibiotics in animal feed. The medical profession uses the same antibiotics to treat infectious diseases in humans as are used on livestock. The advent of antibiotic resistant bacteria makes humans vulnerable to life-threatening diseases and increases the cost of treatment. This has clearly raised concerns about the risks to human health resulting from the routine addition of antibiotics to animal feedstock.

D7 ANTIVIRALS

D.7.1 State how viruses differ from bacteria.

D.7.2 Describe the different ways in which antiviral drugs work.

D.7.3 Discuss the difficulties associated with solving the AIDS problem.

Bacteria are single cell microorganisms, measuring between 0.3 and 2.0 microns in diameter. Each cell contains a single chromosome consisting of a circular strand of DNA, which is coiled and which occupies part of the cell. The rigid cell walls are made of protein-sugar (polysaccharide) molecules. Inside the cell membrane is the cytoplasm which contains enzymes to break down food and build cell parts.

Viruses, on the other hand are submicroscopic, non-cellular infectious particles capable of reproduction only inside a living cell using the enzymatic machinery of that cell. Viruses attach themselves to a variety of cells, called host cells, and assume control of them. Viruses have a central core of DNA surrounded by a protein coat known as a capsid. However, viruses are not cellular as they have no nucleus, cytoplasm or cell membrane (though some have a membrane outside their protein coats). Viruses do not feed or grow but do reproduce inside the cells of living organisms using the ribosomes of host cells. Viruses are much smaller than bacteria.

Different ways in which Antiviral Drugs Work

Antibiotics control bacterial infections. Whether an antibiotic works against viruses depends very much on its mechanism of action. An antibiotic may be effective against viruses if it is able to block the transfer of genetic information. Most antibiotics do not do this and thus control only a few viruses. For the most part viruses are controlled most effectively by innoculations. Polio, smallpox and yellow fever (all caused by viruses) are prevented by innoculations today, as is influenza, which is caused by several different strains of viruses. The UN Smallpox Innoculation Program has been so successful that the virus is now thought to be extinct in humans. Nonetheless, controlling viral infections remains one of the major challenges for scientists.

Viruses consist of nucleic acid surrounded by a protein coat. They attach themselves to host cells and stimulate the cell to make viral nucleic acid instead of host nucleic acid. The viral nucleic acid is then coated with protein, and the viral particle emerges to infect other cells. A number of enzymes are essential for at least some of these steps, and one of the goals of research into antiviral agents is to find chemical ways to block such enzyme activity within the host cell. Doing so stops the viruses and prevents replication in host cells. Once replication is stopped, the virus is defeated. Antiviral drugs may also work by altering the cell's ribosomes (its genetic material) so that the virus cannot use them to multiply.

A handful of drugs that work against viral infections have been developed. Among them is Acyclovir® (Zovirax®) which is for general topical and oral use against herpes viruses. Acyclovir® relieves pain and itching in genital herpes and shortens the duration of the outbreak. It is most effective when used at the time of initial infection but it does not prevent recurrences. Also, while Acyclovir® succeeds in shortening the contagious period, it does not work on all patients.

Some cancers are caused by viruses that don't cause the immediate production of a tumour but insert their genetic material into the genome of an animal or plant cell. The viral genetic material becomes part of the host cell and is duplicated and passed on to new cells at cell division. Latent viruses of this type are very common. A familiar latent virus is the herplex simplex virus which, when stimulated by various factors, leaves its latent state in nerve cells (where it hides), is reproduced, and causes the cell damage known as a 'cold sore'.

Problems Associated with solving the problems of AIDS

Viruses can cross species (influenza originated from domestic birds) and can mutate frequently as is the case with the Human Immunodeficiency Virus. HIV is a retrovirus that contains Ribonucleic Acid, RNA instead of Deoxyribonucleic Acid (DNA).

AIDS, (Acquired Immuno Deficiency Syndrome) was first reported in the US in 1981 and has since become a major worldwide epidemic. AIDS is caused by HIV. By killing or damaging particular cells, especially the white blood cells of the immune system in the body, HIV progressively destroys the body's ability to fight infections, leading to life threatening infections such as pneumonia (called opportunistic infections) that do not generally threaten healthy people. The term AIDS applies to the most advanced stages of HIV infection.

Specific proteins on the surface of the HIV virus bind to a receptor glycoprotein (called CD4) on a certain type of the cell membrane of the white blood cells, namely the T4 lymphocytes. The T4-cells are immune cells that circulate in the blood stream; the crucial T4-cells are disabled by the virus and killed during the course of infection, and are unable to play their central role in the immune response (of signalling other cells in the immune system to perform their functions). The ability of the HIV virus to mutate, together with its similar metabolism to that of the human cell, makes effective treatment with antiviral drugs and vaccine development very difficult. The control and treatment of HIV is excerbated by the high price of antiretroviral agents and socio-economic issues as are found in many African countries including South Africa, Swaziland and Kenya amongst other third-world and developing countries.

HIGHER LEVEL

D8 DRUG ACTION (HL)

D.8.1 Describe the importance of geometrical isomerism in drug action.

Stereoisomers are isomers with the same molecular formula and the same structural formula, but a different arrangement of atoms in space. In organic chemistry, if a pair of stereoisomers contains a double bond, then it is possible to obtain cis (on the same side) and trans (across/opposite) arrangements of substituents at each end of the double bond. These are referred to as geometric or cis-trans-isomers (refer to Chapter 10).

Physical properties

Geometric isomers have different physical properties such as polarity (dipole moment), boiling point, melting point and solubility.

CHEMICAL PROPERTIES

Geometric isomers can undergo different chemical reactions. Since they contain the same functional groups, they do show some similar chemical properties but not all their chemical properties are identical, and the two different isomers can have different pharmacological effects.

Such isomerism can occur in inorganic complexes where the two different cis and trans isomers can have different pharmacological effects.. A square planar 4-coordinated inroganic complex of the form MA_2B_2 also experiences geometric isomerism, for example $Pt(NH_3)_2Cl_2$. See Figure 1520.

cis-diamminedichloroplatinum(II)

Figure 1520 An example of geometric isomerism

The cis-isomer, called cisplatin is an anti-cancer drug which is used in chemotherapy. It is a square planar molecule, making geometric isomerism possible (note that if it was tetrahedral, like a saturated carbon atom, it would not exhibit this isomerism). The trans-isomer is found to be chemotherapeutically inactive. Cisplatin is a heavy metal complex with the two chlorine ligands and two NH_3 groups in the cis position. Because of the cis-arrangement the anticancer ability arises from its ability to enter the nucleus of a cancerous cell in which the two Cl atoms are replaced by bonds that are eventually formed with guanine bases of the same DNA strand (figure 1521); as a result this prevents replication.

Figure 1521 Interaction of cisplatin

DB.8.2 Discuss the importance of chirality in drug action.

Optical isomers, differ from geometric isomers in two ways – the molecules are chiral (i.e., asymmetric, containing, for example, 4 different groups on a carbon atom). Optical isomers are non-superimposable mirror images of each other (called a pair of **enantiomers**). These isomers differ in their optical activity; optical activity is the ability to rotate the plane of polarised light. One optical isomer will rotate plane polarised light clockwise, and its non-superimpossable mirror image will rotate it anti-clockwise by the same amount. 2-butanol, is an example of a molecule with a chiral carbon atom. See Figure 1522.

Figure 1522 An example of optical isomers

An equi-molar mixture of the two enantiomers will not rotate the plane of polarised light and is said to be optically inactive. This is known as a **racemic mixture**.

Many drugs come from natural sources, often plants, either directly or they are prepared semi-synthetically (i.e. they are chemically modified natural substances). They are usually chiral and are generally found only as single enantiomers in nature rather than as racemic mixtures. Penicillin V which is isolated from penicillium mould is one such example. Its enantiomer does not occur naturally, but can be synthesised and is found to be pharmacologically inactive. Thus the different spacial arrangements of atoms in the two enantiomers lead to different pharmacology.

Drugs synthesised entirely in a laboratory, if chiral, are generally formed as racemic mixtures. Ibuprofen, sold as Advil® and Motrin IB® is an example. One of its enantiomers has analgesic and anti-inflammatory properties, the other does not. It is, however, sold as a racemic mixture to reduce costs. However, the 'wrong'/inactive enantiomer may have unintended effects of its own. An example is the thalidomide tragedy. Thalidomide was designed as a mild non-addictive sedative. In the 1950s, it was prescribed to alleviate morning sickness in pregnant women. It was marketed as a racemic mixture of the two enantiomers. One enantiomer alleviates morning sickness, but the other entantiomer causes deformities in the limbs of fetuses and hence birth defects. It is still marketed as a racemic mixture for leprosy patients. Incidentally, the thalidomide

OPTION

molecule does not contain a chiral carbon centre, but a less common chiral nitrogen atom located in a five membered glutamiride ring.

D 8.3 Explain the importance of beta-lactam ring action of penicillin

The structure of penicillin consists of three important structural groups, the presence of the R group, the carboxylic acid group and the beta-lactam ring as shown in Figure 1523.

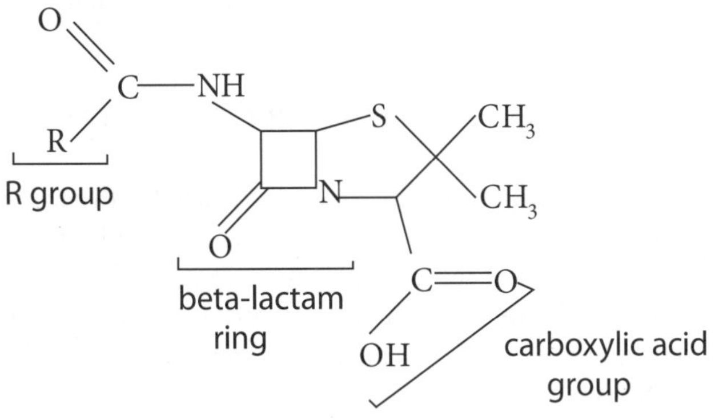

Figure 1523 Structure of penicillin

The beta-lactam ring is a heteroatomic four-membered ring structure consisting of one nitrogen atom and three carbon atoms. The four atoms are bonded to produce a square planar structure with bond angles of 90°. Based on the Valence Shell Electron Pair Repulsion Theory, the carbon atoms with four bonded electron pairs and the nitrogen (with its one lone electron pair and three bonded electron pairs) would prefer tetrahedral angles of about 109° and the carbon double bonded to the oxygen would expect a 120° angle. Thus the 90° in the beta-lactam places the ring under chemical stress and increases its chemical reactivity, opening up the ring. The open structure is able to covalently bond to the enzyme transpeptidase that is responsible for the synthesis of the bacterial cell walls, thus blocking the action of the enzyme. The reaction of the penicillin with the enzyme is not reversible and thus it inhibits the synthesis and growth of the bacterial cell wall. Specifically, it prevents the cross linking of the peptides; the bacteria burst without the linkage between the bacterial cell walls.

D.8.4 Explain the increased potency of diamorphine (heroin) compared to morphine:

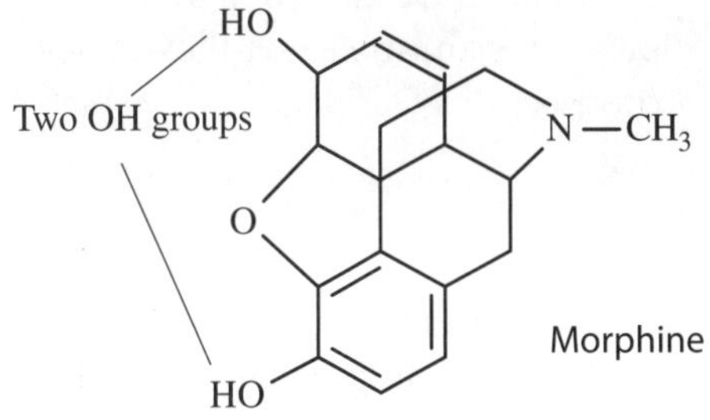

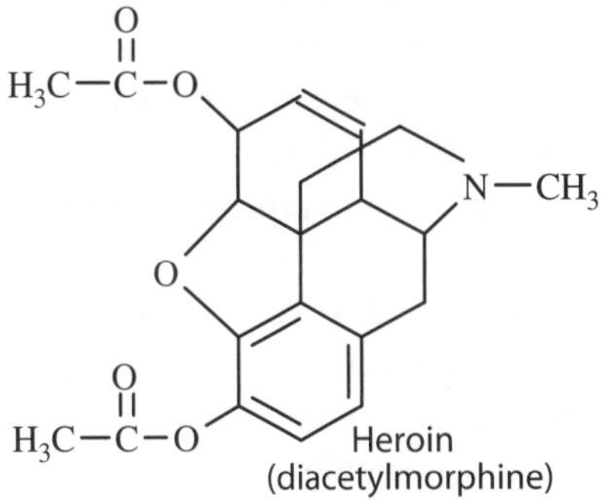

Figure 1524 The structures of morphine and heroin

Heroin is a semisynthetic narcotic which contains the same carbon skeleton as morphine, but in which the two polar hydroxyl groups are replaced by the two less polar ester groups (see Figure 1524). The presence of the ester groups makes a heroin molecule more fat-soluble and therefore more rapidly absorbed into the non-polar environment of the central nervous system and the brain. This increases the potency of heroin, making it a more powerful painkiller than morphine, but it is also a more addicitve drug.

D9 DRUG DESIGN (HL)

D.9.1 Discuss the use of a compound library in drug design

D.9.2 Explain the use of combinatorial and parallel chemistry to synthesise new drugs.

As discussed earlier, the research, development and testing of new pharmaceutical drugs is an extremely expensive, time consuming process, akin to finding a needle in the proverbial haystack. Research almost always starts with a potential drug that shows some pharmacological activity. This is called the 'lead' compound. Keeping the main chemical structure of the lead compound, changes are made to its structure to produce more effective drugs in terms of their potency, fewer side effects, etc. That is, a large number of related compounds are synthesized individually and evaluated for their biological properties. Two such simple examples discussed in this chapter include aspirin and penicillin.

COMBINATORIAL CHEMISTRY

Combinatorial chemistry involves a variety of techniques and technologies for creating a large number of molecules and testing them quickly for desirable biological properties. Thus combinatorial chemistry (**combi-chem**) is considered a much better way of synthesising potential new drugs. Since designing chemicals for biological activity is difficult, this technology allows the testing of thousands of possible chemicals in order to find the right one. Combi-chem basically involves reacting a set of starting materials in all possible combinations. This new and important method is being increasingly used to reduce the time and costs associated with producing effective new drugs.

Combinatorial chemistry uses the same methods as organic synthesis; however, instead of making one compound at a time, combi-chem takes advantage of technology and computerisation to make very large libraries of related chemicals. Larger, more diverse compound libraries can only increase the chances of finding better drugs. A pharmacophore, or receptor site, represents the essential molecular structure features based on the functional groups and geometry that are responsible for a drug's activity. Molecules with the same structural features can then be identified from a library data base of chemicals.

The term 'library' (or compound library or combinatorial library) is used to describe a collection of compounds that are screened to determine their pharmacological activity. Libraries of a very large number of related compounds have been produced by the combi-chem technique. This involves the use of robotics to carry out identical chemical processes between chemicals such as adding fixed volumes of substances using syringes. This technique is called **parallel synthesis** which can produce smaller, more focused libraries. The products of such reactions (called 'libraries') are then tested *en masse* for their potential pharmacological activities. Initial testing for many drugs can be achieved in the laboratory, rather than on animals, by studying the effects of each chemical on enzymes and their ability to bind to receptor sites.

An example of parallel synthesis in organic chemistry will help explain the principle involved. Carboxylic acids react with an alcohol in the presence of an acid catalyst to produce an ester:

$$R_1\text{-COOH} + \text{HO-}R_2 \longrightarrow R_1COOR_2 + H_2O$$

Eight different carboxylic acids can be reacted with each of eight different alcohols in the presence of an acid catalyst in 64 separate test tubes by computer controlled addition of fixed volumes of each reactant using syringes. Each test tube then contains a particular ester after the parallel synthesis.

Combinatorial chemistry started with peptides – parts of protein molecules. A condensation reaction between two amino acids produces the dipeptide containing the amide linkage or the peptide bond (and water) (see Figure 1525).

$$\text{HO(O)C}-CH_2\text{-NH}_2 + \text{HO(O)C}-CH_2\text{-NH}_2 \longrightarrow \text{HO(O)C}-CH_2\text{-}\underbrace{\text{N(H)}-\text{C(=O)}}_{\text{peptide linkage}}-CH_2\text{-}NH_2 + H_2O$$

Figure 1525 An example of combinatorial chemistry

A method was developed in the 1960s to make peptides by solid-state or solid-phase synthesis; this was followed by a technique to produce a large number of peptides by solid-phase parallel synthesis. The technique of 'mix and split' allows for the synthesis of a very large number of polypeptides by combination of amino acids using solid state chemistry (with resin beads). This is described below and illustrates the importance of solid-phase chemistry in the synthesis of organic molecules.

The formation of a peptide link requires a bond between the N atom on one amino acid (for example, A) and the carbon atom containing the acid group of another amino acid (for example, B). First a 'linking group' is chemically attached to a plastic bead. In vessel 1 (Figure 1526) a chemical reaction allows amino acid A (via its acid group) to be attached to the linking group on the plastic bead (with the elimination of HCl: H coming from the -OH group of the amino acid, and Cl from the linking group). Vessel 2 contains the amino acid B. The bead from vessel 1 is washed and reacted with amino acid B in vessel 2 to produce the dipeptide A-B attached to the linkage. The linkage to the plastic resin can be broken at any stage or subsequent condensation can be carried out to produce a polypeptide.

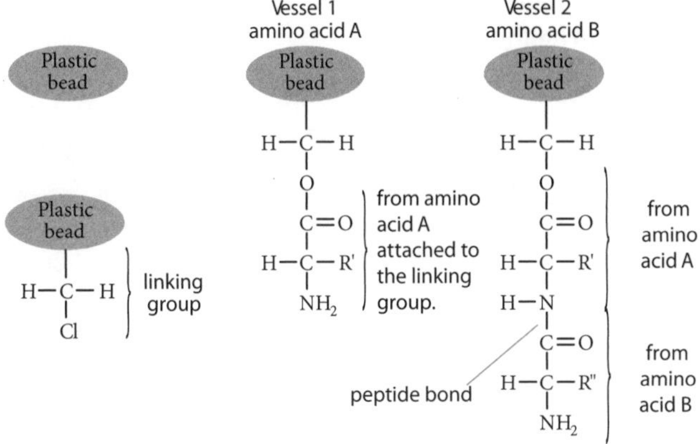

Figure 1526 An example of a solid-phase reaction

The above procedure can be extended so that the first step commences with reacting two amino acids A and B with the beads through a linking group to give bead-A and bead-B. These can then be split into two containers so that each now contains half of bead-A and half of bead-B. In the second stage, one container is reacted with A and therefore produces bead-A-A and bead-B-A. The second one is reacted with B and will produce bead-A-B and bead-B-B. Thus a two amino acid, two-stage process will provide 4 (2^2) dipeptides A-A, A-B, B-A and B-B. Starting with three different amino acids A, B and C and using three stages would lead to the formation of $3^3 = 27$ tripeptides. A four amino acid, four-stage process would produce $4^4 = 256$ different compounds, leading to the formation of a library of compounds.

Once a compound has been de-linked from the resin bead, mass spectrum and nuclear magnetic resonance spectroscopy can be used to determine its structure.

The linkage to the resin can be broken at any stage or subsequent condensation reactions can be carried out to produce a polypeptide.

Example

Consider three aminoacids A, B and C. Calculate the number of dipeptides that could be created from a two stage combi-chem process.

Solution

1st stage: bead-A , bead-B, bead-C

2nd stage: Divide so that each container now contains ⅓ bead-A, ⅓ bead-B and ⅓ bead-C. Next, react each one with A, B and C. The first container will have beads with -A-A, -A-B and -A-C, the second container, beads -B-A, -B-B and -B-C and the third container, beads -C-A, -C-B and -C-C for a total of 9 (3^2).

Ten compounds in ten reaction vessels in a four-stage reaction sequence would produce $10^4 = 10 \times 10 \times 10 \times 10 = 10\,000$ compounds with 40 (10+10+10+10) reactions. Scientists realised that this method need not be restricted to making polymeric structures like the polypeptides. Chemicals such as organic heterocyclics can be synthesised - compounds that are often used as starting materials to make drugs. A cyclic compound can often be a very good library starting point to which different branches can be added, eventually leading to new and better drugs.

D.9.3 Describe how computers are used in drug design

Over the past 20 years, more powerful computers have been manufactured whose power has doubled approximately every 18 months or so. At the same time, the cost has decreased making it possible for researchers to access such technology. Simultaneously, molecular modelling software that allows scientists to mimic or model molecular behaviour has been developed. These have allowed computational chemists to use computers in drug design. Molecular modelling now plays an important role in the development of new molecules with medcinal properties leading to a technological revolution in drug discovery. Currently it takes years and hundreds of millions of dollars for a new drug to be approved. **Rational Drug Design** (RDD) is the use of molecular modelling software to discover safe drugs in as short a time as possible.

The mode of action of many drugs involves some form of interaction with biological molecules such as enzymes. For example, HIV drugs interfere with the enzyme reverse transcriptase or protease that is important for viral function. The presence of functional groups and the orientation of the drug molecule may make it possible for it to interact with the enzyme protein structure active site, thus interfering with its biological action. NMR and X-ray crystallography are two powerful tools available to chemists to determine the three dimensional structure of such proteins.

In particular, computer programs that can convert two dimensional diagrams into their 3-D equivalent structures have been instrumental in drug research. Three dimensional molecular models can be created *in silico* (that is, performed on a computer or via computer simulation). The 3-D structure of the target biological enzyme molecules together with those of the drug molecules are stored on the computer for retrieval purposes. Computer modelling can then be used to design smaller molecules that are capable of binding or interfering with the active site of the protein. Such ligand molecules are called **inhibitors**. Molecular modelling software can thus be used to virtually develop and evaluate new inhibitor drug molecules.

D.9.4 Discuss how the polarity of a molecule can be modified to increase its aqueous solubility and how this facilitates its distribution around the body.

In the past salicylic acid (2-hydroxybenzoic acid), the active ingredient in the bark of the willow tree was widely used as a fever reducer (anti-pyretic drug) and pain killer (mild analgesic). However, salicylic acid is a relatively strong acid due the presence of the carboxylic acid (–COOH) and the hydroxyl group (–OH) on the benzene ring. Its highly acidic nature makes it rather unpleasant to take orally and it damages the membranes lining the mouth, oesphagus and stomach. Thus salicylic acid was chemically modified to overcome these two negative effects of its use. Initially, sodium salicylate, a soluble ionic salt of salicylic acid, produced by reacting salicylic acid with sodium hydroxide, was used (see FIgure 1527).

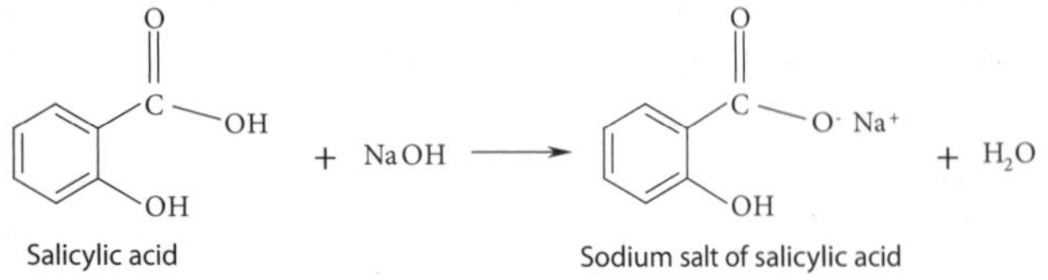

Salicylic acid + NaOH ⟶ Sodium salt of salicylic acid + H_2O

Figure 1527 Formation of sodium salt of salicylic acid

This has a bitter taste and is, again, highly irritating to the stomach lining where it is changed to salicylic acid. However, the acetate (ethanoate) ester of salicylic acid, called Acetyl Salicylic Acid (ASA) named Aspirin retains the beneficial properties of salicylic acid but is less irritating to the stomach. Addition of the acetyl group reduces the acidity sufficiently to make it relatively non-irritating. Because ASA is relatively tasteless, it can be taken orally. Refer to Figure 1528 (a). This type of research where a drug is chemically altered to minimise side effects but retain beneficial properties is very common in the modern drug industry.

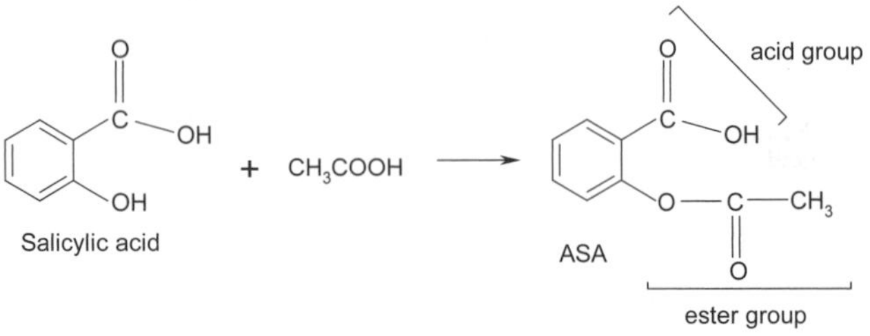

Salicylic acid + CH_3COOH ⟶ ASA (acid group; ester group)

Figure 1528 (a) Formation of ASA

ASA is a less active form of the drug that is converted to the active form sometime after administration. ASA reacts with water in a hydrolysis reaction to form salicylic acid only after reaching the alkaline (basic) conditions in the small intestines.

Salicylic acid and methyl salicylate are virtually insoluble in water due to the presence of the aromatic ring and no ionic bonding. Aspirin can be purchased in two forms: one is insoluble in water (the ester) due to the presence of the aromatic ring and no ionic bonding and the other, the salt of ASA which is ionic and water soluble. Insoluble aspirin takes longer to dissolve; the longer it takes, the less effective it is. In the case of aspirin, the ability of the acidic (carboxylic acid) group to form an ionic salt makes it possible for the insoluble ASA to form a soluble salt which is more effective,see Figure 1528 (b).

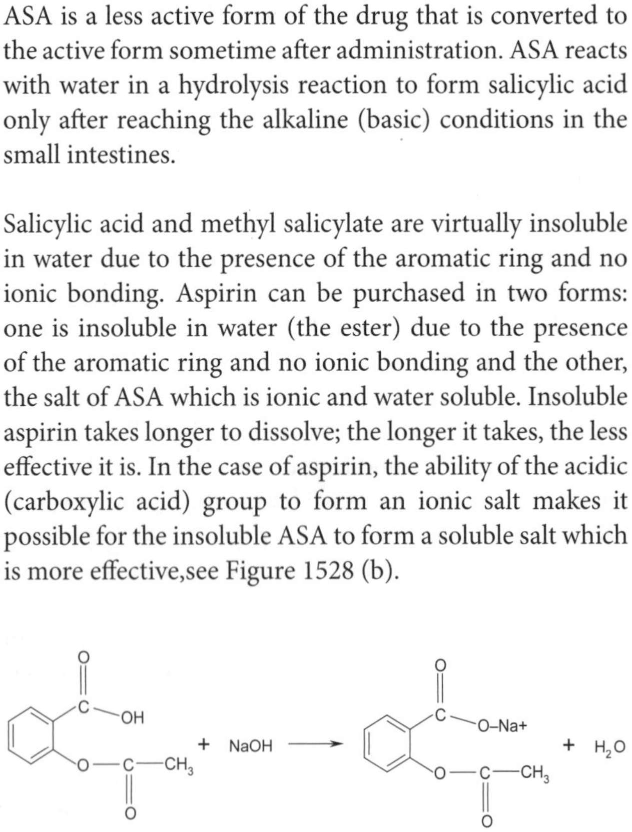

ASA + NaOH ⟶ salt of ASA (O–Na+) + H_2O

FIgure 1528 (b) Formation of a salt of ASA

It is also possible for a drug with a basic group, such as an amine, to form ionic salt (by reaction with hydrochloric acid). This is the case with the anti-depressant drug, Prozac®, called fluoxetine hydrochloride (see Figure 1529).

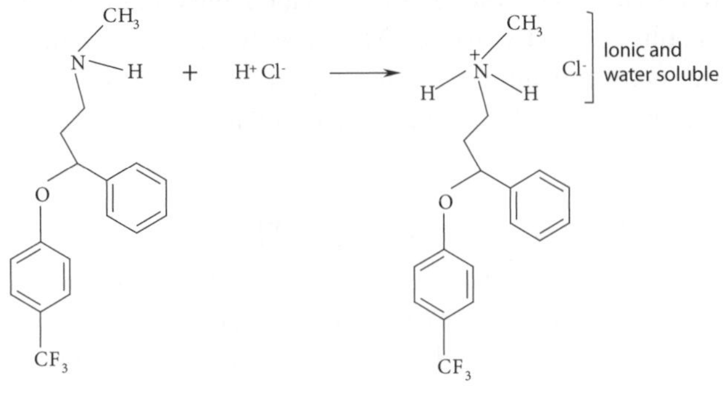

Ionic and water soluble

Figure 1529 Structure of fluoxetine and fluoxetine hydrochloride

D.9.5 Describe the use of chiral auxiliaries to form the desired enantiomer.

The separation of racemic mixtures into respective enantiomers can be very difficult since the enantiomers have identical chemical properties in relation to non-chiral reagents but the interaction of a pair of enantiomers with other chiral molecules is not identical. This enables scientists to devise methods of asymmetric synthesis, which allows them to prepare only a single enantiomer rather than a racemic mixture, a so called stereospecific synthesis.

Chiral auxiliaries play a key role in the synthesis of optically active compounds, specifically converting a non-chiral molecule into the desired enantiomer, thus avoiding the need to resolve enantiomers from a racemic mixture (an 'auxiliary' is a 'helping hand'). It works by attaching itself chemically to the non-chiral molecule to create the stereochemical conditions necessary to force the reaction to follow a certain stereo-specific path. Once the new molecule has been formed, the auxiliary can be removed (and recycled) to leave the desired enantiomer. An example is the synthesis of Taxol, an anti-cancer drug, effective against breast cancer.

Use of chiral auxilliary example

Propanoic acid, CH_3–CH_2–COOH does not contain a chiral centre and it is not optically active. However, if a hydrogen on C2 is replaced by OH, it introduces a chiral centre in the product and a racemic mixture of the two enantiomers is formed (see Figure 1530):

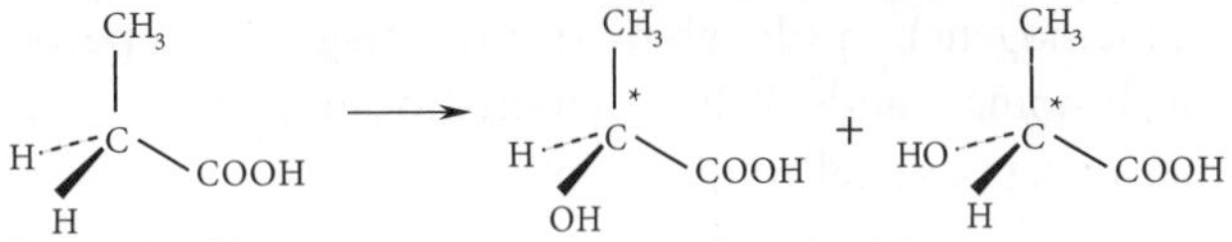

Propanoic acid

Racemic mixture

Figure 1530 Formation of a racemic mixture starting from propanoic acid

If a chiral optically active auxilliary is attached to the propanoic acid, the orientation of the attached auxilliary can allow for the formation of only the one enantiomer. Namely, bonding a non-chiral molecule containing a planar sp^2 hybrid carbon to a 'molecular surface' forces attack from only one side and hence produces only one isomer. On removal of the auxilliary, the desired enantiomer is left behind (see Figure 1531).

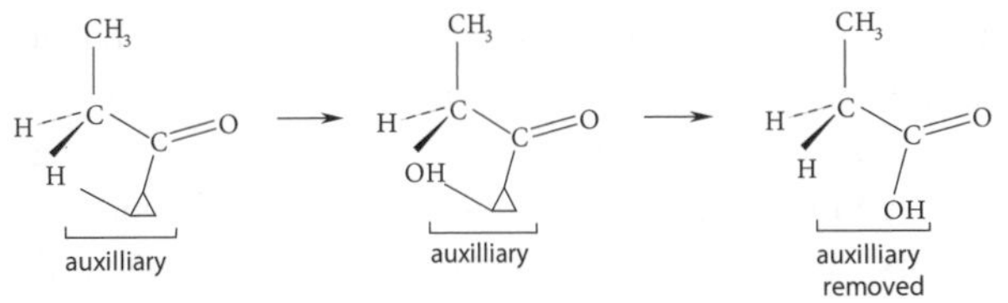

auxilliary

auxilliary

auxilliary removed

Figure 1531 The role of an active auxilliary

D10 MIND ALTERING DRUGS (HL)

D.10.1 Describe the effects of lysergic acid diethylamide (LSD), mescaline, psilocybin and tetrahydrocannabinol (THC).

Mind altering drugs are also called psychedelic drugs or **psychotomimetics** (i.e. simulating 'madness') or hallucinogens. A hallucination is a mistaken notion, that is a perception or feeling that has no external cause. The word psychedelic means something causing an abnormal stimulation of feeling or consciousness. These 'mind bending' or 'mind altering' drugs produce a qualitative change in thought, perception or mood and can cause vivid illusions and fantasies ('imagination unrestrained by reality'). These drugs can cause remarkable distortions in touch, smell, hearing and vision, thereby causing illusions. For example walls may appear to move, colour may appear brilliant, users may claim to "see" sound and "hear" colours and jumping from a high building may appear safe.

Examples of mind altering drugs include LSD (lysergic acid diethylamide), mescaline (one of the oldest known hallucinogens), psilocybin (from 'magic' or peyote mushrooms) and THC (tetrahydrocannabinol) from marijuana (also called grass, pot, etc.).

Effects of mind altering drugs

Lysergic acid diethylamide (LSD)

LSD is a powerful hallucinogen manufactured from lysergic acid, which is found in ergot, a fungus that grows on rye and other grains. An LSD experience is a highly personal one and the effect varies with the dose, physiological condition (state of vital processes) and psychological condition (state of mind) of the user, and the user's expectations. Perception is magnified many fold. It can destroy the sense of judgement (i.e. jumping from a high building). LSD can cause strong opposite emotions at the same time e.g. relaxation and tension. The physical effects of a 'trip' on LSD are dilation of the pupils, an increase in heart rate, blood pressure and body temperature, as well as sweating, sleeplessness and tremors. It can produce frightening 'bad' trips as well as flash backs after the event. It does not tend to produce physical addiction, but tolerance develops and disappears rapidly. Psychological dependence can appear but not as strongly as with other drugs. LSD appears to interact with serotonin receptors on neurons by preventing the neurotransmitters from facilitating, or helping to make, connections between neurons in the brain.

Mescaline

The peyote cactus found in Central and South America has been a source of hallucinogens for centuries. Like LSD it produces visual colour hallucinations (vivid colour perceptions). although its potency is considerably less than that of LSD. A mescaline trip usually lasts about 12 hours, and often leads to a decrease in appetite. Like many other drugs, mescaline produces much worse effects when used with alcohol, and liver damage is possible with long term use.

Psilocybin

Psilocybin is the major hallucinogenic drug found in 'magic mushrooms'. It is a mild hallucinogen. Effects of psilocybin are similar to LSD where perception is magnified although the drug is less potent. In low doses it produces feelings of relaxation similar to those of cannabis. At high doses the effect is closer to that of LSD. Users experience an intensification of colour, hallucinations and a sense of well-being. A 'magic mushroom' trip tends to last about 4 hours (as opposed to 8 or more with LSD). Psilocybin seems not to be addicitve in nature although users tend to develop some tolerance to it. Psiliocybin and mescaline are physcho-active like LSD because they closely resemble the neurotransmitter serotonin and bind with the same receptors in the brain and 'over stimulate' them.

Tetrahydrocannabinol (THC)

Cannabis (marijuana) is extracted from the plant *Cannabis sativa*. Hashish is made from the resin of the flowering tops of *Cannabis sativa* and is a very psychoactive product of the plant. The main psychoactive ingredient in cannabis is tetrahydrocannabinol (THC). THC is a mild hallucinogen and has some effects similar to alcohol. At low doses users feel excited and silly. As the dose is increased, it produces changes in perception - the user sees bright colours and has a keener sense of hearing. Still higher doses produce visual hallucinations (objects in odd shapes). The initial feeling of joy can turn to extreme anxiety, depression, uneasiness, panic attack and fearfulness. Decisions become harder to make, and a person is more likely to follow the suggestions of others. Tasks like driving that require clear thinking and good reflexes become difficult. No tolerance develops, but regular use can lead to moderate psychological dependence. The smoking of marijuana produces smoke that has composition similar to cigarette smoke, and therefore produces simlair risks to smoking cigareattes including cancer.

D.10.2 Discuss the structural similarities and differences between LSD, mescaline and psilocybin.

Indole is an example of a heterocyclic amine compound in which the nitrogen atom is part of a ring. Indole is a fused-ring heterocyclic structure containing a benzene ring and a heterocyclic ring sharing a common C=C bond. The N atom bonded to two carbons and an H atom is a secondary amine.

H–N
O
N
H
N
CH_3
Secondary amine
Diethyl amine side chain

Figure 1532 The structure of LSD

LSD, a fat soluble compound, easily diffuses into the brain. It readily crosses the placental barrier into a fetus. LSD contains the diethylamide side chain (see Figure 1532).

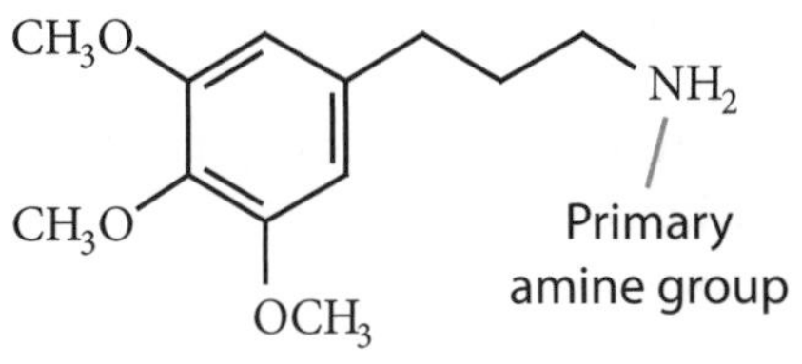

Figure 1533 The structure of mescaline

Mescaline contains the benzene ring, but does not contain the fused-ring heterocyclic structure. Instead it contains a primary amine group $-NH_2$ where the N atom is bonded to only one C atom (see Figure 1533).

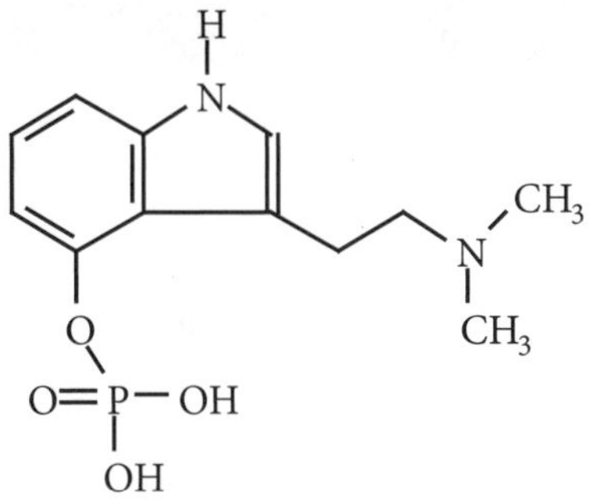

Figure 1534 The structure of psilocybin

Besides the indole ring found in LSD, psilocybin also contains the dimethylamine $—N(CH_3)_2$ side chain, as well as the dihydrogen phosphate group on the benzene ring (see Figure 1534).

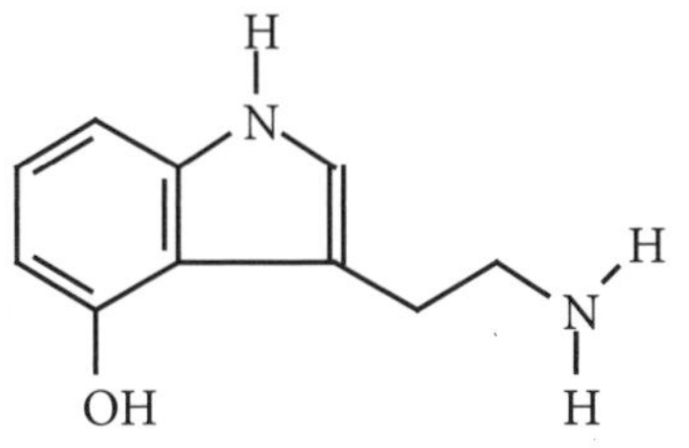

Figure 1535 The structure of serotonin

The backbone structure of psilocybin is the same as that of serotonin (a neurotransmitter) but with different side chains (see Figure 1535). The difference in the properties of the various hallucinogens is due to presence of different functional groups attached to the indole skeleton. This in turn affects their solubility in fats. The greater their solubility in fats, the more readily they penetrate the fatty cell membranes of nerve cells and the greater their potency. This effect is enhanced by the presence of non-polar groups like methyl groups ($-CH_3$) and reduced by the presence of polar groups like the phosphoric acid group ($-OPO(OH)_2$).

D.10.3 Discuss the arguments for and against the legalization of cannabis.

The cannabis plant, *cannabis sativa*, contains pharmacologically active compounds, the cannabinoids. Arguments for the legalisation of cannabis include its ability to offer relief from certain diseases and ailments such as AIDS, cancer and glaucoma. The 'wasting syndrome' seen in AIDS patients due to loss of appetite leads to drastic weight loss. The causes of this wasting are not completely known. It is claimed that marijuana use produces beneficial effects from its ability to increase appetite. Treatment using chemotherapy often causes nausea and thus reduces the patient's ability to keep food down. It has been suggested that cannabis relieves nausea, allowing cancer patients to gain weight. In some countries, it is medically given to terminally ill cancer patients to relieve tension and anxiety. Similarly marijuana is reported to help glaucoma patients by decreasing pressure inside the eyeball which can damage eyes. Another argument given is that legalisation would allow better control of quality and fewer problems with regard to harmful impurities. Also it would move it away from the environments where 'hard' drugs are readily available.

Regular intake of marijuana can lead to respiratory ailments associated with inhaling smoke. It has been suggested that regular use may suppress the body's immune system, thus increasing susceptibility to disease. Also, decreased fertility has been observed in some human males. There is some evidence that marijuana use causes brain damage in rats (to a lesser extent than is caused by alcohol) and some research has reported chromosomal damage which may lead to birth defects. It has also been suggested that cannabis users could possibly move on to 'hard' drugs. This may be true of illegal drug users, but whether medicinal users of cannabis would do the same is considered questionable.

A significant danger in the use of prohibited drugs is that users have to obtain their supplies from criminal sources. Addicts pay much more than the true cost of the drug and are often forced into crime and/or prostitution to support their habit. This produces a very negative impact on society at large and is the main reason why a few governments have decided to supply drugs to addicts under controlled conditions. This does not mean that these drugs (mainly in the 'hard' category) have become, in the strictest sense 'legal'. A case that could be discussed in this context is that of the prohibition of alcohol in the USA in the early part of the last century. This was widely disobeyed and produced such a spate of organised crime that it had to be scrapped.

The issue of how to contain the damage done to both individuals and society at large by the abuse of both legal and illegal drugs remains one of the most challenging issues facing us all.

OPTION D: MEDICINES AND DRUGS

QUESTIONS

D1 Pharmaceutical products

1. (a) List the effects of medicines and drugs on the functioning of the body.

(b) State what a *placebo* is and describe the *placebo effect.*

(c) Outline the stages involved in testing a new drug.

(d) Outline four methods of drug administration and state their relative advantage and disadvantage.

2. (a) Discuss the terms *therapeutic window, tolerance,* and *side effects.*

(b) Distinguish between physical and psychological dependence.

D2 Antacids

3. (a) The normal pH of gastric juices is in the 1.0 – 3.0 range. State two purposes of this acidic solution and explain what causes heartburn.

(b) Describe what an antacid is made of and explain its purpose.

(c) (i) Name four antacids each containing a different metal.

(ii) For each antacid in (i) above, write a balanced chemical equation for its reaction with excess stomach acid.

(iii) Explain why some antacids contain the chemical called dimethicone.

(d) Two solid antacid products containing the same mass of different active ingredients are on sale for the same price. One contains magnesium hydroxide, the other calcium carbonate as the active ingredient. Without detailed calculations, deduce which one is a better buy and explain your reasoning.

D3 Analgesics

4. (a) Define the terms *analgesic, mild analgesic* and *strong analgesic.*

(b) Explain the difference in mode of action of a mild analgesic compared to a strong analgesic.

(c) Give two examples each of a mild and a strong analgesic.

5. (a) From the structures in the Data Booklet:

(i) Identify two functional groups present in the structure of aspirin.

(ii) Name the nitrogen containing functional group in acetaminophen.

(iii) Name the nitrogen containing functional group in codeine.

(iv) Suggest how heroin can be chemically prepared from morphine.

6. (a) Besides the use of aspirin as an analgesic, list three other uses of the drug.

(b) State three disadvantages of using aspirin.

(c) Discuss the advantages and disadvantages of using morphine and its derivatives as strong analgesics.

D4 Depressants

7.(a) (i) Define the term *depressants* and suggest how these work.

(ii) List the effects of depressants on the body.

(iii) Explain why depressants are often described as anti-depressants.

(b) (i) The effect of a depressant is dose dependent. Describe how increasing the dose affects human body.

(ii) Differentiate between the following depressants: tranquilizers, sedatives and hypnotics.

8. (a) Discuss the social and physiological effects of the use and abuse of ethanol.

(b) Explain the *synergetic effect*. Describe the synergistic effects of ethanol with sleeping pills and aspirin.

9. The roadside breathalyser test done by law enforcement officers involves a redox reaction in which acidified potassium dichromate(VI) $K_2Cr_2O_7$ is used as the oxidising agent:

(a) Give the name and formula of the organic reactant and product in the redox reaction.

(b) Describe the colour change that takes place as the reaction progresses.

(c) Write a balanced reduction and oxidation half reaction and the equation for the overall reaction that takes place in an acidic medium.

(d) (i) In many countries a 0.080% blood alcohol level is the legal limit for driving cars. Determine what this is equal to in terms of mass of alcohol per 100 cm^3 of blood.

(ii) Determine the concentration of ethanol in mol dm^{-3} for the legal limit for driving.

10. Describe and explain two other methods that are used to detect alcohol in the breath.

D5 Stimulants

11.(a) Define the term *stimulant* and state its effect on the body. List three commonly used stimulants.

(b) Based on the structures given in the Data Booklet, identify the structural similarity between the structures of the hormone adrenaline, amphetamine and the street drug 'Speed'.

(c) Identify the difference in the amine group in amphetamine compared to the one in adrenaline or 'Speed'.

(d) Define the term *sympathomimetic drug* and state three short term effects of it.

12.(a) List three similarities in the structures of caffeine and nicotine.

(b) Discuss the short- and long-term effects of nicotine consumption.

D6 Antibacterials

13.(a) Define the term *antibacterial.*

(b) Outline the historical development of penicillins.

(c) Explain how penicillins work and discuss the effects of modifying the side chain.

(d) Discuss and explain the importance of patient compliance and the effect of penicillin over-prescription.

D7 Antivirals

14.(a) State how viruses differ from bacteria.

(b) Describe the different ways in which antiviral drugs work.

(c) Discuss the difficulties associated with solving the AIDS problem.

[HL] D8 Drug action

15. (a) Define the term *stereoisomerism* and describe the importance of geometrical isomerism in drug action.

(b) Describe and explain how physical properties (such a boiling point and polarity) and chemical reactions of geometric isomers compare.

(c) Draw the geometric isomers of the 4-coordinated inorganic complex $Pt(NH_3)_2Cl_2$, describe its shape, the type of bonding present in the isomers and the type of reaction that occurs on bond formation.

(d) Explain why the cis isomer is chemo-therapeutically active and describe how it prevents replication of cancer cells.

(e) Explain the importance of clinical trials on different enantiomers and justify your answer with an example.

16.(a) Describe the similarity and two differences between geometric and optical isomers.

(b) Define *racemic mixture* and deduce its optical activity.

(c) Explain why some medicines such as ibuprofen are sold as racemic mixtures.

(d) Define the term *chiral auxiliary* and describe how a chiral auxiliary can be used to separate two enantiomers.

17.(a) List the three important structural features of penicillin and explain the importance of the beta-lactam ring action of penicillin.

(b) Explain the increased potency of heroin compared to morphine.

[HL] D9 Drug design

18.(a)

(i) Define the term *combinatorial chemistry* and *pharmacophore.*

(ii) Define the term *compound library* and discuss the use of a compound library in drug design.

(iii) 'Parallel synthesis' can produce smaller, more focused libraries. Use the example of the formation of esters from carboxylic acids and alcohols to explain parallel synthesis.

19.(a) Define the term *rational drug design.*

(b) Describe how computers are used in drug design.

20. Use acetyl salicylic acid and the anti-depressant drug Prozac® as examples to discuss how the polarity of a molecule can be modified to increase its aqueous solubility and how this facilitates its distribution around the body.

[HL] D10 Mind-altering drugs

21.(a) Define the term *hallucinogen.*

(b) Describe the structural similarities and differences between LSD, mescaline and psilocybin.

(c) Describe the effects of lysergic acid diethylamide (LSD), mescaline, psilocybin and tetrahydrocannabinol (THC).

22. Discuss the arguments for and against the legalization of cannabis.

ENVIRONMENTAL CHEMISTRY

16

E1 Air pollution
E2 Acid deposition
E3 Greenhouse effect
E4 Ozone depletion
E5 Dissolved oxygen in water
E6 Water treatment
E7 Soil
E8 Waste
E9 Ozone depletion (HL)
E10 Smog (HL)
E11 Acid Deposition (HL)
E12 Water and soil (HL)

Human activities involve intensive use of limited resources found in air, water and soil. Many of these activities produce waste products that build up in the environment to produce pollution with increasingly local and global effects. An understanding of this impact is essential within and beyond the study of chemistry. This option has many opportunities for discussing aim 8 issues and the international dimension.

E1 AIR POLLUTION

E.1.1 Describe the main sources of carbon monoxide (CO), oxides of nitrogen (NO_x) oxides of sulfur (SO_x), particulates and volatile organic compounds (VOCs) in the atmosphere.

Dry air that is not polluted contains about 78% nitrogen gas, N_2, 21% oxygen gas, O_2, 1% argon, Ar, 0.03% carbon dioxide, CO_2 together wth trace amounts of other gases. An air pollutant is a substance present in sufficient concentration in the air to produce a harmful effect on humans or other animals, vegetation or materials. It can be produced, naturally by processes such as volcanic activity and bacterial action, or produced by human activity ('man made') due to increased urbanization, industrialization (such as electrical power plants), transportation, forest fires, incineration of solid wastes amongst others.

A primary air pollutant is one which is added directly to the air from a given source, such as carbon dioxide from the burning of fossil fuels. A secondary air pollutant, on the other hand, is formed in the atmosphere through chemical reaction(s), such as the formation of ozone in photochemical smog. The five major primary pollutants in the atmosphere are: carbon monoxide (CO), oxides of nitrogen (NO_x), oxides of sulfur (SO_x), particulates and volatile organic compounds (VOCs).

Carbon monoxide

:C≡O: (CO) is a polar molecule with covalent bonding between the atoms. It is a colorless, odorless, tasteless, toxic compound which is not very soluble in water. It is formed due to the incomplete oxidation of carbon and carbon-containing compounds such as fossil fuels.

Main sources of carbon monoxide

Almost 90% of all CO production comes from natural sources – most of it from the atmospheric oxidation of methane gas, CH_4.

$$2CH_4\,(g) + 3O_2\,(g) \rightarrow 2CO\,(g) + 4H_2O\,(l)$$

Methane is produced from the decomposition of organic matter in swamps and tropical regions (for example rice fields, rivers and lakes) under anaerobic (lack of oxygen) conditions, as well as from algae and other organic matter in oceans.

OPTION

The other 10% CO comes from man-made sources, such as the combustion of fossil fuels used in industry, in particular gasoline (petrol) used in the internal combustion engine for transportation, and from forest fires. Carbon monoxide is a product if there is insufficient oxygen present such as in forest fires, or in automobiles when poor mixing of fuel and air takes place, or if there is insufficient oxygen present in an internal combustion engine. One example of incomplete combustion is:

$$C_7H_{16}\,(l) + 7\tfrac{1}{2}O_2\,(g) \rightarrow 7CO\,(g) + 8H_2O\,(l)$$

Whereas the natural sources of CO tend to be widely distributed, two major problems with CO from human activity include:

(1) localization, that is, it is produced in compact areas such as down-town core areas and on highways and major thoroughfares

(2) high emission rates at rush hours.

Fungi in soil act as 'soil sinks' converting CO to CO_2:

$$2\,CO(g) + O_2(g) \rightarrow 2\,CO_2(g)$$

Hovever, localization and high emission rates of CO occur in urbanized areas with less soil than rural areas and therefore fewer microorganisms to reduce CO concentrations. Refer to Figure 1601.

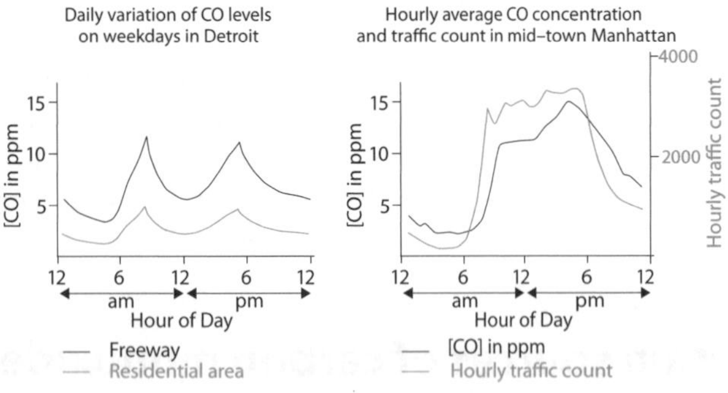

Figure 1601 The variation in CO levels in two large cities

OXIDES OF NITROGEN (NO_x)

There are several (8) known oxides of nitrogen of which nitrous oxide (N_2O; systematic name: dinitrogen monoxide) is found naturally and nitric oxide or nitrogen monoxide (NO) and nitrogen dioxide (NO_2) are found to be important components of polluted air (see Figure 1602).

There is no reaction between nitrogen gas (N_2, :N≡N:) and oxygen gas at room or moderately high temperatures due to the very high stability of the nitrogen–nitrogen triple bond. Any reaction between nitrogen and oxygen gas is highly endothermic. Under conditions of high temperatures (around 1500 °C found in automobile engines) a reaction between the two gases can take place, producing nitrogen oxides, NO_x.

Principal Sources

Human activity produces about 10% of NO_x. Most human sources of NO_x are emitted as NO and a small amount as NO_2 gas during the high temperature combustion that takes place in an automobile engine, airplanes and rail engines; stationary sources such as furnaces fuelled by natural gas, coal, fuel oil and wood; industrial processes such as nitric acid manufacture as well as agricultural burning and forest fires.

$$N_2(g) + O_2(g) \rightarrow 2\,NO(g)$$

$$N_2(g) + 2\,O_2(g) \rightarrow 2\,NO_2(g)$$

In the atmosphere the NO gas present (a primary pollutant) is rapidly converted to NO_2, a secondary pollutant according to this equation.

$$2\,NO(g) + O_2(g) \rightarrow 2\,NO_2(g)$$

Thus, most of the man-made NO_x pollution enters the environment as NO gas. The natural decomposition of nitrogen-containing compounds by bacterial action is, however, responsible for most of the N_2O and NO found in the environment. The high energy in lightning also results in some formation of N_2O and NO; natural NO is rapidly oxidised to NO_2, a secondary pollutant. As with carbon monoxide, natural sources of NO_x are widely distributed, however, man made sources of NO_x are localized and can be present in high concentrations due to the use of automobiles.

OXIDES OF SULFUR (SO_x)

Sulfur dioxide, SO_2, is produced by far in the largest amount and sulfur trioxide, SO_3, is produced in very small amounts. Once SO_2 is in the atmosphere, it is slowly oxidised to SO_3. The presence of heavy metal pollutants and finely divided particulates such as ash can speed up the reaction, as can the presence of O_3, hydroxyl free radical, ·OH and sunlight as follows.

$$2\,SO_2(g) + O_2(g) \rightarrow 2\,SO_3(g)$$

	N_2O nitrous oxide	NO nitric oxide	NO_2 nitrogen dioxide
Oxidation number of nitrogen:	+ 1	+ 2	+ 4
Lewis Structure	:N=N=Ö:	:Ṅ=Ö: odd # electrons	N with O: and :O: odd # of electrons
Sources	All produced by natural sources from decomposition of nitrogen containing compounds by bacterial action in soil and from lightning.	80% from natural sources (bacterial action); 20% from human sources from high temperature oxidation of N_2 in air in automobile and aircraft engines.	Nearly all made as secondary pollutant from NO.

Figure 1602 The oxides of nitrogen

Principal sources

(a) From sulfur containing fossil fuels such as coal: Low grade coal can contain up to 7% sulfur impurity (although the common percentage of sulfur in coal is between 1 and 5%). Coal contains sulfur as elemental sulfur, as iron pyrite FeS_2 and as organic sulfur compounds, since it was present in the proteins of the trees from which it was derived. The combustion process converts any sulfur to sulfur dioxide:

$$S(s) + O_2(g) \rightarrow SO_2(g)$$

$$4\ FeS_2(g) + 11\ O_2(g) \rightarrow 2\ Fe_2O_3(s) + 8\ SO_2(g)$$

Coal combustion is the major contributor to sulfur oxide pollution. Petroleum and natural gas contribute little to this as most of the sulfur is removed, by reacting with hydrogen gas in the presence of a catalyst, during petroleum refining and natural gas processing. Some heavy fuels (used by ships and power stations) can however have a high sulfur content, contributing to SO_2 pollution.

(b) From smelting plants which oxidise sulfide ores to the metal oxides:

$$Cu_2S_{(s)} + 2\ O_{2(g)} \rightarrow 2\ CuO_{(s)} + SO_{2(g)}$$

(c) Sulfuric acid factories also release some sulfur dioxide. Sulfuric acid, H_2SO_4 is produced by the oxidation of sulfur dioxide, SO_2 gas by oxygen in the presence of vanadium(V) oxide, V_2O_5 as a catalyst to form sulfur trioxide, SO_3 gas which reacts with water to produce the acid as shown:

$$SO_2(g) + O_2(g)) \rightarrow SO_3(g)$$

$$SO_3(g) + H_2O(l) \rightarrow H_2SO_4(l)$$

Natural sources

No major natural primary sources of sulfur dioxide are known although probably very small amounts are produced through volcanic and bacterial activity. However, sulfur dioxide is formed as a secondary pollutant in the atmosphere as a result of the atmospheric oxidation of hydrogen sulfide gas, H_2S:

$$2\ H_2S(g) + 3\ O_2(g) \rightarrow 2\ SO_2(g) + 2\ H_2O(l)$$

Hydrogen sulfide gas is produced most importantly by the anaerobic decay of organic matter (in swamps, oceans, etc.) and also some by volcanic activity.

PARTICULATES

These are solid particles suspended or carried in the air and are generally large enough to be seen. Natural sources of particulates include sandstorms, volcanoes and forest fires started by lightning.

Typical particulates from man–made sources include:

(a) Smoke and soot produced by the combustion of coal, petroleum, wood etc.

(b) Dust from mechanical break–up of solid matter.

(c) Asbestos from industrial plants: asbestos is a fibrous material composed of silicate crystals. Having used asbestos in the past in the insulation of buildings, demolition of such buildings releases asbestos particles. Many countries now ban the use of asbestos as it causes scarring of lung tissue.

(d) Metallic particles such as beryllium, mercury and arsenic from industrial plants and lead compounds in places where leaded gasoline is still in use. Beryllium oxide is used in spark plugs and as lining in high temperature furnaces (because of its very high melting point and high electrical resistivity). Mercury is present in fly ash and is also used in the manufacture of fungicides, pulp and paper.

(e) When coal is burnt, most of the ash is carried away in the exhaust gases as finely divided powder called fly ash which consists of unburnt carbon and oxides of many metals including iron, magnesium and calcium, as well as sulfates. A typical coal burning power plant produces 1000 tons of fly ash a day.

Volatile Organic Compounds

Volatile Organic Compounds (VOCs) are primary pollutants introduced directly into the environment. These include hydrocarbon gases or volatile organic liquids that are easily converted into gases which escape into the air. Recall that C_1 to C_4 hydrocarbons are gases and C_5 to C_{18} hydrocarbons are liquids due to the weak van der Waals' forces between these generally non–polar molecules which increase as their size increases.

Similarly to CO and NO_x, most hydrocarbons enter the environment from natural sources involving biological processes including a little from geothermal activity. Methane, the simplest alkane, and the largest natural source of hydrocarbons, is produced by the anaerobic bacterial decomposition of organic matter in bodies of water including swamps and oceans. Methane is also produced as a digestive gas in many animals. Trees and plants produce most of the rest of the natural volatile organic compounds called terpenes.

Petroleum, a complex mixture of very useful organic compounds, is the key source of VOC pollution produced by human activities. These include extracting, refining, transporting and using petroleum products, air pollution resulting at each stage. The fraction from petroleum that is used as vehicle fuel contains volatile hydrocarbons with C_5 to C_{16} carbons. These evaporate easily in the internal combustion engine and produce vapor during storage and the filling of fuel tanks. Incomplete combustion of fuel, especially in gasoline and diesel engines, also produces VOCs that are released into the atmosphere through exhausts. Photochemical smog, which is secondary pollution from automobile exhausts, contains large amounts of methyl benzene, $C_6H_5CH_3$, as well as reactive benzene derivatives. Solvents used in paints and other similar products are also human sources of volatile hydrocarbons.

E.1.2 Evaluate current methods for the reduction of air pollution.

Current Methods for the Reduction of Air Pollutants

Several methods are being used including implementing policies to encourage the use of mass transportation. Others being tested include the use of alternate fuels such as solar and battery operated cars, 'hybrid' cars, fuel cells, hydrogen as a fuel and changes to engine design. Most solutions are directed towards the automobile as it is the largest man made source of primary pollutants.

The combustion of hydrocarbon fuel and air mixture produces very high temperatures. The consequence of this sudden and rapid chemical process is that some VOCs remain unreacted, some undergo partial oxidation to carbon monoxide, and the high temperatures make a reaction between oxygen and highly stable nitrogen gas possible. By far the most common method for the reduction of these air pollutants includes exhaust systems that make it possible for the oxidation of carbon monoxide to carbon dioxide (which although it is a greenhouse gas is not a metabolic poison). However, the problem is complicated by the presence of other pollutants, namely oxides of nitrogen, particulates and VOCs also produced by the automobile.

Figure 1613 summarizes sources of major air pollutants, their health effects and methods of control.

OPTION

	Human source	Natural Source	Effect on Health	Methods of Control
Carbon monoxide (CO)	Incomplete combustion of fossil fuels used for transportation and industry; forest fires. Localized, high emissions produced. $C_7H_{16}+7½O_2 \rightarrow 7CO + 8H_2O$	From atmospheric oxidation of CH_4 (from anaerobic decomposition of organic matter). $2CH_4 + 3O_2 \rightarrow 2CO + 4H_2O$	Metabolic poison. Interferes with O_2 transport; prevents haemoglobin from carrying O_2; deprives body cells of O_2 leading to asphyxiation. Heart has to pump faster.	1. Catalytic converter 2. Lean burn engine (less fuel present with higher air/fuel ratio) 3. Thermal exhaust reactor
Oxides of Nitrogen (NO_x): N_2O, NO and NO_2	High temperature combustion in automobiles produces mostly NO, nitric oxide. This is oxidised to NO_2 in the atmosphere.	Decomposition of N-containing compounds by bacterial action produces N_2O, and NO. NO is oxidized to NO_2 in the atmosphere.	NO_2 causes breathing problems, respiratory distress and pulmonary edema. HNO_3 (from NO_2) irritates the respiratory tract	1. Catalytic converter. 2 Lean burning engines. 3. Recirculation of exhaust gases.
Oxides of sulfur (SO_x): SO_2 and SO_3	Combustion of sulfur containing coal, smelting plants, sulfuric acid plants: $S + O_2 \rightarrow SO_2$	No major direct sources of SO_x in nature, but oxidation of H_2S gas from decay of organic matter and volcanic activity. $2H_2S+3O_2 \rightarrow 2SO_2+2H_2O$	Acid rain formed from SO_x pollution irritates the respiratory tract and adversely affects the elderly, the young and asthma sufferers.	1. Alkaline scrubbing. 2. Limestone-based fluidized beds 3. Sulfur removed from fossil fuels before burning
Particulates	Combustion of fossil fuel use by industry, transportation, breakup of solid matter, industrial plants which produce smoke, soot, ash, dust	Blowing dust, volcanic activity, forest fires, biological sources such as pollen.	Irritation of the mucous membranes and lungs causing emphysema. Asbestosis and berylliosis cause scarring of lung tissue.	1. Electrostatic precipitators. 2. Gravity settling chambers. 3. Cyclone separators.
Volatile organic compounds (VOCs)	Petroleum extracting, refining, transporting and use; solvents, incomplete combustion of gasoline, coal and wood.	CH_4 from biological anaerobic bacterial decomposition of organic matter; trees and plants produce terpenes.	Aromatic compounds cause irritation of mucous membrane; some, such as benzene and benzo(α)pyrene are carcinogenic.	1. Catalytic converters.

Figure 1603 Summary of air pollutant sources, health effects and methods of control

Reduction of CO, NO_x and VOCs using catalytic converter

Catalytic converters are quite remarkable in their ability not only to oxidize carbon monoxide to carbon dioxide, but also to convert NO (nitrogen monoxide) to nitrogen gas as follows.

$$2\,CO(g) + 2\,NO(g) \rightarrow 2\,CO_2(g) + N_2(g)$$

In the presence of small amounts of platinum-based catalysts, the pollutants CO and NO are converted to CO_2 and harmless nitrogen gas. The principal source of VOCs is from automobile exhausts. The catalytic converter effectively removes these as it can also oxidize volatile organic compounds (hydrocarbons) to carbon dioxide and water.

The average cost of an automobile is increased by about US $600 – 800 and it also requires the use of high octane, non-leaded fuel since the catalyst in the converter is inactivated by the lead in leaded gasoline. Similarly, sulfur impurities in gasoline also poison the catalyst and have to be removed before the gasoline can be used as fuel.

Use of Air to Fuel Ratio to reduce automobile pollution

Gasoline mixture consists of VOCs containing C_5 to C_8 hydrocarbons. Consider the complete combustion of C_7H_{16} represented by the equation:

$$C_7H_{16} + 11O_2 \rightarrow 7CO_2 + 8H_2O;\ M_r(C_7H_{16}) = 100;\ M_r(O_2) = 32$$

1 mol C_7H_{16} (= 100g) requires 11 mol O_2 (= 352g) for complete combustion. Thus, 1.0 g C_7H_{16} requires 3.52 g oxygen. By mass, air contains about 22% oxygen and 78% nitrogen. Thus the mass of air required for 1.0 g C_7H_{16} is: $(100/22) \times 3.52 = 16$g, that is a theoretical air to fuel ratio by mass of 16:1. A similar calculation with C_8H_{18} gives a ratio of 14 to 1. Since gasoline is a mixture of hydrocarbons, an average value of air to fuel ratio of about 15 to 1 should give rise to complete combustion. However, the control of pollutants from automobiles is complicated because of the presence of other primary pollutants.

(a) Lower air to fuel ratio: If there is more fuel present (a richer fuel mixture, that is a lower air to fuel ratio), then complete combustion does not take place. some unreacted VOCs remain and more carbon monoxide is produced but the lack of air reduces the amount of nitrogen oxides produced. Air can then be injected into the exhaust gases containing CO and unburnt HCs to oxidize these to carbon dioxide and water. This Thermal Exhaust Reactor method however requires expensive engine design.

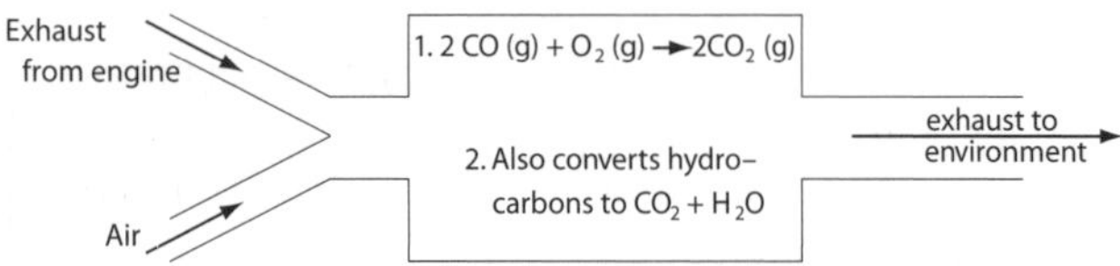

Figure 1604 A Thermal exhaust reactor

(b) **Lean Burn Engines:** If there is excess air and less fuel present, this represents a lean mixture with higher air to fuel ratio. In this case, less carbon monoxide and volatile organic compounds will be present in the exhaust, but nitrogen oxides levels will increase. The graph shows the variation in concentration of exhaust emission gases with the composition of the air to fuel mixture. 'Lean burn' engines with modification use an air:fuel ratio of approximately 18:1 by volume to minimise the production of pollutants.

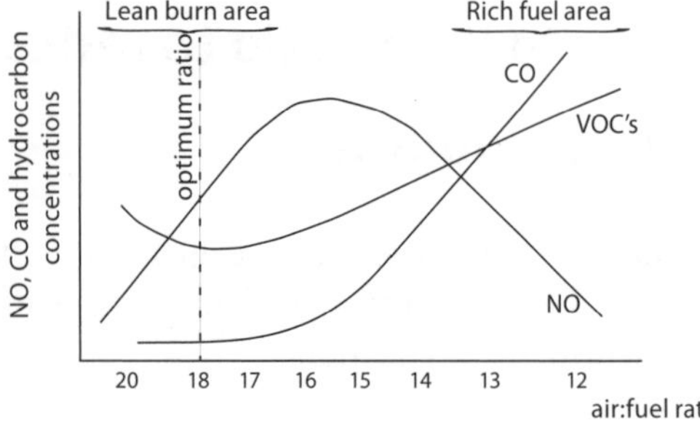

Figure 1605 Lean burn engines are better for the environment

The graph shows that CO% and VOCs% decrease as air to fuel ratio increases, NO_x% increases up to about 16:1 air to fuel ratio. Thus, changing the air to fuel ratio changes the amount of these three pollutants, but does not reduce all three without affecting performance.

Reduction of oxides of sulfur by post-combustion methods

Post combustion methods, involve the removal of sulfur dioxide from exhaust gases after burning the coal but before releasing to the atmosphere:

(1) Limestone fluidized beds involve adding powdered limestone, $CaCO_3$, with the coal in the combustion process. The heat from the combustion decomposes the limestone to calcium oxide:

$$CaCO_3(s) + heat \rightarrow CaO(s) + CO_2(g)$$

The calcium oxide reacts with the SO_2 produced to form $CaSO_3$, calcium sulfate(IV), and in the presence of oxygen $CaSO_4$, calcium sulfate(VI) forms:

$$CaO(s) + SO_2(g) \rightarrow CaSO_3(s);$$

$$2\ CaO(s) + 2\ SO_2(g) + O_2(g) \rightarrow 2\ CaSO_4(s)$$

The calcium sulfate, any unreacted calcium oxide and sulfur dioxide together with fly ash (particulates) are then absorbed into water in a wet–scrubber.

(2) A wet alkaline scrubber (Figure 1606) is a cleaning device that uses a liquid, usually water based, to remove contaminants. This uses a counterflow method in which the alkaline liquid is sprayed downward while the gas stream moves upwards. The effectiveness depends on the contact between the alkaline liquid and the acidic sulfur dioxide:

$$CaO(s) + H_2O(l) \rightarrow Ca(OH)_2(aq)$$

$$Ca(OH)_2(aq) + SO_2(g) \rightarrow CaSO_3(aq) + H_2O(l)$$

$$CaCO_3(s) + SO_2(g) \rightarrow CaSO_3(aq) + CO_2(g)$$

OPTION

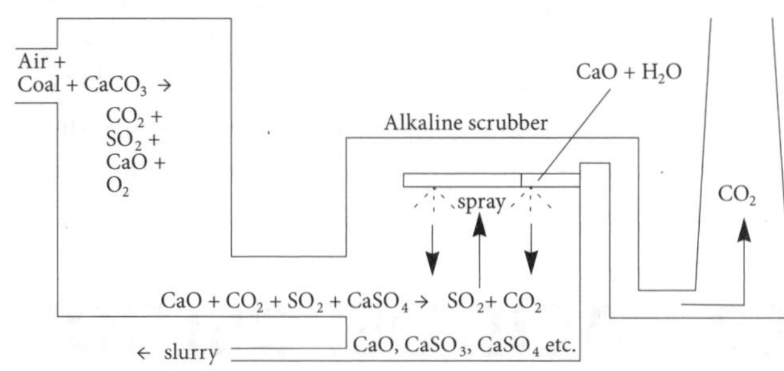

Figure 1606 The principle of a 'wet scrubber'

The waste slurry is transferred to settling ponds. Problems include the tendency of $CaSO_3$ to deposit on scrubber surfaces and the need for extremely large amounts of limestone, $CaCO_3$ which is converted to CaO by heating. Note that, by this method, the sulfur dioxide is being replaced by carbon dioxide, a greenhouse gas.

Other wet alkaline scrubbers use magnesium hydroxide as the alkaline material:

$$Mg(OH)_2(aq) + SO_2(g) \rightarrow MgSO_3(s) + H_2O(l)$$

Magnesium sulfate(IV) formed in the slurry can be heated to convert it to MgO:

$$MgSO_3(s) + heat \rightarrow MgO(s) + SO_2(g)$$

SO_2 formed can be used for the manufacture of sulfuric acid and the magnesium oxide treated with water to form magnesium hydroxide and recycled:

$$MgO(s) + H_2O(l) \rightarrow Mg(OH)_2(s)$$

However, the heating requires large amounts of energy and is therefore very expensive.

Other methods of reducing oxides of sulfur in the atmosphere

(1) Converting high sulfur coal to synthetic natural gas, SNG, CH_4 and the removal of most of the sulfur in the process of coal gasification. In this method, any sulfur is converted to hydrogen sulfide gas which is acidic and easily removed:

$$S(s) + H_2(g) \rightarrow H_2S(g)$$

One major disadvantage is that it requires about 30% of the energy for the conversion of coal to SNG.

(2) Using low sulfur, cleaner burning coal such as anthracite (hard coal) that has a high heat content. This type of coal is however much scarcer and more expensive.

(3) During petroleum refining and natural gas processing, sulfur is removed by reaction with hydrogen gas, in the presence of a catalyst. Any sulfur present is reduced to hydrogen sulfide gas which is an acidic gas and easily removed (considered a pre-combustion method).

(4) To desulfurize (remove sulfur from) high sulfur coal, the method of coal washing is used. Coal is finely ground and washed with water. Iron pyrites, FeS_2, has high density, settles rapidly and is removed. However, even in finely ground coal, a lot of sulfur is trapped below the surfaces of the particles and is therefore not removed. Organic sulfur, chemically bonded to carbon atoms in coal cannot be removed by this physical process (also considered a pre-combustion method).

Reduction of Particulates

Electrostatic precipitation is the most important and effective method for the removal of very tiny particles suspended in the air.

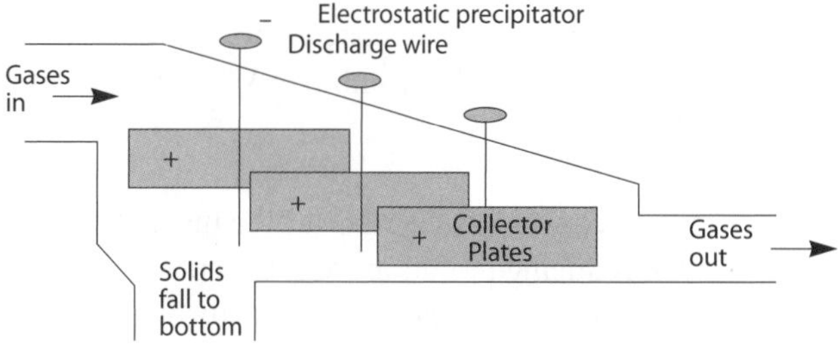

Figue 1607 The principle of electrostatic precipitation

In an electrostatic precipitator, a very high voltage is applied between the discharge wires and the collector plates which ionizes the gas molecules present:

$$G \rightarrow G^+ + e^-$$

The electrons produced collect on the particulates and the negatively charged particles are attracted to the positively charged collector plates. The collector plates have to be periodically shaken to remove the collected solid particles. This method can remove more than 98% of all particulate matter see Figure 1607.

Summary of Automobile Pollution

The sheer number of automobiles around the world makes this mode of transportation the major source of air pollution. These include unburnt VOC fuels that escape from the fuel tank, the engine and exhaust as well as carbon dioxide, carbon monoxide, particulates (soot) and oxides of nitrogen produced after combustion as well as lead (released as lead(II) bromide) if leaded gasoline is used. Methods of control of pollution from the automobile include:

(a) use of non–leaded gasoline to eliminate lead pollution.

(b) valves on gas tanks so gasoline can be pumped into the tank, but gasoline vapor cannot escape.

(c) different air to fuel ratios produce different amounts of pollutants. Lower air to fuel ratios produce less NO_x but more CO and VOCs due to incomplete combustion. Higher air to fuel ratios produce more complete combustion, thus less CO and VOCs but more NO_x as the more complete combustion produces higher temperatures and the presence of more oxygen favors NO_x production.

(d) thermal exhaust reactor, where the exhaust gases are mixed with air to oxidize carbon monoxide to carbon dioxide and any unburnt VOCs to CO_2 and H_2O.

(e) catalytic converters seem by far the most effective way of reducing pollution from the automobile. They use platinum–based catalysts through which the exhaust gases pass and they convert unburnt VOCs to CO_2 and H_2O, CO to CO_2 and NO to N_2. Because lead poisons the catalyst, an added advantage is that catalytic converters require the use of non-leaded gasoline thus eliminating lead pollution from automobiles.

E2 ACID DEPOSITION

E.2.1 State what is meant by the term acid deposition and outline its origins.

The term **acid deposition** refers to acidic particles and gases that deposit or fall to the Earth. It includes both wet deposition of acidic gases such as oxides of sulfur and nitrogen and acidic particles brought down as precipitation by rain, fog and snow and dry deposition of acidic gases and particles in the absence of rain or precipitation.

Pure rain water is naturally acidic, pH ≈ 5.6 ($[H^+] \approx 2.5 \times 10^{-6}$ mol dm^{-3}) due to dissolved carbon dioxide reacting to form carbonic acid, a very weak acid:

$$CO_2(g) + H_2O(l) \rightleftharpoons H_2CO_3(aq)$$

$$H_2CO_3(aq) \rightleftharpoons H^+(aq) + HCO_3^-(aq)$$

The environmental pollution called acid rain is any rain with pH less than 5.6. Recall that pH is a logarithmic scale with one pH unit corresponding to a difference in

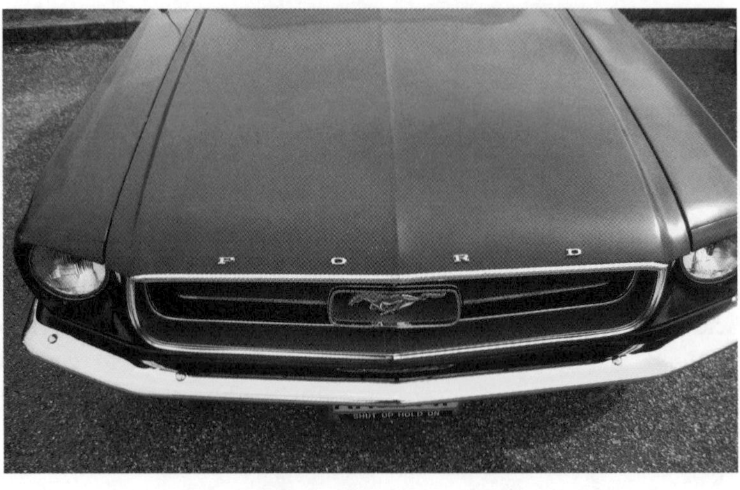

hydrogen ion concentration of a factor of 10. Thus acid rain of pH 4.2 has hydrogen ion concentration 25 times greater than pure rain water. Although extreme acid rain (pH of 1.7 recorded in Los Angeles in December 1982) is rare, the average rainfall in industrialized areas of the world has $[H^+]$ about 4 to 40 times greater than pure rain water (that is, pH 4 to 5 is common compared to a pH of 5.6). A pH of 4.0 in lakes is sufficient to kill fish life and such dead lakes do exist in North America, China and Russia among other places. Note that the pH of any water sample can be measured using pH paper showing colors of various pH values, or using a universal indicator, or a calibrated pH meter.

Research shows that acid deposition is associated with parts of a country where heavy industries are situated and also down–wind from such sites. Analysis of acid deposition indicates that oxides of sulfur, SO_x, and oxides of nitrogen, NO_x, are mostly responsible for the rain acidity (recall that many non–metallic oxides are acidic). Snow, fog, sleet, hail and drizzle all become contaminated with acids when SO_x and NO_x are present as pollutants.

FORMATION OF ACID DEPOSITION:

From oxides of sulfur

In the presence of moisture, sulfur dioxide produces sulfurous acid, a weak acid, but significantly stronger than carbonic acid:

$$SO_2(g) + H_2O\ (l) \rightarrow H_2SO_3(aq)$$

Sulfur dioxide can be oxidized in the presence of O_2, O_3, ·OH (hydroxyl free radical) and sunlight to sulfur trioxide:

$$SO_2(g) + \tfrac{1}{2}\ O_2(g) \rightarrow SO_3(g)$$

In the presence of moisture, sulfur oxides can be converted to sulfuric acid, a strong acid:

$$2\ SO_2(g) + O_2(g) + 2\ H_2O(l) \rightarrow 2\ H_2SO_4(aq)$$

$$SO_3(g) + H_2O(l) \rightarrow H_2SO_4(aq)$$

From oxides of nitrogen

In the absence of oxygen, nitrogen dioxide can dissolve in water to produce a mixture of nitrous acid (HNO_2), a weak acid, and nitric acid (HNO_3), a strong acid:

$$2\ NO_2(g) + H_2O(l) \rightarrow HNO_2(aq) + HNO_3(aq)$$

Nitrogen dioxide gas can be converted to nitric acid, HNO_3, a strong acid, in the presence of oxygen gas and moisture through a series of complicated reactions which can be summarized as:

$$4\ NO_2(g) + 2\ H_2O\ (l) + O_2(g) \rightarrow 4\ HNO_3(aq)$$

The conversion of nitrogen dioxide to nitric acid can be accelerated by the presence of other pollutants present in the air, such as the hydroxyl free radical, •OH, which is formed during photochemical smog can react with nitrogen dioxide, itself a free radical (with a lone electron):

$$\bullet NO_2(g) + \bullet OH(g) \rightarrow HNO_3(aq)$$

E.2.2 Discuss the environmental effects of acid deposition and possible methods to counteract them.

Acid deposition affects humans, aquatic life, materials, soil, vegetation and visibility as follows

EFFECTS OF ACID RAIN ON HUMANS

Breathing air containing fine droplets of acid irritates the whole respiratory tract from mucous membranes in the nose and throat to the lung tissues. Also, it can cause severe eye irritation. Sulfate aerosols are also powerful irritants. The small sulfate particles penetrate the lungs where they become embedded and have adverse effects on asthmatics, the elderly and the young. Increased concentrations of $Al^{3+}(aq)$ in water due to acidic conditions may lead to Alzheimer's disease.

EFFECT ON AQUATIC LIFE

Salmon cannot survive if pH is as low as 5.5. If acidification of lakes and rivers takes place, it affects aquatic life. One major effect on fish is the increased concentration of Al^{3+} resulting from the leaching of soil by acid rain. Al^{3+} affects the function of the gills. **Eutrophication** results from nitrates in acid deposition (see also E.5.3).

EFFECT ON MATERIALS

Corrosion of basic materials such as marble or limestone ($CaCO_3$) and dolomite ($CaCO_3$ $MgCO_3$) takes place. The insoluble carbonates are converted to more soluble sulfates:

$$CaCO_3(s) + H_2SO_4(aq) \rightarrow CaSO_4(aq) + H_2O\ (l) + CO_2(g)$$

The sulfates can dissolve in water leading to considerable damage to structural and artists' stone. This is called 'stone leprosy' and has caused damage to cultural monuments in places like Egypt, Greece, Mexico and Turkey. The Egyptian sphinx (see Figure 1608) has suffered from both acid rain and being used for artillery target practice.

Figure 1608 The Egyptian sphinx

Corrosion of iron and steel is promoted by acid rain, a problem which is increased by high humidity, high temperatures and the presence of particulates. The overall reaction is:

$$4Fe_{(s)} + x\,H_2O_{(l)} + 3O_{2(g)} \rightarrow 2Fe_2O_3.x\,H_2O_{(s)}$$

Similarly deterioration of electrical equipment takes place as a result of corrosion. Acid rain pollution causes bleaching and weakening of fabrics and leather and discoloration and embrittlement of paper. Acid rain can also leach heavy toxic metals such as lead, cadmium and mercury into the water system (see also E.12.3).

EFFECT ON SOIL AND VEGETATION

The extent to which plants can be damaged depends upon acid concentration and length of exposure. Acute injury due to short term exposure to high acid concentrations leads to attacks on cells producing dead areas of leaves which dry out and usually become bleached. Chronic injury due to long term exposure to even low acid concentrations disrupts chlorophyll synthesis, characterized by yellowing of leaves (as a result of acid entering the stomata of the leaves). Effects include bleached spots, yellowing of leaves, suppression of plant growth and reduction in yield. Acid rain also leaches or removes important nutrients such as Mg^{2+} from soil.

EFFECT ON VISIBILITY

The mist of sulfuric acid and sulfate aerosols in the atmosphere can cause great loss of visibility and can curtail air flights.

Possible methods to counteract acid deposition

Most efforts at reducing acid deposition are directed at the important sources of the pollutants, namely from coal and automobile engines and are discussed in detail in section E.1.2 above. These include the use of catalytic converters to reduce CO and NO_x, control of air to fuel ratio to reduce NO_x, coal pre-combustion methods to desulfurize high sulfur coal or convert it to SNG and post-combustion methods to remove oxides of sulfur by alkaline scrubbing and using limestone fluidized beds.

Other methods include promoting alternative energy sources such as solar and wind power and fuel cells, hybrid automobiles, increased public transportation, etc. Also, lime ($CaO/Ca(OH)_2$) can be added to soil and lakes to neutralize excess acidity.

E3 GREENHOUSE EFFECT

E.3.1 Describe the greenhouse effect.

The temperature of the Earth depends on the amount of sunlight received, the proportions absorbed by the earth or reflected back into space, and the extent to which the atmosphere retains the heat. There is a natural steady state 'greenhouse effect' which keeps the Earth's average temperature warm enough (about 16°C or 60°F) to be habitable. This effect is due to the presence of water vapor and carbon dioxide as **greenhouse gases** found naturally in the atmosphere.

The **Greenhouse Effect** is the trapping of heat in the atmosphere. Short wavlength sunlight penetrates the atmosphere to warm the Earth's surface which absorbs some of the energy. Hence the outgoing radiation, reflected back from Earth is of longer wavelength. This infrared radiation from the Earth is absorbed by the greenhouse gases, water vapor and carbon dioxide and reradiated back to Earth. Thus, greenhouse gases allow incoming solar radiation to reach the Earth, but absorb some of the heat radiated from the Earth, thus maintaining the global temperature. Without the greenhouse effect the Earth would be much colder than it is. Greenhouse gases in the atmosphere act similarly to glass or plastic on a greenhouse, that is, they act as a one way filter.

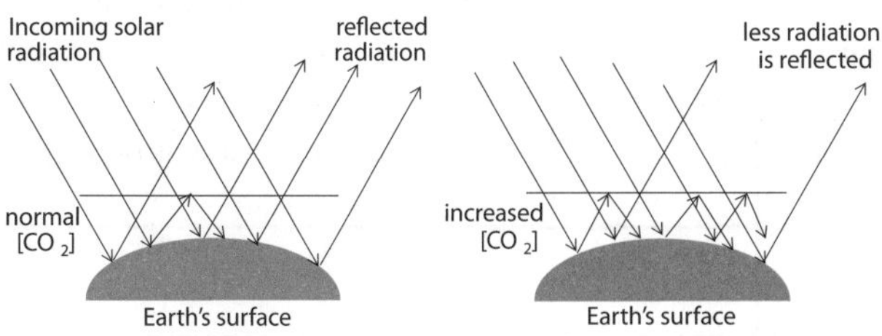

Figure 1609 The 'enhanced' greenhouse effect

In other words, the greenhouse effect allows visible and uv light of short wavelength to pass through the atmosphere to heat the air and the Earth but it traps the longer wavelength infrared heat rays emitted from the warm soil and air, thus raising the temperature of the atmosphere.

Global warming is the gradual increase in planet–wide temperatures. There is evidence to conclude that global warming is taking place. Surface land and ocean temperature records exist for more than a century and indicate that, over that time period, average global temperatures have risen by about half a degree centigrade and the rate of temperature change is significantly faster than any observed changes in the last 10,000 years.

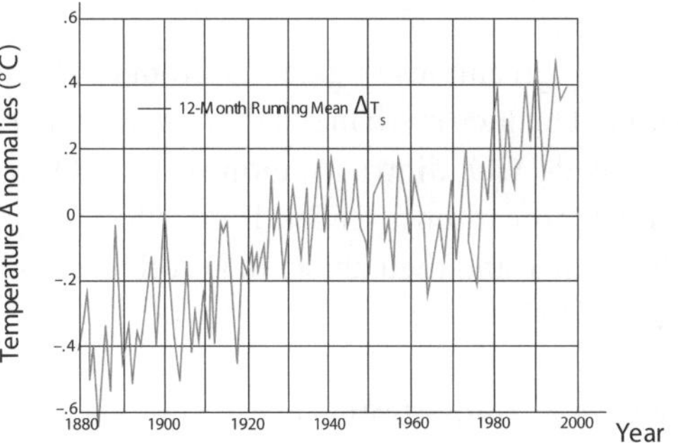

Figure 1610 Global surface air temperature

TOK Is climate change real or is there 'reasonable doubt'?

"There are lies, damned lies and statistics" (variously attributed to Benjamin Disraeli and Mark Twain) - probably nowadays that is starting to apply just as much to some fields of science as it is to the social sciences for which it was originally coined. How much evidence is required to prove something beyond reasonable doubt? The old question of inductive logic, though slightly tainted by hints that the person who is paying the piper might just influence the 'reasonable doubt' judgement. There were many studies on the effects of tobacco funded by cigarette manufacturers and on acid-rain funded by power generating companies, whose conclusions differed from more independent researchers.

With regard to climate change, there is little doubt that there have previously been tremendous differences in climate and not just on a geological timeframe. In the 18th century there were regular winter fairs held on the frozen River Thames, whereas even 50 years ago, before the current global warming scare really began, just a frost in London was unusual, let alone the whole river freezing. Another factor is the fact that the connection between mean global temperature and industrial pollution is a complex one for which we do not have models accepted by all scientists. When people differ it is human nature to speculate on the reasons underlying the fact that people do not agree with you, and then probably use these to impugn their scientific impartiality. It is not only in science that 'reasonable doubt' is a factor – it is interesting to speculate on what kind of world we might now be living in if different recent political leaders had been elected.

E.3.2 List the main greenhouse gases and their sources, and discuss their relative effects.

The major greenhouse gases introduced into the environment include methane CH_4, water vapour, H_2O (g), carbon dioxide, CO_2, dintrogen monoxide, N_2O, ozone, O_3 and chlorfluorocarbons, CFCs. Their effects depend on their abundance and their ability to absorb heat radiation., (see Figure 1611).

The increase in concentrations of greenhouse gases from human activity provide a circumstantial link to global warming. Atmospheric concentrations of greenhouse gases have increased significantly since the industrial revolution: CO_2 is up 25%, CH_4 is up over 145% and N_2O around 15%. The atmospheric concentration of methane is low, but it is about 30 times more effective than carbon dioxide in its ability to trap infrared radiation. However, methane has a relatively short average atmospheric lifetime compared with carbon dioxide. Compared to carbon dioxide, nitrous oxide is about 160 times more effective, whereas water is only a tenth as effective as carbon dioxide in its ability to trap infrared radiation. The concentrations of these gases in the atmosphere also vary, with water vapour being the most, and CFCs the least abundant. Also, the rate of increase of CFCs has been decreasing as their use has been controlled by legislation.

E.3.3 Discuss the influence of increasing amounts of greenhouse gases on the atmosphere.

The effects of Global Warming over the last century have resulted in

- an increase in temperature by about half a degree centigrade,
- a one percent increase in precipitation and
- about 15–20 cm worldwide rise in sea levels resulting from the partial melting of glaciers and polar ice-caps and the physical expansion of ocean water caused by warmer temperatures.

The change in the climate in most regions of the world will grow as the concentration of greenhouse gases continues to increase. The climate change will impact on health, agriculture, forests, water resources, coastal areas, species diversity, species numbers and natural areas.

The latest (2007) scientific reports suggest that consequences of Greenhouse gas emissions are occuring faster than 'worse-case' scenarios. For example, the decrease in ice cover in the Arctic ocean is taking place 30 years sooner than predicted by scientific models.

Gas	H_2O	CO_2	CH_4	N_2O	O_3	CFCs
Main Sources	Evaporation from bodies of water; product of hydrocarbon combustion	Combustion of fossil fuels, forest fires, decay of plants and animals	Anaerobic decomposition of organic matter; from ruminant animals (cows and sheep by bacterial breakdown of cellulose), rice paddies, oil and gas fields	Bacterial action, use of nitrogen-based fertilizers	Photo-chemical smog	In spray can propellants, old refrigerators and air conditioners, as solvents, production of plastic foams (no natural sources of CFCs)
% Vol.	0 – 4%	3.7×10^{-2}	1.7×10^{-4}	3×10^{-5}	4×10^{-6}	2×10^{-8}
Relative effectiveness*	0.1	1	30	160	2000	10 000 – 25 000
Contribution to global warming	-	50 – 60%	15 – 18%	6%	12%	8 – 14%
Atmospheric life / years	-	200 – 500	7 - 10	120 - 150		80

* In comparison to arbitrary assigned value of 1 for CO_2

Figure 1611 Greenhouse gases, sources and effectiveness

OPTION

Health	Agriculture	Forests	Water Resources	Coastal Areas	Species and Natural Areas
Life cycles of pathogens and insects such as mosquitoes are affected by climate; greater chance of malaria, etc.	Effect on crop yields and geographic distribution of crops; some crops will thrive, others will not.	Insects and diseases may increase; increase in summer droughts would produce more forest fires. Higher temperatures and more rain should help forests grow more rapidly.	Decreased water quality due to flooding; floods more likely due to more intense rainfall; droughts more severe due to increased evaporation and drier soil.	Raise the level of seas eroding beaches, inundating low lands, increasing coastal flooding.	Loss of cold water fish habitat, shift in ecological areas, loss of habitats and species; desertification.

Figure 1612 Effects of Global Warming

E4 OZONE DEPLETION

E.4.1 Describe the formation and depletion of ozone in the stratosphere by natural processes.

E.4.2 List the ozone-depleting pollutants, and their sources.

E.4.3 Discuss alternatives to CFCs in terms of their properties.

Ozone, O_3, is a naturally occurring component of the stratosphere. It is a very pale bluish gas with an acrid (pungent–smelling) odor. Chemically it is very reactive (a powerful oxidizing agent) and hence it has harmful effects on living matter. Inhaling a small amount of ozone can be harmful, yet it is essential to life and health by its presence in the ozone layer, where it plays a vital role. The ozone layer is about 15 to 45 km above the Earth's surface and holds much of the air's ozone.

Formation of Ozone

The photo–dissociation of molecular oxygen by ultraviolet (uv) light represents the principle mechanism of ozone's formation in the upper atmosphere. High energy, very short wavelength uv light from the sun splits the strong double bond in O_2 molecules into oxygen atoms which are extremely reactive free radicals containing unpaired electrons (represented by •):

$$O_2(g) + \text{uv light} \rightarrow 2\ \bullet O$$

These oxygen atoms react with other oxygen molecules, O_2 to form O_3:

$$O_2(g) + \bullet O(g) \rightarrow O_3(g)$$

Depletion of ozone

Unlike O_2 that contains a O=O double bond, the resonance structures of ozone (see Figure 1613) suggest that two (π) bonding electrons are spread over the entire structure of the molecule with a bond order of 1½ in ozone (between a single and a double bond), and it is thus a weaker bond than in O_2. This means that the bonds in ozone can be broken by light of a longer wavelength, and hence less energy, than that required to dissociate O_2 molecules.

Figure 1613 The resonance structure of ozone

The reverse reaction takes place when O_3 absorbs rather longer wavelength uv light of less energy to form O_2 molecule and oxygen free radical:

$$O_3(g) \rightarrow O_2(g) + \bullet O_{(g)}$$

The oxygen free radicals react with ozone to form O_2 gas:

$$O_3(g) + \bullet O(g) \rightarrow 2\ O_2(g)$$

Thus O_3 is constantly being formed and broken down. The ozone layer acts as a shield by absorbing 99% of the sun's harmful uv light of longer wavelength than that absorbed by O_2 and N_2.

Ozone-depleting pollutants and their sources

Satellite data shows a clear decline over the last 30 years in ozone concentration in the latitudes 60° south to 60° north. Similarly satellite measurements show the greatest destruction of the ozone layer at the South Pole, covering an area almost equal in size to the North American continent. Satellite data over the North and South Poles clearly indicate that the ozone holes, where depletion of ozone has taken place, are seasonal with the lowest levels being found in the antarctic region during the antarctic spring.

Ozone in the ozone layer is being depleted by:

(1) CFCs, chlorofluorocarbons (freons) are used in spray cans as a propellant and in old refrigerators and air conditioners, in fire extinguishers and as solvents. When released, the CFCs, because they are chemically very inert, do not decompose but float slowly through the atmosphere into the stratosphere. When they reach the unfiltered ultraviolet rays of the sun, they are turned into extremely reactive chlorine atoms with an unpaired electron, called chlorine free radicals. These react readily with the ozone as follows

$$CCl_2F_2 + \text{uv light} \rightarrow \bullet CClF_2 + \bullet Cl$$

Note that the average bond enthalpy of C–F bond is 484 kJ mol^{-1} and only 338 kJ mol^{-1} for the C–Cl bond; the C–Cl bond is weaker and breaks. The Cl atom, also a free radical, is very reactive and readily reacts with O_3 to produce O_2:

$$\bullet Cl + O_3 \rightarrow ClO\bullet + O_2$$

(2) Nitric oxide, formed from the high temperature reaction of N_2 and O_2 in aircraft engines, reacts with ozone reducing its concentration:

$$NO + O_3 \rightarrow NO_2 + O_2$$

A decrease in O_3 concentration in the stratosphere means more uv light reaches the Earth, thus increasing cases of skin cancer and eye cataracts, more sunburn and damage to animals and plants including suppression of plant growth, genetic mutations and changes in the world's climate.

Alternatives to CFCs

CFCs are used because of their lack of reactivity, low toxicity and low flammability. Alternatives to CFCs must possess similar properties, but with no C–Cl bonds and it is preferable if they show little absorption of infrared radiation in order not to behave as greenhouse gases:

1. Hydrocarbons, such as propane, C_3H_8 and 2–methylpropane, $CH_3CH(CH_3)_2$, are used as refrigerant coolants. Although these do not lead to ozone depletion, they are flammable as well as being greenhouse gases (able to absorb infrared radiation) and would lead to global warming.

2. Hydrochlorofluorocarbons, HClFCs contain hydrogen, chlorine, fluorine and carbon atoms in their molecules, for example: CHF_2Cl, Chlorodifluoromethane. The presence of a hydrogen atom makes the compound decompose less easily since the C–H bond is stronger (412 kJ mol^{-1}) than the C–Cl bond. Nonetheless, these do reduce the ozone layer because of the presence of a C–Cl bond in the molecule and can only be considered a temporary solution.

3. Fluorocarbons: For example, CF_4, tetrafluoro-methane; C_2F_6, hexafluoroethane. These have low reactivity, are neither toxic nor flammable and the very strong C–F bond makes them stable to uv radiation so they cannot catalyze ozone depletion. However, these are greenhouse gases, absorb infrared radiation and would eventually lead to an increase in the global temperature.

4. HFCs hydrofluorocarbons: For example, CF_3CH_2F, 1,1,1,2-tetraflouroethane, without any chlorine atoms, are considered good alternatives to CFCs as no chlorine atoms, which are primarily responsible for ozone depletion, are involved. These also have low reactivity, low toxicity and low flammability, but do contribute to global warming.

E5 DISSOLVED OXYGEN IN WATER

The importance of dissolved oxygen

Human beings and land animals obtain oxygen for respiration from the air. For animals to survive in aquatic systems, water must contain a minimum concentration of dissolved oxygen. The dissolved–oxygen (DO) content of a body of water is one of the most important indicators of its quality. Recall that whereas water is a highly polar, bent molecule, diatomic oxygen is a non–polar molecule and hence its solubility in water is very low. At 20°C, it is about 2.8×10^{-4} mol dm^{-3}. This is equivalent to 9 mg of oxygen per dm^{-3} of water (or 1000g water or a million mg of water) and is best expressed as 9 ppm (parts per million). As the temperature rises, the solubility of any gas decreases, in contrast to that of most solids.

The quality of water, at any temperature, can be determined by the amount of oxygen present. At 20°C, DO content of 8 to 9 ppm O_2 at sea level is considered to be water of good quality. As the DO level reaches 4.5 ppm oxygen, it is considered moderately polluted and below that concentration, highly polluted. The quality of water depends on several factors including oxygen demanding wastes and disease causing pathogens or microorganisms that can affect health. Organic substances such as plants, animal and human waste, waste from industrial processes such as meat packing and food processing plants and paper mills, are the main oxygen demanding wastes.

E.5.1 Outline biochemical oxygen demand (BOD) as a measure of oxygen-demanding wastes in water.

BOD, the **Biochemical Oxygen Demand** (some refer to it as the Biological Oxygen Demand), is a measure of the amount of oxygen consumed by the biodegradable organic wastes and ammonia in a given amount of water over a time period, normally 5 days, at 20°C. The effluent sample is diluted in oxygen saturated water and enclosed without any air space in a BOD sample bottle. After the 5 day incubation period, the decrease in dissolved oxygen is measured using an oxygen electrode. The greater the amount of oxygen–demanding wastes, the higher is the BOD:

ppm BOD	Quality of Water
< 1	Almost pure water
5	Doubtful purity
20	Unacceptable purity

Figure 1614 BOD Values for Water

Untreated municipal sewage can be in the 100 to 400 ppm BOD range, whereas food processing plants can be up to 10 000 ppm, indicating very high oxygen demanding wastes present in the effluent of such plants.

E.5.2 Distinguish between *aerobic* and *anaerobic* decomposition of organic material in water.

Aerobic decomposition of organic matter in water in the presence of oxygen is a natural biological process in which bacteria that thrive in oxygen-rich environments break down and digest the organic matter. This is an oxidation process where the complex organic matter is broken down into simple organic material, carbon dioxide and water. Any organic nitrogen is converted into nitrates, NO_3^-, organic sulfur to sulfates, SO_4^{2-} and organic phosphorus to phosphates, PO_4^{3-}. Aerobic decomposition removes oxygen from the water, thus causing a decrease in dissolved oxygen (DO). The DO may decrease to zero if too much organic matter is present, killing aquatic life that depends on oxygen.

Anaerobic decomposition of organic matter in water takes place in the absence of oxygen by microorganisms that do not require oxygen. Typical anaerobic decomposition reaction products due to the reduction of organic matter in the presence of water include:

- ammonia and amines (with a strong fishy smell) from nitrogen and hydrogen
- methane (biogas or marsh gas), from the carbon and hydrogen
- hydrogen sulfide, H_2S (foul rotten egg smell) from organic sulfur
- phosphine, PH_3 from phosphorus.

OPTION

E.5.3 Describe the process of eutrophication and its effects.

Plant nutrients such as nitrates from nitrogen-containing animal and human waste and fertilizers, and phosphates from detergents and fertilizers lead to excessive growth of aquatic plant life, often in the form of algal blooms. This can make water taste and smell bad and can kill shell fish, as in the case of 'red tides'. Red tides are caused by several species of marine plankton (microscopic plant-like cells) that can produce chemical toxins. Dead plants fall to the bottom of bodies of water where, in the presence of oxygen, they are broken down or decay due to bacterial activity, thus depleting the concentration of oxygen. Consequently, fish die of asphyxiation (lack of oxygen); anaerobic processes produce toxic substances such as hydrogen sulfide and phospine and that part of the water becomes lifeless. This process is known as **eutrophication**.

E.5.4 Discuss the source and effects of thermal pollution in water.

Power plants and many industrial processes use huge quantities of fresh water to cool and condense steam. The cooling water subsequently becomes warm (or hot) and if this is dumped into streams, rivers or lakes, it leads to **thermal pollution**. Two major effects of thermal pollution on bodies of water include that on dissolved oxygen and that on the metabolic rates of aquatic life.

The concentration of any gas such as oxygen dissolved in a liquid decreases as temperature is increased (that is, more of the gas bubbles out). This is complicated by the fact that if the less dense warm water is not rapidly mixed with a body of deep, cooler, more dense water, it can stay on the top, is unable to absorb as much oxygen from the atmosphere and leads to overall reduced levels of dissolved oxygen.

Temperature /°C	0	20	40
Solubility /ppm	15	9	6.5

Figure 1615 The Effect of Temperature on the Solubility of Oxygen Gas in Water

A moderate increase in temperature generally speeds up the rate at which biochemical reactions occur, thus, not only is the DO (dissolved oxygen) level decreased as temperature increases, but the metabolic rates of aquatic animals increase and require more oxygen. As a result, thermal pollution has adverse effects on both dissolved oxygen and the rate of consumption of oxygen in bodies of water.

E6 WATER TREATMENT

Approximately three quarters of the Earth's surface is covered by water with the world's oceans containing most of it, as shown in the table below:

	oceans	glaciers, ice caps	ground water	lakes, rivers	atmosphere
%	97.3	2.1	0.6	0.015	0.001

Figure 1616 The distribution of Water on Earth

E.6.1 List the primary pollutants found in waste water and identify their sources.

Water is a unique, highly polar substance capable of hydrogen bonding and this property allows it to dissolve many chemicals. Thus some toxic substances as well as bacteria and viruses can be carried by water. Water used by humans, whether for personal use or by industry, becomes impure and is returned to the environment into lakes, rivers, oceans, reservoirs or aquifers (natural underground reservoirs). Water that is unsuitable for drinking, irrigation, industrial use or washing is considered **polluted water** (see Figure 1617 for details).

E.6.2 Outline the primary, secondary and tertiary stages of waste water treatment, and state the substance that is removed during each stage.

Sewage is the water-carried wastes (that is used water) that flows away from any community. It can contain domestic, sanitary, commercial and industrial wastes. Such sewage may contain disease causing microorganisms, organic materials as well as other toxic substances such as heavy metal ions. The purpose of sewage treatment is to remove hazardous materials, reduce the BOD (Biological Oxygen Demand) of the sewage and kill microorganisms prior to discharge.

OPTION

Pollutants	Sources
Heavy metals (for example, Cadmium, Copper, Mercury, Lead, Zinc)	Cd: Rechargeable batteries, metal plating and pigments Cu: household plumbing, copper mining and smelting Hg: Batteries, mercury salts as fungicides, mercury cells in chlor-alkali industry, discharge from pulp and paper mills
Pesticides (include DDT, fungicides and herbicides)	Agricultural practices.
Dioxins	From by-products of industrial processes such as waste incineration, forest fires and burning fuels, manufacture of chlorinated pesticides; used in Agent Orange as a defoliant in Vietnam war.
Polychlorobiphenyls (PCBs)	Very stable compounds that were used widely as coolants and lubricants in capacitors, transformers, and other electrical equipment.
Organic matter	Waste treatment plants, decomposition of plants and animals, oil spills, industrial waste
Nitrates (present as highly soluble salts)	Agriculture: Chemical nitrate fertilizers for farming; from acid rain.
Phosphates	Detergents and chemical phosphate fertilizers.

Figure 1617 Sources of primary pollutants in waste water

Different types of sewage treatment with different levels of effectiveness are carried out in the world depending on the availability of resources since the cost increases with more advanced treatment. These are classified as primary, secondary and tertiary stages of sewage treatment. Each level of treatment reduces the level of the pollutants in the sewage and thus the original BOD, with the tertiary treatment being the most effective but by far the most expensive to build and operate.

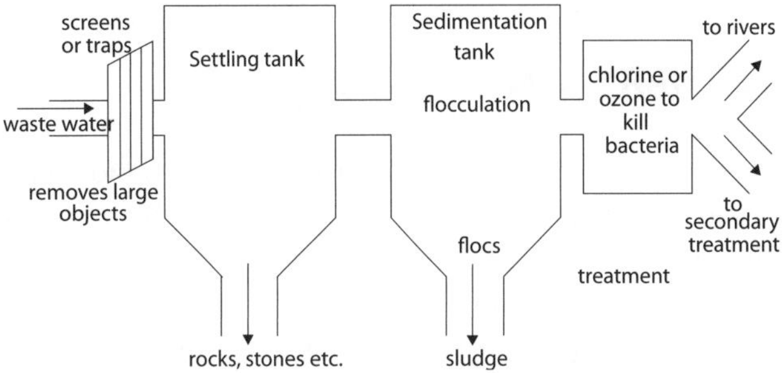

Figure 1618 Primary sewage treatment

Primary Sewage Treatment

The effluent is first passed through screens and traps which filter out large objects such as trash and debris and, from the surface, remove floating objects including grease (which has a high BOD). It then passes through settling tanks where smaller heavier objects such as rocks and stones settle and can be transferred to land fills. Next, the sewage passes through holding or sedimentation tanks or ponds where it is allowed to settle and sludge is removed from the bottom. The mechanical process of **sedimentation** can be speeded up by adding chemicals which allow suspended particles to join together to form large clumps. This process is called **flocculation** (the large clumps formed are called flocs) and can be achieved by the addition of aluminium sulfate, $Al_2(SO_4)_3$, the aluminium ions cause particles to clump together and precipitate out. The flocs formed settle to the bottom, see Figure 1618.

Depending on the amount of BOD wastes, primary treatment is generally not sufficient to improve the quality of water to safe levels, even if it is treated with chlorine or ozone to kill pathogens. A typical primary treatment domestic sewage plant can remove about 30 – 40% of the BOD waste and secondary treatment is essential to further reduce BOD levels.

Secondary Sewage Treatment

This involves microbial activity and requires aeration in which air, or air enriched with oxygen, is bubbled, using large blowers, through sewage mixed with bacteria–laden sludge. This allows aerobic bacteria to thoroughly mix with the sewage in order to oxidize and break down most of the organic matter. The process is thus biological in nature and is called an **activated sludge process**.

Then the water, containing decomposed suspended particles, is passed through a sedimentation tank where large quantities of biologically active sludge collect. Part of this is recycled and the rest has to be disposed off. Secondary sewage treatment can remove most (about 90%) organic oxygen-demanding wastes and suspended particles. Primary and secondary treatments cannot remove dissolved inorganic substances such as nitrates, phosphates and heavy metal ions, which require further treatment. The effluent from secondary treatment may then be sent to a tertiary plant for further treatment or released into lakes, rivers etc. before which it may be treated with chlorine or ozone gas to kill pathogenic bacteria.

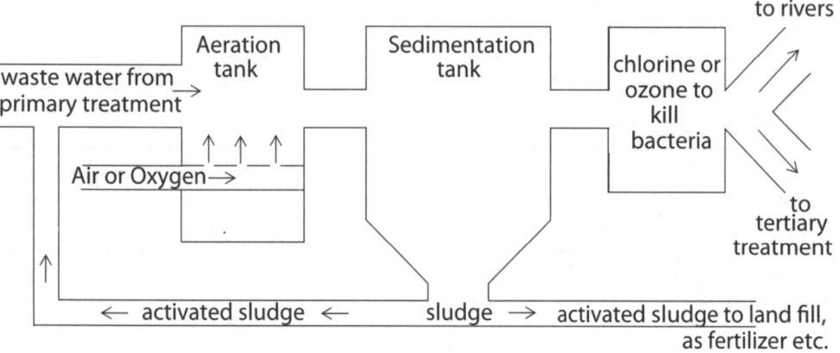

Figure 1619 Secondary sewage treatment

TERTIARY SEWAGE TREATMENT

These processes involve specialized chemical, biological and or physical treatment that further purify the water after it has undergone primary and secondary treatments. It can remove the remaining organic materials, nutrients and substances not taken out by the biological processes in secondary treatment, such as toxic metal ions as well as nitrate and phosphate ions. Examples of tertiary treatment include carbon bed, chemical precipitation and biological processes.

Carbon bed method

This uses activated carbon black. It consists of tiny carbon granules with large surface areas which have been treated and activated by high temperatures. This then has the ability to readily adsorb organic chemicals from the waste waters. Adsorption is the attraction of a substance to the surface of a solid substance. Carbon beds are effective against many toxic organic materials and charcoal filters are often used to further purify tap water for drinking purposes.

Chemical Precipitation

Certain toxic heavy metal ions such as cadmium, lead and mercury can easily be precipitated as their sulfide salts whose solubilities in water are incredibly small. For the reaction:

$$MS\ (s) \rightleftharpoons M^{2+}\ (aq) + S^{2-}\ (aq)$$

the K_c value (also called K_{sp}, the solubility product constant) at 25°C is of the order of 10^{-28} for CdS and PbS, and for HgS it is of the order of 10^{-52}. Thus if carefully controlled amounts of hydrogen sulfide gas are bubbled through a solution containing heavy metal ions, these can be precipitated as the corresponding sulfides which can then be filtered out. Excess hydrogen sulfide (being acidic) can then be easily removed:

$$M^{2+}\ (aq) + H_2S\ (g) \rightarrow MS(s) + 2\ H^+\ (aq)$$

Similarly, the presence of phosphate ions, PO_4^{3-}, can be reduced to very low levels by the addition of calcium ions, Ca^{2+}, since the solubility product constant K_{sp} of calcium phosphate is very small (1.2×10^{-26}).

$$3\ Ca^{2+}\ (aq) + 2\ PO_4^{3-}\ (aq) \rightarrow Ca_3(PO_4)_2\ (s)$$

Anaerobic biological process

This is **denitrification** which turns the nitrogen in nitrates back to atmospheric nitrogen, N_2. This is achieved by anaerobic organisms (denitrifying bacteria). This is a reduction process in which the oxidation number of nitrogen is reduced from +5 in the nitrate ion, NO_3^- to zero in N_2. At the same time, carbon in the organic matter is oxidized to CO_2. The net ionic half-equation for the reduction reaction can be summarized as:

$$6H^+ + NO_3^- + 5e^- \rightarrow N_2 + 3H_2O$$

Denitrification therefore reduces nitrate contamination in ground water.

E.6.3 Evaluate the process to obtain fresh water from sea water using multi-stage distillation and reverse osmosis.

DISTILLATION

Sea water, containing on average about 3.5% dissolved salts by mass, is not fit for human consumption. It is equally unfit for agricultural and industrial uses where the high salt content would cause dehydration of plants (water loss by the process of osmosis) and lead to corrosion of

OPTION

equipment. **Desalination** processes remove salts from sea water and brackish water to produce fresh water. Two methods in common use to desalinate sea water are multi-stage distillation and reverse osmosis.

Distillation is the process that allows the separation of a volatile liquid from non-volatile materials. Heating the solution allows for the volatile water to be converted to water vapor that can be separated and collected as fresh water leaving behind the non-volatile salts in solution. Large scale desalination by distillation is made more efficient by using a multistage process to maximize the use of heat so that when condensation of vapor produces heat in one stage, it is used to heat water in the second stage and so on (see Figure 1621).

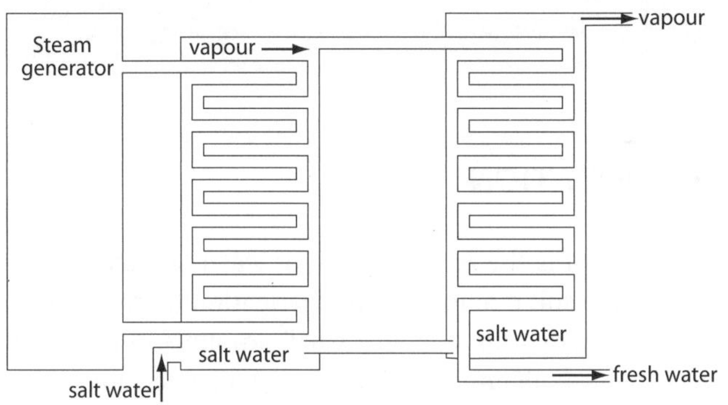

Figure 1621 The Distillation process

Reverse osmosis

Osmosis is the natural tendency of a solvent such as water to move from a region of high solvent concentration (purer water) to one of lower solvent concentration (less pure water) through a **semi-permeable membrane**. Thus, it is a tendency to equalize concentrations across the membrane. A semi-permeable membrane allows water, but not ions or large molecules, to pass through. If pure water and salt water are separated by a semipermeable membrane then, due to osmosis, pure water (of higher solvent concentration) will move into the salt water thus diluting it. This flow of water can in fact be stopped if a pressure equal to the osmotic pressure of the solution is applied. Indeed, if the pressure applied is greater, then the flow of the solvent takes place in the opposite direction and the process is called **reverse osmosis** (see Figure 1622).

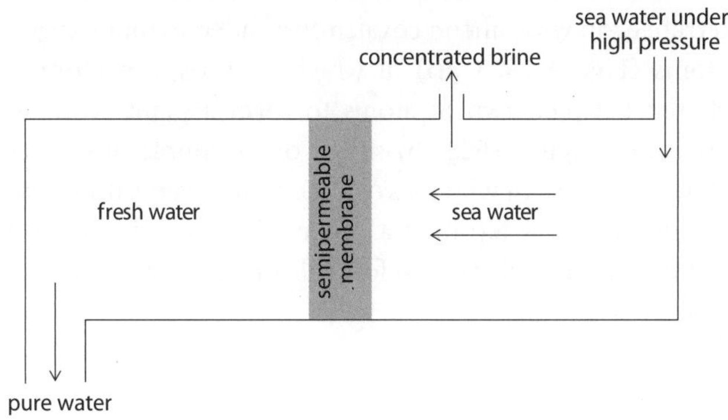

Figure 1622 Reverse Osmosis

Because reverse osmosis does not require a phase change as does distillation, it requires less energy. Energy is still however required to produce the pressure necessary for reverse osmosis, hence this process is still too expensive for many nations to use. The world's largest desalination reverse osmosis plant is in Saudi Arabia, producing about 50% of that nation's drinking water.

E7 SOIL

Over 80% of the Earth's crust is made of the elements oxygen, silicon and aluminium with smaller amounts (between 1 – 5% each) of calcium, iron, potassium, magnesium and sodium. Lesser amounts of other elements such as phosphorus and sulfur are also present. Soil, a vital part of the Earth, is a complex, heterogeneous mixture of interacting materials. It results from the weathering of rocks due to its breakdown by biological decay of organic matter by microbial action due to bacteria and fungi in the soil and by physical and chemical means. For example, chemical weathering of limestone, calcium carbonate, produces dissolved ions and the rate of reaction of weathering depends on the temperature and the surface area.

$$CaCO_3(s) + H_2O(l) + CO_2(g) \rightarrow Ca^{2+}(aq) + 2HCO_3^-(aq)$$

Soil consists of four components: inorganic matter (the largest component in soil due to weathering of rocks), water, air and smaller amounts of organic matter. The amount of air and water in the soil affects how life forms survive and decay after death. Bacteria and fungi convert the organic matter into a typically water insoluble mixture called humus containing about half its mass as carbon and about 5% nitrogen. As a result, soil composition varies tremendously depending on how and where it is formed and what life forms live in it. Inorganic matter contains mostly silica, silicates and aluminosilicates.

The structure of silica, silicon(IV) oxide, SiO_2, is a tetrahedron with silicon covalently bonded to four oxygen atoms (Figure 1623 (a)) in which each oxygen atom is shared between two Si atoms to form a giant covalent structure. Figure 1623 (b) shows one example of silicate chain structure in which two of the four oxygen atoms are bonded to other tetrahedra. Since Al^{3+} has a similar size to Si^{4+}, Al can replace Si to form aluminosilicate structure (Figure 1623 (c).

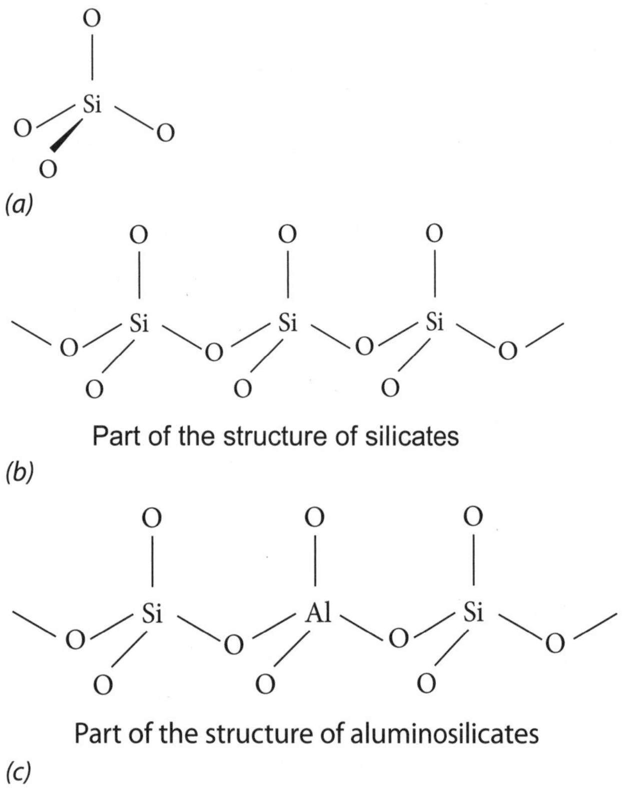

(a)

Part of the structure of silicates

(b)

Part of the structure of aluminosilicates

(c)

Figure 1623 (a), (b) and (c)

In the silica structure, SiO_2, if one in every four tetrahedrons contain Al^{3+} instead of Si^{4+}, then the structure will be short one electron, making it an anion with a one negative charge and an empirical formula $AlSi_3O_8^-$ instead of SiO_2. Similarly, if two in every four tetrahedrons contain Al^{3+} instead of Si^{4+}, then the structure will be short two electrons, making it an anion with two negative charges and an empirical formula $Al_2Si_2O_8^{2-}$ instead of SiO_2. The existence of these ions in inorganic matter and the presence of the highly electronegative oxygen explains its ability to hold on to plant nutrient cations such as K^+, NH_4^+, Ca^{2+}, Mg^{2+} and to form salts such as $NaAlSi_3O_8$ and $CaAl_2Si_2O_8$.

The soil food web is incredibly complex and is made of a great diversity of organisms from the simplest bacteria and algae to earthworms and plants. Some, like plants and algae, use the sun's energy to convert carbon dioxide to sugar. Others use the energy and nutrients. Soil sustains life. Nutrients found in soil that occur as dissolved ions, such as Ca^{2+}, K^+, NH_4^+ and Mg^{2+}, are absorbed through the roots and are essential for plant growth. Calcium is used in plant cell wall synthesis. Potassium controls the amount of water that enters via osmosis. Nitrogen is used in the synthesis of amino acids and thus proteins, and iron, nitrogen and magnesium are used in the synthesis of chlorophyll. Decaying plants replace nutrients. However, several factors such as acid deposition, water runoff from soil, pollution, pesticides and harvesting of crops change and deplete the amounts of essential soil nutrients. Soil management includes crop rotation and the addition of fertilizers to replenish plant nutrients.

E.7.1 Discuss salinization, nutrient depletion and soil pollution as causes of soil degradation.

SALINIZATION

Salinization is the accumulation of water soluble ions or salts in the soil due to continual irrigation to grow crops. Water for irrigation contains small amounts of dissolved salts such as calcium chloride ($CaCl_2$), magnesium sulfate ($MgSO_4$) and sodium chloride (NaCl). As the water is used by plants or evaporates due to high atmospheric temperature, and where salts are not washed away due to poor drainage or low rainfall, the salts accumulate over time, leading to salinization of the soil. Another major cause of salinization in some parts of the world (for example Australia) is the rise of the water table. This is caused in part by the removal of large native plants and a consequent reduction in evapo-transpiration. This in turn allows the soil water to get close enough to the surface to evaporate and in doing so increase the salt concentration on or near the surface.

Salinization reduces plant growth as the increased concentrations of ions reduce the ability of the roots to take up water. For example, the effect of sodium chloride on seed germination and plant growth can be easily studied in the laboratory by keeping all variables such as time, temperature, size of seeds, amount and type of soil, amount of water etc. constant and varying only the concentration of ions. This is due to the phenomenon of osmosis which is the movement of water from a region of low ion concentration in the roots to high ion concentration in the soil (to eventually reach infinite dilution). According to UN Food and Agricultural Organization article, *The salt of the earth: hazardous for food production,* "Irrigation produces much of the world's food, but about a tenth of the world's irrigated land has been damaged by salt. This has become a profound threat to food security."

Nutrient depletion or loss

This is the removal of essential nutrients and minerals from the soil food web by crops that grow and are continually harvested due to agricultural practices, and leads to soil degradation. **Nutrient depletion** or loss results in decreased soil quality and can lead to a serious decline in the yield of crops, thus affecting food supply. Replenishing the mineral nutrients and carrying out crop rotation so that the same nutrients are not used each time is important to improve soil quality. However, overuse of nitrate and phosphate fertilizers can lead to environmental pollution as the chemicals can end up in ground and surface water. This can lead to eutrophication, which is the excess growth of aquatic life such as algal blooms.

Soil pollution or contamination

This arises from the presence of man-made chemicals such as **pesticides** and **herbicides**. Pesticides provide better harvests by killing insect pests. Herbicides kill unwanted plants or weeds and fungi are controlled using **fungicides**. Pesticides can lead to lower crop yields by destroying very small flora and fauna, and similarly to fertilizers, they leach into ground water polluting it. Soil pollution also arises from the addition of nitrate and phosphate fertilizers to replenish the soil with nitrogen and phosphorus. Soil contamination is also caused by domestic and industrial waste added directly to soil or by wastes leached from land fill sites. These may contain heavy metals such as arsenic, chromium, copper, mercury, lead and zinc and organic contaminants such as polychlorobiphenyls (PCBs,) and polyaromatic hydrocarbons (PAHs). Similar to leaching of fertilizers, these poisonous chemicals can pollute ground water, affect water supplies and create health risks.

E.7.2 Describe the relevance of the soil organic matter (SOM) in preventing soil degradation and outline its physical and biological functions.

The term **soil organic matter** (SOM) refers to the mixture of non-living organic components present in the soil in various stages of decomposition arising from the chemical and biological action on plant matter and organisms. The amount of carbon in the organic constituents in the soil is a measure of the organic matter present; the organic carbon can be determined experimentally by titration with a dichromate(VI) solution. Soil organic matter includes humic substances, the organic matter converted into a mixture by bacteria and fungi, smaller molecules such as sugars and amino acids and high molecular mass polysaccharides and proteins.

Humic acids of different composition and molar masses containing the phenolic acid (ArOH) and carboxylic acid functional groups (RCOOH) are present in the soil organic matter. These are weak acids and dissociate partially:

$$RCOOH \rightleftharpoons RCOO^- + H^+$$

The anion $RCOO^-$ is able to chelate or bind to plant nutrients containing multivalent cations such as Ca^{2+}, Fe^{2+}, Mg^{2+}, as well a trace metal ions: Zn^{2+}, Mn^{2+}, Co^{3+}. The strength of the bond depends on the charge to size (charge density) of the hydrated ion: the higher the charge density, the stronger the binding, for example: $Al^{3+}(aq) > Mg^{2+}(aq) > K^+(aq)$.

Relevance of soil organic matter in preventing soil degradation

SOM plays an important role in soil quality, and thus in producing high crop yields, in a variety of ways. In deserts, for example, organic matter (called 'sweet soil' which stinks of organic fertilizer) added to sand can greatly improve plant growth. Soil organic matter contains a pool of mineral nutrients it can exchange with plant roots, it holds on to water, improves soil structure and reduces soil erosion. The functions of SOM are biological, physical and chemical and involve interactions between all three (see Section E.12.4 for chemical function):

Biological

Organic soil matter binds to many nutrients and is a substantial reservoir of the mineral nutrients nitrogen, phosphorus and sulfur that are made available to microbes and plants for growth. Nitrogen is used in the synthesis of proteins and chlorophyll. Phosphorus is used in the synthesis of enzymes and the storage of energy. Sulfur is used in the synthesis of some amino acids, the building blocks of proteins. Typically soil organic matter contains about 5% nitrogen. Bacteria and fungi decompose the organic matter and release the nutrients to the plant roots in the soil.

OPTION

Mineralization

This is the slow process by which organic matter containing nitrogen and phosphorus is broken down or mineralized to release nitrogen and phosphorus to roots. Thus a biological function of soil organic matter is to provide a source of mineral nutrients N, P and S. Soil/plant system resilience is maintained since plant residue contains nutrients that contribute to soil organic matter upon decomposition. Thus, SOM becomes a reservoir of nutrients that are stored in the soil and released to plants on an ongoing basis.

Physical

Soil clusters collect together in stable forms due to the presence of organic matter. This reduces soil erosion, and increases the ability of air and water to move through the soil. As a result, like a sponge, soil organic matter can absorb several times its mass of water and thus influences soil's water retention property. It also improves soil structure since the porous soil makes it possible for roots to spread through the soil.

Organic matter also affects soil thermal properties by influencing soil temperature. Thermal properties are related to soil temperature and the transfer of heat through the soil. Moist soil has higher heat capacity than dry soil due to the higher heat capacity of water. Thus, soil with higher water content (and thus higher thermal capacity) experiences smaller temperature changes. Recall:

Heat absorbed, $Q = mc\Delta T$

If c, the heat capacity is large then, for the amount of heat absorbed, the change in temperature, ΔT will be small. For dry soil, the heat capacity is smaller and for the same heat absorbed, the change in temperature will be larger.

E.7.3 List common soil pollutants and their sources.

We live in a world where the population and the demand for petroleum products continue to increase at an alarming rate and there is wide spread use of chemicals for

Common Organic Soil Pollutants	Sources
Petroleum hydrocarbons	Discharges and accidents from petroleum industry from oil fields, tankers, pipelines, refining plants
Agrichemicals including fertilizers and pesticides containing organochlorine compounds	Agriculture: over-application of fertilizers, use of pesticides which leach into ground; chlorine-organic pesticides with long half lives remain in the soil for many years
Volatile organic compounds (VOCs): these include ethylene glycol (ethan-1,2-diol), methylbenzene, methanal	Household products, fuels from gasoline, cleaning and degreasing products, chemicals from copiers and printers, glues, markers, paints
Solvents such as hexane, methyl benzene, acetone, dimethyl sulfoxide (DMSO), ethanol, 2-propanol, 1-butanol	Dry cleaning, electronics industry, manufacture of paints
Polyaromatic hydrocarbons (PAHs) such as benzo(α)pyrene (a carcinogen)	Tar, coal, crude oil spills, incomplete combustion of wood, vegetation, waste incineration, industrial emission and waste
Polychlorinated biphenyls (PCBs)	Incinerator stacks, leaks from enclosed electrical equipment (where PCBs were used as insulating fluids), leaks from hydraulic fluids
Organotin compounds, for example, triphenyl tin (TPhT)	PVCs (where alkyl tin compounds are used as stabilizers), ship paints which are used as biocidal agents as an antifoulant coating to hulls of ships below the water line, stopping plants and marine life forms attaching to the hull
Semi-volatile organic compounds (SVOCs), those with boiling points greater than 200°C such as PCBs, PAHs	From pesticides and fungicides in agriculture and chemicals used in preserving wood, propellants, fuels

Figure 1624 Common organic soil pollutants and their sources

industry and agriculture. Waste in landfill sites and sludge from treatment plants continue to pollute the earth but often there is a lack of laws and regulations to minimize pollution and protect health, (see Figure 1624).

E8 WASTE

According to the World Wildlife Fund's 2006 *Living Planet Report*, we are now turning resources into waste at a pace 25% faster than the Earth can turn waste back into resources, with first world countries having a considerably larger 'ecological footprint' than poor ones. A combination of population increase and rise in the standard of living has led to an increase in mining, biological waste containing high organic biodegradable waste, medical waste from hospitals and veterinary practices, nuclear waste, fly ash from power plants, industrial and municipal waste amongst others. Excessive use of plastics, packaging and non-recyclable materials adds to the problem. Recyclable materials such as paper, glass, and metals are dumped into garbage, further complicating the waste problem.

E.8.1 Outline and compare the various methods for waste disposal.

Methods of waste disposal include landfill sites, incineration, large scale composting, recycling and the burial of radioactive wastes, (see Figure 1625).

E.8.2 Describe the recycling of metal, glass, plastic and paper products and outline its benefits.

See Figure 1626 on the next page.

E.8.3 Describe the characteristics and sources of different types of radioactive waste.

The French physicist Henri Becquerel (1896) accidentally discovered **radioactivity** which is the ability of some isotopes to undergo reactions involving nuclear change or transformation. There are three common types of radioactive emissions, as follows.

Alpha particles are positively charged helium nuclei, ${}^{4}_{2}He$, that have low penetrating power (a few centimeters of air) and can be stopped by clothing, paper or skin.

Beta particles or β-rays are a stream of electrons that are negatively charged that have moderator penetrating power (about a hundred times the penetrating power of alpha particles). They can penetrate a few meters of air and can be stopped by 1 mm thick aluminium foil.

Gamma rays are high energy electromagnetic radiation that have high penetrating power (about 100 times the penetrating power beta particles). They can penetrate a few kilometers of air and several centimeters of lead but can be stopped by about 10 cm of lead or several meters of concrete.

	Landfill sites	Incineration
Waste	Waste volume is increasing whereas availability of landfill sites is decreasing and are often at capacity; takes up precious land space; leaves ugly, smelly sites.	On incineration, reduces volume; slag produced sent to landfill sites, but can also be used in building roads and in construction industry.
Costs	Involves transportation costs as landfill sites tend to be away from cities and towns (for years, Toronto waste was transported to Michigan for disposal).	Involves transportation costs as incinerator sites tend to be away from cities and towns. Uses energy in running incinerator plants; however, the energy produced from the combustion of the waste in a closed-loop process can be used to reduce energy costs.
Pollution	Source of underground water and soil pollution due to leaching which can be reduced by lining the landfill site. Anaerobic decomposition of organic waste releases methane, CH_4, a greenhouse gas; also produces toxic substances such as ammonia, hydrogen sulfide, etc. Medical waste has to be sterilized before being disposed of in landfill sites.	Emission of pollutants on burning plastics release dioxins into the environment. Incineration destroys disease causing microorganisms.

Figure 1625 Comparison of landfill sites and incineration

OPTION

	Recycling process	Benefits
Metals	Involves collecting and separating these out into ferrous and non-ferrous metals (e.g., Al cans from steel and tin cans which are iron cans coated with tin; tin cans are de-tinned and the tin sold). The metal products are cut up and powerful magnets used to separate ferrous metals from the mixture. In the non-ferrous mixture, the lighter aluminium is separated from other high density metals by flotation.	Recycling metals conserves natural resources (the raw materials) Reduces energy, water and landfill usage: recycling Al uses about 95% less energy and steel uses about 50% less energy Less energy use means less greenhouse gases released Aluminium and steel are the most recycled metals, and can be recycled over and over again.
Glass	Glass is separated by colour, namely: colourless, amber and green (coloured glass maintains its colour permanently). However, glass mirrors, window panes, light bulbs are made of different compositions and often are not recyclable; glass containers for food and drinks are of similar composition and are recyclable. Crushed waste glass called 'cullet' is exposed to a magnet to remove any ferrous metals and to a vacuum to remove paper and plastic. It is then mixed with raw materials (sand, limestone and soda ash) and melted at 1200°C. The glass formed is moulded or blown into new products such as bottles, jars and tiles.	Saves raw materials and mining wastes Takes about one-third less energy compared to virgin glass from raw materials Uses about half the water compared to virgin glass Reduces use of landfill sites Glass cullet can be used in highway construction and landscaping Glass can be recycled over and over again.
Plastics	Plastics have different properties due to their different compositions (for example, polyethene versus polystyrene) and are thus difficult and expensive to separate and recycle. The numbering system used in some countries facilitates separation and recycling of similar plastics. Low density polyethylene (LDPE) or polypropylene (PP) plastics used for packaging bakery and food products and polystyrene (PS) plastics are typically not recyclable. However, plastics made of polyethylene terephthalate (PET) and high density polyethylene (HDPE) include many dairy product containers, juice and household containers can be recycled by melting these and re-moulding into new shapes.	Recycling plastics saves landfill sites as it occupies a great deal of space and reduces the need for more incinerators Uses less petrochemical raw materials Uses less energy and water compared to virgin plastics Recycled PET has many uses including fibre for pillows, jackets, automobile seats and insulation material.
Paper products	Waste paper has to be separated as paper coated with wax or plastic cannot be recycled. Paper is chopped and mixed with water and chemicals such as clay as filler, calcium oxide (CaO, lime) and $CaCO_3$ and heated for alkaline pulping. This breaks the paper into fibres (small pieces of cellulose) and produces pulp (a soggy mixture). Spinning the pulp in cylinders removes heavy objects like paper clips and staples. Ink is removed from pulp by washing with water. Surfactant chemicals are added to remove ink and glue from the pulp. Other chemicals remove colours (dyes). Often fresh pulp is added and if it is not treated to remove lignin, the glue in wood that holds fiber together, the paper turns yellow with time when exposed to light as is the case with paper used to make newspapers. Hydrogen peroxide, H_2O_2 or chlorine dioxide, ClO_2 is typically used to bleach paper to produce white recycled paper.	Recycled paper uses about half the energy and water used to produce virgin paper Reduces the number of trees that have to be cut down and preserves forests Saving forests means less greenhouse gas, carbon dioxide is reduced and forests provide habitat for wildlife Extends the life of landfill sites However, paper cannot be recycled over and over again as the fibre loses strength on recycling Economic benefit: all recycling produces jobs

Figure 1626 Recycling processes and its benefits

Half-life, $t_{½}$ of a radioactive substance is the time required for one-half of the amount of radioactive material to decay; it is independent of the amount of the radioactive sample present and follows first order kinetics, namely an exponential decay. Each radioisotope has its own characteristic half-life which can range from 10^{-7} seconds ($^{212}_{84}Po$ has $t_{½} = 3 \times 10^{-7}$ s) to a few billion years ($^{238}_{92}U$ has $t_{½} = 4.5 \times 10^{9}$ years). Pu-239, a product of nuclear reactions and a highly toxic substance has $t_{½} = 24\,000$ years.

If one starts with 100 g of Pu-239 at time zero, then after one half-life (24 000 years), 50 g of the original isotope will remain as half will have been converted to decay products.

After two half-lives, the mass remaining will be $\frac{100}{2^2} = 25$ g.

After seven half-lives (= 7 × 24 000 = 168 000 years), the amount remaining will be ≈ 0.8 g. Thus, the Pu-239 produced in nuclear power plants as a waste product will last for tens of thousands of years before it decays to less than 1% of its present amount.

E.8.4 Compare the storage and disposal methods for different types of radioactive waste.

Radioactive waste storage and disposal depends on the amount and type of activity it produces and the half-life of the radioisotopes involved, (see Figure 1627).

Low level radioactive waste decreases to background radiation within 500 years with about 90% of it decreasing to general levels within 100 years. This waste can be compacted to reduce volume and buried in shallow lined, land-burial trenches. Together with intermediate level nuclear waste, they can also be stored in steel containers in concrete vaults below ground. Combustible dry low-level waste can be incinerated with regulations on how much radiation can be released into the environment. Dumping into landfill sites or diluting by dumping into the sea are generally banned. Caesium and strontium, products of fission are low-level nuclear wastes; these can be removed by the use of ion-exchange resins.

High-level waste comprises a small volume of all nuclear waste but contains most of the radioactivity. Spent fuel is temporarily stored in pools of water to absorb the heat produced by high level radioactivity. Long term storage of high-level nuclear waste seems most problematic. One method used is to contain it securely by making liquid waste into glass (vitrifying it) followed by burial deep underground in geologically stable (earthquake free), non-leachable environments such as granite rock, or used salt mines. The containers are meant to be non-corrosive (to decrease the possibility of leaching by water) and kept intact for hundreds of thousands of years for the radioactivity to decrease to background levels.

HIGHER LEVEL

E9 OZONE DEPLETION (HL)

E.9.1 Explain the dependence of O_2 and O_3 dissociation on the wavelength of light.

Diatomic oxygen, O_2, and ozone (triatomic oxygen), O_3, are allotropes. An oxygen molecule has a double bond between the oxygen atoms (bond order of two).

$$\ddot{\underset{..}{O}}=\ddot{\underset{..}{O}}$$

Type of radioactive waste	Characteristics of radioactive waste	Sources of radioactive waste
Low-level waste (> 90% of the volume of nuclear waste but contains only about 1% of the radioactivity).	Contain small amounts of radioisotopes producing low activity alpha and low-energy beta particles of short half-lives; thus radioactivity is low.	Include clothes, gloves, paper, plastic and glass products from nuclear fuel cycle, hospitals and nuclear research facilities; radioisotopes from industry monitoring thickness of paper, plastics.
Medium or intermediate-level waste.	Contain greater amounts of radioisotopes with intermediate activity and generally of intermediate half-lives.	Mostly from nuclear reactor parts and processing nuclear fuel.
High-level waste (occupies a small volume of nuclear waste but contains most of the radioactivity).	Contain large amounts of radioisotopes of high activity due to high energy beta and gamma rays with generally long half-lives that remain radioactive for long periods.	Mostly from spent fuel rods and processing of spent nuclear fuel.

Figure 1627 Characteristics and sources of radioactive wastes

Ozone, on the other hand is triatomic and can be represented by two resonance structures (bond order of one and a half) (see Figure 1628):

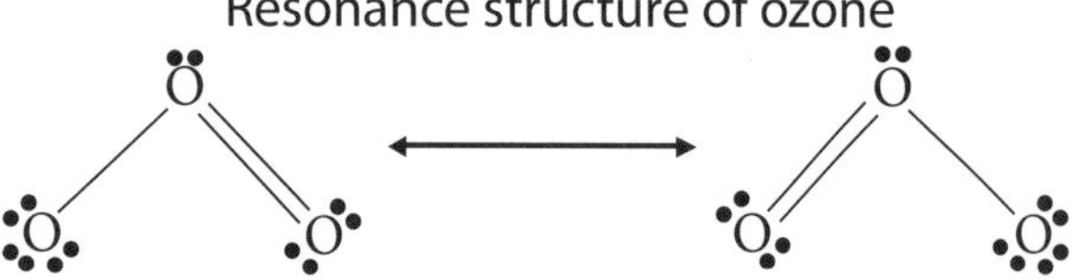

Figure 1628 The resonance structure of ozone

The double bond in the oxygen molecule results in a stronger bond compared with ozone. To dissociate an oxygen molecule, therefore, requires greater energy than to dissociate an ozone molecule. Since the wavelength of light is inversely proportional to its energy, the stronger double bond in the oxygen molecule requires radiation of lower wavelength (242 nm or less) compared with the dissociation of ozone which requires higher wavelength (330 nm or less). Thus, ozone absorbs harmful uv rays in the range 240 to 330 nm that oxygen does not absorb.

E.9.2 Describe the mechanism in the catalysis of O_3 depletion by CFCs and NO_x.

Chlorofluorocarbons (CFCs) are stable compounds with a variety of uses such as in refrigeration and as propellants in aerosol sprays. In the upper atmosphere, uv light is able to break the weaker C–Cl bonds by homolysis to produce chlorine free radicals, this is the initiation step.

$$CCl_2F_2 + h\nu \rightarrow \bullet CClF_2 + \bullet Cl$$

The chlorine free radicals can react with ozone to produce oxygen molecules and •ClO (this is the propagating step where one free radical is used up and another is formed in its place):

$$\bullet Cl + O_3 \rightarrow ClO\bullet + O_2$$

The newly formed free radical •ClO can also react with an oxygen free radical to form a diatomic oxygen molecule and regenerate the chlorine free radical (termination step):

$$ClO\bullet + O\bullet \rightarrow O_2 + Cl\bullet$$

These two steps combined, remove both ozone and atomic oxygen in the upper atmosphere by converting them to diatomic oxygen. In the process a chlorine free radical is reformed, that is, it effectively catalyses the conversion of ozone and atomic oxygen to oxygen gas:

$$O_3\,(g) + O\,(g) \xrightarrow{\bullet Cl} 2\,O_2\,(g)$$

Similarly, nitrogen monoxide, NO, formed by the high temperature reaction between nitrogen and oxygen gases in supersonic aircraft engines, reacts with ozone, reducing its concentration:

$$NO + O_3 \rightarrow NO_2 + O_2$$

The nitrogen dioxide formed can react with an oxygen free radical:

$$NO_2 + O \rightarrow NO + O_2$$

The net result of the presence of nitrogen monoxide is the depletion of ozone:

$$O_3 + O \rightarrow 2O_2$$

Any NO_2 formed either by this reaction or by oxidation with O_2 also undergoes photo-dissociation in the presence of uv light to promote other photochemical reactions:

$$NO_2\,(g) + h\nu \rightarrow NO\,(g) + O\bullet\,(g)$$

E.9.3 Outline the reasons for greater ozone depletion in polar regions.

Data shows a decrease in ozone concentrations in Antarctica in the 1980s and 1990s compared with earlier data. This was caused by increased ozone depleting pollutants. Data also indicates that the ozone concentrations over Antarctica show a seasonal variation with a greater depletion around October during the polar spring producing the ozone hole. A return to more normal concentrations occurs in November as the spring progresses.

The ozone hole can be explained by the fact that during the South Pole winter from June to September, the temperatures are frigid, trapping very cold air at the pole and immediately converting any water vapor present into ice crystals. These ice particles behave as surface catalysts and provide the surface area over which pollutants present in the polar atmosphere combine to produce reactive chemicals such as chlorine molecules. After the long, cold winter darkness, when the sun comes out in October, the photo-dissociation of chlorine molecules takes place in the presence of ultra violet light from the sun's rays. This produces chlorine free radicals which catalyze the destruction of ozone over Antarctica to produce the ozone hole.

$$Cl_2 (g) + \text{uv light} \rightarrow 2 \bullet Cl (g)$$

$$\bullet Cl (g) + O_3 (g) \rightarrow \bullet ClO (g) + O_2 (g)$$

$$\bullet ClO (g) + O (g) \rightarrow O_2 (g) + \bullet Cl_{(g)}$$

$$O_3 (g) + O (g) \rightarrow 2 O_2(g)$$

As the spring progresses in Antarctica, the ice crystals in the stratosphere melt and are no longer available as surface catalysts for the production of chlorine molecules. This, combined with the flow of air containing ozone from the lower altitude warmer regions, replaces the destroyed ozone and by November the ozone concentration increases. Similar, but not as drastic ozone depletion, has also been observed over the North Pole during the Arctic spring. The temperatures around the North Pole do not go down to the same extremes as those at the South Pole (down to –90°C) and the air with the ozone from lower altitudes is better able to diffuse, reducing the overall effect on the ozone layer.

E10 SMOG (HL)

Smog, a term coined from the words 'smoke' and 'fog' arose from the conditions of coal smoke and fog experienced by the city of London in the early part of the 19th Century. The so-called 'London smog', also known as industrial or reducing smog is one of two types of smog. It is caused by the combustion of sulfur containing coal used for heating, manufacturing processes and the generation of electricity. It consists of water droplets, sulfur dioxide and trioxide, soot and ash (particulate matter) and sulfuric acid.

The reducing smog can be found in coal burning cities such as Chicago and Beijing which can experience cool or cold, wet winters and where thermal inversion can trap cold, still air close to the Earth's surface. As a result of increased pollution controls, bans on the use of coal as a domestic fuel, and measures such as the use of alkaline scrubbers which remove SO_x and particulates pollution, severe episodes of industrial smog are on the decline.

> E.10.1 State the source of primary pollutants and the conditions necessary for the formation of photochemical smog.
>
>

The other type of smog, called **photochemical smog** is an oxidizing smog. This is a chemical soup containing hundreds of different substances formed in the atmosphere as a result of free radical reactions brought about by ultraviolet radiation from the sun (thus called photochemical smog). It was first observed in Los Angeles in the 1940s. Automobile pollution is the main source of this type of smog and unlike industrial smog it is almost free of sulfur dioxide.

The main sources of primary pollutants for photochemical smog are volatile organic chemicals (VOCs) and nitrogen oxides (NO_x), especially nitrogen monoxide, NO from automobile exhaust and the furnaces of power plants. The main condition that promotes photochemical smog is the ultraviolet radiation from sunlight. Temperature or thermal inversion, windlessness and bowl-shaped cities such as Mexico City allow the collection of pollutants which are not dispersed and worsen the smog.

Under normal conditions, there is a gradual decrease in the temperature as the altitude increases. The warmer, less dense air near the Earth's surface, warmed by the earth, rises. At the same time, pollutants produced near the surface of the Earth move with the warm air to the upper atmosphere. Cooler air takes the place of the rising warmer air near the Earth's surface, warms up and rises, in turn creating air currents which allow the pollutants produced to be dispersed. **Thermal inversion** (also called temperature inversion) is the abnormal temperature arrangement of air masses where a layer of warmer air is trapped between two layers of colder air (Figure 1629).

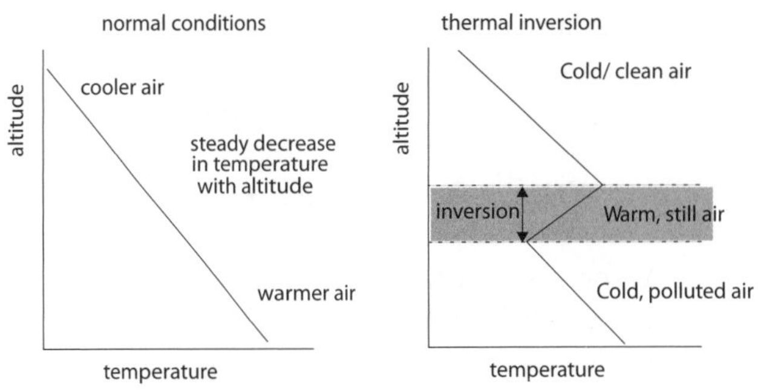

Figure 1629 Thermal inversion

Prevailing winds give rise to the horizontal movement of air. However, surrounding hills, mountains or valleys in places such as Mexico City and Los Angeles hinder the horizontal movement of air. The flow of cold air from the surrounding hills and mountains into these cities creates the cool lower layer. Under windless conditions, pollutants can collect over a city without being dispersed. This creates a situation where warm air on top stays over a polluted air mass and the cooler, more dense, air stays near the earth, stopping vertical movement. The warm air mass effectively acts as a lid, trapping polluted air close to the ground. The warm, dry, cloudless conditions of thermal inversion are ideal for the formation of photochemical smog as any ultraviolet light from the sun's rays is easily able to reach the Earth.

E.10.2 Outline the formation of secondary pollutants in photochemical smog.

Research has clearly identified the role of sunlight in initiating photochemical smog in which particulates and unburnt volatile organic chemicals (VOCs) act as catalysts and reactants in the formation of secondary pollutants. It is found that photochemical smog follows a general, daily, cyclic pattern:

1. The release of VOCs, nitrogen oxides and particularly nitrogen monoxide, NO, as primary pollutants from the combustion of fossil fuels at high temperature in internal combustion engines and in the furnaces of power plants, cause smog. The automobile is the main source; nitrogen monoxide, along with volatile organic chemicals and particulates peaks during morning rush hours:

   $N_2(g) + O_2(g) \rightarrow 2\,NO_{(g)}$; primary pollutant

2. With the increase in the concentration of nitrogen monoxide, it is oxidized to brown nitrogen dioxide gas either by oxygen or primarily by ozone:

   $$2\,NO(g) + O_2(g) \rightarrow 2\,NO_2(g)$$

   $$NO(g) + O_3(g) \rightarrow NO_2(g) + O_2(g)$$

3. As soon as solar radiation is available in the morning, photo-dissociation of the nitrogen dioxide takes place to produce oxygen atoms:

   $$NO_2(g) + \text{uv light} \rightarrow NO(g) + \bullet O(g)$$

   The atomic oxygen formed is a highly reactive species containing unpaired electrons and is called a free radical.

4. The oxygen free radicals initiate a series of important reactions to produce secondary pollutants such as ozone and hydroxyl free radicals, ·OH:

   $$O\bullet + O_2 \rightarrow O_3$$

   $$O\bullet + H_2O \rightarrow 2\,\bullet OH$$

   Ozone and hydroxyl free radical levels therefore peak later in the day. These are photochemical oxidants capable of oxidizing other substances not easily oxidized by diatomic oxygen under atmospheric conditions. For example:

   The hydroxyl free radical reacts with nitrogen dioxide to produce nitric acid:

   $$\bullet OH + NO_2 \rightarrow HNO_3$$

5. The photochemical oxidants carry out the oxidation of VOCs to produce a wide variety of secondary pollutants including aldehydes (RCHO) and toxic substances such as peroxyacyl nitrates, PANs, which are powerful lachrymators (cause eyes to water). These then disperse in the atmosphere reaching a maximum concentration in the afternoon. A sequence of reactions involving free radicals leading to the formation of PAN can be shown as follows:

   Propagation of free radicals takes place where one radical is used up but another formed:

   $$RH + \bullet OH \rightarrow R\bullet + H_2O$$

   $R\bullet + O_2 \rightarrow ROO\bullet$, peroxide free radical.

   Termination of free radicals takes place when two free radicals combine:

   $$ROO\bullet + \bullet NO_2 \rightarrow ROONO_2$$

   A specific example is the formation of PAN:

$$R-C(=O)-O-O + NO_2 \rightarrow R-C(=O)-O-O-NO_2$$

Figure 1630 The formation of peroxyacyl nitrates

OPTION

E11 ACID DEPOSITION (HL)

E11.1 Describe the mechanism of acid deposition caused by the oxides of nitrogen and oxides of sulfur.

Oxides of nitrogen include nitrogen monoxide, NO and nitrogen dioxide, NO_2. Photo-dissociation of NO_2 in the presence of sunlight produces oxygen free radicals:

$$NO_2 + \text{uv light} \rightarrow NO + \bullet O$$

The oxygen free radicals initiate a series of important reactions to produce secondary pollutants such as ozone and hydroxyl free radicals, •OH, the later being a propagation step, where one free radical, O• is replaced by another, •OH:

$$O\bullet + O_2 \rightarrow O_3$$

$$O\bullet + H_2O \rightarrow 2\ \bullet OH$$

The ozone formed can also react with water to form the hydroxyl free radicals:

$$H_2O + O_3 \rightarrow 2\ \bullet OH + O_2$$

The hydroxyl free radicals react with nitrogen monoxide and nitrogen dioxide to produce nitrous acid and nitric acid respectively:

$$\bullet OH + NO \rightarrow HNO_2$$

$$\bullet OH + NO_2 \rightarrow HNO_3$$

Sulfur dioxide is a primary pollutant produced from the combustion of sulfur containing coal. The hydroxyl free radicals react with sulfur dioxide to produce $HSO_3\bullet$ ($HOSO_2\bullet$):

$$HO\bullet + SO_2 \rightarrow HOSO_2\bullet$$

Another propagation step leads to the formation of sulfur trioxide, the anhydride of sulfuric acid. SO_3 reacts rapidly with moisture present in the air to produce sulfuric acid, a strong acid:

$$HOSO_2\bullet + O_2 \rightarrow HO_2\bullet + SO_3$$

$$SO_3 + H_2O \rightarrow H_2SO_4$$

E11.2 Explain the role of ammonia in acid deposition.

Ammonia, NH_3 contains a lone electron pair on the nitrogen, is able to accept a proton and is a weak base:

$$NH_3 + H^+ \rightleftharpoons NH_4^+$$

In the atmosphere, sulfuric acid and nitric acid formed as acid deposition pollutants can be neutralized by ammonia to form ammonium salts, ammonium sulfate, $(NH_4)_2SO_4$ and ammonium nitrate, NH_4NO_3:

$$2\ NH_3 + H_2SO_4 \rightarrow (NH_4)_2SO_4$$

$$NH_3 + HNO_3 \rightarrow NH_4NO_3$$

Both $(NH_4)_2SO_4$ and NH_4NO_3 are salts of a weak base and a strong acid; the conjugate acid of the weak base, NH_4^+ is therefore weakly acidic whereas both anions SO_4^{2-} and NO_3^- are neutral, making the salts weakly acidic in aqueous solution:

$$NH_4^+ + H_2O \rightleftharpoons NH_3 + H_3O^+$$

The weakly acidic salts formed in the atmosphere fall to the ground or are removed from the atmosphere by rain and enter the soil as NH_4^+. Plants use nitrogen as nitrates, NO_3^- with its highest oxidation of +5. Thus, the ammonium ion with an oxidation number of –3 must be oxidized to +5. This process is called **nitrification** and is catalyzed by bacteria. The overall reaction is:

$$NH_4^+ + 2O_2 \rightarrow 2H^+ + NO_3^- + H_2O$$

The process also makes the soil more acidic with the formation of H^+.

E12 WATER AND SOIL (HL)

E.12.1 Solve problems relating to the removal of heavy-metal ions and phosphates and nitrates from water by chemical precipitation.

Many metal ions form sparingly or slightly soluble salts. Chemical precipitation of such salts is a major method of removing heavy-metal ions and phosphates. For example, hydrogen sulfide, H_2S or soluble sulfides such as sodium sulfide, Na_2S, can be used to remove ions of heavy metals such as mercury, cadmium, lead and zinc by chemical precipitation:

$$Hg^{2+}\,(aq) + S^{2-}\,(aq) \rightarrow HgS\,(s)$$

Similarly, heavy metal ions such as copper, cobalt and iron can be removed as hydroxides from water sewage and soil by chemical precipitation:

$$Cu^{2+}\,(aq) + 2\,OH^{-}\,(aq) \rightarrow Cu(OH)_2\,(s)$$

The following general solubility rules help explain the concept of using chemical precipitation for the removal of heavy-metal ions and phosphates from water and soil:

1. All carbonates, CO_3^{2-} and phosphates, PO_4^{3-} except those of Li^+, Na^+, K^+ and NH_4^+ are insoluble.
2. All sulfides, S^{2-} except those of Groups I, II and NH_4^+ are insoluble.
3. All hydroxides and oxides except alkali metals are insoluble (those of Sr^{2+}, Ca^{2+} and Ba^{2+} are sparingly soluble).
4. All Cl^-, Br^- and I^- salts are water soluble except those of Ag^+, Hg_2^{2+} and Pb^{2+}.
5. All sulfates are water soluble except those of Ba^{2+}, Ca^{2+}, Pb^{2+} and Sr^{2+}.
6. Most nitrate (NO^{3-}) salts are water soluble.
7. Most salts of Na^+, K^+, and NH^{4+} are water soluble

Quantitative aspects of solubility equilibria

Barium ions in water can be precipitated out by adding sulfate ions. The resulting barium sulfate is only slightly soluble in water and establishes the following equilibrium:

$$BaSO_4(s) \rightleftarrows Ba^{2+}(aq) + SO_4^{2-}(aq)$$

The equilibrium constant expression for such a precipitation reaction is given by :

$$K_{sp} = [Ba^{2+}][\,SO_4^{2-}]\ (= 1.0 \times 10^{-10}\ mol^2\ dm^{-6}\ at\ 25°C)$$

K_{sp} is called the **solubility product constant** (note the concentration of solid does not appear because it is also a constant) and, because K_{sp} is temperature dependent, the particular temperature at which it is measured must be quoted. Thus, in a saturated solution of a slightly soluble ionic compound, the product of the concentrations of the individual ions raised to the powers indicated by the coefficients is a constant at a given temperature. Precipitation depends on K_{sp}; a precipitate will form if the product of the ions in the mixture of solutions, when substituted into the K_{sp} expression, exceeds the numerical value of K_{sp} at that temperature.

The value of the solubility product is related to the solubility of the salt and the solubility can be calculated given the value of K_{sp}:

For example, if the solubility is x mol dm^{-3}, in the case of, $BaSO_4$, where one Ba^{2+} is produced for each SO_4^{2-}:

$$BaSO_4(s) \rightleftarrows Ba^{2+}(aq) + SO_4^{2-}(aq)$$

$$K_{sp} = [Ba^{2+}][\,SO_4^{2-}] = x^2 = 1.0 \times 10^{-10}\ (mol^2\ dm^{-6})$$

$$x = 1.0 \times 10^{-5}\ mol\ dm^{-3}$$

Consider the solubility of $BaSO_4$ in a 0.10 mol dm^{-3} sodium sulfate, $Na_2\,SO_4$, a strong electrolyte that is fully dissociated in solution. If the solubility of $BaSO_4$ in solution is now y mol dm^{-3}, we can calculate this value as follows:

$$BaSO_4(s) \rightleftarrows Ba^{2+}(aq) + SO_4^{2-}(aq)$$

$$y + 0.10 \approx 0.10\ (since\ y << 0.10)$$

$$K_{sp} = [Ba^{2+}][\,SO_4^{2-}] = y \times 0.10 = 1.0 \times 10^{-10}$$

$$y = 1.0 \times 10^{-9}\ mol\ dm^{-3}\ (and:\ y + 0.10 \approx 0.10\ is\ correct)$$

OPTION

Thus, in pure water, $BaSO_4$ has a solubility of 1.0×10^{-5} mol dm^{-3} whereas in the presence of a common ion, the solubility is reduced by 10^4 to 1.0×10^{-9} mol dm^{-3}. This is called the common ion effect, a qualitative aspect of solubility equilibria. If a salt containing one of the ions is added, stress is placed on the system. The equilibrium is disturbed and the reverse reaction is favoured according to **Le Chatelier's principle,** to use up some of the ions added. More precipitate is formed and its solubility decreases in the presence of a common ion, as illustrated in the $BaSO_4$ example above. Thus, the solubility of a solid is always lower in a solution of a salt containing any common ions. Refer to Figure 1632 for some common K_{sp} values.

$CaSO_4$: 3.2×10^{-4}	$Mg(OH)_2$: 1.2×10^{-11}	FeS: 5.0×10^{-18}
$CaCO_3$: 4.8×10^{-9}	$Ca(OH)_2$: 2.5×10^{-16}	HgS: 1.0×10^{-26}

Figure 1632 Some K_{sp} values

Application of precipitation in water and soil chemistry

Sludge and hard water contain calcium ions, $Ca^{2+}(aq)$, which can be precipitated out as calcium sulfate by adding sodium sulfate. The net ionic equation for the precipitation reaction is as follows:

$$Ca^{2+}(aq) + SO_4^{2-}(aq) \rightleftarrows CaSO_4(s);$$
$$K_{sp}(CaSO_4) = 3.0 \times 10^{-5} \text{ mol}^2 \text{ dm}^{-6} \text{ at } 25°C$$

Lead ions, Pb^{2+} can be precipitated out as lead chloride by adding sodium chloride or as lead sulfate by adding sodium sulfate:

$$Pb^{2+}(aq) + 2\,Cl^-(aq) \rightleftarrows PbCl_2(s);$$
$$K_{sp}(PbCl_2) = 1.73 \times 10^{-7} \text{ mol}^3 \text{ dm}^{-9} \text{ at } 25°C$$

$$Pb^{2+}(aq) + SO_4^{2-}(aq) \rightleftarrows PbSO_4(s);$$
$$K_{sp}(PbSO_4) = 6.3 \times 10^{-7} \text{ mol}^2 \text{ dm}^{-6} \text{ at } 25°C$$

Phosphate ions form a precipitate with iron or aluminium oxide or with calcium ions :

$$Ca^{2+}(aq) + PO_4^{3-}(aq) \rightarrow Ca_3(PO_4)_2(s)$$

Metal salts such as aluminium nitrate, iron(III) chloride or iron(III) sulfate can be used to remove arsenic (as arsenate) and phosphate from water by chemical precipitation:

$$Al^{3+}(aq) + AsO_4^{3-}(aq) \rightleftarrows AlAsO_4(s)$$

$$Fe^{3+}(aq) + PO_4^{3-}(aq) \rightleftarrows FePO_4(s)$$

The very low solubility of heavy metal sulfides can be used to remove Cd, Hg, Pb, Zn from water and soil:

$$Pb^{2+}(aq) + S^{2-}(aq) \rightleftarrows PbS(s)$$

Example 1

1. Write the solubility product constant expression for the following compounds and indicate K_{sp} value in terms of x, if x is its molar solubility:

(a) AgCl (b) $PbCl_2$ (c) As_2S_3 (d) $Ca_3(PO_4)_2$ (e) $Fe(OH)_3$

Solution

(a) $AgCl(s) \rightleftarrows Ag^+(aq) + Cl^-(aq)$; x, x

$K_{sp} = [Ag^+][Cl^-] = x^2$

(b) $PbCl_2(s) \rightleftarrows Pb^{2+}(aq) + 2\,Cl^-(aq)$; x, $2x$

$K_{sp} = [Pb^{2+}][Cl^-]^2 = x(2x)^2 = 4x^3$ (note that $[Cl^-] = 2x$)

(c) $As_2S_3(s) \rightleftarrows 2\,As^{3+}(aq) + 3\,S^{2-}(aq)$; $2x$, $3x$

$K_{sp} = [As^{3+}]^2[S^{2-}]^3 = (2x)^2(3x)^3 = 108x^5$

(d) $Ca_3(PO_4)_2(s) \rightleftarrows 3\,Ca^{2+}(aq) + 2\,PO_4^{3-}(aq)$; $3x$, $2x$

$K_{sp} = [Ca^{2+}]^2[PO_4^{3-}]^3 = (3x)^3(2x)^2 = 108x^5$

(e) $Fe(OH)_3(s) \rightleftarrows Fe^{3+}(aq) + 3\,OH^-(aq)$; x, $3x$

$K_{sp} = [Fe^{3+}][OH^-]^3 = x(3x)^3 = 27x^4$

Example 2

2. (a) Calcium ions present in hard water are precipitated by adding sulfate ions. Write the net ionic equation for the reaction.

OPTION

(b) Given K_{sp} $(CaSO_4) = 3.0 \times 10^{-5}$ mol^2 dm^{-6} at 25°C, calculate its molar solubility in water at 25°C.

(c) Determine if a precipitate will form when the ion concentrations are: $[Ca^{2+}] = 1.0 \times 10^{-3}$ mol dm^{-3} and $[SO_4^{2-}] = 1.0 \times 10^{-2}$ mol dm^{-3}.

(d) Calculate the minimum concentration of sulfate ion required in (c) to precipitate the Ca^{2+}.

Solution

(a) Ca^{2+} (aq) + SO_4^{2-} (aq) → $CaSO_4$ (s)

(b) $CaSO_4$ (s) ⇄ Ca^{2+} (aq) + SO_4^{2-} (aq)

If the solubility is x mol dm^{-3}, then:

$K_{sp} = [Ca^{2+}][SO_4^{2-}] = x^2 = 3.0 \times 10^{-5}$

$x = 5.5 \times 10^{-3}$ mol dm^{-3}

(c) $[Ca^{2+}][SO_4^{2-}] = 1.0 \times 10^{-3} \times 1.0 \times 10^{-2} = 1.0 \times 10^{-5} < K_{sp}$. Thus there is no precipitate formed and no equilibrium present.

(d) $K_{sp} = [Ca^{2+}][SO_4^{2-}] = 0.0010\,x = 3.0 \times 10^{-5}$

$x = 3.0 \times 10^{-2}$ mol dm^{-3}

Example 3

3. Water containing 0.010 mol dm^{-3} magnesium ions precipitates magnesium hydroxide on the addition of sodium hydroxide.
Given K_{sp} $(Mg(OH)_2) = 1.0 \times 10^{-11}$ mol^3 dm^{-9}:

(a) Calculate the concentration of Mg^{2+} left in solution if enough NaOH is added to produce a hydroxide concentration of 0.010 mol dm^{-3}.

(b) Calculate the percentage of Mg^{2+} remaining in solution.

Solution

$Mg(OH)_2$ (s) ⇄	Mg^{2+} (aq)	+	2 OH^- (aq)
	x		0.010

$K_{sp} = [Mg^{2+}][OH^-]^2 = x \times (0.010)^2 = 8.9 \times 10^{-12}$

$x = 8.9 \times 10^{-8}$ mol dm^{-3}

(b) %Mg left = $\dfrac{8.9 \times 10^{-8}}{1.0 \times 10^{-2}} \times 100 = 0.00089\%$ $(8.9\times10^{-4}\,\%)$

Example 4

4. Magnesium hydroxide has a K_{sp} value of 8.9×10^{-12} mol^3 dm^{-9}. Calculate the concentrations of the ions in a saturated solution of $Mg(OH)_2$ and its pH.

Solution

If $[Mg^{2+}] = x$, then $[OH^-] = 2x$

$Mg(OH)_2$ (s) ⇄ Mg^{2+} (aq) + 2 OH^- (aq)

$K_{sp} = [Mg^{2+}][OH^-]^2 = x\,(2x)^2 = 4x^3 = 8.9 \times 10^{-12}$

$x = [Mg^{2+}] = 1.3 \times 10^{-4}$ mol dm^{-3} and

$[OH^-] = 2x = 2.6 \times 10^{-4}$ mol dm^{-3}

pOH = – $\log_{10}[OH^-]$ = – $\log_{10}[2.6 \times 10^{-4}]$ = 3.58

pH = 14.00 – pOH = 14.00 – 3.58 = 10.42

Example 5

5. From a consideration of the data below, determine the order of decreasing molar solubility (highest one first) of the salts AgCl, Ag_2CO_3 and Ag_3PO_4.

Solution

K_{sp} (AgCl) = 1.0×10^{-10} mol^2 dm^{-6};

K_{sp} $(Ag_2CO_3) = 6.3 \times 10^{-12}$ mol^3 dm^{-9};

K_{sp} $(Ag_3PO_4) = 2.0 \times 10^{-21}$ mol^4 dm^{-12}

Note : The order cannot be deduced from the K_{sp} values as all these do not contain 1:1 ions.

AgCl (s) ⇄ Ag^+ (aq) + Cl^- (aq)

OPTION

$K_{sp} = [Ag^+][Cl^-] = x^2 = 1.0 \times 10^{-10}$;

$x = 1.0 \times 10^{-5}$ mol dm^{-3}

$Ag_2CO_3 (s) \rightleftarrows 2Ag^+ (aq) + CO_3^{2-} (aq)$

$K_{sp} = [Ag^+]^2[CO_3^{2-}] = (2x)^2 \cdot x = 4x^3 = 6.3 \times 10^{-12}$;

$x = 1.16 \times 10^{-4}$ mol dm^{-3}

$Ag_3PO_4 (s) \rightleftarrows 3Ag^+ (aq) + PO_4^{3-} (aq)$

$K_{sp} = [Ag^+]^3[PO_4^{3-}] = (3x)^3 \cdot x = 27x^4 = 2.0 \times 10^{-21}$;

$x = 2.9 \times 10^{-6}$ mol dm^{-3}

Thus, order of decreasing solubility is: Ag_2CO_3 > AgCl > Ag_3PO_4

Selective Precipitation

Consider a solution containing 0.010 mol dm^{-3} each of barium chloride and strontium chloride.

Given K_{sp} ($BaSO_4$) = 1.5×10^{-9} mol^2 dm^{-6} and K_{sp} ($SrSO_4$) = 7.6×10^{-7} mol^2 dm^{-6}, and since both contain 1:1 ions, we can deduce that $BaSO_4$ will precipitate first if sulfate ions are added to the mixture. This is because the sulfate ion concentration required to precipitate Ba^{2+} ions will be less than that required to precipitate Sr^{2+} ions as shown by the calculation:

K_{sp} ($BaSO_4$) = $[Ba^{2+}][SO_4^{2-}]$. For the precipitation of $[Ba^{2+}]$:

$$[SO_4^{2-}] = \frac{K_{sp}(BaSO_4)}{[Ba^{2+}]} = \frac{1.5 \times 10^{-9}}{0.010} = 1.5 \times 10^{-7} \text{ mol dm}^{-3}$$

K_{sp} ($SrSO_4$) = $[Sr^{2+}][SO_4^{2-}]$. For the precipitation of $[Sr^{2+}]$:

$$[SO_4^{2-}] = \frac{K_{sp}(SrSO_4)}{[Ba^{2+}]} = \frac{7.6 \times 10^{-7}}{0.010} = 7.6 \times 10^{-5} \text{ mol dm}^{-3}$$

Sr^{2+} ions will not begin to precipitate until the sulfate ion concentration reaches 7.6×10^{-5} mol dm^{-3}. Until this concentration of $[SO_4^{2-}]$, the concentration of Ba^{2+} left in solution will be:

$$[Ba^{2+}] = \frac{K_{sp}(BaSO_4)}{[SO_4^{2-}]} = \frac{1.5 \times 10^{-9}}{7.6 \times 10^{-5}} = 2.0 \times 10^{-5} \text{ mol dm}^{-3}$$

The original concentration of $[Ba^{2+}]$ = 0.010 mol dm^{-3}, and the concentration of $[Ba^{2+}]$ left = 2.0×10^{-5} after the addition of sufficient $[SO_4^{2-}]$ to begin Sr^{2+} precipitation. At this point, the percentage of $[Ba^{2+}]$ left in solution is:

$$\frac{2.0 \times 10^{-5}}{0.010} \times 100 = 0.20\%$$

Thus, 99.8% Ba^{2+} is selectively precipitated out of solution before Sr^{2+} precipitation begins.

Consider the equilibrium between the precipitate AgCl and its ions, Ag^+ and Cl^-:

$AgCl (s) \rightleftarrows Ag^+ (aq) + Cl^- (aq)$

$K_{sp} = [Ag^+][Cl^-]$; thus, $[Ag^+] = \frac{K_{sp}}{[Cl^-]}$ where K_{sp} is a constant.

The mathematical relation between the concentrations of the ions can be represented neatly in a graphical form, as shown in Figure 1633.

A: The curve represents concentrations at precipitation. This suggests an infinite concentration of ions that can lead to equilibrium.

B: Where a solution contains a lower concentration of ions, no precipitate forms and no equilibrium is present.

C: A solution contains a higher concentration of ions than it can precipitate at equilibrium, a precipitate forms and an equilibrium is established between the solid precipitate and ions in solution.

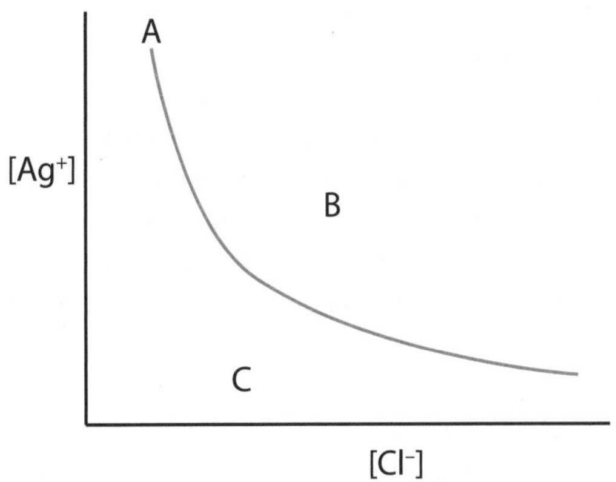

Figure 1633 Relation between $[Ag^+]$ and $[Cl^-]$ ions

Applications of K_{sp}:

1. Calculate the water solubility of a solid given its K_{sp} value.

2. Determine the effect of adding a common ion on the solubility.

3. Calculate the concentration of one ion in equilibrium with the solid when the concentration of the other ion is given.

OPTION

4. When two ionic solutions are added, determine whether a precipitate will form or not.

5. In a mixture of two slightly soluble ionic compounds, can selectively precipitate one.

E.12.2 State what is meant by the term cation-exchange capacity (CEC) and outline its importance.

Cation-exchange capacity (CEC) is the extent to which the negative charges on clay and/or humus in the soil can exchange nutrient cations at the roots of plants. CEC is an indicator of soil fertility. Some cations such as K^+, $Ca^{2+}$and Mg^{2+} are important plant nutrients, but others for example Na^+ and Al^{3+} are not.

CEC values depend on the type of soil and how much organic matter is present. Soil organic matter contains humic acid anions that are able to bind to nutrient cations. Thus, sand with little organic matter has low CEC value. Soil with clay and organic matter has high CEC value; the larger the CEC value, the more cations the soil can absorb and make available to plants. The importance of CEC is the availability of the key mineral nutrients to plants and reflects the soil's ability to exchange and adsorb cation nutrients.

Adsorption occurs due to electrical attraction in which the positively charged cations are held by particles containing negative charges in the soil organic matter and in clay. Clay in which Si(IV) and Al(III) have been replaced, for example, by Fe(II) result in a net negative charge on the surface. These negative charges attract cations. The higher the number of negative charges, the higher its CEC.

Humus in soil organic matter occupies a large surface area and contains many anionic sites due to the partial dissociation of the presence of phenolic and carboxylic acid groups (see also E.7.2). Thus it can adsorb large amounts of nutrient cations and humus is a very good storehouse for plant nutrients. Thus, adding SOM increases CEC. As plants take up nutrients from the soil, cation exchange takes place and these cations are replaced by hydrogen ions.

E.12.3 Discuss the effects of soil pH on cation-exchange capacity and availability of nutrients.

Water in the soil plays several key roles. For example, Group 1 metal ions such as Na^+ and K^+ are water soluble and are removed on regular irrigation of soil. Potassium ions control the amount of water that enters via osmosis; thus removal of potassium ions affects its ability to control water by osmosis.

Carbon dioxide in the air reacts with water to form H_2CO_3, a weak acid:

$$H_2O(l) + CO_2(g) \rightleftharpoons H_2CO_3(aq) \rightleftharpoons H^+(aq) + HCO_3^-(aq)$$

Natural rain water therefore is acidic and has a pH ~ 5.6. This makes the soil acidic (lowers its pH) making it possible for more metal ions to dissolve. For example, zinc sulfide is insoluble in water, but dissolves in an acid by reacting with H^+ ions by forming H_2S:

$$ZnS(s) + 2H^+(aq) \rightarrow Zn^{2+}(aq) + H_2S(g)$$

Similarly, zinc hydroxide, a base, is insoluble in water but reacts with H^+ ions:

$$Zn(OH)_2(s) + 2H^+(aq) \rightarrow Zn^{2+}(aq) + 2H_2O(l)$$

H^+ from acid deposition can replace nutrient cations in the soil such as Zn^{2+} and Mg^{2+}.

Alumina, Al_2O_3 is insoluble in water and is amphoteric: it reacts as a base with H^+ ions to form soluble Al^{3+} (aq) ions:

$$Al_2O_3(s) + 6H^+(aq) \rightarrow 2Al^{3+}(aq) + 3H_2O(l)$$

In basic conditions, Fe^{3+} and Al^{3+} react with OH^- to form insoluble hydroxides:

$$Fe^{3+}(aq) + 3OH^-(aq) \rightarrow Fe(OH)_3(s)$$

$$Al^{3+}(aq) + 3OH^-(aq) \rightarrow Al(OH)_3(s)$$

Hydrated ions such as $[Al(H_2O)_6]^{3+}$ and $[Fe\ (H_2O)_6]^{3+}$ with the high charge densities (charge to size ratio of the metal ion) attract the negative part of the water dipole to produce weakly acidic solutions:

$$[Al(H_2O)_6]^{3+} \rightleftharpoons [Al(H_2O)_5OH]^{2+} + H^+$$

$$[Fe\ (H_2O)_6]^{3+} \rightleftharpoons [Fe\ (H_2O)_5OH]^{2+} + H^+$$

Ions such as Al^{3+}, Fe^{3+} and Mn^{2+} are soluble in acidic solutions, but Al^{3+} and Mn^{2+} are toxic to plants. Al^{3+} is not a plant nutrient. However, its presence in soil below pH 5 is problematic. Due to its high charge density (charge to size ratio) and thus high chelating effect of binding onto the negative surfaces in clay and humus, it is able to displace important plant nutrient cations such as Ca^{2+} and Mg^{2+} from the soil:

$$3Mg^{2+}(soil) + 2Al^{3+}(aq) \rightarrow 2Al^{3+}(soil) + 3Mg^{2+}(aq)$$

These can then be lost, for example, due to irrigation. The soil pH needs to stay above pH 5 in order to avoid losing plant nutrients by the presence of Al^{3+} ions by the above process.

In acidic soil, insoluble calcium carbonate and magnesium carbonate are converted to soluble Ca^{2+} and Mg^{2+} ions respectively and can be lost to water drainage:

$$CaCO_3(s) + 2H^+(aq) \rightarrow Ca^{2+}(aq) + H_2O(l) + CO_2(g)$$

$$MgCO_3(s) + 2H^+(aq) \rightarrow Mg^{2+}(aq) + H_2O(l) + CO_2(g)$$

In such cases, $CaCO_3$ or $MgCO_3$ can be added to the acidic soil to replenish the nutrients:

$$2RCOOH + CaCO_3(s) \rightarrow 2RCOO^- Ca^{2+}(aq) + H_2O(l) + CO_2(g)$$

Acidic soil below pH 5.5 affects microbes' ability to fix NH_4^+ to N_2. Thus below about pH 5.5, NH_4^+ ions, which are weakly acidic, accumulate in the soil. Soil below pH 4 is too acidic and leads to poor plant growth. Lime can be added judiciously to reduce soil acidity and increase its pH to a more acceptable level (about pH 6 to 6.5). If soil pH increases too much, ions such as Fe^{3+} precipitate out as insoluble hydroxides leading to deficiency of important nutrients:

$$Fe^{3+}(aq) + 3OH^-(aq) \rightarrow Fe(OH)_3(s)$$

Soil pH affects the amount of phosphate ion present in solution. Phosphoric(V) acid, H_3PO_4 is a weak, triprotic acid. It's first dissociation is at low pH where as the third dissociation is at high pH, both typically out of soil pH range:

$$H_3PO_4(aq) \rightleftarrows H^+(aq) + H_2PO_4^-(aq);\ pH < 4$$

$$H_2PO_4^-(aq) \rightleftarrows H^+(aq) + HPO_4^{2-}(aq);\ pH \sim 7$$

$$HPO_4^{2-}(aq) \rightleftarrows H^+(aq) + PO_4^{3-}(aq);\ pH > 10$$

Thus, as plants absorb inorganic phosphorus from the soil as $H_2PO_4^-$ and HPO_4^{2-}, its supply depends on having a soil pH between about 6 and 7.5. In acidic soil below pH 5, the presence of Al^{3+} and Fe^{3+} produce insoluble phosphate compounds thus decreasing the availability of phosphorus to plants. Above pH 7, phosphates of Ca^{2+} and Mg^{2+} precipitate out.

Micro-nutrients such as iron, manganese and zinc are available in acidic soil. As soil pH approaches 7, their availability decreases as they precipitate out as hydroxides and may have to be supplemented. If soil is too basic, soil organic matter containing humic acids or acidic ammonium sulfate, $(NH_4)_2SO_4$ can be added. Ammonium sulfate is a salt of a weak base, NH_3 and a strong acid, H_2SO_4. It therefore consists of the cation, NH_4^+ that is weakly acidic (and anions, SO_4^{2+}, that are neutral):

$$NH_4^+(aq) \rightleftarrows NH_3(aq) + H^+(aq)$$

CEC depends on soil pH. SOM contains humic acids which exhibit buffering capacity over the pH 6.5 to 7.5 range. For example, the weakly acidic carboxylic acid group dissociates as follows:

$$RCOOH(aq) \rightleftarrows H^+(aq) + RCOO^-(aq)$$

Increased soil pH reduces H^+ in the above equation. This pushes the equilibrium to the right (Le Chatelier's principle) and produces more anions in the organic soil matter. This is able to bind to more cation nutrients and thus increase the soil's CEC. Increasing soil pH to 7 increases soil CEC; thus checking and maintaining soil pH is essential.

E.12.4 Describe the chemical functions of soil organic matter (SOM).

The major chemical functions of soil organic matter (SOM) are that it :

- has the ability to increase CEC of the soil
- behaves as a buffer and hence controls soil pH
- removes heavy metals and pesticides through its chelating ability.

Soil organic matter can greatly increase the cation exchange capacity (CEC, the extent to which it can exchange nutrient cations at the roots) of soil due to the presence in humic acid anions from carboxylic acid and phenolic functional groups ($RCOO^-$ and ArO^-). This makes it possible to chelate to nutrient cations, hence SOM prevents these from precipitating out as insoluble compounds. If cations such as Fe^{3+} are not able to bind to anions in SOM, these ions form insoluble oxides, hydroxides or carbonates and thus become unavailable to plants through the roots:

$$Fe^{3+}(aq) + 3\ H_2O(l) \rightarrow Fe(OH)_3(s) + 3H^+(aq)$$

$$2Fe(OH)_3(s) \rightarrow Fe_2O_3(s) + 3H_2O(l)$$

SOM thus acts as a nutrient reservoir for plants. It is not able to bind to anions such a nitrate, NO_3^-, phosphates ($H_2PO_4^-$ and HPO_4^{2-}) and sulfate, SO_4^{2-}. However, N, P and S are bonded in the organic matter and made available to plants due to microbial activity in the soil organic matter. These effects are further enhanced by the large surface area of SOM.

A buffer system is able to minimize the effect on pH (that is, its pH changes only slightly) when small amounts of an acid or a base are added to it. Soil organic matter is an important buffer system that maintains soil pH due to changes in the hydrogen ion concentration. Consider the dissociation of the weak carboxylic acid groups present in humus:

$$RCOOH(aq) \rightleftharpoons RCOO^-(aq) + H^+(aq)$$

If H^+ is added to the system, the equilibrium is disturbed; the reverse reaction is favoured using up some of the acid added, a new equilibrium is established and the change in pH of the soil is minimised. Similarly, if $OH^-(aq)$ is added, it reacts with the H^+ present; the equilibrium is disturbed, the forward reaction is favoured to replace some of the acid used up, a new equilibrium is established and again the change in pH of the soil is minimised.

Plants require phosphorus for early root development and growth; phosphorus deficiency may lead to fewer flowers, yellowing of leaves and stunted growth. Calcium phosphate is the main inorganic phosphorus source but it is not always available. Organic phosphorus, which comes from the phosphate used by living organisms, is relatively immobile in the soil. Organic phosphate is converted slowly into inorganic ions; the process is called mineralization and organic soil matter is an important source of phosphorus to the plants. The ability of humic acid anions from the carboxylic acid and phenolic group to chelate or bind plant nutrient cations is very important in soil chemistry. For example, soil organic matter enhances phosphorus availability through its chelating ability.

Soil organic matter is able to chelate and hold on to toxic cations such as Al^{3+} and heavy metals ions such as Hg^{2+}. It can also deactivate pesticides as they can be broken down by soil organisms. This decreases the amount of pollution that reaches and affects the water supply. Soil organic matter is able to bind to soil mineral nutrients such as iron cations which can otherwise precipitate out as insoluble salts and make them available to plants.

OPTION E: ENVIRONMENTAL CHEMISTRY QUESTIONS

E1 Air pollution

1. List the five major primary pollutants in the atmosphere and describe their main natural and anthropogenic sources. Illustrate your answer with appropriate equations. State methods that can be used to reduce each of the pollutants.

2. (a) Describe the electrostatic precipitation method of reducing the release of particulate matter into the atmosphere.

(b) Describe five methods for reducing the release of sulfur dioxide into the atmosphere.

E2 & E11 Acid deposition

3.(a) Define acid deposition and explain why natural rain water is acidic.

(b) State the pH of pure rain water and, with the aid of an equation, explain why rain is naturally acidic.

(c) Determine how many times more concentrated is rain of pH 4 acidic compared to that of pH 6.

4. (a) List two major pollutants responsible for acid deposition and give one man-made and one natural source of each. Write equations for the formation of acids from the pollutants.

(b) Outline the effect of acid deposition on marble objects and on plant growth.

(c) Describe two methods each for the reduction of each of the two pollutants.

E3 Greenhouse effect

5. (i) Describe and explain the *'greenhouse effect'.*

(ii) List five greenhouse gases other than CFCs and list the main source for each.

(iii) CFCs are produced in much less amount compared to the other greenhouse gases. State one reason why CFC is considered an important greenhouse gas.

(iv) Discuss the effects of global warming.

E4 & E 9 Ozone depletion

6. (a) Without external influence, explain how the environment is able to maintain more or less constant ozone concentration in the upper atmosphere. Illustrate your answer with appropriate equations.

(b) Explain why the allotropes of oxygen require energies of different wavelengths to undergo dissociation.

(c) (i) State two sources of chlorofluorocarbons in the atmosphere.

(ii) Explain how the presence of CFCs may lead to ozone depletion. Use dichlorodifluoromethane as an example to illustrate your answer with appropriate equations.

(iii) Explain why the ozone layer depletion in the polar regions seems the greatest in the winter months.

(iv) List three harmful effects on the human health of the decrease of ozone in the upper atmosphere.

(v) Suggest four possible alternatives to CFCs and list their advantages and disadvantages.

E5 Dissolved oxygen in water

7. (a)

(i) Explain the importance of dissolved oxygen in water.

(ii) List three factors that affect the concentration of dissolved oxygen in water, and explain the effect of increasing each one on dissolved oxygen content and on the quality of the water.

(b) Define the term *Biological oxygen demand.*

(c) Define the term *eutrophication* and explain how nitrates are involved in the process.

(d) Distinguish between aerobic and anaerobic decomposition of organic material in water and list products of C, N, S and P in each process.

E6 Water treatment

8. Explain why many substances dissolve in water.

9. (i) State the purpose of sewage treatment.

(ii) List the main materials removed during various methods of sewage treatment.

(iii) Explain the purpose of adding aluminium sulphate in primary sewage treatment.

(iv) Describe how waste in sewage is removed in secondary treatment

10.(a) State the names of two methods used for obtaining pure water from sea water. Explain the principle behind each method.

(b) Explain why nitrates and phosphates are not removed during primary and secondary treatment. Explain how ions such as Cd and phosphate can be removed. Illustrate your answer with appropriate equations.

E7 & 12 Soil

11 (a)

(i) List three major and three minor elements present in the Earth's crust.

(ii) List the four components of soil and identify the one in the largest amount and its source.

(iii) Define the term *humus* and list its carbon and nitrogen content.

(iv) Describe the structure of silica, SiO_2 and explain the consequence of replacing one in every four tetrahedrons contain Al^{3+} instead of Si^{4+} in the silica structure.

12. Define the terms *salinization, nutrient depletion* and *soil pollution*, describe how each arises and discuss their impact on the quality of soil.

13.(i) Define the term *soil organic matter* (SOM).

(ii) List the composition of SOM and state how its carbon content can be measured experimentally.

(iii) Describe the relevance of SOM.

14. Define the process of *mineralization* and describe the relevance of SOM in terms of biological, physical and chemical functions.

15.(a) Calcium ions present in hard water are precipitated by adding sulfate ions. Write the net ionic equation for the reaction.

(b) Given K_{sp} ($CaSO_4$) = 3.0×10^{-5} mol^2 dm^{-6} at 25°C, calculate its molar solubility in water at 25°C.

(c) Determine if a precipitate will form when the ion concentrations are: $[Ca^{2+}] = 1.0 \times 10^{-3}$ mol dm^{-3} and $[SO_4^{2-}] = 1.0 \times 10^{-2}$ mol dm^{-3}.

(d) Calculate the minimum concentration of sulfate ion required to precipitate the Ca^{2+}.

16. State the meaning of the term cation-exchange capacity (EC) and outline its importance.

17.(a) Use relevant equations to discuss the effects of soil pH on cation-exchange capacity and availability of:

(i) Zn (ii) Al

(b) Explain how soil pH affects the amount of phosphate ions present in solution.

E8 Waste

18. Outline and compare the two main methods of disposing of waste.

19. List five commonly recycled materials and identify the appropriate benefits for each type of recycled material.

20. Describe the characteristics, sources and storage methods of different types of radioactive waste.

E10 Smog

21.(i) List the primary pollutants produced in photochemical smog and state its main cause.

(ii) Explain why the concentration of the primary pollutants increases in the mornings and the role of sunlight in the formation of chemical smog. Use appropriate equations to illustrate your answer.

(iii) State two health problems caused by chemicals in photochemical smog.

(iv) Outline three methods of reducing photochemical smog.

FOOD CHEMISTRY

17

F1 Food groups

F2 Fats and oils

F3 Shelf life

F4 Colour

F5 Genetically modified foods

F6 Texture

F9 Stereo-chemistry in food (HL)

(Note that HL material from F7, F8 and F10 has been integrated)

Food chemistry is a study of the composition and properties of food, the chemical changes it undergoes during handling, processing and storage, and the principles underlying the improvement of food. The aim of this option is to give students an understanding of the chemistry of important molecules in food and the contribution that chemistry has made (and continues to make) towards maintaining and improving the quality and cost of food, adequacy of food supplies and food safety. Students should be able to recognize some important structures and relevant functional groups and to distinguish between them. It is not necessary to memorize complex formulas, as structures and examples of some food molecules are given in the *Chemistry data booklet*.

F1 FOOD GROUPS

F.1.1 Distinguish between a food and a nutrient.

F.1.2 Describe the chemical composition of lipids (fats and oils), carbohydrates and proteins.

Like all matter, food is composed of chemicals. These chemicals are particularly important because they provide the fuel from which we gain our energy and the materials required for essential bodily functions, as well as the building blocks for the growth and regeneration of our bodies. A balanced diet is vital for good health, hence the need to study the chemistry of food.

A food may be considered any substance that we deliberately take into our mouths and swallow. That is any natural or artificial material intended for human consumption. Ideally, a food must contain one or more nutrients. Some foods are rich in nutrients, whereas others have very little nutrient value. A **nutrient** is a component of food that is used by the body to provide energy, or for the growth and repair of tissue. The major nutrients are lipids, carbohydrates and proteins. Other nutrients are vitamins and minerals, which are required in much smaller quantities. Water, which is essential for biochemical processes to occur, is also considered a nutrient. A lack of these nutrients in the diet eventually gives rise to **malnourishment**.

Lipids (fats and oils) are esters of a glycerol (propan-1.2.3-triol) and three fatty acids (long chain carboxylic acids) as shown in Figure 1701.

$$\begin{array}{l} CH_2\text{-}O-C(=O)-R_1 \\ | \\ CH-O-COR_2 \\ | \\ CH_2\text{-}O-C(=O)-R_1 \end{array}$$

Figure 1701 The chemical structure of lipids

Here R_1, R_2 and R_3 represent long hydrocarbon chains, which may be the same or may be different. The hydrocarbon chains may also be saturated, unsaturated (containing a carbon-carbon double bond) or poly-unsaturated (containing a number of carbon-carbon double bonds). The nature of the R group determines the physical and chemical properties of the lipid. For example, saturated fats tend to be solids at room temperature whereas unsaturated ones (as in vegetable oils) are liquids. Lipids are a source of energy and are also vital in constructing cell membranes.

Carbohydrates, as their name would imply, have the empirical formula CH_2O. **Monosaccharides** with the general formula $(CH_2O)_n$ (n>2) are the simplest carbohydrates. Each monosaccharide contains one carbonyl group (C=O) and at least two hydroxyl groups (-OH). Condensation of two monosaccharides forms a **disaccharide**. Carbohydrates comprise sugars and polymers such as starch and cellulose derived from monosaccharides. The main function of carbohydrates is as a source of energy, though they are also used for cell construction. One of the simplest sugars is glucose, shown in Figure 1702.

```
      H
      |
      C=O
      |
   H–C–OH
      |
  HO–C–H
      |
   H–C–OH
      |
   H–C–OH
      |
      CH2OH
```

Figure 1702 The chemical structure of carbohydrates

Proteins are polymers of amino acids. All proteins contain C, H, O and N and some also have P and S. A typical section of a protein is shown in Figure 1703.

```
–NH–CH–CO–NH–CH–CO–NH–CH–CO–
     |          |          |
     R1         R2         R3
```

Figure 1703 The chemical structure of proteins

Here R_1, R_2 and R_3 represent the side chains of the amino acids involved and they may be the same or different.

F2 FATS AND OILS

F.2.1 Describe the difference in structure between saturated and unsaturated (mono- and poly-unsaturated) fatty acids.

F.2.2 Predict the degree of crystallization (solidification) and melting point of fats and oils from their structure, and explain the relevance of this property in the home and in industry.

F.2.3 Deduce the stability of fats and oils from their structure.

F.2.4 Describe the process of hydrogenation of unsaturated fats.

F.2.5 Discuss the advantages and disadvantages of hydrogenating fats and oils.

As stated in the previous section, fats and oils (sometimes referred to collectively as lipids) are esters of glycerol (propan-1.2.3-triol) and fatty acids (long chain carboxylic acids). Refer back to Figure 1701.

The groups R_1, R_2 and R_3, which may be the same or different, represent hydrocarbon chains, typically 15-25 carbon atoms long, though in most oils and fats the total number of carbons in the chain (including the –O-CO- one) is even because they are synthesised from two carbon units. These hydrocarbon chains may be saturated (all C-C bonds single), mono-unsaturated (containing one C=C) or poly-unsaturated (containing more than one C=C). In any given oil there is usually a mixture of chain lengths and degrees of saturation, though the relative proportions of these has an effect on the properties of the lipid.

Chemically oils and fats are similar, the main difference being in their melting point with fats being solid at room temperature and oils being liquid. The melting point of the lipid and hardness (degree of crystallinity) of the solid will depend on a number of factors:

- The mean length of the hydrocarbon chains.
- The degree of unsaturation.
- Whether the hydrocarbon chain is *cis-* or *trans-* around the double bond.

The longer the carbon chain, then the greater the molar mass, the stronger the van der Waals' forces and the higher the melting point. The presence of double bonds means that the hydrocarbon chain is less 'straight', so weakening the van der Waals' forces by reducing the close contact between the chains. As a result the greater the degree of unsaturation, the lower the melting point. The effect of double bonds on the 'straightness' of the hydrocarbon chain is much greater if these are *cis-* (H-atoms on the same side of the carbon chain) than if they are *trans-* (H-atoms on the opposite side of the carbon chain) as shown in Figure 1704.

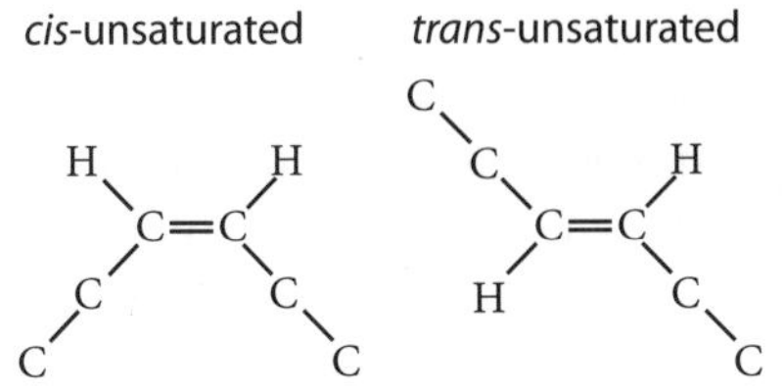

cis-unsaturated *trans*-unsaturated

Figure 1704 Cis and trans forms

As a result *cis*-unsaturated oils (the sort most commonly found naturally) have lower melting points than the equivalent *trans*-unsaturated oils.

Lipids that are solids at room temperature (such as coconut fat, butter and lard) tend to have saturated hydrocarbon chains and form more crystalline solids which are relatively hard. Oils, which are liquid at room temperature and give less crystalline, softer solids when solidified, are unsaturated. Poly-unsaturated oils (such as sunflower oil, corn oil and fish oil) have lower melting points and form softer solids than mono-unsaturated oils (such as olive oil, canola oil and peanut oil).

As might be expected from the underlying chemistry (unsaturated hydrocarbons are much more reactive than saturated ones) unsaturated oils are less stable and therefore keep less well than saturated fats. The major problem is reaction of the carbon-carbon double bond with oxygen (**auto-oxidation**), especially in the presence of light (**photo-oxidation**), which is why the surface of margarine is often discoloured. Unsaturated lipids are also more prone to hydrogenation and hydrolysis as well as enzyme-catalysed degradation by microbes.

Unsaturated oils are often hydrogenated using hydrogen at high pressure and a temperature of about 200°C in the presence of catalysts such as nickel, to produce products that are more saturated and in some cases fully saturated, as shown in Figure 1705.

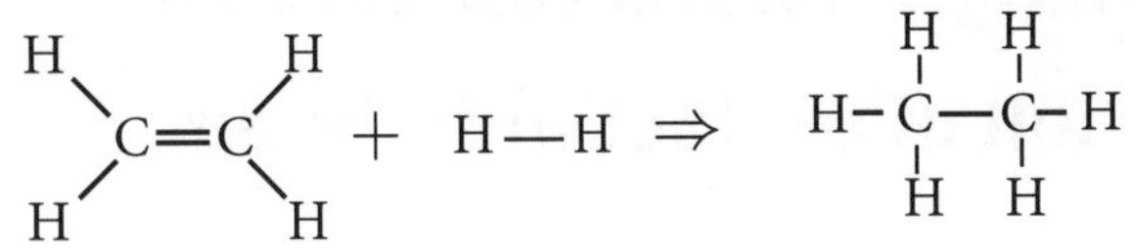

$$H_2C{=}CH_2 + H{-}H \Rightarrow H_3C{-}CH_3$$

Figure 1705 Using a catalyst to increase saturation

Whilst this has some practical advantages, such as:

- the product is a semi-solid or solid, rather than a liquid, which is more convenient for some cooking techniques.
- the product is more stable because the rate of oxidation is decreased.
- the texture (hardness and plasticity) of the product can the controlled.

This comes at a health cost because mono- and poly-unsaturated fats are healthier for the heart than saturated fats. Also partial hydrogenation can lead to the formation of *trans*-fats which, as they do not occur naturally, are difficult to metabolise and hence they accumulate in the fatty tissues of the body. *Trans*-fats also cause an increase in the levels of LDL cholesterol, which can lead to atherosclerosis (narrowing of the arteries) and a resultant increase in the probability of strokes and heart problems.

F3 SHELF LIFE

F.3.1 Explain the meaning of the term shelf life.

F.3.2 Discuss the factors that affect the shelf life and quality of food.

One problem with all foodstuffs is that they gradually degrade so that because of changes in flavour, smell, texture and appearance, or because of the growth of organisms, they become undesirable and/or unfit for consumption. The length of time a product can be stored without this occurring is known as its **shelf life** and obviously maximising shelf life is desirable.

This degradation can result from a number of different processes.

Change in water content as a result of contact with the air

Loss of water from moist foods can result in them becoming dry and changing in texture. The increased exposure to air of the solid food can result in an increase in the rate of oxidation leading to a decrease in nutrient value, discolouration of the surface and rancidity. Conversely if dry foods absorb water vapour from the air they become moist and more vulnerable to microbial degradation.

Chemical reaction

Chemical changes occurring within the food can result in pH changes (e.g. becoming sour) or the development of other undesirable flavours. Chemical changes can also result in colour changes in the food and a decrease in its nutritional value. The presence of oxygen often leads to oxidative degradation of foodstuffs.

Light

Light provides energy for photochemical reactions to occur leading to rancidity, the fading of the colour of foodstuffs and the oxidation of nutrients, especially vitamins.

Temperature

As with all chemical changes, an increase in temperature leads to an increase in the rate of degradation of foods.

Note that water is an important component of food. It determines its texture, softness and how juicy it is depending on how the water molecules are present. These can either be chemically bonded to carbohydrate and protein polar groups amongst others or be 'free' but linked via hydrogen bonding to protein and polysaccharides. A change in the forces of attraction that hold carbohydrate or protein chains in place will influence how much water it can hold. Thus a change in pH or increased temperature disrupts these forces, changing the amount of water it can hold and thus affecting texture, softness and how juicy it remains.

F.3.3 Describe the rancidity of fats.

F.3.4 Compare the processes of hydrolytic and oxidative rancidity in lipids.

F.3.5 Describe ways to minimize the rate of rancidity and prolong the shelf life of food.

F.3.6 Describe the traditional methods used by different cultures to extend the shelf life of foods.

One common form of food degradation is **rancidity** in lipids. Rancidity is the development of unpleasant smells in fats and oils, which are often accompanied by changes in their texture and appearance. There are two distinct ways in which rancidity can develop; **hydrolytic rancidity** and **oxidative rancidity**. In the former, the ester bond is broken down in the presence of lipase, heat and moisture to yield free fatty acids. See Figure 1706.

$$\underset{\text{oil/fat}}{C-O-CO-R} + \underset{\text{water}}{H_2O} \Rightarrow \underset{\text{glycerol}}{C-O-H} + \underset{\text{free fatty acid}}{HO-CO-R}$$

Figure 1706 Rancidity in lipids

The free fatty acids with 4-8 carbon atoms such as butanoic acid, hexanoic acid and octanoic acid have an unpleasant smell giving a rancid smell and taste to milk and butter (which is made from milk) that have been stored too long. Longer chain acids are less volatile, so the smell is less noticeable, but the presence of the free fatty acids such as palmitic, stearic and oleic acids or lauric acid affects the texture to give a fatty or soapy feel to the product, as for example in old samples of chocolate or cocoa butter. The rate of hydrolysis is significantly increased by the presence of enzymes, such as lipase, produced by micro-organisms and deep frying, can produce a hydrolytic reaction between the cooking oil and moisture in the food.

A second way in which rancidity occurs is oxidative rancidity (auto-oxidation) which involves the reaction of the carbon-carbon double bond in unsaturated lipids with oxygen from the air. This results in complex free radical reactions to produce a wide variety of products, many of which have unpleasant odours or tastes. The presence of light (which can produce free radicals leading to photo-oxidation), and of enzymes produced by, for example, micro-organisms, accelerates the rate at which oxidative rancidity occurs. Obviously this is much less of a problem with saturated lipids, but in highly unsaturated lipids, such as fish oils, oxidative rancidity can be a major problem.

HL F.7.1 Describe the steps in the free-radical chain mechanism occurring during oxidative rancidity.

Auto-oxidation is a free radical process chain reaction that involves the reaction of oxygen molecules with the double bonds of unsaturated lipids. Like other free radical chain reactions there are three stages to the reaction:

Initiation

The initial formation of free radicals has a very high activation energy and usually occurs by exposure of unsaturated lipids to light (photo-oxidation) which causes homolytic fission of a carbon-hydrogen bond:

$$R\text{-}H \rightarrow R\bullet + \bullet H$$

Initiation may also occur as a result of the decomposition of hydroperoxides, a product of the reaction, catalysed by traces of transition metal ions.

Propagation

Once formed the hydrocarbon free radicals react rapidly with oxygen molecules to form peroxide radicals, which then abstract hydrogen from other substrate molecules reforming the hydrocarbon radicals:

$$R\bullet + O_2 \rightarrow R\text{-}O\text{-}O\bullet$$

$$R\text{-}O\text{-}O\bullet + H\text{-}R \rightarrow R\text{-}O\text{-}O\text{-}H + R\bullet$$

These propagation reactions continue until a termination reaction destroys the free radicals. As these involve radicals encountering each other they are relatively rare and so one initiation step can produce very many hydroperoxide products.

Termination

This involves the removal of free radicals from the system by reactions between radicals. An inspection of the propagation steps above shows that there are three possible combinations:

$$R\bullet + R\bullet \rightarrow R\text{-}R$$

$$R\text{-}O\text{-}O\bullet + R\bullet \rightarrow R\text{-}O\text{-}O\text{-}R$$

$$R\text{-}O\text{-}O\bullet + R\text{-}O\text{-}O\bullet \rightarrow [R\text{-}O\text{-}O\text{-}O\text{-}O\text{-}R] \rightarrow R\text{-}O\text{-}O\text{-}R + O_2$$

The hydroperoxides formed (R-O-O-H) in the propagation step are very reactive molecules and are gradually converted to aldehydes and ketones. These, and the long chain fatty acids that the aldehydes are further oxidised to, have unpleasant smells and tastes and it is these that are responsible for the spoiling of the food.

Increasing the time required for the onset of rancidity is a major factor in increasing the shelf life of products containing high proportions of oils and fats. There are number of ways in which rancidity can be controlled:

Packaging

Using opaque packaging and coloured glass bottles will reduce light induced oxidative rancidity. Gas impermeable wrapping film will reduce the exposure of the product to oxygen and water vapour in the air and the free space in the container should be kept to a minimum to reduce the amounts of these present. Even better is vacuum packaging or filling the package with an inert gas. A good example is potato crisps which are usually packed in thick foil packets filled with nitrogen.

Storage

Refrigeration will reduce the rate of most reactions that produce rancidity and storing fat and oil rich foods in the dark will reduce the rate of photo-oxidation, which is less affected by temperature. Dairy products for example are almost always stored at low temperatures. Reducing the water level, by *drying* or *smoking*, and then storing away from moisture reduces hydrolytic rancidity and discourages the growth of micro-organisms.

Additives

There are many substances that can be added to foodstuffs to reduce the occurrence of rancidity. Some processing, for example **salting** (as in preparing bacon) and having a high sugar content (as in **preserves**), reduces the amount of water in the foodstuff by osmosis. This reduces the rate of hydrolytic rancidity as well as making the environment less suitable for the growth of micro-organisms. Other substances, such as sulfur dioxide and sodium sulfites used with fruit products, along with sodium and potassium nitrites and nitrates used in curing meats, are reducing agents and prevent the oxidative reactions that for example lead to the browning of many substances when stored too long.

Anti-microbial agents

Many methods of delaying the onset of rancidity depend on preventing the growth of micro-organisms in the foodstuff. Traditionally in **pickling** the use of vinegar creates an environment that is too acidic for micro-organisms. Many other organic acids and their salts (indicating that this is not purely a pH effect) are added to discourage the growth of moulds and bacteria in foods. Specific examples include the addition of benzoic acid and sodium benzoate to fruit juices as well as propanoic acid, along with its sodium and calcium salts, to bread and cheese. **Fermentation** also produces ethanol which limits bacterial growth, so wine keeps much better than fresh fruit juice and distilled spirits, with an even higher alcohol concentration, last longer still.

Quite a few of the methods mentioned above, particularly those in **bold**, have been traditionally used by cultures worldwide for many centuries to preserve foodstuffs.

F.3.7 Define the term antioxidant.

F.3.8 List examples of common naturally occurring antioxidants and their sources.

F.3.9 Compare the structural features of the major synthetic antioxidants in food.

F.3.10 Discuss the advantages and disadvantages associated with natural and synthetic antioxidants.

F.3.11 List some antioxidants found in the traditional foods of different cultures that may have health benefits.

An **antioxidant** is a substance that can be added to food to increase its shelf life by delaying the onset of oxidative degradation. Many of the antioxidants work by reacting with oxygen containing free radicals, so preventing these species degrading food by, for example, oxidative rancidity. There are many naturally occurring antioxidants present in foods, common examples being:

- Vitamin C (ascorbic acid) - found in citrus fruits and most green vegetables.
- Vitamin E (a tocopherol) - found in nuts, seeds, soya beans, whole grains, and some vegetable oils like canola oil.
- β-carotene - found in vegetables such as carrots and broccoli as well as fruits such as tomatoes and peaches.
- Selenium – an important trace element found in fish, shellfish, meat, eggs and grains.

Increasingly, synthetic antioxidants are being added to foodstuffs to increase their shelf life. Some of the most common are BHA (2- and 3-tert-butyl-4-hydroxyanisole), BHT (3,5-di-tert-butyl-4-hydroxytoluene), PG (propyl gallate), THBP (2,4,5-trihydroxybutyrophenone) and TBHQ (tertbutylhydroquinone). Almost all have phenolic type structures, that is they have a hydroxyl group attached to a benzene ring, a structural feature that is not found in naturally occurring antioxidants. The use of synthetic antioxidants is not without controversy as there are many who feel that they can have harmful side effects, but there is no clear evidence on the issue. Studies have however shown that naturally occurring antioxidants, such as vitamin C, vitamin E and β-carotene reduce the risk of cancer and heart disease by reacting with free radicals. There are also other health benefits of these as vitamin C is vital for the production of hormones and collagen, whilst β-carotene can act as a precursor for vitamin A. Even though synthetic antioxidants are more effective than the natural ones. they require strictly enforced codes for their safe use in foods. These may be difficult to police, especially in developing countries and many feel that their safety has yet to be satisfactorily proven.

That being said many substances traditionally used in different cultures as promoting good health are rich in natural antioxidants. Common examples of such foods include green tea, turmeric, oregano, blueberries, cranberries and dark chocolate. Many claims are made for these such as the lowering levels of LDL cholesterol, blood sugar levels and high blood pressure as well as preventing cancerous cell development. In many cases these claims have not been subjected to the stringent tests of modern science.

F.8.1 Explain the differences between the three main types of antioxidants.

The antioxidants added to foods may interfere with the auto-oxidation process in a number of ways:

FREE RADICAL QUENCHERS

These are species (represented as H-A in the equation below) that react with the free radicals present and produce less reactive free radicals (A• in the mechanism below):

$$R\text{-}O\text{-}O\bullet + H\text{-}A \rightarrow R\text{-}O\text{-}O\text{-}H + A\bullet$$

There are also many naturally occurring antioxidants, such as tocopherol (vitamin E) that can be used as free radical quenchers and many people prefer these to synthetic antioxidants such as BHA (2- and 3-tert-butyl-4-hydroxyanisole), TBHQ (tertbutylhydroquinone) and BHT (3,5-di-tert-butyl-4-hydroxytoluene).

CHELATING AGENTS

Free radicals may be formed by the reaction of transition metal ions with the hydroperoxides initially produced by the auto-oxidation reaction, for example:

$$R\text{-}O\text{-}O\text{-}H + Fe^{2+} \rightarrow R\text{-}O\bullet + OH^- + Fe^{3+}$$

Chelating reagents form very stable complex ions with transition metals and hence reduce the occurrence of these reactions. Many plants such as rosemary, tea and mustard, contain natural chelating agents. Salts of EDTA (ethylenediaminetetraacetic acid) are sometimes added as artificial chelating agents.

REDUCING AGENTS

Reducing agents (electron donors) can react with both oxygen in the food and with the hydroperoxides initially produced by auto-oxidation. Examples of naturally occurring reducing agents include ascorbic acid (vitamin C) and carotenoids. Artificial preservatives that are reducing agents, such as sulfur dioxide, sulfites and nitrites, may act in a similar manner.

F4 COLOUR

F.4.1 Distinguish between a dye and a pigment.

F.4.2 Explain the occurrence of colour in naturally occurring pigments.

Many foods have distinctive colours and we often use the appearance of the food to judge its quality and freshness. The colouring materials naturally present in foods are referred to as **pigments**, but **dyes** (i.e. coloured compounds, either synthetic or from a different natural source) are often added to enhance the appearance of processed products. These dyes, which are usually water soluble, have to be thoroughly tested to prove that they are safe for human consumption. Both groups of compounds owe their colour to the fact that they absorb certain frequencies of visible light, whilst reflecting others which are able to stimulate the retina in the eye. For example green spinach looks green because it absorbs red light and blue light, but **does not** absorb (and hence reflects) green light.

Note that the structures of the pigments shown overleaf all involve extensive delocalised π-bonds (HL material).

F.4.3 Describe the range of colours and sources of the naturally occurring pigments anthocyanins, carotenoids, chlorophyll and heme.

F.4.4 Describe the factors that affect the colour stability of anthocyanins, carotenoids, chlorophyll and heme.

F.10.1 Compare the similarities and differences in the structures of the natural pigments: anthocyanins, carotenoids, chlorophyll and heme.

There are various groups of compounds that are found as natural pigments in foods. Some of the most common of these are listed below along with the way that cooking, which, as well as subjecting them to heat, may involve changes of pH and an acceleration of oxidative reactions which can modify their colour:

Anthocyanins

These are the most commonly found pigments. They are responsible for red, pink, purple and blue colours found in berries as well as the colour of beetroot and red cabbage. **Anthocyanins** also cause the colour of many flowers. Some typical anthocyanins are shown below; it will be noted that they all have very similar 3-ring $C_6C_3C_6$ structures with conjugated double bonds, but they vary in the number and position of the hydroxyl groups and alkoxy side chains. Anthocyanins are often found bonded to sugar side chains which also modify their precise colour. Refer to Figure 1707.

Pelargonidin

Cyanidin

Delphinidin

Figure 1707 The structure of some anthocyanins

The structure of anthocyanins is very dependent on pH, not only because of acid base effects, but also because of the effect of pH on the ease of hydration reactions. As a result the colour of foods coloured by anthocyanins can vary significantly during the cooking process, especially when mixed with acidic or alkaline ingredients. Anthocyanins form complex ions with metal ions such as Fe^{3+} and Al^{3+}, hence prolonged contact with these metals, from which saucepans are often made, may also contribute to changes in colour during the cooking process. At high temperatures, like many organic compounds, anthocyanins decompose and this may lead to browning in some cooking processes.

There are four closely related structural forms of anthocyanins which are often in equilibrium, the exact position depending on factors such as pH and temperature, which allows these compounds to be used as acid-base indicators. The most brightly coloured forms (A and B below) however are stable at low temperature and, for A, at low pH. The structures of these forms and the equilibria linking them are illustrated below, with the changes in structure highlighted:

The absorption spectra of the anthocyanins therefore vary with pH, causing the colour changes discussed above. At low pH the flavylium cation (AH^+) predominates and the mixture is red, at neutral pH values there is a sufficient concentration of hydroxide ions for this to hydrolyse and the solution becomes almost colourless as it is converted to the carbinol pseudobase (B) and chalcone (C). At even greater pHs the flavylium cation (AH^+) in equilibrium with this is converted to the quinoidal base (A) so all the equilibria are shifted to yield this product and the solution turns blue. This is illustrated in the Figures 1708 and 1709.

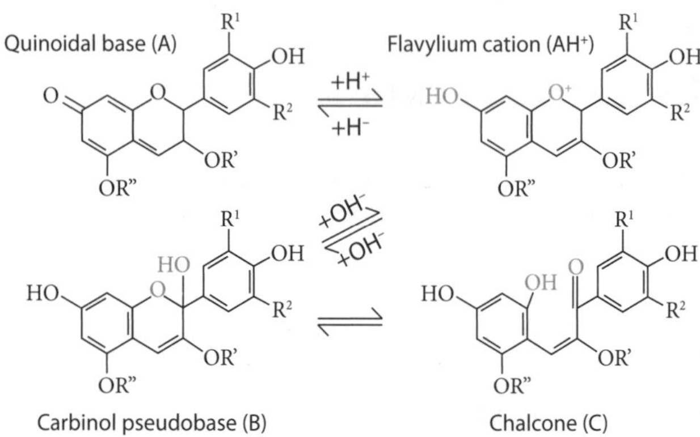

Figure 1708 Colour changes in anthocyanins

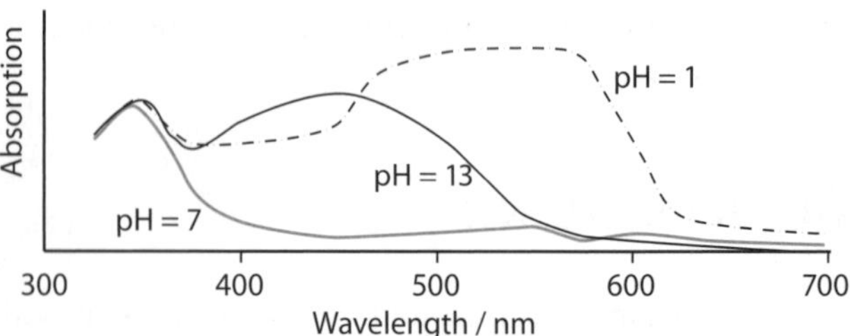

Figure 1709 Absorption of anthocyanins at various pH levels

Flavanones, of which quercetin (shown below) found as the colouring material in red grapes and many berries is a typical example, are closely related to anthocyanins. See Figure 1710.

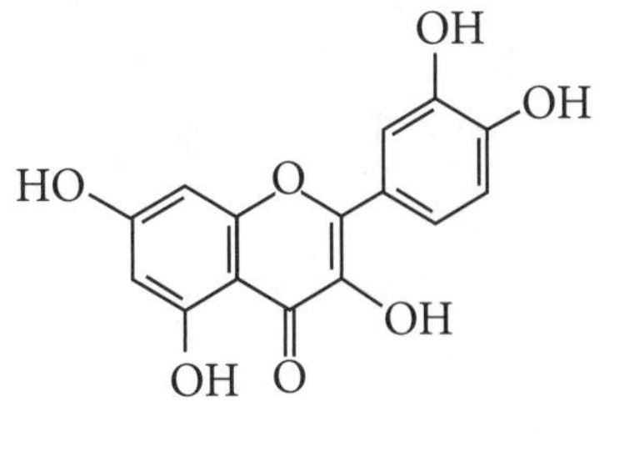

OH
OH
HO
O
OH
OH O

Figure 1710 Quercetin

Carotenoids – These are widely found in all living things, especially in algae. They are responsible for yellow, orange and red colours and, as well as being responsible for the colour of carrots, they cause the colour in bananas, tomatoes and saffron. Because their low levels in grass are concentrated in milk fats they also give butter its colour. Carotenoids also have nutritional value because they can be converted into vitamin A, as well as being effective antioxidants. The structures of some typical carotenoids are illustrated below. The essential feature of carotenoids is the long hydrocarbon chain, which may also have methyl groups attached. In some cases there may be ring structures at the ends of the chain, in other cases not. Similarly some caretenoids have hydroxyl groups near the end of the chain or on the ring, whereas others, sometimes called **carotenes** (see Figures 1711, 1712), have a hydrocarbon structure. Vitamin A, as can be seen from Figure 1713, is very closely related to the carotenes which act as precursors for it.

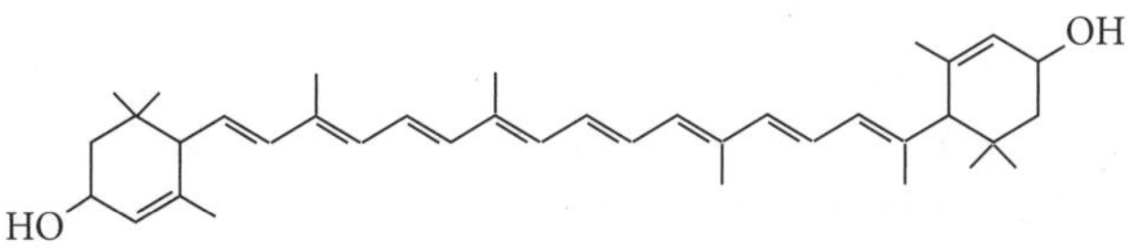

OH
HO

Figure 1711 Xanthophyll – a typical carotenoid

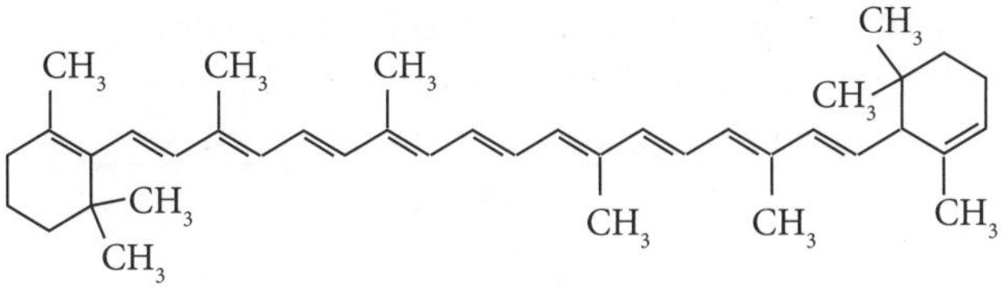

CH_3 CH_3 CH_3 CH_3 CH_3 CH_3 CH_3 CH_3 CH_3 CH_3

Figure 1712 Beta-carotene

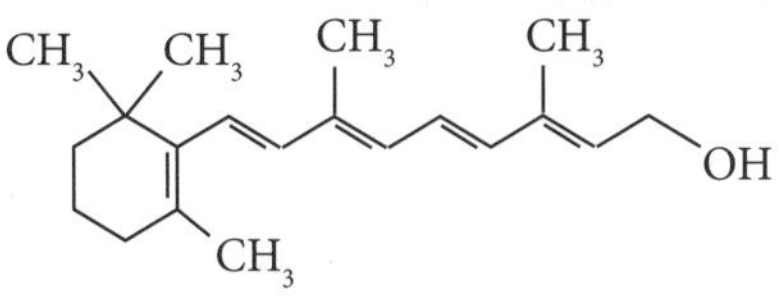

CH_3 CH_3 CH_3 CH_3 OH CH_3

Figure 1713 Vitamin A

Carotenoids are stable under most conditions used for processing foods so little loss of colour occurs, though heating can cause some discolouration and the *trans*-coordination around double bonds to change to *cis*-coordination. The presence of the polyunsaturated hydrocarbon chain means that, like poly unsaturated oils carotenoids are subject to oxidative degradation. As could be expected, this is accelerated by light, which can produce hydroperoxide free radicals and which is catalysed by the presence of transition metal ions. This oxidation as well as causing discoloration also means that the carotenoids can no longer be converted to vitamin A.

Astaxanthin is a red pigment closely related to carotenoids (compare the structures). When it is found naturally it is usually bonded to proteins, which modify the frequencies of light it absorbs so that it gives the blue and green colours found in live lobsters and crabs. High temperatures disrupt the bonding to the protein, hence the startling change in colour when these animals are cooked. Like carotenoids it acts as an antioxidant, hence the health benefits ascribed to eating the shells of shrimps and prawns. This pigment is also responsible for the pink colour of salmon meat.

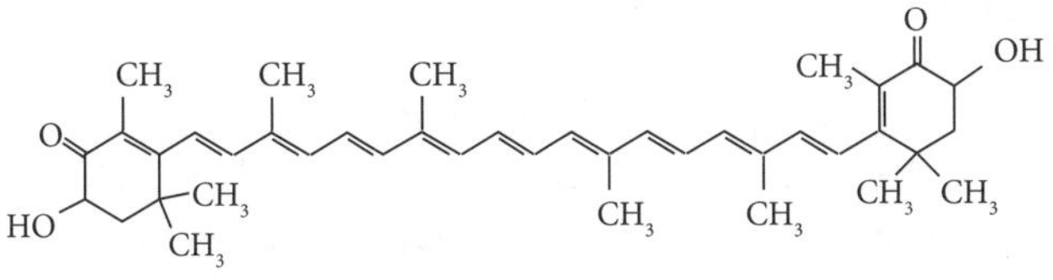

O OH
CH_3 CH_3 CH_3 CH_3
O
CH_3 CH_3 CH_3 CH_3 CH_3
HO CH_3

Figure 1714 Astaxanthin

CHLOROPHYLL

This is the green coloured pigment responsible for catalysing the photosynthetic process in green plants and hence is widely found in green vegetables. In the structure (See Figure 1415), which is actually that of chlorophyll a, note the presence of magnesium at the centre of the ring. There are actually two very closely related forms of chlorophyll, chlorophyll a and chlorophyll b, which differ only in whether a side chain is a methyl group (a) or an aldehyde group (b).

OPTION

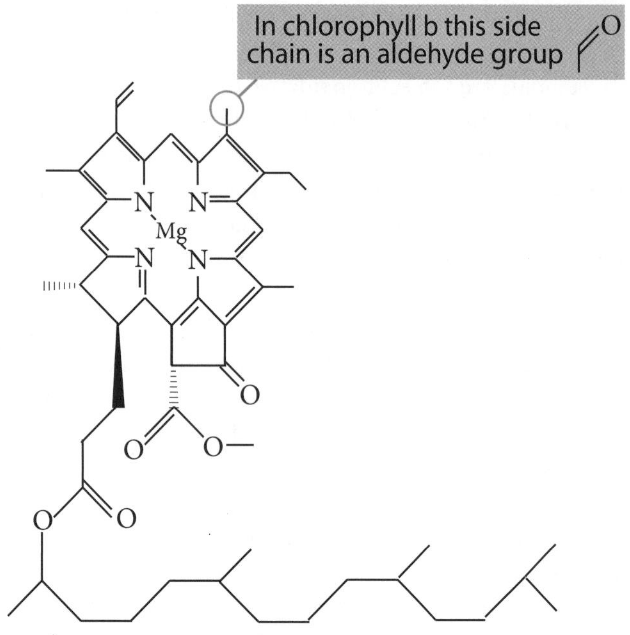

In chlorophyll b this side chain is an aldehyde group

Figure 1715 Chlorophyll a and b

During cooking plant cells break down and this releases acids, decreasing the pH of the solution. Whilst stable in neutral and alkaline solution, in acidic solution hydrogen ions displace the magnesium ion from the ring into solution, resulting in a colour change to olive-brown. These changes also make the pigment less stable to light and **photodegradation** can occur.

HEME

This is the red pigment found in the red blood cells of higher animals. Its structure is shown in Figure 1716. Note the similarity of structure to that of chlorophyll, but in this case iron(II), rather than magnesium is found at the centre of the ring. The essential features of both chlorophyll and heme are the planar ring systems in which the metal ion is bonded to four nitrogen atoms, which act as **ligands**. This is referred to as a **porphyrin ring**.

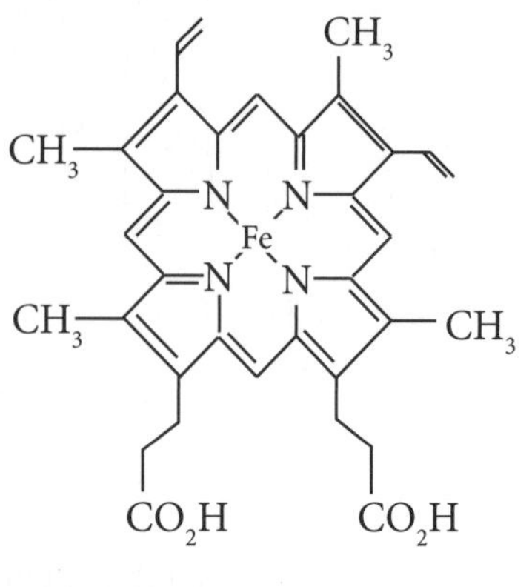

Figure 1716 The Heme group

In muscles, heme is found associated with **myoglobin**, a protein molecule, and this has a purplish-red colour. It binds easily to oxygen molecules, hence its role in oxygen transportation, and this results in a colour change to bright red. A much slower reaction with oxygen, called **auto-oxidation**, results in the oxidation of the iron from iron(II) to iron(III), forming **metmyoglobin** and the colour changes to a brownish red colour, which is considered less desirable. These changes are summarised in the diagram below:

$$\underset{\text{Bright red}}{O_2\text{-}Fe^{2+}\text{-}Mb} \underset{+O_2}{\overset{-O_2}{\rightleftarrows}} \underset{\text{Purple-red}}{Fe^{2+}\text{-}Mb} \underset{[Red]}{\overset{[Ox]}{\rightleftarrows}} \underset{\text{Brown-red}}{Fe^{3+}\text{-}Mb}$$

The colour of the meat can be preserved by storing it in an oxygen free environment, by vacuum packing it, or packing it in an inert gas (such as CO_2), using polymers with low gas permeability.

F.10.2 Explain why anthocyanins, carotenoids, chlorophyll and heme form coloured compounds while many other organic molecules are colourless.

F.10.3 Deduce whether anthocyanins and carotenoids are water- or fat-soluble from their structures.

It is interesting to enquire why all of these compounds absorb light in the visible region of the spectrum and hence appear coloured. The answer to this is that they all have extensive systems of delocalised π-bonding. The greater the extent of delocalisation, the closer together in energy the bonding and antibonding π-orbitals become. Hence the region in which photons can excite an electron from one to the other shifts from the ultraviolet region (as in benzene) into the visible region. In the structures drawn the extensive system of delocalisation is indicated by alternate single and double bonds ('conjugated' double bonds). In anthocyanins this can be seen to extend over all three rings and closely related molecules in which this does not occur (such as **carbinol**, see below, in which it is disrupted by the sp^3 hybridised carbon indicated). See Figure 1717.

Figure 1717 Carbinol

In carotenoids, even though the rings themselves are not fully delocalised, the delocalised system spreads from the sections of the rings closest to the chain and along the entire hydrocarbon chain. In chlorophyll and heme the delocalised system is essentially the ring that surrounds the central metal ion, though it does extend slightly into some of the side chains. The colour of the food depends on the reflected rather than the absorbed light, hence chlorophyll, which absorbs red and blue light, appears green because light of this wavelength is reflected rather than absorbed.

It can be seen that anthocyanins have many hydroxyl groups attached to their ring structure. These can hydrogen bond to water molecules and as a result anthocyanins tend to be water soluble. In contrast carotenoids have a long hydrophobic hydrocarbon chain and the hydroxyl groups on the rings are not sufficient to confer water solubility, so carotenoids are soluble in oils and fats.

F.4.5 Discuss the safety issues associated with the use of synthetic colourants in food.

Many synthetic dyes are quite biochemically active and hence pose health threats. It is obviously important that such materials are not used to colour foodstuffs, hence in most countries the dyes that can be used in foods are regulated and there are authorities responsible for testing and licensing food additives. Unfortunately there are no international standards on this and colouring materials permitted in one country may be banned in another, posing difficulties for international trade. Synthetic dyes, such as malachite green and sudan red, are sometimes found in imported foodstuffs even though they are not permitted in many countries. Another problem is that whilst short term, acute toxicity is easy to test for, chronic effects are less easy to prove, especially with substances that may be suspected of having long term carcinogenic effects.

F.4.6 Compare the two processes of non-enzymatic browning (Maillard reaction) and caramelization that cause the browning of food.

Cooking foods often causes them to turn brown and this colour change is often used as an indication of whether they have been sufficiently cooked. There are two distinct processes that lead to this colour change. The first process is known as the **Maillard reactions** (after the French chemist Louis-Camille Maillard). These are responsible for the smell and colour change of many common cooking processes, such as grilling meat, toasting bread, malting barley and making fudge (Maillard reactions are also used in some self-tanning treatments.). In these condensation reactions the aldehyde group in reducing sugars (such as glucose and lactose) reacts with the free amino group of an amino acid, or amino groups on the side chains of peptides and proteins. Because there is such a variety of possible reactants, many Maillard reactions are known and over a thousand different products have been identified. The polymeric ones are often brown and hence responsible for the colour change, whilst the lower molar mass products are thought to be responsible for many of the aromas of cooking and resulting changes in flavour. The equation for the first stage of these reactions can be written as:

$$HO\text{-}CH_2\text{-}[CH(OH)]_4\text{-}CH{=}O + H_2N\text{-}CHQ\text{-}COOH \rightarrow HO\text{-}CH_2\text{-}[CH(OH)]_4\text{-}CH{=}N\text{-}CHQ\text{-}COOH + H_2O$$

Reducing sugar + Amino acid → Initial condensation product

The initial products then polymerise to form brown pigments (known as melanoidins). Maillard reactions usually only occur at temperatures over about 140°C, though their rate varies significantly, especially with the nature of the amino acid involved. Cysteine is one of the least reactive, whereas lysine is much more reactive, so foods that contain a lot of this (such as milk) brown readily (as for example in the formation of fudge).

The second process is referred to as **caramelisation**. This occurs when foods with a high carbohydrate concentration,

OPTION

especially sugars, are heated and start to dehydrate. Initially this process leads to polymerisation and produces a wide variety of products responsible for the appearance of the brown colouration. If continued this eventually leads to the production of carbon and the burning of the food:

$$C_n(H_2O)_n \rightarrow n\,C + n\,H_2O$$

The rate of caramelisation varies with the sugar involved, with fructose, found in fruits, being the most easily caramelised. Extremes of pH, both high and low, also promote caramelisation. Because the Maillard reaction requires proteins or amino acids, the browning of foods that do not contain these, such as making toffee from sugar, or the crisp sugar topping of *crème brulée*, results from caramelisation. In practice however the browning of food on cooking usually involves both processes.

F5 GENETICALLY MODIFIED FOODS

F.5.1 Define a genetically modified (GM) food.

F.5.2 Discuss the benefits and concerns of using GM foods.

Modern biological techniques mean that it is possible to artificially modify the DNA sequence of micro-organisms, plants and animals. Using organisms modified in this way, it is possible to produce foods that are different from those that occur naturally. Foods produced from these organisms are collectively known as genetically modified (or GM) foods. There are a number of possible advantages to GM foods, some of which are listed below.

Pest and disease resistance

The yields from many plants and animals are reduced by pests and diseases. **Genetic modification** can increase their resistance to these, reducing the need to treat with herbicides, pesticides, vaccines etc., all of which add to production costs and may leave potentially toxic residues in the food. Examples are the production of potatoes that are resistant to fungal diseases and bananas that are resistant to attack by nematodes.

Improved quality and range

Many crops are geographically limited because of the conditions required for their growth. Genetic modification can enable the production of varieties that can grow in a wider range of climatic conditions as well as produce greater yields and mature in a shorter time. Examples are the development of higher yielding rice varieties and maize that can grow in areas of lower rainfall.

Production of medicinal and other novel products

Genetic modification can be used to enable plants and animals to produce products that they would not normally produce, such as biologically active molecules that can be used as medicines. Examples are GM hens that lay eggs containing human interferon and cows that produce milk rich in nutritionally desirable omega-3 fatty acids.

There are however many people and organisations that are very concerned about the proliferation of genetically modified organisms and food produced from them. The main reasons for this concern are:

Are GM foods safe?

Some people who have no problems with natural foods will develop allergic reactions to GM varieties. The composition of GM foods may be different from the equivalent natural foods and hence subtly alter the balance of our diets.

Will the production of GM foods damage natural ecosystems?

Even though genetically modified plants are currently limited to certain farms, there is the risk that pollen from them will escape into the wild population with unforeseen consequences.

Do we understand enough about genetic modification?

Genetic modification is a relatively recent technique. Do scientists understand enough about the process, or could we be tampering with things that could have a catastrophic effect we currently cannot predict?

F6 TEXTURE

F.6.1 Describe a dispersed system in food.

F.6.2 Distinguish between the following types of dispersed systems: suspensions, emulsions and foams in food.

F.6.3 Describe the action of emulsifiers.

TOK What conflict of concepts and values are raised by GM foods?

If you have studied Option D you may remember the TOK Box on scientific responsibility and if you studied Option E I said a little about 'reasonable doubt' and the impartiality of scientific opinion. These two concepts sort of come together in the idea of 'acceptable risk' which is what probably governs the GM food debate. I don't think any scientist maintains that it is totally risk free, nor does any environmentalist deny that there are huge potential advantages. The debate would seem to be over whether one justifies the other. Facts, even when agreed on by both sides of the debate (in itself a rarity), can sometimes be manipulated by statistics to back both causes, but it is rare to see a debate on this issue that centres around the differing interpretations of agreed facts, or even the reasons why one side finds unacceptable a particular body of evidence quoted by the other side.

Our scientific name is *Homo sapiens*, but maybe *Homo emotionalis* might be more appropriate? Do we use logic for the important decisions in life – which university to go to, who to get married to, what kind of pizza to order? The answer is a resounding "No". We might use logic to narrow things down a little bit (e.g. with the weather, food and friends) but when it comes down to it our final call is a gut reaction, an emotional one. Knowing that, both sides have tried to move the discussion to an emotional level, though this has been achieved with spectacularly more success by the environmentalist lobby. *Do a search with Google to see what I mean.*

The texture of food depends on its physical properties, such as its hardness and its elasticity. These are almost always affected by cooking, such as meat and vegetables becoming softer as their cell structure breaks on heating or biscuits becoming crisp as water is lost. Contrasts in texture, such as a crisp crust on soft bread, are very attractive to the palate. A creamy texture is something that is often sought in foods and often this comes from a **disperse system**, i.e. a stabilised, macroscopically homogenous mixture of two immiscible phases. There are many types of disperse systems and their naming depends on the physical states of the components, those most important in food chemistry all contain a liquid as one component:

Liquid-solid

In fact there are two types of disperse liquid-solid systems that do not separate; a **suspension** or **sol** comprises solid particles suspended in a liquid, whereas as a **gel** has liquid particles suspended in a solid medium. An example of a sol would be blood in which the solid red and white cells remain suspended in the plasma, or the fine precipitate of sulfur that forms when very dilute acid is added to aqueous sodium thiosulfate. A fruit jelly, in which water is trapped in a protein matrix would be an example of a gel.

Liquid-liquid

A stable blend of two immiscible liquids is known as an **emulsion**. Mayonnaise, which is a suspension of oil droplets in an aqueous system would be a good example.

Liquid-gas

Again there are two types of stable disperse liquid-gas systems. **Foams** are comprised of gas bubbles trapped in a liquid medium. Whipped cream or egg whites, would provide a good example. **Aerosols**, which comprise liquid droplets suspended in a gas, may well be responsible for many of the smells of food and cooking.

A question that arises with disperse systems is why they do not separate. In fact often they do, but only very slowly. Gravity, coupled with the differing densities of the components will often cause a disperse system to slowly settle out. Some disperse systems, referred to as **colloids**, do not however separate. Often this is because the suspended particles are electrically charged and hence repel each other. In food preparation substances, known as **emulsifiers**, are frequently used to promote mixing of the two phases, and stabilisers are often added to slow down their separation. Emulsifiers are molecules that can bond to both phases so they are found at the surface between the phases and hence are known as **surfactants**. This is very similar to the action of soap as shown in Figure 1718.

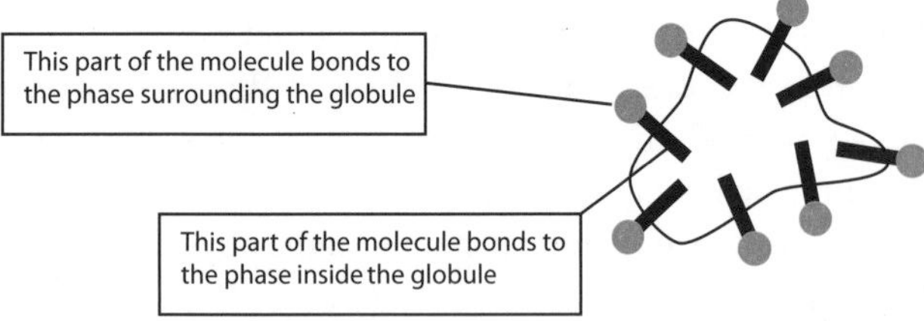

Figure 1718 The action of soap

In food preparation one of the most commonly used emulsifiers is lecithin, a phospholipid which occurs naturally in egg yolks. As can be seen from its structure below, lecithin has many charge centres and oxygen atoms at one end of the molecule which bond strongly to water (hydrophilic). It also has two hydrocarbon chains which will tend to break the hydrogen bonds in water, but be unable to form any bonds of their own to replace these. As a result these parts of the molecule will avoid water (hydrophobic) and bond to the non-aqueous phase. See Figure 1719.

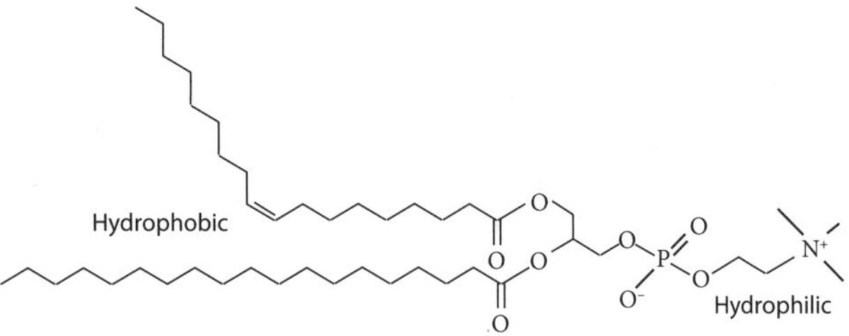

Figure 1719 Lecithin is an emulsifier

In mayonnaise, made by beating oil and vinegar with egg yolks, the hydrophilic end of lecithin will bond to the vinegar and the hydrophobic hydrocarbon tails will bond to the oil. Each oil droplet will therefore be surrounded by a layer of lecithin molecules. Note that it is important to physically beat the mixture so that small droplets of the suspended phase are formed, maximising the surface area on which the surfactant can be adsorbed. Stabilisers are often also added to stabilise disperse states. Inorganic phosphates, such as trisodium phosphate, are effective at stabilising emulsions. Chefs often prefer metal bowls for beating egg whites and recent research has shown that minute traces of the metal are in fact incorporated into the foam and stabilise it.

F9 STEREO-CHEMISTRY IN FOOD

F.9.1 Explain the three different conventions used for naming the different enantiomeric forms.

You may recall that if a molecule contains a chiral carbon atom (one that is bonded to four different groups) then two distinct spatial arrangements of the molecule, called enantiomers, are possible. These enantiomers are mirror images of each other and have identical physical and chemical properties, except that one of them will rotate the plane of polarisation of plane polarised light in a clockwise direction, whilst the other will rotate the plane of polarisation of plane polarised light in an anticlockwise direction. The clockwise rotating enantiomer is said to be **dextrorotatory**, {+ or (*d*)}, and has a positive specific rotation value, whilst the other enantiomer is said to be **laevorotatory**, {- or (*l*)}, and it has a negative specific rotation value. Whether it is dextrorotatory or laevorotatory does not however give any indication as to the spatial arrangement of the components, their absolute configuration. Unfortunately there are two separate systems used to indicate this.

The first system, known as the D,L system (it is most unfortunate that upper case D and L are used for this and lower case *d* and *l* for the totally unrelated dextrorotatory and laevorotatory) is an older convention and used for sugars and amino acids. In this the absolute configuration of the molecule is related to that of glyceraldehyde, the absolute configuration of which was defined originally by guesswork. Fortunately a correct guess now confirmed by X-ray crystallography. See Figure 1720.

H-C=O
*C
HOCH$_2$ H OH

Mirror images

O=C-H
*C
HO H CH$_2$OH

D - glyceraldehyde L - glyceraldehyde

Figure 1720 D and L forms of glyceraldehyde

The absolute configuration of other sugars about each chiral centre is then named by analogy, that is, if the molecule is viewed along the chain with the C=O pointed away, the D-isomer has the –OH group on the right. The system is also applied to amino-acids, where a useful rule of thumb is the **'CORN' rule**. The molecule is viewed with the C-H bond pointing away from the observer (fortunately the same as in the R,S system below). If the groups **COOH, R, NH_2** (where R- is the side chain) are arranged clockwise around the carbon atom then it is the D-form. If anticlockwise, it is the L-form.

Consider applying this to the alanine (2-aminopropanoic acid) enantiomer illustrated in Figure 1721.

Figure 1721 The 'CORN' rule

It can therefore be seen, applying the 'CORN' rule, that this is L-alanine (COOH -> R -> NH_2 anticlockwise). In fact almost all naturally occurring amino acids are the L-form. These are usually tasteless, whereas the synthetic D-amino acids taste sweet. Conversely most naturally occurring sugars are the D-form, which taste sweet. Often the enantiomer that does not occur naturally cannot be metabolised by our bodies.

The second system, the **R,S system** (or **CIP system**, after Cahn, Ingold and Prelog, who first proposed it) is used for most other groups of compounds. In this system there are three steps:

1. The atoms bonded to the chiral carbon are ranked in order of increasing atomic number ($H<C<N<O<F<Cl<Br$ for the most common atoms).

2. Where two or more atoms have the same atomic number (e.g. there are two C-atoms, one a $-CH_3$ and the other a –COOH), the second atoms are used to rank the substituents (so in this case the order would be $-CH_3<-COOH$ as 3 × atomic number of H is less than that of O). If the second atoms are also the same, the sums on the third are used, and so on (in this case a double bond counts as double, so that the –COOH would be equal to 3×O).

3. Imagine you are viewing the molecule with the lowest ranking substituent pointing away from you, the other three substituents must either decrease in order in a clockwise direction, in which case it is the R-enantiomer, or they must decrease in an anticlockwise direction, in which case it is the S-enantiomer.

Consider applying these to 2-bromobutane as shown in Figure 1722.

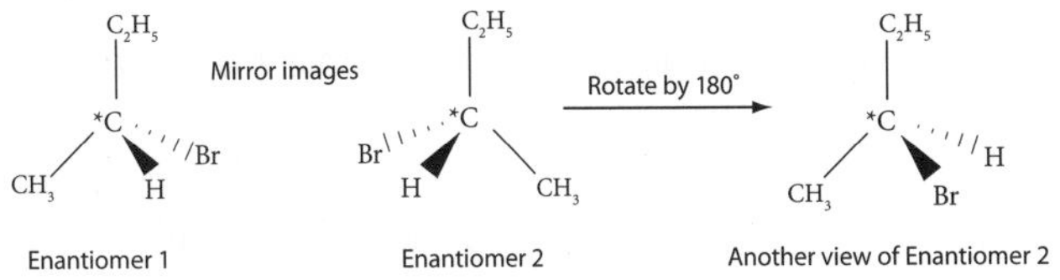

Figure 1722 The CIP system

1. Applying the first rule, the order of the substituents attached to the central carbon is $H<(C,C)<Br$.

2. Applying the second rule, the order of the two carbons is $CH_3<CH_2\text{-}CH_3$ (as $3\times H<C$), so the complete order is $H<CH_3<C_2H_5<Br$.

3. Consider looking at the two enantiomers with the C-H bond pointing away from you (so the H-atom is below the page). The order of the substituents will be:

Figure 1723

It can be seen that in Enantiomer 1 the order decreases clockwise and in Enantiomer 2 the order decreases anticlockwise. Enantiomer 1 is therefore R-2-bromobutane and Enantiomer 2 is S-2-bromobutane.

> F.9.2 Distinguish between the properties of the different enantiomeric forms of stereoisomers found in food.
>
> © IBO 2007

Even though they are so similar, different enantiomeric forms of molecules found in food often have different smells, tastes and toxicity. One well known example of this is the molecule **carvone**, a terpenoid. Refer to Figure 1724

OPTION

(R) (S)

Figure 1724 R and S forms of the molecule carvone

The R-form (which is laevorotatory, has a smell and flavour of spearmint, whilst the S-form has a smell and flavour of caraway seeds. Similarly the closely related molecule limonene has a +(d)-enantiomer which smells of oranges and a -(*l*)-enantiomer that smells of lemons.

Sometimes a natural flavour is a pure enantiomer, because biosynthesis tends to be stereospecific, whereas the synthetic equivalent is often a racemic mixture (a mixture of equal amounts of the enantiomers) because this is much easier to synthesise. An example of this is alpha-ionone, one of the flavours present in raspberries where the natural material is the pure R- alpha-ionone. The toxicity of molecules can also vary tremendously between the different enantiomers, as became tragically apparent in the thalidomide disaster.

QUESTIONS FOR OPTION F

Note that questions intended for HL students only are marked with an asterisk [*].

F1 Food Groups

1. Distinguish between a food and a nutrient. Is it possible to have a food that is not a nutrient? What about a nutrient that is not a food?

2. Describe the common chemical structure of oils and fats? Given this common structure, in what way do oils and fats differ and how may this be explained.

3. Proteins are comprised of many 2-amino acid units. Draw the structural formula of a typical 2-amino acid and show how amino acids join together to form proteins. What name is given to the bond linking the amino acid units?

4. Glucose has the chemical formula $C_6H_{12}O_6$. To what group of chemical compounds does it belong? Name a food component that comprises many glucose units joined together. Give an example of a food that is rich in this component.

5. For the following foods, identify firstly the major food group that they belong to and also give the major use that is made of this by the body.

Olive oil	Flour	Honey
Eggs	Rice	Chocolate

6. The major food groups are carbohydrates, lipids and proteins. Explain why it is that other substances, such as minerals, vitamins and water can be considered as nutrients.

OPTION

F2 Fats and oils

7. Olive oil is mainly mono-unsaturated, whereas sunflower oil is mainly poly-unsaturated. Explain what is meant by these terms. How would you expect the melting points of these two oils to compare? Explain why this is so.

8. Most naturally occurring unsaturated oils are the *cis*-isomer, but hydrogenation of poly-unsaturated oils can give the *trans*-isomer of unsaturated oils. Explain how *cis*- and *trans*- isomers differ and state what differences you would expect between these isomers firstly with regard to melting point and secondly with regard to nutritional value.

9. You are planning to make a 'strawberry candy' with a texture similar to chocolate by blending together a lipid base, sucrose, food colouring and artificial strawberry essence. What kind of lipid would you choose for this? Justify your choice.

10. Going from lard, through olive oil to canola oil to corn oil the degree of unsaturation increases. How would you expect the chemical stability of these lipids to vary? Explain this.

11. Vegetable oils are frequently hydrogenated. Give the reagents and conditions used for these reactions. Give two advantages for the food industry of doing this and two health concerns that the general public might have about the products.

F3 Shelf life

12. Give three specific examples of changes you might notice in specific foods that would indicate that they had been in storage beyond their shelf life.

13. Many cultures have traditional ways of preserving foods. Some that are common across a number of cultures are fermentation, pickling, salting and drying. For each of these give an example of a food that is preserved in this way and explain the reason why this method of preservation works.

14. What is meant by the term 'rancidity'? State which food group becomes rancid and give two changes you could make to the way in which the food is stored which would decrease this effect.

15. Adding antioxidants can increase the shelf life of foods. What is meant by the term antioxidant and what type of food degradation does it combat? Name one synthetic and one naturally occurring antioxidant used in foods.

16. Rancidity can occur by two distinct processes. Describe a way in which substances become rancid that

i) affects all types of lipids.

ii) affects unsaturated lipids much more than saturated ones.

In the case of the latter what other conditions are likely to accelerate the reaction?

17. If you were wanting to increase your consumption of antioxidants, name two foods that you would be advised to eat more of and for each food name the active antioxidant present in it.

18. In food storage often:

i) the moisture level is kept very low.

ii) the packaging excludes air.

iii) the wrapping is opaque.

iv) the product is stored at a low temperature.

Explain how each of these will help to increase the shelf life of the product.

19. Additives are often introduced into foods to delay the onset of microbial growth. Name two specific additives used for this along with one example for each of a foodstuff they are generally added to.

20. Auto-oxidation occurs by a free radical chain reaction. Explain what this means. Write equations for the two reactions that are responsible for generating the major product.

21. Antioxidants added to food can reduce oxidative degradation in three specific ways. Outline these mechanisms and give a specific example of an antioxidant that operates in this manner.

22*. The initiation stage of the auto-oxidation reaction of lipids has a very high activation energy and so occurs relatively infrequently. Explain therefore why auto-oxidation can rapidly lead to the deterioration of foods containing a high proportion of oils.

23*. Explain why it is that trace quantities of transition metals can rapidly accelerate the rate at which lipids become rancid.

F4 Colour

24. Name three groups of compounds that are responsible for the colours of foodstuffs and, for each, give two examples of specific foodstuffs in which they produce the colour.

25. One group of naturally occurring pigments has a structure closely related to that of vitamin A. Which group of pigments is this and what are the principal structural features of this group of compounds?

26. The colour of red cabbage often changes when it is cooked or preserved. What is the principal colouring agent in red cabbage? Give three factors that might affect the colour of this group of compounds when being prepared as foodstuffs.

27. Heme and chlorophyll are both frequently responsible for the colour of foods. Which groups of foods are they found in? They have closely related structures; state one similarity and one difference in their structures. What is the principal change that occurs when heme is converted into myoglobin, the major pigment in muscle tissue?

28. Discuss some health concerns that people have with regard to the use of synthetic dyes in processed foods. What regulatory changes, other than banning their use, would you propose that could reduce public concerns in this regard.

29. When heated on their own, carbohydrates undergo changes that result in the formation of a brown colour. What name is given to this process and how does it occur?

When carbohydrates are heated with proteins a second group of browning processes can also occur. What name is given to this second group? Describe how these food groups interact to produce brown products.

30. What is the normal oxidation state of iron in heme. Under some conditions this may alter and lead to undesirable changes in the appearance of meat – describe this change and the conditions required. Give suggestions of two ways in which the storage of meat could be altered to delay this undesirable change.

31*. Anthocyanins, carotenoids and chlorophyll all have very different structures. Why is it that all are coloured?

32*. When beetroot is boiled the water becomes a bright purple colour, but when carrots are boiled little colouration of the water is noticed, but if carrots are fried, the oil becomes orange coloured. Use your knowledge of the compounds responsible for the colour of these vegetables to explain these observations.

33*. If a molecule of β-carotene was subject to catalytic hydrogenation, would you expect the product to be coloured? Explain.

F5 Genetically modified foods

34. Briefly describe the process by which a plant or animal can be modified to produce a genetically modified (GM) food.

35. Give three separate ways in which genetic modification might improve the yield from a food crop.

36. As well as improving the viability of plants and animals, genetic modification can also result in novel substances being produced by organisms. Give a specific example of such a modification.

37. Many people are opposed to the introduction of genetically modified plants and animals. Explain what their major concerns are.

F6 Texture

38. What physical properties of a food contribute to its texture? Disperse systems often display highly desirable textures. What is meant by a disperse system?

39. Three common disperse systems are suspensions, emulsions and foams. Distinguish between these in terms of the states of the components.

40. The production of stabilised disperse systems often depends on additives such as emulsifiers and stabilisers. Explain the role of these two groups of substances and name a synthetic example of each.

41. What characteristics do all emulsifiers have? Explain how these characteristics allow an emulsifier to produce a stable disperse system from two immiscible components.

42. As well as requiring an emulsifying agent, the production of an emulsion always involves vigorous beating of the components. Explain why this mechanical agitation is necessary.

F7 Stereochemistry in food

43*. What is meant by an absolute configuration? Place the following substituents in increasing order for the R-S system of indicating absolute configurations:

-CO-CH_3 -CH_2-CH_3 -F -C=CH_2
-OH -CO-OH

44*. Is the compound shown the D or L enantiomer of the amino acid leucine?

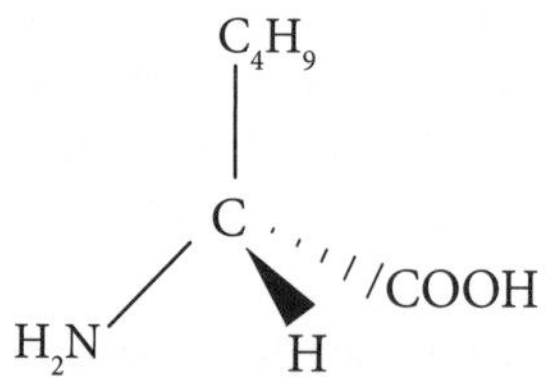

C_4H_9 | C ; H_2N, H (wedge), COOH (dashed)

45*. Draw the R-isomer of 2-chloropropanoic acid.

46*. Is the compound illustrated below the R-isomer or the S-isomer of 2-methylbut-3-enal?

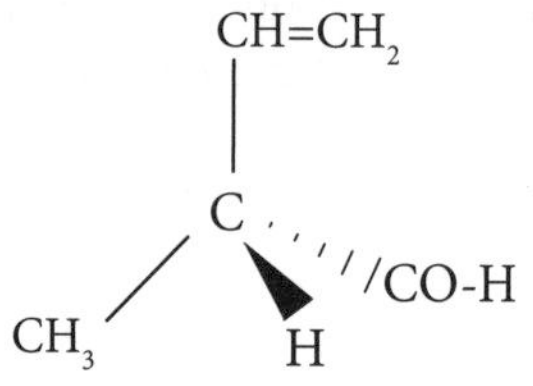

CH=CH_2 | C ; CH_3, H (wedge), CO-H (dashed)

47*. Draw the D-isomer of the 4-carbon sugar erythrulose (HO-CH_2-CO-CH(OH)-CH_2OH).

48*. The specific rotation of naturally occurring sucrose is +66.5°. Is it dextrorotatory or laevorotatory? What would be the specific rotation of its enantiomer?

49*. Explain how it may be possible to tell whether a food colouring containing a chiral centre comes from a natural or a synthetic source.

50*. Give a specific example of a compound for which the two enantiomers have different smells or tastes.

FURTHER ORGANIC CHEMISTRY

18

G1 Electrophilic addition reactions
G2 Nucleophilic addition reactions
G4 Addition–elimination reactions
G3 Elimination reactions
G5 Arenes
G6 Organometallic chemistry
G7, G11 Reaction pathways (SL and HL)
G8 Acid–base reactions
G9 Addition–elimination reactions (HL)
G10 Electrophilic substitution reactions (HL)

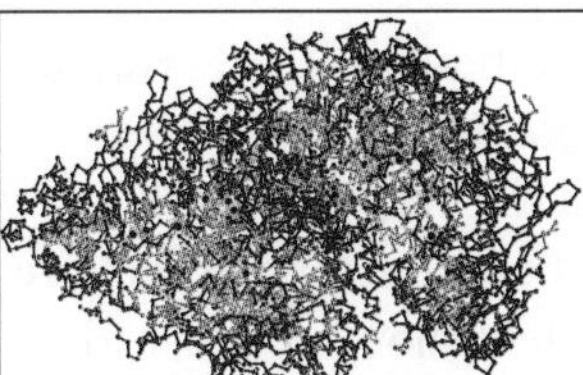

G1 ELECTROPHILIC ADDITION REACTIONS

G.1.1 Describe and explain the electrophilic addition mechanisms of the reactions of alkenes with halogens and hydrogen halides.

G.1.2 Predict and explain the formation of the major product in terms of the relative stabilities of carbocations.

The typical reactions that alkenes undergo are addition reactions in which the double bond is converted to a single bond and two new bonds are formed. These reactions occur in two stages and are initiated by species known as **electrophiles**. These are species that will attack a molecule at a region of high electron density, such as a double or triple bond by accepting an electron pair. First the electrophile attacks the double bond, which you may recall comprises a **σ-bond** and a **π-bond**. This results in the destruction of the π–bond and the electrons from that bond form a new σ-bond to the electrophile, which itself undergoes heterolytic fission. This results in the formation of an intermediate **carbocation** (a species in which the carbon carries a positive charge and has only three electron pairs around it). If a neutral molecule, such as a halogen, is the electrophile, the approach of the molecule to the double bond causes a movement of electrons in the halogen–halogen bond and hence an induced dipole is produced. Using ethene and bromine as the example, the mechanism of the first stage of the addition is

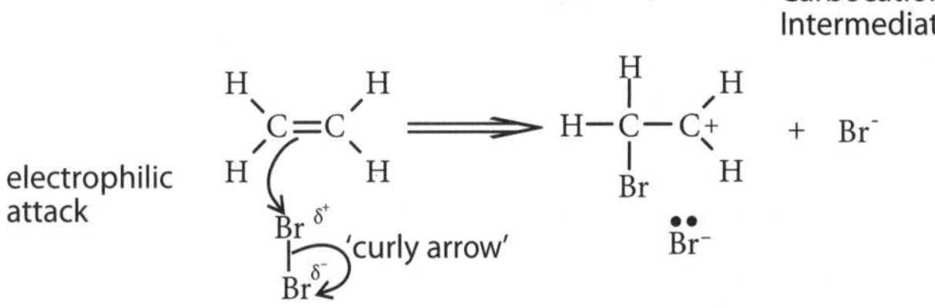

Figure 1801 The first step of electrophilic addition

Then in the second step (or stage), this carbocation will react with an anion present to complete the addition process:

1,2-dibromoethane

Figure 1802 The second step of electrophilic addition

Note the use of 'curly arrows' in the equations above. These curly arrows should start at the bond or lone pair initially containing the electrons and should end at the atom the bond is formed to, or where the electron pair creates a **lone pair**. Evidence in favour of an ionic mechanism comes from the fact that if the reaction is carried out in the presence of NaCl(aq), where Cl^- anions are present,

OPTION

the carbocation intermediate reacts not only with Br^- but also with Cl^- to also produce $CH_2Br–CH_2Cl$, 1-bromo-2-chloroethane.

The example above involves a symmetrical electrophile, for example, where the two bromine atoms are identical. The reaction can also occur with polar non–symmetrical electrophiles, such as H–Br or I-Cl. In this case, the more positively charged of the two atoms (the one with the lower electronegativity) will be the one that attacks the alkene. This is important where the alkene is also non–symmetrical (such as propene, $CH_2=CHCH_3$) as the addition reaction can then result in two different products. In these cases, the initial electrophilic attack can produce two different carbocations. So for example, the addition of HX to propene can form the secondary carbocation $CH_3–C^+H–CH_3$ or the primary carbocation $CH_3–CH_2–C^+H_2$. These carbocations will have different stabilities and the more stable will always predominate and lead to the major product.

It is found that the lower the electrical charge carried by a particular atom, then the more stable the species is. In the case of carbocations, the **inductive effect** (that is the ability of the covalent bond to polarise and reduce the charge) of the atoms bonded on to the carbon carrying the positive charge must be considered. Empirically it appears that alkyl groups attached to this atom reduce the charge that it carries more than hydrogen atoms do. This means that tertiary carbocations (with three carbon atoms attached to the charged one) are more stable than secondary carbocations (two carbon atoms) which in turn are more stable than primary carbocations (one carbon):

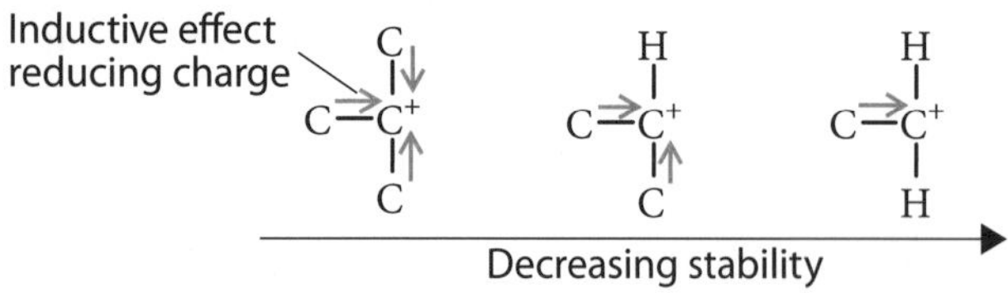

Figure 1803 The relative stability of carbocations

Combining a knowledge of the polarity of the attacking electrophile with that of the stability of the intermediate carbocations allows the prediction of the major product from an addition reaction between an asymmetrical electrophile and an asymmetrical alkene. Consider the reaction of iodine monochloride with propene as an example. Iodine is less electronegative than chlorine and so it will have a partial positive charge as a result of the polarity of the Cl-I bond. This means that the iodine atom is the one that attacks the double bond. There are also two possible carbocations that could form, a more stable secondary carbocation and a less stable primary carbocation. The major product from the reaction is therefore the one that results from the secondary carbocation as shown in Figure 1804.

Figure 1804 The addition of iodine monochloride to propene

Therefore the major product of this reaction is $CH_3–CHI–CH_2Cl$ rather than $CH_3–CHCl–CH_2I$.

Empirical observation led to the formulation of **Markovnikov's Rule**:

"When a molecule H–X adds to a multiple carbon–carbon bond, the hydrogen atom will always attach itself to the carbon atom that already has most hydrogens attached to it".

Some people like to memorise this as "the rich get richer". The reason for this is that in electrophiles involving hydrogen, the hydrogen is almost always the atom that carries the partial positive charge owing to its relatively low electronegativity. In addition the carbocation with the least number of hydrogens on the charged carbon is the more stable, so that this hydrogen attaches itself to the carbon that already has most hydrogens. Consider the addition of hydrogen bromide to methylpropene, there are two possible products as shown in Figure 1805.

Figure 1805 The reaction of hydrogen bromide and methylpropene

The reaction, in accordance with Markovnikov's Rule, gives a product that is almost entirely 'A' with very little 'B'. This is in keeping with the explanation in terms of the stability of the intermediate carbocations shown.

OPTION

Exercise G1

1. Which one of the following is the major product when propene reacts with hydrogen bromide?

   A CH_3-CH_2-CH_2-Br
   B CH_3-CHBr-CH_3
   C Br-CH_2-CH_2-CH_2-Br
   D CH_3-CHBr-CH_2-Br

2. Which one of the methylbutane carbocations below would you expect to be the more stable?

   A CH_3-(CH_3)CH-CH_2-CH_2^+
   B CH_3-(CH_3)CH-CH^+-CH_3
   C CH_3-(CH_3)C^+-CH_2-CH_3
   D $^+CH_2$-(CH_3)CH-CH_2-CH_3

3. Draw the mechanism for the reaction of iodine monochloride (I-Cl) with 2-methylbut-1-ene. State which of the two possible products will predominate and explain why this is the case.

4. Methylpropene can react with hydrogen bromide to produce two isomeric bromoalkanes.

   a) Draw the structural formulae of the two possible products and state which you would expect to predominate.
   b) These bromoalkanes can be hydrolysed to give two different alcohols:

      i What reagent and conditions are required for this?
      ii Give the names of the two alcohols and state whether they are primary, secondary or tertiary alcohols.

5. The hydration of propene to produce propan–2–ol is reversible. Discuss, in terms of Le Chatelier's principle, how the reaction conditions can be varied to favour the forward or reverse reaction. Why is the major product propan–2–ol rather than propan–1–ol?

G2 NUCLEOPHILIC ADDITION REACTIONS

G.2.1 Describe, using equations, the addition of hydrogen cyanide to aldehydes and ketones.

G.2.2 Describe and explain the mechanism for the addition of hydrogen cyanide to aldehydes and ketones.

G.2.3 Describe, using equations, the hydrolysis of cyanohydrins to form carboxylic acids.

The **carbonyl group**, found in **aldehydes** and **ketones**, is quite polar with the carbon atom being the positive end of the dipole. This carbon atom is therefore electron deficient and hence susceptible to **nucleophilic attack** and through this **addition** to the carbon–oxygen double bond occurs. A **nucleophile** is a molecule or ion that has a lone pair of electrons that it can use to form a new bond to a centre of positive charge. A good example of this type of reaction is the addition of hydrogen cyanide to the carbonyl group, as shown in Figure 1806.

$$-\overset{\displaystyle O}{\overset{\|}{C}}- \; + \; H-C{\equiv}N \;\Rightarrow\; -\overset{\displaystyle H-O}{\overset{|}{\underset{\underset{\displaystyle C{\equiv}N}{|}}{C}}}-$$

Figure 1806 The addition of hydrogen cyanide to the carbonyl group

This reaction requires a base catalyst to convert the hydrogen cyanide into the more nucleophilic cyanide ion and the carbon of the cyanide ion then acts as a nucleophile, attacking the carbonyl carbon to produce an intermediate anion. This reacts with the water present to form the hydroxynitrile product (also known as a cyanohydrin) containing an alcohol with a nitrile group on it, regenerating the base catalyst:

OPTION

$$HCN + OH^- \rightleftharpoons CN^- + H_2O$$

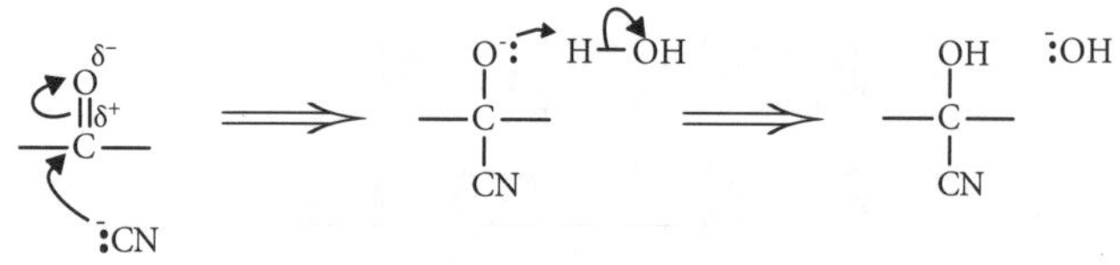

Figure 1807 The mechanism of the nucleophilic attack of hydrogen cyanide to a carbonyl group

This hydroxynitrile can be hydrolysed by refluxing with either dilute acid (or dilute alkali) to produce an ammonium salt (or ammonia) and a carboxylic acid (or its anion). The acid produced contains one more carbon atom than the original aldehyde or ketone and so this reaction is a means of lengthening the carbon chain, see Figure 1808.

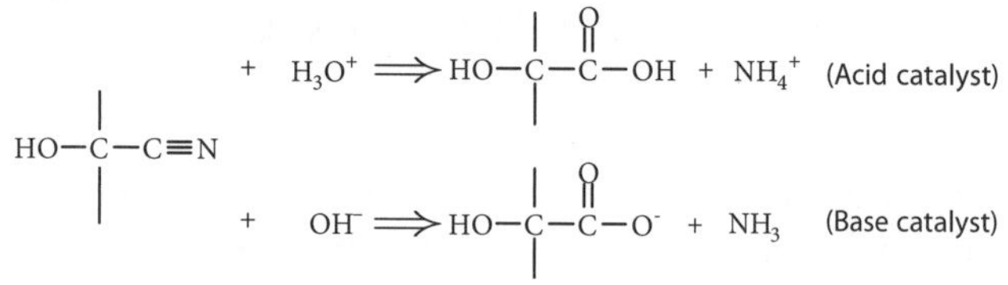

(Acid catalyst)

(Base catalyst)

Figure 1808 The lengthening of a carbon chain via the addition of hydrogen cyanide to an aldehyde

The hydrolysis of the addition product from the reaction of hydrogen cyanide with ethanal, is therefore 2-hydroxypropanoic acid (lactic acid which is formed when milk goes sour).

$$CH_3CHO + HCN \rightarrow CH_3CH(OH)\text{-}CN$$

$$CH_3CH(OH)\text{-}CN + 2\,H_2O \rightarrow CH_3CH(OH)\text{-}COOH + NH_3$$

G4 ADDITION–ELIMINATION REACTIONS

G.4.1 Describe, using equations, the reactions of 2,4-dinitrophenylhydrazine with aldehydes and ketones.

With some nucleophiles that have a hydrogen atom attached to the same atom that acts as the **nucleophile**, the initial addition product from the reaction with the **carbonyl** group can eliminate water (hence they are sometimes called '**condensation reactions**') to reform the double bond resulting in an **addition–elimination** reaction. Carbonyl compounds can react in this way with molecules containing the -NH_2 group, as shown in Figure 1809:

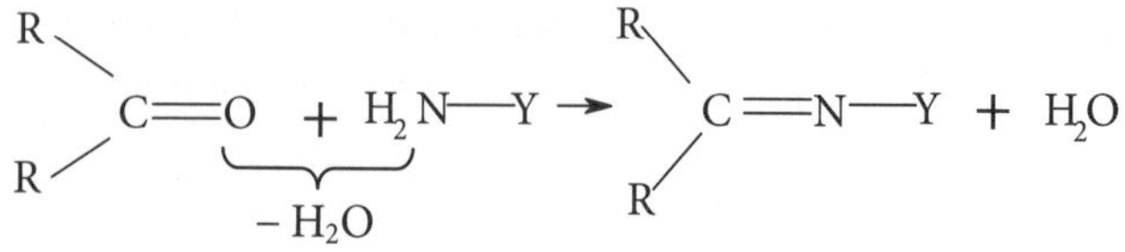

$$R_2C{=}O + H_2N{-}Y \rightarrow R_2C{=}N{-}Y + H_2O$$

Figure 1809 A typical nucleophilic addition-elimination reaction

The most commonly encountered reaction of this type is that which occurs between carbonyl compounds and 2,4–dinitrophenylhydrazine (2,4-DNP). In this a lone pair on the terminal nitrogen acts as the nucleophile and an addition reaction occurs, by a mechanism similar to that in Figure 1807, followed by the gain and loss of hydrogen ions, to form the intermediate. This then eliminates a hydrogen ion and a hydroxide ion (that is water overall) to give the final product, as shown in Figure 1810.

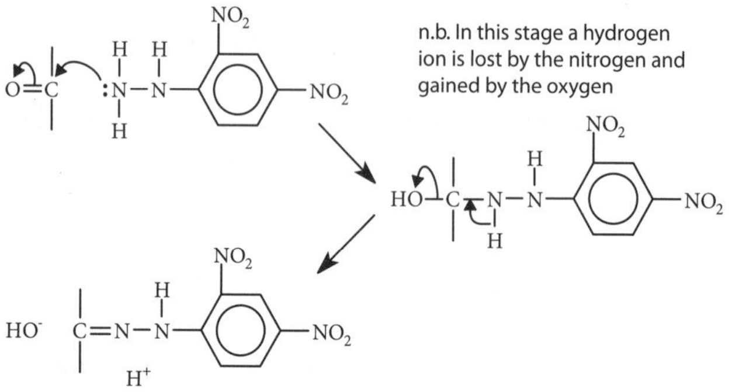

n.b. In this stage a hydrogen ion is lost by the nitrogen and gained by the oxygen

Figure 1810 The addition-elimination reaction of 2.4-dinitrophenylhydrazine with the carbonyl group

This final product is an orange–yellow crystalline solid. Its formation is used as a test for aldehydes and ketones. The sharp melting point of these crystalline derivatives was formerly used to identify the aldehyde or ketone that they were formed from. Some examples are given in Figure 1811:

Carbonyl compound	melting point of 2,4-dinitrophenylhydrazone / °C
methanal	167
ethanal	164
propanal	156
propanone	128
butanal	123
butanone	115

Figure 1811 The melting points of some 2.4-dinitrophenylhydrazones

OPTION

Exercise G4

1. When propanal is reacted with hydrogen cyanide and the initial product hydrolysed, the final product will be:

A CH_3- CH_2-COOH
B CH_3-CH(OH)-COOH
C CH_3-CH_2-CH_2-COOH
D CH_3-CH_2-CH(OH)-COOH

2. In the reaction between a carbonyl compound and hydrogen cyanide a base is usually added to convert the hydrogen cyanide into the cyanide ion. This is done because the cyanide ion is:

A a stronger reducing agent.
B a stronger oxidising agent.
C a stronger acid.
D a stronger nucleophile.

3. The product of the reaction between butanone and 2,4-dinitrophenylhydrazine is likely to be:

A a purple liquid.
B a red solid.
C a yellow solid.
D a green liquid.

4. 2-hydroxypropanoic acid may be prepared from ethanal by a two stage process via an intermediate compound (X).

a) Draw the stuctural formulae of these two compounds.
b) Draw the structure of the probable intermediate (X).
c) Give the reagents and conditions required to convert ethanal into X.
d) Outline the mechanism of this reaction.
e) Give the reagents and conditions required to convert X into hydroxypropanoic acid.
f) Hydroxypropanoic acid can exist as a pair of enantiomers. Explain why this occurs and draw diagrams to illustrate how the enantiomers differ.
g) What is meant by 'optical activity' and how is this related to enantiomers?
h) In view of this why is the hydroxypropanoic acid produced in the above process optically inactive? Explain in terms of your answer to (d) why this occurs.

5. Phenylethanone (acetophenone) is the molecule (C_6H_5-CO-CH_3). Write the formula for the organic product formed when:

a) It reacts with hydrogen cyanide.
b) When this product is hydrolysed.
c) It reacts with 2,4-dinitrophenylhydrazine.

The melting point of this final product is 238°C. What use was made historically of this melting point and that of related compounds?

G3 ELIMINATION REACTIONS

G.3.1 Describe, using equations, the dehydration reactions of alcohols with phosphoric acid to form alkenes.

G.3.2 Describe and explain the mechanism for the elimination of water from alcohols.

An **elimination reaction** is the opposite of an addition reaction. In it a multiple bond is formed between two neighbouring atoms and a small molecule is formed from the groups that were originally attached to these atoms.

When alcohols are heated to a temperature of ~170°C with an excess of concentrated phosphoric or sulfuric acid, they undergo dehydration to form an alkene. For example, ethanol loses water to form ethene:

$$C_2H_5OH \longrightarrow C_2H_4 + H_2O$$

In this reaction, the acid protonates the hydroxyl group, so that water, a much better leaving group than the hydroxide ion, is lost in the second elimination step, in which the conjugate base of the acid accepts a hydrogen ion from the carbon next to the one attached to the –OH group, as shown in Figure 1812.

$$H_3C\text{-}CH_2\text{-}OH + H\text{-}O\text{-}PO_3H_2 \Longrightarrow H_3C\text{-}CH_2\text{-}OH_2^+ + {:}O^-\text{-}PO_3H_2$$

$$H_2PO_3\text{-}O^- + H\text{-}CH_2\text{-}CH_2\text{-}OH_2^+ \Longrightarrow H_2PO_3\text{-}O\text{-}H + H_2C{=}CH_2 + H_2O$$

Figure 1812 Mechanism of the acid catalysed elimination reaction of an alcohol

OPTION

Note that if the hydroxyl group is in the middle, rather than at the end of the hydrocarbon chain, then the elimination can occur in more than one direction. Hence a mixture of products may result. So that whilst in the dehydration of ethanol or cyclohexanol only one product is possible, the dehydration of 2-methylbutan-2-ol yields a mixture of 2-methylbut-1-ene and 2-methylbut-2-ene, as shown in Figure 1813:

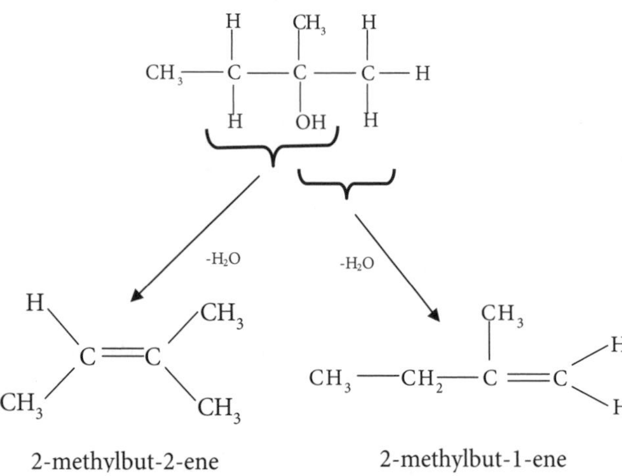

Figure 1813 Mixed products from the dehydration of 2-methylbutan-2-ol

It is interesting to note that, as shown in Figure 1814, the dehydration reaction at a slightly lower temperature in the presence of excess ethanol yields ethoxyethane through a nucleophilic substitution reaction:

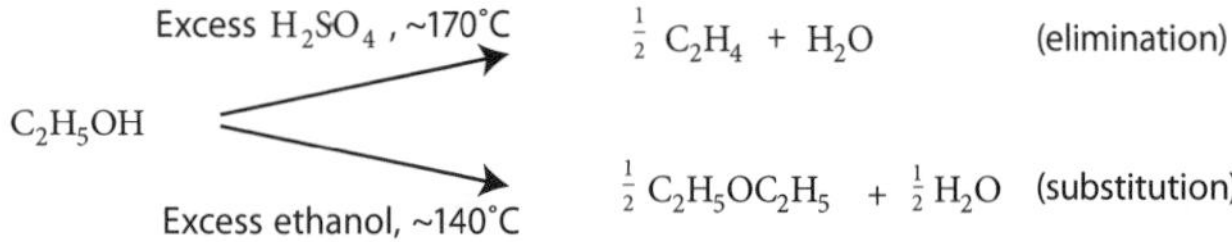

Figure 1814 Competing dehydration reactions of ethanol

Exercise G3

1. Which one of the following will give more than one product when it undergoes dehydration to form an alkene?

   A Propan-1-ol.
   B Propan-2-ol.
   C Butan-1-ol.
   D Butan-2-ol.

2. When alcohols dehydrate the reaction goes via

   A a carbocation.
   B a carbanion.
   C a free radical.
   D an alkane.

3. Give the mechanism for the dehydration of cylohexanol. State the conditions required to bring about this reaction and explain why only one product is possible.

G5 ARENES

G.5.1 Describe and explain the structure of benzene using physical and chemical evidence.

G.5.2 Describe and explain the relative rates of hydrolysis of benzene compounds halogenated in the ring and in the side-chain.

Benzene a, hydrocarbon with the formula C_6H_6, is a typical **arene** (indeed the term is used to describe hydrocarbons involving a ring structure or fused ring structure? similar to that of benzene. The fact that there are three different structural isomers with the formula $C_6H_4X_2$ indicates that benzene probably contains a six membered ring and for a long time it was thought to be a cyclic molecule equivalent to 'cyclohexatriene'. There are however many pieces of evidence that lead to the conclusion that this is not in fact the correct structure for benzene. Briefly these are:

1. 'Cyclohexatriene' would not be symmetrical owing to the fact that double bonds are shorter than single bonds (C–C = 0.154 nm, C=C = 0.134 nm), yet X–ray crystallography shows that benzene has

sixfold rotational symmetry and its bonds are all of an equal intermediate length (0.139 nm).

2. Benzene most commonly undergoes substitution reactions, rather than the addition reactions that characterise alkenes. For example it does not decolourise bromine water, a common test for carbon–carbon double bonds.

3. Benzene is found to be more thermodynamically stable than would be predicted for 'cyclohexatriene'. For example the enthalpy changes for both the hydrogenation and the combustion of benzene are significantly less exothermic than would be predicted for cyclohexatriene.

Cyclohexene reacts with hydrogen to form cyclohexane and this reaction releases 119 kJ mol^{-1} of heat energy. If benzene was cyclohexatriene and contained three double bonds then it would be reasonable to expect it to release three times this amount of energy (that is 357 kJ mol^{-1}). In fact only 207 kJ mol^{-1} of heat energy is released so that the delocalisation of the double bonds results in benzene being stabilised by about 150 kJ mol^{-1}. This is illustrated in Figure 1815.

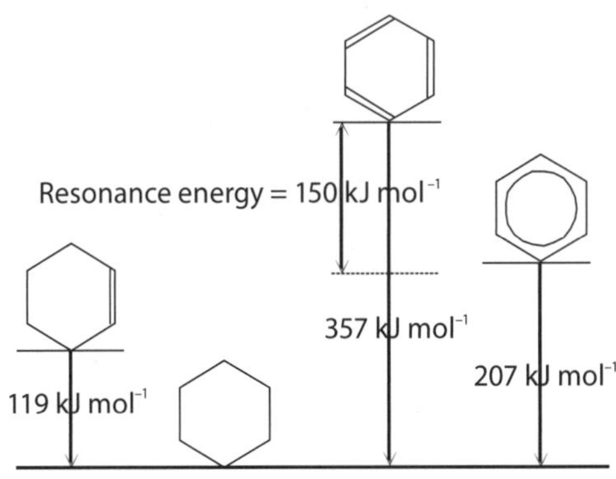

Figure 1815 The thermochemistry of the hydrogenation of benzene

Whilst most **halogenoalkanes** readily undergo nucleophilic substitution reactions, halogenated benzene derivatives, in which the halogen is attached directly to the benzene ring:

C_6H_5–Cl

are very resistant to nucleophilic substitution, requiring heating to over 300°C under high pressure. This is the result of three factors:

- The charge on the carbon atom that is attached to the halogen is much reduced by distortion of the delocalised π–bond.
- Attack on the carbon atom from the side opposite to the carbon–halogen bond is blocked by the presence of the benzene ring.
- The p–electrons on the halogen interact with the π–bond of the benzene ring to produce a carbon-halogen bond that has a partial double bond character and is stronger than the usual bond.

If the halogen is not directly attached to the benzene ring (such as in C_6H_5–CH_2–Cl), then the reactivity is similar to halogenoalkanes. Early insecticides, such as DDT, contained chlorine atoms directly bonded on to a benzene ring and their resistance to substitution reactions is part of the reason why they are so persistent in the environment.

Exercise G5

1. Which one of the following would you expect to undergo most rapid hydrolysis?

   A Cl-C_6H_4-CH_3

   B Br-C_6H_4-CH_3

   C C_6H_5-CH_2-Cl

   D C_6H_5-CH_2-Br

2. Which one of the following implies that benzene does not contain carbon-carbon double bonds?

   A It is a cyclic molecule.
   B It is planar.
   C It has a regular hexagonal shape.
   D It is a liquid at room temperature and pressure.

OPTION

3. How many isomers, involving a benzene ring, are there of $C_6H_4Cl_2$?

   A 2
   B 3
   C 4
   D 5

4. Does delocalisation in the benzene ring increase or decrease thermodynamic stability? Explain the evidence for this involving the hydrogenation reactions of cyclohexene (C_6H_{10}) and benzene (C_6H_6).

5. A research chemist considers the possible conversion of 4-chloro(chloromethyl)benzene (Cl-⌬-CH_2Cl) to 4-hydroxy(chloromethyl) benzene (HO-⌬-CH_2Cl) and to 4-chlorophenylmethanol (Cl-⌬-CH_2OH). State which is likely to be successsful and explain in detail why this conversion is much more feasible than the other.

G6 ORGANOMETALLIC CHEMISTRY

G.6.1 Outline the formation of Grignard reagents.

G.6.2 Describe, using equations, the reactions of Grignard reagents with water, carbon dioxide, aldehydes and ketones.

Usually metals form ionic bonds, though a number of exceptions to this have already been met (anhydrous $AlCl_3$ and ions such as $Cr_2O_7^{2-}$). In organometallic compounds metal atoms are bonded to carbon by polar covalent bonds. Some of the first compounds of this type to be discovered were the **Grignard reagents** in which magnesium is covalently bonded to a hydrocarbon chain. They are usually formed by the reaction between magnesium metal and a halogenoalkane:

$$\text{Mg} + \text{R-X} \rightarrow \text{R-Mg-X}$$

Grignard reagents react very readily with moisture and so their formation requires very anhydrous conditions. Hence the solvent usually used for this reaction is ethoxyethane that has been dried by having sodium wire in it. The reaction is also often initiated by a trace of iodine. In the above reaction, X can be Cl, Br or I; fluorides do not react because of the strength of the C–F bond.

Grignard reagents are not isolated, but are used as prepared. Because of the polarity of the Mg-C bond, in many of their reactions Grignard reagents react as if they contained a **carbanion** (a carbon with a negative charge, R^-). As mentioned they react with water to yield the corresponding alkane:

$$\text{R-MgX} + H_2O \rightarrow \text{R-H} + \text{Mg(OH)X}$$

The most important reactions of Grignard reagents however are those in which they form new carbon-carbon bonds, so extending the length of the hydrocarbon chain. For example they react with **carbon dioxide** to form an intermediate, which is readily hydrolysed by dilute acid to a carboxylic acid containing one more carbon than the Grignard reagent:

$$\text{R-MgX} + CO_2 \rightarrow [\text{R-}CO_2\text{MgX}]\ (+ H^+_{(aq)}) \rightarrow \text{R-COOH}_{(aq)} + Mg^{2+}_{(aq)} + X^-_{(aq)}$$

Grignard reagents also undergo similar addition reactions with the **carbonyl** group:

$$\text{R-MgX} + \text{C=O} \rightarrow [\text{R-COMgX}] + (H^+_{(aq)}) \rightarrow \text{R-COH}_{(aq)} + Mg^{2+}_{(aq)} + X^-_{(aq)}$$

Hence with methanal the product is a primary alcohol. With an aldehyde it is a secondary alcohol and with a ketone it is a tertiary alcohol. The equations below, which do not show the intermediate, give specific examples of reactions of this type:

$$C_2H_5\text{-MgX} + H_2C\text{=O}\ (+ H^+) \rightarrow C_2H_5\text{-}CH_2\text{-OH} + Mg^{2+} + X^-$$

$$C_2H_5\text{-MgX} + CH_3\text{-CHO}\ (+ H^+) \rightarrow C_2H_5\text{-CH(}CH_3\text{)-OH} + Mg^{2+} + X^-$$

$$C_2H_5\text{-MgX} + CH_3\text{-CO-}CH_3\ (+ H^+) \rightarrow C_2H_5\text{-C(}CH_3)_2\text{-OH} + Mg^{2+} + X^-$$

OPTION

Exercise G6

1. The carbon atom bonded to the magnesium in a Grignard reagent acts as a strong:

   A electrophile.
   B nucleophile.
   C acid.
   D oxidising agent.

2. Which one of the following is most important for the successful preparation of a Grignard reagent?

   A A high temperature.
   B A high pressure.
   C Anhydrous conditions.
   D Anaerobic conditions.

3. Which one of the following reacts with a Grignard reagent to produce a product containing the same hydrocarbon skeleton as the halogenoalkane from which it was formed?

   A H_2O
   B CH_2O
   C CH_3CHO
   D CH_3COCH_3

4. Describe how you would go about preparing a Grignard reagent from magnesium turnings and 1-bromobutane.

5. Outline a reaction, involving ethylmagnesium bromide, that you could use to prepare a sample of 3-methylpentan-3-ol ($(C_2H_5)_3COH$).

G7, G11 REACTION PATHWAYS (SL AND HL)

G.7.1 & G 11.1 Deduce reaction pathways given the starting materials and the product.

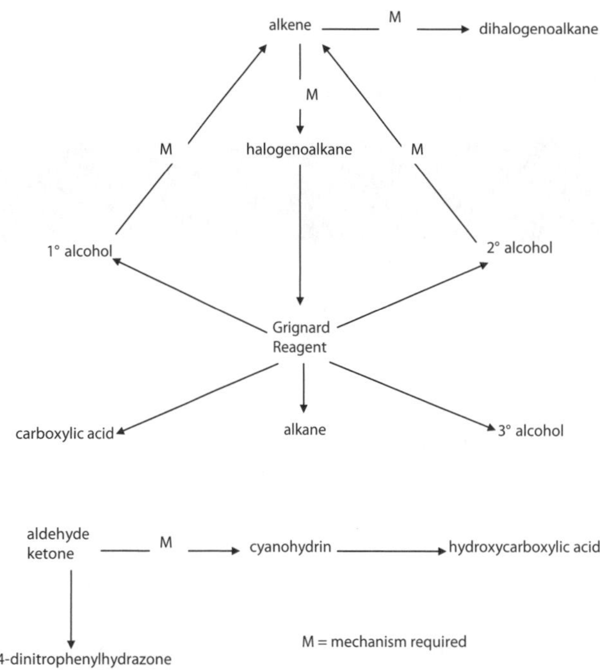

Figure 1816 A summary reactions for SL students

As previously encountered, it is important to be able to devise synthetic pathways by which one compound can be converted into another even if a direct conversion is not possible. This can be done by considering what possible products the reactant could be converted to and what reactions can produce the desired product, in order to find an appropriate intermediate compound. If a lengthening of the hydrocarbon chain is required, then this may be achieved through the formation of a nitrile or via a Grignard reagent. The conditions required to bring about these reactions are also important, and in some cases the mechanism should also be known. The groups of compounds for which such knowledge is expected of Standard Level students studying the Further Organic Chemistry Option is given in Figure 1816 and those for students studying it at Higher Level is given in Figure 1817. Further details of these reactions can be found from the relevant sections of the text.

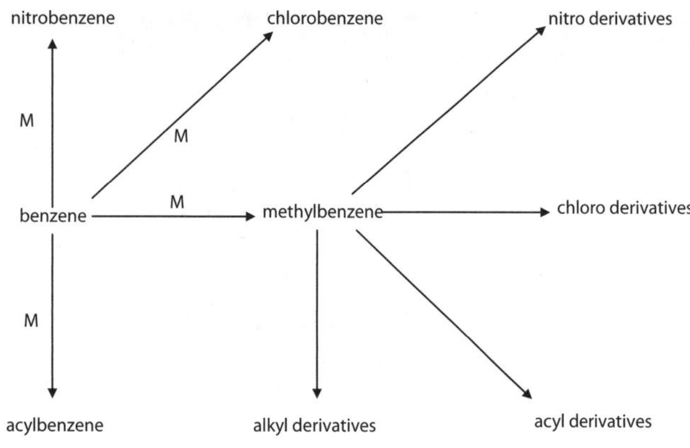

Figure 1817 A summary reactions for HL students

Exercise

*(Note that questions with an asterisk * are for HL students only.)*

1. Give reagents and conditions for a scheme to convert ethanal (CH_3CHO) to 2-hydroxypropanoic acid ($CH_3CH(OH)COOH$).

2. What reagents and conditions would you require to produce methylpropan-2-ol from propanone?

3. How could you produce a sample of benzene from chlorobenzene? Give appropriate reagents and conditions.

4.* If you required a sample of 4-nitromethylbenzene (O_2N-⌬-CH_3)and you had only benzene as the organic starting material, describe, giving reagents and conditions for each step. How you might achieve this. What would be the probable major impurity in the product?

5.* Give appropriate reagents and conditions for the conversion of benzene into chloromethylbenzene (⌬-CH_2-Cl).

G8 ACID–BASE REACTIONS

G.8.1 Describe and explain the acidic properties of phenol and substituted phenols in terms of bonding.

G.8.2 Describe and explain the acidic properties of substituted carboxylic acids in terms of bonding.

G.8.3 Compare and explain the relative basicities of ammonia and amines.

The **acidity** of a compound to a large extent depends on the stability of the anion formed when it dissociates. This in turn is mainly dependent on the degree to which the charge on the anion formed can be distributed amongst other atoms in the molecule.

In **alcohols**, if the molecule loses a hydrogen ion, the charge on the resultant anion is concentrated onto a single oxygen atom. In the case of **phenols**, some of the charge may be distributed on to the benzene ring through interaction of a lone pair of electrons on the oxygen with the delocalised π–electrons. The reduction in charge that this produces is much less than that from the complete delocalisation between two oxygen atoms found in carboxylic acids, so that phenol is only very weakly acidic. Like carboxylic acids, phenols will form salts with strong bases such as sodium hydroxide, but unlike carboxylic acids, simple phenols will not produce carbon dioxide when they react with carbonates because they are weaker acids than 'carbonic acid'. This is summarised in Figure 1818.

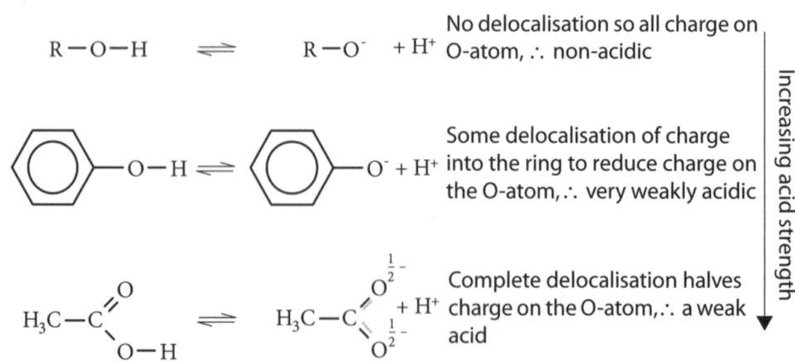

Figure 1818 The relationship between redistribution of charge and acid strength

In the case of a substituted phenol, a group that donates electrons (such as $-CH_3$) will increase the charge density in the ring and hence on the oxygen, making the anion less stable and the acid weaker. Conversely groups that withdraw electrons (such as $-Cl$ and $-NO_2$) will further reduce the electron density and hence make the acid stronger, as shown below. In the case of 2,4,6-trinitrophenol the effect of the three nitro groups is so large as to make it quite a strong acid. This is as summarised in Figure 1819.

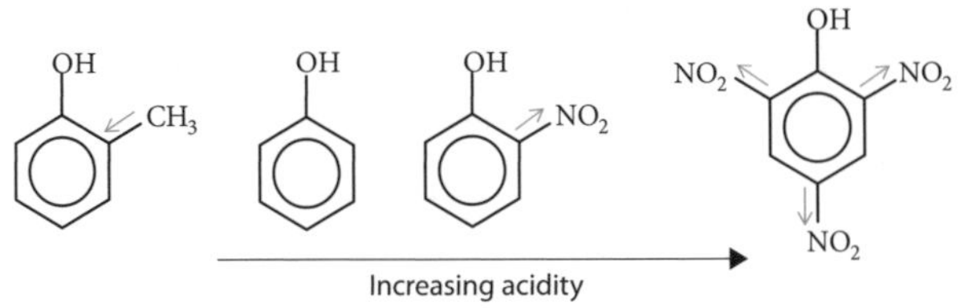

OH, CH_3 | OH | OH, NO_2 | OH, NO_2, NO_2, NO_2

Increasing acidity →

Figure 1819 The effect of substituents on the acidity of substituted phenols

The same is true for carboxylic acids. Substituents that donate electrons (e.g. $-CH_3$) make the acid weaker, whereas electron withdrawing substituents (e.g. $-Cl$) make the acid stronger; see Figure 1820.

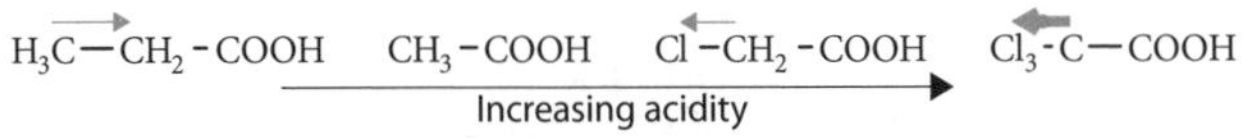

H_3C-CH_2-COOH CH_3-COOH $Cl-CH_2-COOH$ $Cl_3-C-COOH$

Increasing acidity →

Figure 1820 The effect of substituents on the acidity of carboxylic acids

Amines are closely related to ammonia and many of their reactions are analogous to those of ammonia. Like ammonia they have an unpleasant 'fishy' smell. When dissolved in water, like ammonia, they act as weak bases and form an alkaline solution:

$$R\text{-}NH_2 + H_2O \rightleftharpoons R\text{-}NH_3^+ + OH^-$$

Acids drive this equilibrium to the right and convert the amine into a salt:

$$R\text{-}NH_2 + HCl \rightarrow R\text{-}NH_3^+ Cl^-$$

For example ethylamine and hydrochloric acid form ethylammonium chloride. These salts are white crystalline solids. When they are warmed with an alkali such as aqueous sodium hydroxide, the equilibrium is driven to the left and the free amine regenerated:

$$R\text{-}NH_3^+ + OH^- \rightarrow R\text{-}NH_2 + H_2O$$

The principle of reducing the electrical charge on the atom to stabilise the ion also applies to the cations formed when these species act as weak bases. In this case however a positive charge needs minimising, so that electron donating groups, such as alkyl groups, help to stabilise the cation. This means that alkyl amines are stronger bases than ammonia and the base strength increases from methylamine (primary amine), through dimethylamine (secondary amine) to trimethylamine (tertiary amine), which is quite a strong base.

In **amides** ($-CO-NH_2$) the lone pair of electrons on the nitrogen is involved in a delocalised π-bond with the electrons in the carbon–oxygen double bond. This means that this pair of electrons is not available to form a bond to a hydrogen ion. Hence amides are non-basic. The relative base strengths of compounds containing the $-NH_2$ group are summarised in Figure 1821.

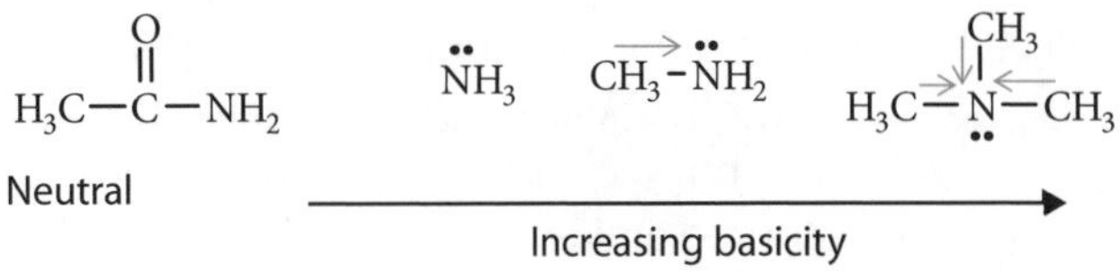

$H_3C-C(=O)-NH_2$ (Neutral) | NH_3 | CH_3-NH_2 | $H_3C-N(CH_3)-CH_3$

Increasing basicity →

Figure 1821 Factors affecting the basicity of the $-NH_2$ group

Exercise

1. Which one of the following will have the highest pH when in aqueous solution?

   A $CH_3\text{-}CH_2\text{-}COOH$
   B $Cl\text{-}CH_2\text{-}COOH$
   C NH_3
   D $CH_3\text{-}NH_2$

2. Phenols are stronger acids than alcohols because:

   A They are solids rather than liquids.
   B They form stronger hydrogen bonds to water.
   C They have a stronger C-O bond.
   D The charge on the conjugate base is partly delocalised.

3. Which one of the following gives the correct order of increasing base strength?

   A $CH_3CONH_2 < NH_3 < CH_3NH_2 < (CH_3)_3N$
   B $CH_3CONH_2 < (CH_3)_3N < CH_3NH_2 < NH_3$
   C $(CH_3)_3N < CH_3NH_2 < NH_3 < CH_3CONH_2$
   D $NH_3 < CH_3NH_2 < (CH_3)_3N < CH_3CONH_2$

4. Explain why ethanol is neutral, phenol a very weak acid, ethanoic acid a weak acid, and trichloroethanoic acid a quite strong acid.

5. Explain why adding a methyl group makes a carboxylic acid a weaker acid (HCOOH is a stronger acid than CH_3COOH), but an amine a stronger base (CH_3NH_2 is a weaker base than $(CH_3)_2NH_2$).

G9 ADDITION–ELIMINATION REACTIONS

G.9.1 Describe, using equations, the reactions of acid anhydrides with nucleophiles to form carboxylic acids, esters, amides and substituted amides.

G.9.2 Describe, using equations, the reactions of acyl chlorides with nucleophiles to form carboxylic acids, esters, amides and substituted amides.

G.9.3 Explain the reactions of acyl chlorides with nucleophiles in terms of an addition–elimination mechanism.

As was seen above the **carbonyl group** in aldehydes and ketones can undergo a nucleophilic addition-elimination reaction, with for example 2,4-dinitrophenylhydrazine. The carbonyl group in compounds related to carboxylic acids, such as **acid anhydrides** (R-CO-O-CO-R) and **acyl chlorides** (R-CO-Cl) is even more polar than that in aldehydes and ketones as a result of the electron withdrawing power of the additional chlorine or oxygen bonded to it. As a result, these compounds are much more reactive. The carbonyl group in them can also undergo addition-elimination reactions but in this case, because the compound has a good 'leaving group' (i.e. $R\text{-}CO\text{-}O^-$ and Cl^- respectively), the C=O bond in the carbonyl group is reformed in the final product so that the leaving group appears to have been substituted by the nucleophile. Using water as the nucleophile, which gives a carboxylic acid as the final product, the reactions can be represented in Figure 1822.

Figure 1822 The mechanism of the nucleophilic addition-elimination reaction of acid anhydrides and acyl chlorides with water

The reactions of acid anhydrides and acyl chlorides are very similar, with acyl chlorides being slightly the more reactive of the two. They react with a wide variety of nucleophiles which, in effect, replace the halogen or alkanoate group. These reactions are summarised in Figure 1823.

Figure 1823 A summary of the nucleophilic addition-elimination reactions of acid anhydrides and acyl chlorides

Specific examples are given below, and more complex examples are of commercial importance in the manufacture of the pain killers aspirin and paracetamol.

$CH_3\text{-}CO\text{-}O\text{-}CO\text{-}CH_3 + H_2O \rightarrow CH_3\text{-}CO\text{-}OH + CH_3\text{-}CO\text{-}OH$

$CH_3\text{-}CO\text{-}Cl + CH_3\text{-}CH_2\text{-}OH \rightarrow CH_3\text{-}CO\text{-}O\text{-}CH_2\text{-}CH_3 + HCl$

$CH_3\text{-}CO\text{-}O\text{-}CO\text{-}CH_3 + NH_3 \rightarrow CH_3\text{-}CO\text{-}NH_2 + CH_3\text{-}CO\text{-}OH$

$(+ NH_3 \rightarrow CH_3\text{-}CO\text{-}O^- NH_4^+)$

$CH_3\text{-}CO\text{-}Cl + C_2H_5\text{-}NH_2 \rightarrow CH_3\text{-}CO\text{-}NH\text{-}C_2H_5 + HCl$

$(+ C_2H_5\text{-}NH_2 \rightarrow C_2H_5\text{-}NH_3^+ Cl^-)$

Exercise G9

1. When ethanoyl chloride reacts with an alcohol the organic product is:

   A an ester.
   B an aldehyde.
   C a ketone.
   D a carboxylic acid.

2. Which one of the following substances would you react with ethanoic anhydride to produce CH_3-CO-NH-CH_3?

   A NH_3
   B CH_3-NH_2
   C CH_3-CO-NH_2
   D CH_3-NH-CH_3

3. When 0.1 moles of ethanoic anhydride and ethanoyl chloride are added to two separate beakers each containing 1 dm^3 of water, which one will give the solution with the lowest pH?

   A Neither as both are insoluble.
   B Neither as they both give the same product.
   C Ethanoic anhydride.
   D Ethanoyl chloride.

4. When ethanoyl chloride is added to pure propan-2-ol a vigorous reaction takes place.

   a) Write a balanced equation for the reaction. Give the name of the product and state to what homologous series of compounds it belongs.
   b) Show the accepted mechanism by which this reaction takes place.
   c) Why is pure propan-2-ol used rather than an aqueous solution of the reagent?
   d) If no ethanoyl chloride were available, what other reagent could be substituted to give the required product? Would you expect the reaction with this second reagent to be more or less vigorous (under the same experimental conditions)?

5. Ethanoic anhydride reacts with ammonia.

   a) Write a balanced equation for the reaction. Give the name of the product and state to what homologous series of compounds it belongs.
   b) Show the accepted mechanism by which this reaction takes place.
   c) How many moles of ammonia would be required for each mole of ethanoic anhydride to give an approximately neutral mixture?
   d) Draw the formula of the product if ethylamine were used instead of ammonia. Name this new product.

G10 ELECTROPHILIC SUBSTITUTION REACTIONS

G.10.1 Describe, using equations, the nitration, chlorination, alkylation and acylation of benzene.

G.10.2 Describe and explain the mechanisms for the nitration, chlorination, alkylation and acylation of benzene.

G.10.3 Describe, using equations, the nitration, chlorination, alkylation and acylation of methylbenzene.

G.10.4 Describe and explain the directing effects and relative rates of reaction of different substituents on a benzene ring.

The **benzene ring**, like the double bond, has a high electron density owing to the presence of π-electrons and this means that it too is susceptible to electrophilic attack to form a carbocation intermediate. In this case however, if it underwent a normal addition reaction, the product would not have a **delocalised π-bond** and so would lose the added stability that results from this. For this reason the intermediate carbocation loses a hydrogen ion to give a **substitution** product, which retains the delocalised π-electron system. The opposite is true for alkenes, where the **addition** product is the more stable.

The nitration of benzene is an example of such a reaction. Benzene is warmed with a mixture of concentrated nitric and sulfuric acids. In this mixture there is an equilibrium resulting in the formation of the nitronium ion (NO_2^+):

$$HNO_3 + 2\,H_2SO_4 \rightleftharpoons NO_2^+ + 2\,HSO_4^- + H_3O^+$$

This then acts as the electrophile, attacking the benzene ring to produce an intermediate carbocation in which the delocalised π-electron system is disrupted, as shown in Figure 1824.

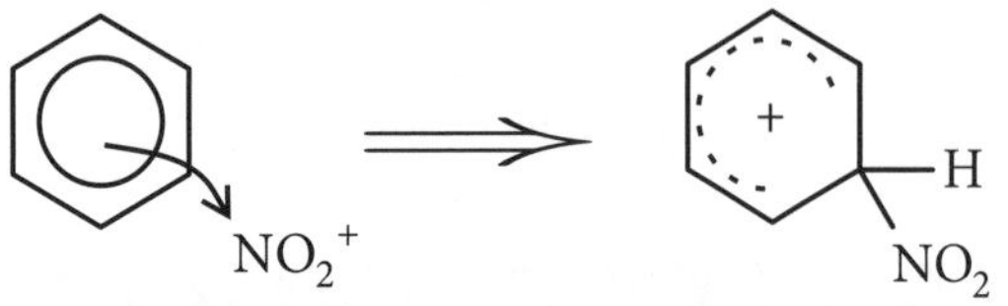

Figure 1824 The electrophilic atack of the nitronium ion on the benzene ring

If an anion were now added on to the carbocation to complete the addition reaction, then the additional stability associate with the delocalised π-bond would be permanently lost. Alternatively the carbocation can eliminate a hydrogen ion, restoring the delocalised π-electron system as shown in Figure 1825. This latter alternative is much more favourable energetically and results in an overall **electrophilic substitution** reaction.

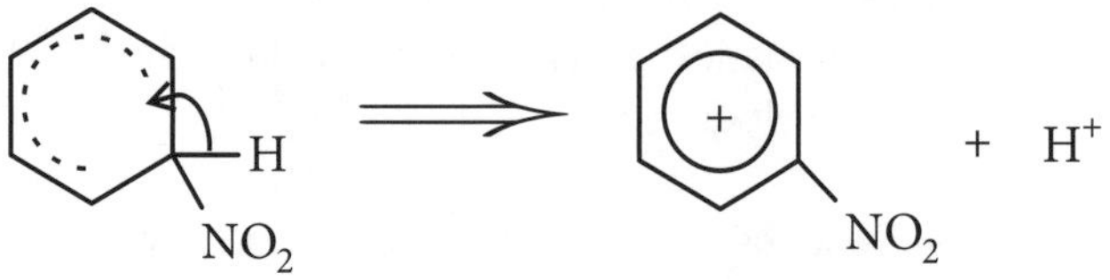

Figure 1825 The elimination of a hydrogen ion from the intermediate carbocation to form nitrobenzene

Benzene and related compounds, such as methylbenzene, undergo electrophilic substitution reactions with a range of other electrophiles, some of which are given in Figure 1826.

These reactions occur by similar mechanisms to the nitration reaction above. As they all employ similar catalysts these are collectively known as **Friedel Crafts reactions.** In each case the electrophile results from the positive end of the polar species produced by the bonding of the reactant to the trivalent electron deficient metal chloride (MCl_3) catalyst (sometimes referred to as a halogen carrier) which acts as a Lewis acid.

$$^{\delta+}Cl - Cl^{\delta-} \rightarrow MCl_3$$

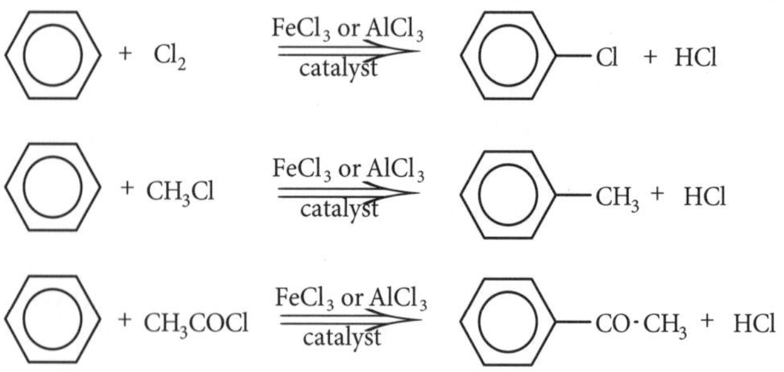

$$C_6H_6 + Cl_2 \xrightarrow[\text{catalyst}]{FeCl_3 \text{ or } AlCl_3} C_6H_5{-}Cl + HCl$$

$$C_6H_6 + CH_3Cl \xrightarrow[\text{catalyst}]{FeCl_3 \text{ or } AlCl_3} C_6H_5{-}CH_3 + HCl$$

$$C_6H_6 + CH_3COCl \xrightarrow[\text{catalyst}]{FeCl_3 \text{ or } AlCl_3} C_6H_5{-}CO{\cdot}CH_3 + HCl$$

Figure 1826 Some electrophilic substitution reactions of benzene

As this complex attacks the benzene ring the Cl–Cl bond breaks heterolytically to form the carbocation and the MCl_4^- anion breaks free, so that in fact the attacking chlorine atom behaves as if it were a Cl^+ ion. In the second step of the reaction this acts as a base and accepts the H^+ lost to form hydrogen chloride and regenerates the MCl_3 catalyst. In bromination, finely divided iron is simply added to the dry reaction mixture where it reacts with the bromine to produce the iron(III) bromide catalyst. In the case of the reactions with chloroalkanes and acyl chlorides, the aluminium chloride catalyst acts as a Lewis acid and binds to the chlorine, causing the carbon-chlorine bond to be even more strongly polarised. This results in the carbon in each case behaving as if it were a carbocation:

$$R^{\delta+} - Cl{:}^{\delta-} \rightarrow AlCl_3$$

$$R - \overset{\overset{\displaystyle O}{\|}}{C}{}^{\delta+} - Cl{:}^{\delta-} \rightarrow AlCl_3$$

The presence of a substituent group on the benzene ring can significantly affect its reactivity with respect to electrophilic substitution reactions. Generally speaking groups which increase the electron density of the π-electron system, either through an **inductive effect** (for example $-CH_3$) or by donating a pair of electrons to the delocalised π-electron system (known as a **mesomeric effect**, occurring for example with –OH), are activating groups and increase the reactivity of the ring whereas those that withdraw electrons (for example $-NO_2$) are deactivating groups and decrease the reactivity. Substituents usually affect the reactivity of the 2,4,6 positions more than that of the 3,5 positions (though the halogens are an exception to this) hence the reaction of methylbenzene with the common electrophiles yields a mixture of the 2- and 4- substitution products as shown in Figure 1827.

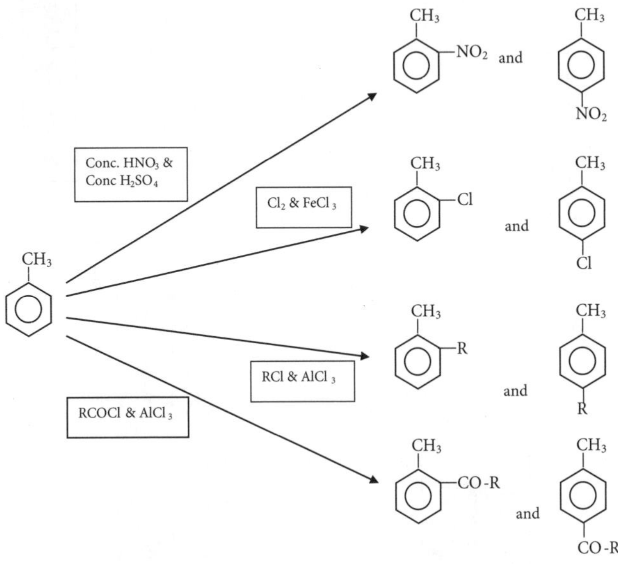

Figure 1827 Some electrophilic substitution reactions of methylbenzene

The effect of the major substituents on the reactivity and position of further substitution is summarised in Figure 1828.

Position	More reactive than benzene	Less reactive than benzene
2- or 4- substitution	Slighty: $-CH_3$	-Cl
3- substitution	-	$-NO_2$ $-CO_2CH_3$

Figure 1828 The effect of substituents on the reactivity and positional preference for electrophilic substitution reactions of the benzene ring

The directional effects can be explained in terms of the charge distribution of the intermediates. The decreased reactivity due to the presence of $-NO_2$ can be explained in terms of its electron-withdrawing nature and lack of a non-bonded electron pair. The slightly increased reactivity due to the presence of $-CH_3$ can be explained in terms of its electron-releasing nature. The greatly increased reactivity due to the presence of –OH can be explained in terms of its partial donation of a non-bonded electron pair. This increase in activity is so great that, for example phenol (C_6H_5OH), will react rapidly with aqueous chlorine at room temperature and pressure to produce 2,4,6–trichlorophenol (the antiseptic, TCP) even without a Friedel Crafts catalyst. See Figure 1829.

Figure 1829 The reaction of phenol with chlorine

It should be noted that with methylbenzene, two possible chlorination reactions are possible. In the presence of ultraviolet light a free radical substitution of the side chain occurs, whereas in the dark with a Friedel Crafts catalyst (normally $FeCl_3$ or $AlCl_3$) the substitution occurs on the ring, as summarised in Figure 1830.

Figure 1830 The effect of reaction conditions on the chlorination reactions of methylbenzene

The next page show a summary of the major reaction pathways.

OPTION

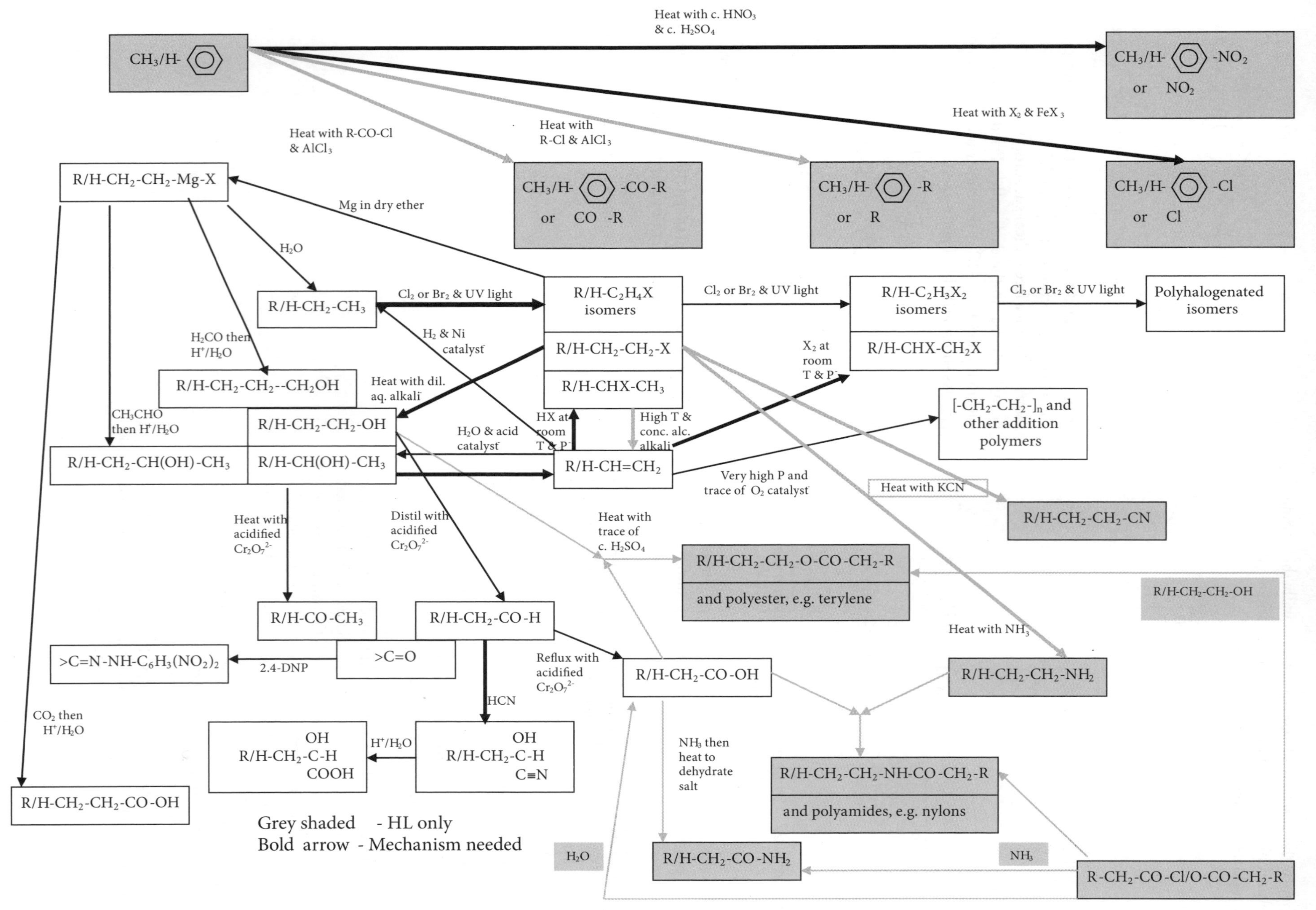
CH3/H-(benzene)
Heat with c. HNO3 & c. H2SO4
CH3/H-(benzene)-NO2 or NO2
Heat with X2 & FeX3
CH3/H-(benzene)-Cl or Cl
Heat with R-CO-Cl & AlCl3
CH3/H-(benzene)-CO-R or CO -R
Heat with R-Cl & AlCl3
CH3/H-(benzene)-R or R
R/H-CH2-CH2-Mg-X
Mg in dry ether
H2O
R/H-CH2-CH3
Cl2 or Br2 & UV light
R/H-C2H4X isomers
R/H-CH2-CH2-X
R/H-CHX-CH3
Cl2 or Br2 & UV light
R/H-C2H3X2 isomers
R/H-CHX-CH2X
Cl2 or Br2 & UV light
Polyhalogenated isomers
H2 & Ni catalyst
H2CO then H+/H2O
R/H-CH2-CH2--CH2OH
Heat with dil. aq. alkali
X2 at room T & P
CH3CHO then H+/H2O
R/H-CH2-CH2-OH
R/H-CH2-CH(OH)-CH3
R/H-CH(OH)-CH3
H2O & acid catalyst
HX at room T & P
High T & conc. alc. alkali
R/H-CH=CH2
[-CH2-CH2-]n and other addition polymers
Very high P and trace of O2 catalyst
Heat with KCN
R/H-CH2-CH2-CN
Heat with acidified Cr2O7 2-
Distil with acidified Cr2O7 2-
Heat with trace of c. H2SO4
R/H-CH2-CH2-O-CO-CH2-R
and polyester, e.g. terylene
R/H-CH2-CH2-OH
R/H-CO-CH3
R/H-CH2-CO-H
>C=O
>C=N-NH-C6H3(NO2)2
2.4-DNP
Reflux with acidified Cr2O7 2-
R/H-CH2-CO-OH
Heat with NH3
R/H-CH2-CH2-NH2
HCN
CO2 then H+/H2O
OH R/H-CH2-C-H COOH
H+/H2O
OH R/H-CH2-C-H C≡N
NH3 then heat to dehydrate salt
R/H-CH2-CH2-NH-CO-CH2-R
and polyamides, e.g. nylons
R/H-CH2-CH2-CO-OH
Grey shaded - HL only
Bold arrow - Mechanism needed
H2O
R/H-CH2-CO-NH2
NH3
R-CH2-CO-Cl/O-CO-CH2-R

Exercise

1. When methylbenzene is nitrated the product will contain significant quantities of

   A 2-nitro(methylbenzene) and 3-nitro(methylbenzene).
   B 3-nitro(methylbenzene) and 4-nitro(methylbenzene).
   C 2-nitro(methylbenzene) and 4-nitro(methylbenzene).
   D 2-nitro(methylbenzene), 3-nitro(methylbenzene) and 4-nitro(methylbenzene).

2. Which one of the following will be the most reactive when heated with ethanoyl chloride and anhydrous aluminium chloride?

   A ⌬-NO_2
   B ⌬-H
   C ⌬-CH_3
   D ⌬-OH

3. Methylbenzene can react with bromine under different conditions to form two different products.

   a) Write balanced equations for the two reactions stating the conditions required in each case.
   b) Give the name and structural formula of both products.
   c) State the type of mechanisms by which the two reactions occur.

4. Benzene is readily converted to nitrobenzene.

   a) To what class of reactions does this belong?
   b) State the reagents and conditions required to bring this about and write a balanced equation for the reaction.
   c) Write the mechanism by which this reaction occurs.

5. Benzene, methylbenzene and phenol will all undergo nitration reactions with nitric acid.

   a) How would you expect the reactivity of these three compounds with nitric acid to vary? How can this variation be explained?
   b) Write the mechanism for the nitration of benzene.
   c) Would you expect the replacement of a second hydrogen on the benzene ring to take place more readily or less readily than the first one? Explain.
   d) Give the structural formulas of the major products you would expect from the nitration of methylbenzene, phenol and nitrobenzene.

GENERAL EXERCISE FOR OPTION G

*The questions below involve a knowledge of various sections of the option. Note that questions marked with an asterisk * are for HL students only.*

1. For each of the following mechanisms, give the balanced equation for a specific example of a reaction that occurs by each mechanism, and then draw the mechanism for the reaction.

   Elimination
   Nucleophilic addition
   Addition–elimination
   Electrophilic addition

2. Write the structural formula of the major product from each of the following reactions:

   a) Reacting butanal with ethylmagnesium bromide and hydrolysing the product.
   b) Warming propanal with 2,4–dinitrophenylhydrazine solution.
   c) Reacting butan–2–ol with methylmagnesium chloride.
   d)* Reacting ethanoyl chloride with ammonia.
   e)* Refluxing methylbenzene with a mixture of concentrated nitric and sulfuric acids.

OPTION

3. What would be seen in each of the following reactions?

   a) Adding water to a solution of methylmagnesium iodide in ethoxyethane.
   b) Adding 2,4–dinitrophenylhydrazine solution to propanone.
   c) Propan-2-ol is warmed with concentrated phosphoric acid.

4. Explain why:

   a) a solution of methylamine in water has a pH ~11.
   b) a pungent smelling gas is evolved when a white, crystalline salt, CH_3NH_3Cl is warmed with aqueous sodium hydroxide.
   c) ethanamide is a crystalline solid.
   d) a solution of trimethylamine is even more alkaline than a solution of methylamine of the same concentration, whereas a solution of ethanamide is almost neutral.

5. This is a question about phenylethanone (acetophenone) (C_6H_5-CO-CH_3).

   a)* Write a balanced equation for the preparation of this compound from benzene, giving the required conditions.
   b) How could you show that phenylethanone is a ketone?
   c) Phenylethanone will react with ethylmagnesium bromide. Draw the structural formula of the final product that results from the hydrolysis of the intermediate. To what class of compounds does it belong?

Activation energy
The minimum amount of combined total kinetic energy a colliding pair of ions, atoms or molecules require for a chemical reaction to occur. It may be thought of as the size of the energy barrier that has to be overcome to form the transition state.

Active site
The region of an enzyme, usually a pocket or groove, that binds the substrate molecule(s) and catalyses a reaction.

Active transport
An energy-requiring process that involves the transport of ions or molecules across a cell membrane, usually in the direction of increasing concentration (that is, against a concentration gradient).

Acyclic
Molecules that have an open-chain molecular structure rather than a ring-shaped structure.

Acyl group
A group of atoms fitting the general formula, RCO-, where R is typically a benzene ring or alkyl group.

Acylation
The introduction of an acyl group into an organic molecule.

Addition
A reaction in which two (or more) molecules combine together to form a single molecule. Alkenes undergo addition reactions which involve atoms and/or groups of atoms adding to opposite faces of a carbon-carbon double bond. They are characteristic of unsaturated compounds, such as the alkenes and carbonyl compounds.

Addition polymerisation
A type of polymerisation which occurs when alkene-based monomers undergo repeated addition reactions to form a single molecule.

Adsorption
The accumulation, usually temporarily, of gases, liquids, or solutes on the surface of a solid or liquid through the formation of weak intermolecular interactions.

Aerobic
Containing or requiring molecular oxygen.

Air pollutant
a substance present in sufficient concentration in the air to produce a harmful effect on humans or other animals, vegetation or materials

Alcohols (monohydric)
A homologous series of organic compounds containing the functional group -OH and the general formula $C_nH_{2n+1}OH$.

Aldehydes
A homologous series of compounds with the general formula, RCHO, where the –CHO group (the aldehyde group) consists of a carbonyl group attached to a hydrogen atom. R is an alkyl or aryl group.

Algal bloom
Rapid growth of algae on the surface of freshwaters in response to a supply of nitrogen and/or phosphorus, leading to depletion of light and oxygen below the water surface.

Alginates
Salts of alginic acid, a hydrophilic colloidal carbohydrate which is extracted from marine kelp.

Alkali
An alkali is a strong base which is soluble in water. Alkalis are Group 1 metal hydroxides, aqueous solution of ammonia, aqueous solution of amines and barium hydroxide.

Alkali metals
The group of very reactive metals in Group 1 of the Periodic Table. They react with water to release hydrogen gas and form strongly alkaline solutions:

Alkaline earth metals
The group of reactive metals in Group 2 of the Periodic Table. They all react with water to give suspensions of their hydroxides.

Alkaline solution
An alkaline solution is an aqueous solution that has an excess of hydroxide ions.

Alkaloid
nitrogen containing organic compound of plant origin whose structure consists of a tertiary amine group heterocyclic rings such as cocaine, codeine, caffeine and morphine

Alkanals (aldehyde)
A homologous series of compounds with the general formula, RCHO, where the –CHO group (the aldehyde or alkanal group) consists of a carbonyl group attached to a hydrogen atom.

Alkanes
Saturated hydrocarbons which have the general formula C_nH_{2n+2}(if acyclic).

Alkanoic (carboxylic) acids
A homologous series of organic compounds with the general formula RCOOH. They can be formed by the oxidation of a primary alcohol or alkanal (aldehyde).

Alkanones (ketones)
A homologous series of compounds with the general formula RCOR', having two alkyl groups bonded to a carbonyl group.

Alkenes
Unsaturated hydrocarbons a carbon-carbon double bond and with the general formula C_nH_{2n} (if acyclic).

Alkylation
The introduction of an alkyl group into an organic molecule.

Alkyl group
A group, with the general formula C_nH_{2n+1}, obtained by removing a hydrogen atom from an alkane, and usually represented by R.

Alkynes
Unsaturated hydrocarbons with a carbon-carbon triple bond and with the general formula C_nH_{2n-2} (if acyclic).

Allotropy
The ability of an element to exist in different crystalline forms or allotropes.

Alloy
A mixture which is made up of two or more metals, or which contains metals and carbon.

Alpha helix
A right-handed helical conformation of a protein chain, held together by intra-molecular hydrogen bonding. It is a common protein secondary structure.

Alpha decay
Alpha decay is the emission of an alpha particle from the nucleus of a radioactive atom. Alpha decay results in a decrease of the atomic number by two and an increase in the mass number by four.

Alpha particle
An alpha particle ($^4_2He^{2+}$) is a helium nucleus or ion emitted by an atom undergoing alpha decay.

Amalgam
An alloy which contains mercury. They may be solid or liquid depending on their composition.

Amide (primary)
A homologous series of organic compounds with the general formula $RCONH_2$.

Amine
Organic compounds derived by replacing one or more of the hydrogen atoms in ammonia by alkyl groups. All are basic and react with acids to form amine salts.

α-Amino acid
A group of soluble organic compounds that possess a carboxylic acid group (-COOH) and a primary amine group ($-NH_2$) bonded to a common carbon atom. α-amino acids are the monomers of proteins. They are also known as 2-amino acids.

Amino group
The $-NH_2$ functional group found in primary amines and amino acids.

Amino-terminal residue (N-terminus)
The amino acid residue at one end of a polypeptide chain that contains a free amino group.

Ammine
A complex ion in which ammonia molecules act as ligands and are coordinated to a metal ion.

Amount
A physical quantity indicating the number of moles of a substance present in a sample.

Amphetamines
Synthetic amines which stimulate the central nervous system (brain and spinal cord) and make people feel more alert.

Amphipathic
Molecules containinf non-polar tails and polar heads.

Amphiprotic
A solvent, for example, water, which undergoes self-ionisation and can act as both a proton donor and proton acceptor.

Amphoteric
A chemical species capable of accepting and donating protons, thus able to behave as both as an acid and a base.

Amphoteric oxide
An oxide of a metal that will react and dissolve in a solution of an acid and a solution of a strong base (alkali). They can react as both acidic and basic oxides.

Amylopectin
The water-soluble component of starch. It consists of highly branched chains of glucose molecules.

Amylose
The water-insoluble component of starch. It consists of between 100 and 1000 linear chains of glucose molecules.

Anabolic steroid
A group of synthetic hormones that promote the storage of protein and the growth of tissue, sometimes used by athletes to increase muscle size and strength.

Anaerobic
Lacking or not requiring molecular oxygen.

Analyte
A sample component whose concentration is being measured (i.e. analyzes).

Analytical chemistry
The qualitative and quantitative analysis of a sample to determine its chemical composition and structure.

Anaesthetic
A substance which reduces or removes the feeling of pain.

Analgesic
A drug used to alleviate the sensation of pain.

Anion
A negatively charged ion which migrates to the anode (positive electrode) during electrolysis.

Anode
The anode is where oxidation (the loss of electrons) occurs during an electrochemical process. In an electrolytic cell the anode is the positive electrode. In an electrochemical cell the anode supplies electrons since oxidation has occurred in that half cell. It is therefore the negative electrode of the cell.

Anodising
A process for protecting aluminium with a thin oxide layer formed in an electrolytic cell containing dilute sulfuric acid where the aluminium object is the anode..

Anomers (of a sugar)
Two stereoisomers which differ only in the configuration about the carbonyl carbon atom.

Antacids
Substances, basic in nature, used to reduce the pH of the gastric juice in the stomach with the aim of relieving indigestion.

Antibiotic
A substance or a semi-synthetic substance derived from a microorganism, usually a bacterium or fungus, and able in dilute solution to inhibit or kill another microorganism, usually a bacterium.

Antibody
A defence protein synthesised by the immune system.

Antifoulant coating
coating to hulls of ships below the water line to stop plants and marine life forms attaching to the hull

Antioxidant
A chemical compound or substance that inhibits oxidation.

Anti-pyretic
a drug that reduces fever

Antiviral
Natural or synthetic substance that kills viruses directly or prevents their replication.

Aqua-ions
Transition and aluminium metal ions in aqueous solution are bonded to six molecules of water to form octahedral complex ions. The bonds are co-ordinate (dative) covalent bonds from the water ligands.

Aqueous solution
A solution in which the water is the solvent.

Aromatic compound
A compound containing one (or more) benzene rings in its structure and typified by its propensity to undergo substitution reactions.

Arrhenius constant
A constant that appears in the Arrhenius equation in front of the exponential term. It is a term which includes the frequency of collisions and their orientation in space.

Arrhenius equation
An equation that relates the rate constants for a reaction obtained at different absolute temperatures to the activation energy of the reaction.

Arrhenius plot
A plot of the natural logarithm of the rate constant (y-axis) against 1/(absolute temperature) (x-axis). A straight line will be obtained with a gradient of $-\frac{E_a}{R}$. The value of the activation energy, Ea, will be in J mol-1.

Arrhenius temperature dependence
A rise in temperature results in an increase in the rate constant, thereby increasing the rate of reaction. For many reactions (with an activation energy ~50 kJ mol^{-1}) a rise in temperature of ten degrees Celsius leads to an approximate doubling of the initial rate. Reactions that follow this dependence are said to exhibit Arrhenius temperature dependence.

Arrhenius theory
The theory of acidity and alkalinity that defines an acid as a solution containing hydrogen ions as the positive ions and an alkali as a solution as one containing hydroxide ions as the only negative ions.

Aryl group
A group derived by removing a hydrogen atom from a benzene ring, or other aromatic structure.

Asymmetric carbon atom
A common term for a carbon atom that is attached to four different atoms or groups of atoms.

Asymmetric molecules
Molecules with no centres, axes or planes of symmetry. Asymmetric molecules are chiral and can exist as a pair of enantiomers or optical isomers.

Atactic
A polymer chain in which the substituents, or side chains, are randomly distributed along the chain.

Atmospheric pressure
The pressure exerted by the atmosphere on the surface of the Earth due to the weight of the atmosphere.

Atom
The smallest particle of an element that can take part in a chemical reaction. All atoms of the same element have the same number of protons in the nucleus.

Atomicity
The number of atoms in a molecule.

Atomic mass
The weighted average mass (according to relative abundances) of all the naturally occurring isotopes of an element compared with an atom of the $^{12}_{6}C$ carbon isotope which has a mass of exactly 12.

Atomic number
The number of protons in the nucleus of an atom.

Atomic radius
Half the distance of the closest approach of atoms in the crystal or molecule of a chemical element (for a particular allotrope).

Atomic theory
The theory that all substances are composed of atoms (that cannot be created or destroyed).

Atomisation
The process in which an element or compound is converted into gaseous atoms.

Atmosphere
The unit atmosphere is used to measure pressure. 1 atm = 101,325 Pa. It is, however, not an SI unit.

Aufbau principle
A principle that the order in which orbitals are filled with electrons is the order of increasing energy.

Autocatalysis
Autocatalysis occurs when the product of a reaction acts as a catalyst in the reaction and causes its rate to increase.

Auto-oxidation
The direct combination of a substance with molecular oxygen at ordinary temperature.

Avogadro constant, NA
The Avogadro constant (6.02×10^{23}) is the number of atoms in exactly 12 grams of carbon-12. It has units of per mol (mol^{-1}).

Azeotrope
A mixture of liquids that will distil without changing in composition. When a mixture that forms a low-boiling point is distilled, the vapour has the composition of the azeotropic mixture.

Avogadro's law
The law states that at a specified temperature and pressure, equal volumes of (ideal) gases contain equal numbers of moles of particles. There is a directly relationship between the volume of gas, V, and the amount of particles, n: $V \alpha n$.

B

Back titration
A back titration typically consists of two consecutive acid-base titrations and is performed when an insoluble and slowly reacting reagent is treated with an excess of an acid or base. The excess acid or base is then titrated with base or acid solution of a primary standard.

Backward reaction
The backward reaction refers to the conversion of products into reactants in an equilibrium reaction.

Bacteriophage
A virus capable of replicating in a bacterial cell.

Bacterium

A single celled organism lacking a nucleus.

Bacterial infections
infections caused by bacteria include tetanus, tuberculosis (TB), cholera, typhoid fever, syphilis, gonorrhea.

Balanced equation
A summary of a chemical reaction using chemical formulas. The total number of any of the atoms or ions involved is the same on the reactant and product sides of the equation.

Balmer series
A series of lines in the emission spectrum of visible light emitted by excited hydrogen atoms. The lines correspond to the electrons falling down into the second lowest energy level, emitting visible light.

Barbiturates
drugs which depress the central nervous system.

Base (DNA or RNA)
One of the nitrogen-containing compounds that occurs attached to the sugar component of DNA or RNA.

Base
A substance which neutralises an acid, producing a salt and water as the only products. Common bases are aqueous ammonia, amines, carbonate ions and the oxides and hydroxides of metals. In the Brønsted-Lowry theory a base is a proton acceptor; a Lewis base is an electron donor.

Base dissociation constant
The equilibrium constant for the reaction in which base reacts with water to produce the conjugate acid and hydroxide ions. It is a measure of the extent to which weak bases accept hydrogen ions in solution.

Base pair
two nucleotides in nucleic acid chains that are paired together by intermolecular hydrogen bonding between the bases.

Basic oxide
An ionic oxide, usually an oxide of a metal, that reacts with acids to form salts and water. Some basic oxides react with water to form alkaline or basic solutions.

Basic oxygen convertor
In the basic oxygen process scrap steel and a small amount of limestone are dissolved in molten iron. Pure oxygen is then blown into the molten mixture to remove impurities.

Base pair
Two nucleotides in nucleic acid chains that are paired together by intermolecular hydrogen bonding between the bases.

Batch process
A process which produces a specified amount of a product in a single operation.

Battery
A group of galvanic or electrochemical cells connected in series or in parallel.

Beer-Lambert law
The concentration of a substance in moles is proportional to the absorbance of a given wavelength of light by a solution of the substance (provided the solution is dilute). $A=\varepsilon cl$, where c is the concentration of the substance and l is the length of the radiation through the substance. T

Bergius process
A process formerly used for making hydrocarbon fuels from coal. A powdered mixture of coal, heavy oil and a catalyst was heated with hydrogen at high pressure.

Beta(-) particle
A high speed electron ejected from the nucleus following the decay of a neutron into a proton.

beta-lactam ring
heteroatomic four-membered ring structure consisting of one nitrogen atom and three carbon atoms

Beta sheet
An extended, zigzag arrangement of a protein chain; a common secondary structure held together by intramolecular hydrogen bonding.

Bidentate ligand
A ligand able to form two coordinate (dative) covalent bonds with a central metal atom or ion.

Bimolecular
An elementary step in a reaction involving the collision between two reactant species to form one large particle or two particles.

Bimolecular layer
A structure, such as a cell membrane, consisting of two molecular layers.

Binary compound
A compound that contains only two elements.

Binary liquid mixture
A mixture that consists of two miscible liquids which mutally dissolve in each other.

Biological oxygen demand (BOD)
This is the amount of oxygen taken up by bacteria that decompose organic waste in water. The BOD is calculated by keeping a sample of water containing a known amount of oxygen for five days at 20°C. The oxygen content is then measured again after this time. A high BOD value indicates the presence of a large number of micro-organisms, which suggests a high level of pollution. Unpolluted water has a very low BOD value.

Biogas
Methane gas produced by the action of bacteria on animal and plant wastes under anaerobic conditions (absence of oxygen).

Biotechnology
The use of microorganisms, such as bacteria or yeasts, or biological substances, such as enzymes, to perform specific industrial or manufacturing processes.

Blast furnace
A furnace in which iron oxide is reduced to iron by tradiationally using a very strong blast of air to produce carbon monoxide from coke, and then using this gas as the active reducing agent for the iron.

Bleach
A substance used to decolourise materials by a process of oxidation or reduction.

Bohr theory
A classical model of atomic structure with energy levels for electrons.

Boiling
The change of a liquid into a gas at constant temperature. This occurs when the vapour pressure of the liquid is equal to the external pressure exerted on the liquid. It is characterised by the appearance of bubbles of vapour throughout the liquid.

Boiling point
The temperature at which a liquid is converted to a gas at the same temperature; a liquid boils when the vapour pressure of the liquid equals the surrounding pressure.

Bomb calorimeter
A device used to measure energy changes (at constant volume) that occur when substances, for example, alcohols or hydrocarbons, are burnt in excess oxygen in a sealed container.

Bond angle
An angle formed by the location of three atoms or two covalent bonds in space. They are used to describe the shapes of molecules.

Bond enthalpy
The bond enthalpy is the amount of energy (in kiloJoules) required to break one mole of a particular covalent bond in the gaseous state into gaseous atoms (under standard thermodynamic conditions). It is a measure of the strength of the bond.

Bond length
The equilibrium distance between the nuclei of two atoms linked by a covalent bond or bonds.

Bond order
A theoretical index of the degree of bonding between two atoms relative to that of a normal single bond, that is, the bond provided by one localised electron pair. In the valence-bond theory it is a weighted average of the bond numbers between the respective atoms in the contributing structures.

Bonding pair
A pair of electrons (with opposite spins) located in the space between the nuclei of two adjacent atoms.

Born-Haber cycle
An energy or enthalpy cycle commonly used in calculating the lattice energies of ionic solids. It is a series of reactions (and the accompanying enthalpy changes) which, when summed, represents the hypothetical one-step reaction in which elements in their standard states are converted into crystals of the ionic compound (and the accompanying enthalpy changes) under standard thermodynamic conditions.

Boyle's law
The gas law stating that the product of pressure and volume (for a fixed mass of ideal gas at constant temperature) is a constant.

Brady's reagent
A solution of 2,4-dinitrophenylhydrazine in either hydrochloric or phosphoric acid. It is used to test for the carbonyl group in aldehydes or ketones and to identify the aldehyde or ketone via the formation of a 2,4-dinitrophenylhdrazone derivative with a characteristic melting point.

Breathalyser
An instrument for estimating the concentration of alcohol in the blood by measuring the concentration of ethanol in a sample of the air from the lungs.

Breeder reactor
A nuclear reactor in which fissionable fuel is produced while the reactor runs.

Brine
A concentrated aqueous solution of sodium chloride. It is used to make sodium hydroxide and sodium chlorate(I), a bleach.

Broad spectrum antibiotic
An antibiotic that is effective against a wide range of strains of bacteria.

Bromination
A reaction in which a bromine atom or a pair of bromine atoms is introduced into a molecule of benzene, alkane or alkene.

Bromine water
An aqueous solution of bromine that contains hydrated bromine molecules and bromic(I) acid. It is commonly used to test for the presence of a carbon-carbon double bond, which turns the yellow/orange solution colourless.

Brønsted-Lowry theory
A theory of acidity that describes an acid as a proton or hydrogen ion donor, and a base as a proton or hydrogen ion acceptor.

Buffer
A buffer is an aqueous solution consisting of a weak base and its conjugate acid that resists a change in pH when small amounts of either hydroxide ions (from a base) or hydrogen ions (from an acid) are added. Buffers typically consist of a weak acid and its corresponding salt (an acidic buffer) or a weak base and its corresponding salt (a basic buffer).

Buffer capacity
The ability of a buffer to absorb hydrogen ions or hydroxide ions without a significant change in pH. It is determined by the concentrations of the weak acid and its conjugate base.

By-products
Unwanted products of a chemical synthesis or manufacturing process.

C

Caffeine
A drug that exerts its central nervous system stimulant action by working inside nerve cells to increase their rates of cellular metabolism.

Calibration
A quantitative procedure performed in order to relate the known concentration of standard solutions of the analyte to the detector signal which is generated from the analyte in the unknown solutions.

Calibration curve
The relationship of instrument response (absorbance) as a function of concentration. Ideally, this should be a linear relationship, under conditions that obey Beer's Law, where absorbance = (slope × concentration) + intercept.

Calorie
A calorie is notionally the energy required to raise the temperature of 1 g of water by 1 °C.

Calorific value
The amount of heat released by a unit mass of a substance, for example, a food, (or of a unit volume of gas) being burnt.

Calorimeter
A piece of insulated apparatus for measuring the energy released or absorbed during a chemical reaction.

Capacity (of a galvanic cell)
The capacity of a cell or battery is measured by the number of amp-hours (Ah) of charge it can deliver.

Caramelisation
Caramelisation is the oxidation of sugar, a process used extensively in cooking for the resulting nutty flavour and brown colour. Caramelisation is a type of non-enzymatic browning reaction and as the process occurs, volatile chemicals are released producing the characteristic caramel flavour. Caramelisation is a complex, poorly understood process that produces hundreds of chemicals. The reactions occurring include: inversion, condensation, dehydration and fragmentation.

Carbocation
A carbocation is an organic ion with a positive charge on an electron deficient carbon atom. They are intermediates during nucleophilic substitution via an SN1 mechanism or electrophilic addition to alkenes.

Carbohydrate
Carbohydrates are organic compounds that contain the elements carbon, hydrogen and oxygen. The ratio of hydrogen to oxygen atoms is usually 2:1 and their formulas are of the form $C_x(H_2O)_y$.

Carbon cycle
The combined processes, including photosynthesis, combustion and respiration (including that in decomposition), by which carbon as a component of various compounds alternates between its major reservoirs the atmosphere, oceans, and living organisms.

Carbonyl
The functional group, >C=O, which occurs in aldehydes, ketones, amides and carboxylic acids. However, the characteristic properties of carbonyl compounds, for example, condensation reactions, are only exhibited in aldehydes and ketones

Carboxylic acid
(See alkanoic acid).

Carboxyl-terminal residue
The only amino acid residue at one end of a polypeptide chain that contains a free carboxyl group.

Carcinogen
A substance that causes or induces cancer.

Carrier gas
The inert gas used to carry the sample in gas chromatography (GC).

Cast iron
The solidified iron direct from the blast furnace. It is brittle, but very hard.

Catalyst
A substance which, when present in relatively small amounts, increases the rate of a chemical reaction but which is not consumed during the overall process. The function of a catalyst is to provide a new reaction pathway with a lower activation energy.

Catalysis
A reaction process accelerated by the presence of a substance (a catalyst) which is neither consumed nor produced during the overall reaction.

Catalytic convertor
Part of the exhaust system of a modern car running on unleaded petrol. It consists of a platinum/rhodium catalyst in a honeycomb structure which converts carbon monoxide, nitrogen monoxide and unburnt hydrocarbons into carbon dioxide, nitrogen and dinitrogen oxide.

Catalytic cracking
Cracking carried out in the presence of a heated catalyst, for example, aluminium oxide (alumina) or silicon dioxide (silica).

Catalytic methanation
Methanation is used to remove residual carbon monoxide and carbon dioxide from synthesis gas. It involves passing the pressurised gas over a heated nickel catalyst.

Cathode
The cathode is where reduction (the gain of electrons) occurs during an electrochemical process. In an electrolytic cell the anode is the negative electrode. In an electrochemical cell the cathode consumes electrons since reduction has occurred in that half cell. It is therefore the positive terminal or pole of the cell.

Cation
A positively charged ion attracted to the cathode during electrolysis.

Cation exchange
The process by which a cation in a liquid phase exchanges with another cation present as the counter-ion of a negatively charged solid polymer (cation exchanger).

Cation exchange capacity
The cation exchange capacity (CEC) is a value given on a soil analysis report to indicate its capacity to hold cation nutrients.

Cell diagram
A shorthand form of summarising the electrodes and electrolytes present in an electrochemical cell. The cell diagram traces the path of the electrons. The reduced form of the metal to be oxidised at the anode is written first, followed by its oxidised form, then the oxidised form of the metal to be reduced at the cathode, and finally the reduced form of the metal at the cathode.

Cell potential
The cell potential is the potential difference between the two electrodes (in their standard states) of an electrochemical cell.

Celsius scale (of temperature)
This scale of temperature is based on a one hundred degree range between the normal melting point of pure ice (0 °C) and the normal boiling point of pure water (100 °C).

Chain reaction (chemical)
A chain reaction occurs when a reaction intermediate generated in one step reacts in such a way that this intermediate is regenerated.

Change of state
The inter-conversion of a substance between the solid, liquid and gaseous states.

Charge density (of a metal ion)
The ratio of the charge of a metal ion to its radius. The higher the charge density the greater its polarising power on neighbouring water molecules and the lower the pH of the resulting solution.

Charles' law
The gas law stating that the volume of a fixed mass (at constant pressure) of an ideal gas is directly proportional to absolute temperature.

Chemical compound
A substance formed by the chemical combination of two or more chemical elements in fixed proportions.

Chemical element
A substance which cannot be decomposed or broken down into simpler substances by chemical methods; all the atoms of an element contain the same number of protons.

Chemical environment
The chemical environment refers to the number and types of atoms a particular atom within a molecule is bonded to.

Chemical feedstock
The raw materials required for an industrial process.

Chemical library
A large collection of molecules prepared by conventional chemical synthesis or, more usually, combinatorial chemistry.

Chemical reaction
A change in which a new substance or substances are formed.

Chemical shift (δ)
The position of a resonance in the NMR spectrum relative to a standard such as TMS (tetramethylsilane).

Chemical symbol
A chemical symbol consists of one or two letters used to represent each element. The first (or only) letter is always a capital letter, the second a lower case.
Chemotherapy
The use of chemical agents in the treatment or control of disease, particularly cancer, or mental illness.

Chiral (asymmetric) centre
An atom, usually a carbon atom, in a molecule that is attached to four different atoms and/or functional groups.

Chiral molecule
A molecule that is non-superimposable on its mirror image.

Chiral auxillary
A chiral auxiliary is a chiral compound that is covalently attached to the substrate as a controlling factor in a diastereo-selective reaction and is subsequently cleaved from the product.

cis-
Used to describe geometric isomers of 1,2-disubstituted alkenes with functional groups or atoms which are on the same side of the molecule as each other.

***cis-trans* isomerism**
Cis-trans isomerism is a form of stereo-isomerism and describes the orientation of functional groups at the ends of a bond around which no rotation is possible.

Chlor-alkali industry
The chlor-alkali industry refers to the industrial electrolysis of brine which results in the production of sodium hydroxide and chlorine.

Chlorination
The addition of chlorine to drinking water in order to kill harmful bacteria. It also refers to a reaction in which a hydrogen atom in an organic molecule is replaced with a chlorine atom.

Chlorofluorocarbons (CFC)
Chloroflurocarbons are a group of compounds in which some or all of the hydrogen atoms of an alkane have been replaced (substituted) by chlorine and fluorine atoms. They are involved in ozone depletion.

Cholesterol
An important steroid; a key component of cell membranes and precursor for other steroids

Chromatography
A technique for analysing or separating mixtures of gases, liquids, or dissolved substances based upon differential solubility in two phases.

Chromatogram
A record obtained from chromatography.

Chromophore
A group of atoms responsible for absorbing electromagnetic radiation. They usually have delocalised π electrons.

Chromoprotein
One of a group of conjugated proteins, consisting of a combination of pigment (that is, a coloured prosthetic group) with a protein.

Closed system
A closed system is one in which matter and energy cannot be lost or gained from the system. It is a pre-requisite for the establishment of an equilibrium.

Coal
A brown or black deposit composed largely of carbon. It is a fossil fuel formed by the action of heat and pressure on the remains of plants buried under sediments.

Coal gasification
Coal gasification is a process for converting coal partially or completely to combustible gases. After purification, these gases - carbon monoxide, carbon dioxide, hydrogen, methane, and nitrogen - can be used as fuels.

Coal liquification
Coal liquification is a process for converting coal into liquid fuels. The basic process of liquification is that pulverised coal is mixed with a liquid to form a slurry mix which is combined with hydrogen in a reactor. This is treated with heat, pressure and chemical catalysts to produce liquids and gases which can be made into a variety of synthetic fuels.

Coefficient
The coefficients are the numbers that appear to the left of chemical formulas in a balanced equation.

Coenzyme
An organic co-factor required for the action of certain enzymes; often contains a vitamin as the component.

Cofactor
The inorganic complement of an enzyme reaction, usually a metal ion.

Coke
The material left behind when volatile components in coal have been removed by heating. It contains a very high percentage of carbon.

Colligative property
A colligative property is a physical property that depends on the number of solute species present, but not on their chemical identity.

Colloid
A colloid is a dispersion of small particles (less than 500 nm in diameter) of one material in another.

Collision theory
Collision theory is a simple model that accounts for the variation in the rate of reaction with temperature and concentration. It considers particles to be hard spheres that react with each other when they collide with sufficient kinetic energy.

Colorimeter
A device for measuring the concentration of coloured substances in solution by passing visible light through the solution.

Combinatorial Chemistry
the automated, parallel synthesis of a ibrary of chemical structures, usually drug leads. This is in contrast to the traditional approach of synthesising different compounds one at a time, manually.

Combined gas law
The gas law that combines absolute temperature, pressure and volume, but not the amount of gas.

Combustion
A highly exothermic and rapid chemical reaction in which a substance reacts with oxygen during burning.

Combustion analysis
Combustion analysis is a method for determining the empirical formula of a compound via a series of weighings before and after complete combustion.

Common ion effect
The common ion effect is an application of Le Chatelier's Principle. According to Le Chatelier's Principle the equilibrium will respond so as to counteract the effect of the added common ion. This means that the equilibria will shift so that the common ion will be reduced which means a shift to the left thus reducing the solubility of the slightly soluble salt system.

Competitive inhibition
A competitive inhibitor generally competes with the substrate for the enzyme's active site. The percentage of competitive inhibition at fixed inhibitor concentration can be decreased by increasing the substrate concentration. At high concentrations of the substrate it is possible to reach V_{max} even in the presence of the inhibitor; however, the value of KM is decreased.

Complementary colours
One of two colours so related to each other that when blended together they produce white light; so-called because each colour makes up to the other what it lacks to make it white.

Complete protein
A protein that provides all of the essential amino acids.

Completion
Complete consumption of at least one of the reactants in a chemical reaction. A reaction goes to completion if its limiting reactant or reagent is consumed.

Complex ion
A chemical species typically consisting of a metal ion, usually a transition metal ion, surrounded by a fixed number of ligands which form dative or coordinate covalent bonds with vacant orbitals in the metal ion.

Concentrated
A concentrated solution contains a relatively high concentration of solute.

Concentration
The ratio of the amount (or mass) of a substance dissolved in a given volume of solution. Concentrations of solution are typically expressed in g dm-3 or mol dm-3.

Condensation (chemical)
An addition reaction immediately followed by an elimination reaction.

Condensation polymerisation
Overall two or more molecules react or link together with the elimination of a small molecule, usually water.

Condensing
The change of a vapour into a liquid (at constant temperature); during this process latent heat is released to the surroundings.

Configuration
The spatial arrangement of atoms or functional groups within a molecule.

Conjugate acid
The chemical species formed when a proton or hydrogen ion is accepted by a base.

Conjugate acid-base pair
Two chemical species related to each other by the loss or gain of a single proton or hydrogen ion.

Conjugate base
The chemical species formed when an acid loses a proton or hydrogen ion.

Conjugated molecules
Conjugated molecules have double or triple bonds that are separated by one single bond. There is delocalisation of electrons in the π orbitals between the carbon atoms linked by the single bond.

Contact process
An industrial process for the manufacture of sulfuric acid. Sulfur dioxide and air are passed over a heated vanadium(V) oxide catalyst to produce sulfur trioxide which is then dissolved in sulfuric acid to form disulfuric acid which is diluted to produce sulfuric acid.

Continuous spectrum
An emission spectrum that exhibits all the wavelengths or frequencies of visible light.

Control rods
Rods of materials such as cadmium or boron steel that act as neutron absorbers and are used in nuclear reactors to control neutron flows and therefore rates of fission.

Convergence
Convergence occurs as the lines in an emission spectrum become progressively closer to each other (at higher frequency or smaller wavelength) and finally merge.

Cooling curve
A plot of temperature against time for a substance where heat energy is being lost to the surroundings.

Coordinate (dative) bond
A dative covalent bond is formed when one of the atoms supplies both electrons of the shared pair.

Coordination number
The number of ligands surrounding a central metal ion, or the number of nearest neighbours an atom, molecule or ion has in a crystal structure.

Co-polymer
A polymer formed from two or more different monomers.

Core electron
An inner electron in an atom; an electron not in the outer or valence shell.

Corrosion
The process by which a metal undergoes oxidation by air and water.

Coulomb
The SI unit of electrical charge. One coulomb of charge is passed around a circuit when a current of one Ampere is allowed to flow for one second.

Covalent bonding
A chemical bond formed by the sharing of one or more pairs of electrons (with paired spins) between two atoms. Covalent bonds are typically formed between two or more non-metals in molecules and giant covalent structures. The strength of the bond stems from the electron density located between the two nuclei.

Covalent radius
The covalent radius is half of the inter-nuclear distance between two covalently bonded atoms. If the two atoms in the covalent bond are identical, then the covalent radius is equivalent to half the covalent bond length.

Cracking
The process of breaking down long chain alkanes into smaller alkanes and alkenes using heat, usually in the presence of a catalyst.

Critical point
The temperature and pressure at which the liquid and gaseous phases of a pure stable substance are in equilibrium. A liquid does not exist above the critical temperature, and heating a liquid in a container to a temperature above its critical point will result in the disappearance of the physical surface between the two phases.

Cross linking
The existence of covalent bonds between adjacent chains in a polymer, thus strengthening the material.

Crude oil or petroleum
A mixture of hydrocarbons formed originally from marine animals, found beneath the ground trapped between layers of sedimentary rock. It is obtained by drilling.

Curly arrow
An arrow used to show the notional movement of a pair of electrons in a reaction mechanism. The tail of the arrow shows where the electrons come from and the head where they go to.

Current
The rate of flow of electric charge or electrons through a conductor. It is measured in coulombs per second or Amperes.

Cyclic
Molecules having atoms arranged in a ring or closed-chain structure.

Cyclisation
The formation of a cyclic compound from a straight chain compound.

Cyclo-alkane
An alkane containing a ring.

Cystine
A molecule resulting from the enzyme-controlled oxidation reaction between the sulfhydryl (–SH) groups of two adjacent cysteine molecules.

Dalton's law of partial pressures
The total pressure a mixture of ideal gases exerts is the sum of the partial pressures of all the component gases.

Daniell cell
A voltaic or galvanic cell consisting of a copper cathode immersed in 1 mol dm^{-3} copper(II) sulfate solution and a zinc anode immersed in 1 mol dm^{-3} zinc sulfate. They are connected via as salt bridge and an external circuit. It has a standard potential of 1.10 V and is named after JF Daniell, who first constructed the first cell of this type.

Dative covalent bond
A dative covalent bond is formed when one of the atoms supplies both electrons of the shared pair.

d-block metals
A group of transition metals located between groups 2 and 3/13 of the Periodic table. The majority of the d-block metals have two s electrons and d-electrons in the inner shell.

d-d transition
An electronic transition between two d-orbitals. Such transitions are responsible for the colours of many transition metal ions.

Deactivating group
In Organic chemistry, it is a substituent that when present in a benzene ring makes the resulting molecule undergo electrophilic substitution at a slower rate than benzene itself.

Degenerate orbitals
A group of orbitals with the same energy.

Dehydrating agent
A substance that removes water or the elements of water from a compound.

Dehydration
The removal of water or elements of water (that is, hydrogen and oxygen in a 2:1 ratio) to form a new compound.

Deliquescence
The property shown by some salts of absorbing sufficient water from the atmosphere to form a solution.

Delocalisation (of electrons)
Molecules or ions that have p orbitals extending over three or more atoms. Metallic bonding involves the delocalisation of valence electrons between all the ions within a crystal.

Denaturation
Partial or complete unfolding of a protein chain (or nucleic acid). The process is usually reversible and is brought about by heat and a variety of chemicals.

Density
Density is defined as mass per unit volume.
$\text{Density} = \frac{\text{mass}}{\text{volume}}$.

Deoxyribonucleic acid
A large nucleotide polymer having a double helical structure with complementary bases on the two strands. Its major functions are protein synthesis and the storage and transport of genetic information.

Depressant
A drug that reduces excitability and calms a person by producing functional slowing of the brain or spinal cord.

Deprotonation
The loss of a proton from a chemical species.

Desalination
The removal of dissolved salts from an aqueous solution.

Designer drug
A drug with properties and effects similar to a known hallucinogen, steroid or narcotic but having a slightly altered chemical structure, created in order to evade restrictions against illegal substances.

Detection Limit
The minimum amount of an analyte that can be detected reliably.

Detergent
Water-soluble mixtures that can emulsify grease and via this action remove dirt.

Deuterium
The isotope of hydrogen having a single neutron in the nucleus.

Diaphragm cell
An industrial electrolytic cell in which a porous diaphragm is used to separate the electrodes thereby allowing electrolysis of sodium chloride solution, without allowing the products to react.

Diatomic molecule
A molecule containing two atoms of the same element covalently bonded together.

Dietary fibre
Mainly plant material that is found in fruit, grains and vegetables that humans cannot digest

Diffusion
The spontaneous movement of gas or liquid particles from a region where they are at high concentration to a region where they are at low concentration.

Dilute
A dilute solution contains a relatively low concentration of solute.

Dilution
The process of adding more solvent, usually water, to a solution to lower the concentration.

Dimer
A molecule formed by the bonding of two identical monomers. The bonds will be relatively strong hydrogen bonds or covalent bonds.

Dimerisation
The linking together of two molecules.

Diode
An electronic device that allows electricity to flow in only one direction.

Dioxins
Toxic chemicals formed during the high temperature combustion of chloro-organic matter. They persist in the environment and contain chlorine atoms bonded to benzene rings.

Dipolar ion
An ion whose positive and negative charges are separated from each other

Dipole
A pair of separated opposite electrical charges located on a pair of atoms within a molecule.

Dipole-dipole forces
The weak intermolecular forces that exist between non-polar molecules when they are arranged so that the positive and negative ends can interact.

Diprotic
An acid which contains two replaceable hydrogen atoms per molecule. (Also known as dibasic).

Directing effect
In Aromatic Chemistry, this is the ability of substituent functional groups to direct further substitution to certain positions on the benzene ring during the electrophilic substitution of benzene derivatives.

Disaccharide
A carbohydrate consisting of two covalently joined monosaccharide units.

Discharge
the conversion of ions to atoms or molecules during electrolysis.

Displacement reaction
A redox reaction in which a more reactive element displaces a less reactive element from a solution of its ions or salt, often in aqueous solution.

Displacement Reactions (halogens)
A redox reaction in which a more reactive halogen displaces a less reactive halogen in the form of its halide (or salt).

Disproportionation
The simultaneous oxidation and reduction of a single chemical element to produce two products.

Dissociation
The splitting of a molecule into two or more smaller fragments, which could be atoms, molecules, ions of radicals.

Dissociation (of an acid)
The breakdown of an acid molecule into ions in the presence of water.

Distillation
The process of boiling a liquid and condensing the vapour.

Disulfide bridge
A covalent bond (-S-S-) formed (in the presence of an enzyme) between two protein adjacent chains by the reaction between sulfhydryl groups (-SH) of two cysteine residues.

Diuretic
A substance that leads to an increase in the discharge of urine.

DNA profiling
The distinctive pattern of fragments of DNA obtained by restriction enzyme digestion and electrophoretic separation of minisatellite DNA from individual people.

Doping
The incorporation of impurities within the crystal lattice of silicon so as to increase its conductivity.

d orbitals
There are five d orbitals (each of a different shape) in every shell beginning with the third shell.
d-orbital splitting
A splitting caused by the ligands of the d orbitals of the transition metal ion in a complex ion.

Double bond
A covalent bond in which two pairs of bonding electrons are shared by a pair of adjacent atoms. One of the bonds is a pi bond; the other is a sigma bond.

Double helix
The coiled structure of double-stranded DNA in which strands linked by hydrogen bonds form a spiral or helical configuration, with the two strands oriented in opposite directions.

Double reciprocal plot
(see Lineweaver-Burke plot)

Drug
A substance intended for use in the diagnosis, cure, mitigation, treatment, or prevention of disease. They affect natural chemical processes occurring within the body.

Dry cell
A battery in which the electrolyte is in the form of a paste.

Ductility
The ability of metals to be drawn out under tension and stretched into wires.

Dynamic equilibrium
A physical or chemical equilibrium is described as dynamic because although there is no change in macroscopic properties the forward and backward reactions are occurring (at equal rates).

Effective nuclear charge
The actual nuclear charge exerted on a particular electron, equal to the actual nuclear charge minus the effect of electron-electron repulsion.

Efflorescence
The process where water of crystallisation is lost by a hydrated salt stored in an open container.

Electrical conductivity
A measure of the ability of a substance to conduct an electric current due to the presence of charged particles, either ions or delocalised valence electrons, which are free to move.

Electrochemical cell
Electrochemical cells include galvanic and electrolytic cells. They produce a potential difference (voltage) from a redox reaction.

Electrochemical series
A 'reactivity series' for metals based on standard electrode potential data, which is a measure of the energetic tendency of a metal to form positive ions. The elements are arranged in order of increasingly negative electrode potentials, that is, increasing reducing power.

Electrochemistry
The study of electrolysis, electrochemical cells and the properties of ionic solutions.

Electrode
A conductor which dips into the electrolyte of an electrolytic or voltaic cell and allows the current (electrons) to flow to and from the electrodes. Electrodes may be inert, functioning only to transfer electrons, or may be active and be involved in the cell reactions.

Electrolysis
A process in which chemical decomposition of a substance, known as the electrolyte, is caused by the passage of an electric current.

Electrolyte
An electrolyte is an ionic compound, a salt, alkali or acid, which will conduct electricity when it is melted or dissolved in water. An electrolyte will not conduct electricity when solid.

Electromagnetic wave
A wave of oscillating electric and magnetic fields that can move through space.

Electromagnetic spectrum
The entire range of electromagnetic radiation or waves including, in order of decreasing frequency, cosmic-ray photons, gamma rays, x-rays, ultraviolet radiation, visible light, infrared radiation, microwaves, and radio waves.

Electron
Negatively charged particle present in all atoms and located in shells, or energy levels, located outside the nucleus.

Electron affinity (first)
The enthalpy change when one mole of gaseous atoms accepts a mole of gaseous electrons under standard thermodynamic conditions.

Electron bombardment
The process of forming positive ions from atoms (and molecules) in a mass spectrometer by bombarding them with electrons of high kinetic energy. The colliding electron ejects a valence electron and both electrons leave the atom.

Electron carrier
A protein that can reversibly lose or gain electrons; involved in the transfer of electrons from glucose to oxygen.

Electron configuration
A short hand method for describing the arrangement of electrons in the shells or main energy levels of an atom.

Electron deficient compound
A molecule or ion where some atoms do not have filled outer or valence shells.

Electronegativity
A measure of the tendency of an atom in a molecule to attract a pair of shared electrons towards itself. The difference in electronegativities of two atoms in a covalent bond gives an indication of the bond's polarity.

Electron transition
The movement of electrons from one orbital to another.

Electrons-in-boxes notation
A notation system in which atomic orbitals are regarded as boxes into which electrons are placed.

Electron transfer chain
The movement of electrons from the break down products of glucose to oxygen via the respiratory (electron transfer) chain.

Electroplating
Electroplating is the electrolytic process of coating a metal with a thin layer of another metal by electrolysis.

Electrophile
An electrophile is a chemical species that can act as an electron pair acceptor or Lewis acid.

Electrophilic addition (in alkenes)
An addition reaction initiated by the rate determining attack of an electrophile on the pi electrons of the carbon-carbon double bond.

Electrophilic substitution
A reaction involving the substitution of an atom or group of atoms in benzene (or derivative) with an electrophile as the attacking species.

Electrophoresis
Movement of charged ions in response to an electrical field. It is often used to separate mixtures of ions, proteins, or nucleic acids.

Electrostatic forces of attraction
A usually strong force of attraction between particles with opposite charges.

Electrostatic precipitation
The removal of very fine particles suspended in a gas by electrostatic charging and subsequent precipitation onto a collector in a strong electric field.

Elementary steps
Most reactions occur in a series of steps each of which involves one or two reacting particles (atoms, ions or molecules). They are reactions in which no reaction intermediates (other than transition species) have been detected.

Elimination
A reaction in which atoms or small molecules are removed from a single molecule, usually to give a double bond, or between two molecules.

Ellingham diagrams
Diagrams that explain how standard free energies of formation of metal oxides vary with temperature. They allow prediction of the conditions required for metal extraction from oxide ores.

Elution
The process of removing an absorbed material (the adsorbate) from an adsorbent by washing it with a liquid (the eluent). The solution consisting of the adsorbate dissolved in the eluent is the eluate.

Emission spectroscopy
The study of spectra produced by excited gaseous atoms or molecules.

Empirical formula
A formula for a compound which shows the simplest ratio of atoms present.

Enantiomer
A compound whose molecular structure is not superimposable on its mirror image.

Endocrine glands
Groups of cells specialised to synthesise hormones and release them into the blood stream.

Endothermic
A reaction in which heat energy is absorbed from the surroundings when a reaction occurs. There is a fall in temperature when the reaction occurs or heat energy has to be continually supplied to make the reaction occur. In endothermic reactions, there is more enthalpy or potential energy in the bonds of the products than there were in the bonds of the reactants.

End point
The end point is where the indicator changes colour suddenly.

Energy Levels
The allowed energies of electrons in an atom (and molecules), which correspond to the shells. Electrons fill the energy levels, or shells, starting with the one closest to the nucleus.

Enthalpy
The amount of heat energy possessed by a chemical substance. It is stored in the chemical bonds as potential energy. When substances react, the difference in the enthalpy between the reactants and products (at constant pressure) can be measured.

Enthalpy change of combustion
The enthalpy change that occurs when one mole of a compound is completely combusted (burned) in excess oxygen under standard thermodynamic conditions (with no change in volume).

Enthalpy change of formation
The enthalpy change that occurs when one mole of a compound is formed under standard thermodynamic conditions from its elements in their standard states.

Enthalpy change of neutralisation
The enthalpy change that occurs when one mole of acid undergoes complete neutralisation with a base under standard thermodynamic conditions.

Enthalpy change of solution
The enthalpy change when one mole of a substance is dissolved in a solvent to infinite dilution (in practice, to form a dilute solution) under standard conditions.

Enthalpy level diagram
A diagram that traces the relative changes in the enthalpy or potential energy of a chemical system during the course of a reaction.

Enthalpy of atomisation
The enthalpy change when a substance is dissociated into one mole of gaseous atoms under standard thermodynamic conditions.

Enthalpy of hydrogenation
The enthalpy change when hydrogen is added across a multiple bond.

Enthalpy of vaporization
The enthalpy change that occurs when one mole of a pure liquid is vaporised at its boiling point.

Entropy
A thermodynamic function that measures randomness or disorderness in a chemical system and can be used to predict the direction of physical and chemical changes. It can also be interpreted as corresponding to the number of ways of arranging particles in a chemical system or a measure of how energy is distributed among particles. It is defined as the heat absorbed divided by the absolute temperature.

Entropy change
The change in entropy that accompanies a physical or chemical change is given by the sum of the entropies of the products minus the sum of the entropies of the reactants.

Enzyme
A globular protein that catalyses a specific biochemical reaction.

Equilibrium
Equilibrium is said to occur for a reversible reaction when the rate of the forward reaction is equal to the rate of the back ward reaction and consequently there are no changes in the concentrations of reactants and products. It is also where the Gibbs free energy, of the system is minimised with the system maintained at constant temperature and pressure.

Equilibrium constant
The value obtained when equilibrium concentrations of the chemical species are substituted in the equilibrium expression. The value indicates the equilibrium position.

Equilibrium expression
The expression obtained by multiplying the product concentrations and dividing by the multiplied reactant concentrations, with each concentration raised to the power by the coefficient in the balanced equation.

Equilibrium position
A particular set of equilibrium concentrations of reactants and products.

Equivalence point
The point in an acid-base titration where the acid and base have been added in stoichiometric amounts, so that neither is present in excess. If a suitable indicator is chosen it will correspond to the end point.

Essential amino acids
Amino acids that cannot be synthesised by humans and must be obtained from the diet.

Essential fatty acids
These are two fatty acids (linoleic and linolenic) that humans cannot make and must be present in the diet in order for the body to function properly.

Ester
Organic compounds formed by the condensation reaction between alcohols and acids. Esters formed from carboxylic acids have the general formula RCOOR'.

Esterification
The reaction between an acid and alcohol to form an ester and water.

Ether
An organic compound containing the group -O-.

Evaporation
Evaporation occurs at the surface of the liquid and involves a liquid changing into a gas at a temperature below the boiling point of the liquid.

Excess
A reactant is said to be present in excess when after the reaction is complete, some of that reactant remains unreacted.

Excited state
The state of an atom or molecule when one ore more of its electrons is raised to a higher energy level above the stable ground state.

Exothermic
A reaction in which heat energy is released to the surroundings from the reactants. The bonds of the products contain less enthalpy or potential energy than the bonds of the reactants.

F

Faraday
A unit of electrical charge (in Coulombs) equal to the charge required to discharge one mole of a unipositive ion. It is the charge carried by one mole of electrons.

Faraday constant
The quantity of electricity (in coulombs) transferred by one mole of electrons.

Faraday's laws of electrolysis
The amount of a chemical product formed is directly proportional to the quantity of electrons passed. The amount of chemical product formed (for a constant quantity of electricity) is proportional to the relative atomic mass of the ion and its charge.

Fat
A solid ester composed of glycerol (propane-1,2,3-triol) and fatty acids.

Fatty acid
A long chain carboxylic acid which is chemically combined with glycerol (propane-1,2,3-triol) to form fats and oils.

Feedstock
The raw material(s) for a process in the chemical industry.

Fermentation
The conversion of sugars to ethanol and carbon dioxide by yeast under anaerobic conditions.

Fertilisers
A group of chemicals that supply plants with the mineral salts they need for growth.

Fibrous protein
Insoluble proteins that serve in a protective or structural role.

Fingerprint region
The region of the infrared spectrum of a substance between 910 and 1430 cm^{-1} where the pattern of peaks is characteristic of that compound, even though all the peaks may not be known.

First order reaction
A reaction in which the initial rate of reaction is directly proportional to the concentration of one of the reacting substances.

Fischer-Tropsch process
The catalytic hydrogenation of carbon monoxide in the ratio 2:1 hydrogen to carbon monoxide at 200 °C to produce hydrocarbons, especially motor fuel.

Fission (nuclear)
The splitting of a nucleus of an element with a high atomic number into two or more smaller atoms with lower atomic numbers.

Flame Test
An analytical technique in which a small sample of a metal salt is introduced into a hot Bunsen flame on a clean platinum or nichrome wire. The flame vaporises part of the sample which excites some of the atoms, which emit light at wavelengths characteristic of the metal ion in the salt.

Flocculation
The process of aggregating suspended solids in water into larger insoluble clumps.

Formula mass
The formula mass is the sum of the atomic masses of the elements in the formula of an ionic compound.

Formula unit
The symbols used in equations and calculations to represent elements and compounds with giant structures.

Forward reaction
The forward reaction refers to the conversion of the reactant into products in an equilibrium reaction.

Fossil fuel
Non-renewable fuels, such as coal, oil and natural gas, formed underground over geological periods of time from the decaying remains of plants and animals.

Fraction
A mixture of liquids with similar boiling points collected by fractional distillation.

Fractional distillation
Distillation to separate volatile chemical substances in which the products are collected in a series of separate fractions, each with a higher boiling point than the previous fraction.

Freezing
The change of a liquid into a solid at constant temperature.

Freezing point
The temperature at which a liquid turns to a solid.

Free radical
A species with one or more unpaired electrons, often produced by photolysis. They act as highly reactive intermediates in atmospheric chemistry.

Frequency
The number of complete waves passing a point per second.

Friedel-Crafts reaction
A method for substituting an alkyl or acyl group into a benzene ring and forming a C-C bond. It involves the reaction between benzene (or other aromatic compound) with a halogenoalkane or acyl chloride in the presence of a so-called halogen carrier.

Fuel cell
A device which converts chemical energy directly into electrical energy. A gaseous fuel, usually hydrogen or a hydrocarbon, and oxygen are passed over porous electrodes where combustion occurs This is accompanied by the production of an electric current.

Fuels
Chemicals that burn in air or oxygen and release heat energy.

Fullerenes
A group of cage-like hollow molecules composed of hexagonal and pentagonal groups of an even number of carbon atoms.

Functional group
A functional group is an atom or group of atoms (other than hydrogen) that imparts specific physical and chemical properties of a homologous series of organic compounds.

Functional group isomerism
Functional group isomerism is a form of structural isomerism where molecules with the same molecular formula have different functional groups.

Fusion (nuclear)
The forming of a nucleus from two nuclei of lower atomic number. The process releases large amounts of energy and only takes place at very high temperatures.

Galvanic cell
(See voltaic cell).

Gamma waves/radiation (or rays)
High energy electromagnetic radiation of high frequency and extremely short wavelength emitted by changes in the nuclei of atoms.

Gas
A state of matter in which there are little attractive forces operating between the particles. The individual particles move at high velocity in straight lines (until they collide with each other or the walls of the container).

Gas chromatography
A technique for separating or analysing mixtures in the gaseous phase using a carrier gas as an eluent.

Gas-liquid chromatography
A form of partition or adsorption chromatography in which the mobile phase is a gas and the stationary phase a liquid. Solid and liquid samples are vaporized before being introduced to the column.

Gas laws
The various laws that describe the physical behaviour of gases.

Gateway drug
A habit-forming substance whose use may lead to the abuse of drugs that are more addictive or more dangerous.

Gene
A segment of a DNA molecule that contains the genetic code for a protein molecule.

General anaesthetic
An anesthetic that affects the entire body and causes loss of consciousness and insensitivity to pain.

Geometric isomerism
Geometric isomerism occurs in alkenes when there is restricted rotation about a carbon-carbon double bond. It can also occur in ring system where there is restricted rotation about a carbon-carbon single bond.

Geothermal energy
The use of hot water or steam located deep underground, often under pressure, to generate electricity.

Giant covalent structure
A regular arrangement, usually three dimensional, of covalently bonded atoms that extends throughout the substance.

Giant structure
A lattice, usually three-dimensional, of ions or atoms in which the bonding (ionic, covalent or metallic) extends throughout the substance.

Gibbs free energy
A thermodynamic function equal to the enthalpy minus the product of the entropy and the absolute temperature. A negative sign indicates that the reaction is spontaneous under standard conditions. It is the energy available to do work.

Gibbs free energy of reaction
The Gibbs free energy of a reaction is defined as the sum of the Gibbs free energies of formation of the products minus the sum of the Gibbs free energies of formation of the reactants.

Global warming
The increase in the temperature of the Earth's atmosphere since the Industrial Revolution. It is believed to be a consequence of rising levels of greenhouse gases, especially carbon dioxide which are enhancing the Greenhouse effect.

Globular protein
Soluble proteins with a globular or rounded shape.

Glycosidic bond
The covalent bond, -O-, formed between two reacting sugar molecules, or the bond between the sugar and base in a nucleotide, in the presence of enzymes.

Graham's law of diffusion
Gases diffuse at a rate that is inversely proportional to the square root of their density or molar mass (at constant temperature and pressure).

Gravimetric analysis
A method of quantitative analysis for finding the composition and formulas of compounds based on accurate weighing of reactants and products.

Greenhouse effect
A heating effect occurring in the atmosphere because of the presence of greenhouse gases that absorb infrared radiation.

Greenhouse gases
Greenhouse gases are molecules that contribute to the greenhouse effect and global warming by absorbing infrared energy emitted or reflected from the surface of the Earth.

Group
A column of the Periodic table which contains elements with similar chemical properties. Atoms of elements in the same group have the same number of electrons in their outer or valence shell.

Haber Process
The industrial manufacture of ammonia from nitrogen and hydrogen, carried out at high pressure and moderate temperature in the presence of an iron catalyst.

Heme
An iron complex found in the protein hemoglobin.

Hemoglobin
A quaternary protein composed of four polypeptide chains combined with a haem group. It can bond and transport oxygen molecules from the lungs to body tissues.

Half cell
An electrode in contact with a solution of ions.

Half-equation
The two parts of a redox reaction, one describing the oxidation and the other reduction.

Half life (of a chemical reaction)
The time taken for the reactant concentration (in a chemical reaction) of the reactants to reach a value which is the mean or average of its initial and final values.

Half life (of a radioactive sample)
The time take for the radioactivity emitted by a sample of a radioactive isotope to fall to half its original value. The value will be constant for a particular isotope and unaffected by changes in temperature or pressure.

Halide ions
The halide ions are chloride (Cl-), fluoride (F-) bromide (Br-) and iodide (I-). The halides are salts that contain a metal ion combined with the halide ions.

Hallucinogens
Drugs which affect the brain and cause people to experience hallucinations.

Halogen carrier
An electron deficient metal halide that acts as a Lewis acid during electrophilic substitution.

Halogenoalkane
A homologous series of organic compounds in which one or more of the hydrogen atoms of an alkane have been replaced by halogen atoms.

Halogenoarenes
Halogenoarenes are compounds formed by replacing one or more hydrogen atoms in an arene with halogen atoms.

Halogens
A group of reactive non-metals in Group 7 of the Periodic Table. They are composed of diatomic molecules.

Heat capacity
The heat capacity is the amount of heat energy required to raise the temperature of a substance by one degree kelvin (or Celsius).

Heat energy
The energy transferred between two objects due to a temperature difference between them. The source of heat energy is the movement of atoms, ions and molecules, that is their kinetic energy.

Heating curve
A plot of temperature against time for a substance where heat energy is added at a constant rate.

Heavy metals
Heavy metals are toxic and metals, such as cadmium, mercury and lead, which have relatively high relative atomic masses.

Heavy water
Heavy water is the common name for deuterium oxide, D_2O or ${}^2_1H_2O$.

Herbicide
A substance designed to kill plants.

Hertz
The SI unit of frequency (units of s^{-1} or Hz).

Hess's law
It states that the total enthalpy change for a reaction is independent of the route taken.

Heterogeneous catalyst
Heterogeneous catalysis occurs when the catalyst and the reactants are in different phases (or states).

Heterogenous equilibrium
An equilibrium system where the reactants and products are in more than one phase.

Heterolytic fission
The cleavage of a covalent bond so that one of the atoms or groups separates with both bonding electrons and becomes negatively charged, leaving the other atom or group positively charged.

High-pressure liquid chromatography
A technique in which the sample is forced through the chromatography column under pressure. It is sometimes known as High Performance Liquid Chromatography.

Homogenous catalysis
Heterogeneous catalysis occurs when the catalyst and the reactants are in the same phase (or states).

Homogeneous equilibrium
An equilibrium system where the reactants and products are in the same phase.

Homologous series
A homologous series of organic compounds follow a regular structural pattern and have the same general molecular formula and differ only by the addition of $-CH_2-$ groups.

Homolytic fission
The breaking of a covalent bond so that one electron from the bond is left on each fragment. It results in the formation of two free radicals.

Hormone
A chemical substance produced in small amounts by endocrine glands and then carried in the blood to a target organ or tissue.

Hund's rule
A rule that states that the electronic configuration in orbitals of the same energy will have the minimum number of paired electrons. Electrons with parallel spins are lower in energy than a corresponding pair with opposed spins.

Hydrate
A salt associated with a definite number of molecules of water.

Hydrated ion
Ions dissolve in water and attract the polar molecules of water and become associated with a definite number of water molecules.

Hydration
A reaction where an unsaturated molecule adds a molecule of water, or where water molecules interact with ions in aqueous solution.

Hydride
A compound of hydrogen and one other element.

Hydrocarbons
Organic compounds containing only hydrogen and carbon atoms.

Hydrocracking
A process by which the hydrocarbon molecules of crude oil or petroleum are broken into simpler molecules, by the addition of hydrogen under high pressure and in the presence of a catalyst.

Hydrofluorocarbons
Hydrofluorocarbons (HFCs) are compounds containing carbon, hydrogen, and fluorine and because they contain no chlorine atoms they do not directly affect stratospheric ozone. However, they are efficient absorbers of infrared radiation.

Hydrogenation
The addition of hydrogen across a multiple bond.

Hydrogen bonding
An unusually strong dipole-dipole force that occurs among molecules in which hydrogen is bonded to nitrogen, fluorine and oxygen.

Hydrolysis
A chemical reaction involving the reaction of a molecular compound with water. Covalent bonds are broken during the reaction and the elements of water are added to the chemical fragments.

Hydrophobic
Used to describe molecules or functional groups that are poorly soluble or insoluble in water.

Hydrophic interactions (of a protein)
The association of the non-polar groups within the center of a folding protein, driven by the tendency of the surrounding water molecules to maximise their entropy.

Hydrophilic
Used to describe molecules or functional groups that are soluble in water.

Hydroxyl group
The –OH group covalently bonded in a molecular structure. Found in alcohols, alkanoic acids and some inorganic acids.

Ideal gas
An ideal gas is a hypothetical substance that consists of molecules or atoms that occupy almost no space and have virtually no attractive forces operating between them, or between themselves and the walls of the container. All collisions between the molecules or atoms are perfectly elastic. An ideal gas obeys the gas laws exactly under all conditions.

Ideal gas constant
The ideal gas constant is the constant that appears in the ideal gas equation. It is formed by combining all the constants from Boyle's Law, Charles's Law and Avogadro's Law.

Ideal gas equation
It is an equation relating the temperature, pressure, volume and amount of an ideal gas. It is frequently used in experimental work to determine the molar masses of gases.

Immiscible liquids
Immiscible liquids are liquids which do not mix (e.g. oil and water).

Incomplete protein
A protein that does not provides all of the essential amino acids.

Indicator (acid-base)
A substance which changes colour over a particular pH range. They are used to detect the end point during titrations.

Indicator range
The pH range – usually 2 pH units – over which an acid-base indicator changes colour completely.

Induced dipole
A force induced in one molecule by the approach of another molecule which has a dipole, whether temporary or permanent.

Inductive effect
The effect of a functional group or atom in an organic molecule in attracting sigma electrons towards itself, or in repelling them. This results in the formation of a dipole in the molecule.

Inert
A chemical is described as inert if it has little or no tendency to react under given circumstances.

Inhibitor
A substance that slows down the rate of a reaction.

Initial rate method
An experimental method for determining the order of a chemical reactions and its rate equation.

Initiation
The first elementary step in a free radical reaction. It involves the homolytic cleavage of a bond, typically by ultraviolet radiation or high temperature, to generate free radicals.

Interferons
A group of naturally occurring anti-viral compounds.

Interhalogen
A covalent compound formed by the reaction between two different halogens. A molecule containing atoms of different halogens.

Intermediate
A chemical species that is neither a reactant nor a product but is formed and consumed during the overall chemical reaction. Intermediates never appear in a rate expression.

Intermolecular forces
The weak attractive forces operating between molecules.

Internal resistance
The resistance of a cell or a battery.

Intramolecular forces
Forces operating within molecules. They are usually covalent bonds, though hydrogen bonding can occur intra-molecularly. They do not normally break during melting or boiling.

Iodine number (or index)
The amount of iodine in grams which 100 grams of a fat or oil can absorb; it is inversely related to the amount of unsaturated fatty acids present in the fat or oil.

Ion
An ion is charged particle formed by the loss or gain of electrons from an atom (simple ion), or a group of atoms (polyatomic ions).

Ion channel
A membrane-bound protein that provides a path for the regulated transport of a specific ion across a cell membrane.

Ion exchange
The exchange of ions of the same charge between an aqueous solution and a solid (in the form of a resin) in contact with it.

Ion exchange chromatography
In ion exchange chromatography, charged substances are separated via column materials that carry an opposite charge.

Ionic bond
A bond formed when electrons are transferred from a metal atom to one or more non-metal atoms. It is the result of electrostatic forces of attraction between oppositely charged ions.

Ionic bonding
A strong electrostatic force of attraction between oppositely charged ions arranged into a lattice. Ionic bonding typically involves the transfer of one, or more electrons, between a metal atom and one ore more non-metal atoms.

Ionic equation
The simplified equation for a reaction involving ionic substances. Only those ions that actually participate in the reaction are included in the ionic equation; spectator ions are not included.

Ionic product constant of water
The product of the concentrations of hydrogen and hydroxide ions in water under standard thermodynamic conditions.

Ionic radius
A measure of the radius of an ion in the crystalline form of a compound.

Ionisation energy (first)
The energy required to remove one mole of electrons from one mole of isolated gaseous atoms to form one mole of unipositive ions under standard thermodynamic conditions.

Isoelectric point (of an amino acid)
The pH at which an amino acid in solution has no overall electrical charge. At this pH the amino acid does not move when placed in an electric field.

Isoelectronic
Two atoms or ions that have the same number of electrons are described as isoelectronic.

Isomers
Isomers are compounds with the same molecular formula but different molecular structures and physical and/or chemical properties.

Isomerism
Isomerism is the existence of two or more molecules having the same molecular formula, but with different bonding arrangements of atoms or orientation of their atoms in space.

Isotactic
A polymer chain in which the substituents, or side chains, are distributed on the same side of the chain.

Isotope
Two or more atoms of the same element with different numbers of neutrons (and therefore different relative isotopic masses).

Isotopic abundance
The proportions of the different isotopes of an element.

Joule
The SI unit for energy. Symbol J.

Kekulé structure
A representation of a hypothetical localised structure of benzene or a benzene derivative in which there is a six-membered ring with alternate double and single bonds.

Kelvin scale
A temperature scale starting from absolute zero (-273 °C) using degrees the same size or magnitude as degrees Celsius.

Kinetic energy (of particles in a gas)
The energy due to the motion of gas particles; it depends on the mass of the gas particle (atom or molecule) and the square of its velocity (speed in a specified direction).

Kinetics
The quantitative study of the dependence of reaction rate on variables, such as concentration, pressure and temperature.

Kinetic stability
If two chemicals react relatively slowly because the activation energy is relatively high, then the system shows kinetic stability.

Kinetic theory
A theory which explains the physical properties of solids, liquids and gases in terms of the movement of particles (atoms, ions or molecules). The theory also accounts for the changes that occur during a change in state.

Knocking
A knocking noise made by a petrol engine in car, as a result of premature fuel combustion.

Latent heat
The heat needed to bring about a change in state.

Lattice
A regular, repeating three dimensional arrangement of atoms, molecules or ions within a crystal.

Lattice enthalpy
The amount of energy required to dissociate one mole of an ionic compound to its gaseous ions (under standard thermodynamic conditions).

Law of conservation of mass
Mass is not lost or gained during a chemical reaction – the total mass of the reactants equals the total mass of the products.

LD_{50}
LD stands for "Lethal Dose". LD_{50} is the amount of a substance, given all at once, which causes the death of 50% (one half) of a group of test animals. The LD_{50} is one way to measure the short-term poisoning potential (acute toxicity) of a material.

Lead acid battery
A battery (used in cars) in which the anode is lead, the cathode is lead coated with lead(IV) oxide and the electrolyte is sulfuric acid.

Lean burn engine
Lean combustion engines were designed to enhance fuel efficiency without sacrificing power or drive-ability. All engines burn a mixture of air and fuel, but a lean-burn engine has a higher air-to-fuel ratio than conventional engines. This can mean significant savings in petrol, and thus in emissions, such as carbon dioxide.

Leaving group
An atom or group of atoms which breaks away from a molecule during a substitution or an elimination reaction.

Le Chatelier's principle
Le Chatelier's principle states that if a change is imposed on a reaction at equilibrium, the position of the equilibrium will shift in a direction that reduces the effect of that change.

Lethal dosage
The size of dosage that will typically cause death.

Lewis acid
A chemical species that can accept an electron pair to form a dative or coordinate covalent bond.

Lewis base
A chemical species that can donate an electron pair to form a dative or coordinate covalent bond.

Lewis (electron dot) structure
A diagram of a molecule showing how the valence electrons are arranged among the atoms in the molecule.

Ligand
A molecule or negative ion that donates a pair of electrons to a central metal ion to form a dative or coordinate covalent bond. Ligands are Lewis acids.

Ligand exchange/substitution
The process where one or more ligands in a complex ion are replaced, often reversibly, by one another.

Line spectrum
An emission spectrum that has only certain wavelengths or frequencies of visible light. The lines arise from excited electrons falling back to lower energy levels within the atom.

Limiting reactant
The reactant that is completely consumed, or used up, when a reaction goes to completion.

Lineweaver-Burke equation
An algebraic rearrangement of the Michealis-Menten equation which allows its maximum rate, V_{max} and the Michaelis-Menten constant, K_m, by extrapolating the substrate concentration, [S], to infinity.

Liquid
A state of matter in which particles are loosely attracted by intermolecular forces. A liquid always take up the shape of the walls of its container and its particles are not arranged into a lattice.

Lipids
Biological compounds, for example, fats, oils and steroids, which are soluble in organic solvent, but essentially insoluble in water.

Local anaesthetic
An anesthetic that numbs a local area of the body whilst the patient remains conscious.

Localised electrons
Electron pairs forming covalent bonds between two atoms. They are not free to move through a structure.

Lock-and-key hypothesis
A model for the mechanism of enzyme activity postulating that the shapes of the substrate and the enzyme are such that they fit together as a key fits into a specific lock.

Lone pair (of electrons)
A lone or non-bonding pair of electrons are pairs of outer or valence shell electrons which are not used to form covalent bonds within the molecule. Lone pairs affect the shape of a molecule and can be used to form dative or coordinate covalent bonds.

Low level radioactive waste
Radioactive waste which, because of its low radioactivity, does not require shielding during normal transport or handling.

Lyotropic liquid crystal
A solution that shows liquid crystal state at certain concentrations.

Lysergic acid diethylaminde (LSD)
a drug that is a powerful hallucinogen

Lysis
Destruction of a cell's cell membrane or of a bacterial cell wall, releasing the cellular contents and killing the cell. This often occurs during viral infections.

Macromolecule
A very large molecule, usually with a molar mass in the tens of thousands.

Macronutrients
Chemical substances required in relativley large amounts in the diet for metabolism.

Macroscopic properties
Macroscopic properties are properties of substances in bulk that can be observed, for example, colour, or easily measured, for example, pressure of a gas.

Magnetic resonance imaging (MRI)
The use of a nuclear magnetic resonance spectrometer to produce electronic images of specific atoms and molecular structures in solids, especially human cells, tissues, and organs. Because it uses radio frequencies the technique is non invasive.

Malleability
The ability of metals to be bent and beaten into thin sheets.

Markovnikov's rule
A rule that predicts the major and minor products when a hydrogen halide or interhalogen adds across the double bond in an unsymmetrical alkene. The rule states that the major product will be the one in which the hydrogen atom (or less electronegative atom of the interhalogen) attaches itself to the carbon atom with the larger number of hydrogen atoms.

Mass defect
The amount by which the mass of an atomic nucleus is less than the sum of the masses of its constituent particles.

Mass number
The mass number is the sum of the protons and neutrons in the nucleus of the atom or ion.

Mass spectrometer
An instrument in which gaseous atoms are ionised and then accelerated into a magnetic field where the ions are separated according to their mass.

Mass spectrometry
Analysis of individual molecules according to their elemental composition and usually giving information about molar mass, as well as structures of component parts of the molecules.

Mass spectrum
The output plot from the mass spectrometer, which is a bar graph of abundance against mass/charge ratio.

Maxwell-Boltzmann energy distribution curve
A curve describing the distribution of velocities ('speeds') or kinetic energies among the atoms or molecules of an ideal gas. It is often used to explain the effects of a temperature change or the presence of a catalyst on the rate of a chemical reaction.

Mechanism
A detailed description in terms of bond breaking, bond making and intermediate formation that occurs during the series of elementary steps by which an overall chemical reaction occurs.

Medicine
A substance or preparation used in treating disease or to give relief from the symptoms of the disease. It also refers to the practice and study of disease treatment.

Melting
The change of a solid into a liquid at constant temperature.

Melting point
The temperature at which a solid is converted to a liquid at the same temperature.

Mercury cathode cell
An electrolytic cell with a flowing mercury cathode used in the industrial production of chlorine from concentrated sodium chloride solution.

Metabolism
All of the chemical reactions that occur in living organisms.

Metal
Chemical elements which are shiny solids and are good conductors of heat and electricity when solid. They form positive ions (cations). They are located on the left hand side of the Periodic Table and possess one, two or three electrons in the outer shell which take part in chemical bonding.

Metallic bonding
Metallic bonding, found in metals and mixtures of metals (known as alloys), consists of a lattice of cations surrounded by delocalised or mobile valence electrons.

Metalloid
Elements which show some of the physical properties of metals, but the chemical properties of non-metals.

Metallo-protein
A protein that possesses one or more metal ions.

Michaelis-Menten constant
The substrate concentration at which an enzyme-catalysed reaction occurs at one half of its maximum rate.

Michaelis-Menten equation
The equation describing the relationship of the initial rate of an enzyme-controlled reaction and the concentration of the substrate. It takes the form of a hyperbolic curve.

Michaelis-Menten kinetics
Kinetic behaviour, exhibited by enzymes, in which the initial rate of an en enzyme-catalysed reaction shows a hyperbolic dependence on substrate concentration.

Micronutrient
A substance required in small amounts in the diet for proper cell and body function.

Microorganism
A microscopic and usually single celled organism capable of independent existence.

Mineral
A naturally occurring inorganic chemical (element or compound) which is used as a raw material in the chemical industry.

Miscible liquids
Liquids that mix in all proportions, for example, ethanol and water.

Mobile phase
A liquid or gas which percolates through or along the stationary phase during chromatography.

Moderator
A substance, such as water or graphite, that is used in a nuclear reactor to decrease the speed of fast neutrons and increase the likelihood of fission.

Molar extinction coefficient
Absorbance of light per unit path length (usually the centimetre) and per unit concentration (moles per cubic decimetre).

Molar gas volume
One mole of an ideal gas occupies 22.4 cubic decimetres at 0 °C (273 K) and one atmosphere pressure.

Molar mass
The mass in grams of one mole of molecules or the formula units of an ionic compound. It is numerically equal to the relative molecular or atomic mass of a substance, but has units of g mol-1.

Molarity
The amount in moles of solute per volume of solution in cubic decimetres.

Mole
The measure of the amount of a substance. One mole of a substance has a mass equal to its formula mass in grams. One mole of a substance contains 6.02×10^{23} (Avogadro's constant) of atoms, ions or molecules.

Molecular ion
The unipositive ion formed by the unfragmented molecule losing one electron following electron bombardment.

Molecularity
The molecularity indicates the number of chemical species or particles participating in the rate determining step of the mechanism.

Molecular orbitals
Molecular orbitals are formed in molecules when atomic orbitals combine and merge when atoms bond together. Sigma and pi bonds are molecular orbitals.

Mole fraction
A measure of the amount of a component in a mixture. The mole fraction of a component is the ratio of the amount of a particular substance over the total amount of all the substances in a mixture.

Molecular covalent (simple molecular)
A substance consisting of molecules arranged into a lattice held together by intermolecular forces.

Molecular equation
An equation representing a reaction in solution showing the reactants and products in undissociated or unionised form, whether they are strong or weak electrolytes and (acids, salts and bases.

Molecular formula
A chemical formula which shows the actual number of atoms of each element present in a molecule of a covalent compound.

Mole fraction
This is the number of moles of a substance divided by the total number of moles of all the components present in the mixture.

Molecular mass
The molecular mass is the sum of the atomic masses of the elements in the formula of a covalent compound.

Molecule
A group of atoms held together by covalent bonds.

Monochromatic radiation
Electromagnetic radiation with a single wavelength.

Monodentate ligand
A ligand that forms one dative covalent bond to a central metal ion.

Monomer
A small molecule, a large number of which can be polymerised via the formation of covalent bonds to form a polymer.

Monoprotic
An acid which contains one replaceable hydrogen atom per molecule, sometimes also known as monobasic.

Monosaccharide
A sugar that cannot be hydrolysed to simpler sugars.

Multiple bond
A double or triple covalent bond between atoms in a molecule.

Mutation
A change in the nucleotide sequence of a gene.

N

Nanotechnology
Research, development and use of technology in the size range of about 1-100 nm.

Naphtha
A general term used to describe a light hydrocarbon fraction from crude oil distillation with a boiling point between 40 °C and 150 °C. It is an important feedstock used to manufacture other substances.

Narcotic
A drug that doses dulls the senses, relieves pain, and induces profound sleep but in excessive doses causes stupor, coma, or convulsions.

Narrow spectrum antibiotic
An antibiotic that is only effective against a small number of bacterial strains.

Natural gas
Gas obtained from underground deposits and often associated with crude oil or petroleum. It contains a high percentage of methane.

Neutralisation
A chemical reaction between an acid and a base to produce a salt and water only.

Neutral solution
An aqueous solution that is neutral has a pH of seven and contains the same concentrations of hydrogen and hydroxide ions.

Neutron
A neutral particle found in the nucleus of all atoms (except that of the most abundant isotope of hydrogen). It has approximately the same mass as the proton.

Nitration
A type of reaction in which a nitro group ($-NO_2$) is introduced into an aromatic compound, usually via the use of a nitrating mixture.

Nitrating mixture
A 1:2 molar mixture of concentrated nitric and sulfuric acids used to nitrate some aromatic organic compounds. The mixture produces the electrophilic nitronium cation, NO_2^+, via an acid-base reaction.

Nitrile
A compound of the form RCN, where R is an alkyl group or aryl group. Nitriles can be hydrolysed to carboxylic acids.

Nitronium ion
The nitronium ion, NO_2^+, is formed in a nitrating mixture and used to nitrate aromatic compounds. It is a powerful electrophile.

Nitrosamines
A group of organic compounds which contain the functional group NNO and some of which are powerful carcinogens.

Noble gas configuration
An octet of electrons in the valence shell or a pair of electrons in the first shell.

Noble gases
A group of very unreactive gases found in Group 0, 8 or 18 of the Periodic Table. They exist as single atoms and all have filled outer or valence shells.

Nomenclature
Naming rules for compounds.

Non-competititive inhibition
A type of enzyme inhibition not reversed by increasing the substrate concentration.

Non-electrolyte
A substance which, when dissolved in water, gives a non-conducting solution due to the absence of ions.

Non-metal
Chemical elements that are typically poor conductors of heat and electricity. They form covalent bonds and/or form negative ions (anions).

Non-polar molecule
A non-polar molecule is a symmetrical molecule whose individual dipoles sum or cancel to zero.

Normal boiling point
The temperature at which the vapour pressure of a liquid is exactly one atmosphere.

n-type semiconductor
A n-type semiconductor is formed when the impurities added to silicon donate electrons which enter the unoccupied energy level.

Nuclear binding energy
The net energy required to decompose a molecule, an atom, or a nucleus into its component protons, neutrons and electrons.

Nuclear charge
The nuclear charge is the total charge of all the protons in the nucleus.

Nuclear energy
The energy released during nuclear fusion or fission.

Nuclear magnetic resonance
The absorption of radio waves by nuclei with an odd nucleon number.

Nucleon
A particle in a nucleus, either a neutron or proton.

Nucleophile
A nucleophile is a species which contains a lone pair of electrons that can be donated to an electron deficient centre.

Nucleophilic addition
A type of reaction in which the rate determining step is the attachment of a nucleophile to a positive (electron-deficient) part of the molecule (often a C=O bond in a carbonyl compound).

Nucleophilic substitution
A reaction involving the substitution of an atom or group of atoms with as the attacking species.

Nucleoside
A compound consisting of a purine or pyrimidine base covalently bonded to ribose or deoxyribose.

Nucleotide
A monomer of the nucleic acids composed of a five-carbon sugar (a pentose), a nitrogen-containing base, and phosphoric(V) acid

Nucleus
The central part of an atom containing protons and frequently neutrons.

Nuclide
The general term for a unique atom.

Nutrients
Food components which provide growth, energy and replacement for body tissues.

Nylon
A polymer with a long chain of carbon atoms to which amide groups (-NH-CO-) are combined at regular intervals. There is extensive hydrogen bonding between the chains.

Obesity
Excess body mass which often leads to health problems

Octane number
A numerical representation of the antiknock properties of motor fuel, compared with a standard reference fuel, such as iso-octane (2,2,4-trimethylpentane), which has an octane number of 100.

Octet
A set of eight electrons in the valence shell.

Octet rule
Atoms (other than hydrogen) typically fill their valence or electron shell with eight electrons (an octet) when they form compounds.

Oil
A liquid ester composed of glycerol (propane-1,2,3-triol) and fatty acids.

Opiates
A drug, hormone, or other chemical substance having sedative or narcotic effects similar to those containing opium or its derivatives.

Optical isomerism
Optical isomerism typically occurs when a molecule has no plane of symmetry and can exist in left- and right-handed forms that are non-superimposable mirror images of each other. The molecule must possess a chiral centre. Optical isomers rotate plane-polarised light.

Optically active
A compound that is able to rotate plane-polarised light.

Optimum pH and temperature
The characteristic pH and temperature at which an enzyme has maximum activity.

Oral contraceptive
A pill, typically containing estrogen or progesterone, that inhibits ovulation and thereby prevents conception. Also called the birth control pill.

Orbit
The circular path of an electron around the nucleus (in the Bohr theory).

Orbital
A region in space in which an electron may be found in an atom or molecule. Each atomic orbital can hold up to a maximum of two electrons with opposite spins.

Order of a reaction (individual)
The order of a reaction, with respect to a particular reactant, indicates how the rate of a chemical reaction is affected by the changes of concentration in a particular reactant. It is the exponent in the rate expression with respect to a particular reactant. The order can only be determined experimentally; it cannot be deduced from the stoichiometric equation.

Ore
A naturally occurring mineral from which a metal can be extracted.

Organic Chemistry
Organic Chemistry is the study of carbon containing compounds with the exception of the elements itself and its oxides.

Overall order
The sum of the individual orders with respect to each of the reactants in the rate expression.

Oxidant
(see oxidising agent).

Oxidation
Oxidation involves an increase in oxidation number or loss of electrons.

Oxidation number
A number (usually an integer), positive or negative, given to indicate whether an element has been reduced or oxidised during a redox reaction.

Oxide
A compound of oxygen with another element where the oxygen has the oxidation number (-2).

Oxidising agent
A chemical or substance that brings about oxidation; it accepts electrons from the reactant or one of the reactants. In the reaction the oxidising agent itself is reduced.

Oxy acid
An acid in which the acidic proton, or replaceable hydrogen, is covalently bonded to an oxygen atom.

Ozone
A colourless and toxic gas with the chemical formula O_3. It is produced in the stratosphere by the action of high-energy ultra-violet radiation on oxygen molecules, producing oxygen atoms. These oxygen atoms then react with oxygen molecules to form ozone. It is also produced in the lower atmosphere by the action of ultraviolet radiation on nitrogen dioxide, to produce oxygen atoms which can then react with oxygen molecules to give ozone.

Ozone depletion
The production of a region of lower concentration ('hole') in the ozone layer by the action of chlorine atoms released from chlorofluorocarbons (CFC's), which destroy ozone by reactions on the surface of ice crystals.

Ozone layer
A layer of ozone in the stratosphere (between 15 – 30 km) which prevents harmful ultra-violet radiation from reaching the earth's surface.

Paper chromatography
Chromatography carried out using a special grade of filter paper as the stationary phase.

Parallel synthesis
A single-batch method that uses a mixture of reagents at each step of a synthesis to generate a large number of different products.

Parenteral
A drug taken into the body or administered in a manner other than through the digestive tract, as by intravenous, subcutaneous or intra-muscular injection.

Partial pressure
The pressure a gas in a mixture of gases would exert on the container if it were the only gas in the container. It is equal to the mole fraction of the gas multiplied by the total pressure.

Particle
The term particle (in the context of kinetic theory) refers to atoms, molecules or ions.

Particulates
Particulates are any type of solid particle or droplet in the air in the form of haze, smoke or dust, which can remain suspended in the air or atmosphere for extended periods.

Partition
The distribution of a solute between two immiscible solvents.

Pascal
The SI unit of pressure, abbreviated to Pa. One pascal is equivalent to a force of one newton on one square metre.

Pauling scale
A common measure of electronegativity which runs from 0 (least electronegative or most electropositive) to 4 (most electronegative or least electropositive).

p-block element
An element where the valence electrons are in the p-shell. P-block elements are in groups 3, 4, 5, 6, 7 and 8 in the Periodic Table.

Penicillin
An antibiotic derived from the mould Pencillium notatum. They produce their effects by disrupting synthesis of the bacterial cell wall.

Peptide
A bond formed between the amino group of an amino acid and the carboxyl group of another (in the presence of enzymes), with the elimination of water.

Peptide bond
An amide bond resulting from the condensation reaction between the amine group of one amino acid and the carboxylic acid group of another.

Percentage composition
The percentage by mass of each of the elements in a compound.

Percentage yield
The actual or experimental yield as a percentage of the theoretical yield.

Period
A row in the Periodic Table which contains elements with same number of shells, but with an increasing number of electrons in the outer or valence shell.

Periodicity
The regular repetition of chemical and physical properties as you move across and down the Periodic Table.

Periodic Table
A table of the chemical elements arranged in order of increasing atomic (proton) number to show the similar chemical properties of elements with similar electron configurations.

Peroxyacetyl nitrate (PAN)
Peroxyacetyl nitrate is an important by-product in the photochemical production of ozone, and acts as a reservoir for nitrogen dioxide.

Petrochemicals
Organic compounds found in, or derived from petroleum that are used in the manufacture of products other than fuels.

Pharmaceutical
a drug which leads to an improvement in health; medicine

Pharmacology
the scientific study of the interactions of drugs with the different cells found in the body.

Phase
A physically or chemically distinct part of a chemical equilibrium. A phase is homogenous throughout and is separated from other phases by a phase boundary.

Phase equilibrium
An equilibrium in which the amounts of the phases are fixed, with transfer from one phase to another feasible.

Phenol
A group of organic compounds in which a hydroxyl group is bonded directly to one of the carbon atoms of a benzene ring.

Phenolphthalein
A common acid-base indicator, used for strong acid/strong base and weak acid.strong base titrations. It is colourless in acid solution, pink in alkaline solution.

Phenyl
The group $-C_6H_5$.

Phospholipids
Lipids that contain the phosphate group.

Photochemical reaction
A reaction initiated by light.

Photochemical smog
A form of local atmospheric pollution found in large cities in which oxides of nitrogen and unburnt hydrocarbons react in the presence of light to produce a range of harmful products including ozone and PAN.

Photolysis
The splitting of molecules into fragments (often free radicals) by light, usually ultraviolet radiation.

Photon
A 'packet' or quantum of light, or other electromagnetic radiation.

pH
The pH of a solution is the negative logarithm (to the base 10) of the hydrogen ion or proton concentration (in mol dm^{-3}).

pH probe
An electrode that can be used to accurately measure (via voltage) the pH of an aqueous solution.

pH scale
The pH scale runs from 0 to 14 and is used to describe the acidity or alkalinity of an aqueous solution.

Pi bond
A bond formed by the sideways overlap of two p-orbitals. In a pi bond the electron density is concentrated on either side of the line between the nuclei of the two joined by the bond.

Placebo effect
An improvement in the condition of an ill person that occurs in response to treatment but that cannot be considered due to the specific treatment used.

Planck('s) constant
The constant relating the change in energy for a system to the frequency of the electromagnetic radiation absorbed or emitted.

Plane polarised light
Electromagnetic radiation in which both components of the wave oscillate in a single plane. It is used for the detection of optical activity.

Plastic
Materials that can be shaped by applying heat or pressure.

Plasticizer
A substance added to a synthetic (man-made) plastic to make it flexible.

Polar covalent bond
A bond formed when electrons are shared unequally between two atoms due to a difference in electronegativity. One atom has a partial positive charge, and the other atom has an equal but opposite partial negative charge.

Polarimeter
A device used to study optically active substances.

Polarisability or polarising power
The extent to which the electron distribution in a molecule, ion or an atom can be distorted by an externally applied electric field.

Polarity
The dipole possessed by a bond as a consequence of a difference in electronegativity values between the bonded atoms.

Polar molecule
A polar molecule is an unsymmetrical molecule whose individual dipoles do not sum to zero or cancel.

Polar solvents
Solvents composed of polar molecules.

Polyamide
A polymer in which the monomer molecules are linked by amide bonds.

Polyester
A synthetic polymer formed by reacting alcohols with acids, so that the monomers are linked by the group, -O-CO-.

Polymer
A compound containing very large molecules composed of repeating units called monomers.

Polymerisation
A chemical reaction in which small molecules called monomers are joined together covalently to form a polymer.

Polypeptide
A long linear chain of between 10 and 100 amino acids linked via peptide bonds.

Polyprotic acid
An acid with more than one acidic proton or replaceable hydrogen. It dissociates in a stepwise manner , one proton or hydrogen ion at a time.

Polysaccharides
Carbohydrates whose molecules contain chains of monosaccharide molecules.

p orbital
A dumb bell-shaped atomic orbital; there are three per shell, beginning with the second.

Potential difference ('voltage')
A measure of the force pushing electrons around a circuit. If the potential difference between two points is 1 volt, then the passage of 1 coulomb of charge between these points involves 1 joule of energy.

Power (of a galvanic cell)
The power of a cell (measured in watts (W)) is given by the product of the voltage and the current.

Precipitate
A precipitate is an insoluble substance formed by a chemical reaction in solution. It occurs when two soluble salts react to give one soluble and one insoluble salt.

Pressure
A measure of the force pressing onto an object's surface. The pressure that a gas exerts upon its container is caused by the particles colliding with the walls of the container. Pressure is defined as force per unit area.
$\text{Pressure} = \frac{\text{force}}{\text{area}}$

Pressure law
The gas law stating that the pressure of a fixed mass (at constant volume) of an ideal gas is directly proportional to absolute temperature.

Primary alcohol
An alcohol containing the $-CH_2OH$ group.

Primary amine
An amine of the form RNH_2, where R is an alkyl or aryl group.

Primary air pollution
Primary pollutants enter the atmosphere directly from various sources.

Primary cell
A device which produces a flow of electric current. A primary cell cannot be recharged.

Primary Standard
A chemical which can be weighed out accurately to prepare a standard solution for volumetric analysis.

Primary structure (of a protein)
The order or sequence of the amino acids in a polypeptide chain.

Product
A substance produced during a chemical reaction.

Promotion
The movement of an electron from a low energy level to a higher energy level further away from the nucleus.

Propagation
An elementary reaction involving one radical causing the formation of another radical.

Prostaglandins
A group of organic compounds derived from essential fatty acids and causing a range of actions, including inflammation.

Protein
A molecule composed of one or more polypeptide chains, each with a characteristic sequence of amino acids linked via peptide bonds.

Proton
Positively charged particle found in the nuclei of all atoms. It has approximately the same mass as the neutron.

Pseudo order
An order of a chemical reaction that appears to be less than the true order because of the experimental conditions used. Pseudo orders occur when one reactant is present in large excess.

Pseudo order constant
If the rate equation takes the form, rate = k [A] [B] then k [A] is the pseudo first-order rate constant with respect to B. Similarly, k [B] is the pseudo first-order with respect to A.

Psychedelic drugs
(or psychotomimetics or hallucinogens) mind-altering drugs produce a qualitative change in thought, perception or mood and can cause vivid illusions and fantasies

p-type semiconductor
A p-type semiconductor is formed when the impurities added to silicon withdraw electrons from the occupied energy level leaving positive 'holes' which allow conduction to occur.

Purine
A nitrogen containing base found in nucleotides and nucleic acids. It contains one six membered ring fused with a five-membered ring.

Pyrolysis
The breaking up of larger hydrocarbons into shorter chain ones using heat.

Pryimidine
A nitrogen containing base found in nucleotides and nucleic acids. It contains one six membered ring.

Qualitative analysis
Analysis used to determine the nature of the constituents of a material or substance.

Quantitative analysis
Analysis used to determine the amount of each component in a material or substance.

Quantisation
The concept that energy can only be obtained in the form of small 'packets' called quanta.

Quantum (plural quanta)
A packet of energy.

Quaternary structure
The overall three-dimensional structure of a protein composed of two or more polypeptide chains.

Racemic mixture
An equimolar mixture of two enantiomers of the same compound. As their rotation of plane-polarised light is equal but opposite, the mixture is not optically active.

Radiation
The transmission of energy by means of an electromagnetic wave; or the emission of particles from the nucleus of a decaying atom.

Radical
(See free radical).

Radioactive decay
The decay of a radioactive nucleus to form the nucleus of another element by alpha decay or bet decay. Gamma rays may also be emitted.

Radioactive series
A series of isotopes produced one from the other in a sequence of spontaneous radioactive disintegrations.

Random coil
An irregular arrangement of a polypeptide chain in space.

Rate constant
The constant in a rate expression. The rate constant is unaffected by changes in the concentrations of the reactants, but is only affected by changes in temperature.

Rate determining step
The slowest elementary step in a reaction mechanism that controls the rate of the overall reaction.

Rate expression
A rate expression is the experimentally determined relationship between the rate of a reaction and the concentrations of the chemical species that occur in the overall chemical reaction.

Rate of decay
The change in the number of radioactive nuclides in a sample per unit time.

Rate of reaction
The rate of reaction indicates how fast reactants are being converted to products during a chemical reaction. It is the rate of formation of a product, or the rate of consumption of a reactant, divided by the corresponding coefficient in the stoichiometric equation. The rate has units of mol dm^{-3} s^{-1}.

Reactant
A substance that is consumed during a chemical reaction.

Reacting masses
The masses of elements and compounds which take part in a chemical reaction.

Reaction mechanism
A description of the changes in electronic structure that occur during a reaction. The movement of electron pairs is shown by means of curly arrows.

Reaction quotient
A quotient obtained by applying the equilibrium law to initial concentrations, rather than to equilibrium concentrations.

Reactivity series
An order of metal reactivity based on the relative rates of reactions of metals with oxygen, water, dilute aqueous acid and solutions of metal ions or salts.

Reactor core
The part of a nuclear reactor where the fission reaction takes place.

Real gas
A real gas does not obey the gas laws and exhibits non-ideal behaviour. Its molecules have a finite size and there are intermolecular or inter-atomic forces of attraction operating between the molecules or atoms.

Recrystallisation
A technique for the purification of solid crystalline substances. The procedure is based on the fact that solutes are much more soluble in a hot solvent and much less soluble when the solvent is cold.

Redox equation
An equation constructed by combining two half equations so the numbers of electrons on both sides of the equation and cancel.

Redox reaction
A reaction involving reduction and oxidation and which results in one or more electrons being transferred.

Redox titration
A titration used to determine the concentration of a solution of an oxidising agent or of a reducing agent.

Reductant
(See reducing agent).

Reduction
Reduction involves a decrease in oxidation number or gain of electrons.

Reducing agent
A chemical or substance that brings about reduction; it donates electrons to the reactant or one of the reactants. In the reaction the reducing agent itself is oxidised.

Reducing smog
A smog containing soot particles and aqueous sulfur dioxide from the combustion of coal in power stations.

Refining
The processes which separate, convert and purify chemicals in crude oil in oil refinery, or the removal of impurities from metals.

Refluxing
The process of boiling a liquid in a flask fitted with a condenser so that the condensed liquid runs back into the flask.

Reforming
Processes occurring where molecules obtained from crude oil or petroleum are converted into more useful products. The reactions involved are rearrangements and do not involve a change in the molar mass of the molecule.

Relative abundance
The relative abundance is the percentage of a particular isotope of an element relative to other isotopes of the same element in a naturally occurring sample.

Relative atomic mass
The weighted average (according to relative abundances) of the isotopic masses of the atoms in a naturally occurring sample of that element.

Relative isotopic mass
The mass of a particular isotope of an element compared to the mass of one twelfth of a carbon-12 atom. They are measured using a mass spectrometer.

Repeating unit
The unit of a polymer chain that originates from a single monomer, in the case of addition polymers, or from the pair of molecules usually used to make condensation polymers.

Residue (amino acid)
A single amino acid within a polypeptide chain.

Resistance
A measure of an electrical component's opposition to the flow of an electric current. It is measured in ohms (Ω).

Resolution
The separation of a racemic mixture into its two enantiomers (optical isomers).

Restricted rotation
The phenomenon where bonded atoms cannot rotate relative to one another because either the bond between them prevents it, or because the two atoms are part of a ring that restricts rotation.

Restriction enzymes
Enzymes that cause cleavage of both strands of double-stranded DNA at or near specific base sequences.

Retention factor (Rf value)
The retention factor, or Rf, is defined as the distance travelled by the compound divided by the distance travelled by the eluent.

Retrovirus
An RNA virus containing reverse transcriptase.

Reverse osmosis
A method for removing dissolved salts from water, for example, in the desalination of sea water, by the use of a semi-permeable membrane and high pressure.

Reversible reaction
A reversible reaction is a physical or chemical reaction that can go either backwards or forwards depending on the conditions. When a reversible reaction has equal forward and reverse rates the reaction is at equilibrium.

Ribose
A monosaccharide and a component of RNA.

Rusting
The corrosion of iron or steel.

S

Salt
A ionic compound formed by the reaction of an acid with a base, in which the hydrogen of the acid has been replaced by a metal ion. They are usually prepared via neutralisation, precipitation or direct synthesis.

Salt bridge
An ionic connection made between two half cells that contains an electrolyte with ions that do not cause precipitation of the ions in the two half cells. It allows ions to flow while preventing the two solutions from mixing. It prevents a build up of charge which would stop the flow of current.

Saturated
A term used to describe an organic molecule that contains no carbon-carbon multiple bonds and contains only carbon-carbon single bonds.

Saturated fat
A fatty acid containing only fully saturated alkyl chains.

Saturated solution
A solution which contains as much of the dissolved solute as possible at a particular temperature.

Saturated vapour
A vapour that is in equilibrium with a liquid. A saturated vapour is at the maximum pressure (the saturated vapour pressure) at a particular temperature. If the saturated vapour pressure of a liquid is equal to atmospheric pressure, then the temperature is the boiling point of that liquid.

s-block elements
Elements where the valence electrons are in an s-orbital. The s-block comprises groups 1 and 2.

Secondary air pollution
Secondary pollutants, are formed when primary pollutants react with each other or with other compounds present in the atmosphere.

Secondary alcohol
An alcohol where the carbon bearing the –OH group is attached to two other carbon atoms in alkyl or aryl groups.

Secondary amine
An amine where the nitrogen atom bears two alkyl or aryl groups.

Secondary cell
A secondary cell can be recharged by passing an electric current through it in the opposite direction.

Secondary structure (of a protein)
The three-dimensional conformation of sections of polypeptide chains. Common protein secondary structures include the alpha-helix, the beta sheet and the random coil.

Second order
A reaction in which the rate of reaction is proportional to the product of the concentrations of two of the reactants or to the square of the concentration of one of the reactants.

Semiconductor
A crystalline material with a conductivity intermediate between that of a conductor and an insulator. Its conductivity rises with increasing temperature.

Sex hormones
Various hormones, such as oestrogen, progesterone and testosterone, affecting the growth or function of the reproductive organs, the development of secondary sex characteristics, and the behavioral patterns of animals.

Shells
The main energy levels of an atom where the electrons are located.

Shielding (of electrons)
Shielding electrons are the electrons in the energy levels between the nucleus and the outer or valence electrons. They are described as 'shielding' electrons because they 'shield' the valence electrons from the nuclear charge and reduce the pull on them by the protons in the nucleus.

Side effects
A secondary and usually adverse effect of a drug.

Side reactions
Unwanted reactions which reduce the yield of the product being formed by the main reaction.

Sigma bond
A bond formed by the head-on overlap between atomic orbitals along an imaginary line joining the two nuclei (the internuclear axis). The electron density is concentrated along the internuclear axis. Sigma bonds can be formed by the overlap of two s-orbitals, an s-orbital and a p-orbital or two p-orbitals.

Single bond
A covalent bond formed by the sharing of one pair of electrons.

Skeletal formula
A formula representing organic molecules where the carbon and hydrogen atoms are omitted and only the bonds between them are shown.

Slag
A mixture of molten non-metallic oxides produced during the extraction of iron in the blast furnace. It consists of oxide impurities that have reacted with the calcium oxide produced from the decomposition of limestone.

Smog
A form of air pollution consisting of a combination of smoke and fog.

Smoke
Tiny particles of unburnt carbon suspended in air.

S_N1 (halogenoalkanes)
A nucleophilic substitution in which a carbocation intermediate is formed in the rate determining step which then reacts with the nucleophile.

S_N2 (halogenoalkanes)
A nucleophilic substitution where a concerted reaction occurs in which the nucleophile begins to bond with the carbon bearing the halogen as the halogen begins to leave the molecule.

Soap
A sodium or potassium salt of a long-chain organic acid.

Solid
A state of matter whose particles are in fixed positions and are not able to move from one location to another. The particles are held in a lattice by chemical bonds or intermolecular forces.

Solid charge
The mixture of raw materials limestone, coke and iron ore that are fed into a blast furnace.

Solid phase chemistry
Solid phase chemistry involves carrying a synthesis with one of the reactant molecules attached to an insoluble material known as a solid support.

Solubility
The amount of solute required to form a saturated solution in a given volume of solvent.

Solute
A solute is the solid, liquid or gas that has been dissolved to form a solution.

Solution
A solution is formed when a solid, liquid or gas is dissolved into a solvent.

Solvation
The process occurring when ions dissolve in a polar solvent and become surrounded by solvent molecules.

Solvent
A solvent is a liquid that dissolves solids, liquids or gases to form a solution.

s orbital
A spherically symmetrical atomic orbital; there is one per shell. s-orbitals have the lowest energy orbital in a given shell.

Specific heat capacity
The specific heat capacity is the amount of heat energy required to raise the temperature of one kilogram of a substance, by one degree kelvin (or Celsius).

Spectrochemical series
Arrangement of ligands in order of increasing ability to produce d-orbital splitting.

Spectroscopy
The production and analysis of spectra.

Spectator ions
Ions present in solution that do not participate directly in a reaction.

Spectral line
A particular wavelength of light emitted (or absorbed) by an atom, ion (or molecule).

Spectral series
A group of related lines in the emission (or absorption) spectrum of a substance. The lines in a spectral series occur when all the transitions all occur between one particular energy level and a set of different energy levels.

Spectroscope
An instrument for examining the different wavelengths present in electromagnetic radiation.

Spontaneous reaction
A reaction which will occur when the reactants are mixed together under standard conditions. It does not require an input of heat energy and is accompanied by a decrease in free energy.

Stability
A compound is described as being stable if it does not tend to decompose into its elements or into other compounds.

Standard electrode potential
The potential difference generated by a half-cell under standard conditions when connected by a salt bridge and an external circuit to a standard hydrogen electrode .

Standard hydrogen electrode
The standard hydrogen electrode is a half cell used to measure standard electrode potentials. It consists of hydrogen gas (at a pressure of one atmosphere) bubbled over a platinum electrode in a one molar solution of hydrochloric acid at 298 K. It is assigned a voltage of zero.

Standard enthalpy change of reaction
The enthalpy change when molar amounts of substances in a balanced equation react under standard thermodynamic conditions.

Standard solution
A solution with an accurately known concentration. They are made by dissolving a known amount of a primary standard in water.

Standard temperature and pressure (stp)
Standard conditions of 0 °C and 1 atmosphere pressure.

States of matter
Solid, liquid and gas are the three states of matter in which all substances can exist, depending on the conditions of temperature and pressure.

State symbols
Symbols used in equation to describe the physical state of the substances that are participating in the reaction.

Stationary phase
One of the two phases forming a chromatographic system. It may be a solid, a gel or a liquid. If a liquid, it may be distributed on a solid. The liquid may also be chemically bonded to the solid (bonded phase) or immobilised onto it (immobilised phase).

Steam cracking
Cracking out in the presence of steam at very high temperatures.

Steam reforming
The reaction of naphtha with steam over a platinum/alumina catalyst to give a variety of branched-chain alkanes, cycloalkanes and aromatic compounds, used in the blending of fuels.

Stereo-isomerism
Isomerism arising from differences in the shapes of molecules. Includes geometric and optical isomerism.

Steric factor
An effect in which the rate of a chemical reaction depends on the size or shape of groups of atoms within a molecule.

Steric hindrance
The prevention or slowing down of a reaction by atoms or functional groups blocking the access of an attacking molecule or ion.

Steroid
A group of lipids with a characteristic fused carbon-ring structure that includes cholesterol and the sex hormones.

Sticky ends
Two DNA molecules with short overhanging single-stranded sequences that are complementary to one another, facilitating the sealing of the ends.

Stimulants
A drug that temporarily arouses or accelerates physiological activity and prevents sleep.

Stoichiometry
The ratio in which the elements combine in a compound, or the ratio in which compounds react in a reaction.

Standard solution
A solution whose concentration is accurately known and does not change with time.

Standard state
A reference state for a specific element (in a particular allotropic form, where appropriate) according to standard thermodynamic conditions.

State symbols
State symbols indicate whether a substance shown in an equation is a solid (s), liquid (l), gas (g) or in aqueous solution (aq), that is, dissolved in water.

Stereo-isomerism
A type of isomerism in which the connectivity of atoms in the isomers is the same, but the arrangements in space are different.

Stereospecific reactions
Reactions with one of the optical isomers or enantiomers of a compound, but not the other.

Stoichiometric quantities
A reaction where amounts of reactants are reacted together so that all are consumed at exactly the same time.

Storage cell
An electrochemical cell that stores, in the form of chemical energy, useful quantities of electrical energy, for example, lead-acid battery.

Strain
Strain is present in a molecule or transition structure if the energy is enhanced because of unfavourable bond lengths or bond angles, relative to a standard. It is quantitatively defined as the standard enthalpy of a structure relative to a strainless structure (real or hypothetical) made up from the same atoms with the same types of bonding.

Stratosphere
The layer of the atmosphere between 15 and 30 km, above the troposphere.

Strong acid/base
A strong acid or strong base is completely dissociated or ionised when dissolved in water.

Structural analysis
The determination of the structure of a pure substance.

Structural formula
A structural formula shows the connectivity of the atoms in the molecule.

Structural isomers
A type of isomerism in which the connectivity of atoms in the isomeric compounds differs.

Sub-atomic particles
The particles, electrons, protons and neutrons, from which all atoms are made.

Sublimation
The direct change of state from solid to gas (or from gas to solid) without melting or freezing occurring.

Sub-critical reaction (nuclear)
A nuclear reaction in which less than one neutron causes another fission event and the process dies out.

Sub-shell
A sub-division of an electron shell.

Substituent
An atom, radical, or group substituted for another in a chemical compound.

Substitution
A reaction in which one atom or group of atoms is replaced by another atom or functional group.

Substrate
The compound acted upon by an enzyme.

Sugar
A sweet, crystalline and water-soluble mono- or disaccharide.

Sunscreen
A chemical that protects the skin from harmful ultraviolet radiation from the sun.

Synergistic effect
The condition in which the result of the combined action of two or more drugs is greater than the sum of their separate, individual effects.

Synthesis
A series of reactions resulting in the production of a particular chemical

Synthesis gas
A mixture of carbon monoxide and hydrogen gas produced by the steam reforming of natural gas using nickel oxide catalyst.

System
A term used to describe the material or mixture of chemicals being studied. Everything outside the system is the surroundings.

T

Temperature
The measure of the average kinetic energy of the particles in a substance.

Termination
An elementary step in a reaction involving the combination of two radicals to form a molecule.

Tertiary alcohol
An alcohol in which the carbon atom bearing the –OH group is attached to three other carbon atoms, that is, to three alkyl or aryl groups.

Tertiary structure (of a protein)
The overall three-dimensional folded shape of a protein composed of a single polypeptide chain.

Tetramethylsilane
A reference standard for proton nuclear magnetic resonance.

Theoretical yield
The maximum amount or mass of a particular product that can be formed when the limiting reactant is completely consumed and there are no losses or side reactions.

Thermal cracking
Cracking carried out a high temperature in the absence of a catalyst.

Thermal decomposition
The decomposition of a substance by heating.

Thermal dissociation
The process whereby a substance decomposes on heating but is regenerated on cooling. This is provided it has been heated in a closed system and the products have not escaped.

Thermal inversion
A thermal inversion occurs when cold dense air is near the ground, and there is a layer of warmer and therefore lighter air above it. They often occur in valleys and trap pollutants formed during the day in towns and cities located there.

Thermal pollution
Industrial discharge of heated water into a river, lake, or other body of water, causing a rise in temperature that endangers aquatic life by decreasing the solubility of dissolved oxygen.

Thermochemical equation
A chemical equation that describes the reaction occurring and gives the associated enthalpy change.

Thermochemistry
The study of heat changes occurring during chemical reactions.

Thermodynamics
The laws which govern energy transfers and the direction of chemical and physical changes.

Thermoplastics
Plastics which soften when heated and can then be re-moulded. Most addition polymers are thermoplastics.

Thermosetting plastics
Plastics which do not soften on heating but only char and decompose – they cannot be re-moulded.

Thermotropic LC
Pure substances that occur as liquid crystals over a certial temperature range bewteen the solid and liquid phases.

Thin-layer chromatography
A form of chromatography in which compounds are separated by a suitable solvent or solvent mixture on a thin layer of adsorbent material coated onto a flat support.

Tidal power
Tidal power utilises the twice daily variation in sea level caused primarily by the gravitational effect of the Moon to generate electricity.

Titration
A Chemical technique in which one solution is used to analyse another solution and find its concentration or amount.

Titration curve
A plot of the pH of the reaction mixture against the amount of titrant added.

Tolerance
The capacity of the body to endure or become less responsive to a substance (such as a drug) with repeated use or exposure.

trans-
A prefix typically used to describe the geometric isomer of a 1,2-disubstituted alkene with atoms or functional groups on opposite sides of a double bond or ring. It is also used in complex ions to designate two groups located directly across a central metal or ion from each other.

Transition (electronic)
A movement of electrons between energy levels. This can be from to a higher energy level, involving a shell further away from the nucleus, or to a lower energy level closer to the nucleus.

Transition state
(See activated complex).

Transition element/metal
A set of metals in the Periodic Table, located between groups 2 and 3/13, in which filling of electrons in an inner d-shell occurs.

Transmittance
A measure of the extent to which a sample in a spectrometer or colorimeter absorbs electromagnetic radiation of a particular wavelength.

Trend
A term used to describe the way in which a chemical or physical property increases or decreases along a series of elements or organic compounds (homologous series).

Triple bond
A covalent bond formed by the sharing of three pairs of electrons between two atoms.

Troposphere
The layer of the atmosphere closest to the ground and extending upwards (15 – 30 km) to the stratosphere.

U

Ultraviolet/Visible spectroscopy
Ultraviolet/visible spectroscopy involves the absorption of ultraviolet/visible light by a molecule causing the promotion of an electron from a ground electronic state to an excited electronic state.

Unimolecular
An elementary step involving one particle dissociating into two or more particles.

Universal indicator
A mixture of indicators which changes colour several times as the pH of an aqueous solution changes.

Unit cell
The smallest repeating part of a lattice or crystalline structure.

Unsaturated fatty acid
A fatty acid containing one or more carbon-carbon double bonds.

Unsaturation
A term used to describe a molecule, such as an alkene or fat, containing one or more carbon-carbon double or triple (multiple) bonds.

Valence electrons
The electrons in the outermost shell of an atom or ion. They are typically involved in bond formation.

Valence shell electron pair repulsion theory (VSEPR)
A model which states that the shape of bonds around the central atom of a molecule is determined by minimising the repulsion between the regions of high electron density.

Van der Waals' forces
Intermolecular forces, that operate between noble gas atoms and non-polar molecules in the solid and liquid states. They occur when the electrons within an atom or molecule induce a temporary dipole in an adjacent atom or molecule. They occur with increasing molecular or atomic size.

Vapour
A gas in contact with its liquid at a temperature below its boiling point.

Vapour pressure
The pressure of the vapour (gas) over a liquid where the gas and vapour are in equilibrium.

Virus
A simple organism that consists essentially of a core of RNA or DNA surrounded by a protein coat. They are only able to replicate inside a host cell.

Vitamin
Various unrelated fat-soluble or water-soluble organic substances essential in minute amounts for normal growth and activity of the body and obtained naturally from plant and animal foods.

Volatile organic compound (VOC)
Volatile organic compound, present in the atmosphere from evaporation of solvents or hydrocarbon fuels (man-made) or emitted by plants (Biological), and important precursors for photochemical formation of ozone.

Volatility
A qualitative measure of the how readily a liquid or solid is vaporised upon heating or evaporation.

Voltaic cell
Voltaic or galvanic cells contain two half cells, each of which is composed of an electrode in contact with an electrolyte. They are connected with a salt bridge and an external circuit.

Water of crystallisation
Water molecules that are incorporated into the crystal lattice of many inorganic salts when they crystallise from aqueous solution.

Wavelength
The distance between the peaks (or troughs) of one complete wave.

Wavenumber
The reciprocal of the wavelength of a wave. It is the number of complete waves in a particular unit of distance, for example, 1 cm. It is commonly used in infrared spectroscopy.

Weak acid/base
A weak acid is only partially dissociated or ionised when dissolved in water.

Word equation
A summary of a chemical reaction using the chemical names of the reactant and products.

Z

Zeolite
A naturally occurring series of aluminosilicate rocks that contain cations in the cavities of the aluminosilicate framework. They are widely used in ion-exchange columns.

Zero order
A chemical reaction in which the rate of reaction is independent of the concentration of a reactant.

Ziegler-Natta process
A method for the manufacture of high-density polyethene using a catalyst of titanium(IV) chloride and triethylaluminium under slight pressure.

Zone of nuclear stability
The area encompassing the stable nuclides on a plot of their positions as a function of the number of protons and the number of neutrons in the nucleus.

Zone refining
A technique used to reduce the level of impurities in semiconductors. It is based on the fact that the solubility of an impurity may be different in the solid and liquid phases.

Zwitterion
(See dipolar ion).

Zymase
A mixture of enzymes found in yeast involved in fermentation.

Symbols

α-amino acids 325
α helix 327
γ-rays 299, 300
π-bond 495
σ-bond 495

A

absolute uncertainty 292
absorption spectroscopy 301
acceptor atom 394
accuracy 289
acetaminophen 413
acid anhydrides 506
acid deposition 444
acidity 504
acid rain 445
acids 212
activated carbon 454
activated sludge process 453
activation energy 167, 346
activation energy graphs 297
active sites 375
actual uncertainty 292
Acyclovir 425
acyl chlorides 506
addition 497
addition polymerization 389
addition reactions 268, 495
adenine 351, 361
adenosine diphosphate 358
adenosine triphosphate 358
administration of drugs 407
adrenaline 419
adsorption 377, 454, 470
aerobic 356
aerobic cellular 333
aerobic decomposition 451
aerosols 487
AIDS 425
air pollutants 437
air pollution 437
air to fuel ratio 441
alcohol 271, 281
alcoholism 416
alcohols 504
aldehyde 271
aldehydes 497
alkali metals 76
alkalis 212
alkaloid 421
alkalosis 411
alkane 264
alkene 267, 280
alkyne 267
allergies 409
allotropes 130, 461
alloy 366
alternatives to CFCs 450
aluminium 367
amide 282
amides 505
amines 505
ammonia 282
amphetamines 420
amphipathic molecule 335
amphiprotic 208
amphoteric 365
anaemia 342
anaerobic 356
anaerobic biological process 454
anaerobic decomposition 451
anaerobic respiration 357
anaesthetics 412
analgesic 412, 413
analytical chemistry 299
androgens 344
anemia 358
anion 98
annealing 366
anode 250
anodizing 369
antacid 410
anthocyanins 482
antibacterials 422
antibiotics 422
antibodies 330, 422
antioxidant 480
antipyrtic drug 430
antiviral agents 425
arene 500
Arrhenius 207
Arrhenius equation 179
asbestos 440
aspirin 412
astaxanthin 483
asymmetric carbon atom 284
atactic 373
atom 1
atomic absorption spectroscopy 310
atomic number 2, 48
atomic oxygen 464
atomic theory 47
Aufbau principle 61
aureomycin 423
auto-oxidation 477, 484
automobile pollution 441
Avogadro's hypothesis 21

B

bacteria 424
bacterial infections 422
bacteriocidal drug 422, 423
bacteriostatic drug 422
band theory 393
barbiturates 415
base 212
basic oxygen process 365
bauxite 367
Becquerel, Henri 459
Beer-Lambert law 320
benzene 500
benzene ring 260, 507
beriberi 342
beta-lactam ring 427
beta-pleated sheet 327
bilayer 335
bimolecular 175
Biochemical Oxygen Demand 451
biodegradability 374
biological catalysts 330
biotechnology 351
blast furnace 364
blood-brain barrier 408
blood alcohol concentration 417
boiling point 193, 202
bond enthalpies 144
Born-Haber cycle 151
Boyle-Mariotte Law 296
branching 372
breathalyser test 417
brine 397
broad spectrum antibiotic 423
bronchitis 420
Brønsted-Lowry 208
buffers 472
buffer solutions 221, 226
burette 30

C

caffeine 421
calorimetry 138

cannabinoid 433
cannabis sativa 433
caramelisation 485
carbanion 502
carbinol 485
carbocation 495
carbohydrates 331
carbon bed method 454
carbon nanotube 386
carbonyl group 497, 506
carboxylic acid 271, 281
carotenes 483
carotenoids 483
carvone 489
catabolism 356
catalase 346
catalyst 346, 375
catalyst poisoning 378
catalytic converter 441
catalytic cracking 371
cathode 250
cation 98
cation-exchange capacity 470
cell diagram 248
cell potential 247
cellulose 331, 333
CFCs (chlorofluorocarbons) 448, 450
charge density 457
Charles's Law 296
chelating effect 471
chelating reagents 481
chemical bond 1, 97
chemical equation 15
chemical equilibrium 181
chemical feedstock 370
chemical precipitation 466
chemical properties 1, 256
chemical shift 307
chemotherapy 405
chiral auxiliaries 431
chiral centre 284
chlor–alkali industry 397
chlorophyll 320, 483
cholesterol 335, 344
chromatography 312, 328
chromophores 319
CIP system 489
cisplatin 426
clock techniques 165
close-packed lattice 126
coal combustion 439
coal washing 443
codeine 413
colligative properties 203
collision rate 167
collision theory 167
colloids 487
column chromatography 314
combi-chem 428
combinatorial chemistry 428
combustion 265
common ion effect 205, 467
competitive inhibitor 349
complementary base pairs 354
complete protein 324
complex ions 88
compound 1
concentration 27
condensation 192
condensation polymer 282
condensation polymerization 389
condensation reaction 338, 498
conformers 341
conjugate acid 208
conjugate base 208
conservation of energy 141
consistency 291
constant pressure 136
constipation 334
Contact process 91, 189, 375
coordinate bond 103
coordination polymerization 393
CORN rule 489
counterflow method 442
covalent bonding 101
cracking 370
critical temperature 350
Crohn's disease 334
cross-linked polymer 390
cross tolerance 414
cryoscopic constants 202
crystal lattice 98
current 252
cytochromes 358
cytosine 351, 361

D

d–block elements 84
dative bond 103
dative covalent bond 101
decimal places 291
delocalisation 485
delocalized π-bond 118, 507
denaturation 350, 376
denitrification 454
dependence 409
depressants 415
desalination 455
dextro-rotatory 488
diabetes 334
diaphragm cell 398
diatomic 2
dietary fibre 333
dimers 125
diode 394
dipeptide 326
dipole 112
dipole-dipole forces 123
dipole moment 112, 303
diprotic 208
disaccharide 476
disperse system 487
displacement reactions 242
disproportionation 233
dissolved-oxygen 451
distillation 272, 455
diuretic drugs 421
divalent 240
diverticulosis 334
DNA profiling 355
donor atom 394
dopant 394
doping 394
double-beam instrument 302
double helix 353
drug 405
drug addiction 410
drug testing 406
dry cells 380
ductile 126
dye 481
dynamic equilibrium 181

E

emf 245
ebullioscopic constants 202
Effective Nuclear Charge (ENC) 72
electrical conductivity 165
electrochemical cell 243
electrolysis 250
electrolyte 214, 250
electromagnetic radiation 299
electron affinity 152
electronegativity 72, 97, 112
electron hole 394

electronic structure 59
electron transport chain 358
electrophiles 495
electrophoresis 328
electrostatic precipitator 443
element 1
elimination reaction 280, 499
eluant 314
emission spectroscopy 301
emission spectrum 56
emphysema 420
empirical formula 257
emulsifiers 487
emulsion 487
enantiomer 283, 326, 426
endorphins 412
endothermic change 187
endothermic reaction 136
energy level diagrams 136
enkephalins 412
enthalpy 135
enthalpy change 135
enthalpy change of hydration 153
enthalpy change of solution 153
enthalpy of vapourisation 193
entropy 155
enzyme-substrate complex 377
enzymes 346, 376
equi-molar mixture 426
equilibrium constant 184
equilibrium law 194
essential amino acids 324
essential fatty acids 337
ester 281
esterification 338
esterification reaction 281
estrogen 340
estrogens 344
ethanol 268, 271, 416
eutrophication 446, 452
exothermic change 187
exothermic reaction 136
experimental errors 289

F

Faraday constant 253
fatty acid 337
fermentation 351, 480
fingerprint region 304
First Law of Thermodynamics 141
first order kinetics 461
flavanones 482
Fleming Alexander 422
flocculation 453
fluorocarbons 450
foams 487
forensic science 305
fractional distillation 199
fragmentation pattern 305
free-radical mechanism 392
free energy change 247
free radical chain reaction 266
free radical quencher 481
freezing point 202
frequency 299
Friedel Crafts reactions 508
fructose 331
fuel cell 379
fullerenes 130
functional group 255, 261
fungicide 457

G

Gas Chromatography – Mass Spectrometry 315
gas liquid chromatography 314, 418
gel 487
gel electrophoresis 355
Genetic engineering 351
Genetic modification 486
geometrical isomers 283, 425
giant covalent structure 130
Gibbs free energy change 157
Gibbs free energy of formation 159
global warming 447
glucagon 343
glucose 331
glycogen 333
glycolysis 356
goitre 342
greenhouse effect 447
greenhouse gases 447
Grignard reagents 502
guanine 351, 361

H

Haber process 91, 189, 375
haemorrhoids 334
half-life 408, 461
half-neutralisation point 226
half equations 236
half life 173
halogenoalkanes 273, 277, 501
halogens 77
HDPE 372
heat energy 138
helix 327
heme 484
heparin 333
hepatitis B vaccine 351
herbicide 457
heroin 413
Hess's Law 141
heterocyclic compounds 421
heterocyclic ring 419
heterogeneous catalysis 375
heterogeneous equilibrium 194
hexoses 331
high performance liquid chromatography 316, 328
HIV 425
homogeneous catalysis 375
homogeneous equilibrium 194
homologous series 256
homolytic fission 386
hopper 364
hormones 330, 343
host cells 424
humic acids 457
Hund's rule 62
hybridization 114
hybrid orbitals 114
hydrocarbon 264
hydrochlorofluorocarbons, 450
hydrofluorocarbons 450
hydrogen bonding 123
hydrolysis 339
hydrolytic rancidity 478
hydronium ion 207
hypnotics 415

I

ideal gas 24
ideal gas law 296
incineration 374
incomplete combustion 265
indicator 29, 228
indigestion 410
induced fit 346, 349
inductive effect 496, 508
Infra-red Spectroscopy 418
infrared radiation 301

inhibitor 349, 430
initiation 266
insoluble fibre 333
insulin 330
interferons 330, 351
intermediates 175
ntoximeter 418
iodine index 337
ionic bonding 98
ionic equation 16
ionisation energy 63, 72
iron 364
Irritable Bowel Syndrome (IBS) 334
isoelectric point 325, 329
Isoelectronic species 67
isomer 257
isomerism 89, 264
isotactic 373
isotopes 1, 49
isotropic 382
IUPAC 260

K

keratin proteins 327
ketones 497
kevlar 390
kinetic energy 167
knocking 371
kwashiorkor 342

L

lactic acid 357
lactose 331
laevorotatory 488
lattice enthalpy 152
LCD 395
LDPE 372
lead-acid storage battery 380
leaded gasoline 440
lean burn engine 442
Le Chatelier's principle 185, 215, 467
Lenz's law 310
lethal dose 406
leukotrienes 337
Lewis acid 209
Lewis acid–base 88
Lewis base 209
Lewis structure 102
ligands 88, 484
light absorption 165
limestone fluidized bed 442
limiting reagent 20
Lineweaver-Burke plot 348
linoleic and linoeic acids 334
lipids 334, 475
lipolase 351
lipoproteins 336
liquid crystal 382
lithium-ion battery 382
lock and key model 377
London forces 122
lone pair 495
lyotropic LC 383
lysergic acid diethylamide (LSD) 432

M

macronutrients 341
magnetic moment 309
magnetic resonance imaging 308
Maillard reactions 485
Main Effect 409
malachite green 485
malleable 126
malnourishment 475
malnutrition 342
marasmus 342
Markovnikov's Rule 496
mass/charge (m/z) ratio 304
mass number 48
mass spectrometer 52, 304
matter 1
Maxwell-Boltzmann distribution 168
MBBA 383
measurement 290
measurement of the mass of the reaction mixture 165
melanoma 320
mercury cell process 397
mescaline 432
mesomeric effect 508
mesophase 382
metallic bonding 126
methadone 414
methane 437
methyl orange 228, 229
metmyoglobin 484
micelles 383
Michaelis–Menten equation 347
micronutrients 341
microorganisms 422
microwaves 301
Minamata disease 399
mineralization 458, 472
mixed triglyceride 335
mixtures 1
mobile phase 312
mogadon 419
molar volume 22
molecular formula 257
molecularity 175
molecular modelling 397, 429
molecules 2, 106
monatomic 2
monobasic strong acid 225
monobasic strong base 226
monochromatic light 302
monochromator 302
monomer 268, 372
monoprotic 208
monosaccharides 331, 476
morphine 413
multi-stage distillation 455
multidentate ligand 358
myoglobin 484

N

nanoethics 387
nanoparticle 386
nanopolitics 387
nanotoxicology 387
nanotubes 386
narcolepsy 420
narcotics 413
negative feedback 343
nematic LC 383
Nernst equation 248
NiCad batteries 380
nicotine 420
ninhydrin 329
ninhydrin solution 312
nitrification 465
nitrile 279
non-leaded fuel 441
non–competitive inhibitor 349
Nuclear Magnetic Resonance (NMR) spectroscopy 307
nucleic acid 351
nucleons 309
nucleophile 273, 497, 498
nucleophilic attack 497
nucleophilic substitution 273, 277

nucleoside 352
nucleotides 351
nutrient 475
nutrient deficiencies 342
nutrient depletion 457
nylon 282

O

obesity 334
octane number 371
omega-3 fatty acids 486
opiates 413
optical isomer 283, 284, 426
optically active 286
oral contraceptive 345
order of reaction 170
organic chemistry 255
organic soil matter 457
orientation 372
osmosis 203, 455
osmotic pressure 203
osteoporosis 343
oxidant 236
oxidation 232
oxidation number 232
oxidative rancidity 478
oxides of Nitrogen 438
oxides of sulfur 438
oxidised 271
oxidising agent 239, 437
oxidizing smog 463
ozone 449
ozone depletion 449
ozone layer 449

P

pain 412
paper chromatography 313, 328
paracetamol 413
parallel synthesis 428
partial pressure 204
particulates 439
Pauli exclusion principle 63
pellagra 342
penicillin 422
penicillinase 422
pentoses 331
peptide bond 326
peptide linkage 326
percentage yield 21
periodic table 70
peroxyacyl nitrates 464
pesticide 457
PET 390
petrochemicals 370
petroleum 440
pH 215
pharmacology 406
phase equilibrium 192
phenacetin 413
phenolphthalein 228, 319
phenols 504
phospholipids 335, 383
photo-oxidation 477
photochemical smog 463
photodegradation 484
photovoltaic cell 363, 393
physical dependence 409, 414
physical properties 1, 256
pickling 480
pigment 481
pipette 29
pixels 396
placebo effect 406
plane polarised light 286
plant nutrients 452
plaque 336
plasticizer 373
platinum black 245
polar bond 112
polarimeter 286
polarising filter 286
polarizer 384
polluted water 452
poly-unsaturated 476
polyamide 282
polycyclic ring 343
polyester 282
polyethene 268, 372
polymer 268, 372
polymerisation 268
polypropene 269
polyprotic 208
polyurethanes 390
porphyrin ring 484
position of equilibrium 185
post-combustion methods 442
precipitate 26
precision 289
preserves 479
primary 262
primary amine 279, 282
primary sewage treatment 453
primary site of absorption 407
primary standard 29
primary structure 326
progestin 345
progestins 344
propagation 266
prostaglandins 337, 412
protein deficiency 342
proteins 324, 330
prozac 419
psilocybin 432
psychological dependence 410
psychotomimetic 431
psychotomimetics 431
pure substances 1
PVC 269
pyrolysis 370
pyruvic acid 356

Q

qualitative analysis 299
quantitative analysis 299
quantitative apparatus 290
quantum Numbers 63
quenching 367
quercetin 482

R

R,S system 489
racemic mixture 286, 426, 490
radioactive decay 173
radioactive waste 459
radioactivity 459
radiocarbon dating 305
radio waves 301
rancidity 478
random uncertainties 290
Raoult's law 200
rate determining step 175
rate expression 170
rate of a chemical reaction 161
rational drug design 429
reaction order graphs 297
Reaction Rate
Effect of Catalyst 169
Effect of Concentration 168
Effect of Light 169
Effect of Surface Area 168
Effect of Temperature 168

reaction rate graphs 297
reactivity series 241
rechargeable battery 379
recycling 370, 374
redox 233
redox couple 241
reducing agents 239, 481
reductant 236
reduction 232
reflux 272
relative atomic mass 2
restriction enzymes 355
retention time 315
retinol 320
reverse osmosis 455
reverse transcriptase 430
reversible reaction 181
Reye's syndrome 413
rhodopsin 341
rickets 342

S

s-block metals 85
salicylic acid 430
salinization 456
salt 224
salt hydrolysis 224
salting 479
saturated fat 336
saturated hydrocarbon 267
saturated solution 26
Schrödinger wave equation 63
scurvy 342
secondary 262
secondary sewage treatment 453
secondary structure 326
sedative 415
sedimentation 453
selective precipitation 469
selectivity 377
semi-permeable membrane 455
semiconductor 393
serotonin 419
sewage 452
sewage treatment
  aeration 453
  sedimentation 453
shelf life 477
side effect 409
significant figures 291
silicon 393
simple distillation 197
simple triglyceride 335
smectic LC 383
smelting plant 439
smog 463
SN_1 mechanism 277
SN_2 mechanism 277
soil 455
soil organic matter 457
soil pollution 457
solid charge 364
solubility 26, 128
solubility product 205
solubility product constant 466
solubility rules 466
soluble fibre 333
solute 26, 127
solution 26
solvent 26, 127
specific heat capacity 138
spectator ions 16
spectrum 56
spin 309
spontaneous reaction 136
standard electrode potentials 245
standard enthalpy change of atomisation 151
standard enthalpy change of combustion 148
standard enthalpy change of formation 147
standard entropy change 155
standard hydrogen electrode 245
standard solution 29
standard state 147
starch 331
stationary phase 312
statistical validation 407
steam cracking 371
steel 367
stereochemistry 372
stereoisomer 258, 283
stereoisomerism 89
stereoisomers 425
steric factor 167
steroids 335
sterols 335
stimulants 419
strong acid 213
structural analysis 299
structural formula 102, 257
structural isomer 258
subatomic particles 47
substitution reaction 265
sucrose 331
sudan red 485
sulfur dioxide 438
sulfuric acid 91, 439
sun creams 320
supersaturated solution 26
surfactants 488
suspension 26, 487
symbol 2
sympathomimetic drugs 420
synergistic effects 417
synthetic natural gas 443
synthetic opiates 414
systematic errors 290

T

tailings 370
temperature 138
tempering 367
termination 266
terramycin 423
tertiary 262
tertiary sewage treatment 454
tertiary Structure 327
terylene 282
testosterone 340
tetracyclines 423
tetrahydrocannabinol (THC) 432
tetramethylsilane 308
thalidomide 407, 426
therapeutic dose 409
therapeutic window 409
thermal cracking 371
thermal inversion 463
thermal pollution 452
thermal pollution 452
thermochemistry 135
thermotropic LC 383
thin layer chromatography 313
thymine 351, 361
thyroid gland 342
time release capsule 407
titration 29, 164, 225
titre 30
TNLC 395
tolerance 409
toxic substance 409
tranquilizer 415
trans-fats 477
transition elements 84

transition metals 90
transition state 176
transpeptidase 427
twisted nematic liquid crystal 395

U

ultraviolet-visible spectroscopy 318
ultraviolet light 300
uncertainties 289
undissociated acid 213
unimolecular 175
universal indicator 215
unsaturated fat 336
unsaturated hydrocarbon 267
uracil 351
urease 346

V

valence level 98
valium 419
van der Waals' forces 74, 122
vapourisation 192
vapour pressure 192
vapour pressure of mixtures 197
variable systematic error 291
vibrational motion 302
virus 424
viruses 424
visible light 300
vitamin A 341
vitamin solubility 341
Volatile Organic Compounds 440
volatility 127
voltaic cell 243
volumetric flask 29
VSEPR theory 107

W

waste 459
water treatment 452
wavelength 299
wet alkaline scrubber 442

X

X-rays 300
xerophthalmia 342

Z

zeolites 377
Ziegler-Natta catalysts 393
zovirax 425
zwitterion 325